PEARSON

Business Statistics
A First Course

Twelfth Custom Edition for Ryerson University
Ted Rogers School of Management

Compiled by Darryl Smith and Clare Chua, Ph.D.

With materials from:
Business Statistics: A First Course, Sixth Edition
by David M. Levine, Timothy C. Krehbiel, and Mark L. Berenson

Pearson Learning Solutions, 330 Hudson Street, New York, New York 10013
A Pearson Education Company
www.pearsoned.com

Printed in the United States of America

1 2 3 4 5 6 7 8 9 10 V3N4 17 16 15

000200010271975384

SK/CC

ISBN 10: 1-323-14971-6
ISBN 13: 978-1-323-14971-3

To our wives,
Marilyn L., Patti K., and Rhoda B.

and to our children,
Sharyn, Ed, Rudy, Rhonda, Kathy, and Lori

About the Authors

The textbook authors meet to discuss statistics at a Mets baseball game. Shown left to right: David Levine, Mark Berenson, and Tim Krehbiel.

David M. Levine is Professor Emeritus of Statistics and Computer Information Systems at Baruch College (City University of New York). He received B.B.A. and M.B.A. degrees in Statistics from City College of New York and a Ph.D. from New York University in Industrial Engineering and Operations Research. He is nationally recognized as a leading innovator in statistics education and is the co-author of 14 books, including such best-selling statistics textbooks as *Statistics for Managers Using Microsoft Excel*, *Basic Business Statistics: Concepts and Applications*, *Business Statistics: A First Course*, and *Applied Statistics for Engineers and Scientists Using Microsoft Excel and Minitab*.

He also is the co-author of *Even You Can Learn Statistics: A Guide for Everyone Who Has Ever Been Afraid of Statistics*, currently in its 2nd edition, *Six Sigma for Green Belts and Champions* and *Design for Six Sigma for Green Belts and Champions*, and the author of *Statistics for Six Sigma Green Belts*, all published by FT Press, a Pearson imprint, and *Quality Management*, 3rd edition, McGraw-Hill/Irwin. He is also the author of *Video Review of Statistics* and *Video Review of Probability*, both published by Video Aided Instruction, and the statistics module of the MBA primer published by Cengage Learning. He has published articles in various journals, including *Psychometrika*, *The American Statistician*, *Communications in Statistics*, *Decision Sciences Journal of Innovative Education*, *Multivariate Behavioral Research*, *Journal of Systems Management*, *Quality Progress*, and *The American Anthropologist*, and given numerous talks at the Decision Sciences Institute (DSI), American Statistical Association (ASA), and Making Statistics More Effective in Schools and Business (MSMESB) conferences. Levine has also received several awards for outstanding teaching and curriculum development from Baruch College.

Timothy C. Krehbiel is Professor of Management and Senior Associate Dean of the Farmer School of Business at Miami University in Oxford, Ohio. He teaches undergraduate and graduate courses in business statistics. In 1996, he received the prestigious Instructional Innovation Award from the Decision Sciences Institute. He has also received the Farmer School of Business Effective Educator Award and has twice been named MBA professor of the year.

Krehbiel's research interests span many areas of business and applied statistics. His work has appeared in numerous journals, including *Quality Management Journal, Ecological Economics, International Journal of Production Research, Journal of Purchasing and Supply Management, Journal of Applied Business Research, Journal of Marketing Management, Communications in Statistics, Decision Sciences Journal of Innovative Education, Journal of Education for Business, Marketing Education Review, Journal of Accounting Education*, and *Teaching Statistics*. He is a co-author of three statistics textbooks published by Prentice Hall: *Business Statistics: A First Course, Basic Business Statistics*, and *Statistics for Managers Using Microsoft Excel*. Krehbiel is also a co-author of the book *Sustainability Perspectives in Business and Resources*.

Krehbiel graduated *summa cum laude* with a B.A. in history from McPherson College and earned an M.S. and a Ph.D. in statistics from the University of Wyoming.

Mark L. Berenson is Professor of Management and Information Systems at Montclair State University (Montclair, New Jersey) and also Professor Emeritus of Statistics and Computer Information Systems at Bernard M. Baruch College (City University of New York). He currently teaches graduate and undergraduate courses in statistics and in operations management in the School of Business and an undergraduate course in international justice and human rights that he co-developed in the College of Humanities and Social Sciences.

Berenson received a B.A. in economic statistics and an M.B.A. in business statistics from City College of New York and a Ph.D. in business from the City University of New York.

Berenson's research has been published in *Decision Sciences Journal of Innovative Education, Review of Business Research, The American Statistician, Communications in Statistics, Psychometrika, Educational and Psychological Measurement, Journal of Management Sciences and Applied Cybernetics, Research Quarterly, Stats Magazine, The New York Statistician, Journal of Health Administration Education, Journal of Behavioral Medicine*, and *Journal of Surgical Oncology*. His invited articles have appeared in *The Encyclopedia of Measurement & Statistics* and *Encyclopedia of Statistical Sciences*. He is co-author of 11 statistics texts published by Prentice Hall, including *Statistics for Managers Using Microsoft Excel, Basic Business Statistics: Concepts and Applications*, and *Business Statistics: A First Course*.

Over the years, Berenson has received several awards for teaching and for innovative contributions to statistics education. In 2005, he was the first recipient of The Catherine A. Becker Service for Educational Excellence Award at Montclair State University.

Brief Contents

Contents

4 Numerical Descriptive Measures 136

5 Basic Probability 202

6 Discrete Probability Distributions 238

7 The Normal Distribution 278

8 Sampling and Sampling Distributions 316

9 Statistical Applications in Quality Management 352

10 Confidence Interval Estimation 382

11 Fundamentals of Hypothesis Testing: One-Sample Tests 426

16 Multiple Regression   704

Preface

Educational Philosophy

Seeking ways to continuously improve the teaching of business statistics is the core value that guides our works. We actively participate in Decision Sciences Institute (DSI), American Statistical Association (ASA), and Making Statistics More Effective in Schools and Business (MSMESB) conferences. We use the Guidelines for Assessment and Instruction (GAISE) reports as well as our reflections on teaching business statistics to a diverse student body at several large universities. These experiences have helped us identify the following key principles:

1. **Show students the relevance of statistics** Students need a frame of reference when learning statistics, especially when statistics is not their major. That frame of reference for business students should be the functional areas of business, such as accounting, finance, information systems, management, and marketing. Each statistics topic needs to be presented in an applied context related to at least one of these functional areas. The focus in teaching each topic should be on its application in business, the interpretation of results, the evaluation of the assumptions, and the discussion of what should be done if the assumptions are violated.

2. **Familiarize students with the statistical applications used in the business world** Integrating these programs into all aspects of an introductory statistics course allows the course to focus on interpretation of results instead of computations. Introductory business statistics courses should recognize that programs with statistical functions are commonly found on a business decision maker's desktop computer, therefore making the *interpretation* of results more important than the tedious hand calculations required to produce them.

3. **Provide clear instructions to students for using statistical applications** Books should explain clearly how to use programs such as Excel and Minitab with the study of statistics, without having those instructions dominate the book or distract from the learning of statistical concepts.

4. **Give students ample practice in understanding how to apply statistics to business** Both classroom examples and homework exercises should involve actual or realistic data as much as possible. Students should work with data sets, both small and large, and be encouraged to look beyond the statistical analysis of data to the interpretation of results in a managerial context.

Acknowledgments

We are extremely grateful to the RAND Corporation and the American Society for Testing and Materials for their kind permission to publish various tables in Appendix E, and the American Statistical Association for its permission to publish diagrams from the *American Statistician*.

A Note of Thanks

We would like to thank Levon R. Hayrapetyan, Houston Baptist University; Jim Mirabella, Jacksonville University; Adam Morris, Crowder College; Ravi Nath, Creighton University; Robert D. Patterson, Penn State-Erie–The Behrend College; Sulakshana Sen, Bethune Cookman University; and Kathryn A. Szabat, LaSalle University for their comments, which have made this a better book.

We would especially like to thank Chuck Synovec, Mary Kate Murray, Ashlee Bradbury, Judy Leale, Anne Fahlgren, and Jane Bonnell of the editorial, marketing, and production teams at Prentice Hall. We would like to thank our statistical reader and accuracy checker Annie Puciloski for her diligence in checking our work; Susan Pariseau, Merrimack College, for assisting in the reading of the page proofs; Julie Kennedy for her proofreading; and Lindsay Bethoney of PreMediaGlobal for her work in the production of this text.

Finally, we would like to thank our families for their patience, understanding, love, and assistance in making this book a reality. It is to them that we dedicate this book.

Concluding Remarks

We have gone to great lengths to make this text both pedagogically sound and error free. Please contact us at **davidlevine@davidlevinestatistics.com** if you require clarification about something discussed in this book, have a suggestion for a future edition, or if you discover an error. Include the phrase "BSFC edition 6" in the subject line of your e-mail. For technical support for PHStat2 beyond what is presented in the appendices and in the PHStat2 readme file that accompanies PHStat2, visit the PHStat2 website, **www.pearsonhighered.com/phstat** and click the **Contact Pearson Technical Support** link.

David M. Levine
Timothy C. Krehbiel
Mark L. Berenson

Business Statistics

1

Data

Learning Objectives
In this chapter, you learn:

• How statistics is used in business
• The sources of data used in business
• The types of data used in business
• The basics of Microsoft Excel
• The basics of SPSS

Statistics is the science of collecting, organizing, presenting, analyzing, and interpreting data to assist in making effective decisions. **Descriptive statistics** focuses on collecting, summarizing, presenting, and analyzing a set of data. **Inferential statistics** uses data that have been collected from a small group to draw conclusions about a larger group. A **statistic** is a numerical measure that describes a characteristic of a sample. A **parameter** is a numerical measure that describes a characteristic of a population.

The first course involves descriptive statistics, in which you learn methods of organizing, presenting, and describing a set of data. Before you learn to summarize a given set of data, you must learn about the nature of the data. The techniques to summarize data are governed by the type of data. For example, if you have a set of data containing a bunch of males and females, you can code "male" as 1 and "female" as 2. Suppose your data consists of 5 males and 5 females. The coded data are 1, 1, 1, 1, 1, 2, 2, 2, 2, 2. The average would be $(1+1+1+1+1+2+2+2+2+2)/10=15/10=1.5$. What does the average of 1.5 mean? Does it make sense? Using the average to summarize qualitative data does not provide any significant meaning in this context.

The first chapter begins by discussing what data are, the different types of data, and the four levels of measurements scales. Statistics are applied daily. For example,

- the article "How to get dieters to lose weight? You pay them, obviously" (source: http://www.theglobeandmail.com/life/style/hannah-sung/how-to-get-dieters-to-lose-weight-you-pay-them-obviously/article1867026/) reported that "According to the Canadian Health Measures Survey, almost a quarter of the Canadian population is considered obese."
- the article "Trade deficit drops 'for all the wrong reasons'" (source: http://www.theglobeandmail.com/report-on-business/economy/trade/trade-deficit-drops-for-all-the-wrong-reasons/article1868347/) reported that "Measured in dollars, energy exports shot up 3.2 per cent in November. Exports of industrial goods and materials rose 6.6 per cent."

These examples show that statistics are facts and figures. But in fact, they are something more than that. In the broadest sense, "statistics" refers to a range of techniques and procedures for describing, summarizing, graphically presenting, measuring, and analyzing data. This is the focus of this course.

1.1 What Are Data?

There are many methods of collecting data. Data collection is a process of gathering information using questionnaires, interviews, experiments, and field study. In the business world, information is usually gathered using questionnaires. A questionnaire is a data collection instrument containing sequences of questions to meet a research objective. The purpose of having the questionnaire is to gather information from respondents for various objectives. An example of a survey questionnaire is shown below in Table 1.1.

TABLE 1.1
Survey

1. Did you bring your textbook to class today?
   - ❏ Yes
   - ❏ No
2. How much time (in hours) do you usually spend studying per week? _____
3. How many courses did you enroll in this semester? _____
4. Your Class Year: _____ *(please check your answer below)*
   - ❏ Freshman
   - ❏ Sophomore
   - ❏ Junior
   - ❏ Senior
5. How did you come to school today?
   - ❏ Walk
   - ❏ Drive
   - ❏ Take public transport
   - ❏ Car pool

A random sample of 12 students was asked to fill out the survey questionnaire shown above. The data collected from the 12 students were tabulated in the table displayed in Table 1.2.

TABLE 1.2
Results of the Survey

Student	Did you bring your textbook to class today?	How much time (in hours) do you usually spend studying per week?	How many courses did you enroll in this semester?	Class Year	How did you come to school today?
1	Yes	20.3	3	Freshman	Take public transport
2	Yes	12.5	5	Sophomore	Drive
3	No	10.3	6	Junior	Walk
4	Yes	2.5	4	Junior	Drive
5	No	0.5	5	Senior	Take public transport
6	Yes	7.2	2	Sophomore	Drive
7	Yes	5.5	5	Freshman	Take public transport
8	No	10.0	4	Freshman	Walk
9	No	4.8	4	Freshman	Walk
10	Yes	3.2	3	Freshman	Drive
11	Yes	17.0	5	Senior	Take public transport
12	Yes	4.3	6	Freshman	Take public transport

The responses collected from the question "Did you bring your textbook to class today?" are a collection of "Yes" and "No." The responses collected from the question "How much time (in hours) do you usually spend studying per week?" are a collection of numbers ranging from 0.5 to 20.3. These numbers are elicited by the respondents. Later you will learn to classify these responses by type of data and measurement scale.

Data are a collection of numbers and/or attributes of an entity. The students' responses are called data. You will see that the responses can be expressed either numerically (for example, 3.2 17.0, 3, 5, etc.) or non-numerically (for example, Yes, No, Drive, Walk, etc.). The numeric data is identified as quantitative data, and the non-numeric data is identified as qualitative data.

Examples of data are shown in Examples 1.1 and 1.2. Example 1.1 is a set of consumer price index data that is classified as quantitative data. Example 1.2 is a set of language data that is classified as qualitative data.

EXAMPLE 1.1

A Set of Consumer Price Index Data
Source: *http://www40.statcan.gc.ca/l01/cst01/ECON45A-eng.htm*

Consumer Price Index, by city (Index)					
All-items	2006	2007	2008	2009	2010
			2002=100		
St. John's (N.L.)	109.1	110.7	114.0	114.7	117.4
Charlottetown and Summerside (P.E.I.)	111.0	113.2	116.9	117.1	119.2
Halifax (N.S.)	109.8	112.0	115.2	115.3	117.6

TABLE 1.3

Saint John (N.B.)	109.2	111.2	113.2	113.7	116.3
Québec (Que.)	108.7	110.1	112.4	113.2	114.8
Montréal (Que.)	108.6	110.3	112.6	113.5	114.8
Ottawa–Gatineau, (Ont. part)	108.6	110.7	113.1	113.7	116.6
Toronto (Ont.)	108.4	110.5	113.1	113.6	116.5
Thunder Bay (Ont.)	106.9	108.1	110.4	110.5	112.8
Winnipeg (Man.)	108.5	110.8	113.3	113.9	114.8
Regina (Sask.)	108.9	111.7	115.2	117.2	118.9
Saskatoon (Sask.)	109.0	112.7	117.1	118.2	119.6
Edmonton (Alta.)	112.0	117.4	121.4	121.6	122.9
Calgary (Alta.)	112.3	118.0	121.8	121.7	122.7
Vancouver (B.C.)	108.0	110.2	112.8	112.9	114.9
Victoria (B.C.)	108.5	109.8	111.8	111.9	113.1
Whitehorse (Y.T.)	106.8	109.5	113.4	113.8	114.7
Yellowknife (N.W.T.)	107.7	110.8	115.2	115.9	117.9

Note: Annual average indexes are obtained by averaging the indexes for the 12 months of the calendar year.
Source: Statistics Canada, CANSIM, table (for fee) 326-0021.
Last modified: 2011-01-24.

EXAMPLE 1.2

A Set of Language Data
Source: *http://www.toronto.ca/ toronto_facts/diversity.htm*

The top five mother tongue languages in 2006 were:

Chinese (420,000);

Italian (195,000);

Punjabi (138,000);

Tagalog/Pilipino (114,000);

Portuguese (113,000).

1.2 Data Collection

As you can see from the examples above, data come in many forms. How do you collect data? Data may be collected from two main sources, namely primary and secondary.

Primary Data

Primary data involves raw data (or original data) that are collected directly from respondents (or participants of a survey) using various instruments such as interviews, surveys (or questionnaires), observations, and laboratory experiments. Collection of data could also involve direct measurement of the item of interest. For example, in the production of a soft drink, the production manager may be interested in measuring the amount of soft drink the machine puts into each bottle.

Secondary Data

Secondary data are collected by another party or source. Secondary data are also recognized as "recycled" data. Examples of secondary data sources are databases from Statistics Canada (http://www.statcan.gc.ca/), CANSIM (Statistics Canada time-series), GDSourcing (Government Data Sourcing), etc.

Definitions

The following are basic statistical terms and definitions you should know.

Variable: a name chosen to describe the data collected. Each variable has a name and a value (also known as a response). The name identifies the variable, and the value relates to the data. For example, the variable for the question "Did you bring your textbook to class today?" could be "textbook." The variable name is usually associated with the question.

Population: includes *all* the items or persons in your study or research. For example, if your study involves the spending habits of the teens in Ontario, the population in your study would include all the teens living in Ontario.

Census: a set of data that includes **all** members of a population.

Sample: a subset of a population.

Sample size: the number of items/persons in a sample. The sample size is denoted as n.

Population size: the number of items/persons in a population. The population size is denoted as N.

1.3 Classification of Data

You can classify data into two types as shown in Figure 1.1.

(1) **Quantitative data (also known as numerical data):** Numeric data resulting from *measuring*.

A set of quantitative data can be either discrete or continuous quantitative data.

(2) **Qualitative data (also known as categorical data):** Usually non-numeric data that describe an attribute or characteristic of the items being studied. For example, yes or no responses, gender, type of car owned, place of birth, etc. Qualitative data can involve numbers. For example, area codes, bank accounts, etc.

FIGURE 1.1
Classification of Data

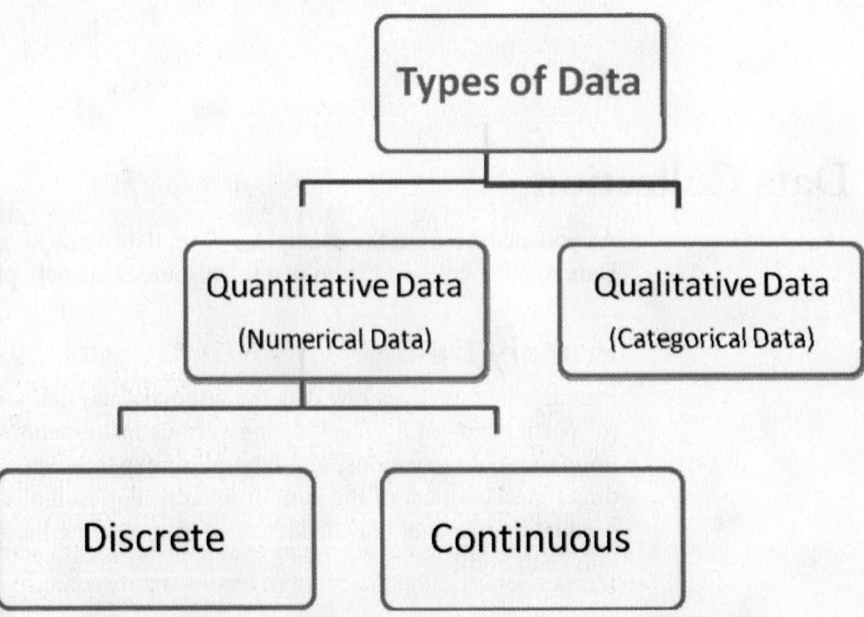

Quantitative Data

Quantitative data consist of data values that can be expressed in numerical values. Numerical values can be either discrete or continuous. Discrete variables have numerical values that arise from a counting process. "The number of premium cable channels subscribed to" is an example of a discrete numerical variable because the response is one of a finite number of integers. You subscribe to zero, one, two, or more channels. "The number of items purchased" is also a discrete numerical variable because you are counting the number of items purchased.

Continuous variables produce numerical responses that arise from a measuring process. The time you wait for teller service at a bank is an example of a continuous numerical variable because the response takes on any value within a continuum, or an interval, depending on the precision of the measuring instrument. For example, your waiting time could be 1 minute, 1.1 minutes, 1.11 minutes, or 1.113 minutes, depending on the precision of the measuring device used. (Theoretically, no two continuous values would ever be identical. However, because no measuring device is perfectly precise, identical continuous values for two or more items or individuals can occur.)

EXAMPLE 1.3
TABLE 1.4

Student	Did you bring your textbook to class today?	How much time (in hours) do you usually spend studying per week?	How many courses did you enroll in this semester?	Class Year	How did you come to school today?
1	Yes	20.3	3	Freshman	Take public transport
2	Yes	12.5	5	Sophomore	Drive
3	No	10.3	6	Junior	Walk
4	Yes	2.5	4	Junior	Drive
5	No	0.5	5	Senior	Take public transport
6	Yes	7.2	2	Sophomore	Drive
7	Yes	5.5	5	Freshman	Take public transport
8	No	10.0	4	Freshman	Walk
9	No	4.8	4	Freshman	Walk
10	Yes	3.2	3	Freshman	Drive
11	Yes	17.0	5	Senior	Take public transport
12	Yes	4.3	6	Freshman	Take public transport

Using the data above, the responses to the question "How much time (in hours) do you usually spend studying per week?" are classified as **quantitative *continuous* data**. Data collected can assume any value within some reasonable range. The values usually result from some form of measurement (e.g., the time it took you to get to class today, the amount of rainfall today, your weight, etc.). Note that the limitations of the measuring instrument are not to be considered when determining whether data is continuous or not. One interesting exception to the general statements above occurs when dealing with <u>money</u> data (such as income and salary). Even though you would think of money as a discrete quantity, this type of data is usually considered continuous.

TABLE 1.5 (A)

These responses are QUANTITATIVE CONTINUOUS data
How much time (in hours) do you usually spend studying per week?
20.3
12.5
10.3
2.5
0.5

The responses to the question "How many courses did you enroll in this semester?" are classified as **quantitative *discrete* data**. The values of the response are whole numbers. **Discrete data** have numerical values that arise from a counting process. "The number of magazines subscribed to" is an example of a discrete numerical variable because the response is one of a finite number of integers. You subscribe to zero, one, two, and so on magazines. The number of items that a customer purchases is also a discrete numerical variable because you are counting the number of items purchased.

TABLE 1.5 (B)

These responses are QUANTITATIVE Discrete data
How many courses did you enroll in this semester?
3
5
6
4
5

Qualitative Data

Qualitative data consist of data values that describe the characteristics or features of an item. Therefore, the data values are non-numeric in nature. For example, a survey asking students to rate an instructor's teaching as excellent, good, fair, or poor gathers qualitative data. "Excellent," "good," "fair," and "poor" are non-numeric values. However, qualitative data can involve numbers (e.g., area codes, bank accounts, etc.).

EXAMPLE 1.4

The responses to the questions "Did you bring your textbook to class today?" and "How did you come to school today?", as well as class year, are classified as **qualitative data**.

TABLE 1.6

These responses are QUALITATIVE data		
Did you bring your textbook to class today?	How did you come to school today?	Class Year
Yes	Take public transport	Freshman
Yes	Drive	Sophomore
No	Walk	Junior
Yes	Drive	Junior
No	Take public transport	Senior
Yes	Drive	Sophomore
Yes	Take public transport	Freshman

Test Your Understanding

Question 1: Which of the following is classified as **qualitative** data?

A. Data on brand of car (e.g., Honda, Toyota, Dodge, Madza, Chrysler, Ford)
B. Data on height (meters) (e.g., 1.7, 1.3, 1.5, 1.6, 1.4)
C. Data on mortgage rate (%) (e.g., 4.2, 2.5, 6.5, 3.6, 4.8, 2.6)
D. Data on income ($) (e.g., 20,000; 35,000; 40,000; 55,000; 43,000)

Answer: A

Question 2: Which of the following is classified as **quantitative** data?

A. Data on brand of car (e.g., Honda, Toyota, Dodge, Madza, Chrysler, Ford)
B. Data on postal code (e.g., N2J-4T3, T3Y-5N4, J5H-2J2)
C. Data on mortgage rate (%) (e.g., 4.2, 2.5, 6.5, 3.6, 4.8, 2.6)
D. Data on brand of laptop (e.g., Dell, Acer, Toshiba, Sony, Samsung)

Answer: C

Question 3: Which of the following data are **_not_** discrete quantitive data?

A. Data on number of child in a family (e.g., 0,1,2,3,4,5,6)
B. Data on number of correct answers on a test (e.g., 0,1,2,3,4,5,6)
C. Data on number of times you travelled a year (e.g., 0,1,2,3,4)
D. Data on income of a household

Answer: D

1.4 Why Do You Classify Your Data?

Data are gathered by using various methods. The most commonly used method in the business field is survey/questionnaires. The questions in a survey are used to collect responses from the respondents. You must learn to classify these response data in order to make informed decisions.

The type of data often dictates what calculations can be performed and what type of graphical display will be appropriate. One of the primary reasons for classifying data according to their types is to ensure proper use of statistical methodology to analyze the data. There are certain statistical analyses that are only meaningful with a certain type of data. For example, with a set of quantitative data, you can take the average of the values.

1.5 Measurement of Scales

Data can be classified according to the type of measurement scale that is involved. The measurement scale is the set of all the possible values that could result when the data is collected. The type of measurement scale often dictates what calculations can be performed and what type of graphical display will be appropriate.

Classify the Data into Different Types of Scales

TABLE 1.7
Classification of Data

Types of Data	Qualitative (Categorical)		Quantitative (Numerical)	
Measurement Scale	Nominal	Ordinal	Interval	Ratio
Numerical Data Value			Continuous/ Discrete	Continuous/ Discrete

To classify the data, you must first figure out the type of data. There are only two types of data: qualitative (categorical) and quantitative (numerical). **Qualitative** data can be classified into two scales: nominal and ordinal. **Quantitative** data can be classified into two scales: interval and ratio. Table 1.5 summarizes how data are classified.

The four levels of measurement scales are the following:

1. Ratio
2. Interval
3. Ordinal
4. Nominal

The highest level of scale is ratio, followed by interval and ordinal. Nominal scale is the lowest level of scale. Qualitative data are usually associated with either a nominal or ordinal scale. Quantitative data are associated with either a ratio or interval scale.

1.6   Define Measurement Scales

Nominal

These data are qualitative data that have no particular order or ranking in their categories. (Note: Alphabetic order is not a consideration.) The categories may be either numeric or non-numeric. In either case, the data is <u>qualitative</u>.

EXAMPLE 1.5

- **Marital Status:** Single, married, divorced, or widowed. On a survey, the results of this question could be recorded as 1 = single, 2 = married, etc. Even though the data are recorded as numbers, it is still <u>qualitative</u>.
- **Check-out lane used in grocery store:** 1, 2, 3, etc. The checkout lanes could have been labelled A, B, C, or if the store had various colour schemes, the lanes could have been indicated by their colour.
- **Sport:** Tennis, swimming, soccer, etc.
- **Colour of your eyes:** Brown, blue, etc.
- **Postal Code:** N2N 5X8, T3M 5H8, etc.
- **Car brand:** Ford, Mazda, Toyota, etc.
- **Country:** Canada, United States, Norway, etc.

FIGURE 1.2

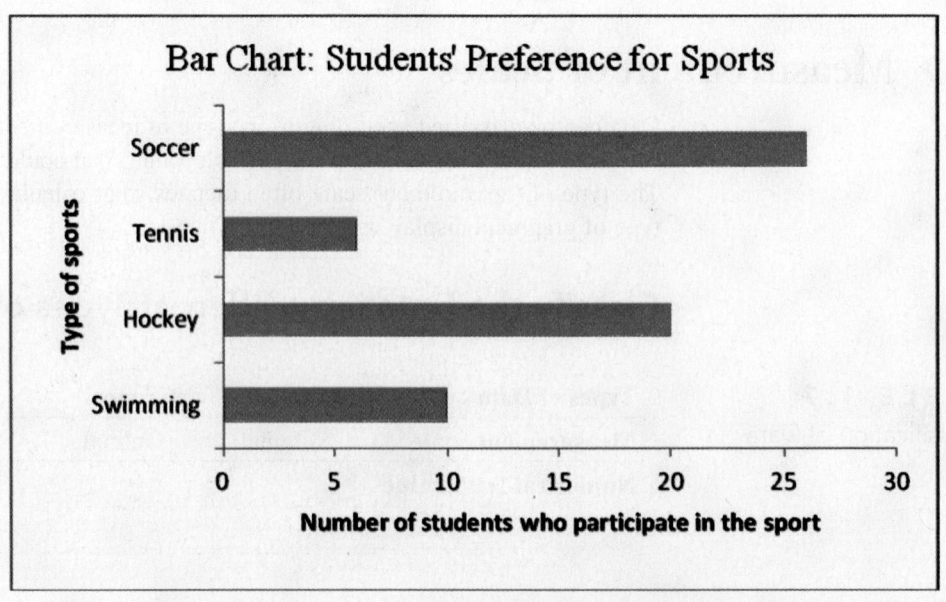

Bar Chart: Students' Preference for Sports

The only calculations that can be performed on nominal data are based on the number of responses in each category. Bar, pie, and Pareto charts (see Chapter 2 for more information on charts) may be useful for displaying the results of this type of data collection. The data on sports (e.g., soccer, tennis, hockey, and swimming) are classified as nominal scale and can be represented graphically in a bar chart as shown in the following figure. Each bar represents the number of students participating in each type of sports.

Ordinal

These data are similar to nominal data in that categories are involved; however, there is a natural <u>order</u> to the categories. We can say that one category is higher or better than another. Again, the categories can be numeric or non-numeric and are considered <u>qualitative</u>. Bar and pie charts are appropriate graphs for displaying results.

EXAMPLE 1.6	•**Professorial rank:** Lecturer, assistant professor, associate professor, and professor •**Rating of a service:** Excellent, good, average, poor, very poor •**Letter grades:** A+, A, A-, B+, etc. •**Medals awarded in Olympic Games:** Gold, Silver, Bronze

Once again, the only type of calculations that can be performed with these data are based on, the number of values in each category.

TABLE 1.8

2010 Winter
Olympic Medals
Summary Table

(source:

http://en.wikipedia.org/wiki/2010

*_Winter_Olympics_medal_table_*

The variable "medals awarded" is an ordinal scale, and the variable "nation" is a nominal scale.

Rank	Nation	Gold	Silver	Bronze	Total
1	Canada (CAN)	14	7	5	26
2	Germany (GER)	10	13	7	30
3	United States (USA)	9	15	13	37
4	Norway (NOR)	9	8	6	23
5	South Korea (KOR)	6	6	2	14
6	Switzerland (SUI)	6	0	3	9
7	China (CHN)	5	2	4	11
7	Sweden (SWE)	5	2	4	11
9	Austria (AUT)	4	6	6	16
10	Netherlands (NED)	4	1	3	8
11	Russia (RUS)	3	5	7	15
12	France (FRA)	2	3	6	11
13	Australia (AUS)	2	1	0	3
14	Czech Republic (CZE)	2	0	4	6
15	Poland (POL)	1	3	2	6
16	Italy (ITA)	1	1	3	5
17	Belarus (BLR)	1	1	1	3
17	Slovakia (SVK)	1	1	1	3
19	Great Britain (GBR)	1	0	0	1

20	● Japan (JPN)	0	3	2	5
21	Croatia (CRO)	0	2	1	3
21	Slovenia (SLO)	0	2	1	3
23	Latvia (LAT)	0	2	0	2
24	✚ Finland (FIN)	0	1	4	5
25	Estonia (EST)	0	1	0	1
25	Kazakhstan (KAZ)	0	1	0	1
Total		**86**	**87**	**85**	**258**

Interval

The distinguishing feature of interval data, as compared to nominal and ordinal data, is that the data have <u>units of measurement</u>. The data must be numeric and are <u>quantitative</u> (either discrete or continuous). As a result, the interval between data values has a meaning. The other characteristic of significance in interval data is that the value "0" (zero) is only an <u>arbitrary reference point</u>. In other words, a value of zero does not mean that there is no amount of the characteristic being measured.

EXAMPLE 1.7

- **Data on temperature:** 0° C does not mean there is no heat.
  The difference between 10° C and 11° C is the same as the difference between 20° C and 21° C. If you had a container of water at 10° C and a similarly sized container at 20° C, then the exact same amount of heat would have to be added to both containers to increase the temperature to 11° C and 21° C, respectively.
- **Calendar scale:** The date "0" is just a reference point.
  The difference between the dates February 2 and February 9 is 7 days, and this is the same amount of time as the difference between March 21 and March 28.

  Note: Interval data is <u>not</u> of great importance to us in business because other than when measuring temperature, we rarely come across this type of data.

Ratio

Ratio data has the characteristics of interval data, but the "0" value does mean the absence of the characteristic being measured (i.e., 0 = "nothing") and the ratio of data values is meaningful. Ratio data may be continuous or discrete.

Examples of <u>discrete</u> ratio data:

- Number of vacations you have taken in the past 10 years
- Number of part-time employees in your company
- Number of DVD movies you own

Examples of <u>continuous</u> ratio data:

- Size of your house (in square meters)
- Gas price (in cents)
- Sales (in dollars)
- Distance (in km)

How Is the *Ratio* of Data Values Meaningful?

The name "ratio" is appropriate because meaningful results occur when two data values are divided.

For example,
The distance between A and B is 10 km and the distance between C and D is 5 km. Compare the two distances. You have

$$\frac{10 \ km}{5 \ km} = 2$$ In other words, the distance of AB is twice the distance of CD.

Also, the same is true for discrete ratio data. Let's consider the variable "number of classes you are currently attending." If you attend 12 classes and your friend attends 6 classes, we can say that you attended twice as many classes as your friend.

All types of calculations can be performed with ratio data. Histograms, polygons, ogives, stem and-leaf displays, and box-whisker plots are all useful graphs of ratio data.

How Do You Differentiate between Interval and Ratio Scales?

Use these two indicators to differentiate between interval and ratio scales. These two indicators are the following:

1. **Using zero**
   For interval scale, "zero" is a reference point, but "zero" is meaningful for ratio scale where zero means "absence of the characteristic." For example, zero textbook means "no textbook." We know that the variable temperature is an interval scale. If your thermometer shows 0° C, does that indicate "absence of temperature" or "no temperature"? You know the answer is no!
2. **Comparing two values**
   Interval scale has meaningful difference between two values, and ratio has meaningful division of two values.

Now consider the following example. The temperature in Location A is 10° C and the temperature in Location B is 5° C. Compare the temperature in the two locations. You have

$$\frac{10° \ C}{5° \ C} = 2$$ In other words, Location A is twice as hot as Location B. Is this correct?

No! You can say that the temperature difference between the two locations is 5° C. Temperature is measured on an interval scale, so the result of a division is not meaningful.

Example of a ratio scale: Salary
Employee A earns $40,000 and employee B earns $20,000. That means employee A earns twice as much as employee B. $\left(\frac{\$40,000}{\$20,000} = 2 \right)$

Test Your Understanding

Question 1. How would you rate the service provided by the Toronto Transit Commission (TTC)?
1. Excellent
2. Good
3. Average
4. Poor

What is the **highest** measurement scale that applies to the set of response data?
A. Nominal
B. Ordinal
C. Interval
D. Ratio – Discrete
E. Ratio – Continuous

Answer: B

Question 2. What are the total sales of your company?
1. less than $200,000
2. between $200,000 and $300,000
3. between $300,000 and $400,000
4. between $400,000 and $500,000
5. between $500,000 and $600,000
6. $600,000 or more

What is the **highest** measurement scale that applies to the set of response data?
  A. Nominal
  B. Ordinal
  C. Interval
  D. Ratio – Discrete
  E. Ratio – Continuous

Answer: E (Note: Although the response data is presented in categories of sales)

Question 3. What is your major in your program?
  1. Accounting
  2. Finance
  3. Human Resources
  4. Management

What is the measurement scale that applies to the set of response data?
  A. Nominal
  B. Ordinal
  C. Interval
  D. Ratio – Discrete
  E. Ratio – Continuous

Answer: A (Note: You cannot rank the program majors in an order.)

Question 4. Which year did you graduate from high school?

What is the measurement scale of the response data?
  A. Ratio
  B. Interval
  C. Ordinal
  D. Nominal
  E. None of the above

Answer: B

1.7 How Do You Transform a Higher-Level Scale to a Lower-Level Scale?

"Downgrading" a scale means transforming a higher-level scale to a lower-level scale. One reason for changing a scale is because of sensitive questions requested in a survey that caused non-response bias. Non-response bias means that respondents will elicit no response. Questions pertaining to age and income may be too personal for respondents to answer. These questions are sensitive questions that respondents may refuse to answer in a survey. By classifying the responses into classes (or categories), the respondents will feel less discomfort when responding to these sensitive questions. For this reason, you may want to transform the data as shown in Examples 1.8 and 1.9. You can downgrade a higher-level scale to the next level of measurement scale. In Example 1.8 of question 1, the age variable is measured on a ratio scale that can be transformed to an ordinal scale by changing the responses to several categories of age as shown in Example 1.8 of question 2.

The possible response categories for the question "What is your age?" are given next:

  [ ] 15–20
  [ ] 20–25
  [ ] 25–30

This "age" variable is now classified as qualitative data because the responses are in categories of age as shown in Example 1.8 of question 2. This age variable is now measured on an ordinal scale because you can order the responses from young to old. So you have "downgraded" quantitative data to qualitative data. By doing so, you lose the ability to summarize the data numerically (e.g., mean, median). It is recommended that you collect data in the highest scale (i.e., ratio scale).

Similarly, in Example 1.9 of question 1, the income variable is measured on a ratio scale that can be downgraded to an ordinal scale by changing the response to categories of income as shown in Example 1.9 of question 2.

EXAMPLE 1.8

Variable: Age	Measurement scale
Question 1: What is your age?_____ years.	Ratio scale
Question 2: What is your age? [ ] 15–20 [ ] 20–25 [ ] 25–30	Ordinal scale

EXAMPLE 1.9

Variable: Salary	Measurement scale
Question 1: What is your salary? $ _____	Ratio scale
Question 2: What is your salary? [ ] 0–10,000 [ ] 10,000–20,000 [ ] 20,000–30,000	Ordinal scale

SUMMARY

Statistics is the collection of methods that help you make better sense of the data used every day to describe and analyze the world. Statistics is a core skill necessary for a complete business education. Businesses use statistics to summarize and reach conclusions from data, to make reliable forecasts, and to improve business processes. In this chapter, you learned the basic vocabulary of statistics and the various types of data used in business. In the next two chapters, you will study data collection and a variety of tables and charts and descriptive measures that are used to present and analyze data.

KEY TERMS

categorical data   6
continuous data   7
descriptive statistics   3
discrete data   8
inferential statistics   3

population   6
primary source   5
qualitative data   6
quantitative data   6
sample   6

statistic   3
parameter   3
secondary source   6
variable   6

PROBLEMS

LEARNING THE BASICS

1.1 Consider the following questions being asked on a survey. The possible responses for each person are given. What is the measurement scale for each response data?

  a. What was the rating of the restaurant in which you last had dinner with your partner?
    a) ★
    b) ★★
    c) ★★★
    d) ★★★★
    e) ★★★★★

  b. What is the rating of your favourite television show?
    a) TV-G
    b) TV-PG
    c) TV-14
    d) TV-MA

  c. What is your marital status?
    a) Married
    b) Common Law

c) Widowed
d) Divorced
e) Separated
f) Single

d. What is your level of education?
  a) Elementary School
  b) High School
  c) College
  d) University-Undergrad
  e) University-Post Grad

e. What stock-exchange are the majority of your stock investments listed on?
  a) TSX
  b) NYSE
  c) AMEX
  d) NASDAQ
  e) VSE

f. What type of accommodation do you usually choose for your overnight stay when on a car trip?
  a) Hotel
  b) Motel
  c) Bed & Breakfast
  d) Country Inn
  e) Cabin/Cottage

g. What was the rating of the last motel that you stayed in?
  a) ★
  b) ★★

c) ★★★
d) ★★★★
e) ★★★★★

h. What is your postal code? Answer: _____

i. What was the rating of the last movie that you saw in a theatre?
  a) G
  b) PG
  c) PG-13
  d) R
  e) NC-17
  f) X

j. What is your favourite meat?
  a) Beef
  b) Pork
  c) Chicken
  d) Veal
  e) Lamb

1.2 Refer to the following chart, from the autumn 1999 issue of *Canadian Social Trends*, that shows data regarding seniors who have driver's licenses and also a health condition. Many seniors were surveyed and much data were obtained from each respondent. The responses to four questions were used to obtain the data to allow the researchers to construct the chart shown. What type of measurement scale is used for each type of data? Are the values discrete or continuous?

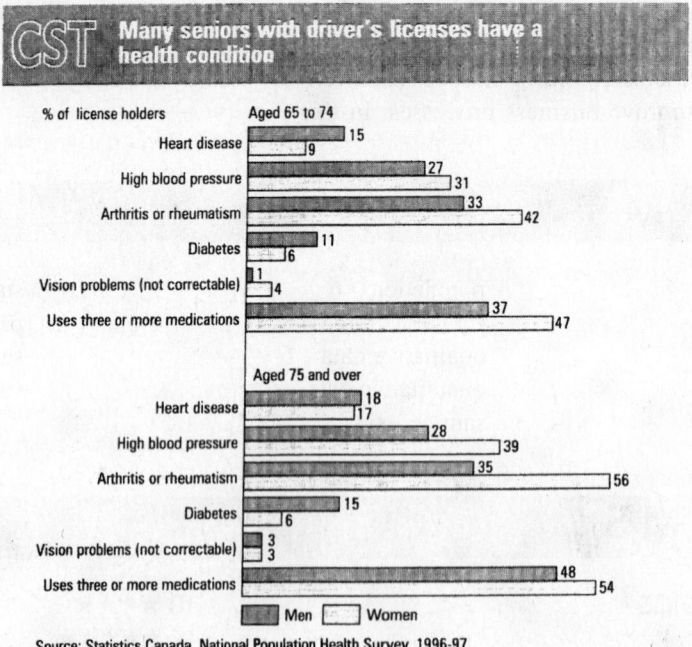

Source: Statistics Canada, National Population Health Survey, 1996-97.

Question	Measurement Scale	Discrete/Continuous

1.3 The responses to two questions in a survey were used by researchers to construct the following bar chart. Assume that this survey was given to the registered nurses employed in the nursing field.

Proportion of registered nurses employed in the nursing field by age and year

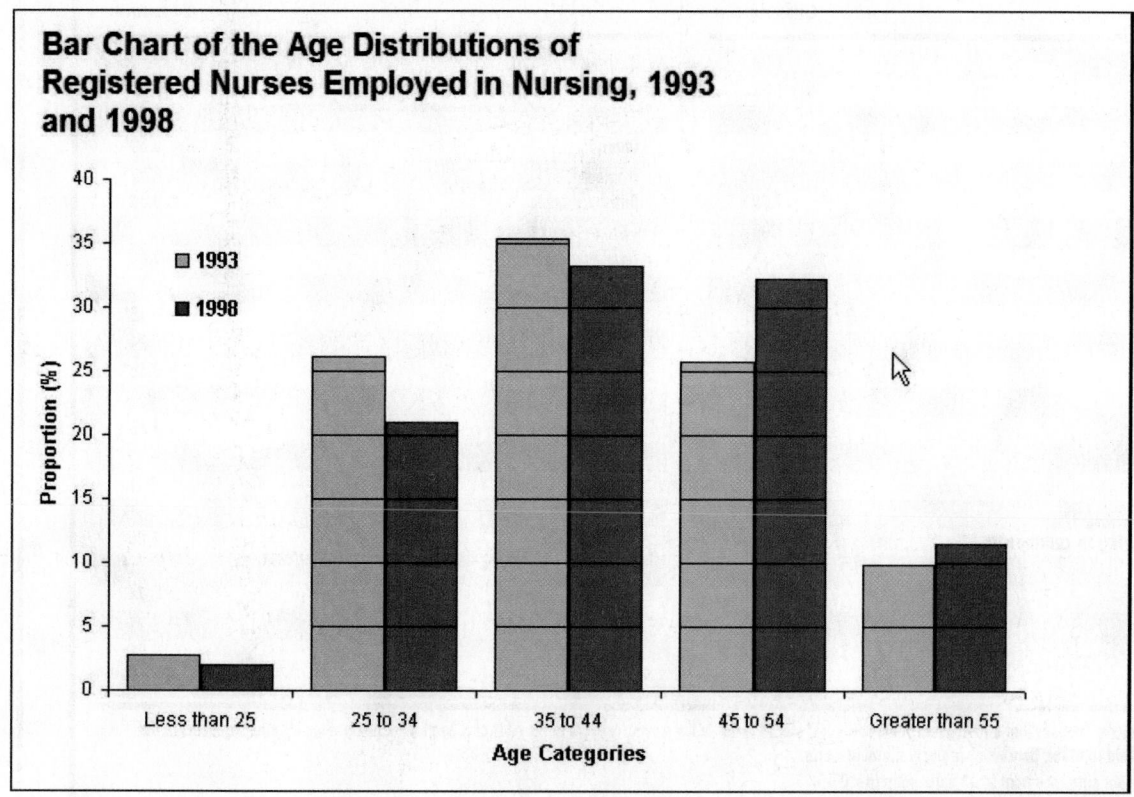

Source: *Registered Nurses Database (RNDB), 1998. (The bar chart appeared on the National Resources Canada's Web site:* http://atlas.nrcan.gc.ca/site/english/maps/health/resources/nursing/nursing_figure7.gif/image_view)

I. What are the two questions?

Question 1: _____

Question 2: _____

II. What is the highest measurement scale that applies to the set of response data from the first question?
a) Nominal
b) Ordinal
c) Interval
d) Ratio – Discrete
e) Ratio – Continuous

III. What is the highest measurement scale that applies to the set of response data from the second question?
a) Nominal
b) Ordinal
c) Interval
d) Ratio – Discrete
e) Ratio – Continuous

1.4 Refer to the table published in *Canadian Social Trends* (CST), that shows data regarding adults aged between 22 and 29 years old with a sense of community and who have higher odds of voting.

Ten questions were asked to obtain data in order to formulate the following table. One of the questions was "What is your gender?" and another was "Did you volunteer in the past year?"

Your task is to identify the remaining eight questions. For each question, identify the type of measurement scale that applies to the set of response data. Use the following measurement scales:
(a) Nominal
(b) Ordinal
(c) Interval - Continuous
(d) Ratio – Discrete
(e) Ratio – Continuous

Use the following table to record your answers.

TABLE 1.9

CST	22- to 29-year-olds with a very strong sense of community have higher odds of voting than those with a weaker sense of belonging			
	Odds ratio			**Odds ratio**
Age[1]	1.03	**Region**		
Youth involvement[2]	1.03	*Quebec*		*1.00*
Number of groups of which a member	1.11[3]	Atlantic		0.38*
		Ontario		0.30*
Sex		Prairies		0.32*
Female	*1.00*	British Columbia		0.36*
Male	1.08	**Educational level**		
Place of birth		*University degree*		*1.00*
Foreign-born	*1.00*	Less than high school		0.25*
Canadian-born	4.27*	High school graduate		0.48*
Religious observance		Some post-secondary		0.74
Rarely/never	*1.00*	Diploma or certificate		0.68*
Weekly	0.86	**Main activity**		
Sometimes	1.40*	*Other[4]*		*1.00*
Volunteer in past year		Labour force		1.10
No	*1.00*	Student		0.81
Yes	1.42*	**Household income**		
Sense of belonging to community		*$60,000 or more*		*1.00*
Very weak	*1.00*	Less than $20,000		0.51*
Very strong	1.74*	$20,000 to $29,999		0.74
Somewhat strong	1.30	$30,000 to $39,999		0.75
Somewhat weak	1.26	$40,000 to $49,999		1.00
		$50,000 to $59,999		0.66*

Note: This table presents the odds that a respondent voted in the last election prior to the survey, relative to the odds of a benchmark group when all other variables in the analysis are held constant. Benchmark group is shown in italics.
*   Statistically significant difference from benchmark group (p<0.05).
1.   For each additional year, the odds of voting increase by 3%.
2.   For each additional activity during youth, the odds of voting increase by 3%.
3.   For each additional group, the odds of voting increase by 11%, which is statistically significant (p<0.05).
4.   "Other" includes activities such as homemaking, retirement, volunteer work or illness.
Source: Statistics Canada, General Social Survey, 2003.

Source: *Canadian Social Trends*, Issue: Winter 2005, page 5. Web site: http://dsp-psd.tpsgc.gc.ca/Collection-R/Statcan/11-008-XIE/0030511-008-XIE.pdf

Question	What is the measurement scale? (a) Nominal (b) Ordinal (c) Interval Continuous (d) Ratio – Discrete (e) Ratio – Continuous
1	
2	
3	
4	
5	
6	
7	
8	

1.5 Refer to the following chart that shows data regarding the majority of young adults who are engaged in at least one non-voting political activity. The chart was produced by asking a question in a survey. What type of measurement scale applies to the set of response data?

FIGURE 1.4

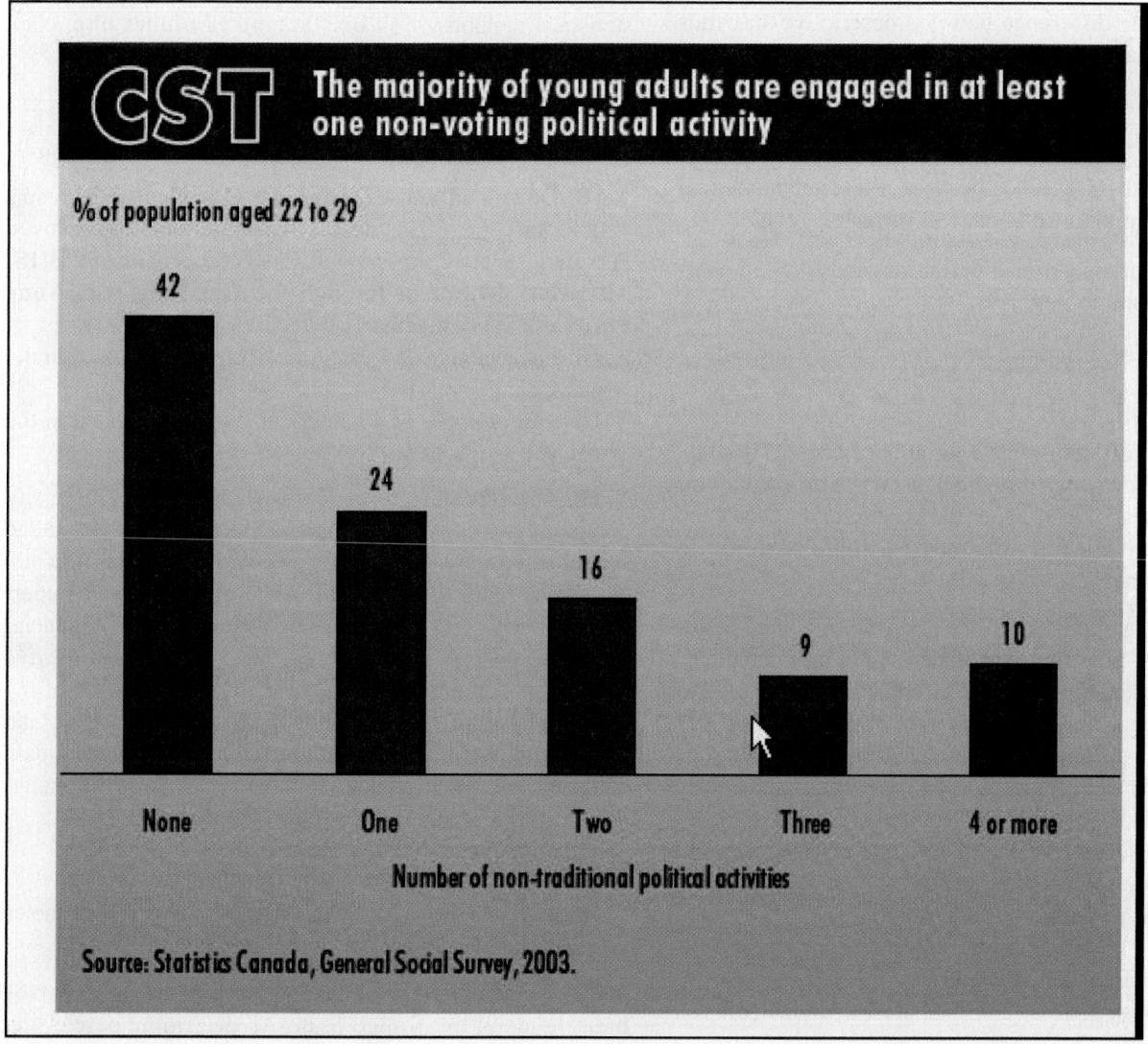

% of population aged 22 to 29

The majority of young adults are engaged in at least one non-voting political activity

CST

| None | One | Two | Three | 4 or more |

42   24   16   9   10

Number of non-traditional political activities

Source: Statistics Canada, General Social Survey, 2003.

Source: *Canadian Social Trends*, Issue: Winter 2005, page 3. Web site: http://dsp-psd.tpsgc.gc.ca/Collection-R/Statcan/11-008-XIE/0030511-008-XIE.pdf

a) Nominal
b) Ordinal
c) Interval – Continuous
d) Ratio – Discrete
e) Ratio – Continuous

CHECKING YOUR UNDERSTANDING

1.6 What is the difference between a sample and a population?

1.7 What is the difference between a statistic and a parameter?

1.8 What is the difference between descriptive statistics and inferential statistics?

1.9 What is the difference between a categorical variable and a numerical variable?

1.10 What is the difference between a discrete numerical variable and a continuous numerical variable?

1.11 What is an operational definition, and why are operational definitions so important?

1.12 What is the difference between a variable and data?

APPLYING THE CONCEPTS

1.13 Visit the official website for either Excel or Minitab, **www.office.microsoft.com/excel** or **www.minitab.com/products/minitab**. Read about the program you chose and then think about the ways the program could be useful in statistical analysis.

1.14 In 2008, a university in the midwestern United States surveyed its full-time first-year students after they completed their first semester. Surveys were electronically distributed to all 3,727 students, and responses were obtained from 2,821 students. Of the students surveyed, 90.1% indicated that they had studied with other students, and 57.1% indicated that they had tutored another student. The report also noted that 61.3% of the students surveyed came to class late at least once, and 45.8% admitted to being bored in class at least once.
a. Describe the population of interest.
b. Describe the sample that was collected.
c. Describe a parameter of interest.
d. Describe the statistic used to estimate the parameter in (c).

1.15 The Gallup organization releases the results of recent polls at its website, **www.gallup.com**. Visit this site and read an article of interest.
a. Describe the population of interest.
b. Describe the sample that was collected.
c. Describe a parameter of interest.
d. Describe the statistic used to describe the parameter in (c).

1.16 A Gallup poll indicated that 74% of Americans who had yet to retire look to retirement accounts as major funding sources when they retire. Interestingly, 40% also said that they looked to stocks or stock market mutual fund investments as major funding sources when they retire. (data extracted from D. Jacobs, "Investors Look Beyond Social Security to Fund Retirement," **www.gallup.com**, March 28, 2011). The results are based on telephone interviews conducted March 24, 2011, with 1,000 or more adults living in the United States, aged 18 and older.

a. Describe the population of interest.
b. Describe the sample that was collected.
c. Is 74% a parameter or a statistic? Explain.
d. Is 40% a parameter or a statistic?

1.17 The Data and Story Library (DASL) is an online library of data files and stories that illustrate the use of basic statistical methods. Visit **lib.stat.cmu.edu/index.php**, click DASL and explore a data set of interest to you.
a. Describe a variable in the data set you selected.
b. Is the variable categorical or numerical?
c. If the variable is numerical, is it discrete or continuous?

1.18 Download and examine the U.S. Census Bureau's "2007 Survey of Business Owners and Self-Employed Persons," directly available at **bhs.econ.census.gov/BHS/SBO/sbo1_07.pdf** or through the **Get Help with Your Form** link at **www.census.gov/econ/sbo**.
a. Give an example of a categorical variable included in the survey.
b. Give an example of a numerical variable included in the survey.

1.19 Three professors at Northern Kentucky University compared two different approaches to teaching courses in the school of business (M. W. Ford, D. W. Kent, and S. Devoto, "Learning from the Pros: Influence of Web-Based Expert Commentary on Vicarious Learning About Financial Markets," *Decision Sciences Journal of Innovative Education*, January 2007, 5(1), 43–63). At the time of the study, there were 2,100 students in the business school, and 96 students were involved in the study. Demographic data collected on these 96 students included class (freshman, sophomore, junior, senior), age, gender, and major.
a. Describe the population of interest.
b. Describe the sample that was collected.
c. Indicate whether each of the four demographic variables mentioned is categorical or numerical.

1.20 A manufacturer of cat food was planning to survey households in the United States to determine purchasing habits of cat owners. Among the variables to be collected are the following:
  i. The primary place of purchase for cat food
  ii. Whether dry or moist cat food is purchased
  iii. The number of cats living in the household
  iv. Whether any cat living in the household is pedigreed
a. For each of the four items listed, indicate whether the variable is categorical or numerical. If it is numerical, is it discrete or continuous?
b. Develop five categorical questions for the survey.
c. Develop five numerical questions for the survey.

1.21 A sample of 62 undergraduate students answered the following survey:
  1. What is your gender? Female _____ Male _____
  2. What is your age (*as of last birthday*)? _____

3. What is your current registered class designation?
   Freshman _____ Sophomore _____ Junior _____
   Senior _____
4. What is your major area of study?
   Accounting _____
   Computer Information Systems _____
   Economics/Finance _____
   International Business _____ Management _____
   Retailing/Marketing _____
   Other _____ Undecided _____
5. At the present time, do you plan to attend graduate school?
   Yes _____ No _____ Not sure _____
6. What is your current cumulative grade point average?
   _____
7. What is your current employment status?
   Full time _____ Part time _____ Unemployed _____
8. What would you expect your starting annual salary (*in $000*) to be if you were to seek full-time employment immediately after obtaining your bachelor's degree?
   _____
9. For how many social networking sites are you registered? _____
10. How satisfied are you with the food and dining services on campus? _____

	1	2	3	4	5	6	7	
Extremely			Neutral				Extremely	
unsatisfied							satisfied	

11. About how much money did you spend this semester for textbooks and supplies? _____
12. What type of computer do you prefer to use for your studies?
    Desktop _____ Laptop _____
    Tablet/notebook/netbook _____
13. How many text messages do you send in a typical week? _____
14. How much wealth (income, savings, investment, real estate, and other assets) would you have to accumulate (in millions of dollars) before you would say you are rich? _____
    a. Which variables in the survey are categorical?
    b. Which variables in the survey are numerical?
    c. Which variables are discrete numerical variables?

The results of the survey are stored in `UndergradSurvey`

1.22 A sample of 44 graduate students answered the following survey:
1. What is your gender? Female _____ Male _____
2. What is your age (*as of last birthday*)? _____

3. What is your current major area of study?
   Accounting _____
   Economics/Finance _____
   Management _____
   Retailing/Marketing _____
   Other _____ Undecided _____
4. What is your current graduate cumulative grade point average? _____
5. What was your undergraduate major?
   Biological Sciences _____ Business _____
   Computers _____
   Engineering _____
   Other _____
6. What was your undergraduate cumulative grade point average? _____
7. What is your current employment status?
   Full time _____ Part time _____ Unemployed _____
8. How many different full-time jobs have you held in the past 10 years? _____
9. What do you expect your annual salary (*in $000*) to be immediately after completion of your graduate studies if you are employed full time? _____
10. About how much money did you spend this semester for textbooks and supplies? _____
11. How satisfied are you with the MBA program advisory services on campus?

	1	2	3	4	5	6	7	
Extremely			Neutral				Extremely	
unsatisfied							satisfied	

12. What type of computer do you prefer to use for your studies?
    Desktop _____ Laptop _____ Tablet/notebook/netbook _____
13. How many text messages do you send in a typical week? _____
14. How much wealth (income, savings, investment, real estate, and other assets) would you have to accumulate (in millions of dollars) before you would say you are rich? _____
    a. Which variables in the survey are categorical?
    b. Which variables in the survey are numerical?
    c. Which variables are discrete numerical variables?

The results of the survey are stored in `GradSurvey`

END-OF-CHAPTER CASES

At the end of most chapters, you will find a continuing case study that allows you to apply statistics to problems faced by the management of the Ashland MultiComm Services, a residential telecommunications provider. You will also find a series of Digital Cases that extend many of the Using Statistics scenarios that begin each chapter.

LEARNING WITH THE DIGITAL CASES

People use statistical techniques to help communicate and present important information to others both inside and outside their businesses. Every day, as in these examples, people misuse these techniques. Identifying and preventing misuses of statistics, whether intentional or not, is an important responsibility for all managers. The Digital Cases help you develop the skills necessary for this important task.

A Digital Case asks you to review electronic documents related to a company or statistical issue discussed in the chapter's Using Statistics scenario. You review the contents of these documents, which may contain internal confidential as well as publicly stated facts and claims, seeking to identify and correct misuses of statistics. Unlike a traditional case study, but like many business situations, not all of the information you encounter will be relevant to your task, and you may occasionally discover conflicting information that you have to resolve in order to complete the case.

To assist your learning, each Digital Case begins with a learning objective and a summary of the problem or issue at hand. Each case directs you to the information necessary to reach your own conclusions and to answer the case questions. You can work with the documents for the Digital Cases offline, after downloading them from this book's download page. Or you can work with the Digital Cases online, chapter-by-chapter, at the companion website.

DIGITAL CASE EXAMPLE

This section illustrates learning with a Digital Case. To begin, open the Digital Case file **GTM.pdf**, which contains contents from the Good Tunes & More website. Recall that the privately held Good Tunes & More, the subject of the Using Statistics scenario in this chapter, is seeking financing to expand its business by opening retail locations. Because the managers are eager to show that Good Tunes & More is a thriving business, it is not surprising to discover the "our best sales year ever" claim in the "Good Times at Good Tunes & More" section on the first page.

Click the **our best sales year ever** link to display the page that supports this claim. How would you support such a claim? With a table of numbers? A chart? Remarks attributed to a knowledgeable source? Good Tunes & More has used a chart to present "two years ago" and "latest twelve months" sales data by category. Are there any problems with the choices made on this web page? *Absolutely*!

First, note that there are no scales for the symbols used, so it is impossible to know what the actual sales volumes are. In fact, charts that incorporate symbols in this way are considered examples of *chartjunk* and would never be used by people seeking to properly use graphs.

This important point aside, another question that arises is whether the sales data represent the number of units sold or something else. The use of the symbols creates the impression that unit sales data are being presented. If the data are unit sales, does such data best support the claim being made, or would something else, such as dollar volumes, be a better indicator of sales at the retailer?

Then there are those curious chart labels. "Latest twelve months" is ambiguous; it could include months from the current year as well as months from one year ago and therefore may not be an equivalent time period to "two years ago." But the business was established in 1997, and the claim being made is "best sales year ever," so why hasn't management included sales figures for *every* year?

Are Good Tunes & More managers hiding something, or are they just unaware of the proper use of statistics? Either way, they have failed to properly communicate a vital aspect of their story.

In subsequent Digital Cases, you will be asked to provide this type of analysis, using the open-ended questions in the case as your guide. Not all the cases are as straightforward as this example, and some cases include perfectly appropriate applications of statistics.

REFERENCES

1. Davenport, T., and J. Harris, *Competing on Analytics: The New Science of Winning* (Boston: Harvard Business School Press, 2007).

2. Davenport, T., J. Harris, and R. Morrison, *Analytics at Work* (Boston: Harvard Business School Press, 2010).

3. McCullough, B. D., and D. Heiser, "On the Accuracy of Statistical Procedures in Microsoft Excel 2007," *Computational Statistics and Data Analysis*, 52 (2008), 4568–4606.

4. McCullough, B. D., and B. Wilson, "On the Accuracy of Statistical Procedures in Microsoft Excel 97," *Computational Statistics and Data Analysis*, 31 (1999), 27–37.

5. McCullough, B. D., and B. Wilson, "On the Accuracy of Statistical Procedures in Microsoft Excel 2003," *Computational Statistics and Data Analysis*, 49 (2005), 1244–1252.

6. *Microsoft Excel 2010* (Redmond, WA: Microsoft Corporation, 2010).

7. *Minitab Release 16* (State College, PA: Minitab, Inc., 2010).

8. Nash, J. C., "Spreadsheets in Statistical Practice— Another Look," *The American Statistician*, 60 (2006), 287–289.

9. New York 1964 World's Fair," *National Geographic*, April 1965, p. 526

10. Thompson, C. "What Is I.B.M.'s Watson?". **http://www.nytimes.com/2010/06/20/magazine/20Computer-t.html**, June 20, 2010, p. MM30 of the Sunday Magazine.

2 Graphical Presentation of Qualitative Data

Learning Objectives

In this chapter, you learn:

- To develop tables and charts for categorical data
- To create tables and charts using the Casio Calculator
- The principles of properly presenting graphs

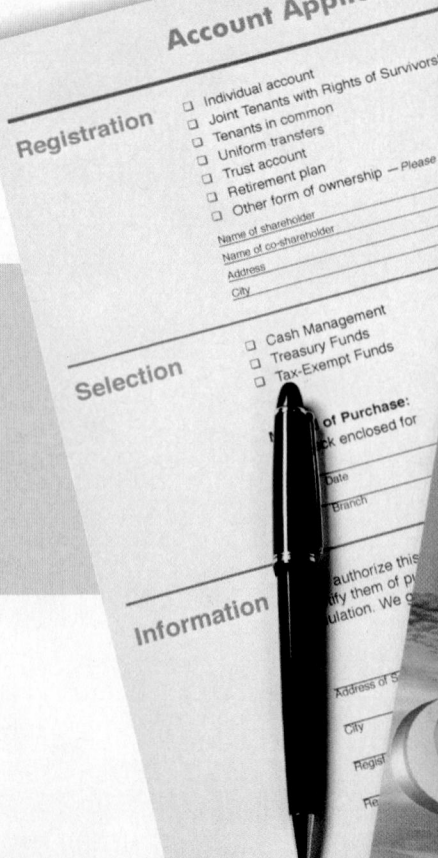

In Chapter 1, you learned to distinguish the types of data and measurement scales. In this chapter, you learn to present qualitative data graphically in the form of a summary table, bar chart, pie chart, and pareto chart.

2.1 How Do You Organize Qualitative Data Graphically?

Qualitative data consist of data values that describe a characteristic or feature of an item. Examples of these types of variables are occupational title, ethnicity, educational level, marital status, types of aircraft, and mode of transportation.

The only calculations that can be performed on **nominal data** and **ordinal data** are based on the number of responses in each category. Bar charts, pie charts, and Pareto charts may be useful for displaying the results of these type of data collection.

EXAMPLE 2.1

A random sample of 100 respondents were asked the question "How do you go to work or school?"

The possible responses to the question are

[   ] Bus
[   ] Train (GO train or TTC)
[   ] Car
[   ] Walk
[   ] None of the above

The response data are qualitative data that are measured on a nominal scale. The data collected from 100 respondents are displayed in Table 2.1.

TABLE 2.1

The code of "1" denotes "Bus"; "2" denotes "Train (GO train or TTC)", "3" denotes "Car"; "4" denotes "Walk"; and "5" denotes "None of the above"

1	2	4	4	4	4	1	1	4	2	4	4	5	4	4	4	2	4	2	5
2	1	3	4	3	1	4	1	1	1	1	2	3	4	2	4	2	4	2	4
3	2	1	1	3	3	2	3	3	5	3	2	3	2	4	4	3	5	4	4
4	3	2	2	1	5	2	3	2	3	4	2	4	3	2	2	2	4	2	4
4	3	1	2	1	1	2	4	5	4	4	4	4	3	3	3	3	4	4	4

The Summary Table

The data shown in Table 2.1 can be summarized in a summary table. A summary table is made up of two columns, where one column specifies the categories and the other column represents the number of occurrences (known as frequency), which can also be expressed as percentage of occurrence.

The summary table in Table 2.2 is based on the question "How do you go to work or school?"

TABLE 2.2
Summary Table of
"How do you go to
work or school?"

How do you go to work or school?	Number of persons
Bus	15
Train (GO train or TTC)	24
Car	20
Walk	35
None of the above	6
Total	100

Bar Chart

The summary table can be displayed graphically as a bar chart. The rectangle bars in the bar chart represent the frequency (or number of occurrences) for each category. The bars can be shown either vertically or horizontally. The vertical bar chart is a graph with vertical bars. Similarly, a horizontal bar chart is a graph with horizontal bars.

How to construct a bar chart using the CASIO Calculator

EXAMPLE 2.2

Create a horizontal bar chart of "How do you go to work or school?" using the CASIO fx-9750GII calculator.

You will learn to use the CASIO fx-9750GII to create a bar chart for modes of transportation based on the data in Table 2.2 and interpret the results.

Follow the calculator procedures to create a __horizontal__ bar chart.

From the **Main Menu** select **STAT** mode and press **EXE**.
If you have difficulty following the instruction, I recommend that you read the "Calculator Lesson 1" at the end of this chapter.

You may enter the data from Table 2.2 in List 1 as follows:

LIST 1
15 EXE
24 EXE
20 EXE
35 EXE
6 EXE

Use the **F6** key (▷) if necessary to get the following menu choices at the bottom of the display:
To create a bar chart, press the **F1** key to select "**GRPH**."

GRPH	CALC	TEST	INTR	DIST	▷
F1	F2	F3	F4	F5	F6

After you have selected "**GRPH**," you will see the following menu choices at the bottom of the display. Press **F6** key to select "**SET**."

GPH1	GPH2	GPH3	SEL		SET
F1	F2	F3	F4	F5	F6

Then enter the following items:

(Note: Use the cursor ▼ arrow. If you accidentally hit the wrong key, use **AC/ON** or **EXIT** to go back.)

StatGraph1

Graph Type   : **F3**(Bar)   (NOTE: Press F6 for ▷ to change the menu choices at the bottom of the display).

Data1   : **List 1** (Press F1 to change the List number)   ▼
Data2   : **None**
Data3   : **None**
Stick Style   : **Horiz (NOTE: For a vertical bar chart, select F1. For a horizontal bar chart, select F2.)**

Now press **EXE**.
Then press **F1** to select **GPH1**.

The horizontal bar chart will appear on your screen as follows:

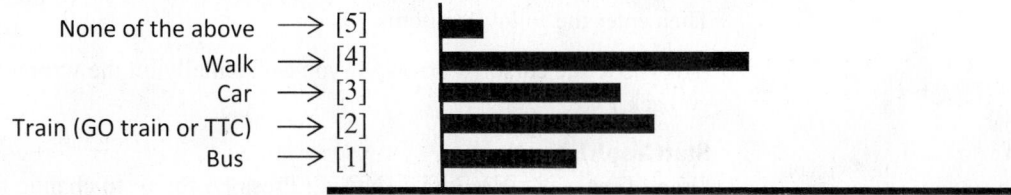

Notations: [1] represents "Bus," [2] represents "Train (GO train or TTC)," [3] represents "Car," [4] represents "Walk," and [5] represents "None of the above."

Interpretation of Results

The most popular mode of transport is walking to work or school, which is the longest bar. The second most popular mode of transport is train (GO train or TTC), which represents the second-longest bar.

EXAMPLE 2.3

Create a vertical bar chart of "How do you go to work or school?" using the CASIO fx-9750GII calculator.

Follow the calculator procedures to create a <u>vertical</u> bar chart.

From the **Main Menu** select **STAT** mode and press **EXE**.
If you have difficulty following the instruction, I recommend that you read the "Calculator Lesson 1" at the end of this chapter.

You may enter the data from Table 2.2 in List 1 as follows:

LIST 1
15 EXE
24 EXE
20 EXE
35 EXE
6 EXE

Use the **F6** key (▷) if necessary to get the following menu choices at the bottom of the display:
To create a bar chart, press the **F1** key to select "**GRPH**."

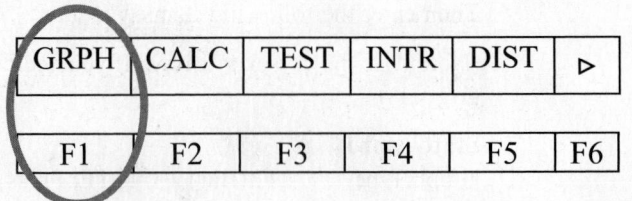

After you have selected "**GRPH**," you get the following menu choices at the bottom of the display. Press the **F6** key to select "**SET**."

GPH1	GPH2	GPH3	SEL		SET
F1	F2	F3	F4	F5	F6

Then enter the following items:

(Note: Use the cursor ▼ arrow. If you accidentally hit the wrong key, use **AC$^{/ON}$** or **EXIT** to go back.)

StatGraph1

Graph Type : **F3**(Bar) (NOTE: Press F6 for ▷ to change the menu choices at the bottom of the display.)

Data1 : **List 1** (Press F1 to change the List number.) ▼

Data2 : **None**

Data3 : **None**

Stick Style : **Length (NOTE: For a vertical bar chart, select F1. For a horizontal bar chart, select F2.)**

Now press **EXE**.

Then press **F1** to select **GPH1**.

The vertical bar chart will appear on your screen as follows:

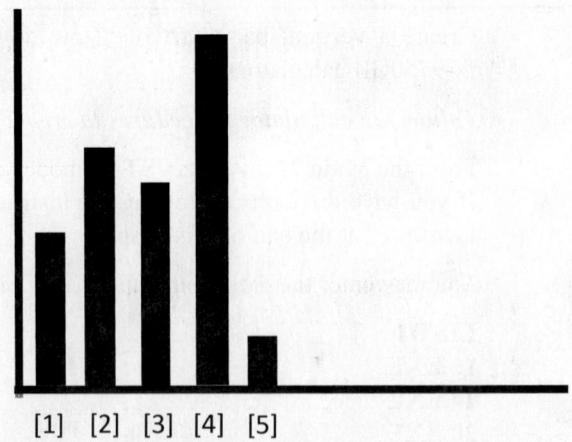

Notations: [1] represents "Bus," [2] represents "Train (GO train or TTC)," [3] represents "Car," [4] represents "Walk," and [5] represents "None of the above."

Interpretation of Results

The most popular mode of transport is walking to work or school, which is the tallest bar. The second most popular mode of transport is train (GO train or TTC), which represents the second tallest bar.

Pie Chart

The summary table can be displayed graphically as a pie chart. In a pie chart, the wedges of the pie (also known as pie slides) denote the frequency (or percentage of occurrences) for each category.

EXAMPLE 2.4

Create a pie chart of "How do you go to work or school?" using the CASIO fx-9750GII calculator.

You will learn to use the CASIO fx-9750 GII to create a pie chart for modes of transport based on the data in Table 2.2 and interpret the results.

Follow the calculator procedures to create a pie chart.

From the **Main Menu** select **STAT** mode and press **EXE**.
If you have difficulty following the instruction, I recommend that you read the "Calculator Lesson 1" at the end of this chapter.

You may enter the data from Table 2.2 in List 1 as follows:

LIST 1
15 EXE
24 EXE
20 EXE
35 EXE
6 EXE

Use the **F6** key (▷) if necessary to get the following menu choices at the bottom of the display:
To create a pie chart, press the **F1** key to select "**GRPH**."

GRPH	CALC	TEST	INTR	DIST	▷
F1	F2	F3	F4	F5	F6

After you have selected "**GRPH**," you will see the following menu choices at the bottom of the display. Press the **F6** key to select "**SET**."

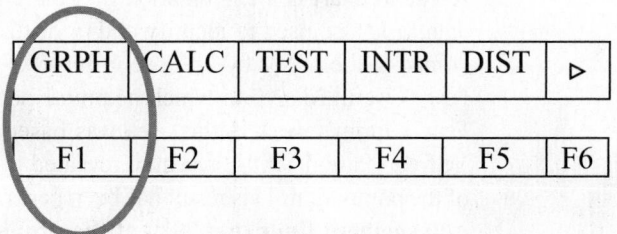

GPH1	GPH2	GPH3	SEL		SET
F1	F2	F3	F4	F5	F6

Then enter the following items:

(Note: Use the cursor ▼ arrow. If you accidentally hit the wrong key, use **AC/ON** or **EXIT** to go back.)

StatGraph1

Graph Type	**: F4**(Pie) (NOTE: Press F6 for ▷ to change the menu choices at the bottom of the display.)
Data 1	**: List 1** (Press F1 to change the List number.) ▼
Display	**: F2 (Data) : in the form of number of occurrences**
% Sto Mem	**: None**

Now press **EXE**.
Then press **F1** to select **GPH1**.

The pie chart will appear on your screen as follows:

A   16
B   24
C   20
D   35
E   6

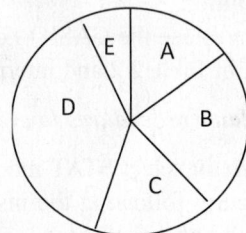

Notations: A represents "Bus," B represents "Train (GO train or TTC)," C represents "Car," D represents "Walk," and E represents "None of the above."

Interpretation of Results

The most popular mode of transportation is walking to school or work, which is the largest wedge of the pie. The second most popular mode of transportation is taking the train (GO train or TTC), which is the second largest wedge of the pie.

Pareto Chart

A Pareto chart is a combination of a bar chart and an OGIVE and is used to analyze attribute data. It is also used to identify and prioritize problem areas. The phrase "Pareto Principle" was coined in the 1950s by Dr. Joseph Juran to focus on his quality management concept of "Vital Few– Useful Many," in which he points out that management should concentrate on the "Vital Few." Juran's work in this area was based on the work of the 19th century Italian economist Vilfredo Pareto, whose research revealed that 80% of the wealth in a country is owned by 20% of the population. This result has been generalized to become the 80/20 rule. **In many instances, management finds that 80% of the problems arise from 20% of the problem sources.**

Pareto charts are often used in *nonmanufacturing applications* of quality improvement methods. Consider the following example:

EXAMPLE 2.5

A quality-improvement team was investigating the purchasing process in a company. The team was particularly interested in errors on purchase orders and hoped to reduce the number of purchase order changes issued by the company. (Each change typically costs around $100, and this company was issuing several hundred purchase order changes each month.)

The team investigated a sample of 2,000 purchase orders and found the following error frequencies.

Type of Error	Frequency
Wrong contract number	74
Wrong part number	14
Wrong price code	60
Wrong schedule date	6
Wrong supplier code	46

To construct the Pareto chart, you first sort the categories in descending order of frequency of occurrence. Then you calculate cumulative percentages. The results are as follows:

Type of Error	Frequency	%	c%
Wrong contract number	74	37	37
Wrong price code	60	30	67
Wrong supplier code	46	23	90
Wrong part number	14	7	97
Wrong schedule date	6	3	100
Total	200	100	

Now you can construct the Pareto chart using SPSS as shown next.

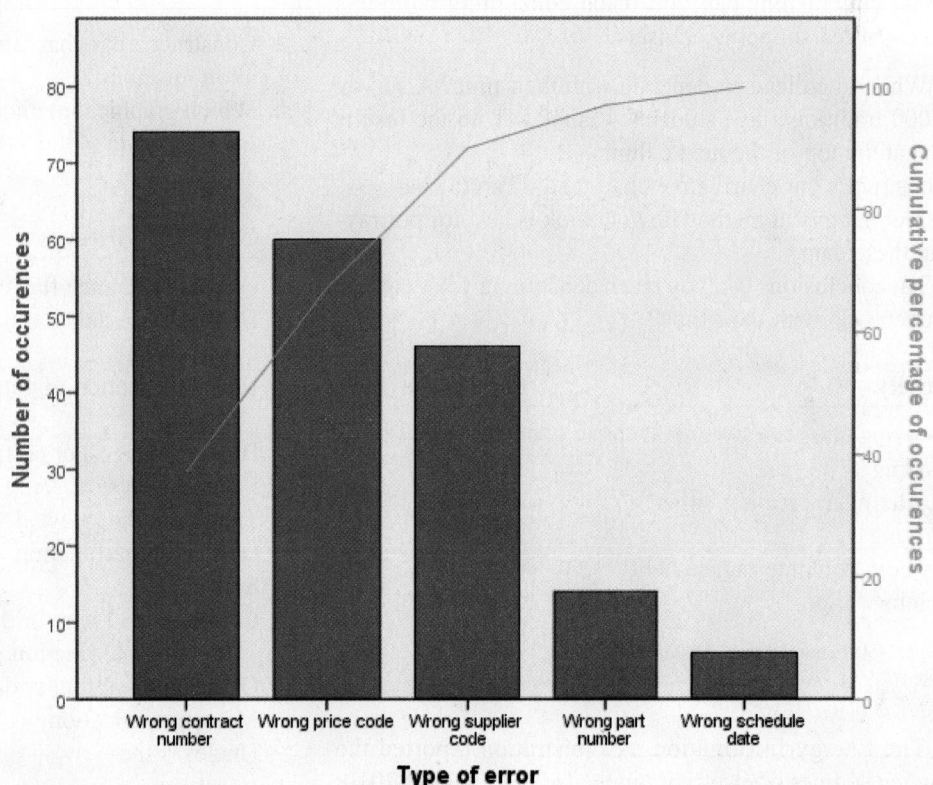

PROBLEMS

APPLYING THE CONCEPTS

2.1 A survey asked 1,264 women who were their most trusted shopping advisers. The survey results were as follows:

Shopping Advisers	Percentage (%)
Advertising	7
Friends/family	45
Manufacturer websites	5
News media	11
Online user reviews	13
Retail websites	4
Salespeople	1
Other	14

Source: Data extracted from "Snapshots," *USA Today,* October 19, 2006, p. 1B.

a. Construct a bar chart, a pie chart, and a Pareto chart.
b. Which graphical method do you think is best for portraying these data?
c. What conclusions can you reach concerning women's most trusted shopping advisers?

2.2 What do college students do with their time? A survey of 3,000 traditional-age students was taken with the results shown at the top of the next column.
a. Construct a bar chart, a pie chart, and a Pareto chart.
b. Which graphical method do you think is best for portraying these data?
c. What conclusions can you reach concerning what college students do with their time?

Activity	Percentage (%)
Attending class/lab	9
Sleeping	24
Socializing, recreating, other	51
Studying	7
Working, volunteering, student clubs	9

Source: Data extracted from M. Marklein, "First Two years of College Wasted?" *USA Today,* January 18, 2011, p. 3A.

2.3 The Energy Information Administration reported the following sources of electricity in the United States in 2010:

Source of Electricity	Percentage (%)
Coal	44
Hydroelectric	7
Natural gas	24
Nuclear	20
Other	5

Source: Energy Information Administration, 2010.

a. Construct a Pareto chart.
b. What percentage of power is derived from coal, nuclear, or natural gas?
c. Construct a pie chart.
d. For these data, do you prefer using a Pareto chart or the pie chart? Why?

2.4 An article discussed radiation therapy and new cures from the therapy, along with the harm that could be done if mistakes were made. The following tables represent the results of the types of mistakes made and the causes of mistakes reported to the New York State Department of Health from 2001 to 2009:

Radiation Mistakes	Number
Missed all or part of intended target	284
Wrong dose given	255
Wrong patient treated	50
Other	32

a. Construct a bar chart and a pie chart for the types of radiation mistakes.
b. Which graphical method do you think is best for portraying these data?

Causes of Mistakes	Number
Quality assurance flawed	355
Data entry or calculation errors by personnel	252
Misidentification of patient or treatment location	174
Blocks, wedges, or collimators misused	133
Patient's physical setup wrong	96
Treatment plan flawed	77
Hardware malfunction	60
Staffing	52
Computer software or digital information transfer malfunction	24
Override of computer data by personnel	19
Miscommunication	14
Unclear/other	8

Source: Data extracted from W. Bogdanich, "A Lifesaving Tool Turned Deadly," *The New York Times,* January 24, 2010, pp. 1, 15, 16.

c. Construct a Pareto chart for the causes of mistakes.
d. Discuss the "vital few" and "trivial many" reasons for the causes of mistakes.

2.5 The following table indicates the percentage of residential electricity consumption in the United States, organized by type of appliance in a recent year:

Type of Appliance	Percentage (%)
Air conditioning	18
Clothes dryers	5
Clothes washers/other	24
Computers	1
Cooking	2
Dishwashers	2
Freezers	2
Lighting	16
Refrigeration	9
Space heating	7
Water heating	8
TVs and set top boxes	6

Source: Data extracted from J. Mouawad, and K. Galbraith, "Plugged-in Age Feeds a Hunger for Electricity," *The New York Times,* September 20, 2009, pp. 1, 28.

a. Construct a bar chart, a pie chart, and a Pareto chart.
b. Which graphical method do you think is best for portraying these data?
c. What conclusions can you reach concerning residential electricity consumption in the United States?

2.6 A study of 1,000 people asked what respondents wanted to grill during barbecue season. The results were as follows:

Type of Food	Percentage (%)
Beef	38
Chicken	23
Fruit	1
Hot dogs	6
Pork	8
Seafood	19
Vegetables	5

Source: Data extracted from "What Folks Want Sizzling on the Grill During Barbecue Season," *USA Today,* March 29, 2009, p. 1A.

a. Construct a bar chart, a pie chart, and a Pareto chart.
b. Which graphical method do you think is best for portraying these data?
c. What conclusions can you reach concerning what folks want sizzling on the grill during barbecue season?

2.7 A survey of 1,085 adults asked "Do you enjoy shopping for clothing for yourself?" The results (data extracted from "Split decision on clothes shopping," *USA Today,* January 28, 2011, p. 1B) indicated that 51% of the females enjoyed shopping for clothing for themselves as compared to 44% of the males. The sample sizes of males and females was not provided. Suppose that the results were as shown in the following table:

a. Construct a side-by-side bar chart of enjoying shopping and gender.
b. What conclusions do you reach from this chart?

| Enjoy Shopping | Gender | | |
for Clothing	Male		Total
Yes	238	276	514
No	304	267	571
Total	542	543	1,085

2.8 Each day at a large hospital, several hundred laboratory tests are performed. The rate at which these tests are done improperly (and therefore need to be redone) seems steady, at about 4%. In an effort to get to the root cause of these nonconformances, tests that need to be redone, the director of the lab decided to keep records over a period of one week. The laboratory tests were subdivided by the shift of workers who performed the lab tests. The results are as follows:

| | Shift | | |
Lab Tests Performed	Day	Evening	Total
Nonconforming	16	24	40
Conforming	654	306	960
Total	670	330	1,000

a. Construct a side-by-side bar chart of nonconformances and shift.
b. What conclusions concerning the pattern of nonconforming laboratory tests can the laboratory director reach?

2.9 Does it take more time to get yourself removed from an email list than it used to? A study of 100 large online retailers revealed the following:

| | Need Three or More Clicks to be Removed | |
Year	Yes	No
2009	39	61
2008	7	93

Source: Data extracted from "Drill Down," *The New York Times,* March 29, 2010, p. B2.

a. Construct a side-by-side bar chart of year and whether you need to click three or more times to be removed from an email list.
b. What do these results tell you about whether more online retailers were requiring three or more clicks in 2009 than in 2008?

CALCULATOR LESSON 1

CASIO
fx-9750GII

Question 1: How do I turn on the calculator?

Press the **AC/ON** key to turn on the calculator.

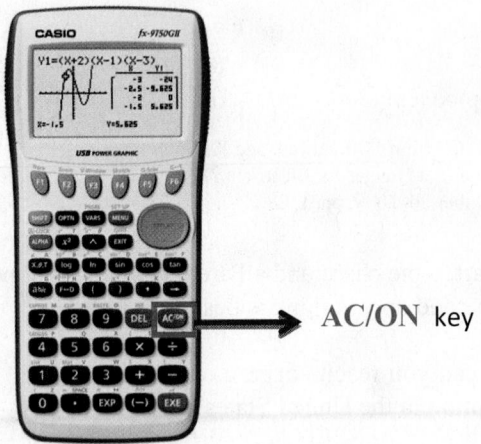

AC/ON key

The diagram is taken from this source: http://www.casio.com/products/Calculators_%26_Dictionaries/Graphing/FX-9750GII/content/Introduction/

Question 2: How do I get to the "Stat" Mode?

Press the **MENU** key. In the main menu, select "**STAT**" by using the cursor keys to move the highlighter to the **STAT** icon and press **EXE**.

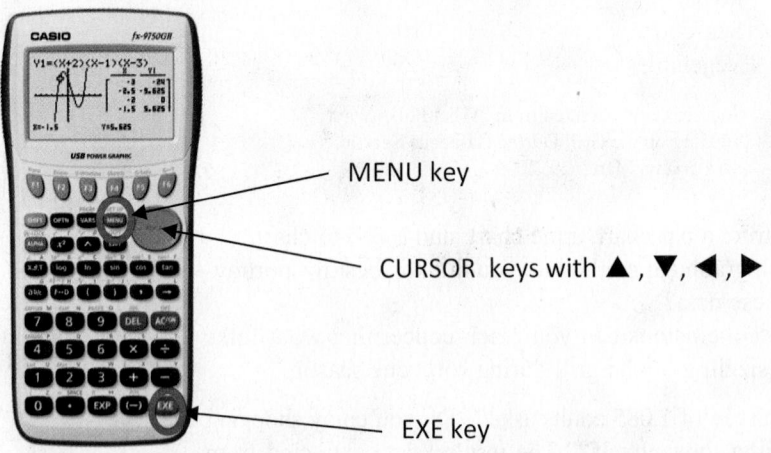

MENU key

CURSOR keys with ▲, ▼, ◄, ►

EXE key

The diagram is taken from this source: http://www.casio.com/products/Calculators_%26_Dictionaries/Graphing/FX-9750GII/content/Introduction/

Question 3: How do I select the Graph function?

Once inside the **STAT** mode, you will see the following screen.

	List 1	List 2	List 3	List 4		
SUB						
1						
2						
3						
4						
GRPH **F1**	**CALC** **F2**	**TEST** **F3**	**INTR** **F4**	**DIST** **F5**	▷ **F6**	

Press function key **F1** to select "**GRPH**."

Question 4: How do I sort data?

Once inside the **STAT** mode, you will see the following screen.

	List 1	List 2	List 3	List 4		
SUB						
1						
2						
3						
4						
GRPH **F1**	**CALC** **F2**	**TEST** **F3**	**INTR** **F4**	**DIST** **F5**	▷ **F6**	

Press function key **F6** to select "▷." This brings you to the next screen with the functions TOOL, EDIT, DEL. DEL-A, INS, and ▷ as shown below.

	List 1	List 2	List 3	List 4		
SUB						
1						
2						
3						
4						
TOOL **F1**	**EDIT** **F2**	**DEL** **F3**	**DEL-A** **F4**	**INS** **F5**	▷ **F6**	

Selecting "**TOOL**" by selecting **F1** function will bring you to another set of functions (**SRT-A**, **SRT-D**, **TOP**, and **BTM**) as shown below.

	List 1	List 2	List 3	List 4
SUB				
1				
2				
3				
4				
SRT-A F1	SRT-D F2	TOP F3	BTM F4	

1. If you wish to sort your data in ascending order, select **F1 (SRT-A)**.
2. If you wish to sort your data in descending order, select **F2 (SRT-D)**.
3. If you wish to go to the TOP of the list, select **F3 (TOP)**.
4. If you wish to go to the BOTTOM of the list, select **F4 (BTM)**.

Press the **EXIT** key to go back to the previous screen.

Question 5: How do I delete data?

Once inside the **STAT** mode, you will see the following screen.

	List 1	List 2	List 3	List 4		
SUB						
1						
2						
3						
4						
GRPH F1	CALC F2	TEST F3	INTR F4	DIST F5	▷ F6	

Press function key **F6** to select " ▷." This brings you to the next screen with the functions TOOL, EDIT, DEL. DEL-A, INS, and ▷ as shown below.

	List 1	List 2	List 3	List 4		
SUB						
1						
2						
3						
4						
TOOL F1	EDIT F2	DEL F3	DEL-A F4	INS F5	▷ F6	

1. If you wish to delete a value from a cell, select **F3 (DEL)**.
2. If you wish to delete a list of data, select **F4 (DEL-A)**. The calculator will ask if you want to proceed to delete the whole list. Press **F1** for Yes. Press **F2** for No.

Press the **EXIT** key to go back to the previous screen.

Question 6: How do I insert a value into a list of data?

Once inside the **STAT** mode, you will see the following screen.

	List 1	List 2	List 3	List 4
SUB				
1				
2				
3				
4				
GRPH F1	CALC F2	TEST F3	INTR F4	DIST F5	▷ F6

Press function key **F6** to select " ▷." This brings you to the next screen with the functions TOOL, EDIT, DEL. DEL-A, INS, and ▷ as shown below.

	List 1	List 2	List 3	List 4
SUB				
1	22			
2	13			
3	10			
4	8			
TOOL F1	EDIT F2	DEL F3	DEL-A F4	INS F5	▷ F6

If you wish to insert a value into List 1, bring the highlighter to the cell where you want to insert the value. Then select **F5 (INS)**.

3 Graphical Presentation of Quantitative Data

Learning Objectives

In this chapter, you learn:

- To construct stem-and-leaf plot
- To construct frequency distribution
- To construct an ogive
- To construct contingency table
- To construct scatter plot

In Chapter 1, you learned the different types of data and scales. In Chapter 2, you learned to present qualitative data in graphical form. In this chapter, you will learn to organize quantitative data in graphical form. Specifically you will learn to group a set of **quantitative** data in the form of the following:

1. Stem-and-leaf plot (section 3.1)
2. Frequency distribution (section 3.6)
3. Histogram
4. Polygon
5. Ogive (cumulative percentage polygon) (section 3.7)
6. Contingency table
7. Scatter plot

How Do You Organize Quantitative Data Graphically?

In this chapter, you can learn to present ratio and interval data using histograms, polygons, Ogives, **stem-and-leaf plots**, frequency distribution, contingency Table and scatter Plot.

3.1 Stem-and-Leaf Plot

Quantitative data can be arranged or summarized either graphically (i.e., charts, graphs, tables) or numerically (i.e., mean, mode, median, standard deviation). In this chapter, you will learn to group the data visually by constructing a stem-and-leaf plot. The purpose of plotting a stem-and-leaf plot is to summarize the distribution (or shape) of a set of quantitative data and at the same time still retain most of the data values (or numbers). A stem-and-leaf plot does look like a bar chart. The advantages of a stem-and-leaf plot are that the plot can be quickly constructed by hand and, most importantly, the values of the individual data can be retrieved from the plot. Stem-and-leaf plots also enable you to find the minimum value, maximum value, and the most frequently occuring value (known as the mode) from just looking at the plot.

A stem-and-leaf plot looks like a horizontal bar chart maintaining most of the original data values. Each data value can be divided into a stem and a leaf.

For example, the value of 84 can be separated into "8" (representing the stem value) and "4" (representing the leaf value).

The stem-and-leaf plot should be considered when the number of data values is not more than 50, which we consider a small set of data.

The following is an example of a stem-and-leaf plot displaying the profits earned by companies in the hospitality industry.

FIGURE 3.1
Stem-and-leaf plot for profits data of the hospitality industry

Hospitality Industry: *Profits ($)*	
Stem (100,000)	**Leaf (10,000)**
1	1234
1	55688
2	2
2	56
3	113
3	79

You must have a title for each stem-and-leaf plot you construct. From the title in Figure 3.1, you know that the data are profits for the hospitality industry. If there is no title provided, the numbers could represent "anything under the sun." So a title is very important because it tells you about the nature of the data. Now, I want you to reverse engineer and give me the list of data values from the stem-and-leaf plot. Each stem is worth 100,000. For stem value 2, we have 200,000. For stem value 3, we have 300,000, and so on. Notice that the first entry has a stem of 1 and a leaf of 1. Since the stem unit is 100,000 and the leaf unit is 10,000, this data value is $1*100,000 + 1*10,000 = 110,000$. Likewise, the second entry has a stem of 1 and a leaf of 2, which corresponds to a value of $1*100,000 + 2*10,000 = 120,000$. Thus, the data can be reconstructed from the entries in the stem-and-leaf plot. Note that if no units are specified for the stem, it should be assumed that the stem unit is 1. While not true in this case, the leaf unit is usually omitted and assumed to be the next single digit after the stem.

Now, let's learn how to construct a stem-and-leaf plot as shown in Figure 3.1.

3.2 Rules and Convention to Construct a Stem-and-Leaf Plot

You must apply these rules to construct a stem-and-leaf plot.

The reasons for applying these rules are (1) to minimize the perception biases and (2) to have an aesthetic appearance graphically.

You will use the following set of rules and conventions.

For the stems:
Stem Rules
1. The number of stems should be from 6 to 13 stems.
2. The stem values should be consecutive numbers or repeated numbers. The numbers may each be repeated twice or 5 times.
3. The stem units must be indicated if the stem is not to be taken at face value.
4. There must be at least one leaf associated with the first and last stem.

For the leaves:
Leaf Rules
1. The leaf for each data value is the next <u>single</u> digit after the stem. When the stems are repeated twice, the leaves values 0 to 4 go to the first stem and the leaves values 5 to 9 go to the second stem of the same values. This order is reversed when the stems are negative values. When the stems are repeated 5 times, the leaves values 0 and 1 go to the first stem, values 2 and 3 go to the second stem, values 4 and 5 go to the third stem, values 6 and 7 go to the fourth stem, and values 8 and 9 go to the fifth stem. This order is reversed when the stems are negative values.
2. There is no rounding off.
3. The leaf values are written in ascending order when positive and descending order when negative.
4. The leaf values must be evenly spaced.
5. No commas or dashes between the numbers are allowed.

I. Illustration of Stem Rule 1: The number of stems should be from 6 to 13 stems.

Title

Stem (10)	Leaf
1	012
2	567
3	1
4	6789
5	02567
6	01
7	35
8	9

There are **8 stems**, which meets the requirement of stems in the plot.

Title

Stem (10)	Leaf
5	02567
6	01
7	35
8	9

There are **4 stems**, which <u>does not</u> meet the requirement of stems in the plot. What should you do? To increase the number of stems, you should apply **Stem Rule 2**.

II. Illustration of Stem Rule 2: The stem values should be consecutive numbers or repeated numbers. The numbers may each be repeated twice or 5 times.

a.) <u>Illustration of stem values as consecutive numbers.</u>

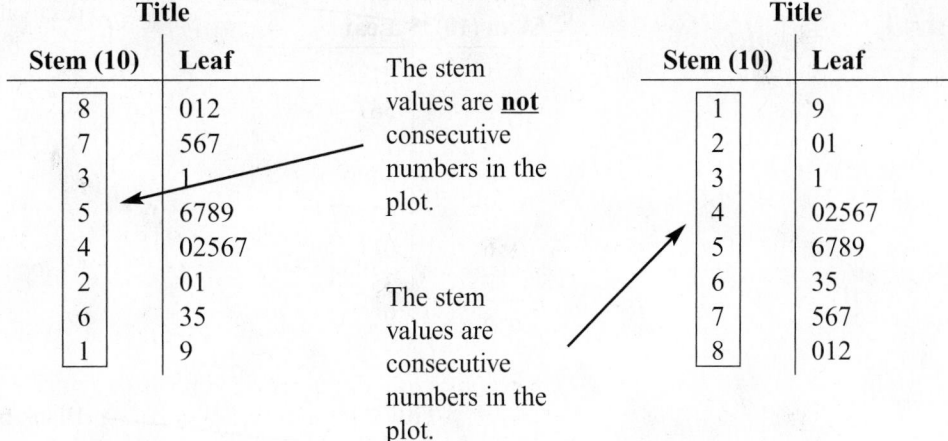

b.) <u>Illustration of few stems and each stem value repeated two times.</u>

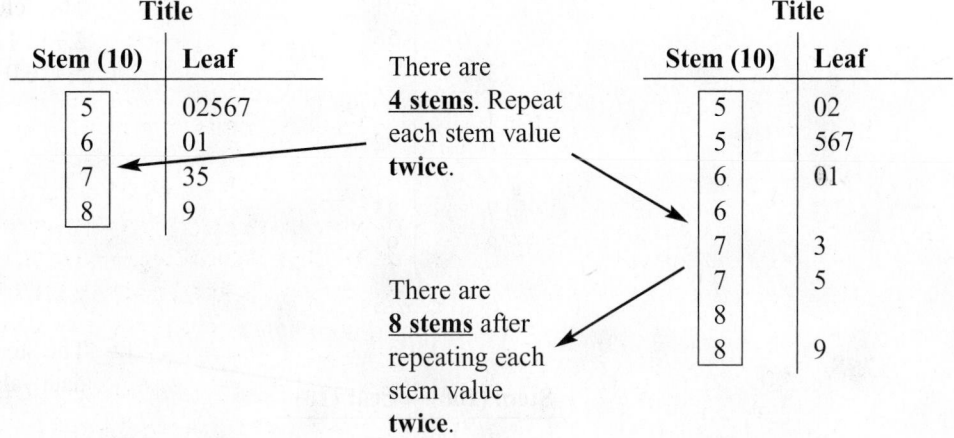

c.) <u>Illustration of few stems and each stem value repeated five times.</u>

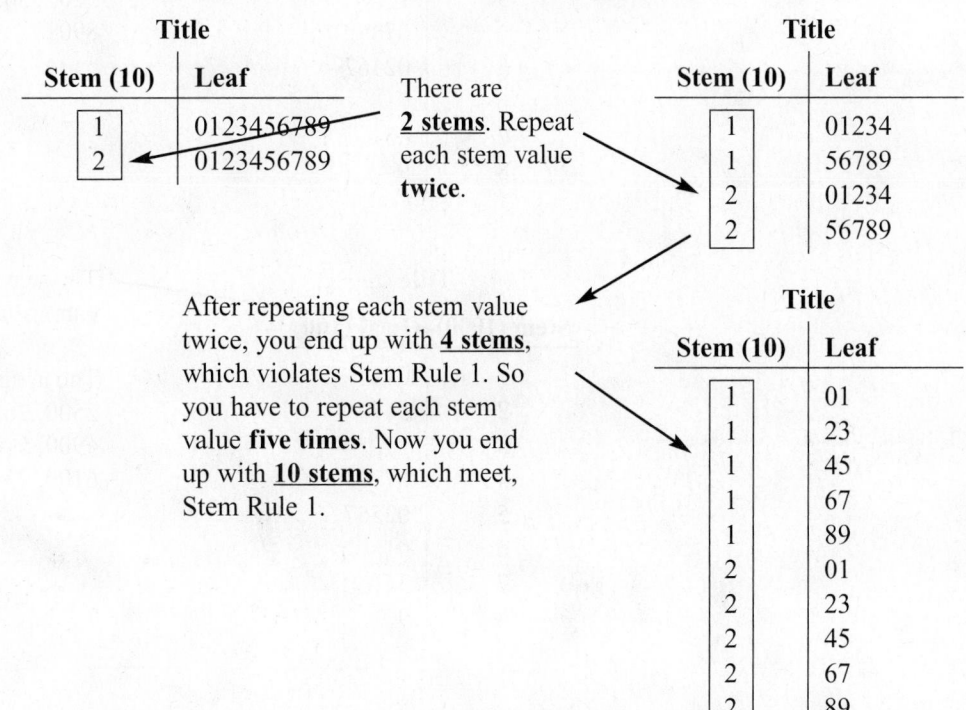

III. Illustration of Stem Rule 3: The stem units must be indicated if the stem is not to be taken at face value.

Title

Stem (10)	Leaf
1	012
2	567
3	1
4	6789
5	02567
6	01
7	35
8	9

The stem unit must represent the actual data value.

The actual data are 10, 11, 12, 25, 26, 27, 31, 46, 47, 48, 49, 50, 52, 55, 56, 57, 60, 61, 73, 75, 89.

Title

Stem	Leaf
1	012
2	567
3	1
4	6789
5	02567
6	01
7	35
8	9

Blank means that the stem should be taken at face value.

The actual data are 1.0, 1.1, 1.2, 2.5, 2.6, 2.7, 3.1, 4.6, 4.7, 4.8, 4.9, 5.0, 5.2, 5.5, 5.6, 5.7, 6.0, 6.1, 7.3, 7.5, 8.9.

Title

Stem (100)	Leaf (10)
1	012
2	567
3	1
4	6789
5	02567
6	01
7	35
8	9

The stem unit must represent the actual data value.

The actual data are 100, 110, 120, 250, 260, 270, 310, 460, 470, 480, 490, 500, 520, 550, 560, 570, 600, 610, 730, 750, 890.

Title

Stem (1000)	Leaf (100)
1	012
2	567
3	1
4	6789
5	02567
6	01
7	35
8	9

The stem unit must represent the actual data value.

The actual data are 1000, 1100, 1200, 2500, 2600, 2700, 3100, 4600, 4700, 4800, 4900, 5000, 5200, 5500, 5600, 5700, 6000, 6100, 7300, 7500, 8900.

The **stem unit** indicated in the stem-and-leaf plot quantified each stem value.

Stem (100)	Leaf (10)
1	2 3 4 5 6
2	6 6 6 7
3	9
4	1 2 5 5
5	3 3
6	0

The stem is recorded on the left-hand side of the column, which displays the hundreds' place. The stem value is in the hundreds' place. The stem values of 1, 2, 3, 4, 5 and 6 are in fact 100, 200, 300, 400, 500, and 600. The leaf is recorded on the right-hand side of the column, displaying the tens' place. The single digit of the leaf value is in the tens' place. In this way, we retain the original data values, which are 120, 130, 140, 150, 160, etc. We do not usually indicate the leaf unit in the stem-and-leaf plot. Leaf Rule 1 states that "The leaf for each data value is the next single digit after the stem." According to this rule, if the stem value is in hundreds (100), then the leaf values should be in tens (10).

You should not record the stem in hundreds as shown next:

Stem	Leaf
100	2 3 4 5 6
200	6 6 6 7
300	9
400	1 2 5 5
500	3 3
600	0

The previous display contains several errors. There are gaps between stem values. How do you record the leaf value in tens? According to Stem Rule 2, you should record the stem values in consecutive numbers such as 10, 11, 12, 13, etc.; 1.2, 1.3, 1.4, 1.5, etc.; or 100, 101, 102, 103, etc.

IV. Illustration of Stem Rule 4: There must be at least one leaf associated with the first and last stem.

Title

Stem (10)	Leaf
1	012
2	567
3	1
4	6789
5	02567
6	
7	35
8	9

There are **three leaves** associated with the first stem.

There is **one leaf** associated with the last stem.

Stem Rule 4 is satisfied.

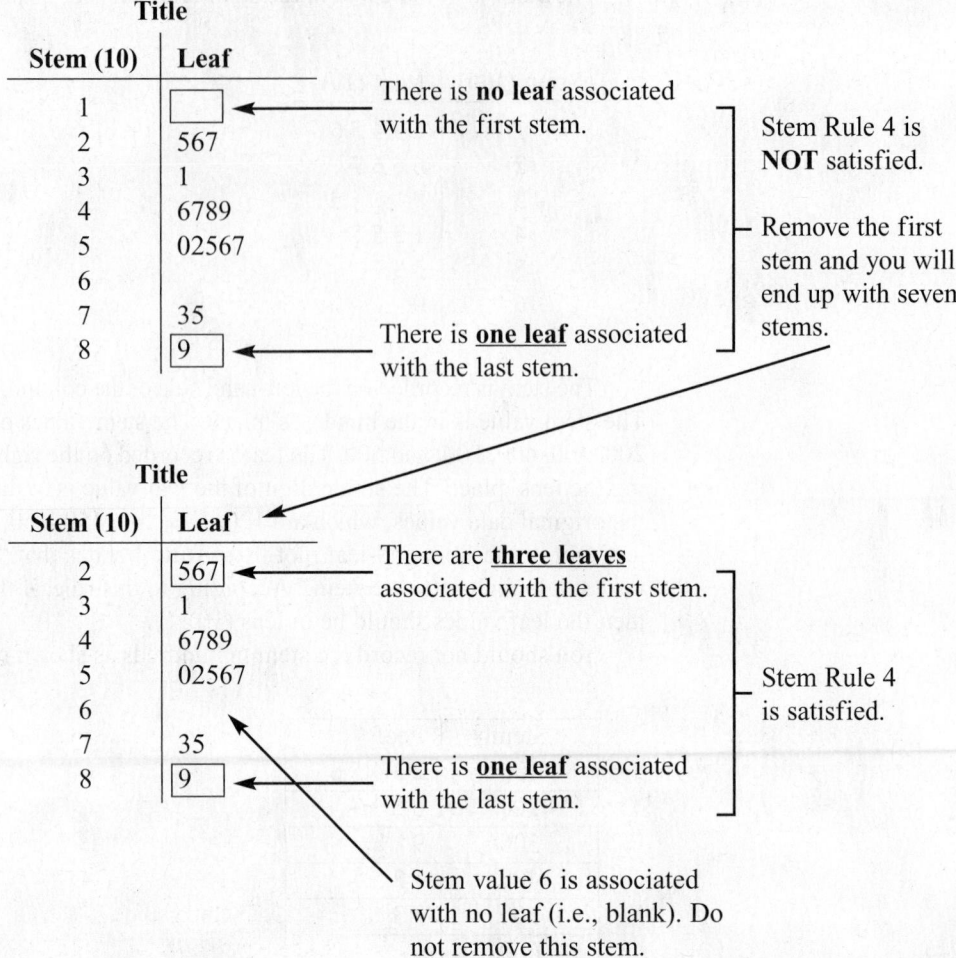

According to Stem Rule 4, there must be at least one leaf associated with the first and last stem.

If the **first stem** has no leaf value (i.e., blank), remove it. *Do not* insert "0," which will give you a data value!

If the **last stem** has no leaf value (i.e., blank), remove it. *Do not* insert "0," which will give you a data value!

For an "intermediate" stem value that is blank (i.e., stem value 6), *do not remove* it.

According to Stem Rule 2, the stem values should be consecutive numbers. Removing this "intermediate" stem value that is blank will violate this rule. If you remove stem value 6, you will end up with stem values 2, 3, 5, 7, and 8. The stem values are not consecutive.

V. Illustration of Leaf Rule 1: The leaf for each data value is the next <u>single</u> digit after the stem. When the stems are repeated twice, the leaves values 0 to 4 go to the first stem and the leaves values 5 to 9 go to the second stem of the same values as shown in Table 3.1. This order is reversed when the stems are negative values as shown in Table 3.2. When the stems are repeated 5 times, the leaves values 0 and 1 go to the first stem, values 2 and 3 go to the second stem, values 4 and 5 go to the third stem, values 6 and 7 go to the fourth stem, and values 8 and 9 go to the fifth stem as shown in Table 3.3. This order is reversed when the stems are negative values as shown in Table 3.4.

TABLE 3.1

Rule for *Positive* Value Stems That Are Repeated Twice

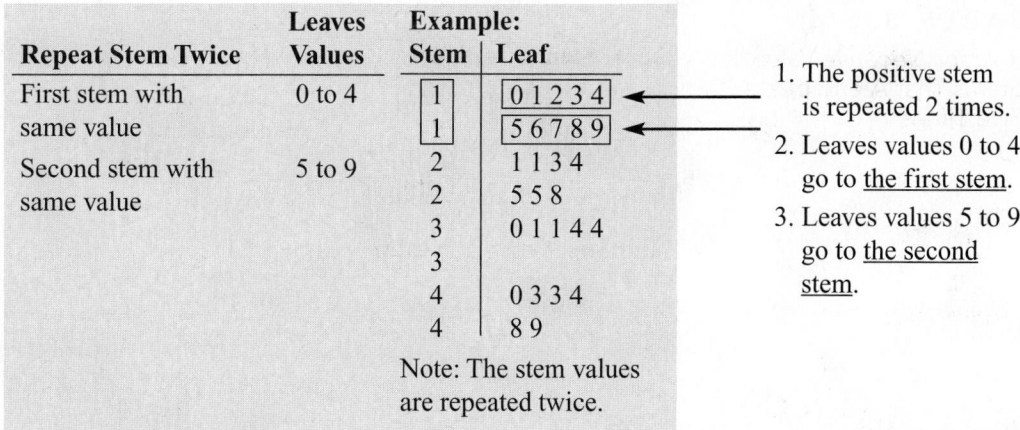

Repeat Stem Twice	Leaves Values	Example: Stem	Leaf
First stem with same value	0 to 4	1	0 1 2 3 4
Second stem with same value	5 to 9	1	5 6 7 8 9
		2	1 1 3 4
		2	5 5 8
		3	0 1 1 4 4
		3	
		4	0 3 3 4
		4	8 9

1. The positive stem is repeated 2 times.
2. Leaves values 0 to 4 go to <u>the first stem</u>.
3. Leaves values 5 to 9 go to <u>the second stem</u>.

Note: The stem values are repeated twice.

Note: For the *positive* stem values, the leaves are arranged in ascending order (i.e., 0, 1, 2, 3, 4, 5, 6, 7, 8, 9)

TABLE 3.2

Rule for *Negative* Value Stems That Are Repeated Twice

Repeat Stem Twice	Leaves Values	Example: Stem	Leaf
First stem with same value	5 to 9	-4	9 8 7 6 5
Second stem with same value	0 to 4	-4	4 3 2 1 0
		-3	
		-3	4 4 2 0 0
		-2	9 8
		-2	4 3 0 0
		-1	9 8 7 6 5
		-1	4 3 2 1 0

1. The negative stem is repeated 2 times.
2. Leaves values 5 to 9 go to <u>the first stem</u>.
3. Leaves values 0 to 4 go to <u>the second stem</u>.

Note: The stem values are repeated twice.

For the *negative* stem values: The leaves are arranged in descending order (i.e., 9, 8, 7, 6, 5, 4, 3, 2, 1, 0)

TABLE 3.3

Rule for *Positive* Value Stems That Are Repeated Five Times

Repeat Stem Five Times	Leaves Values	Example: Stem	Leaf
First stem with same value	0 , 1	5	0 1
Second stem with same value	2 , 3	5	2 3
		5	4 5
Third stem with same value	4 , 5	5	6 7
Fourth stem with same value	6 , 7	5	8 9
		6	0 0 0 0 1
Fifth stem with same value	8 , 9	6	2 2 2 2
		6	4 4 5 5 5
		6	6 6 7
		6	9 9 9 9

Note: The stem values are repeated five times.

Note: For the *positive* stem values, the leaves are arranged in ascending order (i.e., 0, 1, 2, 3, 4, 5, 6, 7, 8, 9)

TABLE 3.4

Rule for *Negative* Value Stems That Are Repeated Five Times

Repeat Stem Five Times	Leaves Values	Example: Stem	Leaf
First stem with same value	8 , 9	−2	9 8
		−2	7 6
Second stem with same value	6 , 7	−2	5 4
Third stem with same value	4 , 5	−2	3 2
		−2	1 0
Fourth stem with same value	2 , 3	−1	9 8
		−1	7 6
Fifth stem with same value	0 , 1	−1	5 4
		−1	3 2
		−1	1 0

Note: The stem values are repeated five times.

For the *negative* stem values: The leaves are arranged in descending order (i.e., 9, 8, 7, 6, 5, 4, 3, 2, 1, 0)

VI. Illustration of Leaf Rule 2: There is no rounding off.

To record value 6786 with a defined stem value of 67, you should record leaf value 8 next to 67. You should not round the leaf value 8 to 9. Otherwise, you will violate Leaf Rule 2.

VII. Illustration of Leaf Rule 3: The leaf values are written in ascending order when positive and descending order when negative.

For the *positive* stem values, the leaves are arranged in ascending order (i.e., 0, 1, 2, 3, 4, 5, 6, 7, 8, 9).

For the *negative* stem values, the leaves are arranged in descending order (i.e., 9, 8, 7, 6, 5, 4, 3, 2, 1, 0).

Refer to Tables 3.1, 3.2, 3.3, and 3.4.

Title

Stem (100,00)	Leaf (10,000)	
-0	9 7 5	Corresponds to the negative stem; the leaves are arranged in descending order.
-0	4 4 3 1	
0	0 0 2 4	
0	5 5 6 8 8	
1	2	
1	5 6	
2	1 1 3	Corresponds to the positive stem; the leaves are arranged in ascending order.
2	7 9	

VIII. Illustration of Leaf Rule 4: The leaf values must be evenly spaced.

Title

Stem (10)	Leaf	
1	0•——•12	These are uneven spaces among the leaves.
2	56••7	
3	1	
4	6••78•—•9	
5	0••25••67	
6	01	
7	35	
8	9	

IX. Illustration of Leaf Rule 5: No commas or dashes between the numbers are allowed.

Title

Stem (10)	Leaf
1	0,1,2
2	5,6,7
3	1
4	6,7,8,9
5	0,2,5,6,7
6	0,1
7	3,5
8	9

Do not insert commas between leaves.

3.3 How Do You Construct a Stem-and-Leaf Plot Using Data with Positive Values?

EXAMPLE 3.1

Data were taken from http://biz.yahoo.com/p/tops/sf.html.

Refer to Table 3.5, which shows annual returns (in %) of the mutual fund top performers in the financial sector.

TABLE 3.5

Mutual Fund Top Performers

Fund Name	Symbol	Ann. Ret.
Prudential Financial Svcs Z	PFSZX	9.80%
Prudential Financial Svcs A	PFSAX	9.49%
Prudential Financial Svcs B	PUFBX	8.71%
Prudential Financial Svcs C	PUFCX	8.71%
Burnham Financial Industries I	BMFIX	6.87%
Burnham Financial Industries A	BURFX	6.80%
Burnham Financial Industries C	BURCX	6.04%
Royce Financial Services Svc	RYFSX	2.19%
FBR Small Cap Financial I	FBRUX	0.90%
FBR Small Cap Financial Investor	FBRSX	0.79%

Using the data listed in Table 3.5, construct stem-and-leaf displays for the annual returns.

Step 1: Sort the annual return data in ascending order.

By sorting the data, the leaves will fall in either ascending or descending order naturally.

 Minimum

 Maximum

Use the Casio calculator to sort your data.

To sort your data, follow these calculator steps.

1. Press the **MENU** key; then press **STAT**.
2. Under STAT mode, input your data in List **1**.
3. After you have entered your data in List 1, select **TOOL**, which corresponds to the **F1** function key.
4. Then select **SRT-A**, which corresponds to **F1**. "SRT-A" stands for "sort lists into ascending order."
5. Then a dialog box will prompt you, "How many Lists?" Press **1**, and then press **EXE**. (Select "1" because you have only one list to sort.) Then a dialog box will prompt you, "Select List   List No: **1** <since you enter your data in List **1**>

Step 2: Find the maximum and minimum values.

> Minimum = 0.79
> Maximum = 9.80

Step 3: Split the minimum and maximum values into stems and leaves.

The value on the left side of the line is the *stem value*, and the value on the right side of the line is the *leaf value*, as shown next.

> Minimum   0. 7 | 9
> Maximum   9. 8 | 0
>   Stem | Leaf

The stem values should be consecutive numbers from 0.7 to 9.8. Count the number of stems from values 0.7, 0.8, and 0.9 all the way to 9.8 without skipping any values, as shown next. There is a total of 92 stems. That is too many stems. You have violated Stem Rule 1.

Stem	Value
0.7	1st stem
0.8	2nd stem
0.9	3rd stem
1	4th stem
1.1	5th stem
1.2	6th stem
1.3	7th stem
1.4	8th stem
1.5	9th stem
etc.	etc.
9.2	86th stem
9.3	87th stem
9.4	88th stem
9.5	89th stem
9.6	90th stem
9.7	91st stem
9.8	92nd stem

The numbers of stems from stem values 0.7 to 9.8 is more than 13 stems. When there are too many stems, you must redefine the stem values by moving the vertical line to the left as shown next.

```
Minimum     0. | 7     9
Maximum     9. | 8     0
```

The new set of stem values are from 0 to 9 (i.e., 0, 1, 2, 3, 4, 5, 6, 7, 8, 9). There is a total of 10 stems. According to Stem Rule 1, "The number of stems should be from 6 to 13 stems." You have enough stems to construct the stem-and-leaf plot.

Step 4: Now construct the stem-and-leaf plot.

Annual returns (in %) of the mutual fund

Stem	Leaf
0	
1	
2	
3	
4	
5	
6	
7	
8	
9	

According to Stem Rule 2, the stem values are in ascending and consecutive order.

Note that you have to check the following stem rules:

1. You have 10 stems. Since you have satisfied this Stem Rule 1, you do not have to repeat each stem twice or five times.
2. Per Stem Rule 2, the stem values are in consecutive numbers.
3. Per Stem Rule 3, leave the stem unit blank because the values are taken at face value. What are these true values: 0, 1, 2, 3, 4, 5, 6, 7, 8 and 9? Are they in units, tens, or hundreds? These numbers are in units, and you leave the stem unit under the stem title blank.
4. You are not able to check Stem Rule 4 at this point because you have not recorded the leaves yet. Come back to check this rule after you have done step 5.

Step 5: Record the leaf values

Record the leaf values, which are one digit after the stem value. You must make sure that the minimum value (which is 0.79) is recorded on the first stem and the maximum value (which is 9.80) is recorded on the last stem.

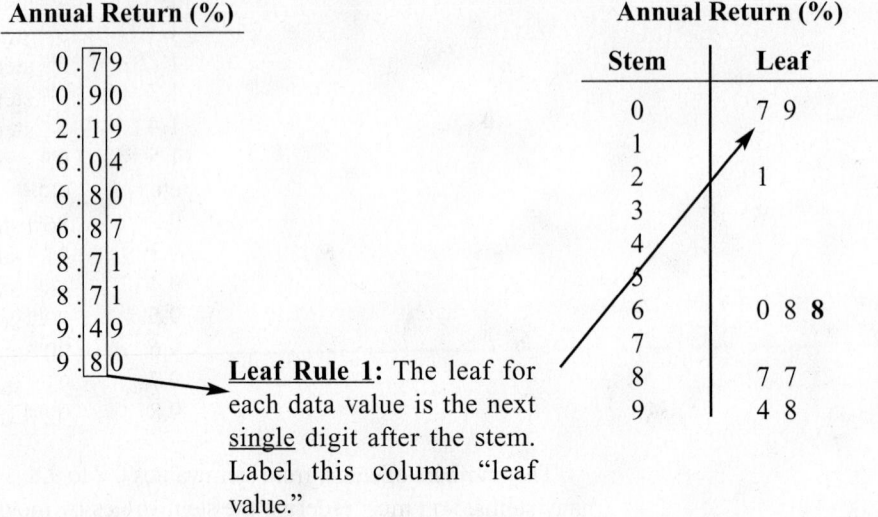

Annual Return (%)

0 .	7 9
0 . 9	0
2 . 1	9
6 . 0	4
6 . 8	0
6 . 8	7
8 . 7	1
8 . 7	1
9 . 4	9
9 . 8	0

Annual Return (%)

Stem	Leaf
0	7 9
1	
2	1
3	
4	
5	
6	0 8 **8**
7	
8	7 7
9	4 8

Leaf Rule 1: The leaf for each data value is the next <u>single</u> digit after the stem. Label this column "leaf value."

Note that you have to check the following leaf rules:

1. There is no rounding off of the leaf values.
2. The leaf values are written in ascending order when positive and descending order when negative.
3. The leaf values must be evenly spaced.
4. No commas or dashes between the numbers are allowed.

EXAMPLE 3.2

Data were taken from http://finance.yahoo.com/actives?e=us.

TABLE 3.6

U.S. Stock Volume Leaders

Refer to Table 3.6, which shows the volume of company stocks traded in the U.S. stock exchange.

Company	Stock Volume
Intel Corporation	72,621,446
iShares MSCI Emerging Index Fun	72,179,486
Microsoft Corporation	63,114,201
Cisco Systems, Inc.	62,747,101
iShares Russell 2000	49,185,710
iShares MSCI Japan Index Fund	48,722,445
Oracle Corporation	43,176,882
Sirius XM Radio Inc.	42,543,054
Micron Technology, Inc.	39,888,893
JDS Uniphase Corporation	39,836,593
Alcatel-Lucent Common Stock	39,399,448
Sprint Nextel Corporation Comm	38,966,215
General Motors Company Common S	33,074,753
Vanguard Emerging Markets ETF	30,592,552
Office Depot, Inc. Common Stock	30,359,092

Using the data listed in Table 3.6, construct stem-and-leaf displays for the stock volume.

Step 1: Sort the stock volume data in ascending order.

Minimum

Maximum

Step 2: Find the maximum and minimum values.

Minimum = 30,359,092
Maximum = 72,621,446

Step 3: Split the minimum and maximum values into stems and leaves.

Minimum	3	0	3	5	9	0	9	2
Maximum	7	2	6	2	1	4	4	6

a) The number of stems from stem values 3035909 to 7262144 is more than 13 stems. There are too many stems, so you have to redefine the stem values again by moving the vertical line to the left.

Minimum	3	0	3	5	9	0	9	2
Maximum	7	2	6	2	1	4	4	6

b) The number of stems from stem values 303590 to 726214 is more than 13 stems. There are too many stems, so you have to redefine the stem values again by moving the vertical line to the left.

Minimum	3	0	3	5	9	0	9	2
Maximum	7	2	6	2	1	4	4	6

c) The number of stems from stem values 30359 to 72621 is more than 13 stems. There are too many stems, so you have to redefine the stem values again by moving the vertical line to the left.

Minimum	3	0	3	5	9	0	9	2
Maximum	7	2	6	2	1	4	4	6

d) The number of stems from stem values 3035 to 7262 is more than 13 stems. There are too many stems, so you have to redefine the stem values again by moving the vertical line to the left.

Minimum	3	0	3	5	9	0	9	2
Maximum	7	2	6	2	1	4	4	6

e) The number of stems from stem values 303 to 726 is more than 13 stems. There are too many stems, so you have to redefine the stem values again by moving the vertical line to the left.

Minimum	3	0	3	5	9	0	9	2
Maximum	7	2	6	2	1	4	4	6

f) The number of stems from stem values 30 to 72 is more than 13 stems. There are too many stems, so you have to redefine the stem values again by moving the vertical line to the left.

Minimum	3	0	3	5	9	0	9	2
Maximum	7	2	6	2	1	4	4	6

The stem values are from 3 to 7 (that is 3, 4, 5, 6, 7). There are a total of 5 stems.

According to Stem Rule 1, "The number of stems should be from 6 to 13 stems." You do not have enough stems to construct the stem-and-leaf plot. According to Stem Rule 2, "The stem values should be consecutive numbers or repeated numbers. The numbers may each be repeated twice or 5 times." Therefore, you have to repeat each stem value twice, that is, 3, 3, 4, 4, 5, 5, 6, 6, 7, 7. You have a total of 10 stems, which satisfies Stem Rule 1. By repeating the stem values, you increase the number of stems so that the distribution does not appear so squeezed or squashed.

Step 4: Now construct the stem-and-leaf plot by repeating each stem value twice.

Per Stem Rule 3, record the stem unit under the stem title in the stem-and-leaf plot. Does stem value 3 represents units (i.e., face value), tens (10), hundreds (100), or thousands (1000). Each stem value is valued at 10,000,000. The stem value of 3 is actually regarded as 30,000,000 (i.e., 3 x 10,000,000), which reflects the original data value (e.g., 30,359,092 etc.). According to Leaf Rule 1, the leaf for each data value is the next <u>single</u> digit after the stem. For value 30,359,092, you record 0 as the leaf value. The rest of the digits after 0 are not recorded.

Stock Volume

Stem (10,000,000)	Leaf
3	
3	
4	
4	
5	
5	A total of 10 stems
6	
6	
7	
7	

Note that you have to check the following stem rules:

1. Per Stem Rule 1, you have 10 stems. Each stem is repeated twice.
2. Per Stem Rule 2, the stem values are consecutive numbers.
3. Per Stem Rule 3, the stem unit is 10,000,000.
4. You are not able to check Stem Rule 4 at this point because you have not recorded the leaves yet. Come back to check this rule after you have done step 5.

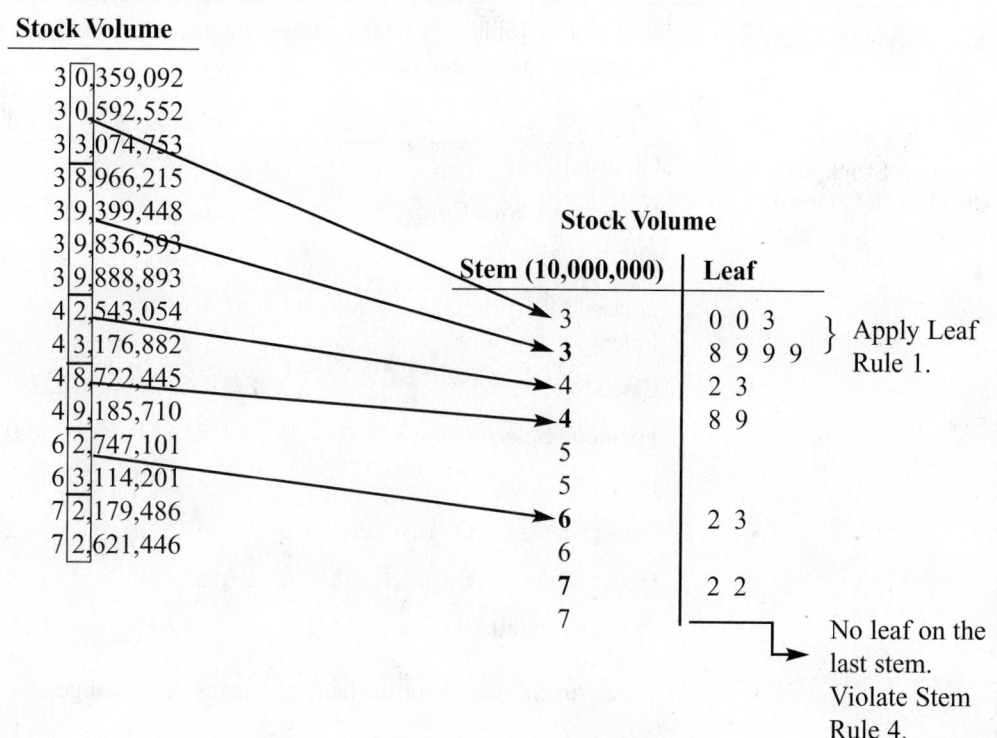

Step 5: Record the leaf values.

These values are **not** recorded.

Minimum	3	0	3	5	9	0	9	2
Maximum	7	2	6	2	1	4	4	6

Stem

According to Leaf Rule 1, record the next *single* digit after the stem.
According to Leaf Rule 2, do not *round off* the single digit of the leaf value.

You have to assign leaf values 0 to 4 to the first stem of the same value. The next leaf values 5 to 9 go to the second stem of the same value.

Record the leaf values, which are one digit after the stem value.

Stock Volume

```
3│0.359,092
3│0.592,552
3│3.074,753
3│8.966,215
3│9.399,448
3│9.836,593
3│9.888,893
4│2.543,054
4│3.176,882
4│8.722,445
4│9.185,710
6│2.747,101
6│3.114,201
7│2.179,486
7│2.621,446
```

Stock Volume

Stem (10,000,000)	Leaf	
3	0 0 3	} Apply Leaf
3	8 9 9 9	Rule 1.
4	2 3	
4	8 9	
5		
5		
6	2 3	
6		
7	2 2	
7		

No leaf on the last stem.
Violate Stem Rule 4.

Note that you have to check the following leaf rules:

1. There is no rounding off with the leaf values.
3. The leaf values are written in ascending order when positive and descending order when negative.
4. The leaf values must be evenly spaced.
5. No commas or dashes between the numbers are allowed.

Stem Rule number 4 "There must be at least one leaf associated with the first and last stem"—is violated. The second stem value 7 has no leaf associated with it, so you have to remove this stem to satisfy Stem Rule 4.

3.4 How Do You Construct a Stem-and-Leaf Plot with Negative and Positive Data Values?

For both positive and negative data values, use positive zero (+0) stem and negative zero (-0) stem to capture the positive and negative values. For example if you have data values -0.8 and +0.9, you would record 9 next to the +0 stem. Where will you record -0.8? If you record 8 next to the +0 stem, you will have a value of +0.8, but the actual value is -0.8. Therefore, you need a -0 to record 8.

Stem	Leaf
-0	8
+0	9

You need both +0 and -0 stems so that you can record 8 next to -0 and 9 next to +0.

EXAMPLE 3.3

Refer to Table 3.7, which shows the stock prices data. The data was taken from http://finance.yahoo.com/actives?e=o.

TABLE 3.7

Data on Stock Volume and the % Change in Volume

Name	Vol (000s)	Last	Change	% Change
Citigroup Inc	790,859	4.42	unch	0.00%
Bank of America Corp	262,174	12.42	−0.4	−3.12%
SPDR S&P 500	210,908	130.56	−1.48	−1.12%
iShares MSCI Emerging Markets Index	93,614	47.9	−1.24	−2.51%
Cisco Systems Inc	86,550	16.73	−0.3	−1.76%
Financial Select Sector SPDR	83,851	15.92	−0.22	−1.36%
iShares Silver Trust	74,937	42.42	0.58	1.38%
PowerShares QQQ Trust Series 1	69,073	56.25	−0.4	−0.71%
General Electric Co	63,659	19.98	−0.06	−0.30%
iShares Russell 2000 Index	58,617	82.13	−1.38	−1.65%

Note: "unch" stands for unchanged, means zero change.

Using the data listed in Table 3.7, construct stem-and-leaf displays for the % change.

Step 1: Sort the % change in ascending order.

% Change	% Change	
0.00%	**−3.12**	← Minimum
−3.12%	**−2.51**	
−1.12%	**−1.76**	
−2.51%	**−1.65**	
−1.76%	**−1.36**	
−1.36%	**−1.12**	
1.38%	**−0.71**	
−0.71%	**−0.30**	
−0.30%	**0.00**	
−1.65%	**1.38**	← Maximum

By sorting the data, it is easy to obtain the minimum and maximum values.

Step 2: Find the maximum and minimum values.

Minimum = −3.12
Maximum = 1.38

Step 3: Split the minimum and maximum values into stems and leaves.

Minimum	−	3	.	1	2
Maximum		1	.	3	8

a) The number of stems from stem values −3.1 to 1.3 is more than 13 stems. There are too many stems, so you have to redefine the stem values again by moving the vertical line to the left.

Minimum	−	3	.	1	2
Maximum		1	.	3	8

b) There are 6 stems from stem values −3 to 1: −3, −2, −1, −0, 0, and 1. According to Stem Rule 1, "The number of stems should be from 6 to 13 stems." You have a sufficient number of stems to construct the stem-and-leaf plot.

Step 4: Now construct the stem-and-leaf plot.

% Change

Stem	Leaf
−3	
−2	
−1	
−0	
0	
1	

A total of 6 stems

Note: Insert a negative zero (−0) stem to capture the positive and negative values.

Next, you have to check that your stem-and-leaf plot follows the stem rules.

Step 5: Record the leaf values.

Record the leaf values, which are one digit after the stem value. The stem unit is the face value; therefore, you leave it blank.

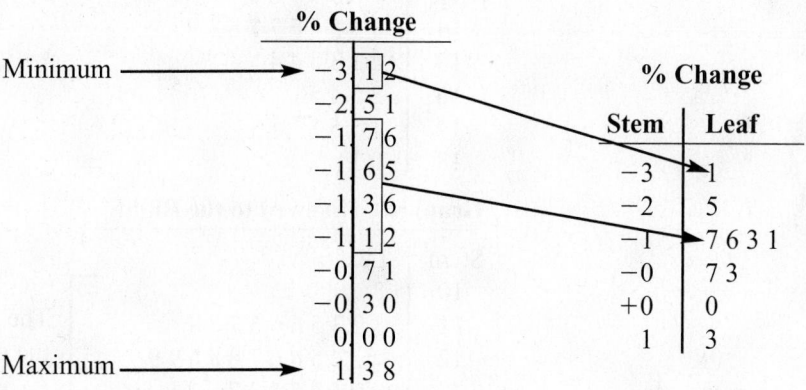

Now you have to check whether the stem and leaf plot follows the following stem rules:

1. The number of stems should be from 6 to 13 stems.

2. The stem values should be consecutive numbers or repeated numbers. The numbers may each be repeated twice or 5 times.
3. The stem units must be indicated if the stem is not to be taken at face value.
4. There must be at least one leaf associated with the first and last stem.

You also have to check the following leaf rules:

1. There is no rounding off with the leaf values.
3. The leaf values are written in ascending order when positive and descending order when negative.
4. The leaf values must be evenly spaced.
5. No commas or dashes between the numbers are allowed.

3.5 Interpretation of Results Using Stem-and-Leaf Plot

A) Using the stem-and-leaf plot to detect the shape of the data distribution.

The symmetry of a data distribution can be classified in three ways: 1) skewed to the left (the bulk of the data is located on the **right** side of the distribution; see Graphic A), (2) symmetrical (the bulk of the data is located in the middle of the distribution; see Graphic B) and (3) skewed to the right (the bulk of the data is located on the **left** side of the distribution; see Graphic C).

Graphic A: Skewed to the Left

Stem	Leaf
10	2
11	1 2
12	3 4 4
13	5 5 6 7 8
14	3 3 5 6 7 7 7
15	2 2 3 3 4 4 5 5 6 7 8
16	2 3 4 5 6 6 7 8 8 8 9 9 9
17	1 5 5 6
18	0 1

The bulk of the data is located on the right side of the distribution.

Graphic B: Symmetrical

Stem	Leaf
10	2
11	1 2
12	3 4 4
13	1 5 5 6 7 8 9
14	3 3 5 6 7 7 7 8 8 9
15	2 2 3 3 4 4
16	2 3 4 5
17	1 5 5
18	0 1

Graphic C: Skewed to the Right

Stem	Leaf
10	2
11	1 2 3 5 6 6 6 7 7 8
12	2 3 4 5 6 6 7 8 8 8 9 9 9
13	0 0 4 4 5 5 6 7
14	3 3 5 6 7 7
15	2 2 3 3
16	3 4 4
17	1 5 8
18	1 2

The bulk of the data is located on the left side of the distribution.

B) Using the stem-and-leaf plot to extract information.

You can extract information from a summarized stem-and-leaf plot. This will be illustrated using the following example.

EXAMPLE 3.4

Hours of Overtime Claimed per Month

A random sample of employees was taken from a technology company, and the hours of overtime claimed per month were recorded and summarized in the following stem-and-leaf plot.

Stem (10)	Leaf
10	2
11	1 2 3 5 6 6 6 7 7 8
12	2 3 4 5 6 6 7 8 8 8 9 9 9
13	0 0 4 4 5 5 6 7
14	3 3 5 6 7 7
15	2 2 3 3
16	3 4 4
17	1 5 8
18	1 2

i. How many employees are being sampled?

Each leaf represents one data value of an employee. Therefore, the sample size is equal to the number of leaves. There are 50 leaves, which means there are 50 employees in this sample.

ii. What percent of employees claimed at least 152 hours per month?

"At least 152" includes the value 152. By counting the values including 152 and greater than 152, you get 12 values. These values are 152, 152, 153, 153, 163, 164, 164, 171, 175, 178, 181, and 182. Each employee has one overtime value. Therefore, 12 values represents 12 employees. Thus, you have (12/50)*100=24% of employees claimed at least 152 hours per month.

iii. What percent of employees claimed less than 130 hours per month?

"Less than 130" does not include the value 130. By counting the values less than 130 and not including 130, you get 24 values. These values are 102, 111, 112, 113, 115, 116, 116, 116, 117, 117, 118, 122, 123, 124, 125, 126, 126, 127, 128, 128, 128, 129, 129, and 129. Each employee has one overtime value. Therefore, 24 values represents 24 employees. Thus, you have (24/50)*100=48% of employees claimed less than 130 hours per month.

iv. What percent of employees claimed more than 163 hours per month?

"More than 163" does not include the value 163. By counting the values more than 163 and not including 163, you get 7 values. These values are 164, 164, 171, 175, 178, 181, and 182. Each employee has one overtime value. Therefore, 7 values represents 7 employees. Thus, you have (7/50)*100 = 14% of employees claimed more than 163 hours per month.

v. What percent of employees claimed at most 115 hours per month?

"At most 115 hours" includes the value 115. By counting the values including 115 and less than 115, you get 5 values. These values are 102, 111, 112, 113, and 115. Each employee has one overtime value. Therefore, 5 values represents 5 employees. Thus, you have (5/50)*100=10% of employees claimed at most 115 hours per month.

Stem and Leaf Plot Problems

3.1 Refer to Table 3.18b (on page 85) that shows data regarding the first 20 companies taken from the FP500 Canada's 500 Largest Corporations table that appeared in the June 2003 issue of *National Post Business*.

Construct stem-and-leaf displays for the following data:

a. Profit rank
b. Asset rank
c. Revenues for 2002
d. Assets for 2002
e. Number of employees
f. Share price Exchange – 1 year percent
g. Profits as a percent of Assets
h. Profits as a percent of Equity

3.2 Refer to Table 3.8, which shows the mutual fund data that appeared in the Canadian Mutual Funds table of the June 3, 2004, issue of the *Globe and Mail*.

Construct stem-and-leaf displays for the following data:

a. Equitable life valuation data
b. Equitable life change data
c. Equitable life percent change data
d. MD management valuation data
e. MD management percent change data

3.3 Refer to Table 3.9 (on page 60), which shows data regarding the first 21 companies taken from the *Financial Post Magazine* Web site (http://www.financialpost.com/magazine/fp500/list.html).

For the 21 companies listed in Table 3.9, construct stem-and-leaf displays for the following data:

a. Revenue amount 2007
b. Profit amount 2007
c. Revenue change
d. Profit change
e. Profit rank

3.4 Refer to Table 3.10 (on page 61), "Telecommunications Industry Annual Ranking of America's Largest Corporations by Revenues, Profits, which appeared in the April 30, 2007, issue of *Fortune* magazine.

Using the data listed in Table 3.10, construct stem-and-leaf displays for the following data:

a. Revenues ($ million)
b. Profits ($ million)
c. Profits % change from 2005
d. Revenues % change from 2005
e. 1000 revenues rank

TABLE 3.8

fund	valuation	chg	% chg
EQUITABLE LIFE			
AIM Cdn Premier 06/01	10.01	+.01	+.07
Accum Income 06/01	23.26	-.03	-.15
American Gwth 06/01	10.48	+.04	+.37
Asian-Pacific 06/01	6.38	+.01	+.17
Asset Allocat 06/01	16.72	-.01	-.06
Dissett Div Inc 06/01	10.19	-.01	-.10
Cdn Bond 06/01	15.55	-.02	-.15
Cdn Stock 06/01	20.17	-.01	-.05
CommonStock 06/01	29.96	-.02	-.05
European Equity 06/01	7.23	-.02	-.22
International 06/01	11.49	+.02	+.17
MB Cdn Eq Value 06/01	18.21	-.04	-.24
Mack US Em Grth 06/01	10.15	+.09	+.84
Templeton Grwth 06/01	9.39	+.02	+.17
Tmplton Glo Bnd 06/01	12.32	+.04	+.36
Trimark Europls 06/01	10.51	+.02	+.15
Trimark Glo Bal 06/01	10.48	+.02	+.17
US Equity 06/01	6.30	+.02	+.32

fund	valuation	chg	% chg
MD MANAGEMENT			
MD Balanced	18.08	-.06	-.33
MD Bnd & Mtg	10.39	-.01	-.10
MD Bond	7.10	-.03	-.42
MD Dividend	16.66	-.03	-.18
MD Equity	19.03	-.03	-.16
MD Glo Bond	11.27	-.03	-.27
MD Glo Equ RSP	7.07	unch	unch
MD Growth	10.37	unch	unch
MD Growth RSP	9.82	unch	unch
MD Int'l Growth	6.64	unch	unch
MD Int'l Value	10.13	unch	unch
MD Intl Gr RSP	6.46	unch	unch
MD Select	15.39	-.04	-.26
MD US LgCpGrRSP	6.07	unch	unch
MD US LiCap Val	8.42	unch	unch
MD US LrCpVIRSP	8.25	unch	unch
MD US Lrg Cp Gr	4.79	unch	unch
MD US Sml Cp Gr	3.68	-.01	-.27
MDPIM Cdn Equ-A	11.01	-.04	-.36
MDPIM US Equ-A	7.39	-.02	-.27

fund	valuation	chg	% chg
MANULIFE MIX FUNDS			
AIM Am MidCp Gw	12.26	-.04	-.33
AIM Cd First Cl	12.25	-.05	-.41
Cd Lg Cap Gw Cl	12.85	-.07	-.54
Cd Lg Cap ValCl	12.12	-.02	-.16
Cd Lg Cp CoreCl	12.05	-.02	-.17
Cdn Equ Val Cl	12.65	-.02	-.16
E&P Gw Opp Cl	14.38	-.04	-.28
E&P US MidCapCl	11.81	-.05	-.42
Fl Can DiscEqCl	13.07	-.08	-.61
Fl Gwth Amer Cl	11.09	-.03	-.27
Fl Intl Port Cl	11.60	-.02	-.17
Global Equ Cl	10.86	-.01	-.09
Global Sect Cl	11.31	-.06	-.53
Global SectCl-H	11.31	-.05	-.44
Global Val Cl	12.48	-.01	-.08
Int'l Growth Cl	11.29	-.01	-.09
Int'l Value Cl	12.27	+.01	+.08
Japanese Class	12.63	-.12	-.94
SM Tot Cd Eq Cl	13.26	+.02	+.15
SM Total Glo Cl	12.00	-.04	-.33
SM Total USEqCl	11.33	-.03	-.26
SMTotal Gl Cl-H	12.00	-.04	-.33
Sht Term Yld Cl	10.21	unch	unch
Str Bond Class	10.30	-.03	-.29
Tri Sel Cdn Cl	12.13	-.03	-.25
Trimark Glo Cl	11.41	+.04	+.35
US Lg Cap Gw Cl	10.40	-.01	-.10
US Lg Cp CoreCl	10.77	-.01	-.09
US Lg Cp Val Cl	10.92	-.02	-.18
US MidCp Val Cl	11.51	-.03	-.26

TABLE 3.8 *(continued)*

fund	valuation	chg	% chg
CI - CLARICA MUTUAL FUNDS			
Alpine CdnRes	10.35	-.08	-.77
Alpine CdnRes A	10.46	-.07	-.66
Alpine GrthEq	13.09	-.04	-.30
Alpine GrthEq A	13.28	-.05	-.38
Cdn Blu Chip Z	11.35	-.04	-.35
Cdn BlueChip	16.34	-.06	-.37
Cdn BlueChip A	16.51	-.07	-.42
Cdn Div Cl Z	10.86	-.04	-.37
Cdn Divers	14.71	-.05	-.34
Cdn Divers A	14.96	-.05	-.33
Cdn Equity	12.80	-.02	-.16
Cdn Equity A	12.82	-.02	-.16
Cdn Lrg Cap Val	10.55	+.01	+.09
Cdn Small/Mid A	21.02	-.04	-.19
Cdn Sml/Mid Cap	18.40	-.03	-.16
Clarica Balance	11.64	-.02	-.17
Glo Lrg Cap Val	10.52	+.04	+.38
Global Bond	9.91	-.04	-.40
Global Bond A	9.91	-.03	-.30
Prem Bond	11.34	-.04	-.35
Prem Bond A	11.49	-.04	-.35
Prem Int'l	12.43	-.03	-.24
Prem Int'l A	12.78	-.03	-.23
Prem Mtg	10.34	-.02	-.19
Prem Mtg A	10.46	-.02	-.19
Sig Corp Bond	9.83	-.02	-.20
Sum Cdn Equ	15.37	-.05	-.32
Sum Cdn Equ A	15.50	-.05	-.32
Sum Div Gwth	15.18	-.02	-.13
Sum Div Gwth A	14.91	-.02	-.13
Sum For Equ	14.46	-.03	-.21
Sum For Equ A	14.96	-.03	-.20
Sum Gwth&Inc	14.09	-.03	-.21
Sum Gwth&Inc A	14.50	-.03	-.21
US Small Cap	8.44	-.02	-.24
US Small Cap A	8.54	-.01	-.12

fund	valuation	chg	% chg
TRANSAMERICA GROWSAFE3 75/100			
AGF Int Val 7510 05/01	4.51	+.00	+.02
AIC AmFoc 7510 06/01	5.07	-.01	-.19
AIC DivCan 7510 06/01	5.38	-.00	-.01
Agg AA GIF 7510	3.63	-.00	-.03
Bal AA GIF 7510	4.47	-.01	-.12
CI Gl Boom 7510 06/01	4.82	-.00	-.10
CI Global 7510 06/01	5.46	-.00	-.01
CanAsian 7510	4.21	-.01	-.14
CanEuro 7510	3.14	+.02	+.75
CanUS 21st 7510	2.86	-.01	-.24
CanUS L Cap 7510	4.16	+.02	+.38
Cdn Bal 7510	4.77	-.02	-.46
Cdn Bond 7510	5.91	-.02	-.34
Cdn Equity 7510	3.40	-.03	-.79
Cdn Lg Cap 7510	4.17	-.01	-.35
Cdn MMF 7510	5.29	+.00	+.00
CdnEqVal 7510 06/01	5.62	+.00	+.04
CdnFixPay 7510 06/01	5.67	-.01	-.18
Con AA GIF 7510	4.88	-.01	-.20
Fid Can AA 7510 06/01	5.66	+.03	+.46
Fid IntPort 7510 06/01	4.78	-.06	-1.19
Fid TrueNrt 7510 06/01	5.75	+.01	+.19
Grow AA GIF 7510	4.11	-.00	-.06
MacIvyGwinc 7510 06/01	5.68	+.01	+.17
TD Div Inc 7510 06/01	6.12	-.00	-.03
TOP AggrGw 7510 06/01	3.66	+.01	+.24
TOP Bal 7510 06/01	4.50	+.01	+.19
TOP CdnMgr 7510 06/01	5.75	+.00	+.02
TOP Cons 7510 06/01	5.00	+.01	+.14
TOP GloMgr 7510 06/01	4.89	+.01	+.13
TOP GloSect 7510 06/01	4.90	+.01	+.29
TOP Growth 7510 06/01	4.24	+.01	+.20
TOP USMgrs 7510 06/01	4.80	+.02	+.39
US EqVal 7510 06/01	5.74	+.03	+.47
US Equity 7510	3.68	-.00	-.01

3.5 Refer to Table 3.11 (on page 61), which shows the stock summary data for companies with names starting with the letter A that were traded on the NASDAQ on May 8, 2008. The data was taken from the *Financial Post Magazine*'s Web site, (*http://www.financialpost.com/markets/market-data/market-nasdaq.html?tmp=nasdaq*).

Using the data listed in Table 3.11, construct stem-and-leaf displays for the following data:

a. Volume
b. High/ask price
c. Low/bid price
d. Close/previous price
e. Net change
f. 52 week high price
g. 52 week low price

TABLE 3.9   FP 500 Ranking of Canada's Companies

FINANCIAL POST
BUSINESS   FP500

Home FP500 Rankings Crown Corps Profit Leaders Largest Subsidiaries Buy the database

Last year's FP500 rankings   **Canada's Top Companies 2008**   *Search*

First · Previous   *1 - 50* ▼   Next · Last

Ranking			Revenue		Profit		
2007	2006	Company	Amt. 2007 (x1000)	Change	Amt. 2007 (x1000)	Change	Rank
1	1	Royal Bank of Canada, Toronto (Oc07) ⇥	$41,307,000	14.6%	$5,492,000	16.2%	2
2	2	Manulife Financial Corp., Toronto ⇥	$35,533,000	3.9%	$4,229,000	6.5%	6
▲ 3	4	George Weston Ltd., Toronto ⇥	$32,815,000	2.0%	$563,000	365.3%	61
▼ 4	3	General Motors of Canada Ltd., Oshawa, Ont. ⇥	$31,675,000	-5.0%	-	-	-
5	5	Power Corp. of Canada, Montreal ⇥	$29,408,000	-3.0%	$1,463,000	5.0%	28
6	6	Magna International Inc.*, Aurora, Ont. ⇥	$27,995,958	2.1%	$712,062	18.9%	52
7	7	Alcan Inc.*, Montreal (De06) ⇥	$26,808,894	8.9%	$2,029,860	1199.4%	22
▲ 8	10	The Bank of Nova Scotia, Halifax (Oc07) ⇥	$26,427,000	17.5%	$4,045,000	13.0%	8
▲ 9	11	The Toronto-Dominion Bank, Toronto (Oc07) ⇥	$25,209,000	13.0%	$3,997,000	-13.2%	9
▼ 10	8	Imperial Oil Ltd., Calgary ⇥	$25,069,000	2.3%	$3,188,000	4.7%	12
▲ 11	15	Onex Corp., Toronto ⇥	$23,433,000	25.8%	$228,000	-77.2%	119
▲ 12	13	Canadian Imperial Bank of Commerce, Toronto (Oc07) ⇥	$23,289,000	15.5%	$3,296,000	24.6%	10
▲ 13	16	EnCana Corp.*, Calgary ⇥	$23,033,004	23.9%	$4,251,966	-33.7%	5
14	14	Petro-Canada, Calgary ⇥	$21,710,000	14.8%	$2,733,000	57.1%	15
▼ 15	9	Sun Life Financial Inc., Toronto ⇥	$21,188,000	-12.8%	$2,290,000	6.8%	17
▼ 16	12	Chrysler Canada Inc., Windsor, Ont. (De06) ⇥	$20,534,000	-1.4%	-	-	-
17	17	Bank of Montreal, Montreal (Oc07) ⇥	$20,344,000	12.1%	$2,131,000	-20.0%	20
▲ 18	19	Bombardier Inc.*, Montreal (Ja08) ⇥	$18,538,854	10.1%	$335,703	10.3%	98
▼ 19	18	BCE Inc., Montreal ⇥	$17,866,000	0.9%	$4,057,000	102.1%	7
▲ 20	21	Suncor Energy Inc., Calgary ⇥	$17,212,000	20.0%	$2,832,000	-4.7%	14
▲ 21	27	Husky Energy Inc., Calgary ⇥	$15,518,000	22.5%	$3,214,000	17.9%	11

Source: http://www.financialpost.com/magazine/fp500/list.html

TABLE 3.10   FORTUNE 1,000: Telecommunications Industry Annual Ranking of America's Largest Corporations by Revenues, Profits

			REVENUES		PROFITS	
Rank	Company	1,000 revenues rank	$ millions	% change from 2005	$ millions	% change from 2005
1	Verizon Communications	13	93,221	24	6,197	−16
2	AT&T	27	63,055	44	7,356	54
3	Sprint Nextel	53	43,531	26	1,329	−26
4	Comcast	84	25,700	15	2,533	173
5	DIRECTV Group	160	14,756	12	1,420	323
6	Qwest Communications	178	13,923	0	593	N.A.
7	Echostar Communications	252	9,818	17	608	−60
8	Alltel	256	9,723	2	1,129	−15
9	Liberty Global	340	6,813	29	706	N.A.
10	Virgin Media	347	6,637	83	−984	−228
11	Cablevision Systems	380	6,007	15	−126	−234
12	Charter Communications	409	5,613	7	−1,370	N.A.
13	Level 3 Communications	465	4,778	30	−744	N.A.
14	Telephone & Data Sys.	501	4,266	8	339	52
15	IDT	755	2,452	−1	−179	N.A.
16	CenturyTel	757	2,448	−1	370	11
17	NII Holdings	772	2,371	36	294	68
18	Citizens Communications	825	2,126	−2	345	70

From the April 30th, 2007, issue
Source: http://money.cnn.com/magazines/fortune/fortune500/

TABLE 3.11   Stock Summary Data for Companies with Names Starting with the Letter A That Were Traded on the NASDAQ.

Stock Description			Daily Trading					52 Week	
Company	Security	Ticker	Volume	High/ Ask	Low/ Bid	Close/ Previous	Net Change	High	Low
A-Power Energy Generation	com	APWR	223,539	10.88	10.09	10.75	+0.73	31.80	3.00
AAON Inc	com	AAON	41,035	21.05	20.62	21.00	+0.50	23.00	12.79
ABIOMED Inc	com	ABMD	93,186	6.98	6.58	6.98	+0.33	20.06	4.67
AC Moore Arts & Crafts	com	ACMR	15,187	3.39	3.26	3.36	−0.01	8.78	0.71
ACADIA Phrmctcls Inc	com	ACAD	84,387	1.94	1.75	1.81	+0.07	8.84	0.73
ACI Worldwide Inc	com	ACIW	194,814	14.33	13.96	14.13	+0.09	22.49	8.86
ADA-ES Inc	com	ADES	900	3.95	3.80	3.86	+0.01	11.98	2.41
ADAM Inc	com	ADAM	3,198	3.33	3.14	3.31	+0.08	7.80	1.96
ADC Telecommuns Inc	com	ADCT	997,080	7.54	7.09	7.43	−0.11	17.45	2.48
ADTRAN Inc	com	ADTN	264,258	20.37	19.56	19.94	+0.19	26.50	12.14
AEP Industries Inc	com	AEPI	15,482	24.63	21.68	23.00	+1.54	28.58	10.43
AEterna Zentaris Inc	com	AEZS	40,060	1.33	1.24	1.32	+0.06	1.48	0.261
AFC Enterprises Inc	com	AFCE	45,533	6.06	5.33	5.62	−0.17	10.14	2.85
AMAG Pharmaceuticals Inc	com	AMAG	155,664	54.65	52.73	54.54	+1.86	55.00	18.33
AMCORE Financial Inc	com	AMFI	12,981	1.40	1.30	1.38	+0.12	14.50	0.59
AMERCO	com	UHAL	14,552	33.45	31.64	33.20	+1.30	59.85	22.01
AMERISAFE Inc	com	AMSF	83,309	17.81	16.85	17.78	+1.00	21.96	12.51
AMICAS Inc	com	AMCS	2,099	2.59	2.44	2.48	+0.01	2.96	1.27
ANADIGICS Inc	com	ANAD	176,563	3.04	2.86	3.04	+0.13	13.94	1.13
ANSYS Inc	com	ANSS	296,247	27.11	26.20	26.65	−0.06	49.81	18.00

Source: http://www.financialpost.com/markets/market-data/commodity-cash_prices.html?tmp=cash_prices

3.6 Frequency Distribution

In this section you will learn to group a set of **quantitative** data into a frequency distribution. Frequency distributions are often used to group data in the form of a table, which gives a general idea of how the data values are being distributed. An advantage of using a frequency distribution is that it can handle a large (typically more than 50) data set. You have to familiarize yourself with the rules and conventions introduced in this chapter to construct your frequency distribution. The guidelines given in this chapter will be useful for a person just learning to make a frequency distribution or for getting a general impression about the distribution of the data. If one has experience and is intimately familiar with the data being organized, several of these general guidelines may not be appropriate.

The following is an example of a frequency distribution displaying the baggage weight for passengers travelling by air.

FIGURE 3.2

Frequency distribution for baggage weight data for passengers travelling by air

Baggage Weight (kg)	Number of passengers
20.0 and under 25.0	4
25.0 and under 30.0	13
30.0 and under 35.0	7
35.0 and under 40.0	4
40.0 and under 45.0	1
45.0 and under 50.0	0
50.0 and under 55.0	1
Total	30

Now, let's learn the general guidelines and how to apply them to construct a frequency distribution as shown in Figure 3.2.

General Guidelines for Constructing a Frequency Distribution

If one has experience and is intimately familiar with the data being organized, several of these general guidelines may not be appropriate.

The frequency distribution for baggage weight data is shown in Figure 3.2 above. The data is grouped into seven **classes** (also known as intervals). The class width for each class is 5 kg. You should know how many classes to use and what class width to apply to your frequency distribution. Before you learn to construct the frequency distribution, you must familiarize yourself with the following guidelines.

1. **Number of classes:** You should not have too few or too **many** classes. For the questions you will solve in this course you should use **5 to 10 classes** in your final constructed frequency distribution.
2. **Notation for indicating classes:** There are several possible notations that are used to designate the classes. In this course we will use the **"and under"** notation (e.g., 260 and under 270). The numerical values used in designating the classes when using the "and under" notation are called **boundaries**.

   You will also likely come across classes that have been set up using the "to" notation (e.g., 260 to 269).

3. **Close-ended classes:** A close-ended class has both a lower and an upper boundary. An open-ended class is missing one of these boundaries. For example, the class "100 and over" is an open-ended class because there is no upper boundary. You should avoid using open-ended classes in this course.

In this course, I do not want you to use "open-ended" classes. I want you to learn the basic rules to construct your frequency distribution—just keep it simple. However, it is not incorrect to use open-ended classes.

Statistics Canada uses open-ended classes in the following frequency distribution of family income by family type.

Family income, by family type (Couple families)					
	2005	2006	2007	2008	2009
	Couple families[1] number of families				
Total, all income groups	7,486,160	7,629,330	7,727,870	7,832,060	7,926,210
Under $10,000	177,840	217,430	198,050	194,670	199,350
$10,000 and over	7,308,320	7,411,900	7,529,820	7,637,400	7,726,860
$15,000 and over	7,180,180	7,291,650	7,416,270	7,527,140	7,613,770
$20,000 and over	6,996,720	7,125,340	7,258,770	7,374,900	7,459,680
$25,000 and over	6,721,450	6,887,120	7,043,530	7,177,060	7,262,910
$30,000 and over	6,370,220	6,552,870	6,734,300	6,876,780	6,958,650
$35,000 and over	6,024,090	6,211,130	6,398,830	6,549,220	6,620,770
$40,000 and over	5,670,370	5,869,210	6,068,570	6,228,650	6,288,200
$45,000 and over	5,313,550	5,524,280	5,734,370	5,900,920	5,949,750
$50,000 and over	4,956,970	5,179,120	5,397,900	5,571,420	5,611,520
$60,000 and over	4,255,720	4,495,550	4,727,730	4,915,080	4,939,370
$70,000 and over	3,589,990	3,838,200	4,077,940	4,277,270	4,292,660
$75,000 and over	3,277,060	3,526,720	3,767,350	3,969,160	3,982,590
$80,000 and over	2,981,070	3,229,670	3,469,550	3,672,840	3,684,990
$90,000 and over	2,443,620	2,684,680	2,915,800	3,119,370	3,129,560
$100,000 and over	1,985,270	2,210,990	2,430,210	2,626,660	2,636,310
$150,000 and over	703,730	824,840	947,310	1,063,240	1,072,990
$200,000 and over	310,260	368,150	424,320	476,110	476,050
$250,000 and over	177,410	209,710	238,760	261,300	256,550

Source: http://www40.statcan.ca/id/cst/FAMIL106A-eng.htm

4. **Class width (denoted as CW):** A class that has an *upper* and a *lower* boundary has a finite class width. The class width is determined by the following formula:

Class Width = Upper boundary − Lower boundary

It is best to select a class width that is an "easy" number to work with. The recommended class widths are shown in Table 3.12.

TABLE 3.12

A List of "Nice" Numbers

For narrower classes				For wider classes		
← Divide by 10				Multiply by 10 →		
	0.01	0.1	1	10	100	
	0.02	0.2	2	20	200	
Etc.	0.025	0.25 (if the data has at least 2 decimals)	2.5 (if the data has at least one decimal)	25	250	Etc.
	0.05	0.5	5	50	500	

Note: In this course, when you are asked to construct a frequency distribution, all classes must have the **same class width**.

5. **No gaps between classes:** Classes are mutually exclusive and are not overlapping. In other words, every possible value must fall into exactly one class. There must be **no gaps** between the classes (i.e., the upper boundary of one class will also be the lower boundary of the next class).

6. **All classes must have the same class width:** When working with continuous data, the upper boundary of one class and the lower boundary of the following class reference the same value. Since the boundary value should fall into only one class, the wording "and under" can be used to clarify that the upper boundaries are not included in the classes. This usage is demonstrated in the next example. To keep it simple, use equal class width for each class. The class width in the following frequency distribution is $20 - 10 = 10$. The frequency distribution has 6 classes with a class width of 10 in each class.

Class	Frequency
10 and under 20	2
20 and under 30	1
30 and under 40	3
40 and under 50	11
50 and under 60	16
60 and under 70	7

7. **The first and last class must contain frequencies:** The lowest value (or minimum value) is in the first class, and the highest value (or maximum value) is in the last class.

8. **Boundaries:** There are several guidelines that should be used to determine the actual numerical values of the boundaries.

   a) The boundaries should *look like* the data, that is, have the same number of decimal places as the data. If the data have one decimal point, then the boundaries should have one decimal point. If the data are whole numbers, then the boundaries should be whole numbers. The reason for having this rule is to retain the information about the type of quantitative data. When we grouped the data, we lost the information about the nature of the data. With the grouped data in the form of a frequency distribution, we only know how many values (i.e., frequency) fall in each class.

   b) Each boundary should be a **multiple** of the chosen class width.

   <u>Example:</u> If the class width is 5 then the boundaries should be a multiple of 5. Then the possible values for your boundaries are 0, 5, 10, 15, 20, 25, 30, 35, 40, 45, 50, etc., which are multiples of 5.

   If the class width is 10 then the boundaries should be multiples of 10. Then the possible values for your boundaries are 0, 10, 20, 30, 40, 50, 60, etc., which are multiples of 10.

Pick a Nice Number for the Class Width

"Nice" numbers are listed in Table 3.12. Always start off with this list of 4 numbers: **1, 2, 2.5, 5**. If you want a larger class width, you can multiply each number in the list of **1, 2, 2.5, 5** by 10 and you will have **10, 20, 25, 50**. If you still want a larger class width, multiply again by 10 and you have **100, 200, 250, 500**. If you want a smaller class width, divide each number in the list of **1, 2, 2.5, 5** by 10 and you have **0.1, 0.2 0.25, 0.5**. If you still want a smaller class width, divide again by 10 and you have **0.01, 0.02, 0.025, 0.05**.

Determine Class Width

To figure out the class width in your frequency distribution, you should estimate the class width using the following formula with the highest value (or maximum value) and lowest value (or minimum value) in a date set. Divide the difference by the minimum number of classes specified by the guideline. The minimum number of classes is 5. The value you obtained is called the "estimated class width" because this value rarely turns out to be 1, 2, 2.5 or 5 (the "nice" numbers).

$$\text{Estimated Class Width} = \frac{\text{Highest value} - \text{Lowest value}}{\text{Minimum number of classes recommended}}$$

$$\text{Estimated Class Width} = \frac{\text{Highest value} - \text{Lowest value}}{5}$$

Choose one of the two recommended class widths (i.e., from a list of "nice" numbers) that enclose the estimated class width. For example, if the estimated class width is 15.3, you may choose either 10 or 20. Whichever class width you choose to construct your frequency distribution, you must always check that the number of classes is between 5 and 10 classes.

Demonstration on How to Select a "Nice" Number for the Class Width

You only need two pieces of information to construct the classes in your frequency distribution —the minimum (also known as lowest) and maximum (or highest) values. To construct the frequency column of the frequency distribution, you need the data values.

EXAMPLE 3.5

Given the lowest value 684 and the highest value 1093, calculate the estimated class width using the formula.

$$\text{Estimated Class Width} = \frac{(1093 - 684)}{5} = 81.8$$

Now let's select the "nice" numbers as shown next.

Start with this list of numbers	Multiply by 10	Multiply by 10 again
1	10	(100)
2	20	200
2.5	25	250
5	(50)	500
Since **81.8** is not in this list, let's move to the next list.		**81.8** is between 50 and 100; thus you will pick either 50 or 100 to construct your classes.

The estimated class width is **81.8**, and this value falls between two nice numbers, which are 50 and 100. After you have picked the two "nice" numbers from the list, you have to make sure that the number of classes is between 5 and 10. The first class should contain the lowest data value, and the last class should contain the highest data value. To obtain the first class **lower boundary**, find the greatest multiple of the class width that is less than or equal to the minimum data value.

Let's start with the class width of 50 (i.e., CW = 50) to construct the classes. The lower boundary is 650 because 650 is the greatest multiple of 50 that is less than or equal to 684. So the first class would be "650 and under 700."

Using CW = 50, you have the following classes:
650 and under 700 (includes the minimum value) is called the first class.
700 and under 750
750 and under 800
800 and under 850
850 and under 900
900 and under 950
950 and under 1000
1000 and under 1050
1050 and under 1100 (includes the maximum value) is called the last class.

There are a total of 9 classes, which meets the guideline (i.e., number of classes are between 5 and 10).

Now use the class width of 100 (i.e., CW = 100) to construct the classes. The lower boundary is 600 because 600 is the greatest multiple of 100 that is less than or equal to 684. You cannot use 680 because 680 is not a multiple of 100. The first class would be "600 and under 700."

600 and under 700 (includes the minimum value = 684)
700 and under 800
800 and under 900
900 and under 1000
1000 and under 1100 (includes the maximum value = 1093)

There are a total of 5 classes, which meets the guidelines.

The results are summarized in Table 3.13.

TABLE 3.13

Summary of the Classes Using the Same Set of Data with Two Class Widths

No	CW = 50	CW = 100
1	650 and under 700	600 and under 700
2	700 and under 750	700 and under 800
3	750 and under 800	800 and under 900
4	800 and under 850	900 and under 1000
5	850 and under 900	1000 and under 1100
6	900 and under 950	
7	950 and under 1000	
8	1000 and under 1050	
9	1050 and under 1100	

If you use CW = 50, you end up with 9 classes (refer to Table 3.13).
If you use CW = 100, you end up with 5 classes (refer to Table 3.13).

For this set of data, you have two class widths that you can use to group your data. Both resulting frequency distributions are correct.

Issues about Picking the Correct Class Width

Recall the guideline that instructs that the boundaries should *look like* the data. In the basic list of "nice" numbers, there is a class width of **2.5** that has one decimal place, but you should not use this class width for whole number data.

Question: Can I only use a nice number with one decimal place if my data only have one decimal place?

The answer is yes; for example, you may use the following nice numbers for your class width: 0.1, 0.2, 0.5, and 2.5. You may not use 0.25 because the data have one decimal place. However, you can use 0.25 if the data have two decimal places.

Symbols: L = Lowest and H = Highest

EXAMPLE 3.6

How to pick the class width with data that have no decimal.

I.   Data: 3   8   10   11   14

L = 3 and H = 14
Estimated CW = (14 – 3) / 5 = 2.2
Estimated CW = 2.2 falls between 2 and 2.5
You cannot use 2.5 as class width because the data has no decimal; you should pick either 2 or 5. Again, you should check that the class widths comply with the guideline (i.e., number of classes are between 5 and 10).

II. Data: 25   67   87   117   164

L = 25 and H = 164
Estimated CW = (164 – 25) / 5 = 27.8
Estimated CW = 27.8 falls between 25 and 50
You can use either 25 or 50, but you have to check that the class widths comply with the guideline.

EXAMPLE 3.7

How to pick the class width with data that have one decimal place.

I.   Data with one decimal: 1.4   4.6   8.7   11.7   14.9

L = 1.4 and H = 14.9
Estimated CW = (14.9 – 1.4) / 5 = 2.7
Estimated CW = 2.7 falls between 2.5 and 5
You can use either 2.5 or 5. The class width of 5 is a whole number. To comply with the guideline, you show 5.0 instead of 5, but you have to check that the number of classes is between 5 and 10 (according to the guideline).

II. Data with one decimal: 13.4   45.7   87.4   106.5   149.5

L = 13.4 H = 149.5
Estimated CW = (149.5 – 13.4) / 5 = 27.22
Estimated CW = 27.22 falls between 25 and 50
You can use either 25 or 50, but now 25 will be 25.0 and 50 will be 50.0. After you decide which CW to use, you should check that the number of classes are between 5 and 10 (i.e., the boundaries must reflect one decimal, 0.0 and under 25.0). Again, you have to check that the number of classes is between 5 and 10.

EXAMPLE 3.8

How to pick the class width with data that have two decimal places.

I.   Data: 1.34   4.57   8.74   10.65   14.95

L = 1.34 and H = 14.95
Estimated CW = (14.95 – 1.34) / 5 = 2.722
Estimated CW = 2.722 falls between 2.5 and 5

You still can use both 2.5 and 5, but now they are 2.50 and 5.00. Again, you have to check that the number of classes is between 5 and 10.

II. Data with two decimal places: 0.25   0.67   0.87   1.17   1.64

L = 0.25 and H = 1.64
Estimated CW = (1.64 – 0.25) / 5 = 0.278
Estimated CW = 0.278 falls between 0.25 and 0.5
You can use either 0.25 or 0.50, but you have to check that that the number of classes is between 5 and 10.

EXAMPLE 3.9

How to pick the class width with data that have three decimals.

Data: 0.134   0.457   0.874   1.065   1.553

L = 0.134 and H = 1.553
Estimated CW = (1.553 – 0.134) / 5 = 0.2838
Estimated CW = 0.2838 falls between 0.25 and 0.5
You still can use 0.25 and 0.5, but now they are 0.250 and 0.500, respectively. Again, you have to check that the number of classes is between 5 and 10.

Test Your Understanding

In a data set, the lowest value (or minimum value) is 112, and the highest value (or maximum value) is 196.

Question 1: What class width(s) did you use in your completed frequency distribution?

A. 10
B. 20
C. 25
D. 50
E. Both a and b

Answer: E

Question 2: What are the number of classes in your completed frequency distribution? Which of the following statements is false?

A. If you use CW = 10, you would have 9 classes
B. If you use CW = 20, you would have 5 classes
C. If you use CW = 25, you would have 5 classes
D. There is insufficient number of classes if you use CW = 25.

Answer: C

Question 3: Suppose you use CW = 50. What is the first class in your completed frequency distribution?

A. 0 and under 50
B. 50 and under 100
C. 100 and under 150
D. 110 and under 160
E. 112 and under 162

Answer: C

Please note that CW = 50 doesn't comply with the guideline. Therefore, you should not use CW = 50 to group your data. This question is only used to test your understanding of obtaining the first class in your data set.

Construct a Frequency Distribution with an Example

Use this example to construct a frequency distribution.

Airlines charge passengers an excess baggage fee for any checked baggage whose weight exceeds a specified limit. A study was conducted to observe how many passengers are being charged with the excess baggage fees. We have taken a random sample of 30 passengers from the airline check-in counter. Their checked baggage weights (measured in kilograms) were recorded as shown next:

25.0 42.9 29.4 25.9 28.7 24.5 30.9 30.5 27.8 28.9 22.8 31.5 23.6 39.5 28.1
31.5 28.1 39.6 27.4 28.9 36.6 25.4 26.9 53.9 33.5 22.5 38.4 26.8 32.4 34.9

The data on baggage weights are classified as quantitative and continuous data. The data have one decimal place.

Next, use the data to construct a frequency distribution by using the following steps.

Step 1: Sort the baggage weights data in ascending order.

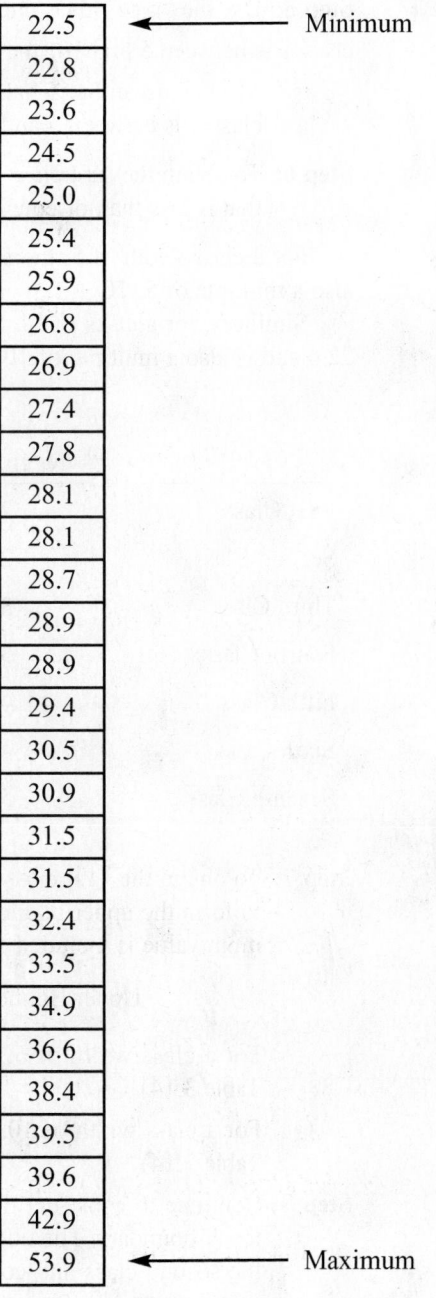

Step 2: Obtain the maximum (highest) and minimum (lowest) values in the data set.

Minimum = 22.5
Maximum = 53.9

Step 3: Estimate the class width by taking the difference between maximum and minimum values and then dividing it by 5.

$$Estimated\ Class\ Width = \frac{(Maximum - Minimum)}{Minimum\ number\ of\ classes\ recommended}$$

$$Estimated\ Class\ Width = \frac{(53.9 - 22.5)}{5} = 6.28$$

Step 4: Pick two nice numbers from Table 3.12 as class widths to construct the class intervals.

The list of nice numbers is 1, 2, 2.5, 5, 10, 20, 25, 50, etc.

The estimated class width of 6.28 falls between 5 and 10.

Step 5: Use the "nice" class widths to construct the classes and make sure that the number of classes is between 5 and 10.

You can use either 5 or10 to construct the boundaries. Then check that the number of classes is between 5 and 10.

Step 6: To obtain the first class **lower boundary**, pick the greatest multiple of the class width that is less than or equal to the minimum data value.

For a class width of 5, the first class lower boundary is 20, which is less than 22.6. 20 is also a multiple of 5 (20 ÷ 5 = 4, that is, 4 times the class width of 5).

Similarly, for a class width of 10, the first class lower boundary is 20, which is less than 22.6 and is also a multiple of 10 (20 ÷ 10 = 2, that is, 2 times the class width of 10).

TABLE 3.14

Class Intervals for Class Widths 5 and 10

	If you use a class width of 5, then the class intervals are	If you use a class width of 10, then the class intervals are
First Class	20 and under 25	20 and under 30
Second Class	25 and under 30	30 and under 40
Third Class	30 and under 35	40 and under 50
Fourth Class	35 and under 40	50 and under 60
Fifth Class	40 and under 45	
Sixth Class	45 and under 50	
Seventh Class	50 and under 55	

Step 7: To obtain the first class **upper boundary**, add the class width to the lower boundary to form the upper boundary of the first class. At this point check to see that the minimum value is included in the first class interval.

Upper Boundary = Lower Boundary + Class Width

For a class width of 5, the first class upper boundary = 20 + 5 = 25 (as shown in Table 3.14)

For a class width of 10, the first class upper boundary = 20 + 10 = 30 (as shown in Table 3.14)

Step 8: Continue to construct the rest of the class intervals by adding the class width to the lower boundary. The upper boundary of the first class becomes the lower boundary of the second class and continues to calculate the rest of the boundaries using the formula just shown. Stop when the last class interval includes the maximum value.

As shown in Table 3.14, we have a total of 7 classes with a class width of 5. For a class width of 10, we have a total of 4 classes.

Step 9: Make sure that the class intervals and boundaries meet the guidelines.

Refer to the guidelines to construct a frequency distribution.

1. **Check the number of classes.** The number of classes you should use is between 5 and 10. Therefore, you can only use a class width of 5 because you have 7 classes in total. If you use a class width of 10, you only have 4 classes, which violates the guideline. If you have too few classes, you can narrow the class width to increase the number of classes.

Thus, you have

baggage weights (measured in kilograms)
20 and under 25
25 and under 30
30 and under 35
35 and under 40
40 and under 45
45 and under 50
50 and under 55

2. **Check that you use "and under" for the classes.**
3. **Check that you use close-ended classes.**
4. **Check the class width.** The class width is a nice number. CW=5 is in the list of "nice" numbers.
5. **Check that there is no gap between classes.**
6. **Check that all classes have the same class width.**
7. **Check the boundaries.**
   a) **The boundaries should look like the data.** The data has one decimal point and therefore the boundaries should have one decimal point. Thus, you have

baggage weights (measured in kilograms)
20.0 and under 25.0
25.0 and under 30.0
30.0 and under 35.0
35.0 and under 40.0
40.0 and under 45.0
45.0 and under 50.0
50.0 and under 55.0

   b) **Each boundary must be a multiple of 5** (which is the selected class width to construct your frequency distribution).
   c) **Boundaries between classes have no gaps.** The upper boundary of the first class becomes the lower boundary of the second class. Thus, there is no gap between classes.

Step 10: To construct the frequencies, you have to count the data and put them into the respective class intervals.

Use the sorted data to put the data values into their respective classes as illustrated next.

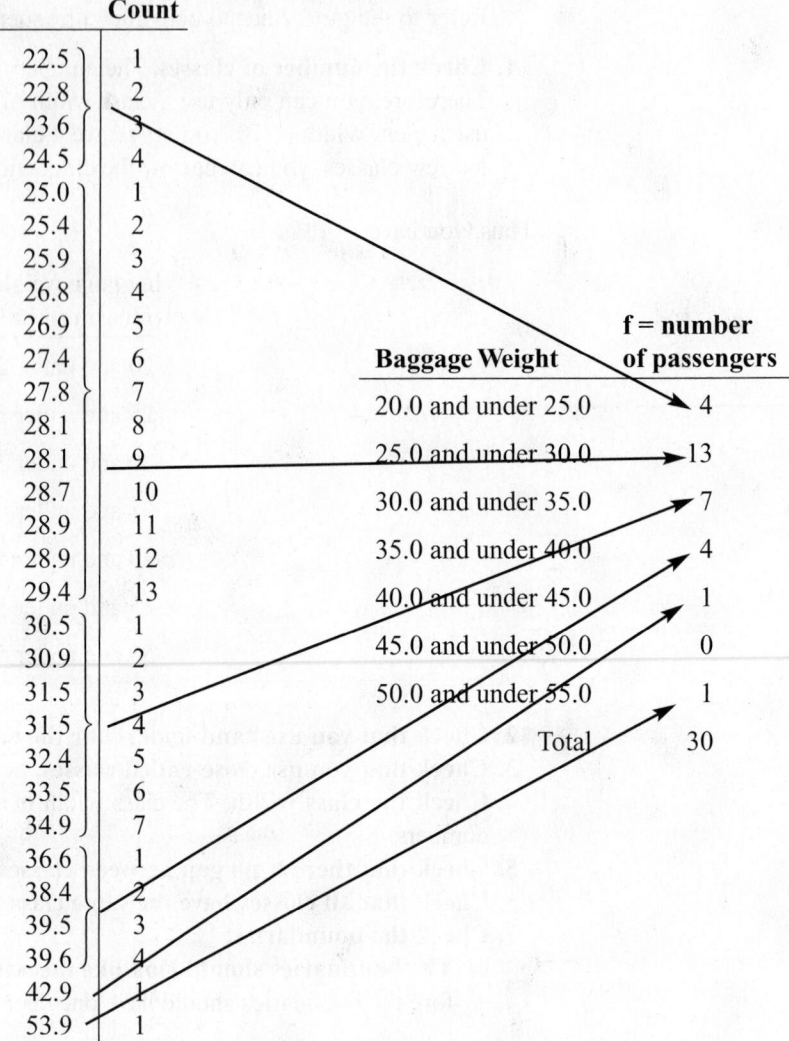

Count

22.5	1
22.8	2
23.6	3
24.5	4
25.0	1
25.4	2
25.9	3
26.8	4
26.9	5
27.4	6
27.8	7
28.1	8
28.1	9
28.7	10
28.9	11
28.9	12
29.4	13
30.5	1
30.9	2
31.5	3
31.5	4
32.4	5
33.5	6
34.9	7
36.6	1
38.4	2
39.5	3
39.6	4
42.9	1
53.9	1

Baggage Weight	f = number of passengers
20.0 and under 25.0	4
25.0 and under 30.0	13
30.0 and under 35.0	7
35.0 and under 40.0	4
40.0 and under 45.0	1
45.0 and under 50.0	0
50.0 and under 55.0	1
Total	30

Note: It is recommended to total the frequencies.

To recap how you construct the frequency distribution:

Referring back to our baggage weight data, you will see that the frequency distribution shown next follows all the recommended guidelines.

FIGURE 3.3

Frequency distribution of baggage weights measured in kgs

Baggage Weight	f = number of passengers
20.0 and under 25.0	4
25.0 and under 30.0	13
30.0 and under 35.0	7
35.0 and under 40.0	4
40.0 and under 45.0	1
45.0 and under 50.0	0
50.0 and under 55.0	1
Total	30

Note: f denotes "frequency"

Your frequency distribution should have proper titles such as "baggage weight," "number of passengers," "percent of passengers," etc. An observer looking at your frequency distribution would understand what you are presenting without having to ask what "frequency," "percent," and "class" stand for. Any graph or chart that you create must have a proper title. In the future, pay attention to the graphs and charts presented in any magazine or newspaper. You will notice that they have proper titles and labelling to explain the data being presented.

Application of Frequency Distribution

By observing the frequencies in the distribution, you can see that most of the data are close to the target values between 25 and 30 kilograms, and there are fewer and fewer data values as we move farther away from the target on the high and low sides.

Frequency distributions are often used to summarize data and give a general idea of where the data values are located. They also give an indication as to the "**shape**" of a set of data.

EXAMPLE 3.10

Consider the following set of data on the GPA scores for a sample of 98 students:

TABLE 3.15

3.56	3.46	3.48	3.50	3.42	3.43	3.52
3.49	3.44	3.50	3.48	3.56	3.50	3.52
3.47	3.48	3.46	3.50	3.56	3.38	3.41
3.37	3.47	3.49	3.45	3.44	3.50	3.49
3.46	3.46	3.55	3.52	3.44	3.50	3.45
3.44	3.48	3.46	3.52	3.46	3.48	3.48
3.32	3.40	3.52	3.34	3.46	3.43	*3.30*
3.46	3.59	3.63	3.59	3.47	3.38	3.52
3.45	3.48	3.31	3.46	3.40	3.54	3.46
3.51	3.48	3.50	*3.68*	3.60	3.46	3.52
3.48	3.50	3.56	3.50	3.52	3.46	3.48
3.46	3.52	3.56	3.52	3.48	3.46	3.45
3.46	3.54	3.54	3.48	3.49	3.41	3.41
3.45	3.34	3.44	3.47	3.47	3.41	3.48

Step 1: Sort your raw data.

Step 2: Obtain the maximum (highest) and minimum (lowest) values in the data set.

Minimum = 3.30
Maximum = 3.68

Step 3: Estimate the class width by dividing the difference between the maximum and minimum values by the minimum number of classes.

$$Estimated\ Class\ Width = \frac{(Maximum - Minimum)}{Minimum\ number\ of\ classes\ recommended}$$

$$Estimated\ Class\ Width = \frac{(3.68 - 3.30)}{5} = 0.076$$

Step 4: Pick a nice number from Table 3.16 as a class width to construct the class intervals. A list of nice numbers are

TABLE 3.16

	"Nice" Class Width	
0.01	(0.1)	1
0.02	0.2	2
0.025	0.25	2.5
(0.05)	0.5	5

The estimated class width of 0.076 falls between 0.05 and 0.1. In the next step, you may use these two nice numbers to construct the classes and then make sure that that the number of classes is between 5 and 10.

Step 5: Use the "nice" class width to construct the classes and make sure that the number of classes is between 5 and 10.

Step 6: To obtain the first class **lower boundary**, find the greatest multiple of the class width that is less than or equal to the minimum data value.

For a class width of 0.05, the first class lower boundary is 3.30, as it is a multiple of 0.05. Similarly, for a class width of 0.1, the first class lower boundary is 3.30, as it is a multiple of 0.1 (3.3 ÷ 0.1 = 33, i.e. 33 times of class width of 0.1).

TABLE 3.17

Class Intervals for Class Widths 0.05 and 0.1

	If you use a class width of 0.05, then the class intervals are	If you use a class width of 0.1, then the class intervals are
First Class	3.30 and under 3.35	3.30 and under 3.40
Second Class	3.35 and under 3.40	3.40 and under 3.50
Third Class	3.45 and under 3.50	3.50 and under 3.60
Fourth Class	3.50 and under 3.55	3.60 and under 3.70
Fifth Class	3.55 and under 3.60	
Sixth Class	3.60 and under 3.65	Note: A total of 4 classes (i.e., not enough classes)
Seventh Class	3.65 and under 3.70	
	Note: A total of 7 classes	

An appropriate frequency distribution would be as follows:

GPA Scores	f = number of students
3.30 and under 3.35	4
3.35 " " 3.40	3
3.40 " " 3.45	15
3.45 " " 3.50	42
3.50 " " 3.55	23
3.55 " " 3.60	8
3.60 " " 3.65	2
3.65 " " 3.70	1

Relative Frequency or Percentage Distributions

Consider the following frequency distributions of manufacturing personnel salaries at ABC Inc. and XYZ Inc.

Salary ($000)	ABC Inc. Number of Employees	XYZ Inc. Number of Employees
20 and under 25	24	10
25 and under 30	41	23
30 and under 35	44	31
35 and under 40	29	14
40 and under 45	15	8
45 and under 50	7	2

Notice that there is a large difference in the number of manufacturing employees in the two companies; therefore, it is difficult to compare the salary distributions by looking at the frequencies.

If you were to set up a **relative frequency** or **percentage** distribution for the two sets of salaries, it would be much easier to make comparisons.

Salary ($000)	ABC Inc.			XYZ Inc.		
	f	rf	%	f	rf	%
20 and under 25	24	0.150	15.0	10	0.114	11.4
25 " " 30	41	0.256	25.6	23	0.261	26.1
30 " " 35	44	0.275	27.5	31	0.352	35.2
35 " " 40	29	0.181	18.1	14	0.159	15.9
40 " " 45	15	0.094	9.4	8	0.091	9.1
45 " " 50	7	0.044	4.4	2	0.023	2.3
Total	160	1.000	100.0	88	1.000	100.0

Notations: f denotes "frequency" (the number of values); rf denotes "relative frequency"

To calculate the relative frequency, use the formula

$$Relative\ Frequency\ (rf) = \frac{Frequency\ (f)}{n}$$

where n denotes sample size (or total number of values).

The relative frequency is also known as proportion of values. The percentage distribution is produced by multiplying the relative frequency in each class by 100.

$$Percentage\ of\ Frequency\ (\%) = \left(\frac{Frequency\ (f)}{n} \right) + 100$$

Note: You will use a maximum of 3 decimals for rf and thus 1 decimal for %.

a) The relative frequency distribution

Use the frequency distribution of baggage weights to create the following relative frequency distribution.

Baggage Weight	f = number of passengers	rf = relative frequency = proportion of passengers
20.0 and under 25.0	4	4/30 = 0.133
25.0 and under 30.0	13	13/30 = 0.433
30.0 and under 35.0	7	7/30 = 0.233
35.0 and under 40.0	4	4/30 = 0.133
40.0 and under 45.0	1	1/30 = 0.033
45.0 and under 50.0	0	0/30 = 0
50.0 and under 55.0	1	1/30 = 0.033
Total	30	

b) The percentage distribution

Use the frequency distribution of baggage weights to create the following percentage distribution.

Baggage Weight	f = number of passengers	Percentage of passengers (%)
20.0 and under 25.0	4	4/30 = 0.133*100 = 13.3
25.0 and under 30.0	13	13/30 = 0.433*100 = 43.3
30.0 and under 35.0	7	7/30 = 0.233*100 = 23.3
35.0 and under 40.0	4	4/30 = 0.133*100 = 13.3
40.0 and under 45.0	1	1/30 = 0.033*100 = 3.3
45.0 and under 50.0	0	0/30 = 0
50.0 and under 55.0	1	1/30 = 0.033*100=3.3
Total	30	

Graphing a Frequency Distribution

I. Graph a histogram

Histogram: A histogram is a graph of "touching rectangles." The horizontal axis represents the class boundaries. No other values are shown on this axis. The vertical axis shows the class frequencies (or relative frequency or percentage). The above rules only apply to histograms where the classes are all of equal width. We are not concerned in this course with how to draw other types of histograms.

EXAMPLE 3.11   The high-voltage output of a certain power supply that is to be used in copying machines must be 300 ± 50 volts (i.e., from 250 to 350 volts). In setting up a quality control chart, data from a sample of 125 power supplies is to be used. The results are given as follows:

333	297	285	300	279	311	298	300	305	262
289	315	305	302	273	282	313	330	300	271
303	330	290	291	300	290	340	293	309	287
292	312	295	296	302	308	268	296	294	306
295	320	322	328	326	316	290	291	320	315
301	292	291	299	298	308	295	296	325	333
309	304	306	292	327	295	302	302	276	331
293	306	286	310	277	309	307	304	323	288
285	292	342	311	316	297	304	316	305	320
303	296	332	336	313	282	294	341	334	317
296	312	307	328	326	301	309	313	275	328
326	303	308	310	285	317	318	319	314	325
284	289	312	319	298					

A possible frequency distribution for the voltage data is

Power Supply Voltage (Volts)	number of power supplies
260 and under 270	2
270 " " 280	6
280 " " 290	11
290 " " 300	29
300 " " 310	31
310 " " 320	21
320 " " 330	14
330 " " 340	8
340 " " 350	3

Use this frequency distribution to create the following histogram.

Frequency Histogram—Power Supply Voltages (using SPSS version 13)

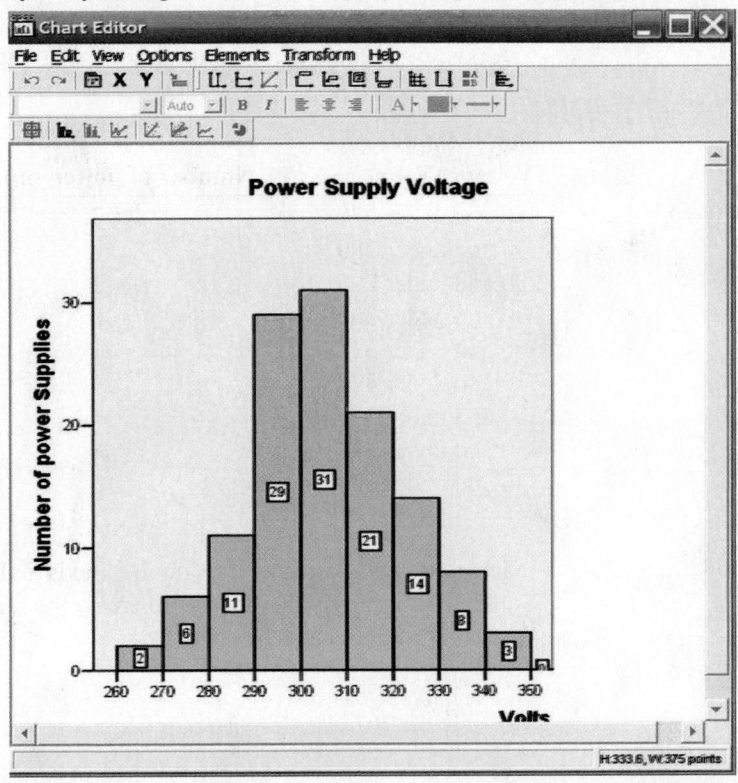

II. Graph a polygon

Polygon: A polygon is a graph in the shape of a many-sided closed figure. (Some texts show a smooth curve, but this is technically not a polygon.) The horizontal axis shows the class **midpoints**. No other values are shown on this axis. The vertical axis shows the class frequencies. In order to close the polygon, an extra class midpoint on the left and right side is used.

The class midpoints may be calculated as follows:

$$m = \frac{lower\ boundary\ +\ upper\ boundary}{2}$$

Notation: m denotes midpoint.

The above rules only apply to polygons where the classes are all of equal width. We are not concerned with how to draw other types of polygons.

EXAMPLE 3.12   The high-voltage output of a certain power supply that is to be used in copying machines must be 300 ± 50 volts (i.e., from 250 to 350 volts). In setting up a quality control chart, data from a sample of 125 power supplies is to be used. The results are given as follows:

333	297	285	300	279	311	298	300	305	262
289	315	305	302	273	282	313	330	300	271
303	330	290	291	300	290	340	293	309	287
292	312	295	296	302	308	268	296	294	306
295	320	322	328	326	316	290	291	320	315
301	292	291	299	298	308	295	296	325	333
309	304	306	292	327	295	302	302	276	331
293	306	286	310	277	309	307	304	323	288
285	292	342	311	316	297	304	316	305	320
303	296	332	336	313	282	294	341	334	317
296	312	307	328	326	301	309	313	275	328
326	303	308	310	285	317	318	319	314	325
284	289	312	319	298					

A possible frequency distribution for the voltage data is

Power Supply Voltage (Volts)	Number of power supplies	Midpoints
260 and under 270	2	(260 + 270) / 2 = 265
270 and under 280	6	(270 + 280) / 2 = 275
280 and under 290	11	(280 + 290) / 2 = 285
290 and under 300	29	(290 + 300) / 2 = 295
300 and under 310	31	(300 + 310) / 2 = 305
310 and under 320	21	(310 + 320) / 2 = 315
320 and under 330	14	(320 + 330) / 2 = 325
330 and under 340	8	(330 + 340) / 2 = 335
340 and under 350	3	(340 + 350) / 2 = 345

The midpoints values will be on the x-axis and the frequency will be on the y-axis. Use this frequency distribution to create the following polygon.

Frequency POLYGON – Power Supply Voltages (using SPSS version 13)

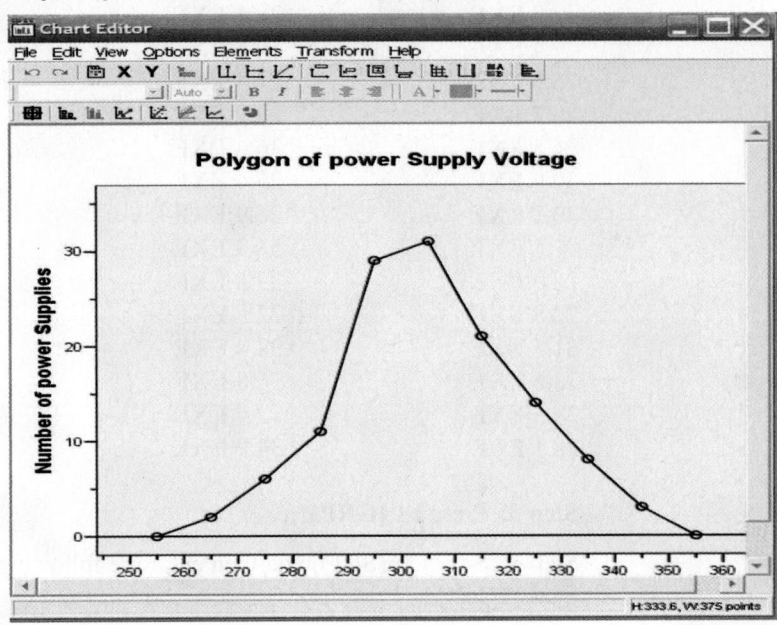

Note: Both graphs, the histogram and the polygon, show that the data has roughly a bell-curve shape.

Using CASIO Calculator to Graph Histogram and Polygon

I.   Graph a Histogram Using the CASIO Calculator

The following baggage weight data were used to construct the frequency distribution:

25.0   42.9   29.4   25.9   28.7   24.5   30.9   30.5   27.8   28.9   22.8   31.5   23.6   39.5   28.1
31.5   28.1   39.6   27.4   28.9   36.6   25.4   26.9   53.9   33.5   22.5   38.4   26.8   32.4   34.9

The baggage weight data frequency distribution is needed to construct the histogram.

Baggage Weight	f = number of passengers
20.0 and under 25.0	4
25.0 and under 30.0	13
30.0 and under 35.0	7
35.0 and under 40.0	4
40.0 and under 45.0	1
45.0 and under 50.0	0
50.0 and under 55.0	1
Total	30

CASIO CALCULATOR INSTRUCTIONS:
Follow these steps to draw the histogram.

Step 1: At the Main Menu, select **STAT** Mode by pressing the **EXE** button.

Step 2: Enter raw data into **List 1**.

On the screen, you will only see List 1 to List 4 at first, but if you move the ▶ cursor key you will be able to scroll over to the other lists. Now, take the values from example 2 and input the values one by one in List 1 as follows. After you have entered each value, press the **EXE** button.

25.0 **EXE**	31.5 **EXE**
42.9 **EXE**	28.1 **EXE**
29.4 **EXE**	39.6 **EXE**
25.9 **EXE**	27.4 **EXE**
28.7 **EXE**	28.9 **EXE**
24.5 **EXE**	36.6 **EXE**
30.9 **EXE**	25.4 **EXE**
30.5 **EXE**	26.9 **EXE**
27.8 **EXE**	53.9 **EXE**
28.9 **EXE**	33.5 **EXE**
22.8 **EXE**	22.5 **EXE**
31.5 **EXE**	38.4 **EXE**
23.6 **EXE**	26.8 **EXE**
39.5 **EXE**	32.4 **EXE**
28.1 **EXE**	34.9 **EXE**

Step 3: Press **F1 (GRPH)**.

Step 4: Select F6(SET), and then enter the following items:
StatGraph1

Graph Type: ▶ (press **F6**) and select **Hist (F1)** and

XList: List (F1) and type **1** (if you input your data in List 1) and

Frequency: 1 (F1)

Now press **EXE**, and then select **GPH1 (F1)** and enter the following items:

Histogram Setting

Start: 20 (the lower boundary of the first class of the frequency distribution)

Width: 5 (choose a "nice" class width in Table 3.8)

Draw:[EXE]

The calculator will now show the histogram. However, there are no major scales on the x-axis. You can refer to the scales from the frequency distribution. That is, the first rectangle will correspond to the first class interval of "20 and under 25."

II. Graph a Polygon Using the CASIO Calculator

The following travel time data were used to construct the frequency distribution:

25.0   42.9   29.4   25.9   28.7   24.5   30.9   30.5   27.8   28.9   22.8   31.5   23.6   39.5   28.1
31.5   28.1   39.6   27.4   28.9   36.6   25.4   26.9   53.9   33.5   22.5   38.4   26.8   32.4   34.9

The frequency distribution of baggage weight data is needed to construct the polygon.

Baggage Weight	f = number of passengers
20.0 and under 25.0	4
25.0 and under 30.0	13
30.0 and under 35.0	7
35.0 and under 40.0	4
40.0 and under 45.0	1
45.0 and under 50.0	0
50.0 and under 55.0	1
Total	30

INSTRUCTIONS:
Follow these steps to draw the polygon.

Step 1: At the Main Menu, select **STAT** Mode by pressing the **EXE** button.

Step 2: Enter raw data into **List 1**.

On the screen, you will only see List 1 to List 4 at first, but if you move the ▶ cursor key you will be able to scroll over to the other lists. Now, take the values from example 2 and input the values one by one in List 1 as follows. After you have entered each value, press the **EXE** button.

25.0 EXE	31.5 **EXE**
42.9 **EXE**	28.1 **EXE**
29.4 **EXE**	39.6 **EXE**
25.9 **EXE**	27.4 **EXE**
28.7 **EXE**	28.9 **EXE**
24.5 **EXE**	36.6 **EXE**
30.9 **EXE**	25.4 **EXE**
30.5 **EXE**	26.9 **EXE**
27.8 **EXE**	53.9 **EXE**
28.9 **EXE**	33.5 **EXE**
22.8 **EXE**	22.5 **EXE**
31.5 **EXE**	38.4 **EXE**
23.6 **EXE**	26.8 **EXE**
39.5 **EXE**	32.4 **EXE**
28.1 **EXE**	34.9 **EXE**

Step 3: Press **F1 (GRPH)**.

Step 4: Select **F6(SET)**, and then enter the following items:
StatGraph1
Graph Type: ▷ (press **F6**) and select **Brkn (F5)**.
XList: List (F1) and type **1** (if you input your data in List 1).
Frequency: 1 (F1)
Now press **EXE**, and then select **GPH1 (F1)** and enter the following items:
Histogram Setting
Start: 15 (the lower boundary of the first class of the frequency distribution with the frequency of zero)
Width: 5 (choose a "nice" class width in Table 3.8)
Draw:[EXE]

The calculator will now show the polygon. However, there are no major scales on the x-axis. You can refer to the midpoint of each class. The lines connect the midpoints of the histogram.

Frequency Distribution Problems

3.6 Refer to Table 3.18a, which shows data regarding the first 32 companies taken from the Top 1000 Ranking by Profits table that appeared in the July 2003 issue of the *Globe and Mail*'s Report on Business.

Construct frequency distributions for the following data:
a. Revenue rank
b. Market capitalization
c. P/E ratio
d. Per share data—price/sales
e. Debt/equity ratio
f. Revenue % change
g. Earnings per share—latest year (Exclude values reported in $US)
h. Number of employees

3.7 Refer to Table 3.9 (on page 60), which shows data regarding the first 21 companies taken from the *Financial Post Magazine* Web site (http://www.financialpost.com/magazine/fp500/list.html).

For the 21 companies listed in Table 3.15, construct frequency distributions for the following data:
a. Revenue amount 2007
b. Profit amount 2007
c. Revenue change
d. Profit change

3.8 Refer to Table 3.11 (on page 61), which shows the stock summary data for companies with names starting with the let-ter A that were traded on the NASDAQ on May 8, 2008. The data was taken from the Financial Post Magazine's Web site (*http://www.financialpost.com/markets/market-data/market-nasdaq.html?tmp=nasdaq*).

Using the data listed in Table 3.11, construct frequency distributions for the following data:
a. Volume
b. High/ask price
c. Low/bid price
d. Close/previous price
e. Net change
f. 52 week High Price
g. 52 week Low Price

3.9 Refer to the mutual fund data in Table 3.19 (on page 86) that appeared in the Canadian Mutual Funds table of the June 3, 2004 issue of The Globe and Mail.

Construct frequency distributions for the following data:
a. Manulife Mix Funds Valuation data
b. Manulife Mix Funds Change data
c. Manulife Mix Funds Percent Change data
d. CI-Clarica Mutual Funds Valuation data
e. Transamerica Growsafe 75/100 Valuation data
f. Transamerica Growsafe 75/100 Percent Change data

TABLE 3.18a

▶Ranking by profits

PROFIT RANK 2002	2001	COMPANY AND YEAR END	PROFIT $000	% CH'GE	REVENUE $000	RANK	%CH'GE	MARKET CAP $ MIL	DIV YIELD %	P/E RATIO	PER SHARE DATA PRICE/SALES	CASH FLOW
1	1	Royal Bank of Canada(Oc02) ON	2,762,000	15	23,234,000	3	-9	36,197	2.79	13.74	1.58	6.59
2	30	BCE Inc.(De02) QC	2,475,000	382	19,809,000	8	2	26.102	4.21	10.40	1.22	6.04
3	2	Bank of Nova Scotia(Oc02) ON	1,797,000	-17	18.310,000	12	-13	23,129	3.16	13.66	1.26	8.44
4	4	Bell Canada(De02) QC	1,504,000	-5	15,685,000	20	7	nm	nm	nm	nm	13.43
5	5	Bank of Montreal(Oc02) ON	1,417,000	-4	13,059,000	21	-24	18,764	3.15	13.96	1.43	4.45
6	10	Manulife Financial(De02) ON	1,378,000	19	16,532,000	18	2	15,923	1.74	11.86	1.03	4.84
7	7	EnCana Corp.(De02) AB	1,224,000	-5	11,031,000	25	112	23.361	.82	16.71	1.85	9.04
8	8	Imperial Oil(De02) ON	1,210,000	-2	15,821,000	19	-2	16,996	1.87	14.06	1.09	4.64
9	14	Sun Life Financial Services(De02) ON	998,000	13	23,101,000	4	37	16,517	2.10	14.52	.63	9.38
10	15	Power Financial(De02) QC	988,000	12	18,700,000	11	3	12,591	2.87	13.35	.68	5.16
11	12	Petro-Canada(De02) AB	974,000	15	9,917,000	28	14	12,892	.82	13.18	1.30	8.66
12	9	Thomson Corp.(De02) ON[1]	(US)615,000	-21	(US)7,768,000	23	7	27,348	2.64	28.77	2.21	(US)4.32
13	29	Great-West Lifeco(De02) MB	962,000	76	16,632,000	16	4	13,648	2.54	14.72	.84	3.79
14	13	Magna International(De02) ON[1]	(US)554,000	-4	(US)13,044,000	7	17	8,417	2.43	9.62	.38	20.25
15	21	TransCanada PipeLines(De02) AB	805,000	17	5,300,000	48	-1	10,990	4.36	14.69	2.10	3.82
16	20	Husky Energy(De02) AB	804,000	23	6,385,000	40	-3	6.882	2.19	8.76	1.08	(US)5.02
17	39	Suncor Energy(De02) AB	761,000	96	4,913,000	52	17	11,090	.69	15.06	2.26	3.21
18	27	Loblaw Companies(De02) ON	728,000	29	23,099,000	5	7	14.905	.89	20.46	.65	4.05
19	24	George Weston Ltd.(De02) ON	690,000	19	27,464,000	1	11	11,938	1.06	17.87	.43	12.25
20	3	Cdn. Imp. Bank of Commerce(Oc02) ON	653,000	-61	17,055,000	13	-20	13.914	4.13	28.29	.82	4.78
21	23	Power Corp.(De02) QC	645,000	4	19,011.000	10	3	7,997	2.21	12.81	.53	8.61
22	31	Enbridge Inc.(De02) AB	610,100	26	4,830.600	54	13	7,233	3.57	11.84	1.50	4.57
23	344	Alcan Inc.(De02) QC[1]	(US)374,000	nm	(US)12,553,000	9	-1	14,894	2.03	25.65	.76	(US)6.39
24	19	Cdn. Natural Resources(De02) AB	574,800	-12	4,114,900	59	15	6,261	1.07	10.49	1.47	17.71
25	18	Canadian National Railway Co.(De02) QC	571,000	-21	6.173,000	41	8	12,891	1.32	22.74	2.10	8.14
26	11	Shell Canada(De02) AB	561,000	-44	7,314,000	35	-5	13,575	1.63	24.24	1.88	4.45
27	17	Talisman Energy(De02) AB	524,000	-29	5,379,000	47	5	7,450	1.06	15.24	1.42	19.74
28	45	Investors Group(De02) MB	511,759	87	1,940,036	102	10	7,058	3.21	14.35	3.63	3.02
29	41	Canada Life Financial(De02) ON	499,000	46	8,598,000	32	7	6,463	1.49	13.21	.77	4.68
30	36	Canadian Pacific Railway Ltd.(De02) AB	496,000	33	3,692,600	62	-1	4,937	1.64	9.95	1.35	5.98
31	44	Great-West Life Assurance(De02) MB	475,000	68	10,766,000	26	7	nm	nm	nm	nm	1,180.76
32	34	Nexen Inc.(De02) AB	452,000	0	3,102,000	77	1	4,212	.88	10.25	1.35	9.75

DEBT/ EQUITY	EARNINGS PER SHARE LATEST YEAR	PREVIOUS YEAR	2 YEARS AGO	RETURN ON COMMON EQUITY ONE-YEAR %	RANK	FIVE-YEAR %	RANK	NUMBER OF EMPLOYEES	INDUSTRY	MAJOR SHAREHOLDER	PROFIT
0.4	3.96	3.55	3.53	15.96	159	17.16	99	59,770	banks	Widely held	1
1.2	2.74	0.56	7.43	17.99	127	26.69	23	66,266	tele	Widely held	2
0.4	3.36	4.12	3.67	12.85	230	15.64	118	44,633	banks	Widely held	3
1.6	3.90	4.18	4.09	19.00	111	21.38	55	54,258	tele	BCE Inc. 100%	4
0.3	2.73	2.72	3.30	13.37	218	14.92	138	33,912	banks	Widely held	5
0.2	2.90	2.40	2.22	16.17	154	14.74	143	13,000	insur	Widely held	6
0.6	2.92	5.02	4.09	13.94	194	19.13	67	3,646	oilprd	Widely held	7
0.3	3.19	3.15	3.40	25.35	62	22.24	50	6.460	integ	Exxon Mobil Corp. (U.S.) 69.6%	8
0.2	1.84	2.08	1.49	8.82	355	na	nr	14,905	insur	Widely held	9
0.3	2.72	2.44	2.18	17.33	136	18.89	72	18.300	fin	Power Corp. of Canada 67.4%	10
0.5	3.71	3.19	3.28	18.29	123	13.00	180	4.470	integ	Government of Canada 18.74%	11
0.5	(US)0.93	(US)1.19	(US)1.96	7.32	397	15.34	131	44.000	serv	Woodbridge Company Ltd.69%	12
0.2	2.53	1.39	1.72	22.86	74	17.53	96	14,000	insur	Power Financial Corp.64.99%	13
0.1	(US)5.83	(US)6.55	(US)7.04	11.85	262	12.45	195	70,800	auto	Stronach Trust 66.3%	14
1.6	1.56	1.30	1.50	13.37	219	8.63	309	2.767	pipeline	Widely held	15
0.5	1.88	1.49	1.39	16.73	146	nm	nr	2,753	integ	Li Ka-sning 71.5%	16
0.8	1.64	0.79	0.79	28.25	51	17.72	93	3.422	integ	Widely held	17
1.0	2.64	2.04	1.71	18.93	113	15.58	122	122,000	food	George Weston Ltd. 61%	18
1.4	5.05	4.42	3.66	18.27	124	21.10	57	142,850	food	W. Galen Weston 62.13%	19
0.3	1.37	4.19	4.97	5.22	461	12.58	189	42,552	banks	Widely held	20
0.4	2.81	2.74	2.93	13.66	205	15.74	117	19,000	mgt	Paul Desmarais and associates 65%	21
1.8	3.60	2.91	2.54	20.08	101	16.94	103	4,000	pipeline	Widely held	22
0.4	(US)1.15	(US)-0.02	(US)2.45	4.32	486	5.76	373	48,100	mining	Widely held	23
0.8	4.46	5.30	6.70	13.51	211	16.29	107	1,573	oilprd	Widely held	24
0.8	2.87	3.72	3.91	8.93	352	10.29	250	23,190	trans	Widely held	25
0.3	2.03	3.67	3.04	11.45	271	17.54	95	3,825	integ	Shell Investments (1996) Ltd. 78%	26
0.7	3.73	5.25	6.41	12.88	229	11.17	226	1,565	oilprd	Widely held	27
0.5	1.86	1.05	1.35	20.01	103	22.45	48	3,285	fin	Power Financial Corp. 56.2%	28
0.1	3.05	2.13	2.22	13.80	200	nm	nr	6,768	insur	Widely held	29
1.0	3.13	2.35	3.36	15.60	165	11.38	217	16,116	trans	Widely held	30
0.2	na	na	na	14.39	185	12.63	187	7,000	insur	Great-West Lifeco Inc. 100%	31
0.8	3.34	3.40	4.52	29.17	45	26.11	26	2,767	oilprd	Ontario Teachers' Pension Plan 20%	32

Reprinted by permission from "Report on Business," the *Globe and Mail*, 2004.

TABLE 3.18b

FP500 CANADA'S 500 LARGEST CORPORATIONS

RANK BY REVENUE 2002	2001	Company	Industry	REVENUES 2002 $'000s	% Change	% Sales Outside Canada	ASSETS 2002 $'000s	% Change	Rank
1	1	General Motors of Canada Ltd., Oshawa, ON	Vehicle	37,000,000	n.a.	n.a.	n.a.	n.a.	n.a.
2	4	George Weston Ltd., Toronto	Conglom	27,446,000	11.3	n.a.	16,630,000	2.2	34
3	7	Bombardier Inc., Montreal (Ja03)	High-tech	23,664,900	9.4	n.a.	29,009,400	4.5	20
4	8	Ford Motor Co. of Canada, Ltd., Oakville, ON	Vehicle	23,328,700	8.1	n.a.	11,398,000	8.0	48
5	3	Royal Bank of Canada, Montreal (Oc02)	Bank	23,234,000	(9.0)	n.a.	376,956,000	4.9	1
6	18	Sun Life Financial Services of Canada, Toronto	Life	23,101,000	38.4	72	123,438,000	53.7	6
7	5	Onex Corp., Toronto	Conglom	22,653,000	(4.8)	85	19,890,000	(4.7)	27
8	17	Magna International Inc.*, Aurora, ON	Vehicle	20,364,470	19.3	70	16,004,076	27.1	35
9	6	BCE Inc., Montreal	Telecom	19,768,000	(8.9)	n.a.	39,563,000	(27.2)	14
10	13	Alcan Inc.*, Montreal	Mining	19,687,800	0.7	94	27,674,964	(0.4)	21
11	12	DaimlerChrysler Canada Inc., Windsor, ON	Vehicle	19,353,000	(5.2)	n.a.	n.a.	n.a.	n.a.
12	14	Power Corp. of Canada, Montreal	Conglom	19,017,000	3.6	30	70,136,000	2.0	11
13	10	The Bank of Nova Scotia, Toronto (Oc02)	Bank	18,310,000	(13.0)	n.a.	296,380,000	4.2	2
14	9	Canadian Imperial Bank of Commerce, Toronto (Oc02)	Bank	17,055,000	(20.3)	n.a.	273,293,000	(4.9)	4
15	16	Imperial Oil Ltd., Toronto	Energy	16,890,000	(1.5)	13	11,868,000	10.3	44
16	11	The Toronto-Dominion Bank, Toronto (Oc02)	Bank	16,680,000	(20.3)	n.a.	278,040,000	(3.4)	3
17	2	Nortel Networks Corp.*, Brampton, ON	High-tech	16,538,380	(39.1)	n.a.	23,382,804	(27.5)	24
18	19	Manulife Financial Corp., Toronto	Life	16,532,000	1.9	80	81,195,000	3.3	9
19	15	Bank of Montreal, Montreal (Oc02)	Bank	13,059,000	(24.2)	n.a.	252,864,000	5.6	5
20	20	Hydro-Québec, Montreal	Utility	13,002,000	3.4	28	59,078,000	(1.3)	12

PROFITS 2002 $'000s	% Change	Rank	EPS $0.00	PROFITS AS % OF... Revenue	Assets	Equity	GROWTH 5-Year % Profit Growth	Share Price Change 1 Year %	5 Year %	Employees	Symbol	Exchange	Major Shareholder(s)	% Foreign	RANK 2002
n.a.	n.a.	n.a.	n.a.	n.a.	n.a.	n.a.	n.a.	n.a.	n.a.	24,500	(Pr)		General Motors, US	100	1
690,000	18.6	24	5.05	2.5	4.2	17.2	182.8	(19.4)	106.9	139,000	WN	T	W. Galen Weston 62%		2
(615,200)	(257.4)	569	(0.47)	(2.6)	(2.2)	(18.0)	(246.4)	(81.1)	(68.8)	75,000	BBD.B	T	Bombardier family 63%		3
n.a.	n.a.	n.a.	n.a.	n.a.	n.a.	n.a.	n.a.	n.a.	n.a.	15,074	(Pr)		Ford Motor Co., US	100	4
2,762,000	14.6	3	3.96	11.9	0.8	15.0	64.5	9.2	36.7	59,549	RY	T,NY	Widely held	20	5
997,000	13.2	15	1.84	4.3	1.0	8.8	95.1	(17.6)	n.a.	11,800	SLF	T,NY	Widely held		6
(145,000)	(118.2)	546	(0.90)	(0.6)	(0.7)	(8.9)	(366.4)	(36.9)	55.0	98,000	OCX	T	Gerald Schwartz 67% voting		7
869,780	(3.0)	19	9.15	4.3	6.1	11.1	44.1	(32.8)	(26.8)	73,000	MG.A	T,NY	Stronach Trust 58%		8
2,475,000	373.2	4	2.74	12.5	5.3	16.6	259.4	(2.3)	(53.7)	66,266	BCE	T,NY	Widely held	14	9
587,180	7,486.3	31	1.81	3.0	2.1	4.3	(9.4)	(33.1)	(8.5)	50,000	AL	T,NY	Widely held		10
n.a.	n.a.	n.a.	n.a.	n.a.	n.a.	n.a.	n.a.	n.a.	n.a.	n.a.	(Pr)		DaimlerChrysler Corp., US	100	11
645,000	4.4	27	2.81	3.4	0.9	12.8	94.9	(5.9)	31.1	28,000	POW	T	Paul Desmarais Sr. 65%		12
1,797,000	(17.2)	7	3.36	9.8	0.6	12.2	18.7	(0.5)	39.6	49,000	BNS	T,NY	Widely held		13
653,000	(61.3)	26	1.37	3.8	0.2	5.4	(57.9)	(15.7)	(3.3)	42,552	CM	T, NY	Widely held		14
1,210,000	(2.7)	14	3.19	7.2	10.7	25.1	42.9	(0.7)	73.4	6,460	IMO	T,AM	Exxon Mobil Corp., US	70	15
(76,000)	(105.5)	533	(0.25)	(0.5)	n.a.	(0.6)	(107.0)	(24.3)	5.9	42,817	TD	T	Widely held		16
(5,549,950)	86.9	574	(1.43)	(33.6)	(19.9)	(106.6)	n.a.	(56.3)	(86.4)	52,600	NT	T,NY	Widely Held		17
1,370,000	17.4	12	2.90	8.3	1.7	16.1	(65.8)	(18.5)	n.a.	32,400	MFC	T,NY	Widely held		18
1,417,000	(3.7)	11	2.73	10.9	0.6	12.6	8.6	4.9	4.4	33,000	BMO	T,NY	Widely held		19
1,526,000	37.7	9	n.a.	11.7	2.6	10.5	94.1	n.a.	n.a.	20,972	(Cr)		Quebec government		20

Reprinted from National Post Business, courtesy of Postmedia Network, Inc..

TABLE 3.19

fund	valuation	chg	% chg
EQUITABLE LIFE			
AIM Cdn Premier 06/01	10.01	+.01	+.07
Accum Income 06/01	23.26	-.03	-.15
American Gwth 06/01	10.48	+.04	+.37
Asian-Pacific 06/01	6.38	+.01	+.17
Asset Allocat 06/01	16.72	-.01	-.06
Dissett Div Inc 06/01	10.19	-.01	-.10
Cdn Bond 06/01	15.55	-.02	-.15
Cdn Stock 06/01	20.17	-.01	-.05
CommonStock 06/01	29.96	-.02	-.05
European Equity 06/01	7.23	-.02	-.22
International 06/01	11.49	+.02	+.17
MB Cdn Eq Value 06/01	18.21	-.04	-.24
Mack US Em Grth 06/01	10.15	+.09	+.84
Templeton Grwth 06/01	9.39	+.02	+.17
Tmplton Glo Bnd 06/01	12.32	+.04	+.36
Trimark Europls 06/01	10.51	+.02	+.15
Trimark Glo Bal 06/01	10.48	+.02	+.17
US Equity 06/01	6.30	+.02	+.32

fund	valuation	chg	% chg
MD MANAGEMENT			
MD Balanced	18.08	-.06	-.33
MD Bnd & Mtg	10.39	-.01	-.10
MD Bond	7.10	-.03	-.42
MD Dividend	16.66	-.03	-.18
MD Equity	19.03	-.03	-.16
MD Glo Bond	11.27	-.03	-.27
MD Glo Equ RSP	7.07	unch	unch
MD Growth	10.37	unch	unch
MD Growth RSP	9.82	unch	unch
MD Int'l Growth	6.64	unch	unch
MD Int'l Value	10.13	unch	unch
MD Intl Gr RSP	6.46	unch	unch
MD Select	15.39	-.04	-.26
MD US LgCpGrRSP	6.07	unch	unch
MD US LrCap Val	8.42	unch	unch
MD US LrCpVIRSP	8.25	unch	unch
MD US Lrg Cp Gr	4.79	unch	unch
MD US Sml Cp Gr	3.68	-.01	-.27
MDPIM Cdn Equ-A	11.01	-.04	-.36
MDPIM US Equ-A	7.39	-.02	-.27

fund	valuation	chg	% chg
MANULIFE MIX FUNDS			
AIM Am MidCp Gw	12.26	-.04	-.33
AIM Cd First Cl	12.25	-.05	-.41
Cd Lg Cap Gw Cl	12.85	-.07	-.54
Cd Lg Cap ValCl	12.12	-.02	-.16
Cd Lg Cp CoreCl	12.05	-.02	-.17
Cdn Equ Val Cl	12.65	-.02	-.16
E&P Gw Opp Cl	14.38	-.04	-.28
E&P US MidCapCl	11.81	-.05	-.42
FI Can DiscEqCl	13.07	-.08	-.61
FI Gwth Amer Cl	11.09	-.03	-.27
FI Intl Port Cl	11.60	-.02	-.17
Global Equ Cl	10.86	-.01	-.09
Global Sect Cl	11.31	-.06	-.53
Global SectCl-H	11.31	-.05	-.44
Global Val Cl	12.48	-.01	-.08
Int'l Growth Cl	11.29	-.01	-.09
Int'l Value Cl	12.27	+.01	+.08
Japanese Class	12.63	-.12	-.94
SM Tot Cd Eq Cl	13.26	+.02	+.15
SM Total Glo Cl	12.00	-.04	-.33
SM Total USEqCl	11.33	-.03	-.26
SMTotal Gl Cl-H	12.00	-.04	-.33
Sht Term Yld Cl	10.21	unch	unch
Str Bond Class	10.30	-.03	-.29
Tri Sel Cdn Cl	12.13	-.03	-.25
Trimark Glo Cl	11.41	+.04	+.35
US Lg Cap Gw Cl	10.40	-.01	-.10
US Lg Cp CoreCl	10.77	-.01	-.09
US Lg Cp Val Cl	10.92	-.02	-.18
US MidCp Val Cl	11.51	-.03	-.26

fund	valuation	chg	% chg
CI - CLARICA MUTUAL FUNDS			
Alpine CdnRes	10.35	-.08	-.77
Alpine CdnRes A	10.46	-.07	-.66
Alpine GrthEq	13.09	-.04	-.30
Alpine GrthEq A	13.28	-.05	-.38
Cdn Blu Chip Z	11.35	-.04	-.35
Cdn BlueChip	16.34	-.06	-.37
Cdn BlueChip A	16.51	-.07	-.42
Cdn Div Cl Z	10.86	-.04	-.37
Cdn Divers	14.71	-.05	-.34
Cdn Divers A	14.96	-.05	-.33
Cdn Equity	12.80	-.02	-.16
Cdn Equity A	12.82	-.02	-.16
Cdn Lrg Cap Val	10.55	+.01	+.09
Cdn Small/Mid A	21.02	-.04	-.19
Cdn Sml/Mid Cap	18.40	-.03	-.16
Clarica Balance	11.64	-.02	-.17
Glo Lrg Cap Val	10.52	+.04	+.38
Global Bond	9.91	-.04	-.40
Global Bond A	9.91	-.03	-.30
Prem Bond	11.34	-.04	-.35
Prem Bond A	11.49	-.04	-.35
Prem Int'l	12.43	-.03	-.24
Prem Int'l A	12.78	-.03	-.23
Prem Mtg	10.34	-.02	-.19
Prem Mtg A	10.46	-.02	-.19
Sig Corp Bond	9.83	-.02	-.20
Sum Cdn Equ	15.37	-.05	-.32
Sum Cdn Equ A	15.50	-.05	-.32
Sum Div Gwth	15.18	-.02	-.13
Sum Div Gwth A	14.91	-.02	-.13
Sum For Equ	14.46	-.03	-.21
Sum For Equ A	14.96	-.03	-.20
Sum Gwth&Inc	14.09	-.03	-.21
Sum Gwth&Inc A	14.50	-.03	-.21
US Small Cap	8.44	-.02	-.24
US Small Cap A	8.54	-.01	-.12

fund	valuation	chg	% chg
TRANSAMERICA GROWSAFE 75/100			
AGF Int Val7510 06/01	4.51	+.00	+.02
AIC AmFoc 7510 06/01	5.07	-.01	-.19
AIC DivCan 7510 06/01	5.38	-.00	-.01
Agg AA GIF 7510	3.63	-.00	-.03
Bal AA GIF 7510	4.47	-.01	-.12
CI Gl Boom 7510 06/01	4.82	-.00	-.10
CI Global 7510 06/01	5.46	-.00	-.01
CanAsian 7510	4.21	-.01	-.14
CanEuro 7510	3.14	+.02	+.75
CanUS 21st 7510	2.86	-.01	-.24
CanUS L Cap7510	4.16	+.02	+.38
Cdn Bal 7510	4.77	-.02	-.46
Cdn Bond 7510	5.91	-.02	-.34
Cdn Equity 7510	3.40	-.03	-.79
Cdn Lg Cap 7510	4.17	-.01	-.35
Cdn MMF 7510	5.29	+.00	+.00
CdnEqVal 7510 06/01	5.62	+.00	+.04
CdnFixPay 7510 06/01	5.67	-.01	-.18
Con AA GIF 7510	4.88	-.01	-.20
Fid Can AA 7510 06/01	5.66	+.03	+.46
Fid IntPort7510 06/01	4.78	-.06	-1.19
Fid TrueNrt7510 06/01	5.75	+.01	+.19
Grow AA GIF7510	4.11	-.00	-.06
MacIvyGwinc7510 06/01	5.68	+.01	+.17
TD Div Inc 7510 06/01	6.12	-.00	-.03
TOP AggrGw 7510 06/01	3.66	+.01	+.24
TOP Bal 7510 06/01	4.50	+.01	+.19
TOP CdnMgr 7510 06/01	5.75	+.00	+.02
TOP Cons 7510 06/01	5.00	+.01	+.14
TOP GloMgr 7510 06/01	4.89	+.01	+.13
TOP GloSect7510 06/01	4.90	+.01	+.29
TOP Growth 7510 06/01	4.24	+.01	+.20
TOP USMgrs 7510 06/01	4.80	+.02	+.39
US EqVal 7510 06/01	5.74	+.03	+.47
US Equity 7510	3.68	-.00	-.01

Fund Name	Mstar Rating	Fund Type	Fund Sub-Type	Fund Categy	% Ret YrEnd May08	Quart YrEnd May08	% Ret YrEnd May07	Quart YrEnd May07	% Ret YrEnd May06	Quart YrEnd May06	% Ret YrEnd May05	Quart YrEnd May05	% Ret YrEnd May04	Quart YrEnd May04	Exp Ratio	Total Asset $Mill
RBC O'Shaughnessy US Value	5	Equity	US Eq	USEq	-16.5	3	21.4	1	4.9	1	13.4	1	21.5	1	1.57	1271.9
Dynamic Power American Growth Class	5	Equity	US Eq	USEq	9.9	1	17.3	2	0.6	1	13.4	1	27.7	1	2.59	93.9
IG AGF US Growth Class B	5	Equity	US Eq	USEq	-4.2	1	18.8	1	-1	2	-5.2	4			3.29	221.1
Dynamic Power American Growth	5	Equity	US Eq	USEq	8.8	1	17.5	2	-0.5	1	12	1	28.6	1	2.55	198
Dynamic American Value	5	Equity	US Eq	USEq	-2	2	16.9	2	16.7	1	1.6	1	26.4	1	2.55	0
SEI US Large Cap Synthetic Class P	5	Equity	US Eq	USEq	-9.2	1	19.1	1	5.1	1	6.3	1	17.9	2	1.5	119.1
TD US Index Currency Neutral - e	5	Equity	US Eq	USEq	-8.1	1	20.6	1	6.6	1	7.8	1	19.2	1	0.48	
IG AGF US Growth B	5	Equity	US Eq	USEq	-4.3	1	19.2	1	-0.9	1	-5.2	4			3.14	119.1
TD US Index Currency Neutral - I	5	Equity	US Eq	USEq	-8.4	1	20.2	1	6.2	2	7.3	1	19	1	0.85	729.3
McLean Budden American Equity	5	Equity	US Eq	USEq	-10.7	2	19.2	1	-3.9	2	-1.4	2	19.2	1	1.25	104.9
IG AGF US Growth A	5	Equity	US Eq	USEq	-4.2	1	19.4	1	-0.8	1	-5.1	4			2.99	349.2
CI American Value Corporate Class	5	Equity	US Eq	USEq	-5.9	1	19.1	1	-5.9	3	7.4	1	17.9	1	2.31	122.6
Altamira Precision US Curr Neutral Idx	5	Equity	US Eq	USEq	-8.5	2	20.5	1	6.5	1	7.2	1	18.8	1	0.53	313.1
RBC US Index Currency Neutral	5	Equity	US Eq	USEq	-8.4	2	20	1	6.6	1	7.1	1	18.7	2	0.7	6.2
Emissary US Small/Mid Cap	4	Equity	US Eq	USEq	-11.5	2	18.5	2	-4.4	2	-4	3	21	1	2.93	37
IA Clarington Navellier US All Cap A	4	Equity	US Eq	USEq	-9.3	2	10.8	4	10.5	1	-1.4	3	23.7	1	2.88	505.3
BMO US Equity	4	Equity	US Eq	USEq	-12.5	2	18.7	1	-2.5	2	7	1	16.8	2	2.44	130
BMO US Equity Index	4	Equity	US Eq	USEq	-11.1	2	15.9	3	2.3	1	4.3	1	16.8	2	1.22	2887
RBC US Equity	4	Equity	US Eq	USEq	-6.5	1	15.8	3	-1.9	2	-1.1	2	15.6	3	2.02	28.2
RBC US Equity Advisor	4	Equity	US Eq	USEq	-6.5	1			-2.1	2	-1	2			2.2	15.6
GGOF American Equity Ltd Mutual	4	Equity	US Eq	USEq	-19.6	4	20.2	1	-5.3	3	-0.3	2	20.4	1	2.75	5.4
GGOF American Equity Ltd Classic	4	Equity	US Eq	USEq	-19.2	4	20.8	1	-4.8	3	0.3	1	21.1	1	2.21	16.7
Marquis US Equity Pool	4	Equity	US Eq	USEq	-5.1	1	11.3	4	2.4	1					2.9	4
Mac Universal US Gr Lead (Unhed) CI	4	Equity	US Eq	USEq	1	4	9.8	4	-3.8	2	-8.5	4			2.69	322.5
imaxx US Equity Growth	4	Equity	US Eq	USEq	-7.8	4	8.8	4	2.1	2	-1.3	2			2.84	8.2
CI American Equity	4	Equity	US Eq	USEq	-19.6	4	21.8	1	-3	2	0.1	1	19.7	1	2.31	211.6
CI American Equity Corporate Class	4	Equity	US Eq	USEq	-19.4	4	21.9	1	-3.1	2	-0.6	2	23.1	1	2.31	16
Investors US Large Cap Growth A	4	Equity	US Eq	USEq	-4.5	1	14.5	3	-6.7	4	-5.6	4	23.4	1	2.71	317.4
Franklin Flex Cap Growth Corp Class	4	Equity	US Eq	USEq	-6.8	4	12.4	4	-8.6	4	-3.4	3			2.65	267.1
CI American Managers Corporate Class	4	Equity	US Eq	USEq	-14.3	3	15.7	3	-0.5	2	4.7	1	26.6	1	2.31	27.6
CI American Value	4	Equity	US Eq	USEq	-6.1	1	19.9	1	-5.3	4	8.7	1	20.7	1	2.31	112.4
Marquis US Equity Pool Series V	4	Equity	US Eq	USEq	-2.5	1	14.2	3	5	1	-1.1	2	19.3	1	0.32	
MD American Value	4	Equity	US Eq	USEq	-10.6	2	13.3	3	-1.8	4	-1.7	2	13.6	3	1.72	
IG AGF US Growth C	4	Equity	US Eq	USEq	-4.3	1	19.2	3	-0.9	2	-5.3	4	19.3	1	3.17	
Investors US Large Cap Growth B	4	Equity	US Eq	USEq	-4.6	1	14.3	3	-6.8	4	-5.8	4	11.1	4	2.86	
Investors US Large Cap Growth Class B	4	Equity	US Eq	USEq	-5.2	3	14.2	3	-6.7	4	-6.1	4			3.01	240.6
North Growth US Equity	4	Equity	US Eq	USEq	-14.8	3	15.9	3	-7.8	4	11.3	1	25.4	1	1.2	1.6
Investors US Large Cap Value C	4	Equity	US Eq	USEq	-15.6	3	17.6	2	-3.4	2	0	2	9.4	4	2.43	8.4
Middlefield US Growth Class	4	Equity	US Eq	USEq	-3.6	1	10.7	4	-0.1	1	3.1	1	16.8	2	2.88	1.9
Investors US Opportunities C	4	Equity	US Eq	USEq	-17.4	3	22.7	1	-8.5	4	-0.7	2	16.1	2	2.65	69.7
Fidelity American Disciplined Eq Sr T8	4	Equity	US Eq	USEq	-8.3	1	19.7	1	2.2	1	5.3	1	13.7	3	2.45	77.6
Fidelity American Disciplined Eq Sr S8	4	Equity	US Eq	USEq	-8.1	1	19.9	1	2.2	1	5.5	1	13.7	3	2.45	4.1
Fidelity American Disciplined Eq Sr B	4	Equity	US Eq	USEq	-8.1	1	19.9	1	2.4	1	5.5	1	13.5	3	2.65	300.9
Fidelity American Disciplined Eq Sr A	4	Equity	US Eq	USEq	-8.3	1	19.6	1	2	1	5.4	1	13.5	2		14.1
Standard Life US Equity Legend Series	4	Equity	US Eq	USEq	-11.2	2	17.7	2	-7.2	4	-0.7	2	18.4	3	1.15	16.5
Synergy American	4	Equity	US Eq	USEq	-7.6	1	15.7	3	0.7	1	9.7	1	12.6	3	2.31	13.1
Synergy American Corporate Class	4	Equity	US Eq	USEq	-7.5	1	15.1	3	0.4	1	10	1	11.8	3	2.31	
Fidelity American Disciplined Eq CI B	4	Equity	US Eq	USEq	-8.2	1	19.7	1	1.9	1	5	1	13.4	3	2.65	
Fidelity American Disciplined Eq CI A	4	Equity	US Eq	USEq	-8.4	1	19.4	1	1.7	1	4.9	1	13.4	3	2.85	

IG AGF US Growth Class A	4	Equity	US Eq	USEq	-4.1	1	19	1	-0.9	1	-5.1	4	11	4	3.14	12
TD Dow Jones Industrial Avg Index - I	4	Equity	US Eq	USEq	-12.7	2	19.8	1	-5.3	3	-4.7	4	15.4	3	0.85	43.8
AGF American Growth Class D	4	Equity	US Eq	USEq	-3.4	1	20	4	0.3	1	-4.3	3	12.3	3	2.45	27.1
IG Mackenzie Universal US Gr Leaders CLB	4	Equity	US Eq	USEq	0.3	1	9	4	-3.8	2	-8.8	4			3.16	43.8
IG Goldman Sachs US Equity C	3	Equity	US Eq	USEq	-19.6	4	10.2	4	-2.1	1	-3.2	3	20	1	3.17	16.2
Leith Wheeler US Equity Series B	3	Equity	US Eq	USEq	-21.5	4	17.2	1	-0.3	3	-3.4	3	19.3	1	1.34	
TD Dow Jones Industrial Avg Index - e	3	Equity	US Eq	USEq	-12.3	2	20.3	3	-4.9	2	-4.2	3	15.9	2	0.31	137.5
Emissary US Value	3	Equity	US Eq	USEq	-18.6	4	13	1	-3.4	2	-2.3	2	17.2	2	2.92	31.7
Investors US Opportunities Class B	3	Equity	US Eq	USEq	-17.2	3	22.2	1	-8.4	3	-1.2	2			2.97	741.5
Férique American	3	Equity	US Eq	USEq	-16.7	1	18.9	2	-4.9	3	-1.6	1	17	2	0.96	15.1
DFA US Value	3	Equity	US Eq	USEq	-22.4	4	16.8	3	3.5	1	5.2	4	13.6	4	1.61	65.1
TD US Blue Chip Equity - A	3	Equity	US Eq	USEq	-10.8	2	15.9	3	-7.4	4	-5	3	15.7	3	2.44	741.5
Professionals Qc American Index	3	Equity	US Eq	USEq	-14.3	2	17.4	2	-5.9	3	-1.6	2	22.8	1	0.88	0.4
PH&N US Growth A	3	Equity	US Eq	USEq	-11.1	2	13.2	3	-2.2	3	-3.8	3	13.6	3	1.22	5.8
TD US Blue Chip Equity - I	3	Equity	US Eq	USEq	-10.9	2	15.9	2	-7.4	4	-5.1	4			2.44	
Standard Life US Equity E	3	Equity	US Eq	USEq	-11.7	2	16.8	2	-7.9	2	-1.2	2	12.7	3	1.91	13.1
Counsel Select America	3	Equity	US Eq	USEq	-14.3	3	11.1	3	-5.8	3	-0.3	3			2.83	
TD US Equity Advantage Portfolio-A	3	Equity	US Eq	USEq	-14	3	16.3	3	-5.1	3	-2.1	3	16.7	2	2.57	28.4
Standard Life US Equity A	3	Equity	US Eq	USEq	-12.3	3	16.1	3	-8.4	3	-1.8	3	16.2	2	2.43	289.6
CIBC US Index RRSP	3	Equity	US Eq	USEq	-14.4	3	17.9	3	-5.8	3	-1.8	3	16.3	2	0.97	32.7
SEI US Large Co Equity Class P	3	Equity	US Eq	USEq	-15	3	15	3	-4.4	3	-0.7	2	17.9	2	2.43	485.4
CIBC US Equity Index	3	Equity	US Eq	USEq	-13.7	3	17.3	3	-4.1	3	-1.1	2	15.8	2	0.98	112.9
Investors US Opportunities Class A	3	Equity	US Eq	USEq	-17.1	3	22.3	3	-8.3	2	0.6	1	6.5	4	2.82	211.4
Mac Universal US Blue Chip Cl	3	Equity	US Eq	USEq	-7.7	4	12.3	4	0.8	4	-0.7	2			2.43	
Investors US Opportunities B	3	Equity	US Eq	USEq	-17.4	3	22.7	3	-8.5	1	-0.5	2	19.9	2	2.85	3.5
Investors US Opportunities A	3	Equity	US Eq	USEq	-17.3	3	22.9	1	-8.3	1	-1.7	3	19.9	1	2.7	2.4
Fidelity American Value Sr A	3	Equity	US Eq	USEq	-20.1	4	14.9	4	-4.5	3	-1.7	2			2.54	150.8
Fidelity American Value Sr B	3	Equity	US Eq	USEq	-19.9	4	15.1	4	-4.4	3	-0.4	2	8.9	4	2.34	13.1
Investors US Large Cap Value Class B	3	Equity	US Eq	USEq	-15.4	3	17.1	3	-3.2	2	-0.3	2			2.84	22.1
Investors US Large Cap Value Class A	3	Equity	US Eq	USEq	-15.2	3	17.3	2	-3	2	-4.6	2	17.7	2	2.69	45
TD US Equity Advantage Portfolio-I	3	Equity	US Eq	USEq	-13.9	3	16.4	3	-5.1	3	-1.9	2			2.44	359.7
Scotia US Value	3	Equity	US Eq	USEq	-9.8	2	9.5	3	-4.4	3	-1.1	3	16.3	2	2.46	141.1
Scotia US Index	3	Equity	US Eq	USEq	-14.4	2	17.5	3	-5.5	3	0.1	3			0.94	
TD US Index - e	3	Equity	US Eq	USEq	-13.7	3	18.4	2	-5.2	3	-1.5	3	16.8	2	0.33	88.5
Investors US Large Cap Value B	3	Equity	US Eq	USEq	-15.5	3	17.6	2	-3.4	2	-2.4	2	16.8	2	2.84	2213.4
Fidelity Growth America Sr B	3	Equity	US Eq	USEq	-21.2	4	12.7	4	-2.3	2	0.2	2			2.43	
Scotia CanAm Index	3	Equity	US Eq	USEq	-14.8	3	17.4	2	-5.3	2	-4.7	3	15.7	3	1.02	5.1
Investors US Large Cap Value A	3	Equity	US Eq	USEq	-15.4	3	17.8	1	-3.2	3	-5.9	2	11.7	4	2.69	14.1
National Bank American Index Plus	3	Equity	US Eq	USEq	-15.1	3	15.8	1	-7.9	3	-1.3	1	5.4	4	1.89	359.7
Investors US Large Cap Growth Class A	3	Equity	US Eq	USEq	-5.1	1	14.3	2	-6.5	3	-1.6	4	16.6	2	2.86	19
TD US Index - I	3	Equity	US Eq	USEq	-13.9	3	18.2	2	-5.3	3	1.4	2	17.2	1	0.53	681.8
Renaissance US Index	3	Equity	US Eq	USEq	-13.6	2	16.7	2	-6	3	-5.1	3	14.7	3	1.82	76.1
TD US Large-Cap Value - A	3	Equity	US Eq	USEq	-17.6	1	18.9	1	-5.4	1	1.3	1			2.44	681.8
Renaissance US Equity Value	3	Equity	US Eq	USEq	-20	4	17.5	4	-4.4	4	-2.3	4	20.4	1	2.62	17.3
TD US Large-Cap Value - I	3	Equity	US Eq	USEq	-17.7	1	19	1	-5.4	1	-8.5	1			2.44	
Capital Intl-US Equity Cl I	3	Equity	US Eq	USEq	-17.4	3	11.8	3	-2	2			20.6	1	0.08	16.1
Mac Universal US Growth Leaders	3	Equity	US Eq	USEq	0	4	10.4	4	-3.5	2			8	4	2.73	53.7
RBC US Index	3	Equity	US Eq	USEq	-14.2	2	18	2	-5.6	3	-1.6	2	16.1	2	0.85	510.8
TD US Quantitative Equity - I	3	Equity	US Eq	USEq	-17.7	3	15.2	3	-5.4	2	-1.4	2	15.7	3	1.53	18.9
Manulife US Core	3	Equity	US Eq	USEq	-20.8	4	13.4	4	-2.5	3	-1.5	2	21.6	1	2.45	
National Bank American Index	3	Equity	US Eq	USEq	-13	1	19.3	3	-5.3	2	-5	4	15.4	4	1.24	9
Maritime Life Elite American Eq Pooled	3	Equity	US Eq	USEq	-14.1	2	12.8	4	-3.9	4	-4.5	4	15	4	0.44	0.7
Maritime Life Elite US Special Eq Pooled	3	Equity	US Eq	USEq	-10.6	2	14.4	3	-5.8	3	-3.8	4	11.9	3	0.49	0.4

	Name															
3	HSBC US Equity	Equity	US Eq	USEq	-14.9	3	16	3	-5.6	3	-3.3	3	10.4	4	2.33	24.3
3	IA Clarington American	Equity	US Eq	USEq	-12.7	2	17.9	2	-4.3	2	-3.9	3	10.5	4	2.4	29.8
3	Beutel Goodman American Equity	Equity	US Eq	USEq	-11	2	19.6	1	-6.1	1	3.6	1	23.3	1	1.42	1
3	imaxx TOP US Managers GIP 75/75	Equity	US Eq	USEq	-21.6	1	14.4	2	-0.1	3	-2.7	2	7.9	4	3.24	15.3
3	Quadrus Mac Univ US Growth Leaders	Equity	US Eq	USEq	0.1	1	10.4	4	-3.4	3	-8.6	3	20.2	1	2.69	33.6
3	Mawer US Equity	Equity	US Eq	USEq	-6.1	1	12.4	4	-6.9	4	-2.9	3			1.28	8.2
3	MLI US Large Cap Growth Class GIFe2	Equity	US Eq	USEq	-9.3	2	13.4	3	-8.2	4	-3.9	3	13.7	3	3.36	31.5
3	MLI US Large Cap Growth Class GIFe	Equity	US Eq	USEq	-9.8	3	12.9	3	-8.7	4	-4.7	4	11.8	3	3.9	2
3	MLI American Equity Index GIFe2	Equity	US Eq	USEq	-15.9	3	16.5	2	-7.4	4	-3.1	3			2.76	620.7
3	AGF American Growth Class	Equity	US Eq	USEq	-3.9	1	19.4	1	-0.3	1	12.3	1			2.95	2.6
3	imaxx TOP US Managers GIP 75/100	Equity	US Eq	USEq	-21.8	4	14.1	3	15.6	3	-8.6	4			3.49	52.5
3	Acker Finley Select US Value 50	Equity	US Eq	USEq	-27.9	2	18.4	2	-3.7	4	-6.1	4	7.4	4	1.94	151.7
3	IG Mackenzie Universal US Gr Leaders CLA	Equity	US Eq	USEq	0.5	1	9.2	1	-5.4	2	-2.9	2			3.02	6.9
2	MLI Renaissance US Basic Value GIFe2	Equity	US Eq	USEq	-20.8	3	16.5	3	-2.6	2	-3	3			3.52	
2	IG Fidelity US Equity Class B	Equity	US Eq	USEq	-22	4	11.4	4	-2	4	-3.2	3	14.7	3	3.21	241.4
2	IG Goldman Sachs US Equity A	Equity	US Eq	USEq	-19.4	4	10.4	4	-2.1	4	-2.8	3	15.4	3	2.99	
2	IG Goldman Sachs US Equity B	Equity	US Eq	USEq	-19.5	4	10.2	4	-2.4	4	-0.4	3			3.14	15.4
2	IG Fidelity US Equity Class A	Equity	US Eq	USEq	-21.9	4	11.5	4	-2.1	4	-0.5	2	15.4	3	3.06	10
2	IG Goldman Sachs US Equity Class A	Equity	US Eq	USEq	-20	4	10.2	4	-2.3	4	-2.7	3			3.12	
2	IG Goldman Sachs US Equity Class B	Equity	US Eq	USEq	-20.1	4	10	4	-2.7	4	-2.7	3			3.27	
2	IG FI US Equity C	Equity	US Eq	USEq	-21.9	4	11.5	4	-2.7	4	-2.5	3			3.17	
2	IG FI US Equity B	Equity	US Eq	USEq	-21.8	4	11.5	4	-2.5	4	-5.7	3			3.14	89
2	IG FI US Equity A	Equity	US Eq	USEq	-21.7	4	11.7	4	-6.5	4	-6.7	3			2.99	54.2
2	IA Clarington US Dividend T	Equity	US Eq	USEq	-20.7	4	19.3	1	-8.5	3	-6.7	3			2.66	7.1
2	Renaissance US Equity Growth	Equity	US Eq	USEq	-18.1	3	14.1	3	-9.6	4	-6.5	4	16.2	4	2.62	4.1
2	AIM Trimark Core American Equity Cl	Equity	US Eq	USEq	-13.9	3	12.1	4	-8.3	4	-1.5	4	11.7	4	2.68	0.7
2	Putnam US Voyager D	Equity	US Eq	USEq	-12.2	2	11.1	4	-5.9	4	-4.4	3	12.8	3	1.93	10.9
2	MLI Renaissance US Basic Value GIFe	Equity	US Eq	USEq	-21.2	4	15.9	2	-5.1	2	-2.4	3	18.3	1	4.05	9.5
2	Putnam US Value D	Equity	US Eq	USEq	-27.4	3	17	2	-7.8	2	-5.8	4	15.2	3	1.93	5.8
2	Franklin Templeton US Rising Div A	Equity	US Eq	USEq	-17.3	3	10.9	4	-3.3	4	-1.6	3	11.9	3	2.59	4.5
2	MLI Fidelity Growth America GIF encore 2	Equity	US Eq	USEq	-22.1	4	11.6	4	-6.9	4	-1.5	2	16	2	3.4	
2	Investors US Large Cap Growth C	Equity	US Eq	USEq	-4.7	1	14.3	1	-2.5	4	-1.7	4	6.2	4	2.88	
2	Fidelity Growth America Sr T8	Equity	US Eq	USEq	-21.5	4	12.4	4	-5.7	3	-2.9	4	16.7	2	2.63	0.5
2	Saxon US Equity Investor Series	Equity	US Eq	USEq	-19.5	4	13.6	4	-2.3	3	-1.8	2			1.86	8.2
2	Fidelity Growth America Sr S8	Equity	US Eq	USEq	-21.2	4	13	3	-2.5	3	-1.9	3	16.7	2	2.43	0.3
2	Fidelity Growth America Sr A	Equity	US Eq	USEq	-21.5	4	12.4	4	-8	4	-3.4	2	16.8	2	2.63	47.7
2	Scotia US Growth	Equity	US Eq	USEq	-11.1	2	13.1	4	-2.7	4	-3.5	2	10.3	2	2.53	45.8
2	Fidelity Growth America Cl B	Equity	US Eq	USEq	-21.3	4	12.5	4	-2.8	4	-3.8	3	16.2	3	2.58	1.2
2	Fidelity Growth America Cl A	Equity	US Eq	USEq	-21.5	4	12.3	4	-1.1	4	-3.9	3	16.2	3	2.78	1.5
2	Fidelity American Opportunities Sr B	Equity	US Eq	USEq	-12.8	2	11.2	4	-1.3	4	-8.1	4	6.3	3	2.45	8.5
2	Fidelity American Opportunities Sr A	Equity	US Eq	USEq	-13	2	11	4	-1.4	4	1.1	3	6.3	3	2.65	9.4
2	Fidelity American Opportunities Cl B	Equity	US Eq	USEq	-13.1	2	10.8	4	-1.6	4	-2.9	3	5.8	3	2.64	0.5
2	Fidelity American Opportunities Cl A	Equity	US Eq	USEq	-15.7	3	10.6	4	1.1	1	-8.8	3	5.8	4	2.84	0.8
2	Ethical American Multi-Strategy	Equity	US Eq	USEq	-22.5	4	11	4	-3.8	2	-6.3	4	11.3	4	2.31	52.2
2	MLI Fidelity Growth America GIF encore	Equity	US Eq	USEq	-13.3	2	9.3	4	-7.4	4	-2.1	3	15.2	3	3.93	9.8
2	Emissary US Growth	Equity	US Eq	USEq	-11.7	2	12.7	2	-10.5	3	-4.2	4	16.1	2	2.93	12
2	Trimark US Companies Class	Equity	US Eq	USEq	-21	4	18	4	-6.4	3	-2.1	3	11.8	4	2.86	6.1
2	Desjardins American Equity Value	Equity	US Eq	USEq	-21	2	18	2	-6.4	3	-2.1	3			2.49	475
2	MLI American Equity Index GIFe	Equity	US Eq	USEq	-16.4	3	14.8	3	-7.6	3	-4.2	3	13	3	3.34	3.3
2	CIBC North American Demographics	Equity	US Eq	USEq	-16.8	3	15	4	-8.7	3	-2.1	3	10.1	3	2.74	16.4
2	PH&N US Equity A	Equity	US Eq	USEq	-13.7	3	12.9	3	-5.9	4	-7.1	3	15.7	3	1.16	322.5
2	PH&N US Dividend Income A	Equity	US Eq	USEq	-19.1	4	11.2	4	-6.5	4	-3.7	3	18.8	3	1.15	73.7
2	AGF US Value Class	Equity	US Eq	USEq	-34.2	4	19.6	1	2.8	1	-0.2	2	20.5	2	2.85	33.3

Fund				Q	%	Q	%	Q	%	Q	%	Q	%	Q	Expense Ratio	Total Asset ($Mill)
MDPIM US Equity Pool	Equity	US Eq	USEq	2	-18.1	3	17.2	2	-3	2	-2.3	3	9.2	4	1.35	666.1
MD American Growth	Equity	US Eq	USEq	2	-9.9	2	13.7	3	-6.1	3	-7.1	4	11.4	4	1.44	304.2
Capital Intl-US Equity Cl H	Equity	US Eq	USEq	2	-18	3	11.1	4	-2.8	3	-3	3	18.9	1	0.77	17.3
Capital Intl-US Equity Cl D	Equity	US Eq	USEq	2	-18.6	3	10.3	4	-3.4	2	-3.7	3	18.4	2	1.47	17.3
Capital Intl-US Equity Cl A	Equity	US Eq	USEq	2	-19	4	9.8	4	-3.9	2	-4.2	3	13.2	3	1.97	17.3
Manulife US Large Cap Value Class	Equity	US Eq	USEq	2	-20.1	2	17.1	2	-7.3	4	-2.6	3	13.6	3	2.8	4.4
AIM American Growth	Equity	US Eq	USEq	2	-16.1	3	11.3	4	-8.1	4	-6	1	14.4	3	2.93	18
BMO US Growth	Equity	US Eq	USEq	2	-12.6	2	14.7	3	-11.3	1	0.3	4	11.4	1	2.48	71.3
Trimark US Companies	Equity	US Eq	USEq	2	-11.4	2	12.9	3	-10.4	4	-5.7	4	10.6	4	2.61	76.3
Altamira US Larger Company	Equity	US Eq	USEq	1	-11.9	3	12.9	3	-7.3	4	-7.3	3	16.1	4	2.67	34.4
imaxx US Equity Value	Equity	US Eq	USEq	1	-27	4	13.6	4	-6.9	4	-2.6	3	24.6	2	2.74	6
Brandes US Equity	Equity	US Eq	USEq	1	-34.6	4	22.3	4	-6.3	3	-3.6	3	14.6	1	2.6	69.9
AIC Value Corporate Class	Equity	US Eq	USEq	1	-34.6	4	23.5	1	-2.2	3	-6.7	2		3	2.47	8
CI Value Trust Corporate Cl Shares Cl Z	Equity	US Eq	USEq	1	-34	4	16.7	2	-9.9	4	-1.4	4	15.2		2.31	77.7
AIC Value	Equity	US Eq	USEq	1	-35.2	4	23.1	1	-2.3	2	-7.1	2	9.1	3	2.52	131.6
AIC American Focused Corporate Class	Equity	US Eq	USEq	1	-39.4	4	6.2	4	8.7	4	-1.1	2	15.2	2	2.35	37.3
CI Value Trust Corporate Class	Equity	US Eq	USEq	1	-34.1	4	16.4	2	-10.2	2	-1.7	2	8.6	3	2.57	856.4
AIC American Focused	Equity	US Eq	USEq	1	-39.5	4	6.1	4	8.3	1	-0.8	1	11.4	4	2.44	308.4
Meritas US Equity	Equity	US Eq	USEq	1	-17.2	3	13	3	-8.3	3	-6.5	4	14.3	4	2.87	11.8
Northwest US Equity	Equity	US Eq	USEq	1	-27.7	3	14.7	3	-5.9	3	0.2	1	13.5	3	2.86	16.5
Mac Focus America Class	Equity	US Eq	USEq	1	-11	2	8.1	4	-10.7	4	-7.2	4		3	2.43	4.5
Desjardins CI Value Trust Sector	Equity	US Eq	USEq	1	-34.2	4	16.3	4	-10.1	2	-1.6	2	14.4		2.75	297.4
Putnam US Value A	Equity	US Eq	USEq	1	-27.9	2	16.3	2	-5.7	3	-2.1	3	11.6	3	2.62	19.5
First Trust DOW 10 Strategy Trust 2003	Equity	US Eq	USEq	1	-23.7	1	23.9	1	-10.7	1	-5	1	12.1	4	2.74	3.1
Putnam US Voyager A	Equity	US Eq	USEq	1	-12.9	2	10.4	2	-9	4	-7.4	4		3	2.64	1.4

Source: Morningstar Research Inc.

Expense Ratio: The manager's annual fee for managing and administering the fund, expressed as a percentage of total fund value. Some funds charge additional administrative fees not included in this figure. For full information on management and administrative costs, consult the fund prospectus.

Total Asset ($Mill): the current assets plus non-current assets.

Fund Table: Canadian Balanced and US Equity funds as of May 30, 2008.

Annual Returns: An annual return is the fund or portfolio return, for any 12-month period, including reinvested dividends.

Quartile Rankings: The quartile (1 to 4) in which this fund's "% YrEnd MmmYY" is positioned, relative to all others in its peer group. For example, if a mutual fund has a "Quart YrEnd Nov02" value of "1", that means this fund's rate of return for the 12 months ending November 30, 2002 is in the top 25% of all other mutual funds in its fund category. If it was "4" then its indicates the rate of return is amongst the bottom 25% of all its peers (e.g. Canadian Equity mutual funds or Canadian Bond segregated funds). Quartiles are useful since they indicate how the subject fund performs relative to its peers in its category. Many managers set the first (1) or second (2) quartile as their on-going goal as it indicates that the fund is outperforming the median fund within this category of funds.

3.7 Cumulative Distributions and Ogives

What Is an Ogive?

An *ogive* is a graph of a cumulative frequency distribution. By reading an ogive you can retrieve certain "percentile" information very quickly. This type of information is not readily available from a frequency distribution.

A soft drink manufacturer has to check periodically whether bottles marked as 2 litre actually contain 2 litres. Have you ever noticed that some bottles are filled to the top and some are not? To avoid customers' complaints, the manufacturer has to conduct some investigations to ensure that the bottling machine is working properly and filling the bottles with the right amount. A sample of 255 bottles was taken from the production floor, and the volumes of these 255 bottles were recorded. The data that showed how much soft drink was in each bottle were summarized in the following frequency distribution table:

Amount in a 2-litre bottle (ml)	Number of bottles
1999.00 and under 1999.50	5
1999.50 " " 2000.00	10
2000.00 " " 2000.50	20
2000.50 " " 2001.00	35
2001.00 " " 2001.50	55
2001.50 " " 2002.00	50
2002.00 " " 2002.50	40
2002.50 " " 2003.00	30
2003.00 " " 2003.50	10
Total	255

(Note: 1 litre = 1000 ml)

Suppose this frequency distribution is the only data we have available and we would like to know the answers to the following questions.

a. What percent of the bottles had less than 2000.00 ml?
b. What percent of the bottles had less than 2002.70 ml?
c. What percent of the bottles had at least 2001.25 ml?
d. 30% of the bottles have at most ____ml.
e. 25% of the bottles have at least ____ml.

Question (a) is easy to answer because 2000.00 ml is the upper boundary of the second class and you just add the frequencies of the first and second classes, (i.e. 5 + 10). The answer is 15 bottles, which is (15/255)*100 = 5.9% of the bottles had less than 2000.00 ml.

Question (b) is not easy because 2002.7 ml falls between 2002.50 and 2003.00. Similarly, for question (c) 2001.25 ml falls between 2001.00 and 2001.50.

To answer questions (b) and (c), you must plot an ogive.

The ogive for the volume of a 2000 ml bottle is

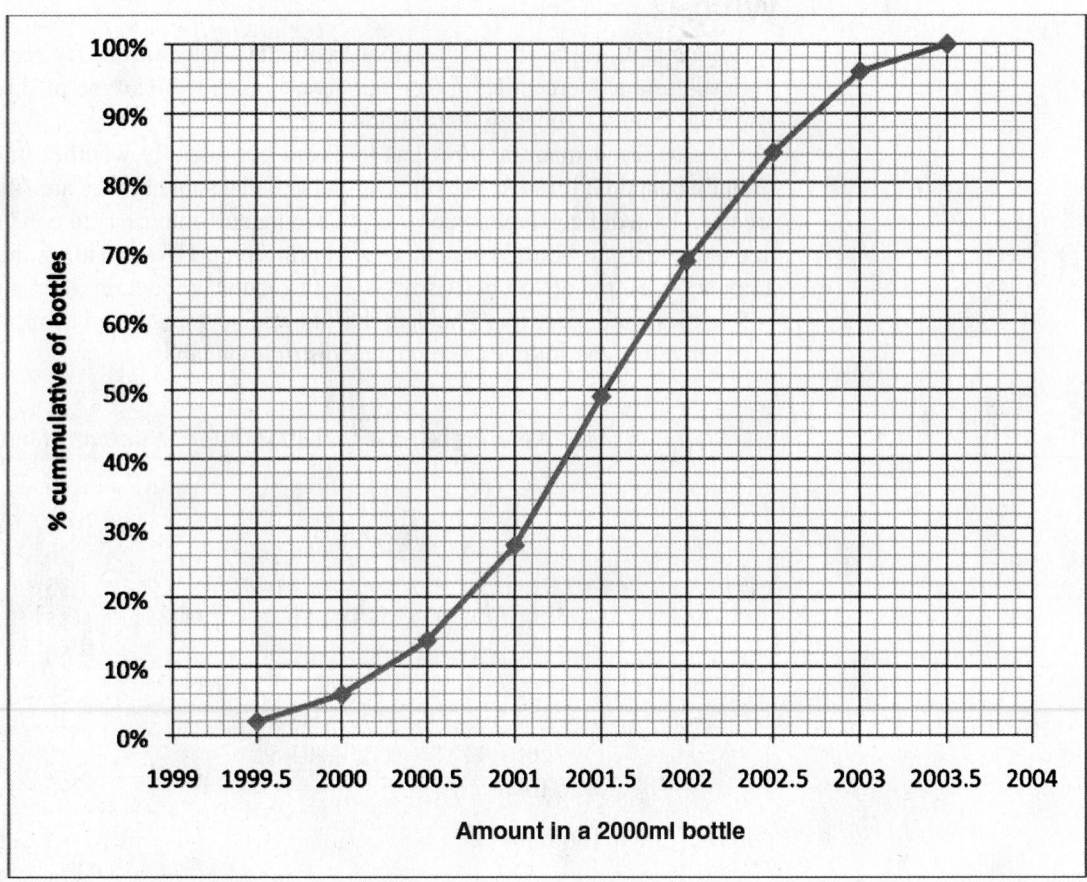

How to Draw an Ogive

Start with a frequency distribution table and add a cumulative frequency column and a cumulative relative frequency column. You may construct two kinds of cumulative relative frequencies. One is the cumulative relative frequency (crf) and the other is the cumulative percentage frequency (c%). Both kinds of cumulative frequency will give you the same answer. However, it is more common to use c% to construct the ogive.

1. Cumulative relative frequency (crf)

crf = relative frequency (rf) of the class + sum of all previous class relative frequencies

Alternatively, crf = Sum of all relative frequencies up to and including the class.

2. Cumulative percentage frequency (c%)

$$c\% = 100 \times \frac{cf}{sum\ of\ all\ frequencies}$$

or

$$c\% = 100 \times crf$$

Amount in a 2 litre bottle (ml)	# of bottles
1999.00 and under 1999.50	5
1999.50 " " 2000.00	10
2000.00 " " 2000.50	20
2000.50 " " 2001.00	35
2001.00 " " 2001.50	55
2001.50 " " 2002.00	50
2002.00 " " 2002.50	40
2002.50 " " 2003.00	30
2003.00 " " 2003.50	10
Total	255

Step 1: Construct the cumulative frequency distribution table as shown.

Amount in a 2 litre bottle (ml)	f = number of bottles	cf = cumulative number of bottles	crf = cumulative proportion of bottles	c% = cumulative percentage of bottles
1999.00 and under 1999.50	5	5	$5 \div 255 = 0.020$	$0.02 \times 100 = 2.0$
1999.50 " " 2000.00	10	$5 + 10 = 15$	$15 \div 255 = 0.059$	$0.059 \times 100 = 5.9$
2000.00 " " 2000.50	20	$5 + 10 + 20 = 35$	$35 \div 255 = 0.137$	$0.137 \times 100 = 13.7$
2000.50 " " 2001.00	35	$5 + 10 + 20 + 35 = 70$	$70 \div 255 = 0.274$	$0.274 \times 100 = 27.4$
2001.00 " " 2001.50	55	125	$125 \div 255 = 0.490$	$0.490 \times 100 = 49.0$
2001.50 " " 2002.00	50	175	$175 \div 255 = 0.686$	$0.686 \times 100 = 68.6$
2002.00 " " 2002.50	40	215	$215 \div 255 = 0.843$	$0.843 \times 100 = 84.3$
2002.50 " " 2003.00	30	245	$245 \div 255 = 0.961$	$0.961 \times 100 = 96.1$
2003.00 " " 2003.50	10	255	$255 \div 255 = 1.000$	$1.00 \times 100 = 100.0$
Total	255			

Step 2: Draw the ogive

To plot the ogive, you need to construct the vertical axis (y-axis) representing the c% and the horizontal axis (x-axis) representing the upper boundary for each class intervals. Start the graph at the first boundary.

The points representing the x-y coordinates on a graph are as follows:

horizontal axis (i.e., x-axis) *upper boundary* for each class	vertical axis (i.e., y-axis) c%
1999.50	2.5
2000.00	5.9
2000.50	13.7
2001.00	27.4
2001.50	49.0
2002.00	68.6
2002.50	84.3
2003.00	96.1
2003.50	100.0

The ogive is plotted as follows:

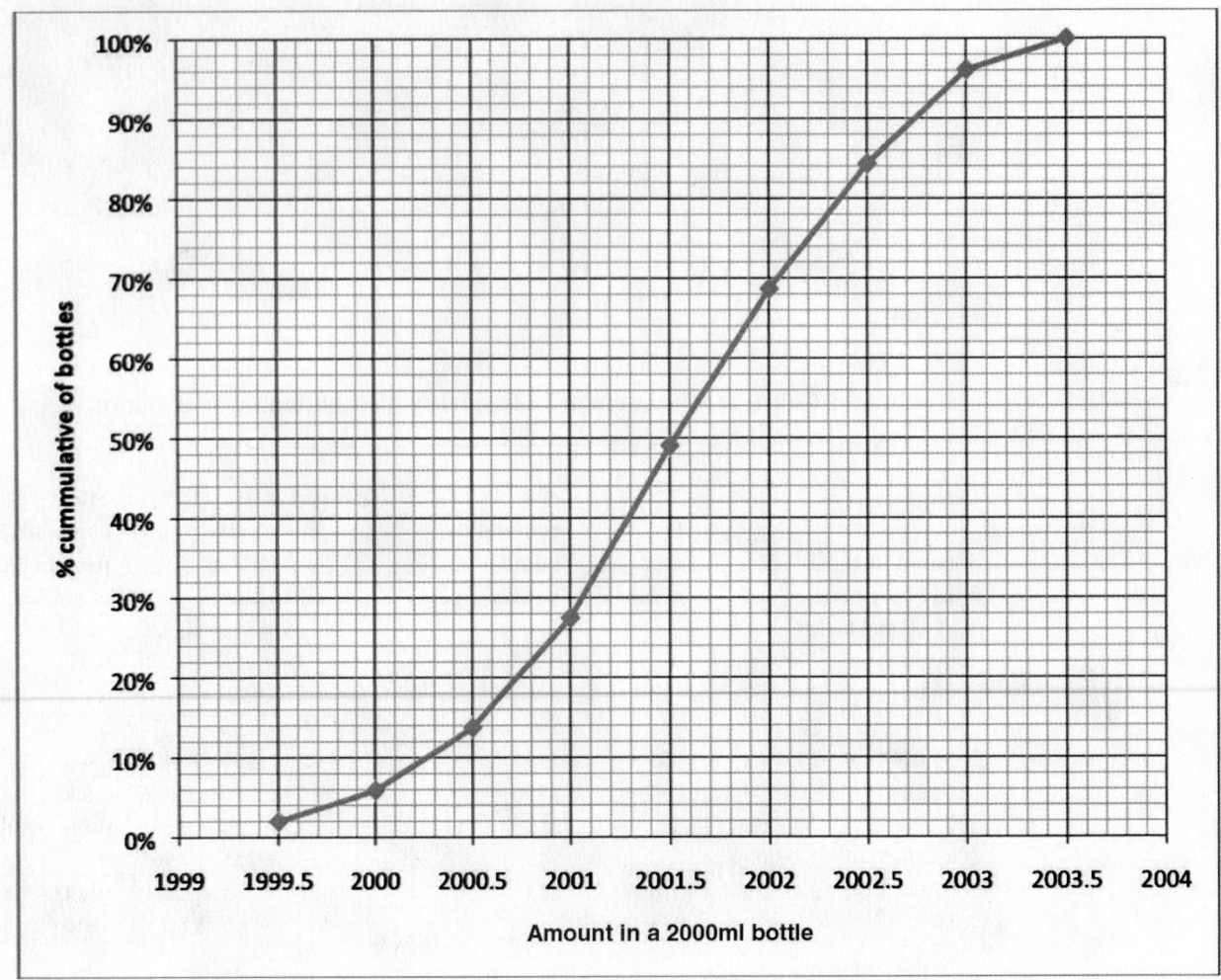

Join the points with a straight line. In the construction of an ogive, an extra upper boundary is added at the beginning so the graph starts with a crf of 0 or 0%.

Use the ogive presented earlier to answer the following questions, part (b) to part (e).

b) What percent of the bottles had less than 2002.70 ml?

To find the "less than 2002.7," go vertically upward at 2002.70 of the x-axis until you hit the ogive line, and then go across to acquire the y value (see A). The y value is 89%; that is, 89% of the bottles had less than 2002.7 ml.

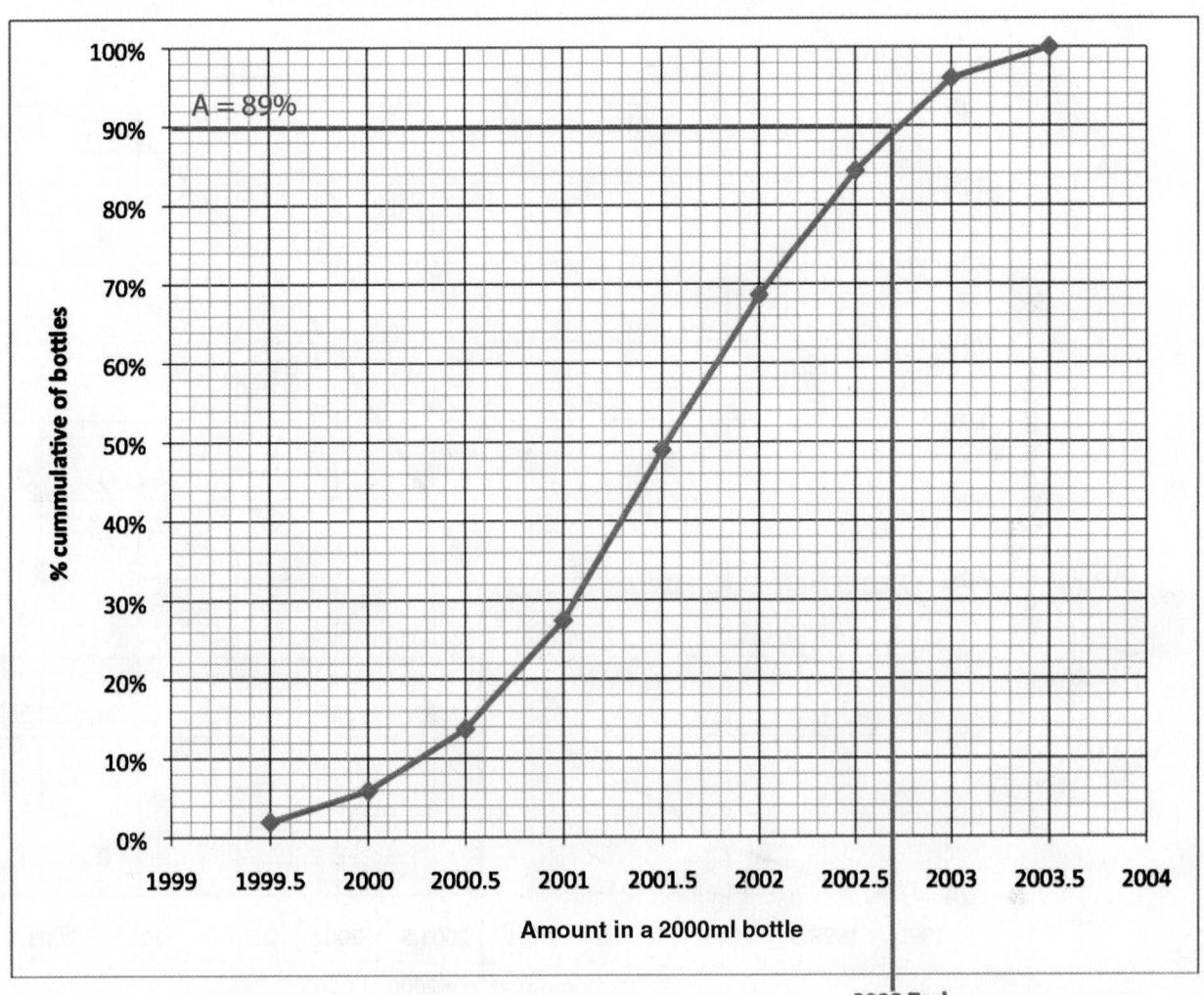

c) What percent of the bottles had at least 2001.25 ml?

To find the "at least 2001.25," go vertically upward at 2001.25 of the x-axis until you hit the ogive line, and then go across to acquire the y value (see B). The y value is 38%. However 38% indicates that 38% of the bottles had less than 2001.25 ml. The question asks for the percent of the bottles that had at least 2001.25 ml. Therefore, 62% (=100%–38%) of bottles had at least 2001.25 ml.

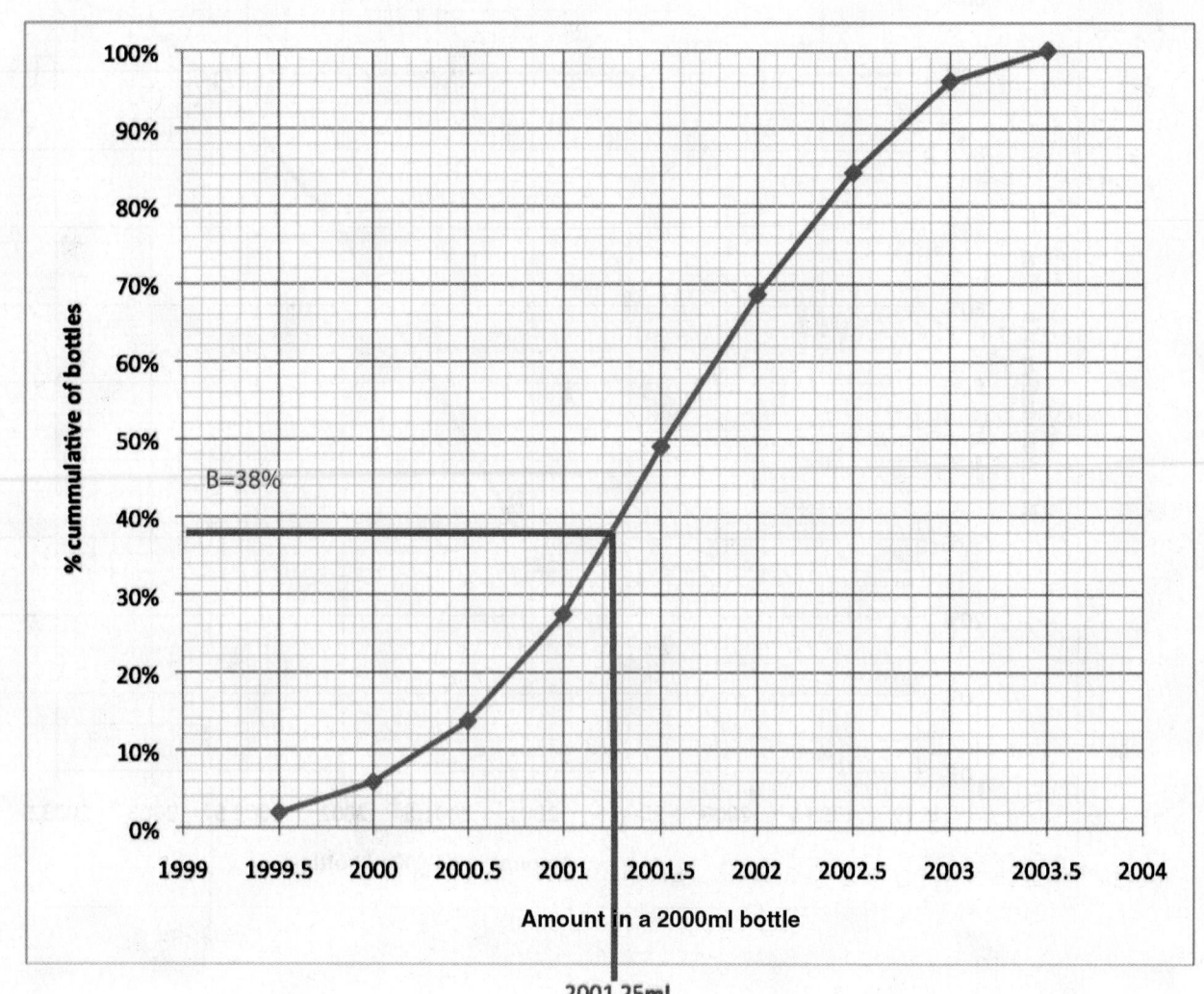

d) 30% of the bottles have at most _____ml.

Go across at 30% of the y-axis until you hit the ogive line, and then go downward to acquire the x value (see C). The x value is 2001.1 ml.

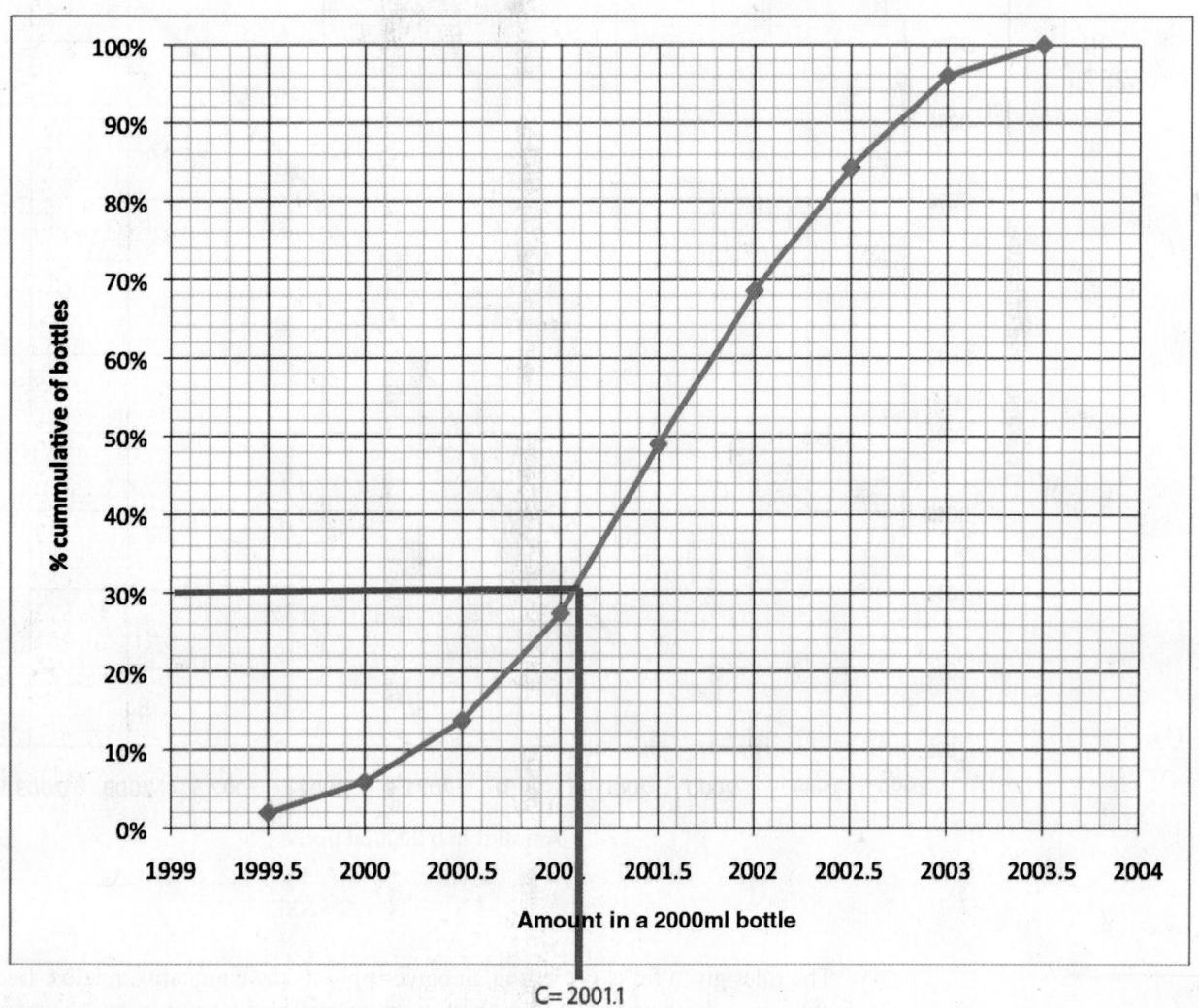

C= 2001.1

e) 25% of the bottles have at least _____ml.

   Go across at 75%(=100%–25%) of the y-axis until you hit the ogive line, and then go downward to acquire the x value (see D). The x value is 2002.2 ml.

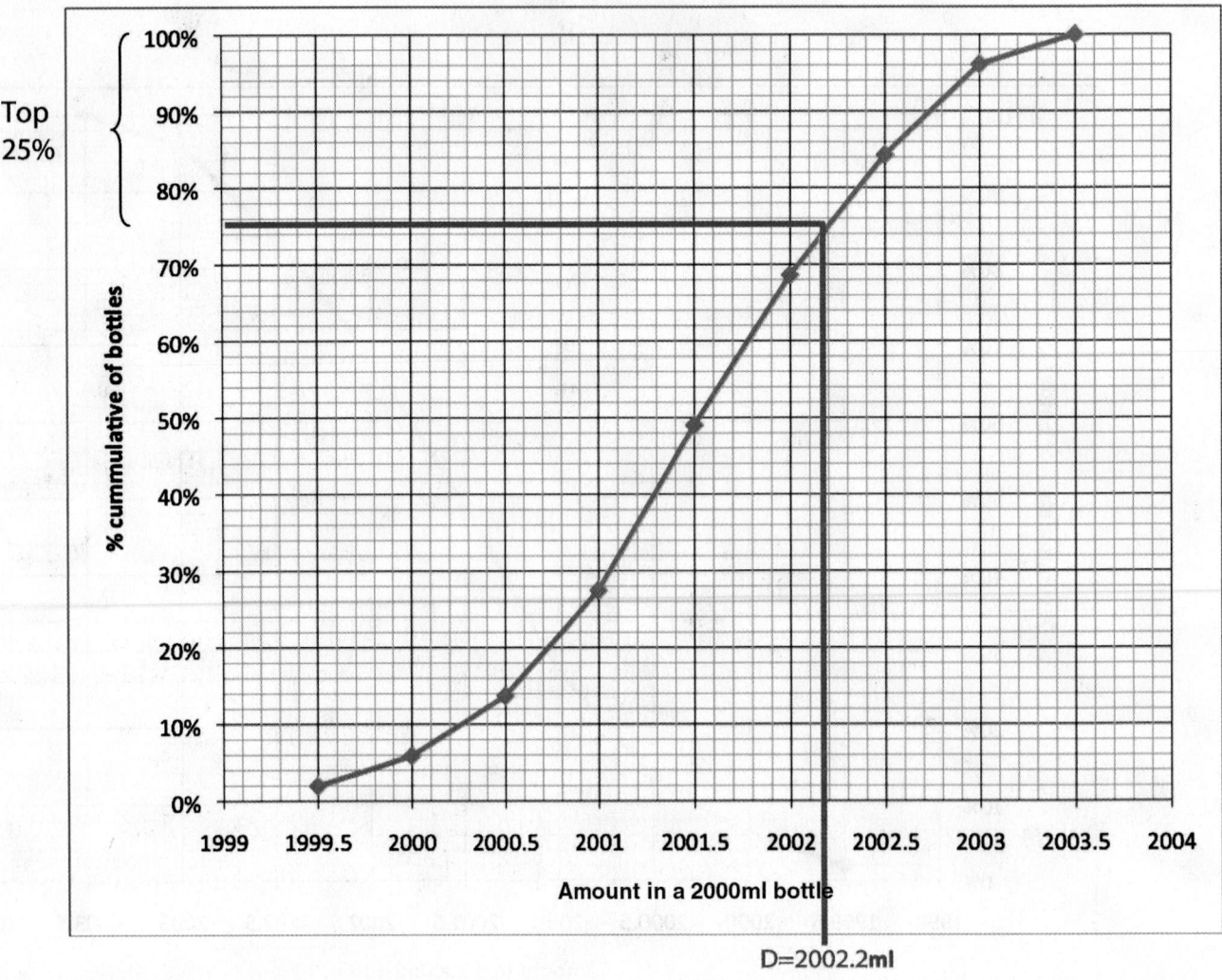

D=2002.2ml

   The rules given for constructing an ogive apply to any cumulative relative frequency distribution, even those where there are classes of unequal width or open-ended classes.

EXAMPLE 3.13   A survey of employees in a large company revealed the following results regarding the amount of time employees had been in their current job position. The results were summarized as follows:

Time in Current Position (years)	Percent
less than 1	15.0
1 and under 3	27.4
3 " " 6	22.2
6 " " 10	13.9
10 " " 20	15.5
20 and over	6.0
Total	100

Based on these results:

a) Approximately what percent of quality professionals had been in their current position for 5 years or more?

b) Seventy percent of quality professionals had been in their current position for less than _____ years.

Step 1: Construct the cumulative frequency distribution table as shown.

The calculations necessary to construct a percentage ogive from the given data are shown next.

Time in current position (years)	Percent	Cumulative Percent
less than 1	15.0	15.0
1 and under 3	27.4	15.0 + 27.4 = 42.4
3 " " 6	22.2	15.0 + 27.4 + 22.2 = 64.6
6 " " 10	13.9	15.0 + 27.4 + 22.2 + 13.9 = 78.5
10 " " 20	15.5	15.0 + 27.4 + 22.2 + 13.9 + 15.5 = 94.0
20 and over	6.0	15.0 + 27.4 + 22.2 + 13.9 + 15.5 + 6.0 = 100.0
Total	100	

Step 2: To draw the ogive

To plot the ogive, you need to construct the vertical axis (y-axis) representing the c% and the horizontal axis (x-axis) representing the upper boundary for each class intervals. Start the graph at the first boundary.

The points representing the x-y coordinates on a graph are as follows:

horizontal axis (x-axis) *upper boundary* for each class	vertical axis (y-axis) c%
1	15.0
3	42.4
6	64.6
10	78.5
20	94.0

The ogive is plotted as follows:

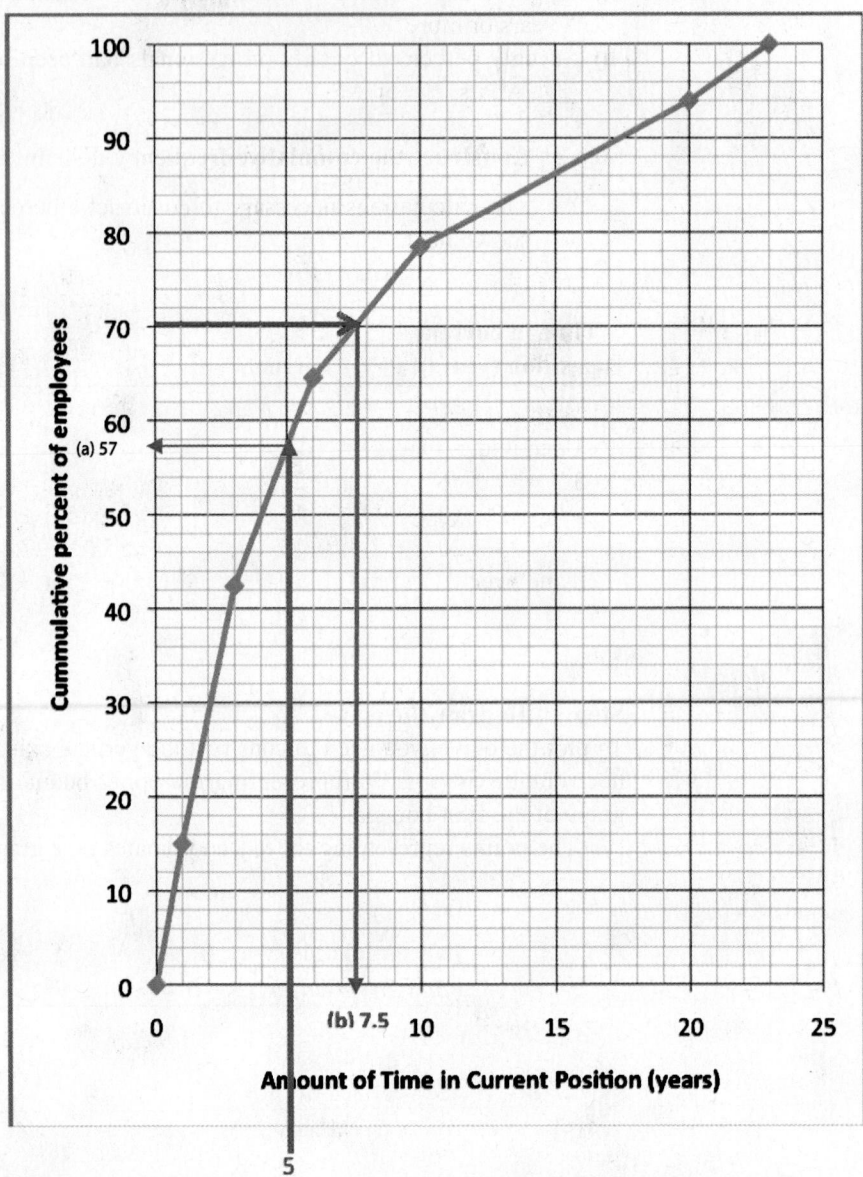

Join the points with straight lines. In the construction of an ogive, an extra upper boundary is added at the beginning so the graph starts with a crf of 0 or 0%.

Use the ogive presented earlier to answer the following questions, part (a) and part (b).

a) Approximately what percent of quality professionals had been in their current position for 5 years or more?

Answer: 100% − 57% = 43%

b) Seventy percent of quality professionals had been in their current position for less than _____ years.

Answer: 7.5 years

Problems for OGIVE

3.10 The National Association of Real Estate Agents has collected the following data on a sample of 170 salespersons. The classes represent their total annual commission.

Total Annual Commission	# people	rf	crf
$ 0 and under $ 5,000	5		
5,000 " " 10,000	9		
10,000 " " 15,000	11		
15,000 " " 20,000	48		
20,000 " " 30,000	62		
30,000 " " 40,000	19		
40,000 " " 50,000	9		
50,000 and over	7		
Total	170		

Construct an ogive that will help you answer the following questions:

a. Approximately what percentage of the salespeople earn more than $27,000?

b. Approximately how much is earned by the "middle" salespeople?

c. Approximately how much would a salesperson have to earn to be in the top 25%?

3.11 A pharmaceutical company sells 78 different products. The distribution of the annual sales amounts last year for these products is as follows:

Annual Sales ($000)	Number of Products
0 and under 10	17
10 " " 50	20
50 " " 100	24
100 " " 150	13
150 " " 250	4
Total	78

Construct an ogive and use it to determine the following:

a. How many products had annual sales of less than $80,000 last year?

b. What percentage of the products had sales of $120,000 or more last year?

3.12 The distribution of a company's stock according to the number of shares held is shown as follows:

Number of Shares Held	% of Shareholders
0 and under 50	25
50 " " 100	19
100 " " 500	41
500 " " 1000	12
1000 " " 2000	3
Total	100

Construct an ogive and use it to determine the following:

a. What percentage of shareholders held 200 or more shares?

b. The 20 percent of shareholders with the most shares each held how many shares or more?

3.8 Measure of Location

In this section, you will learn to estimate percentiles using an ogive. A percentile is the value below which a certain percent of observations fall. So the 30th percentile is the value (or score) below which 30 percent of the observations may be found. There are several ways to analytically determine percentiles, but we will focus on the one used by the calculator.

Symbol for Percentile : $P_k = k^{th}$ percentile.

The kth percentile in a data set is the value such that at most k% of the data is lower than the value and at most $(100 - k)\%$ of the data is higher than the value.

There are three steps involved in calculating percentile value.

Step 1: Arrange the data into an *ascending* data array.

Step 2. Calculate the rank of the kth percentile using the following formula:

$$r = Rank\ of\ P_k = Half\ Round\left[n\frac{k}{100} + \frac{1}{2}\right]$$

NOTATION:

n = number of observations in the data set

k = % of observations less than or equal to P_k

"Half round" means round to the nearest half.

The half-round procedure rounds the non-integer rank (e.g., 7.3, 7.4, etc.) to the nearest half.

Example: Half round (2.3) = 2.5,

Half round (3.8) = 4 , Half round (7.7) = 7.5

Round .25 and .75 *down* if k < 50 or

Round .25 and .75 *up* if k > 50

Step 3. Compute P_k.

$$P_k = x_r\ (\textit{if the rank is an integer})\ or = \frac{x_{r-1/2} + x_{r+1/2}}{2}\ (\textit{if the rank is a fractional half})$$

where x denotes the observation value corresponding to the rank (r).

Quartiles:
Some of the percentiles have special names. These are as follows:

First quartile = Q_1 = 25th percentile = P_{25}

Second quartile = Q_2 = Median = 50th percentile = P_{50}

Third quartile = Q_3 = 75th percentile = P_{75}

Summary
If the computed rank is a whole number (e.g., 12) then you looked for the observation value corresponding to the 12th position. That is why you have to arrange your data in ascending order first.

If the computed rank ends with 0.5 (e.g., 10.5) then you take the midpoint (or average) of the corresponding values to rank 10 and 11 because 10.5 is in the middle of 10 and 11.

How to Compute a Percentile

At this point it would be beneficial to demonstrate the calculation of various percentiles by referring to examples 3.14, 3.15, 3.16, and 3.17.

EXAMPLE 3.14   Consider the following data: 4 , 6, 8, 10, 16.

a) Determine Q_1

Step 1: Arrange the data into an *ascending* data array.

4 , 6, 8, 10, 16

Step 2: Calculate the r (rank).

Note: Q_1 is equivalent to the 25th percentile (i.e., P_{25}).

$$r = Half\ Round\left[5\left(\frac{25}{100}\right) + \frac{1}{2}\right] = Half\ Round\ (1.75) \sim 1.5$$

Since the decimal ends with 0.75 and k is less than 50, *round down* to 1.5.

Step 3: Compute P_k.

	x_1	x_2	x_3	x_4	x_5
Data	4	6	8	10	16
Rank	1	2	3	4	5

Note: Rank = 1.5 is between rank 1 and rank 2, so you take the average of the corresponding values of rank 1 and rank 2, which are 4 and 6 as shown next.

$$P_{25} = Q_1 = \frac{(x_1) + (x_2)}{2} = \frac{4 + 6}{2} = 5$$

b) Determine the median.

Step 1: Arrange the data into an *ascending* data array.

4, 6, 8, 10, 16

Step 2: Calculate the r (rank).

Note the median is equivalent to Q_2, which is equivalent P_{50}.

$$r = Half\,Round\left[5\left(\frac{50}{100}\right) + \frac{1}{2}\right] = Half\,Round\,(3) = 3$$

Step 3: Compute P_k.

	x_1	x_2	x_3	x_4	x_5
Data	4	6	8	10	16
Rank	1	2	3	4	5

$$P_{50} = Q_2 = x_3 = 8$$

c) Determine Q_3.

Step 1: Arrange the data into an *ascending* data array.

4, 6, 8, 10, 16

Step 2: Calculate the r (rank).

Note: Q_3 is equivalent to the 75th percentile (i.e., P_{75}).

$$r = Half\,Round\left[5\left(\frac{75}{100}\right) + \frac{1}{2}\right] = Half\,Round\,(4.25) \sim 4.5$$

Since the decimal ends with 0.75 and k is greater than 50, *round up* to 4.5.

Step 3: Compute P_k.

	x_1	x_2	x_3	x_4	x_5
Data	4	6	8	10	16
Rank	1	2	3	4	5

Note: Rank = 4.5 is between rank 4 and rank 5, so you take the average of the corresponding values of rank 4 and rank 5, which are 10 and 16 as shown next.

$$P_{75} = Q_3 = \frac{x_4 + x_5}{2} = \frac{10 + 16}{2} = 13$$

Calculate Percentile Using the CASIO Calculator

CASIO calculator instruction:
You can use the CASIO calculator to obtain Q_1, the median, and Q_3 by following these calculator procedures:

1. From the Main Menu, select the **STAT** mode.
2. Enter data (4, 6, 8, 10, 16) in List 1.
3. Select **CALC** (F2).
4. Select **SET** (F6).

5. Set the following:

1 Var XList : List 1
1 Var Freq : 1

After you have finished, press **EXIT**.

6. Select "**1 Var**" (**F1**) for the results

RESULTS (from CASIO FX-9750GII)

Scroll down until you get to

Q1   : 5
Med : 8
Q3   : 13

EXAMPLE 3.15   Consider the following data: **3, 5, 9, 13, 17, 21**.

a) Determine Q_1.

Step 1: Arrange the data into an *ascending* data array.

      3, 5, 9, 13, 17, 21

Step 2: Calculate the r (rank).

    Note: Q_1 is equivalent to the 25th percentile (i.e., P_{25}).

$$r = Half\,Round\left[6\left(\frac{25}{100}\right) + \frac{1}{2}\right] = Half\,Round\,(2) = 2$$

Step 3: Compute P_k.

	x_1	x_2	x_3	x_4	x_5	x_6
Data	3	5	9	13	17	21
Rank	1	2	3	4	5	6

$P_{25} = Q_1 = x_2 = 5$

b) Determine the median.

Step 1: Arrange the data into an *ascending* data array.

      3, 5, 9, 13, 17, 21

Step 2: Calculate the r (rank).

    Note the median is equivalent to Q_2, which is equivalent P_{50}.

$$r = Half\,Round\left[6\left(\frac{50}{100}\right) + \frac{1}{2}\right] = Half\,Round\,(3.5) = 3.5$$

Step 3: Compute P_k.

	x_1	x_2	x_3	x_4	x_5	x_6
Data	3	5	9	13	17	21
Rank	1	2	3	4	5	6

Note: Rank = 3.5 is between rank 3 and rank 4, so you take the average of the corresponding values of rank 3 and rank 4, which are 9 and 13 as shown next.

$$P_{50} = Q_2 = \frac{x_3 + x_4}{2} = \frac{9 + 13}{2} = 11$$

c) Determine Q_3.

Step 1: Arrange the data into an *ascending* data array.

      3, 5, 9, 13, 17, 21

Step 2: Calculate the r (rank).

Note: Q_3 is equivalent to the 75th percentile (i.e., P_{75}).

$$r = Half\,Round\left[6\left(\frac{75}{100}\right) + \frac{1}{2}\right] = Half\,Round\,(5) = 5$$

Step 3: Compute P_k.

	x_1	x_2	x_3	x_4	x_5	x_{66}
Data	3	5	9	13	17	21
Rank	1	2	3	4	5	6

$P_{75} = Q_3 = x_5 = 17$

Calculate Percentile Using the CASIO Calculator

CASIO calculator instruction:

You can use the CASIO calculator to obtain Q_1, the median, and Q_3 by following these calculator procedures:

1. From the Main Menu, select the **STAT** mode.
2. Enter data **(3, 5, 9, 13, 17, 21)** in List 1.
3. Select **CALC** (F2).
4. Select SET (F6).
5. Set the following:

   1 Var XList : List 1
   1 Var Freq : 1

   After you have finished, press **EXIT**.

6. Select "**1 Var**" **(F1)** for the results

   RESULTS (from casio FX-9750GII)

   Scroll down until you get to

   Q1   : 5
   Med : 11
   Q3   : 17

Calculator versus Formula to Calculate Percentile

The CASIO calculator function "Calc" gives you the following percentiles.

Q1 = 25th percentile = is the value below which (less than) 25 percent of the observations may be found.

Q2 = median = 50th percentile = is the value below which (less than) 50 percent of the observations may be found.

Q3 = 75th percentile = is the value below which (less than) 75 percent of the observations may be found.

If you wish to find any percentile other than the 25th, 50th, or and 75th, you have to use the formula

$$r = Rank\,of\,P_k = Half\,Round\left[n\,\frac{k}{100} + \frac{1}{2}\right]$$

where n= number of elements in the data set or sample size and k = the kth percentile.

The formula converts the kth percentile to rank (denotes as r) and from rank (r) back to an observation value.

EXAMPLE 3.16

Using Formula to Obtain the Percentile

Consider the following data: **6, 8, 9, 16, 19, 23**.

a) Determine P_{20} (20th percentile).

Step 1: Arrange the data into an *ascending* data array.

6, 8, 9, 16, 19, 23

Step 2: Calculate the r (rank).

$$r = Half\,Round\left[6\left(\frac{20}{100}\right) + \frac{1}{2}\right] = Half\,Round\,(1.7) \sim 1.5$$

Step 3: Compute P_k.

	x_1	x_2	x_3	x_4	x_5	x_6
Data	6	8	9	16	19	23
Rank	1	2	3	4	5	6

Note: Rank = 1.5 is between rank 1 and rank 2, so you take the average of the corresponding values of rank 1 and rank 2, which are 4 and 6 as shown below.

$$P_{20} = \frac{(x_1 + x_2)}{2} = \frac{6 + 8}{2} = 7$$

b) Determine P_{30} (30th percentile).

Step 1: Arrange the data into an *ascending* data array.

6, 8, 9, 16, 19, 23

Step 2: Calculate the r (rank).

$$r = Half\,Round\left[6\left(\frac{30}{100}\right) + \frac{1}{2}\right] = Half\,Round\,(2.3) \sim 2.5$$

Step 3: Compute P_k.

	x_1	x_2	x_3	x_4	x_5	x_6
Data	6	8	9	16	19	23
Rank	1	2	3	4	5	6

Note: Rank = 2.5 is between rank 2 and rank 3, so you take the average of the corresponding values of rank 2 and rank 3, which are 8 and 9 as shown below.

$$P_{30} = \frac{(x_2 + x_3)}{2} = \frac{8 + 9}{2} = 8.5$$

EXAMPLE 3.17

The following data represents the ages, in years, of 20 employees working at a retail outlet. The data has already been arranged in an ascending data array.

18, 18, 18, 20, 20, 20, 20, 21, 22, 22, 24, 25, 28, 29, 29, 38, 40, 45, 52, 63

a) Determine the 80th percentile.

Step 1: Arrange the data into an *ascending* data array.

18, 18, 18, 20, 20, 20, 20, 21, 22, 22, 24, 25, 28, 29, 29, 38, 40, 45, 52, 63

Step 2: Calculate the r (rank).

$$r = Half\,Round\left[20\left(\frac{80}{100}\right) + \frac{1}{2}\right] = Half\,Round\,(16.5) = 16.5$$

Step 3: Compute P_k.

	x_1	x_2	x_3	x_4	x_5	x_6	x_7	x_8	x_9	x_{10}	x_{11}	x_{12}	x_{13}	x_{14}	x_{15}	x_{16}	x_{17}	x_{18}	x_{19}	x_{20}
Data	18	18	18	20	20	20	20	21	22	22	24	25	28	29	29	38	40	45	52	63
Rank	1	2	3	4	5	6	7	8	9	10	11	12	13	14	15	16	17	18	19	20

Note: Rank = 16.5 is between rank 16 and rank 17, so you take the average of the corresponding values of rank 16 and rank 17, which are 38 and 40 as shown below.

$$P_{80} = \frac{(x_{16} + x_{17})}{2} = \frac{38 + 40}{2} = 39 \text{ years}$$

b) Determine the 34th percentile.

Step 1: Arrange the data into an *ascending* data array.

18, 18, 18, 20, 20, 20, 20, 21, 22, 22, 24, 25, 28, 29, 29, 38, 40, 45, 52, 63

Step 2: Calculate the r (rank).

$$r = Half\,Round\left[20\left(\frac{34}{100}\right) + \frac{1}{2}\right] = Half\,Round\,(7.3) = 7.5$$

Step 3: Compute P_k.

	x_1	x_2	x_3	x_4	x_5	x_6	x_7	x_8	x_9	x_{10}	x_{11}	x_{12}	x_{13}	x_{14}	x_{15}	x_{16}	x_{17}	x_{18}	x_{19}	x_{20}
Data	18	18	18	20	20	20	20	21	22	22	24	25	28	29	29	38	40	45	52	63
Rank	1	2	3	4	5	6	7	8	9	10	11	12	13	14	15	16	17	18	19	20

Note: Rank = 7.5 is between rank 7 and rank 8, so you take the average of the corresponding values of rank 7 and rank 8, which are 20 and 21 as shown below.

$$P_{34} = \frac{(x_7 + x_8)}{2} = \frac{20 + 21}{2} = 20.5 \text{ years}$$

c) Determine the 61st percentile.

Step 1: Arrange the data into an *ascending* data array.

18, 18, 18, 20, 20, 20, 20, 21, 22, 22, 24, 25, 28, 29, 29, 38, 40, 45, 52, 63

Step 2: Calculate the r (rank).

$$r = Half\,Round\left[20\left(\frac{61}{100}\right) + \frac{1}{2}\right] = Half\,Round\,(12.7) = 12.5$$

Step 3: Compute P_k.

	x_1	x_2	x_3	x_4	x_5	x_6	x_7	x_8	x_9	x_{10}	x_{11}	x_{12}	x_{13}	x_{14}	x_{15}	x_{16}	x_{17}	x_{18}	x_{19}	x_{20}
Data	18	18	18	20	20	20	20	21	22	22	24	25	28	29	29	38	40	45	52	63
Rank	1	2	3	4	5	6	7	8	9	10	11	12	13	14	15	16	17	18	19	20

Note: Rank = 12.5 is between rank 12 and rank 13, so you take the average of the corresponding values of rank 12 and rank 13, which are 25 and 28 as shown below.

$$P_{34} = \frac{(x_{12} + x_{13})}{2} = \frac{25 + 28}{2} = 26.5 \text{ years}$$

We can use the calculator to give us the values of the quartiles.

$$Q_1 = 20 \text{ years}, Q_2 = 23 \text{ years, and } Q_3 = 33.5 \text{ years}$$

Ogive and Percentile

An ogive for the volume of a 2000 ml bottle is shown. Use this ogive to find the first quartile (Q1), the median (Q2), and the third quartile (Q3).

a. To find Q1, you have to know that Q1 is equivalent to the 25th percentile. You can infer that 25% of the bottles are filled less than a certain value, and that value can be found in the ogive. To find the 25th percentile, go across at 25% of the y-axis until you hit the ogive line, and then go downward to acquire the x value (see A). Based on the ogive, 25% of the bottles are filled less than 2000.9 ml (i.e., 25th percentile = 2000.9, so Q1=2000.9).

b. Based on the same reasoning, Q2 is equivalent to the median value, which is the 50th percentile. To find the 50th percentile, go across at 50% of the y-axis until you hit the ogive line, and then go downward to acquire the x value (see B). Based on the ogive, 50% of the bottles are filled less than 2001.5 ml (i.e., the median is 2001.5, which is the same as saying that Q2 is equal to 2001.5).

c. Q3 is equivalent to the 75th percentile. To find the 75th percentile, go across at 75% of the y-axis until you hit the ogive line, and then go downward to acquire the x value (see C). Based on the ogive, 75% of the bottles are filled less than 2002.2 ml (i.e., Q3 = 2002.2).

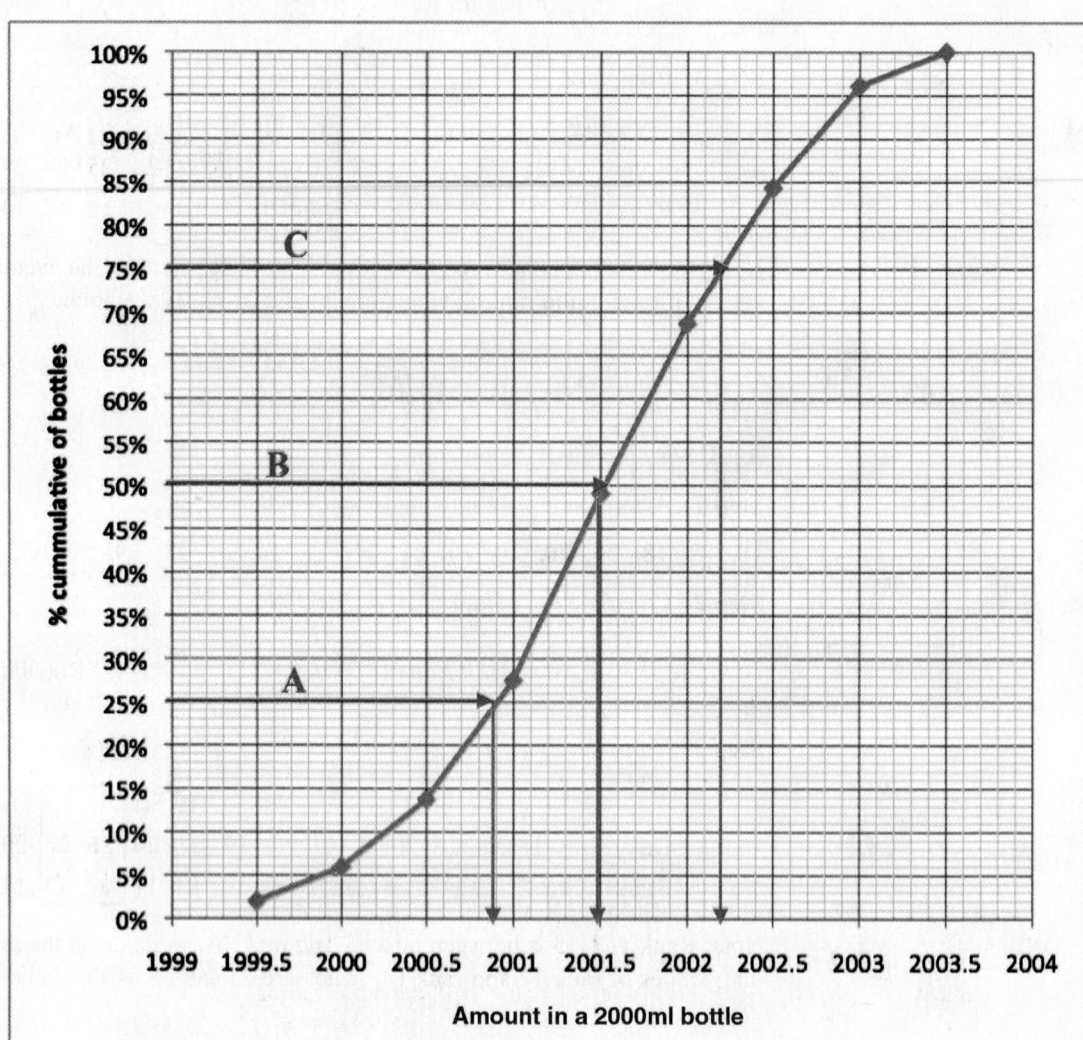

Test Your Understanding

TABLE 3.20

Canadian City Averages

City	Price	Change	Trend
Edmonton, AB	113.748	+0.026	➡
Calgary, AB	116.598	-0.097	➡
Winnipeg, MB	119.718	-0.434	⬇
Victoria, BC	125.717	-0.183	➡
Ottawa, ON	127.247	+1.234	⬆
Abbotsford, BC	127.375	-0.338	⬇
Regina, SK	126.220	+0.185	➡
Saskatoon, SK	126.419	+0.019	➡
London, ON	129.101	+0.329	⬆
Barrie, ON	129.288	-0.068	➡
Hamilton, ON	130.190	+0.316	⬆
Kitchener-Waterloo, ON	130.225	+0.887	⬆
Toronto, ON	131.476	+0.102	➡
Halifax, NS	134.200	-0.014	➡
Quebec City, QC	139.463	+0.030	➡
Montreal, QC	141.103	-0.773	⬇
Vancouver, BC	141.203	+0.592	⬆

Source: http://www.gasbuddy.com/GB_Price_List.aspx

For the gasoline prices in Canadian cities listed in Table 3.20: Canadian City Averages, determine the 43rd percentile value (P_{43}) in cents per litre.

Use the following data for questions 1 and 2.

Question 1: What is the rank for the 43rd percentile value?

        A. 7.81 rounded to 7.5
        B. 7.81 rounded to 8
        C. 7.81 rounded to 7
        D. 7.31 rounded to 7.5
        E. 7.31 rounded to 7

Answer: B

Question 2: What is the 43rd percentile value?

        A. 127.311
        B. 126.419
        C. 126.220
        D. 127.375
        E. None of the above

Answer: D

Problems for Percentile

3.13 Refer to Table 3.21: Divorces by provinces and territories published by Statistics Canada, calculate the following percentiles.

a. For 2002, determine the 25th percentile of number of divorces.

b. For 2002, determine the 50th percentile of number of divorces.

c. For 2002, determine the 75th percentile of number of divorces.

d. For 2002, determine the 80th percentile of number of divorces.

e. For 2002, determine the 43rd percentile of number of divorces.

f. For 2002, determine the 67th percentile of number of divorces.

TABLE 3.21   Divorces by Provinces and Territories

	2000	2001	2002
		number of divorces	
Canada			
Newfoundland and Labrador	1,913	1,755	1,842
Prince Edward Island	1,272	2,246	2,258
Nova Scotia	2,054	2,945	2,990
New Brunswick	2,717	2,570	3,461
Quebéc	7,054	7,094	6,499
Ontario	6,148	6,516	6,170
Manitoba	3,430	3,480	3,396
Saskatchewan	3,194	2,955	3,959
Alberta	9,176	9,252	9,291
British Columbia	11,017	11,115	12,125

Source: Statistics Canada, CANSIM, table 053-0002.
Last modified: 2004-09-02.

3.9 Organizing Categorical Data

You organize categorical data by tallying responses by categories and placing the results in tables. Typically, you construct a summary table to organize the data for a single categorical variable and you construct a contingency table to organize the data from two or more categorical variables.

The Summary Table

A **summary table** presents tallied responses as frequencies or percentages for each category. A summary table helps you see the differences among the categories by displaying the frequency, amount, or percentage of items in a set of categories in a separate column. Table 3.22 shows a summary table (stored in **Bill Payment**) that tallies the responses to a recent survey that asked adults how they pay their monthly bills.

TABLE 3.22

Types of Bill Payment

Form of Payment	Percentage (%)
Cash	15
Check	54
Electronic/online	28
Other/don't know	3

Source: *Data extracted from "How Adults Pay
Monthly Bills,"* USA Today, *October 4, 2007, p. 1.*

From Table 3.22, you can conclude that more than half the people pay by check and 82% pay by either check or by electronic/online forms of payment.

EXAMPLE 3.18

Summary Table
of Levels of Risk
of Bond Funds

The 184 bond funds involved in Part I of the Choice Is Yours scenario are classified according to their risk level, categorized as below average, average, and above average. Construct a summary table of the bond funds, categorized by risk.

SOLUTION From Table 3.23, you can see that about the same number of funds are below average, average, and above average in risk. This means that 69.57% of the bond funds are classified as having an average or above average level of risk.

TABLE 3.23

Frequency and
Percentage Summary
Table Pertaining to Risk
Level for 184 Bond
Funds

Fund Risk Level	Number of Funds	Percentage of Funds (%)
Below average	56	30.43%
Average	69	37.50%
Above average	59	32.07%
Total	184	100.00%

The Contingency Table

A **contingency table** allows you to study patterns that may exist between the responses of two or more categorical variables. This type of table cross-tabulates, or tallies jointly, the responses of the categorical variables. In the simplest case of two categorical variables, the joint responses appear in a table such that the category tallies of one variable are located in the rows and the category tallies of the other variable are located in the columns. Intersections of the rows and columns are called **cells**, and each cell contains a value associated with a unique pair of responses for the two variables (e.g., Fee: Yes and Type: Intermediate Government in Table 3.24). Cells can contain the frequency, the percentage of the overall total, the percentage of the row total, or the percentage of the column total, depending on the type of contingency table being used.

In Part I of the Choice Is Yours scenario, you could create a contingency table to examine whether there is any pattern between the type of bond fund (intermediate government or short-term corporate) and whether the fund charges a fee (yes or no). You would begin by tallying the joint responses for each of the mutual funds in the sample of 184 bond mutual funds (stored in Bond Funds). You tally a response into one of the four possible cells in the table, depending on the type of bond fund and whether the fund charges a fee. For example, the first fund listed in the sample is classified as an intermediate government fund that does not charge a fee. Therefore, you tally this joint response into the cell that is the intersection of the Intermediate Government row and the No column. Table 3.24 shows the completed contingency table after all 184 bond funds have been tallied.

TABLE 3.24

Contingency Table Displaying Type of Fund and Whether a Fee Is Charged

	FEE		
TYPE	Yes	No	Total
Intermediate government	34	53	87
Short-term corporate	20	77	97
Total	54	130	184

To look for other patterns between the type of bond fund and whether the fund charges a fee, you can construct contingency tables that show cell values as a percentage of the overall total (the 184 mutual funds), the row totals (the 87 intermediate government funds and the 97 short-term corporate bond funds), and the column totals (the 54 funds that charge a fee and the 130 funds that do not charge a fee). Tables 3.25, 3.26, and 3.27 present these contingency tables.

Table 3.25 shows that 47.28% of the bond funds sampled are intermediate government funds, 52.72% are short-term corporate bond funds, and 18.48% are intermediate

TABLE 3.25

Contingency Table Displaying Type of Fund and Whether a Fee Is Charged, Based on Percentage of Overall Total

	FEE		
TYPE	Yes	No	Total
Intermediate government	18.48	28.80	47.28
Short-term corporate	10.87	41.85	52.72
Total	29.35	70.65	100.00

government funds that charge a fee. Table 3.26 shows that 39.08% of the intermediate government funds charge a fee, while 20.62% of the short-term corporate bond funds charge

TABLE 3.26

Contingency Table Displaying Type of Fund and Whether a Fee Is Charged, Based on Percentage of Row Total

	FEE		
TYPE	Yes	No	Total
Intermediate government	39.08	60.92	100.00
Short-term corporate	20.62	79.38	100.00
Total	29.35	70.65	100.00

a fee. Table 3.27 shows that of the funds that charge a fee, 62.96% are intermediate government funds. From the tables, you see that intermediate government funds are much more likely to charge a fee.

TABLE 3.27

Contingency Table Displaying Type of Fund and Whether a Fee Is Charged, Based on Percentage of Column Total

	FEE		
TYPE	Yes	No	Total
Intermediate government	62.96	40.77	47.28
Short-term corporate	37.04	59.23	52.72
Total	100.00	100.00	100.00

Problems for Section 3.9

LEARNING THE BASICS

3.14 A categorical variable has three categories, with the following frequencies of occurrence:

Category	Frequency
A	13
B	28
C	9

a. Compute the percentage of values in each category.
b. What conclusions can you reach concerning the categories?

3.15 The following data represent the responses to two questions asked in a survey of 40 college students majoring in business: What is your gender? (M = male; F = female) and What is your major? (A = Accounting; C = Computer Information Systems; M = Marketing):

a. Tally the data into a contingency table where the two rows represent the gender categories and the three columns represent the academic major categories.
b. Construct contingency tables based on percentages of all 40 student responses, based on row percentages and based on column percentages.

Gender:	M	M	M	F	M	F	F	M	F	M	F	M	M	M	M	F	F	M	F	F
Major:	A	C	C	M	A	C	A	A	C	C	A	A	A	M	C	M	A	A	A	C
Gender:	M	M	M	M	F	M	F	F	M	M	F	M	M	M	M	F	M	F	M	M
Major:	C	C	A	A	M	M	C	A	A	A	C	C	A	A	A	A	C	C	A	C

APPLYING THE CONCEPTS

3.16 The Transportation Security Administration reported that from January 1, 2008, to February 18, 2009, more than 14,000 banned items were collected at Palm Beach International Airport. The categories were as follows:

Category	Frequency
Flammables/irritants	8,350
Knives and blades	4,134
Prohibited tools	753
Sharp objects	497
Other	357

a. Compute the percentage of values in each category.
b. What conclusions can you reach concerning the banned items?

3.17 The following table represents world oil consumption in millions of barrels a day in 2009:

Region	Oil Consumption (millions of barrels a day)
Developed Europe	14.5
Japan	4.4
United States	18.8
Rest of the world	46.7

Source: Energy Information Administration, 2009.

a. Compute the percentage of values in each category.
b. What conclusions can you reach concerning the consumption of oil in 2009?

3.18 Federal obligations for benefit programs and the national debt were \$63.8 trillion in 2008. The cost per household (\$) for various categories was as follows:

Category	Cost per Household (\$)
Civil servant retirement	15,851
Federal debt	54,537
Medicare	284,288
Military retirement	29,694
Social Security	160,216
Other	2,172

Source: Data extracted from "What We Owe," *USA Today*, May 29, 2009, p. 1A.

a. Compute the percentage of values in each category.
b. What conclusions can you reach concerning the benefit programs?

3.19 A survey of 1,085 adults asked "Do you enjoy shopping for clothing for yourself?" The results (data extracted from "Split decision on clothes shopping," *USA Today*, January 28, 2011, p. 1B) indicated that 51% of the females enjoyed shopping for clothing for themselves as compared to 44% of the males. The sample sizes of males and females was not provided. Suppose that the results were as shown in the following table: are summarized in the following table:

ENJOY SHOPPING FOR CLOTHING FOR YOURSELF	GENDER		
	Male	Female	Total
Yes	238	276	514
No	304	267	571
Total	542	543	1,085

a. Construct contingency tables based on total percentages, row percentages, and column percentages.

b. What conclusions do you reach from these analyses?

3.20 Each day at a large hospital, several hundred laboratory tests are performed. The rate at which these tests are done improperly (and therefore need to be redone) seems steady, at about 4%. In an effort to get to the root cause of these nonconformances, tests that need to be redone, the director of the lab decided to keep records over a period of one week. The laboratory tests were subdivided by the shift of workers who performed the lab tests. The results are as follows:

LAB TESTS PERFORMED	SHIFT		
	Day	Evening	Total
Nonconforming	16	24	40
Conforming	654	306	960
Total	670	330	1,000

a. Construct contingency tables based on total percentages, row percentages, and column percentages.

b. Which type of percentage—row, column, or total—do you think is most informative for these data? Explain.

c. What conclusions concerning the pattern of nonconforming laboratory tests can the laboratory director reach?

3.21 Does it take more time to get yourself removed from an email list than it used to? A study of 100 large online retailers revealed the following:

	NEED THREE OR MORE CLICKS TO BE REMOVED	
YEAR	Yes	No
2009	39	61
2008	7	93

Source: Data extracted from "Drill Down," *The New York Times,* March 29, 2010, p. B2.

What do these results tell you about whether more online retailers were requiring three or more clicks in 2009 than in 2008?

3.10 Visualizing Two Numerical Variables

Often you will want to explore possible relationships between two numerical variables. You use a scatter plot as a first step to visualize such relationships. In the special case where one of your variables represents the passage of time, you use a time-series plot.

The Scatter Plot

Often, you have two numerical measurements about the same item or individual. A **scatter plot** can explore the possible relationship between those measurements by plotting the data of one numerical variable on the horizontal, or X, axis and the data of a second numerical variable on the vertical, or Y, axis. For example, a marketing analyst could study the effectiveness of advertising by comparing advertising expenses and sales revenues of 50 stores. Using a scatter plot, a point is plotted on the two-dimensional graph for each store, using the X axis to represent advertising expenses and the Y axis to represent sales revenues.

Table 3.28 presents the revenues and value (both in millions of dollars) for all 30 NBA professional basketball teams that is stored in NBAValues . To explore the possible relationship between the revenues generated by a team and the value of a team, you can create a scatter plot.

TABLE 3.28

Values and Revenues for NBA Teams

Team	Value	Revenues	Team	Value	Revenues
Atlanta	306	103	Milwaukee	254	91
Boston	433	144	Minnesota	268	96
Charlotte	278	96	New Jersey	269	92
Chicago	511	168	New Orleans	267	95
Cleveland	476	159	New York	586	202
Dallas	446	154	Oklahoma City	310	111
Denver	321	115	Orlando	361	107
Detroit	479	171	Philadelphia	344	115
Golden State	315	113	Phoenix	429	148
Houston	470	160	Portland	338	121
Indiana	281	97	Sacramento	305	109
Los Angeles Clippers	295	102	San Antonio	398	133
Los Angeles Lakers	607	209	Toronto	386	133
Memphis	257	88	Utah	343	118
Miami	364	126	Washington	313	110

Source: Data extracted from **www.forbes.com/lists/2009/32/basketball-values-09_NBA-Team-Valuations_Rank.html**.

For each team, you plot the revenues on the X axis and the values on the Y axis. Figure 3.4 presents a scatter plot for these two variables.

FIGURE 3.4

Scatter plot of revenue and value

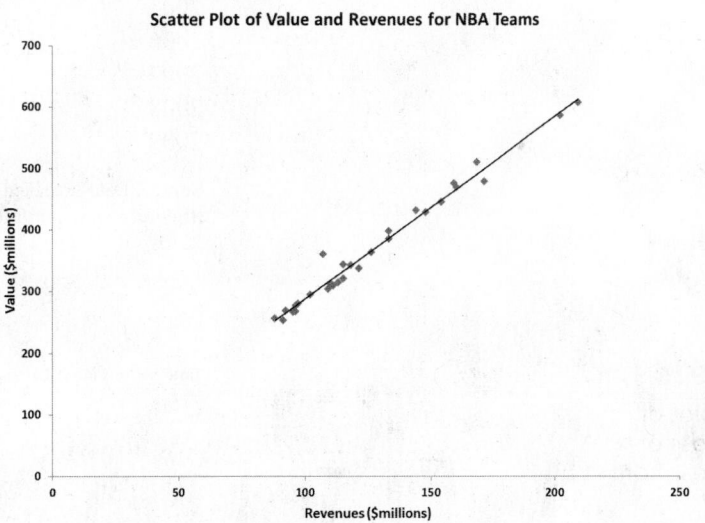

Reviewing Figure 3.4, you see that there appears to be a very strong increasing (positive) relationship between revenues and the value of a team. In other words, teams that generate a smaller amount of revenues have a lower value, while teams that generate higher revenues have a higher value. Notice the straight line that has been superimposed on the plotted data in Figure 3.4. For these data, this line is very close to the points in the scatter plot. This line is a linear regression prediction line that will be discussed in Chapter 15. (In Section 4.5, you will return to this example when you learn about the covariance and the coefficient of correlation.)

Other pairs of variables may have a decreasing (negative) relationship in which one variable decreases as the other increases. In other situations, there may be a weak or no relationship between the variables.

The Time-Series Plot

A **time-series plot** plots the values of a numerical variable on the Y axis and plots the time period associated with each numerical value on the X axis. A time-series plot can help explore trends in data that occur over time. For example, Table 3.29 presents the combined gross (in millions of dollars) of movies released from 1996 to 2009 that is stored in MovieGross . To better visualize this data, you create the time-series plot shown in Figure 3.5.

From Figure 3.5, you see that there was a steady increase in the combined gross of movies between 1996 and 2009. During that time, the combined gross increased from under $6 billion in 1996 to more than $10 billion in 2009.

TABLE 3.29

Combined Gross
of Movies

Year	Combined Gross
1996	5,669.20
1997	6,393.90
1998	6,523.00
1999	7,317.50
2000	7,659.50
2001	8,077.80
2002	9,146.10
2003	9,043.20
2004	9,359.40
2005	8,817.10
2006	9,231.80
2007	9,685.70
2008	9,707.40
2009	10,675.60

Source: Data extracted from **www
.the-numbers. com/movies**, February 16,
2010.

FIGURE 3.5

Time-series plot of
combined gross of
movies per year from
1996 to 2009

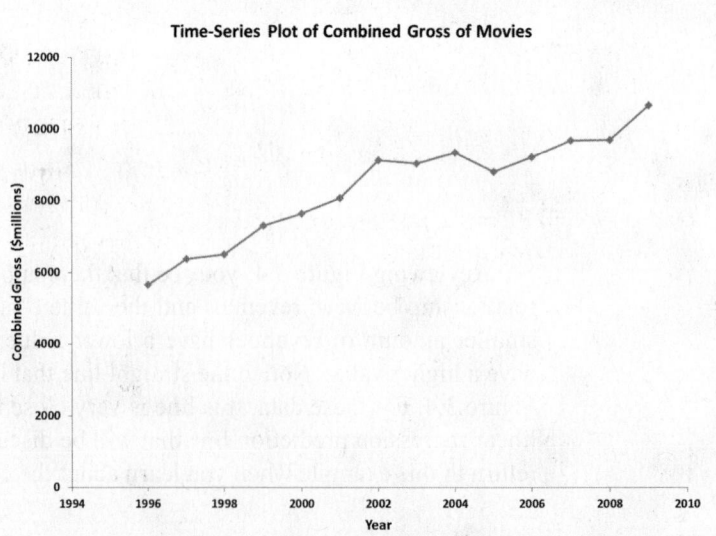

Problems for Section 3.10

LEARNING THE BASICS

3.22 The following is a set of data from a sample of $n = 11$ items:

| X: | 7 | 5 | 8 | 3 | 6 | 0 | 2 | 4 | 9 | 5 | 8 |
| Y: | 1 | 5 | 4 | 9 | 8 | 0 | 6 | 2 | 7 | 5 | 4 |

a. Construct a scatter plot.
b. Is there a relationship between X and Y? Explain.

3.23 The following is a series of annual sales (in millions of dollars) over an 11-year period (2000 to 2010):

| Year: | 2000 | 2001 | 2002 | 2003 | 2004 | 2005 | 2006 | 2007 | 2008 | 2009 | 2010 |
| Sales: | 13.0 | 17.0 | 19.0 | 20.0 | 20.5 | 20.5 | 20.5 | 20.0 | 19.0 | 17.0 | 13.0 |

a. Construct a time-series plot.
b. Does there appear to be any change in annual sales over time? Explain.

APPLYING THE CONCEPTS

3.24 Movie companies need to predict the gross receipts of individual movies once the movie has debuted. The following results, stored in PotterMovies , are the first weekend gross, the U.S. gross, and the worldwide gross (in millions of dollars) of the first six Harry Potter movies.

Title	First Weekend	U.S. Gross	Worldwide Gross
Sorcerer's Stone	90.295	317.558	976.458
Chamber of Secrets	88.357	261.988	878.988
Prisoner of Azkaban	93.687	249.539	795.539
Goblet of Fire	102.335	290.013	896.013
Order of the Phoenix	77.108	292.005	938.469
Half-Blood Prince	77.836	301.460	934.601

Source: Data extracted from **www.the-numbers.com/interactive/comp-Harry-Potter.php**.

a. Construct a scatter plot with first weekend gross on the X axis and U.S. gross on the Y axis.
b. Construct a scatter plot with first weekend gross on the X axis and worldwide gross on the Y axis.

c. What can you say about the relationship between first weekend gross and U.S. gross and first weekend gross and worldwide gross?

3.25 The file VeggieBurger contains data on the calories and total fat (in grams per serving) for a sample of 12 veggie burgers.

Source: Data extracted from *"Healthful Burgers That Taste Good,"* *Consumer Reports,* June 2008, p 8.

a. Construct a scatter plot with calories on the X axis and total fat on the Y axis.
b. What conclusions can you reach about the relationship between the calories and total fat in veggie burgers?

3.26 College basketball is big business, with coaches' salaries, revenues, and expenses in millions of dollars. The file College Basketball contains the coaches' salary and revenue for college basketball at 60 of the 65 schools that played in the 2009 NCAA men's basketball tournament (data extracted from "Compensation for Division 1 Men's Basketball Coaches," *USA Today*, April 2, 2010, p. 8C; and C. Isadore, "Nothing but Net: Basketball Dollars by School," **money.cnn.com/2010/03/18/news/companies/basketball_profits/**).
a. Do you think schools with higher revenues also have higher coaches' salaries?
b. Construct a scatter plot with revenue on the X axis and coaches' salaries on the Y axis.
c. Does the scatter plot confirm or contradict your answer to (a)?

3.27 College football players trying out for the NFL are given the Wonderlic standardized intelligence test. The file Wonderlic contains the average Wonderlic scores of football players trying out for the NFL and the graduation rate for football players at selected schools (data extracted from S. Walker, "The NFL's Smartest Team," *The Wall Street Journal*, September 30, 2005, pp. W1, W10).
a. Construct a scatter plot with average Wonderlic score on the X axis and graduation rate on the Y axis.
b. What conclusions can you reach about the relationship between the average Wonderlic score and graduation rate?

3.28 How have stocks performed in the past? The following table presents the data stored in Stock Performance that shows the performance of a broad measure of stocks (by percentage) for each decade from the 1830s through the 2000s:

Decade	Performance (%)
1830s	2.8
1840s	12.8
1850s	6.6
1860s	12.5
1870s	7.5
1880s	6.0
1890s	5.5
1900s	10.9
1910s	2.2
1920s	13.3
1930s	−2.2
1940s	9.6
1950s	18.2
1960s	8.3
1970s	6.6
1980s	16.6
1990s	17.6
2000s*	−0.5

* Through December 15, 2009.

Source: Data extracted from T. Lauricella, "Investors Hope the '10s" Beat the '00s," *The Wall Street Journal,* December 21, 2009, pp. C1, C2.

a. Construct a time-series plot of the stock performance from the 1830s to the 2000s.
b. Does there appear to be any pattern in the data?

3.29 According to the U.S. Census Bureau, the average price of a new home declined in 2008 and 2009. The file New Home Prices contains the average price paid for a new home from 1990 to 2010 (extracted from **www.census.gov**, April 1, 2011).
a. Construct a time-series plot of new home prices.
b. What pattern, if any, is present in the data?

3.30 The following data (stored in Movie Attendance) represent the yearly movie attendance (in billions) from 2001 through 2010:

Year	Attendance
2001	1.44
2002	1.60
2003	1.52
2004	1.48
2005	1.38
2006	1.40
2007	1.40
2008	1.36
2009	1.42
2010	1.35

Source: Data extracted from Motion Picture Association of America, **www.mpaa.org**, and S. Bowles, "Ticket Sales Slump at 2010 Box Office," *USA Today,* January 3, 2011, p. 1D.

a. Construct a time-series plot for the movie attendance (in billions).
b. What pattern, if any, is present in the data?

3.31 The file Audits contains the number of audits of corporations with assets of more than $250 million conducted by the Internal Revenue Service (data extracted from K. McCoy, "IRS Audits Big Firms Less Often," *USA Today*, April 15, 2010, p. 1B).
a. Construct a time-series plot.
b. What pattern, if any, is present in the data?

3.11 Misuses and Common Errors in Visualizing Data

Good graphical displays clearly and unambiguously reveal what the data convey. Unfortunately, many graphs presented in the media (broadcast, print, and online) are incorrect, misleading, or so unnecessarily complicated that they should never be used. To illustrate the misuse of graphs, the chart presented in Figure 3.6 is similar to one that was printed in *Time* magazine as part of an article on increasing exports of wine from Australia to the United States.

FIGURE 3.6

"Improper" display of Australian wine exports to the United States, in millions of gallons

Source: *Based on S. Watterson, "Liquid Gold— Australians Are Changing the World of Wine. Even the French Seem Grateful," Time, November 22, 1999, p. 68.*

We're drinking more . . .
Australian wine exports to the U.S. in millions of gallons

1.04   2.25   3.67   6.77
1989   1992   1995   1997

In Figure 3.6, the wineglass icon representing the 6.77 million gallons for 1997 does not appear to be almost twice the size of the wineglass icon representing the 3.67 million gallons for 1995, nor does the wineglass icon representing the 2.25 million gallons for 1992 appear to be twice the size of the wineglass icon representing the 1.04 million gallons for 1989. Part of the reason for this is that the three-dimensional wineglass icon is used to represent the two dimensions of exports and time. Although the wineglass presentation may catch the eye, the data should instead be presented in a summary table or a time-series plot.

In addition to the type of distortion created by the wineglass icons in the *Time* magazine graph displayed in Figure 3.6, improper use of the vertical and horizontal axes leads to distortions. Figure 3.7 presents another graph used in the same *Time* magazine article.

FIGURE 3.7

"Improper" display of amount of land planted with grapes for the wine industry

Source: *Based on S. Watterson, "Liquid Gold— Australians Are Changing the World of Wine. Even the French Seem Grateful," Time, November 22, 1999, pp. 68–69.*

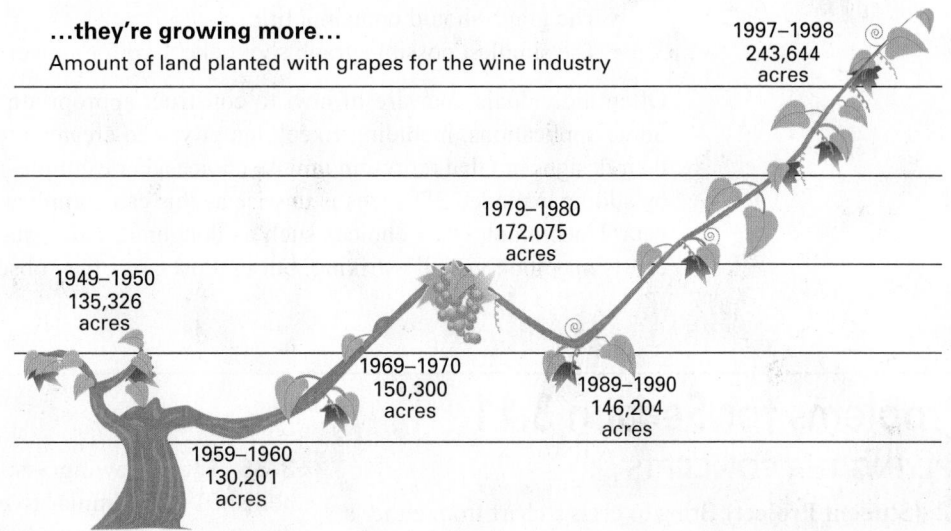

There are several problems in this graph. First, there is no zero point on the vertical axis. Second, the acreage of 135,326 for 1949–1950 is plotted above the acreage of 150,300 for 1969–1970. Third, it is not obvious that the difference between 1979–1980 and 1997–1998 (71,569 acres) is approximately 3.5 times the difference between 1979–1980 and 1969–1970 (21,775 acres). Fourth, there are no scale values on the horizontal axis. Years are plotted next to the acreage totals, not on the horizontal axis. Fifth, the values for the time dimension are not properly spaced along the horizontal axis. For example, the value for 1979–1980 is much closer to 1989–1990 than it is to 1969–1970. Other types of eye-catching displays that you typically see in magazines and newspapers often include information that is not necessary and just adds excessive clutter. Figure 3.8 represents one such display.

FIGURE 3.8

"Improper" plot of market share of soft drinks

Source: *Based on Anne B. Carey and Sam Ward, "Coke Still Has Most Fizz," USA Today, May 10, 2000, p. 1B.*

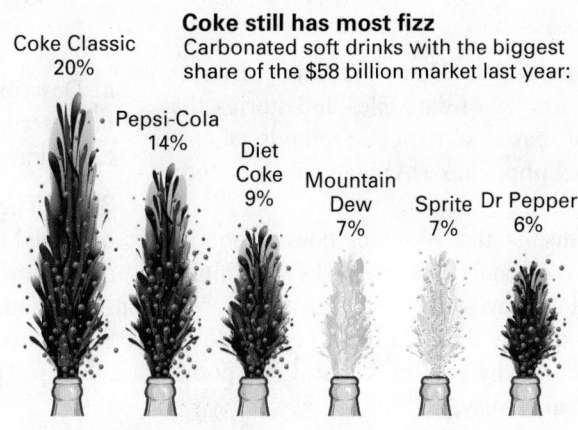

The graph in Figure 3.8 shows the products with the largest market share for soft drinks. The graph suffers from too much clutter, although it is designed to show the differences in market share among the soft drinks. The display of the fizz for each soft drink takes up too much of the graph relative to the data. The same information could be better conveyed with a bar chart or pie chart.

The following are some guidelines for developing good graphs:

- A graph should not distort the data.
- A graph should not contain **chartjunk**, unnecessary adornments that convey no useful information.
- Any two-dimensional graph should contain a scale for each axis.
- The scale on the vertical axis should begin at zero.
- All axes should be properly labeled.
- The graph should contain a title.
- The simplest possible graph should be used for a given set of data.

Often individuals unaware of how to construct appropriate graphs violate these guidelines. Some applications, including Excel, tempt you to create "pretty" charts that may be fancy in their designs but that represent unwise choices. For example, making a simple pie chart fancier by adding exploded 3D slices is unwise as this can complicate a viewer's interpretation of the data. Uncommon chart choices such as doughnut, radar, surface, bubble, cone, and pyramid charts may look visually striking, but in most cases they obscure the data.

Problems for Section 3.11

APPLYING THE CONCEPTS

3.32 (Student Project) Bring to class a chart from either a website, newspaper, or magazine published this month that you believe to be a poorly drawn representation of a numerical variable. Be prepared to submit the chart to the instructor with comments about why you believe it is inappropriate. Do you believe that the intent of the chart is to purposely mislead the reader? Also, be prepared to present and comment on this in class.

3.33 (Student Project) Bring to class a chart from either a website, newspaper, or magazine published this month that you believe to be a poorly drawn representation of a categorical variable. Be prepared to submit the chart to the instructor with comments about why you consider it inappropriate. Do you believe that the intent of the chart is to purposely mislead the reader? Also, be prepared to present and comment on this in class.

3.34 (Student Project) The Data and Story Library (DASL) is an online library of data files and stories that illustrate the use of basic statistical methods. Go to **lib.stat.cmu.edu/index.php**, click DASL and explore some of the various graphical displays.
a. Select a graphical display that you think does a good job revealing what the data convey. Discuss why you think it is a good graphical display.
b. Select a graphical display that you think needs a lot of improvement. Discuss why you think that it is a poorly constructed graphical display.

3.35 The following visual display contains an overembellished chart similar to one that appeared in *USA Today*, dealing with the average consumer's Valentine's Day spending ("USA Today Snapshots: The Price of Romance," *USA Today*, February 14, 2007, p. 1B).

a. Describe at least one good feature of this visual display.
b. Describe at least one bad feature of this visual display.
c. Redraw the graph, using the guidelines given above.

3.36 The following visual display contains an overembellished chart similar to one that appeared in *USA Today*, dealing with the estimated number of hours the typical American spends using various media ("USA Today Snapshots: Minding Their Media," *USA Today*, March 2, 2007, p. 1B).

Media Usage
Estimated number of hours the typical American will spend using various media this year.

Listening to music — 175
Reading newspapers — 175
Using Internet — 195
Listening to Radio — 974
Watching TV — 1555

Courtesy of David Levine

a. Describe at least one good feature of this visual display.
b. Describe at least one bad feature of this visual display.
c. Redraw the graph, using the guidelines given on page 128.

3.37 The following visual display contains an overembellished chart similar to one that appeared in *USA Today*, dealing with which card is safer to use ("USA Today Snapshots: Credit Card vs. Debit Card," *USA Today*, March 14, 2007, p. 1B).

Credit Card vs. Debit Card:
Which one is safer to use?

Don't Mind 49%
Credit Card 32%
Debit Card 19%

a. Describe at least one good feature of this visual display.
b. Describe at least one bad feature of this visual display.
c. Redraw the graph, using the guidelines given on page 128.

3.38 Professor Deanna Oxender Burgess of Florida Gulf Coast University conducted research on annual reports of corporations (see D. Rosato, "Worried About the Numbers? How About the Charts?" *The New York Times*, September 15, 2002, p. B7) and found that even slight distortions in a chart changed readers' perception of the information. Using Internet or library sources, select a corporation and study the most recent annual report. Find at least one chart in the report that you think needs improvement and develop an improved version of the chart. Explain why you believe the improved chart is better than the one included in the annual report.

Choice Is Yours, Part I

In the Using Statistics scenario, you were hired by the Choice Is Yours investment company to assist clients who seek to invest in mutual funds. A sample of 184 bond mutual funds was selected, and information on the funds and past performance history was recorded. For each of the 184 funds, data were collected on eight variables. With so much information, visualizing all these numbers required the use of properly selected graphical displays.

From bar charts and pie charts, you were able to illustrate that about one-third of the funds were classified as having below-average risk, about one-third had average risk, and about one-third had above-average risk. Cross tabulations of the funds by whether the fund charged a fee and whether the fund invested in intermediate government bonds or short-term corporate bonds revealed that intermediate government bond funds are more likely to charge fees. After constructing histograms on the 2009 return, you were able to conclude that the returns were much higher for the short-term corporate bond funds than for the intermediate government bonds. The return for intermediate government bond funds is concentrated between 0 and 10, whereas the return for the short-term corporate bond funds is concentrated between 5 and 15.

With these insights, you can inform your clients about how the different funds performed. Of course, past performance history does not guarantee future performance. In fact, if you look at returns in 2008, stored in BondFunds2008 , you will discover that the returns were much *lower* for the short-term corporate bond funds than for the intermediate government bonds!

Using graphical methods such as these is an important first step in summarizing and interpreting data. Although the proper display of data (as discussed in Section 3.12) helps to avoid ambiguity, graphical methods always contain a certain degree of subjectivity. Next, you will need descriptive statistics to further analyze the past performance of the mutual funds. Chapter 4 presents descriptive statistics (e.g., mean, median, and mode).

SUMMARY

Organizing and visualizing data involves using various tables and charts to help draw conclusions about data. In several different chapter examples, tables and charts helped you reach conclusions about how people prefer to pay their bills and about the cost of restaurant meals in a city and its suburbs; they also provided some insights about the sample of bond mutual funds in the Using Statistics scenario.

The tables and charts you use depend on the type of data you have. Table 3.30 summarizes the proper choices for the type of data and the tables and charts discussed in this chapter. In Chapter 4 you will learn about a variety of descriptive statistics useful for data analysis and interpretation.

TABLE 3.30

Selecting Tables and Charts

	Type of Data	
Type of Analysis	**Numerical**	**Categorical**
Organizing data	Ordered array, frequency distribution, relative frequency distribution, percentage distribution, cumulative percentage distribution	Summary table, contingency table (Section 3.10)
Visualizing one variable	Stem-and-leaf display, histogram, percentage polygon, cumulative percentage polygon (ogive)	Bar chart, pie chart, Pareto chart
Visualizing two variables	Scatter plot, time-series plot (Section 3.11)	Side-by-side bar chart
Organizing multidimensional data	Multidimensional tables	Multidimensional tables

KEY EQUATIONS

Determining the Class Interval Width

$$\text{Estimated Class Width} = \frac{\text{maximum} - \text{minimum}}{\text{minimum number of classes recommended}}$$

Computing the Proportion or Relative Frequency

$$\text{Proportion} = \text{relative frequency} = \frac{\text{number of values in each class}}{\text{total number of values}}$$

KEY TERMS

boundaries 62	midpoints 78	stem-and-leaf plot 39
cells 109	OGIVE 89	stem unit 43
chartjunk 118	quantitative 62	summary table 108
classes 62	relative frequency or percentage 75	time-series plot 114
contingency table 109	scatter plot 112	

PROBLEMS

CHECKING YOUR UNDERSTANDING

3.39 How do histograms and polygons differ in their construction and use?

3.40 Why would you construct a summary table?

3.41 What are the advantages and disadvantages of using a bar chart, a pie chart, and a Pareto chart?

3.42 Compare and contrast the bar chart for categorical data with the histogram for numerical data.

3.43 What is the difference between a time-series plot and a scatter plot?

3.44 Why is it said that the main feature of a Pareto chart is its ability to separate the "vital few" from the "trivial many"?

3.45 What are the three different ways to break down the percentages in a contingency table?

3.46 How can a multidimensional table differ from a two variable contingency table?

3.47 What type of insights can you gain from a three-way table that are not available in a two-way table?

APPLYING THE CONCEPTS

3.48 The following summary table presents the breakdown of the price of a new college textbook:

Revenue Category	Percentage (%)	
Publisher	64.8	
Manufacturing costs		32.3
Marketing and promotion		15.4
Administrative costs and taxes		10.0
After-tax profit		7.1
Bookstore	22.4	
Employee salaries and benefits		11.3
Operations		6.6
Pretax profit		4.5
Author	11.6	
Freight	1.2	

Source: Data extracted from T. Lewin, "When Books Break the Bank," *The New York Times,* September 16, 2003, pp. B1, B4.

a. Using the four categories publisher, bookstore, author, and freight, construct a bar chart, a pie chart, and a Pareto chart.

b. Using the four subcategories of publisher and three subcategories of bookstore, along with the author and freight categories, construct a Pareto chart.

c. Based on the results of (a) and (b), what conclusions can you reach concerning who gets the revenue from the sales of new college textbooks? Do any of these results surprise you? Explain.

3.49 The following table represents the market share (in number of movies, gross in millions of dollars, and in number of tickets sold in millions) of each type of movie in 2009:

Type	Number	Gross ($ millions)	Tickets (millions)
Based on book/short story	66	2042.9	272.4
Based on comic/graphic novel	6	376.2	50.2
Based on factual book/article	5	280.7	37.4
Based on game	3	9.2	1.2
Based on musical/opera	1	13.7	1.8
Based on play	8	172.0	22.9
Based on real life events	95	334.9	44.7
Based on toy	1	150.2	20.0
Based on TV	7	267.5	35.7
Compilation	1	0.6	0.1
Original screenplay	203	4,335.7	578.1
Remake	18	422.6	56.3
Sequel	20	2,064.2	275.2
Spin-off	1	179.9	24.0

Source: Data extracted from **www.the-numbers.com/market/Sources2009.php**.

a. Construct a bar chart, a pie chart, and a Pareto chart for the number of movies, gross (in millions of dollars), and number of tickets sold (in millions).

b. What conclusions can you reach about the market share of the different types of movies in 2009?

3.50 A survey was conducted from 665 consumer magazines on the practices of their websites. The results are summarized in a copyediting table and a fact-checking table:

Copyediting as Compared to Print Content	Percentage
As rigorous	41
Less rigorous	48
Not copyedited	11

a. For copyediting, construct a bar chart, a pie chart, and a Pareto chart.

b. Which graphical method do you think is best for portraying these data?

Fact Checking as Compared to Print Content	Percentage
Same	57
Less rigorous	27
Online not fact checked	8
Neither online nor print is fact-checked	8

Source: Data extracted from S. Clifford, "Columbia Survey Finds a Slack Editing Process of Magazine Web Sites," *The New York Times,* March 1, 2010, p. B6.

c. For fact checking, construct a bar chart, a pie chart, and a Pareto chart.

d. Which graphical method do you think is best for portraying these data?

e. What conclusions can you reach concerning copy editing and fact checking of print and online consumer magazines?

3.51 The owner of a restaurant that serves Continental-style entrées has the business objective of learning more about the patterns of patron demand during the Friday-to-Sunday weekend time period. Data were collected from 630 customers on the type of entrée ordered and organized in the following table:

Type of Entrée	Number Served
Beef	187
Chicken	103
Mixed	30
Duck	25
Fish	122
Pasta	63
Shellfish	74
Veal	26
Total	630

a. Construct a percentage summary table for the types of entrées ordered.

b. Construct a bar chart, a pie chart, and a Pareto chart for the types of entrées ordered.

c. Do you prefer using a Pareto chart or a pie chart for these data? Why?

d. What conclusions can the restaurant owner reach concerning demand for different types of entrées?

3.52 Suppose that the owner of the restaurant in Problem 3.51 also wanted to study the demand for dessert during the same time period. She decided that in addition to studying whether a dessert was ordered, she would also study the gender of the individual and whether a beef entrée was ordered. Data were collected from 600 customers and organized in the following contingency tables:

DESSERT ORDERED	GENDER		
	Male	Female	Total
Yes	40	96	136
No	240	224	464
Total	280	320	600

DESSERT ORDERED	BEEF ENTRÉE		
	Yes	No	Total
Yes	71	65	136
No	116	348	464
Total	187	413	600

a. For each of the two contingency tables, construct contingency tables of row percentages, column percentages, and total percentages.
b. Which type of percentage (row, column, or total) do you think is most informative for each gender? For beef entrée? Explain.
c. What conclusions concerning the pattern of dessert ordering can the restaurant owner reach?

3.53 The following data represent the pounds per capita of fresh food and packaged food consumed in the United States, Japan, and Russia in 2009:

FRESH FOOD	COUNTRY		
	United States	Japan	Russia
Eggs, nuts, and beans	88	94	88
Fruit	124	126	88
Meat and seafood	197	146	125
Vegetables	194	278	335

a. For the United States, Japan, and Russia, construct a bar chart, a pie chart, and a Pareto chart for different types of fresh foods consumed.

PACKAGED FOOD	COUNTRY		
	United States	Japan	Russia
Bakery goods	108	53	144
Dairy products	298	147	127
Pasta	12	32	16
Processed, frozen, dried and chilled food, and ready-to-eat meals	183	251	70
Sauces, dressings, and condiments	63	75	49
Snacks and candy	47	19	24
Soup and canned food	77	17	25

Source: Data extracted from H. Fairfield, "Factory Food," *The New York Times,* April 4, 2010, p. BU5.

b. For the United States, Japan, and Russia, construct a bar chart, a pie chart, and a Pareto chart for different types of packaged foods consumed.
c. What conclusions can you reach concerning differences between the United States, Japan, and Russia in the fresh foods and packaged foods consumed?

3.54 In 2000, a growing number of warranty claims on Firestone tires sold on Ford SUVs prompted Firestone and Ford to issue a major recall. An analysis of warranty claims data helped identify which models to recall. A breakdown of 2,504 warranty claims based on tire size is given in the following table:

Tire Size	Number of Warranty Claims
23575R15	2,030
311050R15	137
30950R15	82
23570R16	81
331250R15	58
25570R16	54
Others	62

Source: Data extracted from Robert L. Simison, "Ford Steps Up Recall Without Firestone," *The Wall Street Journal*, August 14, 2000, p. A3.

The 2,030 warranty claims for the 23575R15 tires can be categorized into ATX models and Wilderness models. The type of incident leading to a warranty claim, by model type, is summarized in the following table:

	ATX Model Warranty Claims	Wilderness Warranty Claims
Tread separation	1,365	59
Blowout	77	41
Other/ unknown	422	66
Total	1,864	166

Source: Data extracted from Robert L. Simison, "Ford Steps Up Recall Without Firestone," *The Wall Street Journal,* August 14, 2000, p. A3.

a. Construct a Pareto chart for the number of warranty claims by tire size. What tire size accounts for most of the claims?
b. Construct a pie chart to display the percentage of the total number of warranty claims for the 23575R15 tires that come from the ATX model and Wilderness model. Interpret the chart.
c. Construct a Pareto chart for the type of incident causing the warranty claim for the ATX model. Does a certain type of incident account for most of the claims?
d. Construct a Pareto chart for the type of incident causing the warranty claim for the Wilderness model. Does a certain type of incident account for most of the claims?

3.55 One of the major measures of the quality of service provided by an organization is the speed with which the organization responds to customer complaints. A large family-held department store selling furniture and flooring, including carpet, had undergone a major expansion in the past several years. In particular, the flooring department had expanded from 2 installation crews to an installation supervisor, a measurer, and 15 installation crews. A business objective of the company was to reduce the time between when the complaint is received and when it is resolved. During a recent year, the company received 50 complaints concerning carpet installation. The data from the 50 complaints, stored in **Furniture**, represent the number of days between the receipt of the complaint and the resolution of the complaint:

```
54    5   35  137   31  27  152    2  123  81  74  27
11   19  126  110  110  29   61   35   94  31  26   5
12    4  165   32   29  28   29   26   25   1  14  13
13   10    5   27    4  52   30   22   36  26  20  23
33   68
```

a. Construct a frequency distribution and a percentage distribution.
b. Construct a histogram and a percentage polygon.
c. Construct a cumulative percentage distribution and plot a cumulative percentage polygon (ogive).

d. On the basis of the results of (a) through (c), if you had to tell the president of the company how long a customer should expect to wait to have a complaint resolved, what would you say? Explain.

3.56 The file **DomesticBeer** contains the percentage alcohol, number of calories per 12 ounces, and number of carbohydrates (in grams) per 12 ounces for 145 of the best-selling domestic beers in the United States.
Source: Data extracted from **www.Beer100.com,** April 1, 2011.

a. Construct a percentage histogram for each of the three variables.
b. Construct three scatter plots: percentage alcohol versus calories, percentage alcohol versus carbohydrates, and calories versus carbohydrates.
c. Discuss what you learn from studying the graphs in (a) and (b).

3.57 The file **CigaretteTax** contains the state cigarette tax ($) for each state as of December 31, 2010.
a. Construct an ordered array.
b. Plot a percentage histogram.
c. What conclusions can you reach about the differences in the state cigarette tax between the states?

3.58 The file **CDRate** contains the yields for a one-year certificate of deposit (CD) and a five-year certificate of deposit (CD) for 25 banks in the United States, as of April 4, 2011.
Source: Data extracted from **www.Bankrate.com**, April 4, 2011.

a. Construct a stem-and-leaf display for each variable.
b. Construct a scatter plot of one-year CD versus five-year CD.
c. What is the relationship between the one-year CD rate and the five-year CD rate?

3.59 The file **CEO-Compensation** includes the total compensation (in millions of $) of CEOs of 161 large public companies and the investment return in 2010. For total compensation:
Source: Data extracted from M. Krantz and B. Hansen, "CEO Pay Sours While Workers' Pay Stalls," "Bargains in the Boardroom," *USA Today,* April 1, 2011, pp. 1B, 2B, and **money.usatoday.com**

a. Construct a frequency distribution and a percentage distribution.
b. Construct a histogram and a percentage polygon.
c. Construct a cumulative percentage distribution and plot a cumulative percentage polygon (ogive).
d. Based on (a) through (c), what conclusions can you reach concerning CEO compensation in 2010?
e. Construct a scatter plot of total compensation and investment return in 2010.
f. What is the relationship between the total compensation and investment return in 2010?

3.60 Studies conducted by a manufacturer of Boston and Vermont asphalt shingles have shown product weight to be a major factor in customers' perception of quality.

Moreover, the weight represents the amount of raw materials being used and is therefore very important to the company from a cost standpoint. The last stage of the assembly line packages the shingles before the packages are placed on wooden pallets. The variable of interest is the weight in pounds of the pallet which for most brands holds 16 squares of shingles. The company expects pallets of its Boston brand-name shingles to weigh at least 3,050 pounds but less than 3,260 pounds. For the company's Vermont brand-name shingles, pallets should weigh at least 3,600 pounds but less than 3,800. Data are collected from a sample of 368 pallets of Boston shingles and 330 pallets of Vermont shingles and stored in Pallet .

a. For the Boston shingles, construct a frequency distribution and a percentage distribution having eight class intervals, using 3,015, 3,050, 3,085, 3,120, 3,155, 3,190, 3,225, 3,260, and 3,295 as the class boundaries.
b. For the Vermont shingles, construct a frequency distribution and a percentage distribution having seven class intervals, using 3,550, 3,600, 3,650, 3,700, 3,750, 3,800, 3,850, and 3,900 as the class boundaries.
c. Construct percentage histograms for the Boston shingles and for the Vermont shingles.
d. Comment on the distribution of pallet weights for the Boston and Vermont shingles. Be sure to identify the percentage of pallets that are underweight and overweight.

3.61 What was the average price of a room at two-star, three-star, and four-star hotels in cities around the world in the summer of 2010? The file HotelPrices contains the prices in English pounds (about US $1.56 as of January 2011). Complete the following for two-star, three-star, and four-star hotels.
Source: Data extracted from **http://www.hotels.com/press/hotel-price-index-summer-2010.html.**

a. Construct a frequency distribution and a percentage distribution.
b. Construct a histogram and a percentage polygon.
c. Construct a cumulative percentage distribution and plot a cumulative percentage polygon (ogive).
d. What conclusions can you reach about the cost of two-star, three-star, and four-star hotels?
e. Construct separate scatter plots of the cost of two-star hotels versus three-star hotels, two-star hotels versus four-star hotels, and three-star hotels versus four-star hotels.
f. What conclusions can you reach about the relationship of the price of two-star, three-star, and four-star hotels?

3.62 The file Protein contains calorie and cholesterol information for popular protein foods (fresh red meats, poultry, and fish).
Source: U.S. Department of Agriculture.
a. Construct a percentage histogram for the number of calories.
b. Construct a percentage histogram for the amount of cholesterol.

c. What conclusions can you reach from your analyses in (a) and (b)?

3.63 The file Natural Gas contains the monthly average wellhead and residential price for natural gas (dollars per thousand cu. ft.) in the United States from January 1, 2008, to January 1, 2011. For the wellhead price and the residential price:
Source: "Energy Information Administration," **www.eia.doe.gov**, April 4, 2011.
a. Construct a time-series plot.
b. What pattern, if any, is present in the data?
c. Construct a scatter plot of the wellhead price and the residential price.
d. What conclusion can you reach about the relationship between the wellhead price and the residential price?

3.64 The following data (stored in Drink) represent the amount of soft drink in a sample of 50 consecutively filled 2-liter bottles. The results are listed horizontally in the order of being filled:

2.109 2.086 2.066 2.075 2.065 2.057 2.052 2.044 2.036 2.038
2.031 2.029 2.025 2.029 2.023 2.020 2.015 2.014 2.013 2.014
2.012 2.012 2.012 2.010 2.005 2.003 1.999 1.996 1.997 1.992
1.994 1.986 1.984 1.981 1.973 1.975 1.971 1.969 1.966 1.967
1.963 1.957 1.951 1.951 1.947 1.941 1.941 1.938 1.908 1.894

a. Construct a time-series plot for the amount of soft drink on the Y axis and the bottle number (going consecutively from 1 to 50) on the X axis.
b. What pattern, if any, is present in these data?
c. If you had to make a prediction about the amount of soft drink filled in the next bottle, what would you predict?
d. Based on the results of (a) through (c), explain why it is important to construct a time-series plot and not just a histogram.

3.65 The file Currency contains the exchange rates of the Canadian dollar, the Japanese yen, and the English pound from 1980 to 2010 where the Canadian dollar, the Japanese yen, and the English pound are expressed in units per U.S. dollar.

a. Construct time-series plots for the yearly closing values of the Canadian dollar, the Japanese yen, and the English pound.
b. Explain any patterns present in the plots.
c. Write a short summary of your findings.
d. Construct separate scatter plots of the value of the Canadian dollar versus the Japanese yen, the Canadian dollar versus the English pound, and the Japanese yen versus the English pound.
e. What conclusions can you reach concerning the value of the Canadian dollar, Japanese yen, and English pound in terms of the U.S. dollar?

3.66 (Class Project) Have each student in the class respond to the question "Which carbonated soft drink do you most prefer?" so that the instructor can tally the results into a summary table.
a. Convert the data to percentages and construct a Pareto chart.
b. Analyze the findings.

3.67 (Class Project) Let each student in the class be cross-classified on the basis of gender (male, female) and current employment status (yes, no) so that the instructor can tally the results.
a. Construct a table with either row or column percentages, depending on which you think is more informative.
b. What would you conclude from this study?
c. What other variables would you want to know regarding employment in order to enhance your findings?

REPORT WRITING EXERCISES

3.68 Referring to the results from Problem 3.60 on pages 121–127 concerning the weight of Boston and Vermont shingles, write a report that evaluates whether the weight of the pallets of the two types of shingles are what the company expects. Be sure to incorporate tables and charts into the report.

3.69 Referring to the results from Problem 3.54 on pages 125–126 concerning the warranty claims on Firestone tires, write a report that evaluates warranty claims on Firestone tires sold on Ford SUVs. Be sure to incorporate tables and charts into the report.

TEAM PROJECT

The file **Bond Funds** contains information regarding nine variables from a sample of 184 mutual funds:

Fund number—Identification number for each bond fund
Type—Bond fund type (intermediate government or short-term corporate)

Assets—In millions of dollars
Fees—Sales charges (no or yes)
Expense ratio—Ratio of expenses to net assets in percentage
Return 2009—Twelve-month return in 2009
Three-year return—Annualized return, 2007–2009
Five-year return—Annualized return, 2005–2009
Risk—Risk-of-loss factor of the mutual fund (below average, average, or above average)

3.70 For this problem, consider the expense ratio.
a. Construct a percentage histogram.
b. Using a single graph, plot percentage polygons of the expense ratio for bond funds that have fees and bond funds that do not have fees.
c. What conclusions about the expense ratio can you reach, based on the results of (a) and (b)?

3.71 For this problem, consider the three-year annualized return from 2007 to 2009.
a. Construct a percentage histogram.
b. Using a single graph, plot percentage polygons of the three-year annualized return from 2007 to 2009 for intermediate government funds and short-term corporate funds.
c. What conclusions about the three-year annualized return from 2007 to 2009 can you reach, based on the results of (a) and (b)?

3.72 For this problem, consider the five-year annualized return from 2005 to 2009.
a. Construct a percentage histogram.
b. Using a single graph, plot percentage polygons of the five-year annualized return from 2005 to 2009 for intermediate government funds and short-term corporate funds.
c. What conclusions about the five-year annualized return from 2005 to 2009 can you reach, based on the results of (a) and (b)?

MANAGING ASHLAND MULTICOMM SERVICES

Recently, Ashland MultiComm Services has been criticized for its inadequate customer service in responding to questions and problems about its telephone, cable television, and Internet services. Senior management has established a task force charged with the business objective of improving customer service. In response to this charge, the task force collected data about the types of customer service errors, the cost of customer service errors, and the cost of wrong billing errors. It found the following data:

Types of Customer Service Errors

Type of Errors	Frequency
Incorrect accessory	27
Incorrect address	42
Incorrect contact phone	31
Invalid wiring	9
On-demand programming error	14
Subscription not ordered	8
Suspension error	15
Termination error	22
Website access error	30
Wrong billing	137
Wrong end date	17
Wrong number of connections	19
Wrong price quoted	20
Wrong start date	24
Wrong subscription type	33
Total	448

Cost of Customer Service Errors in the Past Year

Type of Errors	Cost ($ thousands)
Incorrect accessory	17.3
Incorrect address	62.4
Incorrect contact phone	21.3
Invalid wiring	40.8
On-demand programming errors	38.8
Subscription not ordered	20.3
Suspension error	46.8
Termination error	50.9
Website access errors	60.7
Wrong billing	121.7
Wrong end date	40.9
Wrong number of connections	28.1
Wrong price quoted	50.3
Wrong start date	40.8
Wrong subscription type	60.1
Total	701.2

Type and Cost of Wrong Billing Errors

Type of Wrong Billing Errors	Cost ($ thousands)
Declined or held transactions	7.6
Incorrect account number	104.3
Invalid verification	9.8
Total	121.7

1. Review these data (stored in AMS2-1). Identify the variables that are important in describing the customer service problems. For each variable you identify, construct the graphical representation you think is most appropriate and explain your choice. Also, suggest what other information concerning the different types of errors would be useful to examine. Offer possible courses of action for either the task force or management to take that would support the goal of improving customer service.

2. As a follow-up activity, the task force decides to collect data to study the pattern of calls to the help desk (stored in AMS2-2). Analyze these data and present your conclusions in a report.

DIGITAL CASE

In the Using Statistics scenario, you were asked to gather information to help make wise investment choices. Sources for such information include brokerage firms, investment counselors, and other financial services firms. Apply your knowledge about the proper use of tables and charts in this Digital Case about the claims of foresight and excellence by an Ashland-area financial services firm.

Open **EndRunGuide.pdf,** which contains the EndRun Financial Services "Guide to Investing." Review the guide, paying close attention to the company's investment claims and supporting data and then answer the following.

1. How does the presentation of the general information about EndRun in this guide affect your perception of the business?

2. Is EndRun's claim about having more winners than losers a fair and accurate reflection of the quality of its investment service? If you do not think that the claim is a fair and accurate one, provide an alternate presentation that you think is fair and accurate.

3. Review the discussion about EndRun's "Big Eight Difference" and then open and examine Mutual Funds, a sample of mutual funds. Are there any other relevant data from that file that could have been included in the Big Eight table? How would the new data alter your perception of EndRun's claims?

4. EndRun is proud that all Big Eight funds have gained in value over the past five years. Do you agree that EndRun should be proud of its selections? Why or why not?

REFERENCES

1. Huff, D., *How to Lie with Statistics* (New York: Norton, 1954).
2. Levine, D. and D. Stephan, "Teaching Introductory Business Statistics Using the DCOVA Framework," *Decision Sciences Journal of Innovative Education*, 9, September 2011, p. 393–398.
3. *Microsoft Excel 2010* (Redmond, WA: Microsoft Corporation, 2010).
4. *Minitab Release 16* (State College, PA: Minitab, Inc., 2010).
5. Tufte, E. R., *Beautiful Evidence* (Cheshire, CT: Graphics Press, 2006).
6. Tufte, E. R., *Envisioning Information* (Cheshire, CT: Graphics Press, 1990).
7. Tufte, E. R., *The Visual Display of Quantitative Information*, 2nd ed. (Cheshire, CT: Graphics Press, 2002).
8. Tufte, E. R., *Visual Explanations* (Cheshire, CT: Graphics Press, 1997).
9. Wainer, H., *Visual Revelations: Graphical Tales of Fate and Deception from Napoleon Bonaparte to Ross Perot* (New York: Copernicus/Springer-Verlag, 1997).

CALCULATOR LESSON 2A

**CASIO FX-9750G
OR CFX-9850GB
CALCULATOR**

Introduction

To install the batteries and make the initial adjustments follow the instructions on the pink pages inside the front cover of the owner's manual.

The GFX-9850GB has three keyboards:

i. The Primary keyboard
    –indicated on the keys

ii. The **Shift** keyboard
    –indicated in *yellow* above the keys

iii. The **ALPHA** keyboard
    –indicated in *red* above the keys

Common Operations

Clear screen	**AC/ON**
Insert	**SHIFT INS**
Delete	**DEL**
Move cursor	**Use cursor arrows**
Erase the last entry	**Use cursor arrow and typeover**
Power (exponent)	**^**

The function keys F1, F2 . . . F6 directly under the display are used to select functions shown at the bottom of the display at various times.

Calculations

RUN Mode:

Highlight the RUN icon and press **EXE**

or press **1** when the main menu screen is visible.

Note: If you change your mind about which *mode* you want to select, just press the menu key and this will always return you to the main menu screen.

To calculate the average of 38, 20, 18, and 23:

Enter the following into the calculator:
(38+20+18+23)÷4 EXE   You should get the result 24.75.   Try it.

Correcting errors

Inserting: Suppose we should have entered 148 instead of 18 in the example. Use the replay arrows (◄ or ►) to position the cursor at the end or beginning of the previously entered calculation. Move the cursor until it is located under the 8 in 18. The 8 will flash on and off. Press **SHIFT INS**. A square blank cursor will now be flashing on and off. Press **4** followed by **EXE**.

We now have the following calculation:
(38+20+148+23)÷4 EXE   You should get the result 57.25.   Try it.

Note: You may insert several digits consecutively without pressing **SHIFT INS** each time. The cursor will be in insert mode any time that it appears as a square blank cursor.

Deleting

If, in fact, the original value of 18 is correct, we can delete the 4 as follows. Use the replay cursor followed by any cursor key to position the cursor under the 4. The 4 will flash on and off. Press the **DEL** key followed by **EXE**. We will now get the answer 24.75 of the original calculation.

Using the ANSWER of the Previous Calculation

Suppose we want to add 10 to the previously calculated average. Press + (the word *Ans* will appear on the display) and **10 EXE**. The result 34.75 will appear.

Now suppose we want to calculate 30/34.75. Press **30 ÷ SHIFT Ans EXE** and the result 0.8633093525 appears.

Note: The calculator displayed 10 decimals for the answer above; however, it keeps 15 digits internally in case this number is to be used in further calculations. In this way round off errors are not likely to have occurred in the digits shown on the display.

Note: Suppose the calculator has shut off due to being inactive for several minutes. Use the **AC/ON** key to turn the calculator back on. Choose the RUN icon and press **EXE**. The screen will be blank. Now press the ▲ cursor key followed by **EXE** and the screen will return to the last calculation that was done when the calculator was last on.

Working with DATA LISTS

LIST Mode:

Press the **MENU** key.

Highlight the LIST icon and press **EXE**.

You will now have six blank lists set up on the screen. You can only see the Lists 1 to 4 at first, but if you move the ▶ cursor key you will be able to scroll over to the other two lists.

You can enter the data from the first example in List 1 as follows:

38 EXE
20 EXE
18 EXE
23 EXE

Note: If you make a mistake, use the following options on the bottom of the display (if you are in **STAT mode**, use the F6 key (▷) to bring up these options):

DEL	DEL-A	INS

F3	F4	F5

Now, if you press **F3** you can *delete* a highlighted data value. If you press **F5** you can create a space to *insert* a data value into the list. All other values will shift downward. To *change* a data value just highlight and type over the old value and then key **EXE**.

Sorting a List

When on the list screen, press the **F1** key if you want to sort a list in ascending order. The calculator will ask you how many lists you want to sort. Answer this and press **EXE.** The calculator will now ask which list(s). Answer this and press **EXE.**

The calculator will immediately sort the list(s) specified.

Deleting a List

To delete a list, place the cursor on any entry in the list and press the **F4** key. The calculator will give you one last chance to change your mind. Delete the highlighted list by answering YES (**F1**).

Error Messages

When you make a syntax error (i.e., you key something that the calculator cannot understand) it tries to point out where the error has occurred. Key in the following:

2 ÷ × 5 – 3 ENTER

The calculator will respond **Syn ERROR** at the bottom of the screen.

Press the left or right cursor arrow and the calculator will return to the calculation and the cursor will be flashing on the entry that is causing the problem.

The SET UP Menu

The SET UP menu allows you to modify the default settings for the calculator. For example, you may want your answer to a series of calculations to have only two decimal places (possibly because the numbers represent dollars and cents). In order to fix the number of decimal places to any calculation result you would go to the main calculation (RUN) screen and press **SHIFT SET UP**, scroll to **DISPLAY** and choose F1 (Fix), and then choose the appropriate number of decimal places, in this case **F3** (for two decimals). Now press the **EXIT** key to return to the previous screen.

Now key in the following calculation: **2 ÷ 3 EXE**. The calculator shows **.67**.

To return to the normal 10 digits with floating point, you will have to reenter the **NORM1** setting from the SET UP menu.

APPENDIX 3.2

CALCULATOR LESSON 2B

CASIO FX-9750GII CALCULATOR

Introduction

Common Operations

Clear screen	**AC/ON**
Insert	**SHIFT INS**
Delete	**DEL**
Move cursor	**Use cursor arrows**
Erase the last entry	**Use cursor arrow and typeover**
Power ON	**AC/ON**
Power OFF	**Shift AC/ON**

The function keys F1, F2 … F6 directly under the display are used to select functions shown at the bottom of the display at various times.

Calculations

RUN-MAT Mode: Highlight the RUN icon and press **EXE**

      or   press **1** when the main menu screen is visible.

Note: If you change your mind about which *mode* you want to select, just press the **MENU** key and this will always return you to the main menu screen.

To calculate the average of 54, 36, 27, and 15:

Select **"RUN-MAT"** mode and enter the following into the calculator:
(54+36+27+15)÷4 EXE　　　You should get the result 33.　　　Try it.

Correcting Errors

Inserting: Suppose we should have entered 157 instead of 15 in the example. Use the replay arrows (◄ or ►) to position the cursor at the end or beginning of the previously entered calculation. Move the cursor until it is located under the 5 in 15. The 5 will flash on and off. Press **SHIFT INS**. A square blank cursor will now be flashing on and off. Press **4** followed by **EXE**.

We now have the following calculation:
(54+36+27+157)÷4 EXE　　　You should get the result 68.5.　　　Try it.

Note: You may insert several digits consecutively without pressing **SHIFT INS** each time. The cursor will be in insert mode any time that it appears as a square blank cursor.

Deleting

If, in fact, the original value of 15 is correct, we can delete the 7 as follows. Use the replay cursor followed by any cursor key to position the cursor under the 7. The 7 will flash on and off. Press the **DEL** key followed by **EXE**. We will now get the answer 33 of the original calculation.

Using the ANSWER of the Previous Calculation

Suppose we want to add 20 to the previously calculated average. Press **+** (the word *Ans* will appear on the display) and **20 and del 4 and type 5**. The result 30.4 will appear.

Now suppose we want to calculate 30/30.4. Press **30 ÷ SHIFT Ans EXE** and the result 0.9868421053 appears.

Note: The calculator displayed 10 decimals for the answer above; however, it keeps 15 digits internally in case this number is to be used in further calculations. In this way round off errors are not likely to have occurred in the digits shown on the display.

Note: Suppose the calculator has shut off due to being inactive for several minutes. Use the **AC/ON** key to turn the calculator back on. Choose the RUN icon and press **EXE**. The screen will be blank. Now press the ▲ cursor key followed by **EXE** and the screen will return to the last calculation that was done when the calculator was last on.

Sort Your Data

STAT MODE　　　Press the **MENU** key.
　　　　　　　　Highlight the STAT icon and press **EXE**.

You will now have 26 blank lists set up on the screen. You can only see the Lists 1 to 4 at first, but if you move the ► cursor key you will be able to scroll over to the other lists.

You can enter the data from the first example in List 1 as follows:
Note: Key in the number and then press **EXE**.

54 EXE
27 EXE
36 EXE
15 EXE

Note: If you make a mistake, use the following options on the bottom of the display. If you have other options, use the F6 key (▷) to bring up these options.

OPTIONS	TOOL	EDIT	DEL	DEL-A	INS	►

FUNCTIONS	F1	F2	F3	F4	F5	F6

(1) Option TOOL(F1)

To **sort** the data that was entered in List 1, press **F1 (TOOL)**.
The calculator will show the following options on the bottom of the display.

OPTIONS	SRT-A	SRT-D	TOP	BTM

FUNCTIONS	F1	F2	F3	F4

The option **SRT-A** will sort a list in **A**scending order.

The option **SRT-D** will sort a list in **D**escending order.

The option **TOP** will bring the cursor to the top of the list.

The option **BTM** will bring the cursor to the bottom of the list.

(2) Option EDIT(F2)

If you wish to **change** a data value, place the cursor on the data value you want to change and press **F2 (EDIT)**. Suppose you want to change 15 to 26. Place the cursor on 15, press **DEL** to delete 15, and then enter **26 EXE**.

(3) Option DEL(F3)

If you wish to **delete** a data value, place the cursor on the value you want to delete and press **F3 (DEL)**.

(4) Option DEL-A(F4)

If you wish to **delete** the whole list of data, place the cursor on any entry in the list and press **F4 (DEL-A)**. The calculator will give you one last chance to change your mind. Delete the highlighted list by answering YES **(F1)**. If you do not wish to proceed with the delete procedure, you press **NO (F2)**.

(5) Option INS(F5)

If you wish to **insert** one data value into the list, place the cursor on the value and press **F5 (INS)** to **insert** a data value above the highlighted data value.

Sorting a List

Press the **F1 (SRT-A)** key if you want to sort a list in ascending order. The calculator will ask you how many lists you want to sort. Answer this by entering **1** if you have **one** list to sort and press **EXE**. The calculator will now ask which list(s). Answer this by entering **1** if the data is in List **1**, and press **EXE**.

The calculator will immediately sort the list(s) specified.

4 Numerical Descriptive Measures

Learning Objectives

In this chapter, you learn:

- To describe the properties of central tendency, variation, and shape in numerical data
- To construct and interpret a boxplot
- To compute descriptive summary measures for a population
- To compute the covariance and the coefficient of correlation

@ Choice Is Yours, Part II

The tables and charts you prepared for the sample of 184 bond mutual funds has been useful to the customers of the Choice Is Yours service. However, customers have become frustrated trying to evaluate bond fund performance. Although they know how the 2009 returns are distributed, they have no idea what a typical 2009 rate of return is for a particular category of bond funds, such as intermediate government and short-term corporate bond funds. They also have no idea of the extent of the variability in the 2009 rate of return. Are all the values relatively similar, or do they include very small and very large values? Are there a lot of small values and a few large ones, or vice versa, or are there a similar number of small and large values?

How could you help the customers get answers to these questions so that they could better evaluate the bond funds?

Tax-Exempt Funds

The Growth Fund Prospec
Diversified C
Fund Portfol

The Bond Fund
Diversified Bond
Fund Portfolio

Fund Facts   A Gr

Fund Facts   An Income Fund

Investment Perspectus

In this chapter, you will learn to group quantitative data in numerical form. Specifically, you will learn to group a set of quantitative data in the following forms:

1. Central tendency (Section 4.1): mode, median, and mean
2. Variability (Section 4.2): range, interquartile range, variance, standard deviation

Next, you will learn to group the quantitative data graphically in the form of box-whisker plots (Section 4.4).

4.1   Descriptive Statistics I: Measures of Central Tendency

Descriptive statistics are numbers calculated to describe various aspects of a data set. The two most important types of descriptive statistics are the following:

Measures of Central Tendency: A single value to represent the data set

Measures of Variability: A single value to describe how spread out the data are

In this section you will learn how to calculate various measures of central tendency—that is, mode, mean, and median. These measures can be obtained using the function CALC under the STAT mode in the main menu of the recommended calculator.

Mean

I. Arithmetic Mean (Average):

Symbol:	Population Parameter	Sample Statistic
Mean (Average)	μ	$\bar{x}$
Size (Number of items or elements)	N	n

Symbol: Sample Mean: $\bar{x}$ Population Mean: μ

Formula: $\bar{x} = \dfrac{\sum x}{n}$ $\mu = \dfrac{\sum x}{N}$

where: x = a value in the data set
n = sample size
N = population size
$\sum$ = summation   therefore $\sum x$ = add up the data

EXAMPLE 4.1

The Data Are in the Form of Raw Data

A fast food franchise has many outlets across the country. One small restaurant in the city where you live has seven full-time employees who earn $38, 20, 20, 18, 18, 18, and 23 thousand annually. Calculate the average salary of these employees.

SOLUTION

Formula	Casio Calculator
Use the **formula** to obtain the average salary of these employees, $$\bar{x} = \frac{\sum x}{n} = \frac{38 + 20 + 20 + 18 + 18 + 18 + 23}{7}$$ $= \$22.1$ thousand per employee Note: Regarding the form of the answer, use one more figure than those used in the data if the data have one or two figures. Otherwise, the answer should look like the data. Example: If data are 1.3, 2.4, and 3.6, then $\quad\quad\bar{x} = 2.43$. If the data have three or more figures, the answer should look like the data (e.g., if the data are 234, 315, and 484, then $\bar{x} = 344$.	Use the **Casio Calculator** to obtain the average salary of these employees, Now use the calculator to calculate the average salary of these employees. Refer to Calculator Lesson 2. **INSTRUCTIONS:** 1. Press the **MENU** key to switch to **STAT** mode. Highlight the **STAT** icon and press **EXE.** 2. You can enter the data from Example 4.1 in List 1 as follows: **38 EXE** **20 EXE** **20 EXE** **18 EXE** **18 EXE** **18 EXE** **23 EXE** 3. Press **F2 (CALC).** 4. Press **F6 (SET)**. Highlight **1 Var XList**, press **F1** (List), enter 1 for **List 1**, and press **EXE**. Then highlight **1Var Freq** and choose **1 (F1)**. Now press **EXIT** to return to the display of the data. *Note: Make sure that* 1Var Freq *is set to 1.* 5. Press **F1 (1 VAR)** to obtain a full range of one-variable statistics. The result, $\bar{x} = 22.1428571$, will be at the top of the list.

EXAMPLE 4.2

The Data Are in the Form of Grouped Data

The salaries of all the employees in the outlets in the city where you live are summarized in the following table:

Job Classification	Number of Employees	Annual Salary ($ thousands)
Senior Management	3	52
Middle Management	10	38
Cooking Staff	45	20
Serving Staff	74	18
Maintenance Staff	7	23

Calculate the average salary of these employees.

SOLUTION

Formula	Casio Calculator
Use the **formula** to obtain the average salary of these employees.	Use the **Casio Calculator** to obtain the average salary of these employees.
In this example the salary figures again need to be averaged. However, we realize that it would be incorrect to add the figures and divide by 5 as this would be correct only if there were an equal number of employees in each category. To take into account the differing number of employees in each category, we must use the **weighted** method to calculate the mean salary. Many textbooks call the result of this calculation, the **weighted mean.**	Now use the calculator to calculate the average salary of these employees. Refer to Calculator Lesson 3.
	INSTRUCTIONS
	1. Press the **MENU** key to switch to **STAT** mode. Highlight the STAT icon and press **EXE**.
	2. You can enter the salaries data, **52 EXE, 38 EXE, 20 EXE, 18 EXE**, and **23 EXE**, in **List 1**.
The formula for the weighted mean is as follows:	Then enter the number of employees (frequencies), **3 EXE, 10 EXE, 45 EXE, 74 EXE,** and **7 EXE**, in **List 2**.
$$\bar{x} = \frac{\sum wx}{\sum w}$$	3. Press **F2 (CALC)**.
	4. Press **F6 (SET)**. Highlight **1 VarXList**, press **F1** (List), enter **1** for **List 1**, and press **EXE**. Then highlight **1Var Freq**, choose **List (F2)**, and enter **2** for **List 2**. Now press **EXIT** to return to the display of the data.
where x = a value in the data set and w = weight of each value—that is, a number to indicate the relative importance of each data value in the overall result.	
In this example,	5. Press **F1 (1 VAR)** to obtain a full range of one-variable statistics.
x = the salaries	
w = the number of employees	The result, $\bar{x} = 21.0719424$, will appear at the top of the list.
$$\bar{x} = \frac{\sum wx}{\sum w}$$	
$$= \frac{(3 \times 52) + (10 \times 38) + (45 \times 20) + (74 \times 18) + (7 \times 23)}{3 + 10 + 45 + 74 + 7}$$	
$$= \frac{2929}{139}$$	
$= \$21.1$ thousand per employee	
Note: This formula also is 'logical' in that the denominator is 139, which is the total number of employees.	

EXAMPLE 4.3

The Data Are in the Form of Grouped Data

A Cruise ship does several week-long cruises during a year. The ship is not always fully occupied. There are three types of cabins on this particular ship: interior (no port hole), deluxe exterior (porthole), and luxury exterior (private balcony). The price for each type of cabin and estimated percent of passengers in each type of cabin for the next cruise is shown below.

Cabin Style	Price per Person ($)	Percent of Passengers
Interior	1900	40
Deluxe exterior	2400	45
Luxury exterior	3200	15

Calculate the average revenue per person earned by the cruise company.

SOLUTION

Formula	Casio Calculator
Use the **formula** to obtain the average revenue per person earned by the cruise company.	Use the **Casio Calculator** to obtain the average revenue per person earned by the cruise company.
In this example, x = the price for each person w = the percentages $$\bar{x} = \frac{\sum wx}{\sum w}$$ $$= \frac{(40 \times 1900) + (45 \times 2400) + (15 \times 3200)}{40 + 45 + 15}$$ $$= \$2{,}320 \text{ per person}$$	Now use the calculator to calculate the average revenue per person earned by the cruise company. Refer to Calculator Lesson 3. **INSTRUCTIONS** 1. Press the **MENU** key to switch to **STAT** mode. Highlight the STAT icon and press **EXE**. 2. You can enter the price data, **1900 EXE, 2400 EXE,** and **3200 EXE** in **List 1**. Then enter the percent of passengers (frequencies); **40 EXE, 45 EXE,** and **15 EXE** in **List 2**. 3. Press **F2 (CALC)**. 4. Press **F6 (SET)**. Highlight **1 VarXList**, press **F1 (List)**, enter **1** for **List 1**, and press **EXE**. Then highlight **1Var Freq**, choose **List (F2)**, and enter **2** for **List 2**. Now press **EXIT** to return to the display of the data. 5. Press **F1 (1 VAR)** to obtain a full range of one-variable statistics. The result, $\bar{x}$ = 2320, will appear at the top of the list.

There are two other common scenarios in which the weighted mean is necessary.

    a) Data to be averaged are themselves averages.

    b) Data to be averaged are percentages.

EXAMPLE 4.4

The Data Are in the Form of Grouped Data

A car-manufacturing company has assembly lines in four plants. Some data regarding the car production on these assembly lines for the past week are shown below.

Production Line	Number of Cars Produced	Average Time per Car (minutes)
Toronto	134	257
Montréal	105	248
Calgary	97	272
Vancouver	82	286

Calculate the overall average production time for these cars.

SOLUTION

Formula	Casio Calculator
Use the **formula** to obtain the overall average production time for these cars.	Use the **Casio Calculator** to obtain the overall average production time for these cars.
In this example, x = the average times w = the number of cars $$\bar{x} = \frac{\sum wx}{\sum w}$$ $$= \frac{(134 \times 257) + (105 \times 248) + (97 \times 272) + (82 \times 286)}{134 + 105 + 97 + 82}$$ $$= \frac{110314}{418} = 264 \text{ minutes per car}$$	Now use the calculator to calculate the overall average production time for these cars. Refer to Calculator Lesson 3. **INSTRUCTIONS** 1. Press the **MENU** key to switch to **STAT** mode. Highlight the STAT icon and press **EXE**. 2. You can enter the average times data, **257 EXE, 248 EXE, 272 EXE**, and **286 EXE** in **List 1**. Then enter the number of cars (frequencies), **134 EXE, 105 EXE, 97 EXE**, and **82 EXE** in **List 2**. 3. Press **F2 (CALC)**. 4. Press **F6 (SET)**. Highlight **1 VarXList**, press **F1** (List), enter **1** for **List 1**, and press **EXE**. Then highlight **Var Freq**, choose **List (F2)**, and enter **2** for **List 2**. Now press **EXIT** to return to the display of the data. 5. Press **F1 (1 VAR)** to obtain a full range of one-variable statistics. The result, $\bar{x}$ = 263.90909, will appear at the top of the list.

EXAMPLE 4.5

The Data Are in the Form of Grouped Data

The following data refer to three divisions of a medium-sized business.

Division	Profit Margin (%)	Sales ($ millions)
A	5	10
B	6	5
C	7	35

Calculate the overall average profit margin for the three divisions.

SOLUTION

Formula	Casio Calculator
Use the **formula** to obtain the overall average profit margin for the three divisions	Use the **Casio Calculator** to obtain the overall average profit margin for the three divisions.
In this example, x = the profit margin w = the sales $$\bar{x} = \frac{\sum wx}{\sum w} = \frac{(10 \times 5) + (5 \times 6) + (35 \times 7)}{10 + 5 + 35}$$ $$= \frac{325}{50} = 6.5\% \text{ (per division)}$$	Now use the calculator to calculate the overall average profit margin for the three divisions. Refer to Calculator Lesson 3. **INSTRUCTIONS** 1. Press the **MENU** key to switch to **STAT** mode. Highlight the STAT icon and press **EXE**. *Note: To delete a list, highlight it and press **F4 (DEL A)**. The whole list will be cleared. It may be necessary to press F6 (/>) for the DEL-A option to show up.*

2. You can enter the profit margin values, **5 EXE, 6 EXE**, and **7 EXE** in **List 1**.

Then enter the sales values, **10 EXE, 5 EXE**, and **35 EXE** in **List 2**.

3. Press **F2 (CALC)**.

4. Press **F6 (SET)**. Highlight **1 VarXList**, press **F1** (List), enter **1** for **List 1**, and press **EXE**. Then highlight **1Var Freq**, choose **List (F2)**, and enter **2** for **List 2**. Now press **EXIT** to return to the display of the data.

5. Press **F1 (1 VAR)** to obtain a full range of one-variable statistics. The result, $\bar{x} = 6.5$, will appear at the top of the list.

One final scenario involving the calculating of a mean is also common.

II: Another Type of Mean

EXAMPLE 4.6

In a particular province there are three provincial parks. The Ministry of Natural Resources is interested in the concentration of moose in these parks. The results of a survey yielded the following data.

Provincial Park	Number of Moose	Area of Park (km^2)
Moose Forest	134	2575
Moose Swamp	105	2037
Moosonee	97	2892

Calculate the overall average number of moose per square kilometre.

SOLUTION

$$\bar{x} = \frac{\sum moose}{\sum area} = \frac{134 + 105 + 97}{2575 + 2037 + 2892}$$

$$= \frac{336}{7504} = 0.0448 \text{ moose per km}^2.$$

Note: When no other rule applies to the result of a particular calculation, we will use a general rule of **three significant digits** (or more if the zeros are to the left of the decimal point).

The arithmetic mean is by far the most important measure of central tendency.

III: Grouped Data: Mean

Suppose the only data available to us are in the form of a frequency or relative frequency (or percentage) distribution. Then in order to estimate the mean of the data, we need to use the **class midpoints** to represent the values in each class. We then use the weighted method to calculate the mean, where the frequencies or relative frequencies will be the appropriate weights.

EXAMPLE 4.7

On a particular Saturday, the amount paid for parking in a small downtown parking lot was as summarized in the following table:

Cost of Parking ($)	Number of Cars (f)	%	Midpoint (m)
2.00 and under 4.00	20	18.3	3.00
4.00 '' '' 6.00	37	33.9	5.00
6.00 '' '' 10.00	29	26.6	8.00
10.00 '' '' 15.00	15	13.8	12.50
15.00 '' '' 20.00	8	7.3	17.50
Total	109	99.9	

Estimate the mean amount paid for parking.

SOLUTION: a) Using the frequencies as weights (note the symbols in the formula),

$$\bar{x} = \frac{\sum fm}{\sum f} = \frac{(20 \times 3.00) + (37 \times 5.00) + (29 \times 8.00) + (15 \times 12.50) + (8 \times 17.50)}{20 + 37 + 29 + 15 + 8}$$

$$= \frac{804.50}{109} = \$7.38 \text{ per customer}$$

b) Using the percentages as weights,

$$\bar{x} = \frac{\sum \%m}{\sum \%}$$

$$= \frac{(18.3 \times 3.00) + (33.9 \times 5.00) + (26.6 \times 8.00) + (13.8 \times 12.50) + (7.3 \times 17.50)}{18.3 + 33.9 + 26.6 + 13.8 + 7.3}$$

$$= \frac{737.45}{99.9} = \$7.38 \text{ per customer}$$

CASIO CALCULATOR

Now use the calculator to calculate the mean amount paid for parking. Refer to Calculator Lesson 3 on page 145.

INSTRUCTIONS

1. Press the **MENU** key to switch to **STAT** mode. Highlight the STAT icon and press **EXE**.

Note: To delete a list, highlight it and press F4 (DEL A). The whole list will be cleared. It may be necessary to press F6 (/>) in order for the DEL-A option to show up.

2. You can enter the midpoints of cost of parking data, **3 EXE, 5 EXE, 8 EXE, 12.5 EXE,** and **17.5 EXE** in **List 1**.

Then enter the number of cars (frequencies), **20 EXE, 37 EXE, 29 EXE, 15 EXE, 8 EXE** in **List 2**.

Note: Instead you may use percentages as the weights (or frequencies) by entering 18.3 EXE, 33.9 EXE, 26.6 EXE, 13.8 EXE, and 7.3 EXE in List 2 (or whichever list you wish to use).

3. Press **F2 (CALC)**.

4. Press **F6 (SET)**. Highlight **1 Var XList**, press **F1** (List), enter **1** for **List 1**, and press **EXE**. Then highlight **1Var Freq**, choose **List (F2)**, and enter **2** for **List 2**. Now press **EXIT** to return to the display of the data.

5. Press **F1 (1 VAR)** to obtain a full range of one-variable statistics. The result, $\bar{x} = 7.38073394$, will appear at the top of the list.

CALCULATOR LESSON 3

CASIO FX-9750GII CALCULATOR

Lesson 3—Calculations using STAT mode

STAT Mode: Press the **MENU** key.

Use the cursor keys to move the highlighting to the **STAT** icon and press **EXE**.

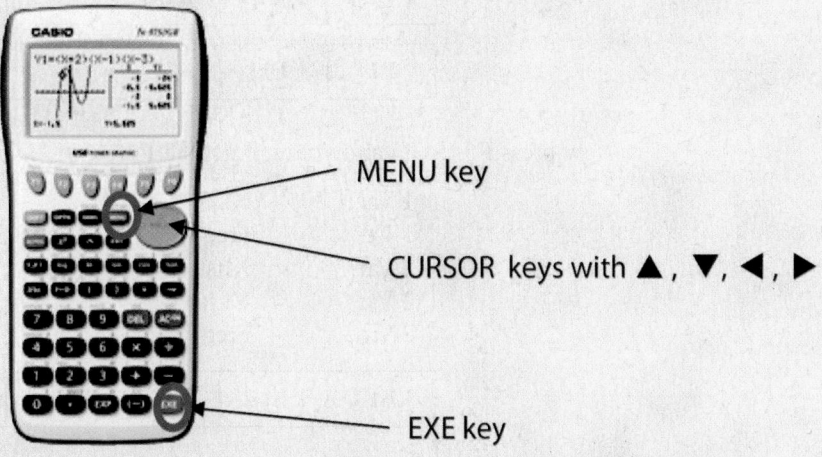

MENU key

CURSOR keys with ▲, ▼, ◄, ►

EXE key

Source: http://www.casio.com/products/Calculators_%26_Dictionaries/Graphing/FX-750GII/content/Introduction/

You will now have 26 blank lists set up on the screen. You can see only List 1 to List 4 at first, but if you move the ► cursor key you will be able to scroll over to the other lists.

You can enter the data from Example 4.1 in the introductory handout in List 1 as follows:

> **38 EXE**
> **20 EXE**
> **20 EXE**
> **20 EXE**
> **18 EXE**
> **18 EXE**
> **23 EXE**

EXAMPLE 1 (revisited)

To calculate the average of the salary data, use the **F6** key (▷) if necessary to get the following menu choices at the bottom of the display:

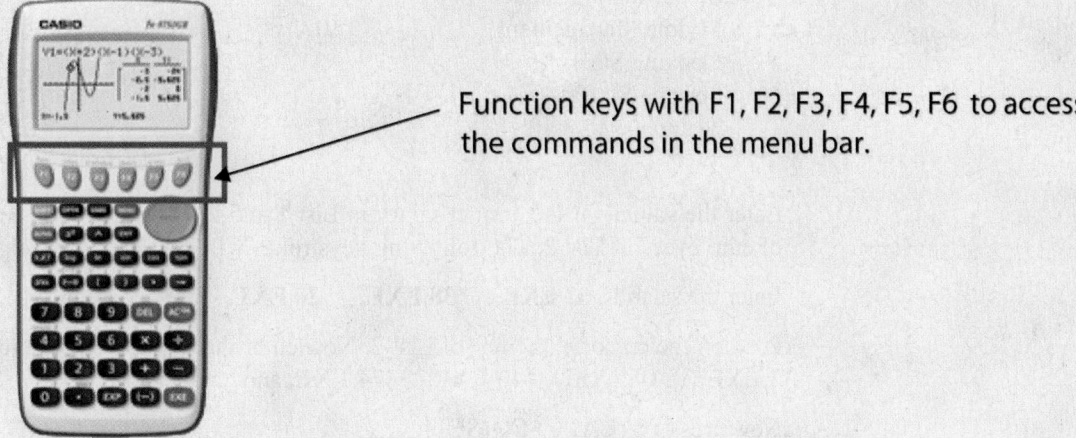

Function keys with F1, F2, F3, F4, F5, F6 to access the commands in the menu bar.

Source: http://www.casio.com/products/Calculators_%26_Dictionaries/Graphing/FX-9750GII/content/Introduction/

GRPH	CALC	TEST	INTR	DIST	$\triangleright$
F1	F2	F3	F4	F5	F6

Now press **F2** (CALC) and you will get the following on-screen menu items:

1 VAR	2 VAR	REG			SET
F1	F2	F3			F6

Now press **F6** (SET) and you will get the following display:

1 Var	XList	:	List1
1 Var	Freq	:	1
2 Var	Xlist	:	List1
2 Var	YList	:	List2
2 Var	Freq	:	1

List 1	List 2	List 3	List 4	List 5	List 6

The first row will be highlighted. To select the desired list for your **1Var XList**, press **F1** (List). The calculator will now ask which list(s). Answer this question (by entering **1** if the data are in List **1**) and press **EXE**.

You also want to have the 1Var Freq as **F1 (1)**.

Now press **EXIT** to return to the display of the data.

Now press **F1 (1 VAR)** and a full range of one-variable statistics will appear. The result, $\bar{x} = 22.4285714$, will be at the top of the list.

Now press **EXIT** to return to the data list display.

Weighted Data

Recall from the Measures of Central Tendency lecture notes that in Example 4.2 we needed to calculate the mean salary for the following group of people:

TABLE 4.1

Job Classification	Number of Employees	Annual Salary ($ thousands)
Senior Management	3	52
Middle Management	10	38
Cooking Staff	45	20
Serving Staff	74	18
Maintenance Staff	7	23

Enter the values for the annual salary in List 1 and the corresponding values for the number of employees in List 2. The following keystrokes will calculate the **weighted** statistics:

Enter the salaries, **52 EXE,   38 EXE,   20 EXE,   18 EXE,** and   **23 EXE** under List 1.

Position the cursor at the top of List 2. Now enter the weights (frequencies),
3 EXE,   10 EXE,   45 EXE,   74 EXE, and   **7 EXE**.

Now press **F2** (CALC) **F6** (SET).

Highlight 1 Var XList, press **F1** (List), enter **1** for List 1, and press **EXE**. Then highlight 1 Var Freq, choose List (**F2**), and enter **2** for List 2. Now press **EXIT**.

Press **F1** (1 VAR) and a full range of one-variable weighted statistics will appear. The result, $\bar{x} = 21.0719424$, will be at the top of the list—that is, the average salary is $21.1 thousand, as we saw in the notes on measures of central tendency.

The Median

The **median** is the middle value in an ordered array of data that have been ranked from smallest to largest. Half the values are smaller than or equal to the median, and half the values are larger than or equal to the median. The median is not affected by extreme values, so you can use the median when extreme values are present.

MEDIAN:

Symbol: sample or population $- \tilde{x}$

The technical definition of the median is that it is the value such that at most 50% of the data values are smaller than the median and at most 50% of the data values are larger than the median. In other words, the median occupies the *middle position* of the data after they are sorted into **an ordered array**, either ascending or descending.

Let **i** denote the position of the median.

To calculate i (position), we use the formula $\quad i = \dfrac{n+1}{2}$.

Once **i** is calculated, there are two possibilities regarding how to determine the median of a data set.

EXAMPLE 4.8

There Is An *Even* Number of Data Values

The following data represent the ages, in years, of 20 employees working at a retail outlet.

$$63, 52, 38, 20, 21, 18, 29, 28, 45, 40, 24, 25, 22, 20, 29, 20, 18, 20, 18, 22$$

The corresponding **data array** in ascending order is the following:

$$18, 18, 18, 20, 20, 20, 20, 21, 22, 22, 24, 25, 28, 29, 29, 38, 40, 45, 52, 63$$

Calculate the median age of the employees.

The **position** of the median is $i = \dfrac{n+1}{2} = \dfrac{20+1}{2} = 10.5^{\text{th}}$ position

Therefore, the median is $\tilde{x} = \dfrac{10^{\text{th}} \text{ value} + 11^{\text{th}} \text{ value}}{2} = \dfrac{22 + 24}{2} = 23$ years

Note: The mean is $\bar{x} = 28.6$ years. The mean is higher than the median because most of the data are in the 18-to-29 range, with a few larger values that will have the effect of increasing the mean.

Calculator Method to Obtain the Median

The **"CALC"** function provides the median as well as the mean.

Use the calculator to calculate the median age of the employees. Refer to Calculator Lesson 3.

INSTRUCTIONS:

1. Press the **MENU** key to switch to **STAT** mode. Highlight the **STAT** icon and press **EXE**.

2. You can enter the age data, **63 EXE, 52 EXE, 38 EXE, 20 EXE, 21 EXE, 18 EXE, 29 EXE, 28 EXE, 45 EXE, 40 EXE, 24 EXE, 25 EXE, 22 EXE, 20 EXE, 29 EXE, 20 EXE, 18 EXE, 20 EXE, 18 EXE,** and **22 EXE** in **List 1**.

3. Press **F2 (CALC)**.

4. Press **F6 (SET)**. Highlight **1 VarXList**, and press **F1** (List), enter **1** for **List 1**, and press **EXE**. Then highlight **1Var Freq** and choose **1 (F1)**. Now press **EXIT** to return to the display of the data. *Note: Make sure that* 1Var Freq *is set to 1.*

5. Press **F1 (1 VAR)** to obtain a full range of one-variable statistics. The result, $\bar{x} = 28.6$, will be at the top of the list. Scroll down the screen to obtain $\tilde{x} = 23$.

EXAMPLE 4.9

There Is An *Odd* **Number of Data Values**

The following data represents the ages, in years, of 17 employees working at a retail outlet.

$$63, 52, 38, 20, 21, 18, 29, 28, 45, 40, 24, 25, 22, 20, 29, 20, 18$$

The corresponding **data array** in ascending order is the following:

$$18, 18, 20, 20, 20, 21, 22, 24, 25, 28, 29, 29, 38, 40, 45, 52, 63$$

The **position** of the median is: $i = \dfrac{n+1}{2} = \dfrac{17+1}{2} = 9^{th}$ position

Therefore, the median is: $\tilde{x} = 9^{th}$ value $= 25$ years

Calculator Method to Obtain the Median

The **CALC** function provides the median as well as the mean.

Use the calculator to calculate the median age of the employees. Refer to Calculator Lesson 3.

INSTRUCTIONS:

1. Press the **MENU** key to switch to **STAT** mode. Highlight the **STAT** icon and press **EXE**.

2. You can enter the age data, **63 EXE, 52 EXE, 38 EXE, 20 EXE, 21 EXE, 18 EXE, 29 EXE, 28 EXE, 45 EXE, 40 EXE, 24 EXE, 25 EXE, 22 EXE, 20 EXE, 29 EXE, 20 EXE,** and **18 EXE**.

3. Press **F2 (CALC)**.

4. Press **F6 (SET)**. Highlight **1 VarXList**, press **F1** (List), enter **1** for **List 1**, press **EXE**. Then highlight **1Var Freq** choose **1 (F1)**. Now press **EXIT** to return to the display of the data. *Note: Make sure that* 1Var Freq *is set to 1.*

5. Press **F1 (1 VAR)** to obtain a full range of one-variable statistics. The result, $\bar{x} = 30.117647$, will be at the top of the list. Scroll down the screen to obtain $\tilde{x} = 25$.

Which Is a Better Measure of Central Tendency? The Mean or the Median?

The following examples show situations in which the median might be the preferred measure of central tendency to represent a data set (i.e., when the median is preferred over the mean).

EXAMPLE 4.10

The following data represent the prices of houses sold last week in a particular neighbour-hood. The data have been put into an array.

$$\$200{,}000 \quad \$205{,}000 \quad \$210{,}000 \quad \$220{,}000 \quad \$225{,}000$$

a) If you read that the mean house price in this neighbourhood was

$$\bar{x} = \$212{,}000$$

then you would get a certain impression as to the size and type of the typical house in the neighbourhood.

b) If you read that the median house price in this neighbourhood was

$$\tilde{x} = \$210{,}000$$

then you would get the same impression as to the size and type of the typical house in the neighbourhood.

Conclusion: If the mean and median are **close**, then the **mean** will give the correct impression and is the preferred measure. How do you measure or evaluate the *closeness* of mean and median? *Closeness* means that the mean is approximately close (or equal) to the median. We proposed a heuristics rule, known as the 10% rule, to evaluate the *closeness*.

EXAMPLE 4.11

The following data represents the prices of houses sold last week in a particular neighbour-hood. The data have been put into an array.

$$\$200{,}000 \quad \$205{,}000 \quad \$210{,}000 \quad \$220{,}000 \quad \$425{,}000$$

a) If you read that the mean house price in this neighbourhood was

$$\bar{x} = \$252{,}000$$

then you would get a certain impression as to the size and type of the typical house in the neighbourhood.

b) If you read that the median house price is this neighbourhood was

$$\tilde{x} = \$210{,}000$$

then you would get a different impression as to the size and type of the typical house in the neighbourhood.

Conclusion: If the mean and median are **not close**, then the **median** will give the correct impression. The reason why the mean and the median are not close is that the data set has **unbalanced extreme values.** *Not close* means that the median is not equal to the mean. Use the 10% rule to evaluate the closeness of mean and median.

Use the 10% rule to evaluate the two values (mean and median) to determine which is the better measure of central tendency (**median** or **mean** (average)) to describe a set of data. Examples 4.10 and 4.11 demonstrate this point.

The following procedure is used to determine whether mean or median is a better measure:

1. Compute the mean.
2. Compute the median.
3. Apply the heuristic rule, which is the 10% rule, to determine if the mean has the same value as or a different value from the median.
4. Select either mean or median to summarize your data based on the heuristic 10% rule.

10% RULE:

To help you determine if the mean and median are really different, use the following rule:

Calculate the *difference* between the mean and median.

Calculate *10% of the smaller value*, be it the mean or median.

Compare the two values, *difference* and *10% of the smaller value* using the following decision rule below.

The decision rules are the following:

If the difference is less than 10% of the smaller value, you conclude that the mean is approximately equal to the median, in which case the *mean* is the preferred measure. This decision also tells you that the distribution is symmetrical. Given a symmetrical distribution, the mean would be a preferred measure of central tendency.

If the difference is greater than 10% of the smaller value, you conclude that the mean is *not equal* to the median, in which case the *median* is the preferred measure. This decision also tells you that the distribution is skewed. Given a skewed distribution, the median would be a preferred measure of central tendency.

Example 4.10: Difference = 2,000, which is **less than** 10% of the smaller value, or 21,000, and you conclude that mean price is a better measure to describe the data set.

Example 4.11: Difference = 42,000, which is **greater than** 10% of the smaller value, or 21,000, and you conclude that median price is a better measure to describe the data set.

The Mode

The **mode** is the value in a set of data that appears most frequently. Like the median and unlike the mean, extreme values do not affect the mode. Often, there is no mode or there are several modes in a set of data. For example, consider the time-to-get-ready data shown as follows:

$$29 \quad 31 \quad 35 \quad 39 \quad 39 \quad 40 \quad 43 \quad 44 \quad 44 \quad 52$$

There are two modes, 39 minutes and 44 minutes, because each of these values occurs twice.

EXAMPLE 4.12

Determining the Mode

A systems manager in charge of a company's network keeps track of the number of server failures that occur in a day. Determine the mode for the following data, which represent the number of server failures a day for the past two weeks:

$$1 \quad 3 \quad 0 \quad 3 \quad 26 \quad 2 \quad 7 \quad 4 \quad 0 \quad 2 \quad 3 \quad 3 \quad 6 \quad 3$$

SOLUTION The ordered array for these data is

$$0 \quad 0 \quad 1 \quad 2 \quad 2 \quad 3 \quad 3 \quad 3 \quad 3 \quad 3 \quad 4 \quad 6 \quad 7 \quad 26$$

Because 3 appears five times, more times than any other value, the mode is 3. Thus, the systems manager can say that the most common occurrence is having three server failures in a day. For this data set, the median is also equal to 3, and the mean is equal to 4.5. The value 26 is an extreme value. For these data, the median and the mode better measure central tendency than the mean.

A set of data has no mode if none of the values is "most typical." Example 4.13 presents a data set with no mode.

EXAMPLE 4.13

Data with no Mode

The bounced check fees ($) for a sample of 10 banks is

$$26 \quad 28 \quad 20 \quad 21 \quad 22 \quad 25 \quad 18 \quad 23 \quad 15 \quad 30$$

Compute the mode.

SOLUTION These data have no mode. None of the values is most typical because each value appears once.

Problems for Section 4.1

4.1 A company has invited its entire human resources staff from each office across the country to attend a conference at the head office in Toronto. The following information is available:

Office	Return Airfare	# of Offices	# of HR Staff per Office
Calgary	$400	2	4
Halifax	350	1	2
Montréal	330	2	3
Ottawa	300	2	3
Vancouver	500	3	5

a. What is the median return airfare per office?
b. What is the mean return airfare per person?

4.2 The following sample data were obtained at 8:00 p.m. at a popular downtown restaurant. There were 15 tables occupied at that time.

Number of Guests at the Table	Food Bill for the Table ($)	Liquor Bill for the Table ($)
2	48.75	15.75
2	36.75	26.00
4	90.55	22.90
4	87.45	42.45
2	41.25	14.00
4	83.30	29.75
6	109.40	44.05
4	88.25	21.55
4	93.45	22.00
2	36.50	16.45
2	42.60	18.00
4	105.80	37.57
4	84.65	18.95
5	110.35	43.95
4	83.55	22.50

a. What is the 40th percentile table liquor bill?
b. What was the average food bill for the 15 tables?

c. How much did the average guest spend on food?
d. In order to be in the top 32% of the amount spent on food, a table would have to spend at least what amount?

4.3 A referendum was held on a particular issue affecting the GTA Megacity. The following table shows the results.

Municipality	Number of Votes	% in Favour
City of Toronto	482,000	45
East York	152,000	63
North York	365,000	27
Etobicoke	298,000	48
Scarborough	456,000	33

What was the overall percent in favour of the issue?

4.4 A specialty bookstore concentrates mainly on selling used books and magazines. Paperbacks sell for $1.00 each, hardcover books are $5.00 each, and magazines sell for $0.50 each. Of the 50 books sold on Tuesday, 40 were paperback and the remainder were hardcover. The bookstore also sold 15 magazines. What was the mean price per item sold?

4.5 Rye Pizza sells soft drinks in three sizes: small, medium, and large. The small size costs $0.75, the medium is $0.90, and the large is $1.15 . On a typical weekday, 25% of the soft drinks sold are small, 45% are medium, and 30% are large. What is the typical daily mean price per soft drink sold?

4.6 A particular oak dining table requires time in three manufacturing stages: 2 hours of cutting, 4 hours of assembly, and 6 hours of finishing. The wood-cutters are paid $10 per hour, the assemblers get $15 per hour, and the finishers get $20 per hour. What is the average hourly labour cost to manufacture one table?

4.7 The personnel director at Recovery Hospital wanted a study made of overtime hours and associated costs of the nurses. Ten (10) nurses were randomly selected and the following data were obtained for August.

Nurse	O/T Hours	Pay ($/hr)	Nurse	O/T Hours	Pay ($/hr)
1	13	35	6	15	25
2	13	35	7	5	30
3	12	20	8	12	35
4	15	25	9	6	30
5	7	30	10	7	25

a. What was the average number of hours of overtime worked per nurse?
b. What was the average hourly overtime pay rate per nurse?
c. What was the average pay rate per hour of overtime?

4.8 The following table shows some data regarding the top four chains of toy stores.

Chain	# of Stores	Average Sales/ Store ($ thousands)
Toys 'R' Us	144	7,236
Child World	79	3,582
Kay bee	361	507
Lionel	56	3,232

a. What is the average sales of a toy store?
b. What is the mean sales of the four toy store chains?
c. Data regarding several retail chains are shown in the table below. What is the overall percent gain in sales for the chains shown?

Company/ Chain	Sales (000,000)	% Gain (Loss)	Number of Stores	% Gain (Loss)
Radio Shack	$1,515	28	4,398	7
Mervyn's	1,336	26	92	15
Toys 'R' Us	1,042	33	144	20
Marshall's	830	35	137	27
Saks Fifth Avenue	710	2	34	6
Lerners	682	(4)	790	3
Nordstrom	613	17	36	6

4.9 The table below shows data dealing with product liability.

		Status of Injured Persons/Parties			
Liability Category Claim	Injured Party	# of Persons Receiving Payment	% of Persons Receiving Payment	% of Total Payment	Average Payment per Person
Bodily Injury	Employee	875	10.6	42.0	$97,884
	Purchaser	5,562	67.5	28.7	10,544
	User	1,441	17.5	22.5	31,836
	Other	364	4.4	6.8	38,016
Property Damage	Employee	12	0.2	0.0	$ 325
	Purchaser	3,928	78.7	64.3	4,372
	User	359	7.2	22.8	22,468
	Employee	695	3.9	12.9	6,176

a. What was the average payment to a person who suffered bodily injury?
b. What was the average payment to a purchaser involved in all types of claims?

4.10 An extensive study was conducted to determine whether there are differences in the characteristics of holiday travellers that are less than 50 years old as compared to those that are more than 50 years old. One of the items of interest was the amount spent for a one-day trip. The results are shown below:

Cost of One-Day Trip	Under 50 Years Old (n = 480)	Over 50 Years Old (n = 325)
$ 0 and under 50	2%	1%
50 " " 100	7	5
100 " " 200	12	9
200 " " 300	20	13
300 " " 400	29	20
400 " " 500	18	17
500 " " 750	6	14
750 " " 1000	3	10
1000 " " 2000	2	7
2000 " " 3000	1	4

a. For which group of travellers, if any, would the median be a better measure of central tendency than the mean?
b. For the under–50 group, 360 of those surveyed would have spent less than $____.

4.11 Based on the data in the following table:
a. What is the overall average tobacco sales revenue per person?
b. What is the mean amount of federal tax per state?
c. Would the mean or median better represent the state tobacco taxes?
d. Which state(s) had the 60th percentile federal tobacco taxes?

	Under-Age Smoking			
	Number of Smokers under 18 Years Old	State Tobacco Taxes ($ millions)	Federal Tobacco Taxes ($ millions)	Sales Revenue ($ millions)
California	300,000	20.6	11.8	125.0
New York	190,000	14.6	7.4	78.2
Texas	200,000	16.6	8.0	76.0
Illinois	130,000	7.8	5.2	49.2
Florida	125,000	8.4	5.0	49.2
Pennsylvania	130,000	8.0	5.2	47.8
Ohio	125,000	4.6	5.0	43.6

Michigan	110,000	5.6	4.4	41.0
New Jersey	85,000	6.6	3.4	33.2
Alabama	50,000	2.8	3.4	31.4

4.12 The following is a portion of a table that appeared in the December 1, 2002 issue of the Toronto Star.

Cancer Surgery Wait Times

In 2002, the average wait time for cancer surgery at the Princess Margaret Hospital and University Health Network was 54 days. This is an increase from 43 days in 2000.

Average wait time from the decision to operate to the date of surgery:

Hospital	Days	Cases
Princess Margaret Hospital	35	144
Toronto General Hospital	33	537
Toronto Western Hospital	5	10

What is the overall average wait time per patient for the three hospitals shown?

4.13 Based on the following table that appeared in *The Globe and Mail*, Classroom Edition, of March 1994, answer the questions:

a. Was the overall mean price per room higher for three-star hotels than for two-star hotels?

b. What is the median number of rooms for all the hotels in the table?

c. It would be reported that 40% of the hotels had a selling price higher than $___ .

Eastern Canada

Hotel	Level of quality	Location	Number of rooms	Selling price $million	Buyer origin
Hotel Strata, Mississauga	2-star	Toronto	129	$2.7	Domestic
Royal Connaught	3-star	Hamilton	206	$4.5	Domestic
Chestnut Park	3-star	Toronto	520	$28.4	Hong Kong
Carlton Place	2-star	Toronto	528	$8.5	Indonesia/Singapore
Howard Johnson, Scarborough	2-star	Toronto	192	$5.6	China
Howard Johnson	2-star	Ottawa	108	$3.7	Domestic
Best Western, Rose City Inn	1-star	Windsor	147	$2.5	Domestic
Sutton Place	4-star	Toronto	280*	$29.2	Hong Kong
Hotel Aurora	2-star	Aurora	98	$3.5	Domestic
Rock Haven Motor Inn	1-star	Peterborough	86	$1.0	Iranian
Skyline Triumph	2-star	Toronto	380	$9.5	Domestic

Western Canada

Hotel	Level of quality	Location	Number of rooms	Selling price $million	Buyer origin
Delta River Inn	4-star	Vancouver	416	$30.0	Domestic/Hong Kong
Skyline Hotel	3-star	Calgary	385	$26.0	Domestic
Cherrywood Inn	2-star	Edmonton	136	$2.9	Domestic
Coast Lakeside Inn	3-star	Penticton	200	$13.5	Domestic
Best Western, Port O'Call	3-star	Calgary	201	$8.5	East African

*Plus 161 apartment units.

Source: Colliers Macaulay Nicolis

4.14 The following data came from the Sales & Marketing Management, Survey of Buying Power, 1998. For the states shown in the table below, answer the following questions:

a. What is the projected overall average retail sales per household in 2002?

b. What is the projected overall percent increase in the number of households from 1998 to 2003?

Survey of Buying Power (Regional and State Summaries for 5-year Projections)

	POPULATION					RETAIL SALES	
REGION STATE	1/1/98 TOTAL POP. (000s)	1/1/2003 TOTAL POP. (000s)	% CHANGE 1998– 2003	1/1/2003 TOTAL HSHLDS. (000s)	% CHANGE 1998– 2003	2002 TOTAL RETAIL SALES ($000)	% CHANGE 1997–2002
NEW ENGLAND							
Connecticut	3,271.1	3,275.2	.1	1,246.1	1.4	39,848,761	15.0
Maine	1,243.7	1,260.1	1.3	496.2	3.5	13,998,071	12.2
Massachusetts	6,133.5	6,241.1	1.8	2,384.6	3.3	66,722,629	12.6
New Hampshire	1,179.1	1,242.3	5.4	472.5	7.0	17,284,399	18.6
Rhode Island	987.0	978.5	-.9	372.5	.1	8,590,400	9.4
Vermont	590.4	601.6	1.9	235.4	4.3	6,407,914	11.4

4.15 A survey of 300 prize winners of a certain contest revealed the following results:

a. What was the mean prize value?

b. How many won prizes of less than $500?

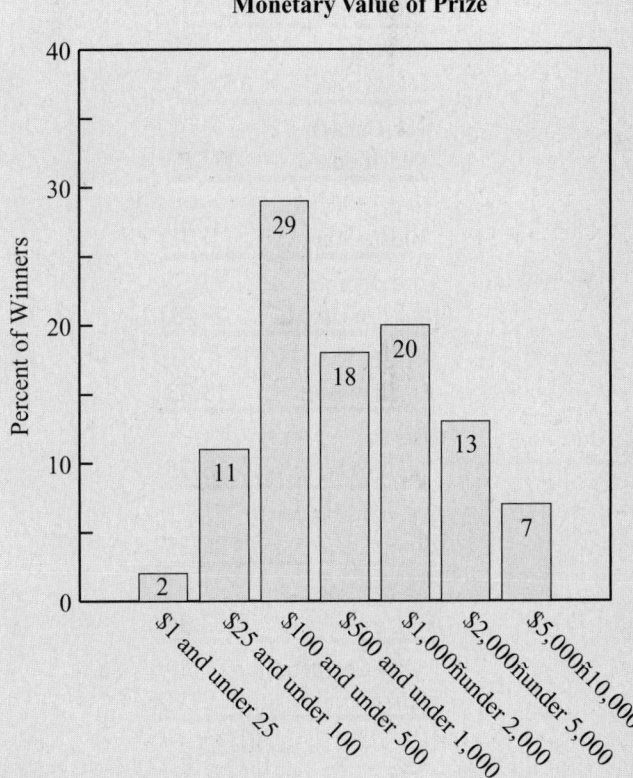

4.16 Based on the following table, what is the mean size of institutions that make extensive use of TQM (Total Quality Management)?

Breakdown by Size of Institution				
Student Population	Number of Institutions Responding	Percent of Institutions Responding	Number of Institutions Extensively Using TQM	Percent of Institutions Extensively Using TQM
0 and under 2,000	19	8	3	7
2,000 " " 5,000	58	24	7	17
5,000 " " 10,000	65	27	13	31
10,000 " " 15,000	41	17	6	14
15,000 " " 25,000	35	14	9	22
25,000 " " 35,000	15	6	3	7
35,000 " " 50,000	10	4	1	2

4.17 The following table appeared in the June 19, 2003 issue of the *Toronto Star*.

Auto productivity

Top 10 assembly plants in North America by labour-hours per vehicle.

Nissan, Smyrna, Tenn.
Midsize car   **15.74**

GM, Oshawa #1
Midsize car   **16.44**

GM, Oshawa #2
Midsize car   **17.08**

Ford, Chicago
Midsize car   **17.71**

Ford, Atlanta
Midsize car   **17.78**

Nissan, Smyrna
Small pickup   **18.23**

Nissan, Smyrna
Small SUV   **18.35**

GM, Lansing, Mich
Compact car   **18.59**

GM, Lansing
Midsize car   **18.64**

Toyota Georgetown #1
Midsize car   **20.06**

SOURCE: Harbour and Associates

Last month there were 2,400 cars produced at Oshawa #1, 3,000 cars produced at Oshawa #2, 1,800 midsize cars produced at Lansing, and 1,500 compact cars produced at Lansing. What was the overall average labour hours per car for these four GM plants?

4.18 The following is a portion of a chart that appeared in the May 25, 2003 issue of the *Toronto Star*.

By the numbers

Housing outlook... Ontario home starts will jump 3 per cent this year to 86,000, but fall back to 80,000 in 2004.

Home sales... Existing-home sales in Canada's 25 major markets declined less than 1 per cent in April, but the average price rose.

Seasonally adjusted

	Apr. 2003	Mar. 2003	% change
Dollar volume (billions)	$4.6	$4.8	-3.6%
Sales	21,905	22,085	-0.8%
Average price	$217,073	$203,589	6.6%
New listings	35,247	34,611	1.8%

What was the overall average price of houses sold in Canada's 25 major markets for March and April 2003?

4.19 The table below appeared in the *Financial Post* of December 2, 1998.

World oil giants

		Profit US$billion	Rev. per employee US$	Employees
1	Exxon Corp./Mobil Corp. (U.S.)	11.8	96,170	122,700
2	Royal Dutch/Shell Group (Britain/Netherlands)	7.8	74,286	105,000
3	British Petroleum/Amoco (Britain)	4.0	70,859	56,450
4	Total SA/Petrofina SA (France)	2.9	67.391	69,066
5	Texaco Inc. (U.S.)	2.7	92,109	29,313
6	Elf Aquitaine (France)	0.96	11,469	83,700
7	ENI (Italy)	3.0	37,417	80,178
8	Chevron Corp. (U.S.)	3.3	84,615	39,362
9	PDVSA (Venezuela)	4.8	84,818	56,592
10	SK (South Korea)	0.125	4,086	30,595

SOURCE: COMPANY REPORTS

a. For the 10 companies shown, what is the mean profit per company?

b. What is the overall mean revenue per employee for the 10 companies shown?

c. What is the overall mean profit per employee?

4.2 Descriptive Statistics II: Measures of Variability

Descriptive statistics comprises numbers calculated to describe various aspects of a data set. The two most important types of descriptive statistics are the following:

Measures of Central Tendency: A single value to represent the data set

Measures of Variability: A single value to describe how spread out the data are

In this section you will learn how to calculate various measures of variability or dispersion. The most common measures of the variability of the data are range, interquartile range, standard deviation, and variance.

We will use the following three data sets to demonstrate the concepts and calculations of variability measures:

Data set A: 1, 2, 3, 4, 5

Data set B: 1, 1, 3, 3, 5, 5

Data set C: 1, 1, 1, 5, 5, 5

It should be noted that for each data set: mean = median = 3.

In other words, the most important measures of central tendency are the same for all three data sets, but the data sets themselves are different; therefore, there must be some other aspect of them that is different. It is the fact that they have different amounts of **variability**.

Range (R)

Symbol: R for sample or population range

Formula: $R = Maximum - Minimum$ **(4.1)**

EXAMPLE 4.14

Data set A: $R = 5 - 1 = 4$

Data set B: $R = 5 - 1 = 4$

Data set C: $R = 5 - 1 = 4$

These results would seem to indicate that the three data sets had the same amount of variability. This would appear not to be true, since our intuition would seem to indicate that the three data sets would have different amounts of variability.

From this example we can see why the range has limited use. It considers only the high and low values of a data set and ignores the values in between. These in-between values should have some input in determining the variability of a data set.

It should be noted, however, that the range can be useful to measure variability in some cases. For many years the range has been the preferred way to measure variability when setting up quality control charts, which are used to monitor the mean and the variability of repeated processes.

In this course, you will calculate the range only if you are told to do so.

EXAMPLE 4.15

Computing the Range in the 2003 Return of Small Cap High-Risk Mutual Funds

The 184 mutual funds that are part of the "Using Statistics" scenario (see page 137) are classified according to the risk level of the mutual funds (low, average, and high) and type (small cap, mid cap, and large cap). Compute the range of the 2003 return for the small cap mutual funds with high risk.

SOLUTION: Ranked from the smallest to the largest, the 2003 return for the nine small cap mutual funds with high risk is the following:

37.3   39.2   44.2   44.5   53.8   56.6   59.3   62.4   66.5

Therefore, using Equation (4.1), the range = 66.5 − 37.3 = 29.2.

The largest difference between any two returns for the small cap mutual funds with high risk is 29.2.

The range measures the *total spread* in the set of data. Although the range is a simple measure of total variation in the data, it does not take into account *how* the data are distributed between the smallest and largest values. In other words, the range does not indicate if the values are evenly distributed throughout the data set, clustered near the middle, or clustered near one or both extremes. Thus, using the range as a measure of variation when at least one value is an extreme value is misleading.

Interquartile Range (IQR)

Symbol: IQR for sample or population

Formula: $IQR = Q_3 - Q_1$ **(4.2)**

EXAMPLE 4.16

Data set A: $IQR = 4.5 - 1.5 = 3$

Data set B: $IQR = 5 - 1 = 4$

Data set C: $IQR = 5 - 1 = 4$

These results would seem to indicate that data set A has less variability than data sets B and C. This is an improvement over the previous results based on the range (as we shall see shortly). However, data sets B and C do not have the same amount of variability.

The interquartile range is often preferred over the range as a measure of variability since the range can easily be influenced by one extreme value.

Consider the following example:

EXAMPLE 4.17

Data set D: 1, 3, 3, 4, 4, 4, 5, 5, 5, 5, 6, 6, 6, 7, 7, 7, 8, 8, 9, 10

Data set E: 1, 3, 3, 4, 4, 4, 5, 5, 5, 5, 6, 6, 6, 7, 7, 7, 8, 8, 9, 20

Suppose we use the *range* to measure the variability of these two data sets:

Data set D: $R = 10 - 1 = 9$ Data set E: $R = 20 - 1 = 19$

Intuitively, we would not expect that data set E would have twice as much variability as data set D (i.e., the range does not seem to be a good measure of variability in this case).

Now, suppose we use the *interquartile range* to measure the variability:

Data set D: $IQR = 7 - 4 = 3$ Data set E: $IQR = 7 - 4 = 3$

Intuitively, we would not say that both data sets have exactly the same variability. However, this appears to be closer to the truth than the conclusion that the range results lead us to. The IQR is not affected by one or two extreme values as the range is.

EXAMPLE 4.18

Computing the Interquartile Range for the 2003 Return of Small Cap High-Risk Mutual Funds

The 184 mutual funds that are part of the "Using Statistics" scenario (see page 137) are classified according to the risk level of the mutual funds (low, average, and high) and type (small cap, mid cap, and large cap). Compute the interquartile range of the 2003 return for the small cap mutual funds with high risk.

SOLUTION: Ranked from smallest to largest, the 2003 return for the nine small cap mutual funds with high risk is the following:

37.3   39.2   44.2   44.5   53.8   56.6   59.3   62.4   66.5

Using Equation (4.2) and the earlier results, $Q_1 = 41.7$ and $Q_3 = 60.85$.

Interquartile range $= 60.85 - 41.7 = 19.15$

Therefore, the interquartile range in the 2003 return is 19.15.

Because the interquartile range does not consider any value smaller than Q_1 or larger than Q_3, it is not affected by a limited number of extreme values. Summary measures such as the median, Q_1, Q_3, and the interquartile range, which are not easily influenced by extreme values, are called **resistant measures**.

Variance

Symbol	Population Parameter	Sample Statistic
Variance	σ^2	s^2
Standard Deviation	$\sqrt{\sigma^2} = \sigma$	$\sqrt{s^2} = s$
Size (Number of items or elements)	N	n

The symbol we use to denote the sample variance is s^2, as shown in the table above. The symbol we use to denote the population variance is $\boldsymbol{\sigma^2}$.

The formula to calculate the variance if you are given **sample** data is $s^2 = \dfrac{\sum (x - \bar{x})^2}{n - 1}$

The formula to calculate the variance if you are given **population** data is $\sigma^2 = \dfrac{\sum (x - \mu)^2}{N}$

Note: For the first time, we will get a different result for a descriptive measure if the data are a sample instead of a population. Previously, only the symbol was different (if anything was different).

We now have a measure of variability that considers *all* the values in a data set.

EXAMPLE 4.19

How to Calculate the Variance Using a Formula?

I. **Data set A: 1, 2, 3, 4, 5**

x	$x - \bar{x}$ or $x - \mu$	$(x - \bar{x})^2$ or $(x - \mu)^2$
1	-2	4
2	-1	1
3	0	0
4	1	1
5	2	4
		10 $\longleftarrow \sum (x - mean)^2 = 10$

If the data are from a **sample**, the sample variance is the following:

$$s^2 = \frac{\sum (x - \bar{x})^2}{n - 1} = \frac{10}{5 - 1} = 2.5$$

If the data are from a **population**, the population variance is the following:

$$\sigma^2 = \frac{\sum (x - \mu)^2}{N} = \frac{10}{5} = 2$$

II.   Data set B: 1, 1, 3, 3, 5, 5

x	$x - \bar{x}$ or $x - \mu$	$(x - \bar{x})^2$ or $(x - \mu)^2$
1	-2	4
1	-2	4
3	0	0
3	0	0
5	2	4
5	2	4
		16 $\longleftarrow$ $\sum(x - mean)^2 = 16$

If the data are from a **sample**, the sample variance is the following:

$$s^2 = \frac{\sum(x - \bar{x})^2}{n - 1} = \frac{16}{6 - 1} = 3.2$$

If the data are from a **population**, the population variance is the following:

$$\sigma^2 = \frac{\sum(x - \mu)^2}{N} = \frac{16}{6} = 2.67$$

III.   Data set C: 1, 1, 1, 5, 5, 5

x	$x - \bar{x}$ or $x - \mu$	$(x - \bar{x})^2$ or $(x - \mu)^2$
1	-2	4
1	-2	4
1	-2	4
5	2	4
5	2	4
5	2	4
		24 $\longleftarrow$ $\sum(x - mean)^2 = 24$

If the data are from a **sample**, the sample variance is the following:

$$s^2 = \frac{\sum(x - \bar{x})^2}{n - 1} = \frac{24}{6 - 1} = 4.8$$

If the data are from a population, the population variance is the following:

$$\sigma^2 = \frac{\sum(x - \mu)^2}{N} = \frac{24}{6} = 4$$

Conclusion: Based on these results, data set A has the least amount of variability, while data set C has the most. These results are reasonable when we understand that variability in statistics has nothing to do with how many different values there are but instead has to do with whether the data seem to be close to the mean or they tend to be further from the mean.

Variance is a good measure of variability in that it takes into account all values. However, variance has a major practical disadvantage: the units don't make sense. The units of variance are (data units)^2. For example, if the data in data set A are $, then the variance is 2.5^2. If the data are people, the variance is 2.5 people^2. Because of this problem, variance does not have a *practical* interpretation. In statistics, variance is used almost exclusively in the theoretical development of formulas.

Standard Deviation

Symbol: Sample standard deviation s Population standard deviation σ

Formula: Sample standard deviation: $s = \sqrt{s^2} = \sqrt{\dfrac{\Sigma(x - \bar{x})^2}{n - 1}}$

Population standard deviation: $\sigma = \sqrt{\sigma^2}$

EXAMPLE 4.20

Data set A: If the data are from a sample, the sample standard deviation is $s = \sqrt{s^2} = \sqrt{2.5} = 1.58$.

In Example 4.19, we found $s^2 = \dfrac{\Sigma(x - \bar{x})^2}{n - 1} = \dfrac{10}{5 - 1} = 2.5$.

Data set B: If the data are from a sample, the sample standard deviation is $s = \sqrt{s^2} = \sqrt{3.2} = 1.79$.

In Example 4.19, we found $s^2 = \dfrac{\Sigma(x - \bar{x})^2}{n - 1} = \dfrac{16}{6 - 1} = 3.2$.

Data set C: If the data are from a sample, the sample standard deviation is $s = \sqrt{s^2} = \sqrt{4.8} = 2.19$.

In Example 4.19, we found $s^2 = \dfrac{\Sigma(x - \bar{x})^2}{n - 1} = \dfrac{24}{6 - 1} = 4.8$.

We can see that the conclusions regarding which data set is the most variable and which is the least variable is the same as when we compared variances.

The main advantage of standard deviation, for practical purposes, is that the units are the *same* as the data.

Rounding Rule for Standard Deviation

Regarding the form of the answer when calculating standard deviation (when rounding is obviously necessary), use three (3) figures or a number that looks like the data, whichever has more figures. This rule also applies to the use of standard deviation in further calculations, although it is sometimes easier to use results stored in the memory of your calculator or computer.

Example 1: If data are 10,	11,	13,	15,	then	$s = 2.22$.
Example 2: If data are 2,315,	4,156,	7,542,	9,587,	then	$s = 3{,}275$.
Example 3: If data are 2,315,	2,320,	2,325,	2,330,	then	$s = 6.45$.
Example 4: If data are 23.46,	56.82,	83.47,	92.61,	then	$s = 31.05$.

Calculator Method to Obtain the Standard Deviation

The **CALC** function provides the mean, median, and standard deviation.

Use the calculator to calculate the standard deviation. Refer to **Data set A: 1, 2, 3, 4, 5**. Follow these steps to obtain the standard deviation:

INSTRUCTIONS
1. From the Main Menu, select the **STAT** mode.
2. Enter data set A (1,2,3,4,5) in List 1.
3. Select **CALC** (F2).
4. Select **SET** (F6).
5. Set the following:
   1 VarXList : List 1

1 VarFreq : "1"

After you are done, press **EXIT**.

6. Select **"1Var"** (F1) for the results.

RESULTS (with Casio FX-9750GII):

σ_x = 1.41421356 (where σ_x is the value of population standard deviation).

s_x = 1.58113883 (where s_x is the value of sample standard deviation).

The Casio calculator does not provide variance. The calculator presents the two standard deviation values: (1) sample standard deviation (with symbols "s_x" or "s_{n-1}" shown in your calculator) and (2) population standard deviation (with symbols" σ_x" or "σ_n" shown in your calculator). To obtain the variance, you square the standard deviation. The calculator symbols for standard deviation are presented below.

	CALCULATORS MODELS			
	Casio fx 9750 plus		Casio fx 9750 GII	
	Population	Sample	Population	Sample
Standard Deviation	xσ_n	xσ_{n-1}	σ_x	S_x

However, you must use the standard statistical symbols: σ (for population standard deviation), s (for sample standard deviation), σ^2 (for population variance) and s^2 (for sample variance).

EXAMPLE 4.21

Computing the Variance and Standard Deviation of the 2003 Return of Small Cap High-Risk Mutual Funds

The 184 mutual funds that are part of the "Using Statistics" scenario (see page 137) are classified according to the risk level of the mutual funds (low, average, and high) and type (small cap, mid cap, and large cap). Compute the variance and standard deviation of the 2003 return for the small cap mutual funds with high risk.

SOLUTION: Table 4.2 illustrates the computation of the variance and standard deviation of the return in 2003 for the small cap mutual funds with high risk. Using the equation below,

$$S^2 = \frac{\sum_{i=1}^{n}(X_i - \bar{X})^2}{n - 1}$$

$$= \frac{(44.5 - 51.53)^2 + (39.2 - 51.53)^2 + \cdots + (66.5 - 51.53)^2}{9 - 1}$$

$$= \frac{891.16}{8}$$

$$= 111.395$$

Using the equation below, the sample standard deviation S is

$$S = \sqrt{S^2} = \sqrt{\frac{\sum_{i=1}^{n}(X_i - \bar{X})^2}{n - 1}} = \sqrt{111.395} = 10.6\%$$

TABLE 4.2

Computing the
Variance of the 2003
Return for the Small
Cap Mutual Funds
with High Risk

$\overline{X} = 51.5333$

Return 2003	Step 1: $(X_i - \overline{X})$	Step 2: $(X_i - \overline{X})^2$
44.5	−7.0333	49.4678
39.2	−12.3333	152.1111
62.4	10.8667	118.0844
59.3	7.7667	60.3211
56.6	5.0667	25.6711
53.8	2.2667	5.1378
37.3	−14.2333	202.5878
44.2	−7.3333	53.7778
66.5	14.9667	224.0011
	Step 3: Sum:	Step 4: Divide by $(n - 1)$:
	891.16	111.395

The following summarizes the characteristics of the range, interquartile range, variance, and standard deviation.

- The more spread out, or dispersed, the data are, the larger the range, interquartile range, variance, and standard deviation.
- The more concentrated, or homogeneous, the data are, the smaller the range, interquartile range, variance, and standard deviation.
- If the values are all the same (so that there is no variation in the data), the range, interquartile range, variance, and standard deviation will all equal zero.
- None of the measures of variation (the range, interquartile range, standard deviation, and variance) can *ever* be negative.

Coefficient of Variation

All of the above measures of variability are *absolute* measures. It is often better (i.e., you get more meaningful results) to compare factors using *relative* measures. The coefficient of variation is a relative measure of variability.

The symbol for the coefficient of variation is CV.
The formulae to compute the coefficient of variation are

With a sample data: $CV = \dfrac{s}{\overline{x}} \times 100\%$

With a population data: $CV = \dfrac{\sigma}{\mu} \times 100\%$

CV is expressed in percentage.

Examples 4.22, 4.23, and 4.24 demonstrate how to determine the coefficient of variation.

EXAMPLE 4.22

The following information for four stocks is to be analyzed.

TABLE 4.3

Stock	Price	Dividend
ABC Company	$25	$0.70
DEF Company	47	1.50
HIJ Company	78	2.00
XYZ Company	92	3.00

Compare the variability of the prices and dividends.

SOLUTION: Since the sizes of the numbers in the two data sets are quite a bit different, it will be best to use a relative measure to compare the variability.

$$\text{Price:} \qquad CV = \frac{s}{\bar{x}} \times 100\% = \frac{30.23}{60.50} \times 100\% = 50\%$$

$$\text{Dividend:} \quad CV = \frac{s}{\bar{x}} \times 100\% = \frac{0.963}{1.80} \times 100\% = 53\%$$

Conclusion: Since $CV_{dividend} = 54\%$ is greater than $CV_{price} = 50\%$, the dividends are relatively more variable than the prices.

Note: If we had just looked at the standard deviation, we would have concluded (rather obviously because of the size of the numbers) that the prices were more variable.

Rounding rule for CV One decimal if $< 10\%$. No decimals if $> 10\%$.

EXAMPLE 4.23

The following table shows data for the houses that are being built on a short street in a new subdivision.

TABLE 4.4

House Number	Size Square ft.	Price ($ thousands)
1002	2400	269
1004	2650	289
1006	2200	225
1008	2150	219
1010	2500	249

Compare the variability of the sizes and the prices.

SOLUTION: Since the *units* of the data are *different,* the only way to compare the variability of these two sets of data is to use the coefficient of variation.

$$\text{Size:} \quad CV = \frac{s}{\bar{x}} \times 100\% = \frac{208}{2380} \times 100\% = 8.7\%$$

$$\text{Price:} \quad CV = \frac{s}{\bar{x}} \times 100\% = \frac{29.4}{250} \times 100\% = 12\%$$

Conclusion: Since $CV_{price} = 12\%$ is greater than $CV_{size} = 8.7\%$, the prices are relatively more variable than the sizes.

EXAMPLE 4.24

Comparing Two Coefficients of Variation When Two Variables Have Different Units of Measurement

The operations manager of a package delivery service is deciding on whether to purchase a new fleet of trucks. When packages are stored in the trucks in preparation for delivery, you need to consider two major constraints—the weight (in pounds) and the volume (in cubic feet) for each item.

The operations manager samples 200 packages and finds that the mean weight is 26.0 pounds, with a standard deviation of 3.9 pounds, and the mean volume is 8.8 cubic feet, with a standard deviation of 2.2 cubic feet. How can the operations manager compare the variation of the weight and the volume?

SOLUTION: Because the measurement units differ for the weight and volume constraints, the operations manager should compare the relative variability in the two types of measurements.

For weight, the coefficient of variation is

$$CV_W = \left(\frac{3.9}{26.0}\right) 100\% = 15\%$$

For volume, the coefficient of variation is

$$CV_V = \left(\frac{2.2}{8.8}\right) 100\% = 25\%$$

Since $CV_V = 25\% > CV_W = 15\%$, the package volume is much more variable than the package weight.

Problems for Section 4.2

4.20 Last year's travel expenditures ($) by the 12 members of a university's business council were as follows:

0	0	173	378	441	733	759
857	958	985	1434	2063		

a. Calculate the mean travel expenditure per member.
b. Determine the median travel expenditure per member.
c. Determine the 80th percentile of these data.
d. Determine the range and the interquartile range of the data.
e. Calculate the coefficient of variation of the data.

4.21 The number of defective items in 12 recent production lots of 1,000 items, each from Plant A, were as follows:

3 1 0 0 2 21 4 1 1 0 2 5

a. Calculate the mean number of defective items per lot.
b. The mean number of defectives per lot in a group of 16 lots from Plant B was 3.5. What was the total number of defective items in these 16 lots?
c. What is the median number of defective items per lot?
d. Why does the median differ substantially from the mean of these data?
e. The median number of defectives per lot for 20 lots from Plant C was 4. What was the total number of defectives in these 20 lots?
f. What is the standard deviation of the number of defectives per lot for Plant A?

4.22 The change in enrollment between this year and last year in seven programs at a particular university are as follows:

−614 −103 41 258 313 387 490

a. Calculate the mean enrollment change per program. Does the fact that the mean is positive imply that the combined total enrollment in the seven programs has increased? Explain.
b. Determine the median enrollment change per program.
c. Calculate the standard deviation of enrollment change. Does the fact that the standard deviation is positive relate to the fact that the mean was positive? Explain.

4.23 Refer to Problem 4.2 in Descriptive Statistics Exercises—Set 1:
What is the standard deviation of the liquor bill for a table?

4.24 Refer to Problem 4.8 in Descriptive Statistics Exercises—Set 1:

What is the standard deviation of the sales of a toy store?

4.25 Refer to Problem 4.10 in Descriptive Statistics Exercises—Set 1:
What is the standard deviation of the cost of a one-day trip for people under 50 years old?

4.26 Refer to Problem 4.15 in Descriptive Statistics Exercises—Set 1:
What is the standard deviation of the monetary value of the prizes?

4.27 Refer to Problem 4.17 in Descriptive Statistics Exercises—Set 1:
What is the standard deviation of the labour hours per car for the four GM plants?

4.28 Refer to Problem 4.19 in Descriptive Statistics Exercises—Set 1:
What is the standard deviation of the company profits?

4.29 A suburban farm grows strawberries in a large field where prospective customers go to pick-their-own. A survey of 200 customers showed that 30% picked one basket, 50% picked two baskets, and the remainder picked three baskets. What is the mean number of baskets of strawberries per customer? What is the standard deviation?

4.30 The means and standard deviations of revenue per farm ($ thousands) and volume harvested per farm (thousands of kg.) for two farm products in Western Canada are as follows:

Grain	Revenue per Farm Mean	Revenue per Farm Std. Dev.	Volume per Farm Mean	Volume per Farm Std. Dev.
Wheat	12.56	4.03	76.7	22.9
Barley	14.49	5.89	106.3	35.4

Is revenue or volume relatively more variable for wheat? Is the same true for barley?

4.31 The table below appeared in the May 1995 issue of *Report on Business*.
a. What is the overall average selling space per store for all 469 stores?
b. What is the overall average sales per store for all 469 stores?

Can Brooks Catch Up

Coutu's current stores outperform its newly acquired Brooks outlets

Coutu stores averaged sales of $6 million in 94

Number of franchises 227
Selling space per store .... 7,700 sq.ft.
System-wide retail sales 1994 .... $1.34 billion

...and the U.S. Maxi outlets averaged $4 million

Number of stores 21
Selling space per store .... 12,000 sq.ft.
1994 sales .... $85 million

...while Brooks lagged far behind at $1.9 million

Number of stores 221
Selling space per store .... 6,000 sq.ft.
1994 sales .... $425.8 million

4.32 The percentage distribution of hourly earnings for the 2,100 plant employees of the ABC Corp. is shown below:

Hourly Earnings ($)	Percent of Employees
14.00 and under 16.00	12
16.00 " " 18.00	24
18.00 " " 20.00	44
20.00 " " 25.00	15
25.00 " " 30.00	5

Calculate the mean and standard deviation of hourly earnings of the employees at ABC Corp.

4.33 Refer to the table 'Who works the hardest' and determine if the five countries indicated were more variable in terms of average hours worked or gross domestic product in 2000.

Who works the hardest
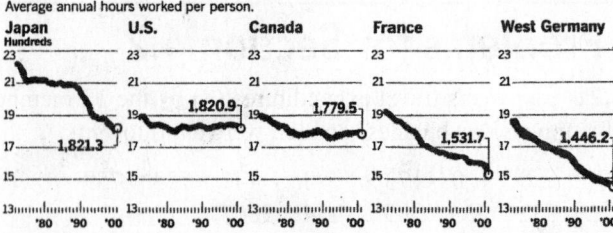

Buying power
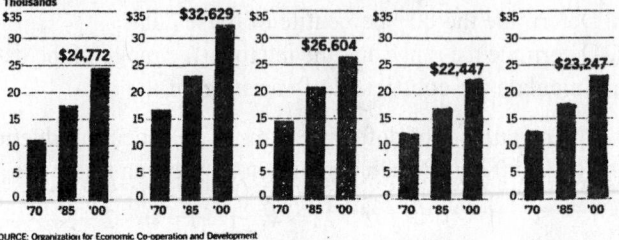

SOURCE: Organization for Economic Co-operation and Development

4.3 Descriptive Statistics III

Shape

Shape is the pattern of the distribution of data values throughout the entire range of all the values. A distribution is either symmetrical or skewed. In a **symmetrical** distribution, the values below the mean are distributed in exactly the same way as the values above the mean. In this case, the low and high values balance each other out. In a **skewed** distribution, the values are not symmetrical around the mean. This skewness results in an imbalance of low values or high values.

Shape also can influence the relationship of the mean to the median. In most cases:

- Mean < median: negative, or left-skewed
- Mean = median: symmetric, or zero skewness
- Mean > median: positive, or right-skewed

Figure 4.1 depicts three data sets, each with a different shape.

FIGURE 4.1
A comparison of three data sets that differ in shape

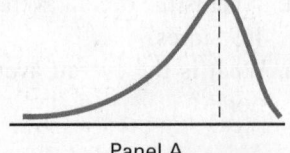

Panel A
Negative, or left-skewed

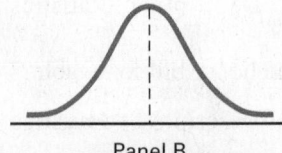

Panel B
Symmetrical

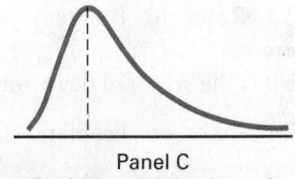

Panel C
Positive, or right-skewed

The data in Panel A are negative, or **left-skewed**. In this panel, most of the values are in the upper portion of the distribution. A long tail and distortion to the left is caused by some extremely small values. These extremely small values pull the mean downward so that the mean is less than the median.

The data in Panel B are symmetrical. Each half of the curve is a mirror image of the other half of the curve. The low and high values on the scale balance, and the mean equals the median.

The data in Panel C are positive, or **right-skewed**. In this panel, most of the values are in the lower portion of the distribution. A long tail on the right is caused by some extremely large values. These extremely large values pull the mean upward so that the mean is greater than the median.

Problems for Section 4.3

LEARNING THE BASICS

4.34 The following set of data is from a sample of $n = 5$:

$$7 \quad 4 \quad 9 \quad 8 \quad 2$$

a. Compute the mean, median, and mode.
b. Compute the range, variance, standard deviation, and coefficient of variation.
c. Compute the Z scores. Are there any outliers?
d. Describe the shape of the data set.

4.35 The following set of data is from a sample of $n = 6$:

$$7 \quad 4 \quad 9 \quad 7 \quad 3 \quad 12$$

a. Compute the mean, median, and mode.
b. Compute the range, variance, standard deviation, and coefficient of variation.
c. Compute the Z scores. Are there any outliers?
d. Describe the shape of the data set.

4.36 The following set of data is from a sample of $n = 7$:

$$12 \quad 7 \quad 4 \quad 9 \quad 0 \quad 7 \quad 3$$

a. Compute the mean, median, and mode.
b. Compute the range, variance, standard deviation, and coefficient of variation.
c. Compute the Z scores. Are there any outliers?
d. Describe the shape of the data set.

4.37 The following set of data is from a sample of $n = 5$:

$$7 \quad -5 \quad -8 \quad 7 \quad 9$$

a. Compute the mean, median, and mode.
b. Compute the range, variance, standard deviation, and coefficient of variation.
c. Compute the Z scores. Are there any outliers?
d. Describe the shape of the data set.

APPLYING THE CONCEPTS

4.38 A survey conducted by the American Statistical Association reported the following results for the salaries of professors teaching statistics in research universities with four to five years in the rank of associate professor and professor.

Title	Median
Associate professor	81,600
Professor	120,000

Source: Data extracted from **magazine.amstat.org/blog/2010/12/01/academic-salary-survey**.

Interpret the median salary for the associate professors and professors.

4.39 The operations manager of a plant that manufactures tires wants to compare the actual inner diameters of two grades of tires, each of which is expected to be 575 millimeters. A sample of five tires of each grade was selected, and the results representing the inner diameters of the tires, ranked from smallest to largest, are as follows:

Grade X	Grade Y
568 570 575 578 584	573 574 575 577 578

a. For each of the two grades of tires, compute the mean, median, and standard deviation.
b. Which grade of tire is providing better quality? Explain.
c. What would be the effect on your answers in (a) and (b) if the last value for grade Y were 588 instead of 578? Explain.

4.40 According to the U.S. Census Bureau, in 2010, the median sales price of new houses was $221,000 and the mean sales price was $272,400 (extracted from **www.census.gov,** April 4, 2011).
a. Interpret the median sales price.
b. Interpret the mean sales price.
c. Discuss the shape of the distribution of the price of new houses.

✓ SELF Test **4.41** The file **FastFood** contains the amount that a sample of nine customers spent for lunch ($) at a fast-food restaurant:

$$4.20 \quad 5.03 \quad 5.86 \quad 6.45 \quad 7.38 \quad 7.54 \quad 8.46 \quad 8.47 \quad 9.87$$

a. Compute the mean and median.
b. Compute the variance, standard deviation, range, and coefficient of variation.

c. Are the data skewed? If so, how?

d. Based on the results of (a) through (c), what conclusions can you reach concerning the amount that customers spent for lunch?

4.42 The file Sedans contains the overall miles per gallon (MPG) of 2011 family sedans:

24 21 25 22 23 34 34
20 20 22 44 32 20 20

Source: Data extracted from "Ratings," *Consumer Reports*, April 2011, pp. 30–31.

a. Compute the mean, median, and mode.

b. Compute the variance, standard deviation, range, coefficient of variation, and Z scores.

c. Are the data skewed? If so, how?

d. Compare the results of (a) through (c) to those of Problem 4.43 (a) through (c) that refer to the miles per gallon of small SUVs.

4.43 The file SUV contains the overall miles per gallon (MPG) of 2011 small SUVs:

20 24 22 23 20 22 21 22 22
19 22 22 26 19 19 23 24 21
21 19 21 22 22 16 16

Source: Data extracted from "Ratings," *Consumer Reports*, April 2011, pp. 35–36.

a. Compute the mean, median, and mode.

b. Compute the variance, standard deviation, range, coefficient of variation, and Z scores.

c. Are the data skewed? If so, how?

d. Compare the results of (a) through (c) to those of Problem 4.42 (a) through (c) that refer to the miles per gallon of family sedans.

4.44 The file ChocolateChip contains the cost (in cents) per 1-ounce serving for a sample of 13 chocolate chip cookies. The data are as follows:

54 22 25 23 36 43 7 43 25 47 24 45 44

Source: Data extracted from "Chip, Chip, Hooray," *Consumer Reports*, June 2009, p. 7.

a. Compute the mean, median, and mode.

b. Compute the variance, standard deviation, range, coefficient of variation, and Z scores. Are there any outliers? Explain.

c. Are the data skewed? If so, how?

d. Based on the results of (a) through (c), what conclusions can you reach concerning the cost of chocolate chip cookies?

4.45 The file DarkChocolate contains the cost per ounce ($) for a sample of 14 dark chocolate bars:

0.68 0.72 0.92 1.14 1.42 0.94 0.77
0.57 1.51 0.57 0.55 0.86 1.41 0.90

Source: Data extracted from "Dark Chocolate: Which Bars Are Best?" *Consumer Reports*, September 2007, p. 8.

a. Compute the mean, median, and mode.

b. Compute the variance, standard deviation, range, coefficient of variation, and Z scores. Are there any outliers? Explain.

c. Are the data skewed? If so, how?

d. Based on the results of (a) through (c), what conclusions can you reach concerning the cost of dark chocolate bars?

4.46 Is there a difference in the variation of the yields of different types of investments? The file CDRate contains the yields for a one-year certificate of deposit (CD) and a five-year certificate of deposit (CD), for 23 banks in the United States, as of April 4, 2011.

Source: Data extracted from **www.Bankrate.com**, April 4, 2011.

a. For one-year and five-year CDs, separately compute the variance, standard deviation, range, and coefficient of variation.

b. Based on the results of (a), do one-year or five-year CDs have more variation in the yields offered? Explain.

4.47 The file HotelUK contains the average room price (in English pounds) paid in six British cities in 2010:

110 98 78 70 76 62

Source: Data extracted from **www.hotels.com/press/hotel-price-index-summer-2010.html**.

a. Compute the mean, median, and mode.

b. Compute the range, variance, and standard deviation.

c. Based on the results of (a) and (b), what conclusions can you reach concerning the room price (in English pounds) in 2010?

d. Suppose that the first value was 160 instead of 110. Repeat (a) through (c), using this value. Comment on the difference in the results.

4.48 A bank branch located in a commercial district of a city has the business objective of developing an improved process for serving customers during the noon-to-1:00 P.M. lunch period. The waiting time, in minutes, is defined as the time the customer enters the line to when he or she reaches the teller window. Data are collected from a sample of 15 customers during this hour. The file Bank1 contains the results, which are also listed here:

4.21 5.55 3.02 5.13 4.77 2.34 3.54 3.20
4.50 6.10 0.38 5.12 6.46 6.19 3.79

a. Compute the mean and median.

b. Compute the variance, standard deviation, range, coefficient of variation, and Z scores. Are there any outliers? Explain.

c. Are the data skewed? If so, how?

d. As a customer walks into the branch office during the lunch hour, she asks the branch manager how long she can expect to wait. The branch manager replies, "Almost certainly less than five minutes." On the basis of the results of (a) through (c), evaluate the accuracy of this statement.

4.49 Suppose that another bank branch, located in a residential area, is also concerned with the noon-to-1 P.M. lunch hour. The waiting time, in minutes, collected from a sample of 15 customers during this hour, is contained in the file `Bank2` and listed here:

9.66 5.90 8.02 5.79 8.73 3.82 8.01 8.35
10.49 6.68 5.64 4.08 6.17 9.91 5.47

a. Compute the mean and median.
b. Compute the variance, standard deviation, range, coefficient of variation, and Z scores. Are there any outliers? Explain.
c. Are the data skewed? If so, how?
d. As a customer walks into the branch office during the lunch hour, he asks the branch manager how long he can expect to wait. The branch manager replies, "Almost certainly less than five minutes." On the basis of the results of (a) through (c), evaluate the accuracy of this statement.

4.4 Box-Whisker Plot

A. What Is the Five-Number Summary?

Sections 4.1 and 4.2 discussed the measures of central tendency and measures of variability. You can graphically display these two measures in a box-whisker plot. The box-whisker plot gives an overall picture of a set of numerical data. You can summarize the numerical data by means of a five-number summary. The "five-number" summarizes the various positions of a set of data. The five-number summary contains the following:

1. Minimum (value)
2. First quartile (Q1)
3. Median (Q2)
4. Third quartile (Q3)
5. Maximum (value)

You can use the five-number summary to construct a box-whisker plot.

B. How to Construct a Box-Whisker Plot

A box-whisker plot is a diagram that can be constructed using the following steps (if it has no outliers values):

1. Draw an evenly spaced scale that covers all of the data values.
2. Using the scale as a reference, draw the box with the *first quartile* (Q_1) and *third quartile* (Q_3) as the sides of the box (see A_1 and A_2 in Figure 4.2). Join the two vertical sides with horizontal sides to form a box.
3. Using the scale as a reference, draw a vertical line across the box to represent the *median* (see **B** in Figure 4.2).
4. Using the scale as a reference, draw a horizontal line linking Q_1 (which is the left-hand side of the box) to the minimum (see **C** in Figure 4.2). The horizontal line from Q_1 to minimum is called the *left whisker*.

FIGURE 4.2
The Box-Whisker Plot

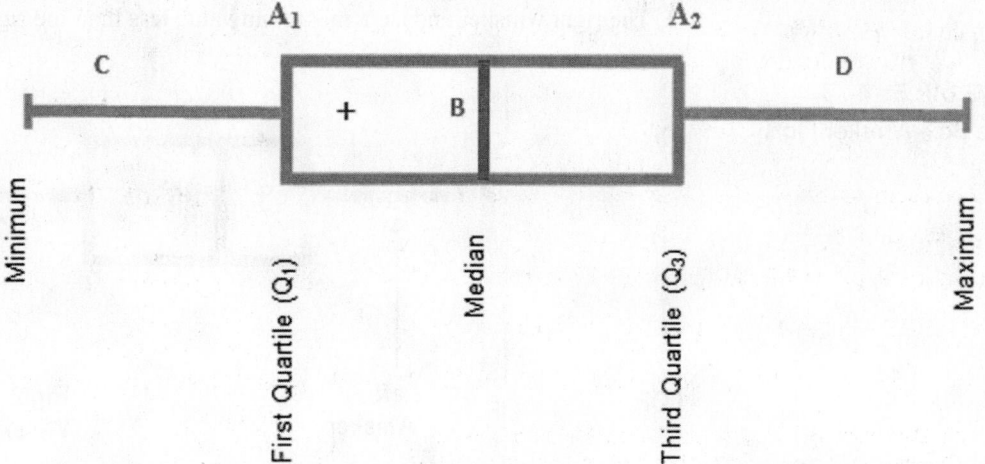

5. Using the scale as a reference, draw a horizontal line linking Q_3 (which is the right-hand side of the box) to the maximum (see **D** in Figure 4.2). The horizontal line from Q_3 to maximum is called the *right whisker*.
6. Similarly, indicate the mean with a '+' sign on the diagram (see Figure 4.2).

The box-whisker plot shown in Figure 4.2 resembles the five-number summary.

However, you have to check whether the minimum and maximum values are either suspect outliers or outliers.

C. How Do You Determine the Suspect Outliers and Outliers?

Suspect Outliers are defined as data values that lie between the inner and outer fences. Suspect outliers are plotted individually using a special symbol, 'o'.

Outliers are defined as data values that lie outside the outer fences. The outliers are plotted individually using a special symbol, '*'.

How to determine the inner and outer fences?

There are four fences, namely

1. Right Inner Fence (RIF) is a value that lies on the right-hand side of the box (see Figure 4.2).
2. Right Outer Fence (ROF) is a value that lies on the right-hand side of the box.
3. Left Inner Fence (LIF) is a value that lies on the left-hand side of the box.
4. Left Outer Fence (LOF) is a value that lies on the left-hand side of the box.

The left and right fences are then calculated but are *not* plotted on the diagram.

The formulae to calculate the fences are as follows:

1. $\text{RIF} = Q_3 + (1.5 \times \text{IQR})$
2. $\text{ROF} = \text{RIF} + (1.5 \times \text{IQR})$
3. $\text{LIF} = Q_1 - (1.5 \times \text{IQR})$
4. $\text{LOF} = \text{LIF} - (1.5 \times \text{IQR})$

Note: IQR stands for *Interquartile Range*. $\text{IQR} = Q_3 - Q_1$, where Q_3 is the third quartile and Q_1 is the first quartile.

What happens if the minimum and maximum values are identified as either suspect outliers or outliers? In this case, you have to redefine the whiskers on both sides of the box.

D. How to Determine the Whiskers

There are two whiskers, one on each side of the box (as shown in Figure 4.3)

There are two rules to determine the whiskers. Each whisker is as long as possible, but

- the whiskers cannot go past the inner fence.
- the whiskers must end at a data point (or value).

Applying these two rules, you have the following:

1. The left whisker ends at a minimum value **greater** than the left inner fence (LIF).
2. The right whisker ends at a maximum value **less** than the right inner fence (RIF).

FIGURE 4.3
The Box-Whisker Plot

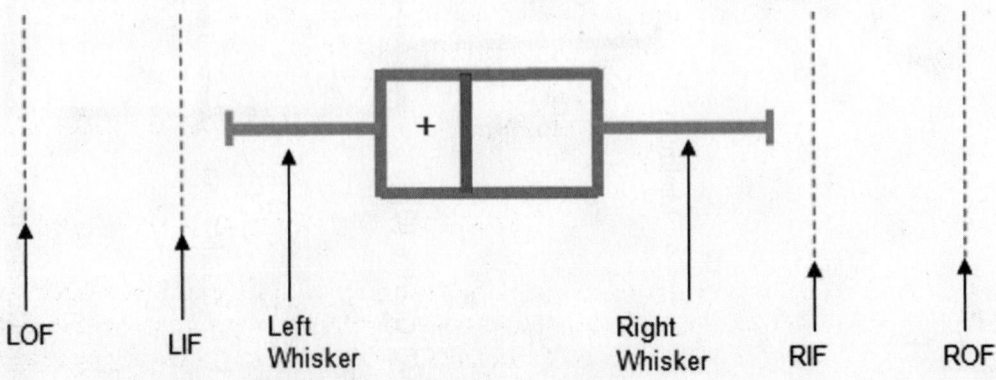

Note:
- The box-whisker plot is not drawn to scale
- The **inner and outer fences** are plotted in this diagram for illustrative purposes.

EXAMPLE 4.25

The following data show the number of days absent from work for 50 employees in a large company. The data have been arranged into an ascending data array.

1	2	4	4	5	5	5	10	10	11
12	13	13	14	19	20	22	23	25	26
26	26	27	27	27	28	29	29	29	30
31	31	32	33	35	35	36	52	54	61
68	74	81	84	95	123	126	137	152	173

The following statistics have been calculated using the CASIO CFX-9850GB calculator.

Mean: 40.7   Min: 1
Median: 27.5   Max: 173
Q1:   13
Q3:   52
IQR: 39

The first step in drawing the box-whisker plot is to lay out an appropriate horizontal scale.

The box is then formed with the first and third quartiles determining the location of the sides. The *mean* may be indicated with a '+' sign. The *median* is indicated by a line across the box.

The **inner left and right fences** are then calculated but are not plotted on the diagram.

The formulae to calculate the **left inner fence (LIF)** and **right inner fence (RIF)** are as followed:

$$\text{LIF} = Q_1 - (1.5 \times \text{IQR}) \qquad \text{RIF} = Q_3 + (1.5 \times \text{IQR})$$

The whiskers may now be drawn using the following procedure:

i. Imagine plotting all the data between the edge of the box and the inner fences (including data that fall on the fence) as points.
ii. Two (2) rules now apply for the whiskers. Each whisker is as long as possible, but
  a) it can't go past the inner fence.
  b) it must end at a data point.

Now we can calculate the location of the **left outer fence (LOF)** and **right outer fence (ROF)** as follows:

$$\text{LOF} = \text{LIF} - (1.5 \times \text{IQR}) \qquad \text{ROF} = \text{RIF} + (1.5 \times \text{IQR})$$

All data values that fall between the fences are called **suspect outliers** and are plotted individually using a special symbol. SPSS uses an 'o' symbol to indicate **suspect outliers**. Suspect outliers are values that are *somewhat unusual* in that they lie away from the majority of the data.

All data values that lie beyond the outer fences are called **outliers** and are also plotted using a special symbol. SPSS uses an '*' symbol to indicate outliers. Outliers are *unusual* values that are often of extreme interest to the statistical analyst.

Using the data in Example 4.25, the values of the fences are calculated as followed:

$$LIF = Q_1 - (1.5 \times IQR) = 13 - (1.5 \times 39) = -45.5$$
$$LOF = LIF - (1.5 \times IQR) = -45.5 - (1.5 \times 39) = -104$$
$$RIF = Q_3 + (1.5 \times IQR) = 52 + (1.5 \times 39) = 110.5$$
$$ROF = RIF + (1.5 \times IQR) = 110.5 + (1.5 \times 39) = 169$$

The complete box-whisker plot is shown below.

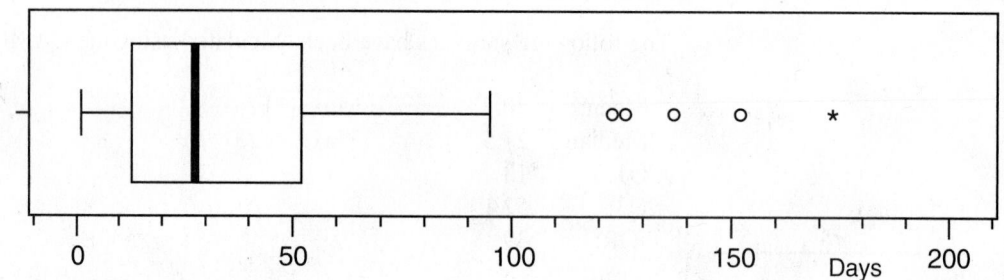

Note: In the diagram, the suspect outliers are indicated by the 'o' symbol. The outliers are indicated by the '*' symbol.

CALCULATOR LESSON 4

CASIO FX-9750GII CALCULATOR

Lesson 4—Graph a Box-Whisker Plot

The following data show the response times, in days, for 50 customer complaints for a large car dealership. The data have been arranged into an ascending data array.

1	2	4	4	5	5	5	10	10	11
12	13	13	14	19	20	22	23	25	26
26	26	27	27	27	28	29	29	29	30
31	31	32	33	35	35	36	52	54	61
68	74	81	84	95	123	126	137	152	173

Follow these steps to draw the box-whisker plot.

Step 1: From the **Main Menu,** select **STAT mode.**

Step 2: Enter data into **List 1**.

Step 3: Press **F1 (GRPH).**

Step 4: Select F6(SET) and then enter the following items:

StatGraph1
Graph Type   : ▶ (press **F6**) and select **BOX (F2)**
XList   : List (F1) and type **1** (if you input your data in List 1)
Frequency   : 1 (F1)
Outlier   : ON (F1)

Now press **EXE**, and then select **GPH1 (F1).**

The calculator will now show the box-whisker plot.

To obtain a full range of one-variable statistics, press **F1 (1 VAR)** at the bottom left-hand corner of the screen. The result is the following:

$$\bar{x} = 40.7$$
$$\Sigma x = 2035$$
$$\Sigma x^2 = 164603$$
$$\sigma x = 40.4421809$$
$$sx = 40.8527719$$
$$n = 50$$
$$\text{minx} = 1$$
$$Q1 = 13$$
$$\text{Med} = 27.5$$
$$Q3 = 52$$
$$\text{maxX} = 173$$
$$\text{Mod} = 5$$
$$\text{Mod} = 26$$
$$\text{Mod} = 27$$
$$\text{Mod} = 29$$
$$\text{Mod:n} = 4$$
$$\text{Mod:F} = 3$$

To go back to view the plot, press **F6(DRAW)**.

The Five-Number Summary

A **five-number summary**, which consists of the following, provides a way to determine the shape of a distribution:

$$X_{smallest} \quad Q_1 \quad \text{Median} \quad Q_3 \quad X_{largest}$$

Table 4.5 explains how the relationships among these five numbers allow you to recognize the shape of a data set.

To further analyze the sample of 10 times to get ready in the morning, you can compute the five-number summary. For these data, the smallest value is 29 minutes, and the largest value is 52 minutes. Calculations done show that the median = 39.5, $Q_1 = 35$, and $Q_3 = 44$. Therefore, the five-number summary is as follows:

$$29 \quad 35 \quad 39.5 \quad 44 \quad 52$$

The distance from $X_{smallest}$ to the median $(39.5 - 29 = 10.5)$ is slightly less than the distance from the median to $X_{largest}$ $(52 - 39.5 = 12.5)$. The distance from $X_{smallest}$ to Q_1 $(35 - 29 = 6)$ is slightly less than the distance from Q_3 to $X_{largest}$ $(52 - 44 = 8)$. The distance from Q_1 to the median $(39.5 - 35 = 4.5)$ is the same as the distance from the median to Q_3 $(44 - 39.5 = 4.5)$. Therefore, the getting-ready times are slightly right-skewed.

TABLE 4.5

Relationships Among the Five-Number Summary and the Type of Distribution

| | Type of Distribution | | |
Comparison	Left-Skewed	Symmetric	Right-Skewed
The distance from $X_{smallest}$ to the median versus the distance from the median to $X_{largest}$.	The distance from $X_{smallest}$ to the median is greater than the distance from the median to $X_{largest}$.	The two distances are the same.	The distance from $X_{smallest}$ to the median is less than the distance from the median to $X_{largest}$.
The distance from $X_{smallest}$ to Q_1 versus the distance from Q_3 to $X_{largest}$.	The distance from $X_{smallest}$ to Q_1 is greater than the distance from Q_3 to $X_{largest}$.	The two distances are the same.	The distance from $X_{smallest}$ to Q_1 is less than the distance from Q_3 to $X_{largest}$.
The distance from Q_1 to the median versus the distance from the median to Q_3.	The distance from Q_1 to the median is greater than the distance from the median to Q_3.	The two distances are the same.	The distance from Q_1 to the median is less than the distance from the median to Q_3.

EXAMPLE 4.26

Computing the Five-Number Summary of the Number of Calories in Cereals

Nutritional data about a sample of seven breakfast cereals (stored in ▇Cereals▇) includes the number of calories per serving. Compute the five-number summary of the number of calories in cereals.

SOLUTION From previous computations for the number of calories in cereals, you know that the median = 110, $Q_1 = 100$, and $Q_3 = 190$.

In addition, the smallest value in the data set is 80, and the largest value is 200. Therefore, the five-number summary is as follows:

$$80 \quad 100 \quad 110 \quad 190 \quad 200$$

The three comparisons listed in Table 4.5 are used to evaluate skewness. The distance from $X_{smallest}$ to the median ($110 - 80 = 30$) is less than the distance ($200 - 110 = 90$) from the median to $X_{largest}$. The distance from $X_{smallest}$ to Q_1 ($100 - 80 = 20$) is the more than the distance from Q_3 to $X_{largest}$ ($200 - 190 = 10$). The distance from Q_1 to the median ($110 - 100 = 10$) is less than the distance from the median to Q_3 ($190 - 110 = 80$). Two comparisons indicate a right-skewed distribution, whereas the other indicates a left-skewed distribution. Therefore, given the small sample size and the conflicting results, the shape is not clearly determined.

EXAMPLE 4.27

The Boxplots of the 2006 Returns of Growth and Value Mutual Funds

The 868 mutual funds (▇Mutual Funds▇) that are part of the Using Statistics scenario are classified according to whether the mutual funds are growth or value funds. Construct the boxplot of the 2006 returns for growth and value mutual funds.

SOLUTION Figure 4.4 shows the 2006 return for the growth and value mutual funds and Figure 4.5 illustrates Minitab boxplots. The median return, the quartiles, and the minimum and maximum returns are much higher for the value funds than for the growth funds. Both the growth and value funds appear to be fairly symmetrical between the quartiles, but the value funds seem to have more extremely high returns.

FIGURE 4.4

FIGURE 4.4

PHStat2 boxplots of the
2006 return for growth
and value mutual funds

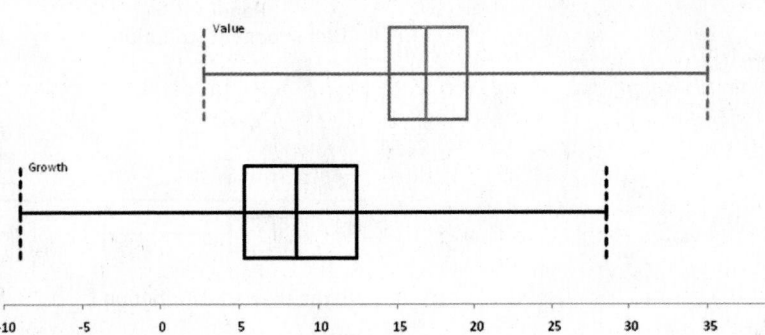

**Boxplots for the Growth and Value Funds
2006 Return**

FIGURE 4.5

Minitab boxplots of the
2006 return for growth
and value mutual funds

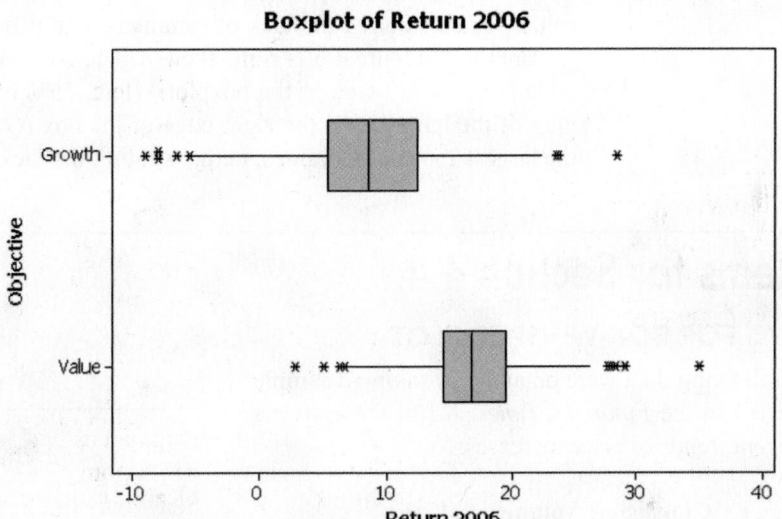

Boxplot of Return 2006

Notice that in Figure 4.5, several * appear in the boxplots. This indicates outliers that are more than 1.5 times the interquartile range beyond the quartiles.

Figure 4.6 demonstrates the relationship between the boxplot and the polygon for four different types of distributions. (*Note:* The area under each polygon is split into quartiles corresponding to the five-number summary for the boxplot.)

Panels A and D of Figure 4.6 are symmetrical. In these distributions, the mean and median are equal. In addition, the length of the left tail is equal to the length of the right tail, and the median line divides the box in half.

Panel B of Figure 4.6 is left-skewed. The few small values distort the mean toward the left tail. For this left-skewed distribution, there is a heavy clustering of values at the high end of the

FIGURE 4.6

Boxplots and corresponding polygons for four distributions

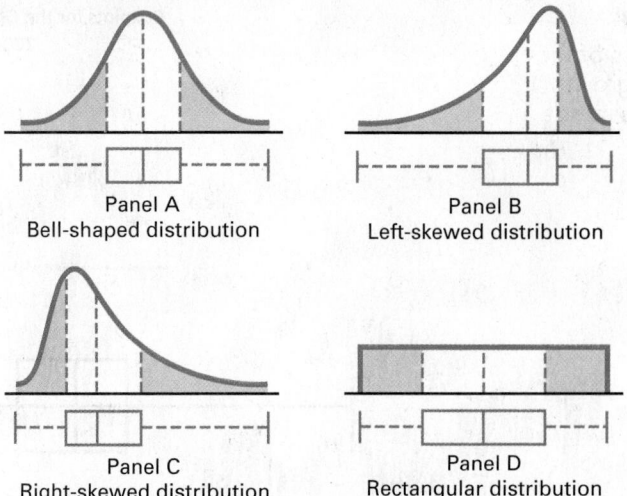

Panel A
Bell-shaped distribution

Panel B
Left-skewed distribution

Panel C
Right-skewed distribution

Panel D
Rectangular distribution

scale (i.e., the right side); 75% of all values are found between the left edge of the box (Q_1) and the end of the right tail ($X_{largest}$). There is a long left tail that contains the smallest 25% of the values, demonstrating the lack of symmetry in this data set.

Panel C of Figure 4.6 is right-skewed. The concentration of values is on the low end of the scale (i.e., the left side of the boxplot). Here, 75% of all values are found between the beginning of the left tail and the right edge of the box (Q_3). There is a long right tail that contains the largest 25% of the values, demonstrating the lack of symmetry in this data set.

Problems for Section 4.4

PROBLEMS FOR BOX-WHISKER PLOT

4.50 The following data were obtained by taking a sample of stocks listed in the *Financial Times*. All of these stocks have had recent trends of price increases.

Stock	Closing Price	Volume ($ hundreds)	Yield %	P/E Ratio
Abitibi-Price	20.25	31435	0.7	67.5
Agnico Eagle	19.38	7529	na	55.4
Air Canada	7.75	13010	na	na
Alberta Energy	20.75	9934	1.9	15.6
Arbor Me	18.50	770	0.3	21.8
Atlantis	1.90	3896	na	14.6
Brascan Cl	19.38	2616	5.4	57.5
Brunswick	11.12	749	3.1	na
Canadex j	33.30	62	na	20.6
Donohue Sv	16.75	1938	1.6	23.8
Electrohom	10.38	920	1.0	7.7
Finning	21.62	1658	1.5	19.3
Gennum	18.50	4	0.4	14.6
Hemlo gold	15.38	3091	1.3	24.4
Ipsco	26.25	1873	1.8	17.5
Jordan Petrol	10.62	356	na	31.3
Kerr Addison	24.50	292	2.5	37.1
Lynx Energy	11.00	10	na	13.6
MDS Helth	14.38	60	1.0	13.2
Noranda	27.50	26426	3.6	32.5
Okanaga	3.30	46	0.6	33.0

Stock	Closing Price	Volume ($ hundreds)	Yield %	P/E Ratio
Pagurian nv	4.50	3898	6.7	13.6
Rio Algom	25.75	24697	2.3	21.6
Shaw Ind	13.75	557	1.0	16.0
Tombill A	5.50	2	3.3	7.6
Versa Services	10.12	699	2.2	21.5
Wetsmin	5.62	388	3.5	na
XL Foods	0.78	1315	na	7.8

a. Draw the box-whisker plot for the Volume data.
b. Draw the box-whisker plot for the Yield data.

4.51 Refer to Problem 4.20 in Descriptive Statistics Exercises—Set 2:

Draw the box-whisker plot for the travel expense data.

4.52 Refer to Problem 4.21 in Descriptive Statistics Exercises—Set 2:

Draw the box-whisker plot for the number of defectives data.

4.53 Refer to Problem 4.22 in Descriptive Statistics Exercises—Set 2:

Draw the box-whisker plot for the university enrollment data.

LEARNING THE BASICS

4.54 The following is a set of data from a sample of $n = 7$:

$$12 \quad 7 \quad 4 \quad 9 \quad 0 \quad 7 \quad 3$$

a. Compute the first quartile (Q_1), the third quartile (Q_3), and the interquartile range.
b. List the five-number summary.
c. Construct a boxplot and describe its shape.
d. Compare your answer in (c) with that from Problem 4.36 (d) on page 165. Discuss.

4.55 The following is a set of data from a sample of $n = 6$:

$$7 \quad 4 \quad 9 \quad 7 \quad 3 \quad 12$$

a. Compute the first quartile (Q_1), the third quartile (Q_3), and the interquartile range.
b. List the five-number summary.
c. Construct a boxplot and describe its shape.
d. Compare your answer in (c) with that from Problem 4.35 (d) on page 165. Discuss.

4.56 The following is a set of data from a sample of $n = 5$:

$$7 \quad 4 \quad 9 \quad 8 \quad 2$$

a. Compute the first quartile (Q_1), the third quartile (Q_3), and the interquartile range.
b. List the five-number summary.
c. Construct a boxplot and describe its shape.
d. Compare your answer in (c) with that from Problem 4.34 (d) on page 165. Discuss.

4.57 The following is a set of data from a sample of $n = 5$:

$$7 \quad -5 \quad -8 \quad 7 \quad 9$$

a. Compute the first quartile (Q_1), the third quartile (Q_3), and the interquartile range.
b. List the five-number summary.
c. Construct a boxplot and describe its shape.
d. Compare your answer in (c) with that from Problem 4.37 (d) on page 165. Discuss.

APPLYING THE CONCEPTS

4.58 The file ChocolateChip contains the cost (in cents) per 1-ounce serving, for a sample of 13 chocolate chip cookies. The data are as follows:

54   22   25   23   36   43   7   43   25   47   24   45   44

Source: Data extracted from "Chip, Chip, Hooray," *Consumer Reports,* June 2009, p. 7.

a. Compute the first quartile (Q_1), the third quartile (Q_3), and the interquartile range.
b. List the five-number summary.
c. Construct a boxplot and describe its shape.

SELF Test **4.59** The file Dark Chocolate contains the cost ($) per ounce for a sample of 14 dark chocolate bars:

0.68   0.72   0.92   1.14   1.42   0.94   0.77   0.57   1.51
0.57   0.55   0.86   1.41   0.90

Source: Data extracted from "Dark Chocolate: Which Bars Are Best?" *Consumer Reports,* September 2007, p. 8.

a. Compute the first quartile (Q_1), the third quartile (Q_3), and the interquartile range.
b. List the five-number summary.
c. Construct a boxplot and describe its shape.

4.60 The file HotelUK contains the average room price (in English pounds) paid in six British cities in 2010:

$$110 \quad 98 \quad 78 \quad 70 \quad 76 \quad 62$$

Source: Data extracted from **www.hotels.com/press/hotel-price-index-summer-2010.html**.

a. Compute the first quartile (Q_1), the third quartile (Q_3), and the interquartile range.
b. List the five-number summary.
c. Construct a boxplot and describe its shape.

4.61 The file SUV contains the overall miles per gallon (MPG) of 2011 small SUVs:

20   24   22   23   20   22   21   22   22
19   22   22   26   19   19   23   24   21
21   19   21   22   22   16   16

Source: Data extracted from "Ratings," *Consumer Reports,* April 2011, pp. 35–36.

a. Compute the first quartile (Q_1), the third quartile (Q_3), and the interquartile range.
b. List the five-number summary.
c. Construct a boxplot and describe its shape.

4.62 The file CD Rate contains the yields for a one-year certificate of deposit (CD) and a five-year CD, for 23 banks in the United States, as of April 4, 2011.

Source: Data extracted from **www.Bankrate.com**, April 4, 2011.

For each type of account:
a. Compute the first quartile (Q_1), the third quartile (Q_3), and the interquartile range.
b. List the five-number summary.
c. Construct a boxplot and describe its shape.

4.63 A bank branch located in a commercial district of a city has the business objective of developing an improved process for serving customers during the noon-to-1:00 P.M. lunch period. The waiting time, in minutes, is defined as the time the customer enters the line to when he or she reaches the teller window. Data are collected from a sample of

15 customers during this hour. The file Bank1 contains the results, which are listed here:

4.21   5.55   3.02   5.13   4.77   2.34   3.54   3.20
4.50   6.10   0.38   5.12   6.46   6.19   3.79

Another bank branch, located in a residential area, is also concerned with the noon-to-1 P.M. lunch hour. The waiting times, in minutes, collected from a sample of 15 customers during this hour, are contained in the file Bank2 and listed here:

9.66   5.90   8.02   5.79   8.73   3.82   8.01   8.35
10.49   6.68   5.64   4.08   6.17   9.91   5.47

a. List the five-number summaries of the waiting times at the two bank branches.
b. Construct boxplots and describe the shapes of the distributions for the two bank branches.
c. What similarities and differences are there in the distributions of the waiting times at the two bank branches?

4.64 For this problem, use the data in Bond Funds2008.
a. Construct a multidimensional table of the mean 2008 return by type and risk.
b. Construct a multidimensional table of the standard deviation of the 2008 return by type and risk.
c. What conclusions can you reach concerning differences between the type of bond funds (intermediate government and short-term corporate) based on risk factor (low, average, and high)?
d. Compare the results in (a)–(c) to the 2009 returns (stored in Bond Funds).

4.65 For this problem, use the data in Bond Funds2008.
a. Construct a multidimensional table of the mean three-year return by type and risk.

b. Construct a multidimensional table of the standard deviation of the three-year return by type and risk.
c. What conclusions can you reach concerning differences between the type of bond funds (intermediate government and short-term corporate) based on risk factor (low, average, and high)?
d. Compare the results in (a)–(c) to the three-year returns from 2007–2009 (stored in Bond Funds).

4.66 For this problem, use the data in Bond Funds2008.
a. Construct a multidimensional table of the mean five-year return by type and risk.
b. Construct a multidimensional table of the standard deviation of the five-year return by type and risk.
c. What conclusions can you reach concerning differences between the type of bond funds (intermediate government and short-term corporate) based on risk factor (low, average, and high)?
d. Compare the results in (a)–(c) to the five-year returns from 2005–2009 (stored in Bond Funds).

4.67 For this problem, use the data in Bond Funds2008.
a. Construct a multidimensional table of the mean 2008 return by type, fees, and risk.
b. Construct a multidimensional table of the standard deviation of the 2008 return by type, fees, and risk.
c. What conclusions can you reach concerning differences between the type of bond funds (intermediate government and short-term corporate) based on fees (yes or no) and risk factor (low, average, and high)?
d. Compare the results in (a)–(c) to the 2009 returns (stored in Bond Funds).

4.5 The Covariance and the Coefficient of Correlation

In Section 3.10, you used scatter plots to visually examine the relationship between two numerical variables. This section presents two measures of the relationship between two numerical variables: the covariance and the coefficient of correlation.

The Covariance

The **covariance** measures the strength of the linear relationship between two numerical variables (X and Y). Equation (4.3) defines the **sample covariance**, and Example 4.28 illustrates its use.

SAMPLE COVARIANCE

$$\text{cov}(X, Y) = \frac{\sum_{i=1}^{n}(X_i - \bar{X})(Y_i - \bar{Y})}{n - 1} \tag{4.3}$$

The Coefficient of Correlation

The **coefficient of correlation** measures the relative strength of a linear relationship between two numerical variables. The values of the coefficient of correlation range from -1 for a perfect negative correlation to $+1$ for a perfect positive correlation. *Perfect* in this case means that if the points were plotted on a scatter plot, all the points could be connected with a straight line.

When dealing with population data for two numerical variables, the Greek letter ρ *(rho)* is used as the symbol for the coefficient of correlation. Figure 4.8 illustrates three different types of association between two variables.

EXAMPLE 4.28

Computing the Sample Covariance

You constructed a scatter plot that showed the relationship between the value and the annual revenue of the 30 teams that make up the National Basketball Association (NBA) (extracted from **www.forbes.com/lists/2009/32/basketball-values-09_NBA-Team-Valuations_Rank.html**; stored in NBAValues). Now, you want to measure the association between the value of a franchise and annual revenue by computing the sample covariance.

SOLUTION Table 4.6 below provides the value and the annual revenue of the 30 teams.

Figure 4.7 contains a worksheet that computes the covariance for these data. The Calculations Area section of Figure 4.7 breaks down Equation (4.3) into a set of smaller calculations. From cell F9, or by using Equation (4.3) directly, you find that the covariance is 3,115.7241:

$$\text{cov}(X, Y) = \frac{90,356}{30 - 1}$$
$$= 3,115.7241$$

The covariance has a major flaw as a measure of the linear relationship between two numerical variables. Because the covariance can have any value, you are unable to use it to determine the relative strength of the relationship. In other words, you cannot tell whether the value 3,115.7241 indicates a strong relationship or a weak relationship. To better determine the relative strength of the relationship, you need to compute the coefficient of correlation.

TABLE 4.6

Values and Annual Revenues of the 30 NBA Teams (in millions of dollars)

Team	Value	Revenue	Team	Value	Revenue
Atlanta	306	103	Milwaukee	254	91
Boston	433	144	Minnesota	268	96
Charlotte	278	96	New Jersey	269	92
Chicago	511	168	New Orleans	267	95
Cleveland	476	159	New York	586	202
Dallas	446	154	Oklahoma City	310	111
Denver	321	115	Orlando	361	107
Detroit	479	171	Philadelphia	344	115
Golden State	315	113	Phoenix	429	148
Houston	470	160	Portland	338	121
Indiana	281	97	Sacramento	305	109
Los Angeles Clippers	295	102	San Antonio	398	133
Los Angeles Lakers	607	209	Toronto	386	133
Memphis	257	88	Utah	343	118
Miami	364	126	Washington	313	110

FIGURE 4.7

Excel worksheet to compute the covariance between the value and the annual revenue of the 30 NBA teams

	A	B	C	D	E	F
1	Covariance Analysis					
2						
3	Revenue	Value	(X-XBar)(Y-YBar)			
4	103	306	1415.2000		Calculations Area	
5	144	433	1174.8000		XBar	126.2000
6	96	278	2687.8000		YBar	367
7	168	511	6019.2000		n-1	29
8	159	476	3575.2000		Σ(X-XBar)(Y-YBar)	90356.0000
9	154	446	2196.2000		Covariance	3115.7241
10	115	321	515.2000			
11	171	479	5017.6000			
12	113	315	686.4000			
13	160	470	3481.4000			
14	97	281	2511.2000			
15	102	295	1742.4000			
16	209	607	19872.0000			
17	88	257	4202.0000			
18	126	364	0.6000			
19	91	254	3977.6000			
20	96	268	2989.8000			
21	92	269	3351.6000			
22	95	267	3120.0000			
23	202	586	16600.2000			
24	111	310	866.4000			
25	107	361	115.2000			
26	115	344	257.6000			
27	148	429	1351.6000			
28	121	338	150.8000			
29	109	305	1066.4000			
30	133	398	210.8000			
31	133	386	129.2000			
32	118	343	196.8000			
33	110	313	874.8000			

In Panel A of Figure 4.8, there is a perfect negative linear relationship between X and Y. Thus, the coefficient of correlation, ρ, equals -1, and when X increases, Y decreases in a perfectly predictable manner. Panel B shows a situation in which there is no relationship between X and Y. In this case, the coefficient of correlation, ρ, equals 0, and as X increases, there is no tendency for Y to increase or decrease. Panel C illustrates a perfect positive relationship where ρ equals $+1$. In this case, Y increases in a perfectly predictable manner when X increases.

Correlation alone cannot prove that there is a causation effect—that is, that the change in the value of one variable caused the change in the other variable. A strong correlation can be produced simply by chance, by the effect of a third variable not considered in the calculation of the correlation, or by a cause-and-effect relationship. You would need to perform addi-

FIGURE 4.8

Types of association between variables

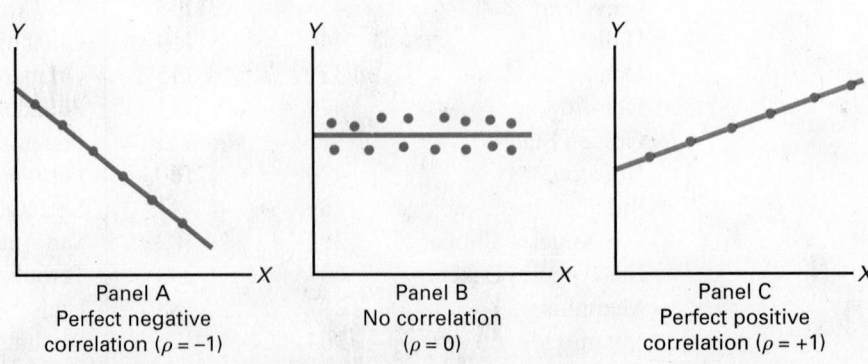

Panel A	Panel B	Panel C
Perfect negative correlation ($\rho = -1$)	No correlation ($\rho = 0$)	Perfect positive correlation ($\rho = +1$)

tional analysis to determine which of these three situations actually produced the correlation. Therefore, you can say that *causation implies correlation, but correlation alone does not imply causation.*

Equation (4.4) defines the **sample coefficient of correlation (r)**.

SAMPLE COEFFICIENT OF CORRELATION

$$r = \frac{\text{cov}(X, Y)}{S_X S_Y}$$

(4.4)

where

$$\text{cov}(X, Y) = \frac{\sum_{i=1}^{n}(X_i - \bar{X})(Y_i - \bar{Y})}{n - 1}$$

$$S_X = \sqrt{\frac{\sum_{i=1}^{n}(X_i - \bar{X})^2}{n - 1}}$$

$$S_Y = \sqrt{\frac{\sum_{i=1}^{n}(Y_i - \bar{Y})^2}{n - 1}}$$

When you have sample data, you can compute the sample coefficient of correlation, r. When using sample data, you are unlikely to have a sample coefficient of correlation of exactly $+1$, 0, or -1. Figure 4.9 presents scatter plots along with their respective sample coefficients of correlation, r, for six data sets, each of which contains 100 values of X and Y.

In Panel A, the coefficient of correlation, r, is -0.9. You can see that for small values of X, there is a very strong tendency for Y to be large. Likewise, the large values of X tend to be paired with small values of Y. The data do not all fall on a straight line, so the association between X and Y cannot be described as perfect. The data in Panel B have a coefficient of correlation equal to -0.6, and the small values of X tend to be paired with large values of Y. The linear relationship between X and Y in Panel B is not as strong as that in Panel A. Thus, the coefficient of correlation in Panel B is not as negative as that in Panel A. In Panel C, the linear relationship between X and Y is very weak, $r = -0.3$, and there is only a slight tendency for the small values of X to be paired with the large values of Y. Panels D through F depict data sets that have positive coefficients of correlation because small values of X tend to be paired with small values of Y and large values of X tend to be associated with large values of Y. Panel D shows weak positive correlation, with $r = 0.3$. Panel E shows stronger positive correlation with $r = 0.6$. Panel F shows very strong positive correlation, with $r = 0.9$.

FIGURE 4.9

Six scatter plots and their sample coefficients of correlation, r

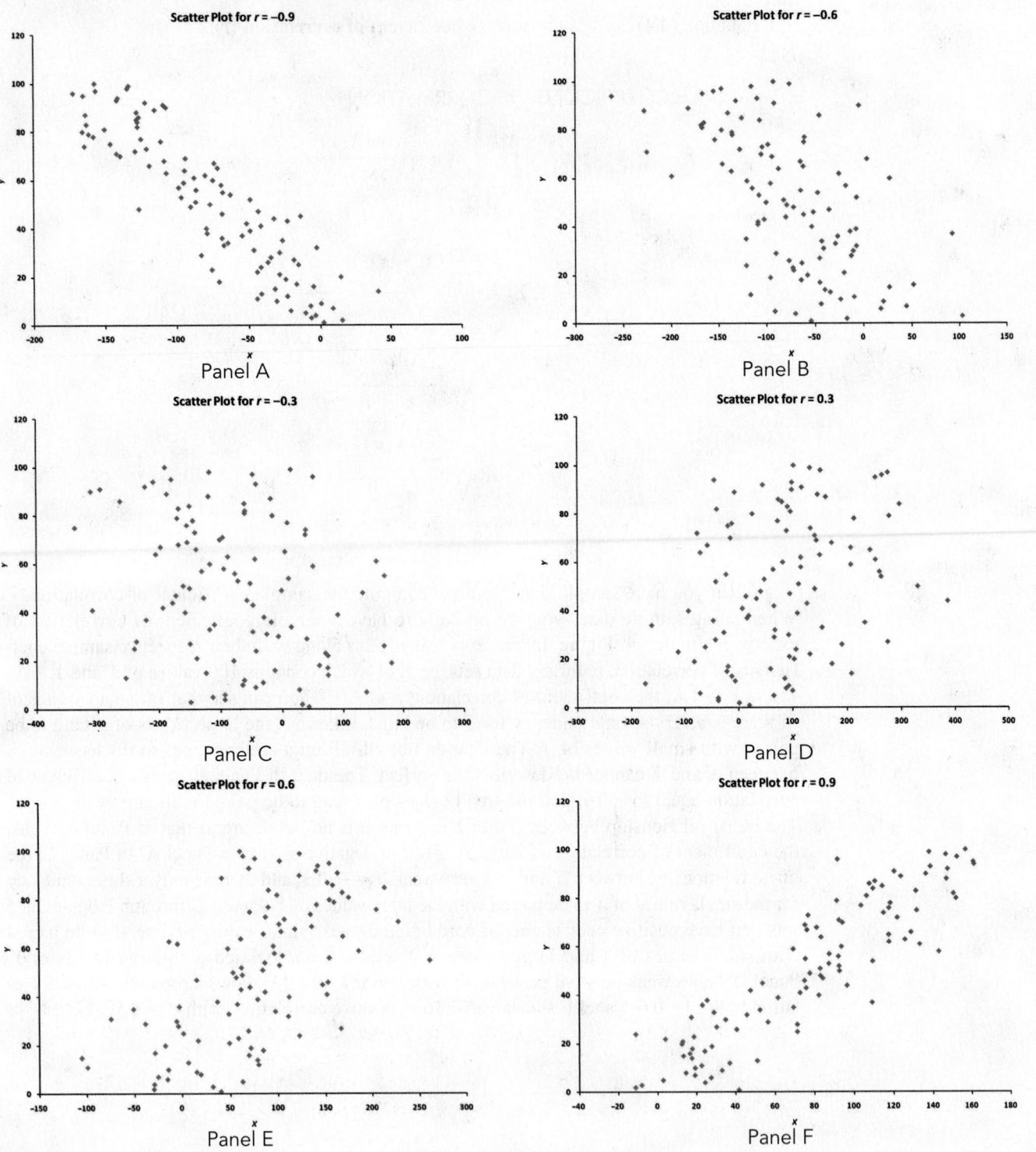

EXAMPLE 4.29

Computing the Sample Coefficient of Correlation

In Example 4.28 on page 177, you computed the covariance of the values and revenues of 30 NBA basketball teams. Using Figure 4.10 and Equation (4.4) on page 179, compute the sample coefficient of correlation.

FIGURE 4.10

Excel worksheet to compute the sample coefficient of correlation, r, between the values and revenues of 30 NBA teams

	A	B	C	D	E	F
1	Coefficient of Correlation Calculations					
2						
3	Revenue	Value	(X-XBar)(Y-YBar)		Calculations Area	
4	103	306	1415.2000		XBar	126.2000
5	144	433	1174.8000		YBar	367.0000
6	96	278	2687.8000		$\Sigma(X-XBar)^2$	30550.8000
7	168	511	6019.2000		$\Sigma(Y-YBar)^2$	272410.0000
8	159	476	3575.2000		$\Sigma(X-XBar)(Y-YBar)$	90356.0000
9	154	446	2196.2000		n-1	29
10	115	321	515.2000			
11	171	479	5017.6000		Results	
12	113	315	686.4000		Covariance	3115.7241
13	160	470	3481.4000		S_X	32.4573
14	97	281	2511.2000		S_Y	96.9198
15	102	295	1742.4000		r	0.9905
16	209	607	19872.0000			
17	88	257	4202.0000			
18	126	364	0.6000			
19	91	254	3977.6000			
20	96	268	2989.8000			
21	92	269	3351.6000			
22	95	267	3120.0000			
23	202	586	16600.2000			
24	111	310	866.4000			
25	107	361	115.2000			
26	115	344	257.6000			
27	148	429	1351.6000			
28	121	338	150.8000			
29	109	305	1066.4000			
30	133	398	210.8000			
31	133	386	129.2000			
32	118	343	196.8000			
33	110	313	874.8000			

SOLUTION

$$r = \frac{\text{cov}(X, Y)}{S_X S_Y}$$

$$= \frac{3{,}115.7241}{(32.4573)(96.9198)}$$

$$= 0.9905$$

The value and revenue of the NBA teams are very highly correlated. The teams with the lowest revenues have the lowest values. The teams with the highest revenues have the highest values. This relationship is very strong, as indicated by the coefficient of correlation, $r = 0.9905$.

In general you cannot assume that just because two variables are correlated, changes in one variable caused changes in the other variable. However, for this example, it makes sense to conclude that changes in revenue would cause changes in the value of a team.

In summary, the coefficient of correlation indicates the linear relationship, or association, between two numerical variables. When the coefficient of correlation gets closer to $+1$ or -1, the linear relationship between the two variables is stronger. When the coefficient of correlation is near 0, little or no linear relationship exists. The sign of the coefficient of correlation indicates whether the data are positively correlated (i.e., the larger values of X are typically paired with the larger values of Y) or negatively correlated (i.e., the larger values of X are typically paired with the smaller values of Y). The existence of a strong correlation does not imply a causation effect. It only indicates the tendencies present in the data.

Problems for Section 4.5

LEARNING THE BASICS

4.68 The following is a set of data from a sample of $n = 11$ items:

X	7	5	8	3	6	10	12	4	9	15	18
Y	21	15	24	9	18	30	36	12	27	45	54

a. Compute the covariance.
b. Compute the coefficient of correlation.
c. How strong is the relationship between X and Y? Explain.

APPLYING THE CONCEPTS

4.69 A study of 218 students at Ohio State University suggests a link between time spent on the social networking site Facebook and grade point average. Students who rarely or never used Facebook had higher grade point averages than students who use Facebook.

Source: Data extracted from M. B. Marklein, "Facebook Use Linked to Less Textbook Time," **www.usatoday.com**, April 14, 2009.

a. Does the study suggest that time spent on Facebook and grade point average are positively correlated or negatively correlated?
b. Do you think that there might be a cause-and-effect relationship between time spent on Facebook and grade point average? Explain.

✓ **SELF** **4.70** The file **Cereals** lists the calories and sugar, **Test** in grams, in one serving of seven breakfast cereals:

Cereal	Calories	Sugar
Kellogg's All Bran	80	6
Kellogg's Corn Flakes	100	2
Wheaties	100	4
Nature's Path Organic Multigrain Flakes	110	4
Kellogg's Rice Krispies	130	4
Post Shredded Wheat Vanilla Almond	190	11
Kellogg's Mini Wheats	200	10

a. Compute the covariance.
b. Compute the coefficient of correlation.
c. Which do you think is more valuable in expressing the relationship between calories and sugar—the covariance or the coefficient of correlation? Explain.

d. Based on (a) and (b), what conclusions can you reach about the relationship between calories and sugar?

4.71 Movie companies need to predict the gross receipts of individual movies after a movie has debuted. The following results, listed in **PotterMovies**, are the first weekend gross, the U.S. gross, and the worldwide gross (in millions of dollars) of the six Harry Potter movies that debuted from 2001 to 2009:

Title	First Weekend	U.S. Gross	Worldwide Gross
Sorcerer's Stone	90.295	317.558	976.458
Chamber of Secrets	88.357	261.988	878.988
Prisoner of Azkaban	93.687	249.539	795.539
Goblet of Fire	102.335	290.013	896.013
Order of the Phoenix	77.108	292.005	938.469
Half-Blood Prince	77.836	301.460	934.601

Source: Data extracted from **www.the-numbers.com/interactive/comp-Harry-Potter.php**.

a. Compute the covariance between first weekend gross and U.S. gross, first weekend gross and worldwide gross, and U.S. gross and worldwide gross.
b. Compute the coefficient of correlation between first weekend gross and U.S. gross, first weekend gross and worldwide gross, and U.S. gross and worldwide gross.
c. Which do you think is more valuable in expressing the relationship between first weekend gross, U.S. gross, and worldwide gross—the covariance or the coefficient of correlation? Explain.
d. Based on (a) and (b), what conclusions can you reach about the relationship between first weekend gross, U.S. gross, and worldwide gross?

4.72 College basketball is big business, with coaches' salaries, revenues, and expenses in millions of dollars. The file **College Basketball** contains the coaches' salaries and revenues for college basketball at 60 of the 65 schools that played in the 2009 NCAA men's basketball tournament

Source: Data extracted from "Compensation for Division 1 Men's Basketball Coaches," *USA Today*, April 2, 2010, p. 8C; and C. Isadore, "Nothing but Net: Basketball Dollars by School," **money.cnn.com/2010/03/18/news/companies/basketball_profits/**.

a. Compute the covariance.

b. Compute the coefficient of correlation.

c. Based on (a) and (b), what conclusions can you reach about the relationship between coaches' salaries and revenues?

4.73 College football players trying out for the NFL are given the Wonderlic standardized intelligence test. The file Wonderlic contains the average Wonderlic score of football players trying out for the NFL and the graduation rate for football players at selected schools.

Source: Data extracted from S. Walker, "The NFL's Smartest Team," *The Wall Street Journal,* September 30, 2005, pp. W1, W10.

a. Compute the covariance.

b. Compute the coefficient of correlation.

c. Based on (a) and (b), what conclusions can you reach about the relationship between the average Wonderlic score and graduation rate?

4.6 Numerical Descriptive Statistics: Pitfalls and Ethical Issues

This chapter describes how a set of numerical data can be characterized by the statistics that measure the properties of central tendency, variation, and shape. In business, descriptive statistics such as the ones you have learned about are frequently included in summary reports that are prepared periodically.

The volume of information available on the Internet, in newspapers, and in magazines has produced much skepticism about the objectivity of data. When you are reading information that contains descriptive statistics, you should keep in mind the quip often attributed to the famous nineteenth-century British statesman Benjamin Disraeli: "There are three kinds of lies: lies, damned lies, and statistics."

For example, in examining statistics, you need to compare the mean and the median. Are they similar, or are they very different? Or, is only the mean provided? The answers to these questions will help you determine whether the data are skewed or symmetrical and whether the median might be a better measure of central tendency than the mean. In addition, you should look to see whether the standard deviation or interquartile range for a very skewed set of data has been included in the statistics provided. Without this, it is impossible to determine the amount of variation that exists in the data.

Ethical considerations arise when you are deciding what results to include in a report. You should document both good and bad results. In addition, when making oral presentations and presenting written reports, you need to give results in a fair, objective, and neutral manner. Unethical behavior occurs when you selectively fail to report pertinent findings that are detrimental to the support of a particular position.

USING STATISTICS @ Choice Is Yours, Part II Revisited

© Steve Cole / iStockphoto.com

In Part II of the Choice Is Yours scenario, you were hired by the Choice Is Yours investment company to assist investors interested in bond mutual funds. A sample of 184 bond mutual funds included 87 intermediate government funds and 97 short-term corporate bond funds. By comparing these two categories, you were able to provide investors with valuable insights.

The 2009 returns for both the intermediate government funds and the short-term corporate bond funds were right-skewed, as indicated by the boxplots. The descriptive statistics allowed you to compare the central tendency and variability of returns of the intermediate government funds and the short-term corporate bond funds. The mean indicated that the intermediate government funds returned an average of 4.4529, and the median indicated that half of the funds had returns of 4.4 or more. The short-term corporate bond funds' central tendencies were much higher than those of the intermediate government funds—they had an average of 9.5959, and half the funds had returns above 9.1. The intermediate government funds showed slightly less variability than the short-term corporate funds with a standard deviation of 5.36 as compared to 5.69. An interesting insight is that while 25% of the intermediate government funds had returns of 6.5 or higher ($Q_3 = 6.5$), 75% of the short-term corporate bond funds had returns of 5.7 or higher ($Q_1 = 5.7$). Although past performance is no assurance of future performance, in 2009, the short-term corporate funds greatly outperformed the intermediate government funds. (To see a situation where the opposite was true, open the `Bond Funds2008` file.)

SUMMARY

In this chapter and the previous chapter, you studied descriptive statistics—how you can visualize data through tables and charts and how you can use different statistics to help analyze the data and reach conclusions. In Chapters 2 and 4, you were able to visualize data by constructing bar and pie charts, histograms, and other charts. In this chapter, you learned how descriptive statistics such as the mean, median, quartiles, range, and standard deviation are used to describe the characteristics of central tendency, variability, and shape.

In addition, you constructed boxplots to visualize the distribution of the data. You also learned how the coefficient of correlation is used to describe the relationship between two numerical variables. Table 4.7 provides a list of the descriptive statistics covered in this chapter.

In the next chapter, the basic principles of probability are presented in order to bridge the gap between the subject of descriptive statistics and the subject of inferential statistics.

TABLE 4.7

Summary of Descriptive Statistics

Type of Analysis	Numerical Data
Describing central tendency, variation, and shape of a numerical variable	Mean, median, mode, quartiles, range, interquartile range, variance, standard deviation, coefficient of variation, Z scores, boxplot (Sections 4.1 through 4.4)
Describing the relationship between two numerical variables	Covariance, coefficient of correlation (Section 4.5)

KEY EQUATIONS

Sample Mean

$$\bar{X} = \frac{\sum_{i=1}^{n} X_i}{n}$$

Median

$$\text{Median} = \frac{n+1}{2} \text{ ranked value}$$

Range

$$\text{Range} = X_{\text{largest}} - X_{\text{smallest}}$$

Sample Variance

$$S^2 = \frac{\sum_{i=1}^{n}(X_i - \bar{X})^2}{n-1}$$

Sample Standard Deviation

$$S = \sqrt{S^2} = \sqrt{\frac{\sum_{i=1}^{n}(X_i - \bar{X})^2}{n-1}}$$

Coefficient of Variation

$$CV = \left(\frac{S}{\bar{X}}\right)100\%$$

Z Score

$$Z = \frac{X - \bar{X}}{S}$$

Interquartile Range

$$\text{Interquartile range} = Q_3 - Q_1$$

Population Mean

$$\mu = \frac{\sum_{i=1}^{N} X_i}{N}$$

Population Variance

$$\sigma^2 = \frac{\sum_{i=1}^{N} (X_i - \mu)^2}{N}$$

Population Standard Deviation

$$\sigma = \sqrt{\frac{\sum_{i=1}^{N} (X_i - \mu)^2}{N}}$$

Sample Covariance

$$\text{cov}(X, Y) = \frac{\sum_{i=1}^{n} (X_i - \bar{X})(Y_i - \bar{Y})}{n - 1}$$

Sample Coefficient of Correlation

$$r = \frac{\text{cov}(X, Y)}{S_X S_Y}$$

KEY TERMS

PROBLEMS

REVIEW PROBLEMS

4.74 The following table appeared in the May 28th, 1998 issue of the *Toronto Star*.

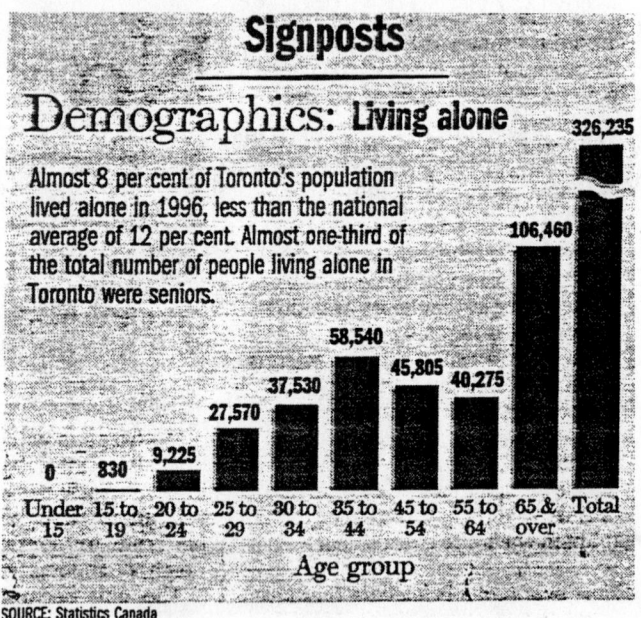

In 1996, excluding seniors (aged 65 and over), what was the average age of people who lived alone in Toronto?

4.75 The following ad appeared in the Feb. 7th, 1997 issue of the *Real Estate News*. It shows the rental costs for various condos in Harbour Square.

HARBOUR SQUARE RENTALS

250 Queens Quay W.#806   2br $1,200 mo.

270 Queens Quay W.#1301 1br $1,295 mo.

270 Queens Quay W.#602   1br $1,295 mo.

270 Queens Quay W.#2302 1br Furnished
                                      $1,595 mo.

77 Harbour Sq.   #2611 1br $1,500 mo.

401 Queens Quay W.#204 1br $1,950 mo.

105 Victoria   #305 1br $1,150 mo.

                   #306 2br $1,450 mo.

                   #807 1br $1,200 mo.

                   #1007 1br $1,200 mo.

Carrie Bynford 203-6636.
Harry Stinson R.E. Ltd.

What is the mean monthly rent for an unfurnished one-bedroom condo?

4.76 Ryerson Memorial Hospital wants to compare its annual patient turnover rate per bed with those of other similar hospitals. The turnover rates for a sample of 80 beds at Ryerson were summarized and organized in the following frequency distribution. (An annual turnover of 21 per bed indicates that, during the year, 21 patients occupied the same hospital bed.)

Annual Turnover Rate Patients per Bed	Number of Beds
10 and under 15	4
15 " " 20	9
20 " " 25	13
25 " " 30	25
30 " " 35	15
35 " " 40	7
40 " " 50	5
50 " " 60	2

a. What is the mean turnover rate?
b. What is the median turnover rate?
c. What is the standard deviation of the turnover rate?

4.77 The following table shows room rates for a resort hotel in Nova Scotia for the time period January 1 to December 31, 2003.

2003 Room Rates	1/1–7/3	8/3–30/3	31/3–31/5	1/6–30/6	1/7–1/9	2/9–8/10	9/10–1/12	2/12–20/12	21/12–31/12
A Oceanfront									
1 double bed	75	125	85	100	150	95	85	75	125
B Oceanfront									
2 double beds	85	135	95	110	160	105	95	85	135
C Oceanfront Effic.									
2 double beds	105	155	115	130	180	125	115	105	155
D 2 room suite									
3 double beds	120	175	130	150	200	140	130	120	175
E Oceanfront Suite									
3 double beds	140	200	150	175	225	165	150	140	200
Extra Person	5	8	5	5	10	7	5	5	10

a. For the nine time periods, what was the mean extra person rate?
b. This hotel has 20% type A rooms, 15% type B, 30% type C, 25% type D and the remainder are type E. If the hotel was fully booked (with no extra people in any room) on October 1, then what was the mean revenue per room? What was the standard deviation?
c. On April 20, the only rooms occupied were 25 type A, 13 type B, and 5 type E. What was the average revenue per bed on that day? If every bed was occupied by two people, what was the mean and standard deviation of the number of people per rented room on that day?

4.78 The following data refer to the OAC average grades of students being accepted into first year of several Ontario universities.

Grade Distribution of New 1st Year Students						
University	60–70	70–75	75–80	80–85	85–90	≥ 90
Brock	5.8	22.1	26.7	26.0	13.1	6.3
Guelph	0	0.2	27.6	37.9	21.4	12.9
McMaster	0.1	10.5	24.2	32.4	19.7	13.1
Queen's	0	0.2	3.2	21.9	36.8	37.9
Ryerson	0.5	23.0	31.0	29.3	12.4	3.8
Toronto	0	1.2	8.9	26.0	36.6	27.3

a. Based on the above data, is the average entering grade higher for Brock or Ryerson, or is the average about the same? How do the standard deviations compare?
b. What about Ryerson compared to Queen's?

4.79 The table below appeared in the April 9, 1998 edition of *The Globe and Mail*.

Municipal salary comparisons		
	Mayor's salary	Councillor's salary
Barrie	$45,000	$11,705
Brantford	$54,758	$11,000
Burlington	$56,000	$27,000
Cambridge	$47,000	$14,500
Gloucester	$69,020	$21,585
Kingston	$52,000	$13,000
Kitchener	$54,440	$22,640
Markham	$60,669	$34,287
Nepean	$72,603	$24,146
Oakville	$45,000	$17,000
Oshawa	$49,610	$18,540
Richmond Hill	$53,074	$29,185
St. Catharines	$51,759	$10,664
Thunder Bay	$57,342	$26,343
Toronto	$101,084	$63,915
Vaughan	$62,792	$38,126
Windsor	$88,236	$26,645
AVERAGE	$60,023	$24,134

Source: KPMG

a. Which are more variable, the mayors' salaries or the councillors' salaries for the 17 cities shown?
b. Draw a box-whisker diagram for the mayors' salaries.
c. Is the mean or median a better indication of the typical councillor's salary?

4.80 The following table and graphical display appeared in the March 21, 1998 issue of *The Globe and Mail*.

Major English-language specialty channels

Year ended Aug. 31, 1997	Total subscribers	Cable revenue per subscriber per month	Advertising revenue per subscriber per month	Profit margin before interest and taxes
TSN	6,401,276	$1.25	$0.66	36.0%
MuchMusic	6,048,240	0.11	0.26	27.5
YTV	7,150,000	0.29	0.32	21.0
Weather	8,167,204	0.22	0.04	19.2
Vision*	6,115,792	0.07	0.02	4.2
Newsworld	7,316,000	0.46	0.14	0.4
WTN	4,676,286	0.32	0.07	14.0
Discovery	4,584,298	0.39	0.15	1.9
Showcase	3,644,440	0.34	0.15	15.7
Life	3,793,871	0.31	0.16	11.5
CMT	6,290,810	0.05	0.08	14.0
Bravo!	3,947,159	0.26	0.05	12.5

* Almost half of Vision's total revenue of $12.5-million a year comes from other revenue such as donations.

Note: Does not include latest tier of channels as pay period started Jan. 18, 1998
Source: Canadian Radio-television and Telecommunications Commission

The growth of specialty TV channels

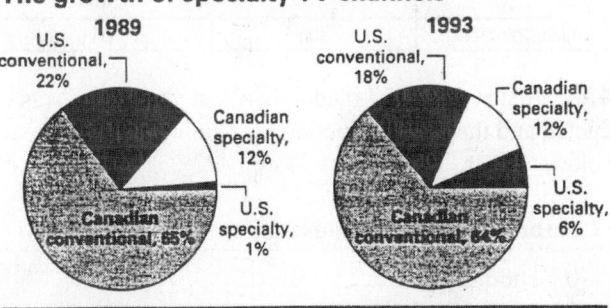
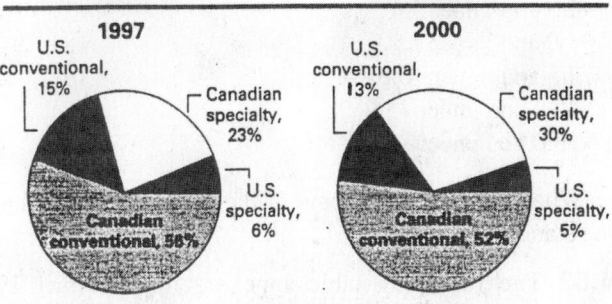

Source: Nielsen People Meter data plus Initiative Media estimates

a. Which factor is more uniform over the 12 stations: (i) cable revenue per subscriber or (ii) advertising revenue per subscriber?
b. Draw the box-whisker plot for the "Advertising revenue per subscriber" data.
c. If the total advertising revenue per channel is $20 per conventional Canadian channel, $15 million per specialty Canadian channel, $12 million per conventional U.S. channel, and $10 million per U.S. specialty channel, will the overall average advertising revenue per channel in the year 2000 be higher or lower than the average was in 1989?

4.81 The following table shows the number of unemployed persons by province for the months of October 1995 and October 1996. Were the numbers of unemployed persons across the provinces relatively more variable in 1995 or 1996?

	Unemployment	(x 1,000)
	October 1995	October 1996
Newfoundland	150	118
P. E. I.	25	31
New Brunswick	75	69
Nova Scotia	79	63
Quebec	250	278
Ontario	300	280
Manitoba	85	85
Saskatchewan	95	87
Alberta	63	43
British Columbia	105	81

4.82 A survey of 137 randomly selected students was conducted and their annual incomes are summarized in the table below.

Annual Income ($ thousands)	# of Students
0.0 and under 2.5	36
2.5 and under 5.0	43
5.0 and under 7.5	18
7.5 and under 10.0	19
10.0 and under 15.0	16
15.0 and under 20.0	5

What is the mean income of the 137 students? What is the standard deviation?

4.83 The following table appeared in the April 1995 *Report on Business Magazine*.

Most Respected: the Top Five

Canada's best corporations excel in profitability, innovation and global reach

Rank	Company	Revenues	Net income
		($ millions)	
1	Royal Bank of Canada (Oc94) financial services	13,434	1,169
2	BCE (De94) telecommunications	21,670	1,178
3	Bombardier (Ja94) aviation, mass transit eqpt.	4,769	176
4	Bank of Montreal (Oc94) financial services	9,108	825
5	Northern Telecom (De94) telecommunications eqpt.	8,874	408

Are the five most respected companies more similar in terms of Revenues or Net Incomes?

4.84 A wholesale appliance distributing firm is studying its accounts receivables for two successive months. Two samples of 50 accounts were selected and the amount of receivables for each has been summarized in the table below.

Accounts Receivables ($)	# of Accounts in March	# of Accounts in April
0 and under 2,000	6	10
2,000 and under 5,000	13	14
5,000 and under 10,000	17	13
10,000 and under 15,000	10	10
15,000 and under 25,000	0	3
25,000 and under 50,000	4	0
Total	50	50

In which month were the accounts receivable amounts more variable?

4.85 The following display appeared in the March 23, 1995 edition of *USA Today*. For all the films made from 1989 to 1994, what was the overall average production cost per movie?

Big picture for film industry

The movie business is thriving despite competition from broadcast and cable TV, home video and other forms of entertainment:

Theater admissions are growing

in millions

1989	1.26
1990	1.19
1991	1.14
1992	1.17
1993	1.24
1994	1.29

Major studios are making more films . . .

Films made		Films to be made in 1995[1]	
1989	157	Buena Vista	25
1990	158	Warner Bros.	35
1991	150	Sony	30
1992	141	Paramount	25
1993	156	Universal	20
1994	168	Fox	25
		New Line	25

. . . and, on average, each one is more expensive

Total cost, in millions

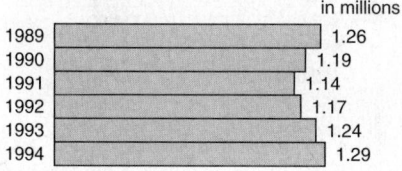

$32.7	$38.8	$38.1	$42.4	$44	$50.4
1989	1990	1991	1992	1993	1994

Average production cost, in millions

$23.5	$26.8	$26.1	$28.9	$29.9	$34.3

Average advertising and print costs, in millions

$9.2	$12.0	$12.0	$13.5	$14.1	$16.1

1 Estimates
Sources: Motion Picture Association of America, Merrill Lynch

4.86 The following table appeared in the March 26, 1998 edition of *The Globe and Mail*.

Average work days lost per year

	Total	For illness	Personal or family
All employees	7.4	6.2	1.2
Men	6.3	5.3	0.9
Men with preschoolers	5.9	4.2	1.8
Women	9.1	7.6	1.5
Women with preschoolers	11.7	7.5	4.2
Company size			
Under 20 employees	6.2	4.9	1.3
Over 500 employees	9.0	7.8	1.2
Union status			
Union member	10.7	9.4	1.3
Non-union member	5.6	4.5	1.1
Job status			
Permanent	7.6	6.4	1.2
Non-permanent	5.4	4.2	1.2

Source: Statistics Canada

The following data are applicable to a new division being set up by the Statistics Consulting Company.

	% Employees	Average Daily Salary
Men	8	$400
Men with preschoolers	62	250
Women	20	320
Women with preschoolers	10	200

a. What is the average number of days lost per employee due to illness during the first year of operation of the new division? What is the standard deviation?

b. What is the difference in the average daily salary between the men and the women of this new division?

c. What is the standard deviation of the daily salary for the men?

4.87 The following chart appeared in the Royal Bank's Business Report of January 1995.

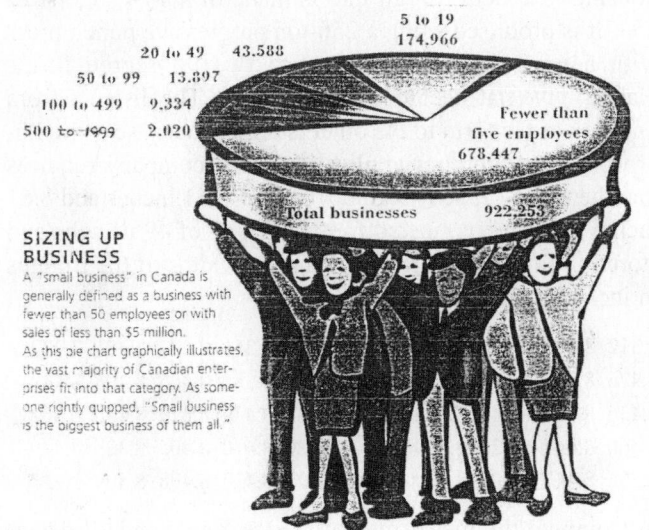

4.88 The following table appeared in the December 8, 1995 issue of the *Toronto Star*.

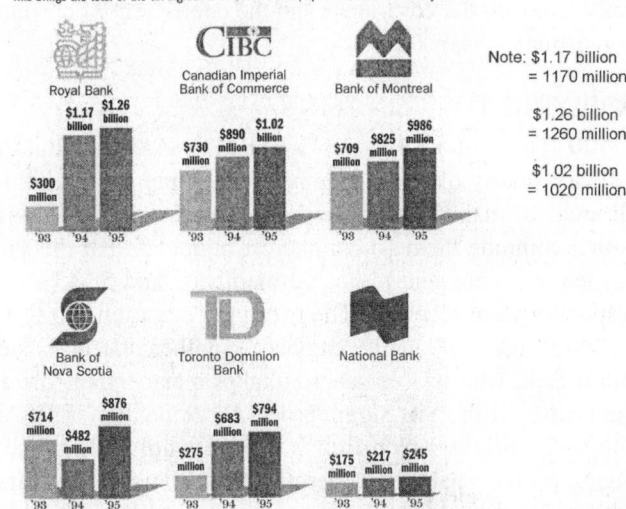

a. Did the median profit increase or decrease in 1994 compared to 1993?

b. For the sample of six banks shown above, were bank profits relatively more variable in 1994 or 1995?

c. In 1993 there were 215 branches of the Royal Bank, 427 branches of CIBC, 385 branches of the Bank of Montreal, 453 branches of the Bank of Nova Scotia, 288 branches of the Toronto Dominion Bank, and 154 branches of the National Bank. What was the overall average profit and per branch in 1993? What was the standard deviation?

CHECKING YOUR UNDERSTANDING

4.89 What are the properties of a set of numerical data?

4.90 What is meant by the property of central tendency?

4.91 What are the differences among the mean, median, and mode, and what are the advantages and disadvantages of each?

4.92 How do you interpret the first quartile, median, and third quartile?

4.93 What is meant by the property of variation?

4.94 What does the *Z* score measure?

4.95 What are the differences among the various measures of variation, such as the range, interquartile range, variance,

a. What is the average employment size of a Canadian business? (Assume that the data cover all Canadian businesses.)

b. What is the standard deviation of employment size?

standard deviation, and coefficient of variation, and what are the advantages and disadvantages of each?

4.96 How does the empirical rule help explain the ways in which the values in a set of numerical data cluster and distribute?

4.97 How do the empirical rule and the Chebyshev rule differ?

4.98 What is meant by the property of shape?

4.99 How do the covariance and the coefficient of correlation differ?

APPLYING THE CONCEPTS

4.100 The American Society for Quality (ASQ) conducted a salary survey of all its members. ASQ members work in all areas of manufacturing and service-related institutions, with a common theme of an interest in quality. For the survey, emails were sent to 56,052 members, and 5,743 valid responses were received. The two most common job titles were manager and quality engineer. Another title is Master Black Belt, who is a person who takes a leadership role as the keeper of the Six Sigma process (see Section 9.4). An additional title is Green Belt, someone who works on Six Sigma projects part-time. Descriptive statistics concerning salaries for these four titles are given in the following table:

Title	Sample Size	Minimum	Maximum	Standard Deviation	Mean	Median
Green Belt	15	24,000	137,000	29,000	75,917	70,000
Manager	1,438	10,400	212,000	26,455	88,993	86,000
Quality Engineer	831	25,000	175,000	19,878	76,239	75,000
Master Black Belt	86	60,000	185,000	26,466	113,276	112,650

Source: Data extracted from J. Seaman and I. Allen, "Revealing Answers," *Quality Progress*, December 2010, p. 31.

Compare the salaries of Green Belts, managers, quality engineers, and Master Black Belts.

4.101 In New York State, savings banks are permitted to sell a form of life insurance called savings bank life insurance (SBLI). The approval process consists of underwriting, which includes a review of the application, a medical information bureau check, possible requests for additional medical information and medical exams, and a policy compilation stage, during which the policy pages are generated and sent to the bank for delivery. The ability to deliver approved policies to customers in a timely manner is critical to the profitability of this service to the bank. During one month, a random sample of 27 approved policies was selected, and the following were the total processing times in days (stored in **Insurance**):

73   19   16   64   28   28   31   90   60   56   31   56   22   18
45   48   17   17   17   91   92   63   50   51   69   16   17

a. Compute the mean, median, first quartile, and third quartile.
b. Compute the range, interquartile range, variance, standard deviation, and coefficient of variation.
c. Construct a boxplot. Are the data skewed? If so, how?
d. What would you tell a customer who enters the bank to purchase this type of insurance policy and asks how long the approval process takes?

4.102 One of the major measures of the quality of service provided by an organization is the speed with which it responds to customer complaints. A large family-held department store selling furniture and flooring, including carpet, had undergone a major expansion in the past several years. In particular, the flooring department had expanded from 2 installation crews to an installation supervisor, a measurer, and 15 installation crews. The business objective of the company was to reduce the time between when the complaint is received and when it is resolved. During a recent year, the company received 50 complaints concerning carpet installation. The data from the 50 complaints, organized in **Furniture** , represent the number of days between the receipt of a complaint and the resolution of the complaint:

54   5   35 137 31 27 152   2 123 81 74 27 11
19 126 110 110 29 61   35 94   31 26   5 12   4
165   32   29   28 29 26   25   1   14 13 13 10   5
27   4   52   30 22 36   26 20   23 33 68

a. Compute the mean, median, first quartile, and third quartile.
b. Compute the range, interquartile range, variance, standard deviation, and coefficient of variation.
c. Construct a boxplot. Are the data skewed? If so, how?
d. On the basis of the results of (a) through (c), if you had to tell the president of the company how long a customer should expect to wait to have a complaint resolved, what would you say? Explain.

4.103 A manufacturing company produces steel housings for electrical equipment. The main component part of the housing is a steel trough that is made of a 14-gauge steel coil. It is produced using a 250-ton progressive punch press with a wipe-down operation and two 90-degree forms placed in the flat steel to make the trough. The distance from one side of the form to the other is critical because of weatherproofing in outdoor applications. The company requires that the width of the trough be between 8.31 inches and 8.61 inches. Data are collected from a sample of 49 troughs and stored in **Trough** , which contains the widths of the troughs in inches as shown here:

8.312 8.343 8.317 8.383 8.348 8.410 8.351 8.373 8.481 8.422
8.476 8.382 8.484 8.403 8.414 8.419 8.385 8.465 8.498 8.447
8.436 8.413 8.489 8.414 8.481 8.415 8.479 8.429 8.458 8.462
8.460 8.444 8.429 8.460 8.412 8.420 8.410 8.405 8.323 8.420
8.396 8.447 8.405 8.439 8.411 8.427 8.420 8.498 8.409

a. Compute the mean, median, range, and standard deviation for the width. Interpret these measures of central tendency and variability.

b. List the five-number summary.

c. Construct a boxplot and describe its shape.

d. What can you conclude about the number of troughs that will meet the company's requirement of troughs being between 8.31 and 8.61 inches wide?

4.104 The manufacturing company in Problem 4.99 also produces electric insulators. If the insulators break when in use, a short circuit is likely to occur. To test the strength of the insulators, destructive testing is carried out to determine how much force is required to break the insulators. Force is measured by observing how many pounds must be applied to an insulator before it breaks. Data are collected from a sample of 30 insulators. The file **Force** contains the strengths, as follows:

```
1,870 1,728 1,656 1,610 1,634 1,784 1,522 1,696 1,592 1,662
1,866 1,764 1,734 1,662 1,734 1,774 1,550 1,756 1,762 1,866
1,820 1,744 1,788 1,688 1,810 1,752 1,680 1,810 1,652 1,736
```

a. Compute the mean, median, range, and standard deviation for the force needed to break the insulator.

b. Interpret the measures of central tendency and variability in (a).

c. Construct a boxplot and describe its shape.

d. What can you conclude about the strength of the insulators if the company requires a force of at least 1,500 pounds before breakage?

4.105 The file **VeggieBurger** contains data on the calories and total fat (in grams per serving) for a sample of 12 veggie burgers.

Source: Data extracted from "Healthful Burgers That Taste Good," *Consumer Reports*, June 2008, p 8.

a. For each variable, compute the mean, median, first quartile, and third quartile.

b. For each variable, compute the range, interquartile range, variance, standard deviation, and coefficient of variation.

c. For each variable, construct a boxplot. Are the data skewed? If so, how?

d. Compute the coefficient of correlation between calories and total fat.

e. What conclusions can you reach concerning calories and total fat?

4.106 A quality characteristic of interest for a tea-bag-filling process is the weight of the tea in the individual bags. If the bags are underfilled, two problems arise. First, customers may not be able to brew the tea to be as strong as they wish. Second, the company may be in violation of the truth-in-labeling laws. For this product, the label weight on the package indicates that, on average, there are 5.5 grams of tea in a bag. If the mean amount of tea in a bag exceeds the label weight, the company is giving away product. Getting an exact amount of tea in a bag is problematic because of variation in the temperature and humidity inside the factory, differences in the density of the tea, and the extremely fast filling operation of the machine (approximately 170 bags per minute). The file **Teabags**, as shown below, contains the weights, in grams,

of a sample of 50 tea bags produced in one hour by a single machine:

```
5.65 5.44 5.42 5.40 5.53 5.34 5.54 5.45 5.52 5.41
5.57 5.40 5.53 5.54 5.55 5.62 5.56 5.46 5.44 5.51
5.47 5.40 5.47 5.61 5.53 5.32 5.67 5.29 5.49 5.55
5.77 5.57 5.42 5.58 5.58 5.50 5.32 5.50 5.53 5.58
5.61 5.45 5.44 5.25 5.56 5.63 5.50 5.57 5.67 5.36
```

a. Compute the mean, median, first quartile, and third quartile.

b. Compute the range, interquartile range, variance, standard deviation, and coefficient of variation.

c. Interpret the measures of central tendency and variation within the context of this problem. Why should the company producing the tea bags be concerned about the central tendency and variation?

d. Construct a boxplot. Are the data skewed? If so, how?

e. Is the company meeting the requirement set forth on the label that, on average, there are 5.5 grams of tea in a bag? If you were in charge of this process, what changes, if any, would you try to make concerning the distribution of weights in the individual bags?

4.107 The manufacturer of Boston and Vermont asphalt shingles provides its customers with a 20-year warranty on most of its products. To determine whether a shingle will last as long as the warranty period, accelerated-life testing is conducted at the manufacturing plant. Accelerated-life testing exposes a shingle to the stresses it would be subject to in a lifetime of normal use via an experiment in a laboratory setting that takes only a few minutes to conduct. In this test, a shingle is repeatedly scraped with a brush for a short period of time, and the shingle granules removed by the brushing are weighed (in grams). Shingles that experience low amounts of granule loss are expected to last longer in normal use than shingles that experience high amounts of granule loss. In this situation, a shingle should experience no more than 0.8 gram of granule loss if it is expected to last the length of the warranty period. The file **Granule** contains a sample of 170 measurements made on the company's Boston shingles and 140 measurements made on Vermont shingles.

a. List the five-number summaries for the Boston shingles and for the Vermont shingles.

b. Construct side-by-side boxplots for the two brands of shingles and describe the shapes of the distributions.

c. Comment on the ability of each type of shingle to achieve a granule loss of 0.8 gram or less.

4.108 The file **Restaurants** contains the cost per meal and the ratings of 50 city and 50 suburban restaurants on their food, décor, and service (and their summated ratings). Complete the following for the urban and suburban restaurants.

Source: Data extracted from *Zagat Survey 2009 New York City Restaurants* and *Zagat Survey 2009–2010 Long Island Restaurants*.

a. Construct the five-number summary of the cost of a meal.

b. Construct a boxplot of the cost of a meal. What is the shape of the distribution?

c. Compute and interpret the correlation coefficient of the summated rating and the cost of a meal.

4.109 The file **Protein** contains calories, protein, and cholesterol of popular protein foods (fresh red meats, poultry, and fish).

Source: U.S. Department of Agriculture.

a. Compute the correlation coefficient between calories and protein.

b. Compute the correlation coefficient between calories and cholesterol.

c. Compute the correlation coefficient between protein and cholesterol.

d. Based on the results of (a) through (c), what conclusions can you reach concerning calories, protein, and cholesterol?

4.110 The file **HotelPrices** contains the average price of a room at two-star, three-star, and four-star hotels in cities around the world in 2010 in English pounds (about US$1.56 as of January 2011). Complete the following for two-star, three-star, and four-star hotels.

Source: Data extracted from **www.hotels.com/press/hotel-price-index-summer-2010.html**.

a. Compute the mean, median, first quartile, and third quartile.

b. Compute the range, interquartile range, variance, standard deviation, and coefficient of variation.

c. Interpret the measures of central tendency and variation within the context of this problem.

d. Construct a boxplot. Are the data skewed? If so, how?

e. Compute the covariance between the average price at two-star and three-star hotels, between two-star and four-star hotels, and between three-star and four-star hotels.

f. Compute the coefficient of correlation between the average price at two-star and three-star hotels, between two-star and four-star hotels, and between three-star and four-star hotels.

g. Which do you think is more valuable in expressing the relationship between the average price of a room at two-star, three-star, and four-star hotels—the covariance or the coefficient of correlation? Explain.

h. Based on (f), what conclusions can you reach about the relationship between the average price of a room at two-star, three-star, and four-star hotels?

4.111 The file **PropertyTaxes** contains the property taxes per capita for the 50 states and the District of Columbia.

a. Compute the mean, median, first quartile, and third quartile.

b. Compute the range, interquartile range, variance, standard deviation, and coefficient of variation.

c. Construct a boxplot. Are the data skewed? If so, how?

d. Based on the results of (a) through (c), what conclusions can you reach concerning property taxes per capita, in thousands of dollars, for each state and the District of Columbia?

4.112 The file **CEO-Compensation** includes the total compensation (in millions of $) of CEOs of 161 large public companies and the investment return in 2010. Complete the following for the total compensation (in millions of $).

Source: Data extracted from M. Krantz and B. Hansen, "CEO Pay Soars While Workers' Pay Stalls," *USA Today*, April 1, 2011, pp. 1B, 2B and **money.usatoday.com**.

a. Compute the mean, median, first quartile, and third quartile.

b. Compute the range, interquartile range, variance, standard deviation, and coefficient of variation.

c. Construct a boxplot. Are the data skewed? If so, how?

d. Based on the results of (a) through (c), what conclusions can you reach concerning the total compensation (in millions of $) of CEOs?

e. Compute the correlation coefficient between compensation and the investment return in 2010.

f. What conclusions can you reach from the results of (e)?

4.113 You are planning to study for your statistics examination with a group of classmates, one of whom you particularly want to impress. This individual has volunteered to use Excel or Minitab to get the needed summary information, tables, and charts for a data set containing several numerical and categorical variables assigned by the instructor for study purposes. This person comes over to you with the printout and exclaims, "I've got it all—the means, the medians, the standard deviations, the boxplots, the pie charts—for all our variables. The problem is, some of the output looks weird—like the boxplots for gender and for major and the pie charts for grade point average and for height. Also, I can't understand why Professor Krehbiel said we can't get the descriptive stats for some of the variables; I got them for everything! See, the mean for height is 68.23, the mean for grade point average is 2.76, the mean for gender is 1.50, the mean for major is 4.33." What is your reply?

REPORT WRITING EXERCISES

4.114 The file **DomesticBeer** contains the percentage of alcohol, number of calories per 12 ounces, and number of carbohydrates (in grams) per 12 ounces for 145 of the best-selling domestic beers in the United States.

Your task is to write a report based on a complete descriptive evaluation of each of the numerical variables—percentage of alcohol, number of calories per 12 ounces, and number of carbohydrates (in grams) per 12 ounces. Appended to your report should be all appropriate tables, charts, and numerical descriptive measures.

Source: Data extracted from **www.Beer100.com**, April 1, 2011.

TEAM PROJECTS

The file **Bond Funds** contains information regarding nine variables from a sample of 184 bond funds:

Fund number—Identification number for each bond fund

Type—Type of bonds comprising the bond fund (inter-mediate government or short-term corporate)
Assets—In millions of dollars
Fees—Sales charges (no or yes)
Expense ratio—Ratio of expenses to net assets
Return 2009—Twelve-month return in 2009
Three-year return—Annualized return, 2007–2009
Five-year return—Annualized return, 2005–2009
Risk—Risk-of-loss factor of the mutual fund (low, average, or high)

4.115 Complete the following for expense ratio in percentage, three-year return, and five-year return.
a. Compute the mean, median, first quartile, and third quartile.
b. Compute the range, interquartile range, variance, standard deviation, and coefficient of variation.
c. Construct a boxplot. Are the data skewed? If so, how?
d. Based on the results of (a) through (c), what conclusions can you reach concerning these variables?

4.116 You want to compare bond funds that have fees to those that do not have fees. For each of these two groups, use the variables expense ratio, return in 2009, three-year return, and five-year return and complete the following.
a. Compute the mean, median, first quartile, and third quartile.
b. Compute the range, interquartile range, variance, standard deviation, and coefficient of variation.
c. Construct a boxplot. Are the data skewed? If so, how?
d. Based on the results of (a) through (c), what conclusions can you reach about differences between bond funds that have fees and those that do not have fees?

4.117 You want to compare intermediate government to short-term corporate bond funds. For each of these two groups, use the variables expense ratio, three-year return, and five-year return and complete the following.
a. Compute the mean, median, first quartile, and third quartile.
b. Compute the range, interquartile range, variance, standard deviation, and coefficient of variation.
c. Construct a boxplot. Are the data skewed? If so, how?
d. Based on the results of (a) through (c), what conclusions can you reach about differences between intermediate government and short-term corporate bond funds?

4.118 You want to compare bond funds based on risk. For each of these three levels of risk (below average, average,

above average), use the variables expense ratio, return 2009, three-year return, and five-year return and complete the following.
a. Compute the mean, median, first quartile, and third quartile.
b. Compute the range, interquartile range, variance, standard deviation, and coefficient of variation.
c. Construct a boxplot. Are the data skewed? If so, how?
d. Based on the results of (a) through (c), what conclusions can you reach about differences between bond funds based on risk?

STUDENT SURVEY DATABASE

4.119 Problem 1.21 on page 20 describes a survey of 62 undergraduate students (stored in UndergradSurvey). For these data, for each numerical variable, complete the following.
a. Compute the mean, median, first quartile, and third quartile.
b. Compute the range, interquartile range, variance, standard deviation, and coefficient of variation.
c. Construct a boxplot. Are the data skewed? If so, how?
d. Write a report summarizing your conclusions.

4.120 Problem 1.21 on page 20 describes a survey of 62 undergraduate students (stored in UndergradSurvey).
a. Select a sample of undergraduate students at your school and conduct a similar survey for those students.
b. For the data collected in (a), repeat (a) through (d) of Problem 4.115.
c. Compare the results of (b) to those of Problem 4.115.

4.121 Problem 1.22 on page 21 describes a survey of 44 MBA students (stored in GradSurvey). For these data, for each numerical variable, complete the following.
a. Compute the mean, median, first quartile, and third quartile.
b. Compute the range, interquartile range, variance, standard deviation, and coefficient of variation.
c. Construct a boxplot. Are the data skewed? If so, how?
d. Write a report summarizing your conclusions.

4.122 Problem 1.22 on page 21 describes a survey of 44 MBA students (stored in GradSurvey).
a. Select a sample of graduate students from your MBA program and conduct a similar survey for those students.
b. For the data collected in (a), repeat (a) through (d) of Problem 4.117.
c. Compare the results of (b) to those of Problem 4.117.

MANAGING ASHLAND MULTICOMM SERVICES

For what variable in the Chapter 3 "Managing Ashland MultiComm Services" case (see page 129) are numerical descriptive measures needed?

1. For the variable you identify, compute the appropriate numerical descriptive measures and construct a boxplot.

2. For the variable you identify, construct a graphical display. What conclusions can you reach from this other plot that cannot be made from the boxplot?

3. Summarize your findings in a report that can be included with the task force's study.

DIGITAL CASE

Apply your knowledge about the proper use of numerical descriptive measures in this continuing Digital Case from Chapter 3.

Open **EndRunGuide.pdf**, the EndRun Financial Services "Guide to Investing." Reexamine EndRun's supporting data for the "More Winners Than Losers" and "The Big Eight Difference" and then answer the following:

1. Can descriptive measures be computed for any variables? How would such summary statistics support EndRun's claims? How would those summary statistics affect your perception of EndRun's record?

2. Evaluate the methods EndRun used to summarize the results presented on the "Customer Survey Results" page. Is there anything you would do differently to summarize these results?

3. Note that the last question of the survey has fewer responses than the other questions. What factors may have limited the number of responses to that question?

REFERENCES

1. Kendall, M. G., A. Stuart, and J. K. Ord, *Kendall's Advanced Theory of Statistics, Volume 1: Distribution Theory*, 6th ed. (New York: Oxford University Press, 1994).
2. *Microsoft Excel 2010* (Redmond, WA: Microsoft Corporation, 2010).
3. *Minitab Release 16* (State College, PA: Minitab, Inc., 2010).

APPENDIX 4.1

Microsoft Excel

Analysis ToolPak Use **Descriptive Statistics** to create a list that contains measures of variation and shape along with central tendency.

For example, to create a worksheet that presents descriptive statistics for the 2009 return for the intermediate government and short-term corporate bond funds, open to the **RETURN2009 worksheet** of the **Bond Funds workbook** and:

1. Select **Data → Data Analysis**.
2. In the Data Analysis dialog box, select **Descriptive Statistics** from the **Analysis Tools** list and then click **OK**.

In the Descriptive Statistics dialog box (shown below):

3. Enter **A1:B98** as the **Input Range**. Click **Columns** and check **Labels in First Row**.
4. Click **New Worksheet Ply**, check **Summary statistics**, and then click **OK**.

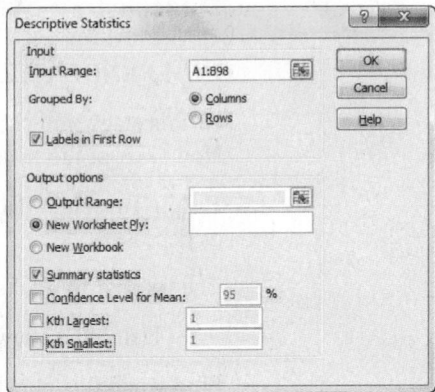

In the new worksheet:

5. Select column C, right-click, and click **Delete** in the shortcut menu (to eliminate the duplicate row labels).
6. Adjust the column headings and cell formatting. (See Appendix B for help with these adjustments.)

To add the coefficient of variation to this worksheet, first enter **Coefficient of variation** in cell **A16**. Then, enter the formula **=B7/B3** in cell **B16** and then copy it to cell **C16**. Finally, format cells B16 and C16 for percentage display.

APPENDIX 4.2

SPSS—Version 15 Lesson 1

Descriptive Statistics

INDEPENDENT READING

At this stage you should read the following help features. Cancel the SPSS opening window. Now look at the following tutorial.

Help / Tutorial / Table of contents (if necessary) / **Working With Output / Next** (as often as necessary)

The tutorial will take you through

Using the Viewer

Stop when this part is finished.

Example 1: The following data show the response times, in days, for 50 customer complaints for a large car dealership. The data have been arranged into an ascending data array.

1	2	4	4	5	5	5	10	10	11
12	13	13	14	19	20	22	23	25	26
26	26	27	27	27	28	29	29	29	30
31	31	32	33	35	35	36	52	54	61
68	74	81	84	95	123	126	137	152	173

Create a SPSS data file where the above raw data are entered and save it as **Lesson 3 - Ex.1.sav.**

Define the variable and fix data at zero decimal places. Give the variable the label **Response Time - Days.**

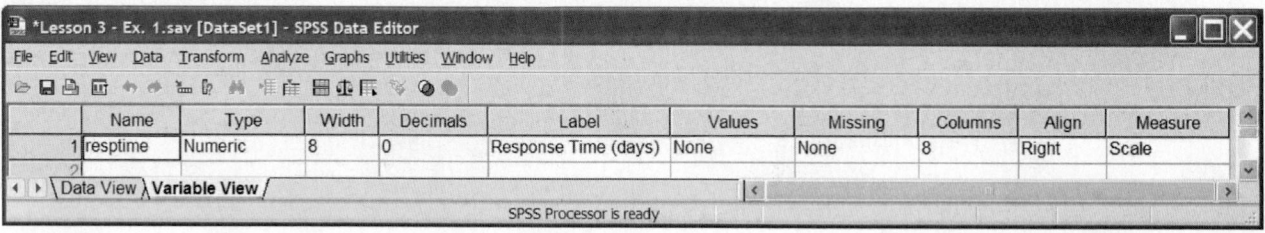

Explore Procedure

Now return to the SPSS Data Editor window. Make the following menu selections:

Analyze / Descriptive Statistics / Explore... / Response Time - Days (Highlight) ▶ (for Dependent List) / **Statistics** (for Display) / **Statistics** / check **Percentiles / Continue / OK**

At this point you will get a set of exploratory information about the data in the SPSS Viewer window. The first table will be a *Case Processing Summary*. This table allows you to check to see how much data were used to produce the results that follow it. This table is of interest only to the researcher and would never be included in any report.

The next table is called *Descriptives* (shown below) and includes several statistics, including measures of centre and measures of variability.

Descriptives

			Statistic	Std. Error
Response Time (days)	Mean		40.70	5.777
	95% Confidence	Lower Bound	29.09	
	Interval for Mean	Upper Bound	52.31	
	5% Trimmed Mean		36.37	
	Median		27.50	
	Variance		1668.949	
	Std. Deviation		40.853	
	Minimum		1	
	Maximum		173	
	Range		172	
	Interquartile Range		40	
	Skewness		1.731	.337
	Kurtosis		2.444	.662

You can customize this table to suit your needs. One way would be by deleting any items that you are not interested in. First activate the table by double-clicking on it so that a fuzzy border appears around the table. (Close the Pivot Trays window.) Then just **Highlight** and **Delete** any items you don't want. You can easily produce the edited table shown below.

Descriptives

		Statistic
Response Time (days)	Mean	40.70
	Median	27.50
	Variance	1668.949
	Std. Deviation	40.853
	Minimum	1
	Maximum	173
	Range	172
	Interquartile Range	39.50
	Skewness	1.731

The next table (shown below) is a table of *Percentiles* that was asked for by checking off the percentiles box.

Percentiles

		Percentiles				
		5	10	25	50	75
Weighted Average (Definition1)	Response Time (days)	3.10	5.00	13.00	27.50	52.50
Turkey's Hinges	Response Time (days)			13.00	27.50	52.00

Percentiles

	Percentiles	
	90	95
Weighted Average (Definition 1)	120.20	143.75

Note: **Tukey's Hinges** are the quartiles calculated with a different formula than the weighted average (definition 1) formula.

Descriptives Procedure

For another method that can be used to calculate descriptive statistics (without the graphing options), choose the following from the SPSS Data Editor window:

Analyze / Descriptive Statistics / Descriptives... / Response Time - Days (Highlight) ► (for Variables)/ **Options /** check **Mean, Std. deviation, Range / Continue / OK**

The output for this procedure is shown below:

Descriptive Statics

	N	Range	Mean	Std. Deviation
Response Time (days)	50	172	40.70	40.853
Valid N (listwise)	50			

Note: This procedure is useful when you know what you want and you don't want a table with a lot of extra items.

Frequencies Procedure

You may also calculate descriptive statistics by using the following procedure:

Analyze / Descriptive Statistics / Frequencies... / Response Time - Days (Highlight) ▶ (for Variables)**/ Statistics /** check **Mean**, **Median**, **Std. deviation**, **Range**, **Quartiles / Cut points for /** key 5 in the equal groups box **/ Percentiles /** key 33 in the percentiles box **/ Add /** key 67 in the percentiles box **Add / Continue /** Now verify that the Display frequency tables option is not selected. **OK**

The Frequencies: Statistics window is shown below.

The 'Frequencies' output is shown below.

Statistics

Response Time (days)

N	Valid	50
	Missing	0
Mean		40.70
Median		27.50
Std. Deviation		40.853
Range		172
Percentiles	20	11.20
	25	13.00
	33	21.66
	40	26.00
	50	27.50
	60	30.60
	67	33.34
	75	52.50
	80	66.60

You may now want to save the results as they appear in the SPSS Viewer window.

File / Save as / Lesson 3 – Ex.1.spo / File / Close / File / Exit

Subgroups of one variable

Recall the file **Lesson – Ex. 1a.sav.**

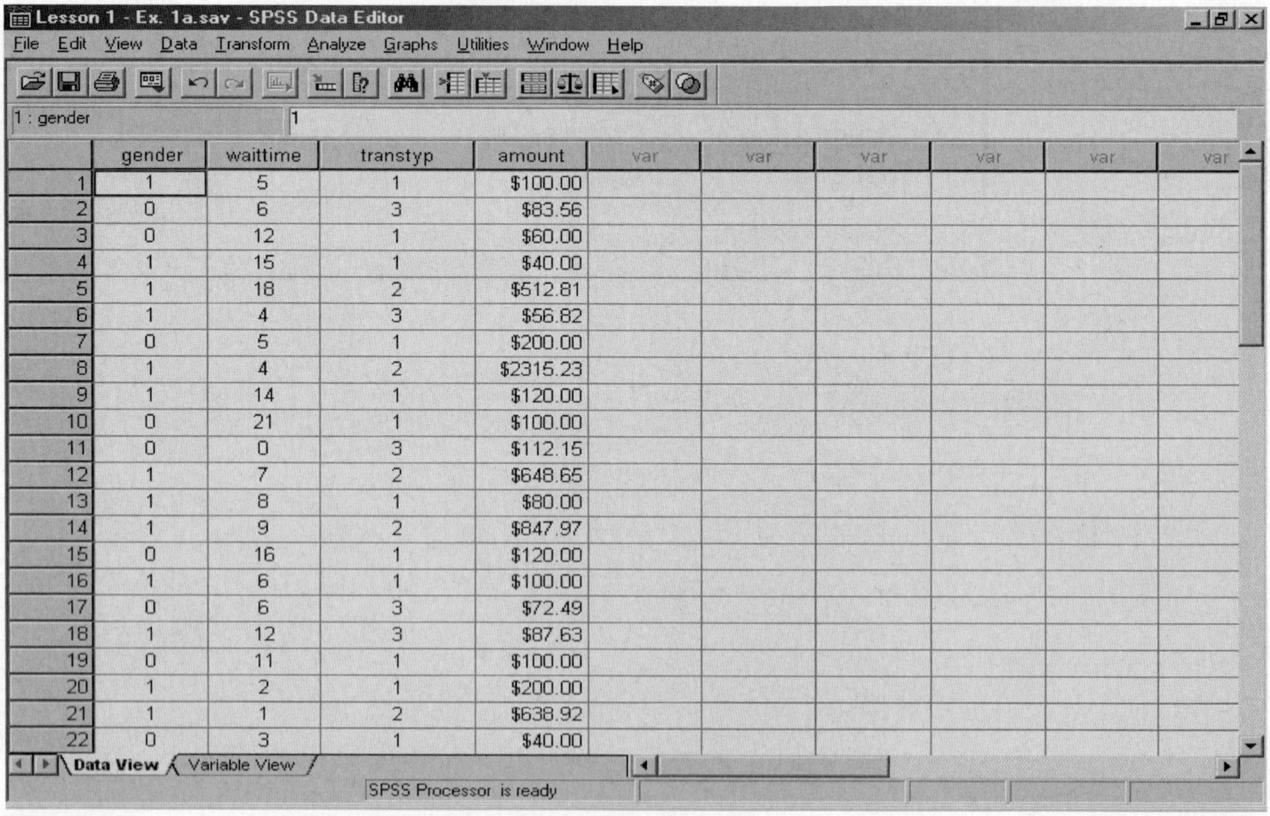

	gender	waittime	transtyp	amount	var	var	var	var	var	var
1	1	5	1	$100.00						
2	0	6	3	$83.56						
3	0	12	1	$60.00						
4	1	15	1	$40.00						
5	1	18	2	$512.81						
6	1	4	3	$56.82						
7	0	5	1	$200.00						
8	1	4	2	$2315.23						
9	1	14	1	$120.00						
10	0	21	1	$100.00						
11	0	0	3	$112.15						
12	1	7	2	$648.65						
13	1	8	1	$80.00						
14	1	9	2	$847.97						
15	0	16	1	$120.00						
16	1	6	1	$100.00						
17	0	6	3	$72.49						
18	1	12	3	$87.63						
19	0	11	1	$100.00						
20	1	2	1	$200.00						
21	1	1	2	$638.92						
22	0	3	1	$40.00						

Suppose we want to calculate the mean and standard deviation of the waiting times for the females and males separately.

Choose **Data / Split file...** and fill in the following window as shown on the next page:

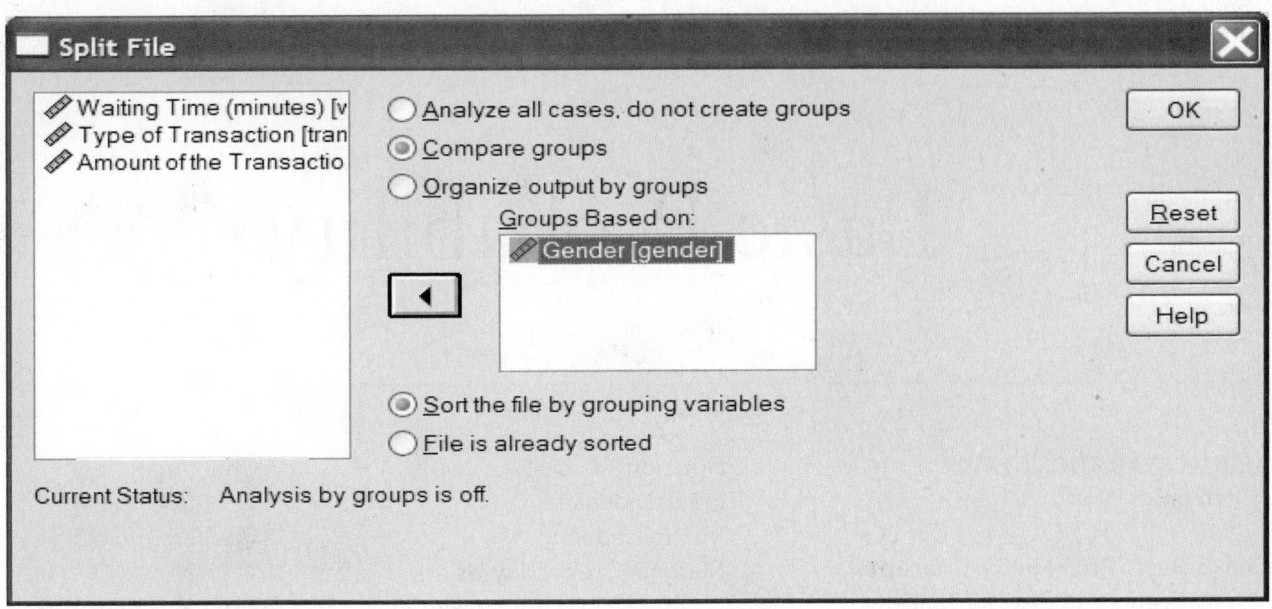

Important note: The **Split file** procedure will cause your, input data file to be sorted by the 'Groups Based on:' variable. Usually you want your original data file *not* to be sorted, therefore *do not save* the sorted data file when you close the file. If you do want the sorted file, then save it under a different name.

Now choose **Analyze / Descriptive Statistics / Frequencies... /** Waiting time (minutes) (Highlight) ▶ (for Variables / **Statistics** check **Mean Std. deviation / Continue / OK**

The results are shown below:

Statistics

Waiting Time (minutes)

Female	N	Valid	10
		Missing	0
	Mean		8.90
	Std. Deviation		6.297
Male	N	Valid	15
		Missing	0
	Mean		8.13
	Std. Deviation		5.303

Note: You may also use the **Descriptives** or **Explore** procedures to get similar results in different layouts. You can also include the 'Gender' variable in the **Factor List:** box of the **Explore** procedure.

5

Basic Probability

Learning Objectives

In this chapter, you learn:

- Basic probability concepts
- Conditional probability
- Bayes' theorem to revise probabilities
- Various counting rules

© Alan Levenson / Corbis

@ M&R Electronics World

As the marketing manager for M&R Electronics World, you are analyzing the survey results of an intent-to-purchase study. This study asked the heads of 1,000 households about their intentions to purchase a big-screen television sometime during the next 12 months. As a follow-up, you plan to survey the same people 12 months later to see whether they purchased televisions. In addition, for households purchasing big-screen televisions, you would like to know whether the television they purchased had a faster refresh rate (120 Hz or higher) or a standard refresh rate (60 Hz), whether they also purchased a Blu-ray disc (BD) player in the past 12 months, and whether they were satisfied with their purchase of the big-screen television.

You are expected to use the results of this survey to plan a new marketing strategy that will enhance sales and better target those households likely to purchase multiple or more expensive products. What questions can you ask in this survey? How can you express the relationships among the various intent-to-purchase responses of individual households?

In previous chapters, you learned descriptive methods to summarize categorical and numerical variables. In this chapter, you will learn about probability to answer questions such as the following:

- What is the probability that a household is planning to purchase a big-screen television in the next year?
- What is the probability that a household will actually purchase a big-screen television?
- What is the probability that a household is planning to purchase a big-screen television and actually purchases the television?
- Given that the household is planning to purchase a big-screen television, what is the probability that the purchase is made?
- Does knowledge of whether a household *plans* to purchase the television change the likelihood of predicting whether the household *will* purchase the television?
- What is the probability that a household that purchases a big-screen television will purchase a television with a faster refresh rate?
- What is the probability that a household that purchases a big-screen television with a faster refresh rate will also purchase a Blu-ray disc player?
- What is the probability that a household that purchases a big-screen television will be satisfied with the purchase?

With answers to questions such as these, you can begin to make decisions about your marketing strategy. Should your strategy for selling more big-screen televisions target those households that have indicated an intent to purchase? Should you concentrate on selling televisions that have faster refresh rates? Is it likely that households that purchase big-screen televisions with faster refresh rates can be easily persuaded to also purchase Blu-ray disc players?

Ljupco Smokovski / Shutterstock

T he principles of probability help bridge the worlds of descriptive statistics and inferential statistics. Reading this chapter will help you learn about different types of probabilities, how to compute probabilities, and how to revise probabilities in light of new information. Probability principles are the foundation for the probability distribution, the concept of mathematical expectation, and the binomial and Poisson distributions, topics that are discussed in Chapter 6.

5.1 Basic Probability Concepts

What is meant by the word *probability*? A **probability** is the numeric value representing the chance, likelihood, or possibility that a particular event will occur, such as the price of a stock increasing, a rainy day, a defective product, or the outcome five dots in a single toss of a die. In all these instances, the probability involved is a proportion or fraction whose value ranges between 0 and 1, inclusive. An event that has no chance of occurring (the **impossible event**) has a probability of 0. An event that is sure to occur (the **certain event**) has a probability of 1.

There are three types of probability:

- *A priori*
- Empirical
- Subjective

In *a priori* **probability**, the probability of an occurrence is based on prior knowledge of the process involved. In the simplest case, where each outcome is equally likely, the chance of occurrence of the event is defined in Equation (5.1).

PROBABILITY OF OCCURRENCE

$$\text{Probability of occurrence} = \frac{X}{T} \qquad (5.1)$$

where

X = number of ways in which the event occurs

T = total number of possible outcomes

Consider a standard deck of cards that has 26 red cards and 26 black cards. The probability of selecting a black card is $26/52 = 0.50$ because there are $X = 26$ black cards and $T = 52$ total cards. What does this probability mean? If each card is replaced after it is selected, does it mean that 1 out of the next 2 cards selected will be black? No, because you cannot say for certain what will happen on the next several selections. However, you can say that in the long run, if this selection process is continually repeated, the proportion of black cards selected will approach 0.50. Example 5.1 shows another example of computing an *a priori* probability.

EXAMPLE 5.1

Finding *A Priori* Probabilities

A standard six-sided die has six faces. Each face of the die contains either one, two, three, four, five, or six dots. If you roll a die, what is the probability that you will get a face with five dots?

SOLUTION Each face is equally likely to occur. Because there are six faces, the probability of getting a face with five dots is 1/6.

The preceding examples use the *a priori* probability approach because the number of ways the event occurs and the total number of possible outcomes are known from the composition of the deck of cards or the faces of the die.

In the **empirical probability** approach, the probabilities are based on observed data, not on prior knowledge of a process. Surveys are often used to generate empirical probabilities. Examples of this type of probability are the proportion of individuals in the Using Statistics scenario who actually purchase big-screen televisions, the proportion of registered voters who prefer a certain political candidate, and the proportion of students who have part-time jobs. For example, if you take a survey of students, and 60% state that they have part-time jobs, then there is a 0.60 probability that an individual student has a part-time job.

The third approach to probability, **subjective probability,** differs from the other two approaches because subjective probability differs from person to person. For example, the development team for a new product may assign a probability of 0.60 to the chance of success for the product, while the president of the company may be less optimistic and assign a probability of 0.30. The assignment of subjective probabilities to various outcomes is usually based on a combination of an individual's past experience, personal opinion, and analysis of a particular situation. Subjective probability is especially useful in making decisions in situations in which you cannot use *a priori* probability or empirical probability.

Events and Sample Spaces

The basic elements of probability theory are the individual outcomes of a variable under study. You need the following definitions to understand probabilities.

> ### EVENT
> Each possible outcome of a variable is referred to as an **event**.
> A **simple event** is described by a single characteristic.

For example, when you toss a coin, the two possible outcomes are heads and tails. Each of these represents a simple event. When you roll a standard six-sided die in which the six faces of the die contain either one, two, three, four, five, or six dots, there are six possible simple events. An event can be any one of these simple events, a set of them, or a subset of all of them. For example, the event of an *even number of dots* consists of three simple events (i.e., two, four, or six dots).

> ### JOINT EVENT
> A **joint event** is an event that has two or more characteristics.

Getting two heads when you toss a coin twice is an example of a joint event because it consists of heads on the first toss and heads on the second toss.

> ### COMPLEMENT
> The **complement** of event A (represented by the symbol A') includes all events that are not part of A.

The complement of a head is a tail because that is the only event that is not a head. The complement of five dots on a die is not getting five dots. Not getting five dots consists of getting one, two, three, four, or six dots.

SAMPLE SPACE

The collection of all the possible events is called the **sample space**.
The sample space for tossing a coin consists of heads and tails. The sample space when rolling a die consists of one, two, three, four, five, and six dots. Example 5.2 demonstrates events and sample spaces.

EXAMPLE 5.2

Events and Sample Spaces

TABLE 5.1

Purchase Behavior for Big-Screen Televisions

The Using Statistics scenario on page 203 concerns M&R Electronics World. Table 5.1 presents the results of the sample of 1,000 households in terms of purchase behavior for big-screen televisions.

PLANNED TO PURCHASE	ACTUALLY PURCHASED		
	Yes	No	Total
Yes	200	50	250
No	100	650	750
Total	300	700	1,000

What is the sample space? Give examples of simple events and joint events.

SOLUTION   The sample space consists of the 1,000 respondents. Simple events are "planned to purchase," "did not plan to purchase," "purchased," and "did not purchase." The complement of the event "planned to purchase" is "did not plan to purchase." The event "planned to purchase and actually purchased" is a joint event because in this joint event the respondent must plan to purchase the television *and* actually purchase it.

Contingency Tables and Venn Diagrams

There are several ways in which you can view a particular sample space. One way involves using a **contingency table** (see Section 3.9) such as the one displayed in Table 5.1. You get the values in the cells of the table by subdividing the sample space of 1,000 households according to whether someone planned to purchase and actually purchased a big-screen television set. For example, 200 of the respondents planned to purchase a big-screen television set and subsequently did purchase the big-screen television set.

A second way to present the sample space is by using a **Venn diagram**. This diagram graphically represents the various events as "unions" and "intersections" of circles. Figure 5.1 presents a typical Venn diagram for a two-variable situation, with each variable having only two events (A and A', B and B'). The circle on the left (the red one) represents all events that are part of A.

The circle on the right (the yellow one) represents all events that are part of B. The area contained within circle A and circle B (center area) is the intersection of A and B (written as $A \cap B$), since it is part of A and also part of B. The total area of the two circles is the union of A and B (written as $A \cup B$) and contains all outcomes that are just part of event A, just part of event B, or part of both A and B. The area in the diagram outside of $A \cup B$ contains outcomes that are neither part of A nor part of B.

You must define A and B in order to develop a Venn diagram. You can define either event as A or B, as long as you are consistent in evaluating the various events. For the big-screen television example, you can define the events as follows:

$$A = \text{planned to purchase} \qquad B = \text{actually purchased}$$
$$A' = \text{did not plan to purchase} \qquad B' = \text{did not actually purchase}$$

In drawing the Venn diagram (see Figure 5.2), you must determine the value of the intersection of A and B so that the sample space can be divided into its parts. $A \cap B$ consists of all 200 households who planned to purchase and actually purchased a big-screen television set.

FIGURE 5.1

Venn diagram for events A and B

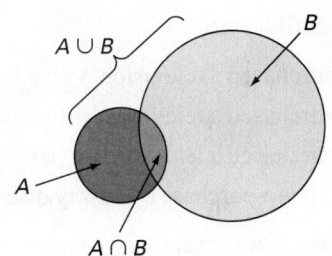

FIGURE 5.2

Venn diagram for the M&R Electronics World example

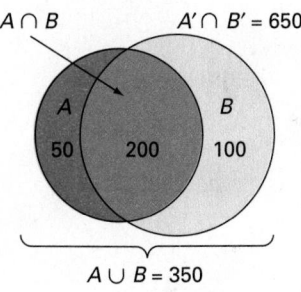

The remainder of event A (planned to purchase) consists of the 50 households who planned to purchase a big-screen television set but did not actually purchase one. The remainder of event B (actually purchased) consists of the 100 households who did not plan to purchase a big-screen television set but actually purchased one. The remaining 650 households represent those who neither planned to purchase nor actually purchased a big-screen television set.

Simple Probability

Now you can answer some of the questions posed in the Using Statistics scenario. Because the results are based on data collected in a survey (refer to Table 5.1), you can use the empirical probability approach.

As stated previously, the most fundamental rule for probabilities is that they range in value from 0 to 1. An impossible event has a probability of 0, and an event that is certain to occur has a probability of 1.

Simple probability refers to the probability of occurrence of a simple event, $P(A)$. A simple probability in the Using Statistics scenario is the probability of planning to purchase a big-screen television. How can you determine the probability of selecting a household that planned to purchase a big-screen television? Using Equation (5.1) on page 204:

$$\text{Probability of occurrence} = \frac{X}{T}$$

$$P(\text{Planned to purchase}) = \frac{\text{Number who planned to purchase}}{\text{Total number of households}}$$

$$= \frac{250}{1,000} = 0.25$$

Thus, there is a 0.25 (or 25%) chance that a household planned to purchase a big-screen television. Example 5.3 illustrates another application of simple probability.

EXAMPLE 5.3

Computing the Probability That the Big-Screen Television Purchased Had a Faster Refresh Rate

In the Using Statistics follow-up survey, additional questions were asked of the 300 households that actually purchased big-screen televisions. Table 5.2 indicates the consumers' responses to whether the television purchased had a faster refresh rate and whether they also purchased a Blu-ray disc (BD) player in the past 12 months.

Find the probability that if a household that purchased a big-screen television is randomly selected, the television purchased had a faster refresh rate.

TABLE 5.2

Purchase Behavior Regarding Purchasing a Faster Refresh Rate Television and Blu-ray Disc (BD) Player

REFRESH RATE OF TELEVISION PURCHASED	PURCHASED BD PLAYER		
	Yes	No	Total
Faster	38	42	80
Standard	70	150	220
Total	108	192	300

SOLUTION Using the following definitions:

$$A = \text{purchased a television with a faster refresh rate}$$
$$A' = \text{purchased a television with a standard refresh rate}$$
$$B = \text{purchased a Blu-ray disc (BD) player}$$
$$B' = \text{did not purchase a Blu-ray disc (BD) player}$$

$$P(\text{faster refresh rate}) = \frac{\text{Number of faster refresh rate televisions}}{\text{Total number of televisions}}$$

$$= \frac{80}{300} = 0.267$$

There is a 26.7% chance that a randomly selected big-screen television purchased has a faster refresh rate.

Joint Probability

Whereas simple or marginal probability refers to the probability of occurrence of simple events, **joint probability** refers to the probability of an occurrence involving two or more events. An example of joint probability is the probability that you will get heads on the first toss of a coin and heads on the second toss of a coin.

In Table 5.1 on page 206, the group of individuals who planned to purchase and actually purchased a big-screen television consist only of the outcomes in the single cell "yes—planned to purchase *and* yes—actually purchased." Because this group consists of 200 households, the probability of picking a household that planned to purchase *and* actually purchased a big-screen television is

$$P(\text{Planned to purchase } and \text{ actually purchased}) = \frac{\text{Planned to purchase } and \text{ actually purchased}}{\text{Total number of respondents}}$$

$$= \frac{200}{1,000} = 0.20$$

Example 5.4 also demonstrates how to determine joint probability.

EXAMPLE 5.4

Determining the Joint Probability That a Household Purchased a Big-Screen Television with a Faster Refresh Rate and a Blu-ray Disc Player

In Table 5.2, the purchases are cross-classified as having a faster refresh rate or having a standard refresh rate and whether the household purchased a Blu-ray disc player. Find the probability that a randomly selected household that purchased a big-screen television also purchased a television that had a faster refresh rate and purchased a Blu-ray disc player.

SOLUTION Using Equation (5.1) on page 204,

$$P\begin{pmatrix}\text{television with a faster refresh} \\ \text{rate } and \text{ Blu-ray disc player}\end{pmatrix} = \frac{\begin{array}{c}\text{Number that purchased a television with a faster} \\ \text{refresh rate } and \text{ a Blu-ray disc player}\end{array}}{\text{Total number of big-screen television purchasers}}$$

$$= \frac{38}{300} = 0.127$$

Therefore, there is a 12.7% chance that a randomly selected household that purchased a big-screen television purchased a television that had a faster refresh rate and a Blu-ray disc player.

Marginal Probability

The **marginal probability** of an event consists of a set of joint probabilities. You can determine the marginal probability of a particular event by using the concept of joint probability just discussed. For example, if B consists of two events, B_1 and B_2, then $P(A)$, the probability of event A, consists of the joint probability of event A occurring with event B_1 and the joint probability of event A occurring with event B_2. You use Equation (5.2) to compute marginal probabilities.

MARGINAL PROBABILITY

$$P(A) = P(A \text{ and } B_1) + P(A \text{ and } B_2) + \cdots + P(A \text{ and } B_k) \quad \text{(5.2)}$$

where $B_1, B_2, \ldots, B_k$ are k mutually exclusive and collectively exhaustive events, defined as follows:

Two events are **mutually exclusive** if both the events cannot occur simultaneously.
A set of events is **collectively exhaustive** if one of the events must occur.

Heads and tails in a coin toss are mutually exclusive events. The result of a coin toss cannot simultaneously be a head and a tail. Heads and tails in a coin toss are also collectively exhaustive events. One of them must occur. If heads does not occur, tails must occur. If tails does not occur, heads must occur. Being male and being female are mutually exclusive and collectively exhaustive events. No person is both (the two are mutually exclusive), and everyone is one or the other (the two are collectively exhaustive).

You can use Equation (5.2) to compute the marginal probability of "planned to purchase" a big-screen television:

$$
\begin{aligned}
P(\text{Planned to purchase}) &= P(\text{Planned to purchase } and \text{ purchased}) \\
&\quad + P(\text{Planned to purchase } and \text{ did not purchase}) \\
&= \frac{200}{1,000} + \frac{50}{1,000} \\
&= \frac{250}{1,000} = 0.25
\end{aligned}
$$

You get the same result if you add the number of outcomes that make up the simple event "planned to purchase."

General Addition Rule

How do you find the probability of event "A or B"? You need to consider the occurrence of either event A or event B or both A and B. For example, how can you determine the probability that a household planned to purchase *or* actually purchased a big-screen television? The event "planned to purchase *or* actually purchased" includes all households that planned to purchase and all households that actually purchased a big-screen television. You examine each cell of the contingency table (Table 5.1 on page 206) to determine whether it is part of this event. From Table 5.1, the cell "planned to purchase *and* did not actually purchase" is part of the event because it includes respondents who planned to purchase. The cell "did not plan to purchase *and* actually purchased" is included because it contains respondents who actually purchased. Finally, the cell "planned to purchase *and* actually purchased" has both characteristics of interest. Therefore, one way to calculate the probability of "planned to purchase *or* actually purchased" is

$$
\begin{aligned}
P(\text{Planned to purchase } or \text{ actually purchased}) &= P(\text{Planned to purchase } and \text{ did} \\
&\quad \text{not actually purchase}) + P(\text{Did not plan to} \\
&\quad \text{purchase } and \text{ actually purchased}) + P(\text{Planned} \\
&\quad \text{to purchase } and \text{ actually purchased}) \\
&= \frac{50}{1,000} + \frac{100}{1,000} + \frac{200}{1,000} \\
&= \frac{350}{1,000} = 0.35
\end{aligned}
$$

Often, it is easier to determine $P(A\text{ or }B)$, the probability of the event $A\text{ or }B$, by using the **general addition rule**, defined in Equation (5.3).

GENERAL ADDITION RULE

The probability of A or B is equal to the probability of A plus the probability of B minus the probability of A and B.

$$P(A\text{ or }B) = P(A) + P(B) - P(A\text{ and }B) \qquad (5.3)$$

Applying Equation (5.3) to the previous example produces the following result:

$$P(\text{Planned to purchase } or \text{ actually purchased}) = P(\text{Planned to purchase})$$
$$+ P(\text{Actually purchased}) - P(\text{Planned to purchase } and \text{ actually purchased})$$
$$= \frac{250}{1,000} + \frac{300}{1,000} - \frac{200}{1,000}$$
$$= \frac{350}{1,000} = 0.35$$

The general addition rule consists of taking the probability of A and adding it to the probability of B and then subtracting the probability of the joint event $A\text{ and }B$ from this total because the joint event has already been included in computing both the probability of A and the probability of B. Referring to Table 5.1 on page 206, if the outcomes of the event "planned to purchase" are added to those of the event "actually purchased," the joint event "planned to purchase *and* actually purchased" has been included in each of these simple events. Therefore, because this joint event has been double-counted, you must subtract it to provide the correct result. Example 5.5 illustrates another application of the general addition rule.

EXAMPLE 5.5

Using the General Addition Rule for the Households That Purchased Big-Screen Televisions

In Example 5.3 on page 207, the purchases were cross-classified in Table 5.2 as televisions that had a faster refresh rate or televisions that had a standard refresh rate and whether the household purchased a Blu-ray disc (BD) player. Find the probability that among households that purchased a big-screen television, they purchased a television that had a faster refresh rate or a BD player.

SOLUTION Using Equation (5.3),

$$P(\text{Television had a faster refresh rate } or \text{ purchased a BD player}) = \begin{array}{l} P(\text{Television had a faster refresh rate}) \\ + P(\text{purchased a BD player}) - P(\text{Television had a faster refresh rate } and \text{ purchased a BD player}) \end{array}$$
$$= \frac{80}{300} + \frac{108}{300} - \frac{38}{300}$$
$$= \frac{150}{300} = 0.50$$

Therefore, of those households that purchased a big-screen television, there is a 50.0% chance that a randomly selected household purchased a television that had a faster refresh rate or purchased a BD player.

Problems for Section 5.1

LEARNING THE BASICS

5.1 Two coins are tossed.
a. Give an example of a simple event.
b. Give an example of a joint event.
c. What is the complement of a head on the first toss?
d. What does the sample space consist of?

5.2 An urn contains 12 red balls and 8 white balls. One ball is to be selected from the urn.
a. Give an example of a simple event.
b. What is the complement of a red ball?
c. What does the sample space consist of?

5.3 Consider the following contingency table:

	B	B'
A	10	20
A'	20	40

What is the probability of event
a. A?
b. A'?
c. A and B?
d. A or B?

5.4 Consider the following contingency table:

	B	B'
A	10	30
A'	25	35

What is the probability of event
a. A'?
b. A and B?
c. A' and B'?
d. A' or B'?

APPLYING THE CONCEPTS

5.5 For each of the following, indicate whether the type of probability involved is an example of *a priori* probability, empirical probability, or subjective probability.
a. The next toss of a fair coin will land on heads.
b. Italy will win soccer's World Cup the next time the competition is held.
c. The sum of the faces of two dice will be seven.
d. The train taking a commuter to work will be more than 10 minutes late.

5.6 For each of the following, state whether the events created are mutually exclusive and collectively exhaustive.
a. Registered voters in the United States were asked whether they are registered as Republicans or Democrats.

b. Each respondent was classified by the type of car he or she drives: sedan, SUV, American, European, Asian, or none.
c. People were asked, "Do you currently live in (i) an apartment or (ii) a house?"
d. A product was classified as defective or not defective.

5.7 Which of the following events occur with a probability of zero? For each, state why or why not.
a. A voter in the United States is registered as a Republican and as a Democrat.
b. A voter in the United States is female and registered as a Republican.
c. An automobile is a Ford and a Toyota.
d. An automobile is a Toyota and was manufactured in the United States.

5.8 Does it take more time to be removed from an email list than it used to take? A study of 100 large online retailers revealed the following:

	NEED THREE OR MORE CLICKS TO BE REMOVED	
YEAR	**Yes**	**No**
2009	39	61
2008	7	93

Source: Data extracted from "More Clicks to Escape an Email List," *The New York Times*, March 29, 2010, p. B2.

a. Give an example of a simple event.
b. Give an example of a joint event.
c. What is the complement of "Needs three or more clicks to be removed from an email list"?
d. Why is "Needs three or more clicks to be removed from an email list in 2009" a joint event?

5.9 Referring to the contingency table in Problem 5.8, if a large online retailer is selected at random, what is the probability that
a. you needed three or more clicks to be removed from an email list?
b. you needed three or more clicks to be removed from an email list in 2009?
c. you needed three or more clicks to be removed from an email list or were a large online retailer surveyed in 2009?
d. Explain the difference in the results in (b) and (c).

5.10 Do people of different age groups differ in their response to email messages? A survey by the Center for the Digital Future of the University of Southern California (data extracted from A. Mindlin, "Older E-mail Users Favor Fast Replies," *The New York Times*, July 14, 2008, p. B3) reported that 70.7% of users over 70 years of age believe that email messages should be answered quickly, as compared to

53.6% of users 12 to 50 years old. Suppose that the survey was based on 1,000 users over 70 years of age and 1,000 users 12 to 50 years old. The following table summarizes the results:

ANSWERS QUICKLY	AGE OF RESPONDENTS		
	12–50	Over 70	Total
Yes	536	707	1,243
No	464	293	757
Total	1,000	1,000	2,000

a. Give an example of a simple event.
b. Give an example of a joint event.
c. What is the complement of a respondent who answers quickly?
d. Why is a respondent who answers quickly and is over 70 years old a joint event?

5.11 Referring to the contingency table in Problem 5.10, if a respondent is selected at random, what is the probability that
a. he or she answers quickly?
b. he or she is over 70 years old?
c. he or she answers quickly *or* is over 70 years old?
d. Explain the difference in the results in (b) and (c).

SELF Test **5.12** According to a Gallup Poll, the extent to which employees are engaged with their workplace varies from country to country. Gallup reports that the percentage of U.S. workers engaged with their workplace is more than twice as high as the percentage of German workers. The study also shows that having more engaged workers leads to increased innovation, productivity, and profitability, as well as reduced employee turnover. The results of the poll are summarized in the following table:

ENGAGEMENT	COUNTRY		
	United States	Germany	Total
Engaged	550	246	796
Not engaged	1,345	1,649	2,994
Total	1,895	1,895	3,790

Source: Data extracted from M. Nink, "Employee Disengagement Plagues Germany," *Gallup Management Journal*, **gmj.gallup.com**, April 9, 2009.

If an employee is selected at random, what is the probability that he or she
a. is engaged with his or her workplace?
b. is a U.S. worker?
c. is engaged with his or her workplace *or* is a U.S. worker?
d. Explain the difference in the results in (b) and (c).

5.13 What is the preferred way for people to order fast food? A survey was conducted in 2009, but the sample sizes

were not reported. Suppose the results, based on a sample of 100 males and 100 females, were as follows:

DINING PREFERENCE	GENDER		
	Male	Female	Total
Dine inside	21	12	33
Order inside to go	19	10	29
Order at the drive-through	60	78	138
Total	100	100	200

Source: Data extracted from **www.qsrmagazine.com/reports/drive-thru_time_study/2009/2009_charts/whats_your_preferred_way_to_order_fast_food.html**.

If a respondent is selected at random, what is the probability that he or she
a. prefers to order at the drive-through?
b. is a male *and* prefers to order at the drive-through?
c. is a male *or* prefers to order at the drive-through?
d. Explain the difference in the results in (b) and (c).

5.14 A survey of 1,085 adults asked "Do you enjoy shopping for clothing for yourself?" The results (data extracted from "Split decision on clothes shopping," *USA Today*, January 28, 2011, p. 1B) indicated that 51% of the females enjoyed shopping for clothing for themselves as compared to 44% of the males. The sample sizes of males and females were not provided. Suppose that the results indicated that of 542 males, 238 answered yes. Of 543 females, 276 answered yes. Construct a contingency table to evaluate the probabilities. What is the probability that a respondent chosen at random
a. enjoys shopping for clothing for themself?
b. is a female *and* enjoys shopping for clothing for herself?
c. is a female *or* is a person who enjoys shopping for clothing?
d. is a male *or* a female?

5.15 Each year, ratings are compiled concerning the performance of new cars during the first 90 days of use. Suppose that the cars have been categorized according to whether a car needs warranty-related repair (yes or no) and the country in which the company manufacturing a car is based (United States or not United States). Based on the data collected, the probability that the new car needs a warranty repair is 0.04, the probability that the car was manufactured by a U.S.-based company is 0.60, and the probability that the new car needs a warranty repair *and* was manufactured by a U.S.-based company is 0.025. Construct a contingency table to evaluate the probabilities of a warranty-related repair. What is the probability that a new car selected at random
a. needs a warranty repair?
b. needs a warranty repair *and* was manufactured by a U.S.-based company?
c. needs a warranty repair *or* was manufactured by a U.S.-based company?
d. needs a warranty repair *or* was not manufactured by a U.S.-based company?

5.2 Conditional Probability

Each example in Section 5.1 involves finding the probability of an event when sampling from the entire sample space. How do you determine the probability of an event if you know certain information about the events involved?

Computing Conditional Probabilities

Conditional probability refers to the probability of event A, given information about the occurrence of another event, B.

CONDITIONAL PROBABILITY

The probability of A given B is equal to the probability of A and B divided by the probability of B.

$$P(A|B) = \frac{P(A \text{ and } B)}{P(B)} \qquad \text{(5.4a)}$$

The probability of B given A is equal to the probability of A and B divided by the probability of A.

$$P(B|A) = \frac{P(A \text{ and } B)}{P(A)} \qquad \text{(5.4b)}$$

where

$$P(A \text{ and } B) = \text{joint probability of } A \text{ and } B$$

$$P(A) = \text{marginal probability of } A$$

$$P(B) = \text{marginal probability of } B$$

Referring to the Using Statistics scenario involving the purchase of big-screen televisions, suppose you were told that a household planned to purchase a big-screen television. Now, what is the probability that the household actually purchased the television? In this example, the objective is to find P(Actually purchased | Planned to purchase). Here you are given the information that the household planned to purchase the big-screen television. Therefore, the sample space does not consist of all 1,000 households in the survey. It consists of only those households that planned to purchase the big-screen television. Of 250 such households, 200 actually purchased the big-screen television. Therefore, based on Table 5.1 on page 206, the probability that a household actually purchased the big-screen television given that they planned to purchase is

$$P(\text{Actually purchased} | \text{Planned to purchase}) = \frac{\text{Planned to purchase } and \text{ actually purchased}}{\text{Planned to purchase}}$$

$$= \frac{200}{250} = 0.80$$

You can also use Equation (5.4b) to compute this result:

$$P(B|A) = \frac{P(A \text{ and } B)}{P(A)}$$

where

$$A = \text{planned to purchase}$$

$$B = \text{actually purchased}$$

then

$$P(\text{Actually purchased}|\text{Planned to purchase}) = \frac{200/1{,}000}{250/1{,}000}$$

$$= \frac{200}{250} = 0.80$$

Example 5.6 further illustrates conditional probability.

EXAMPLE 5.6

Finding the Conditional Probability of Purchasing a Blu-ray Disc Player

Table 5.2 on page 207 is a contingency table for whether a household purchased a television with a faster refresh rate and whether the household purchased a Blu-ray disc player. If a household purchased a television with a faster refresh rate, what is the probability that it also purchased a Blu-ray disc player?

SOLUTION Because you know that the household purchased a television with a faster refresh rate, the sample space is reduced to 80 households. Of these 80 households, 38 also purchased a Blu-ray disc (BD) player. Therefore, the probability that a household purchased a BD player, given that the household purchased a television with a faster refresh rate, is

$$P\binom{\text{Purchased BD player} \mid \text{Purchased}}{\text{television with faster refresh rate}} = \frac{\begin{array}{c}\text{Number purchasing television with}\\ \text{faster refresh rate } and \text{ BD player}\end{array}}{\begin{array}{c}\text{Number purchasing television}\\ \text{with faster refresh rate}\end{array}}$$

$$= \frac{38}{80} = 0.475$$

If you use Equation (5.4b) on page 213:

  A = purchased a television with a faster refresh rate

  B = purchased a BD player

then

$$P(B|A) = \frac{P(A \text{ and } B)}{P(A)} = \frac{38/300}{80/300} = 0.475$$

Therefore, given that the household purchased a television with a faster refresh rate, there is a 47.5% chance that the household also purchased a Blu-ray disc player. You can compare this conditional probability to the marginal probability of purchasing a Blu-ray disc player, which is $108/300 = 0.36$, or 36%. These results tell you that households that purchased televisions with a faster refresh rate are more likely to purchase a Blu-ray disc player than are households that purchased big-screen televisions that have a standard refresh rate.

Decision Trees

In Table 5.1 on page 206, households are classified according to whether they planned to purchase and whether they actually purchased big-screen televisions. A **decision tree** is an alternative to the contingency table. Figure 5.3 represents the decision tree for this example.

FIGURE 5.3

Decision tree for M&R Electronics World example

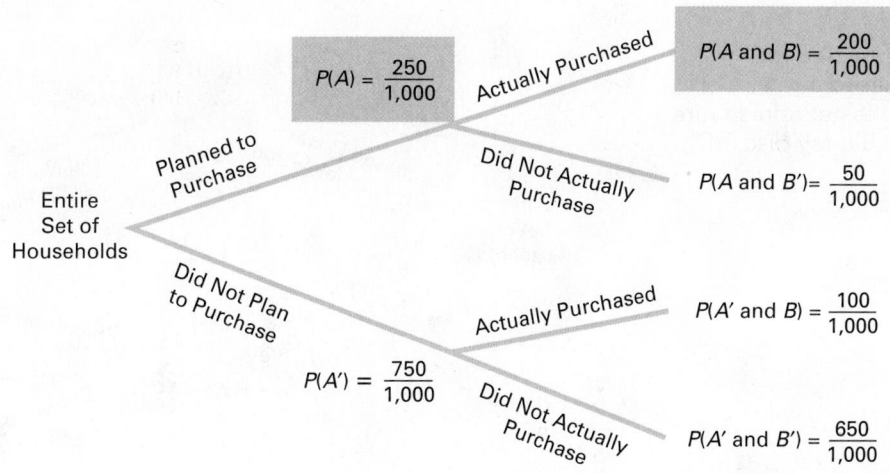

In Figure 5.3, beginning at the left with the entire set of households, there are two "branches" for whether or not the household planned to purchase a big-screen television. Each of these branches has two subbranches, corresponding to whether the household actually purchased or did not actually purchase the big-screen television. The probabilities at the end of the initial branches represent the marginal probabilities of A and A'. The probabilities at the end of each of the four subbranches represent the joint probability for each combination of events A and B. You compute the conditional probability by dividing the joint probability by the appropriate marginal probability.

For example, to compute the probability that the household actually purchased, given that the household planned to purchase the big-screen television, you take P(Planned to purchase *and* actually purchased) and divide by P(Planned to purchase). From Figure 5.3,

$$P(\text{Actually purchased} | \text{Planned to purchase}) = \frac{200/1,000}{250/1,000}$$

$$= \frac{200}{250} = 0.80$$

Example 5.7 illustrates how to construct a decision tree.

EXAMPLE 5.7

Constructing the Decision Tree for the Households That Purchased Big-Screen Televisions

Using the cross-classified data in Table 5.2 on page 207, construct the decision tree. Use the decision tree to find the probability that a household purchased a Blu-ray disc player, given that the household purchased a television with a faster refresh rate.

SOLUTION The decision tree for purchased a Blu-ray disc player and a television with a faster refresh rate is displayed in Figure 5.4 on page 216. Using Equation (5.4b) on page 213 and the following definitions,

$$A = \text{purchased a television with a faster refresh rate}$$
$$B = \text{purchased a Blu-ray disc player}$$

$$P(B|A) = \frac{P(A \text{ and } B)}{P(A)} = \frac{38/300}{80/300} = 0.475$$

FIGURE 5.4

Decision tree for purchased a television with a faster refresh rate and a Blu-ray disc (BD) player

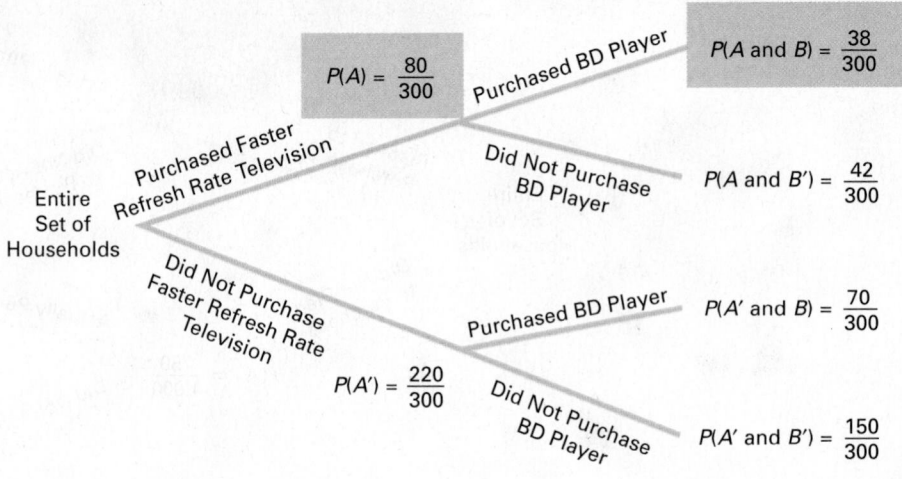

Independence

In the example concerning the purchase of big-screen televisions, the conditional probability is $200/250 = 0.80$ that the selected household actually purchased the big-screen television, given that the household planned to purchase. The simple probability of selecting a household that actually purchased is $300/1,000 = 0.30$. This result shows that the prior knowledge that the household planned to purchase affected the probability that the household actually purchased the television. In other words, the outcome of one event is *dependent* on the outcome of a second event.

When the outcome of one event does *not* affect the probability of occurrence of another event, the events are said to be independent. **Independence** can be determined by using Equation (5.5).

INDEPENDENCE

Two events, A and B, are independent if and only if

$$P(A \mid B) = P(A) \qquad (5.5)$$

where

$$P(A \mid B) = \text{conditional probability of } A \text{ given } B$$

$$P(A) = \text{marginal probability of } A$$

Example 5.8 demonstrates the use of Equation (5.5)

EXAMPLE 5.8

Determining Independence

In the follow-up survey of the 300 households that actually purchased big-screen televisions, the households were asked if they were satisfied with their purchases. Table 5.3 cross-classifies the responses to the satisfaction question with the responses to whether the television had a faster refresh rate.

TABLE 5.3

Satisfaction with Purchase of Big-Screen Televisions

TELEVISION REFRESH RATE	SATISFIED WITH PURCHASE?		
	Yes	No	Total
Faster	64	16	80
Standard	176	44	220
Total	240	60	300

Determine whether being satisfied with the purchase and the refresh rate of the television purchased are independent.

SOLUTION For these data,

$$P(\text{Satisfied}|\text{faster refresh rate}) = \frac{64/300}{80/300} = \frac{64}{80} = 0.80$$

which is equal to

$$P(\text{Satisfied}) = \frac{240}{300} = 0.80$$

Thus, being satisfied with the purchase and the refresh rate of the television purchased are independent. Knowledge of one event does not affect the probability of the other event.

Multiplication Rules

The **general multiplication rule** is derived using Equation (5.4a) on page 213:

$$P(A|B) = \frac{P(A \text{ and } B)}{P(B)}$$

and solving for the joint probability $P(A \text{ and } B)$.

GENERAL MULTIPLICATION RULE

The probability of A and B is equal to the probability of A given B times the probability of B.

$$P(A \text{ and } B) = P(A|B)P(B) \tag{5.6}$$

Example 5.9 demonstrates the use of the general multiplication rule.

EXAMPLE 5.9

Using the General Multiplication Rule

Consider the 80 households that purchased televisions that had a faster refresh rate. In Table 5.3 on page 216 you see that 64 households are satisfied with their purchase, and 16 households are dissatisfied. Suppose 2 households are randomly selected from the 80 households. Find the probability that both households are satisfied with their purchase.

SOLUTION Here you can use the multiplication rule in the following way. If

$$A = \text{second household selected is satisfied}$$
$$B = \text{first household selected is satisfied}$$

then, using Equation (5.6),

$$P(A \text{ and } B) = P(A|B)P(B)$$

The probability that the first household is satisfied with the purchase is 64/80. However, the probability that the second household is also satisfied with the purchase depends on the result of the first selection. If the first household is not returned to the sample after the satisfaction level is determined (i.e., sampling without replacement), the number of households remaining is 79. If the first household is satisfied, the probability that the second is also satisfied is 63/79 because 63 satisfied households remain in the sample. Therefore,

$$P(A \text{ and } B) = \left(\frac{63}{79}\right)\left(\frac{64}{80}\right) = 0.6380$$

There is a 63.80% chance that both of the households sampled will be satisfied with their purchase.

The **multiplication rule for independent events** is derived by substituting $P(A)$ for $P(A \mid B)$ in Equation (5.6).

MULTIPLICATION RULE FOR INDEPENDENT EVENTS

If A and B are independent, the probability of A and B is equal to the probability of A times the probability of B.

$$P(A \text{ and } B) = P(A)P(B) \tag{5.7}$$

If this rule holds for two events, A and B, then A and B are independent. Therefore, there are two ways to determine independence:

1. Events A and B are independent if, and only if, $P(A \mid B) = P(A)$.
2. Events A and B are independent if, and only if, $P(A \text{ and } B) = P(A)P(B)$.

Marginal Probability Using the General Multiplication Rule

In Section 5.1, marginal probability was defined using Equation (5.2) on page 209. You can state the equation for marginal probability by using the general multiplication rule. If

$$P(A) = P(A \text{ and } B_1) + P(A \text{ and } B_2) + \cdots + P(A \text{ and } B_k)$$

then, using the general multiplication rule, Equation (5.8) defines the marginal probability.

MARGINAL PROBABILITY USING THE GENERAL MULTIPLICATION RULE

$$P(A) = P(A \mid B_1)P(B_1) + P(A \mid B_2)P(B_2) + \cdots + P(A \mid B_k)P(B_k) \tag{5.8}$$

where $B_1, B_2, \ldots, B_k$ are k mutually exclusive and collectively exhaustive events.

To illustrate Equation (5.8), refer to Table 5.1 on page 206. Let

$$P(A) = \text{probability of "planned to purchase"}$$
$$P(B_1) = \text{probability of "actually purchased"}$$
$$P(B_2) = \text{probability of "did not actually purchase"}$$

Then, using Equation (5.8), the probability of planned to purchase is

$$P(A) = P(A \mid B_1)P(B_1) + P(A \mid B_2)P(B_2)$$
$$= \left(\frac{200}{300}\right)\left(\frac{300}{1,000}\right) + \left(\frac{50}{700}\right)\left(\frac{700}{1,000}\right)$$
$$= \frac{200}{1,000} + \frac{50}{1,000} = \frac{250}{1,000} = 0.25$$

Problems for Section 5.2

LEARNING THE BASICS

5.16 Consider the following contingency table:

	B	B'
A	10	20
A'	20	40

What is the probability of
a. $A \mid B$?
b. $A \mid B'$?
c. $A' \mid B'$?
d. Are events A and B independent?

5.17 Consider the following contingency table:

	B	B'
A	10	30
A'	25	35

What is the probability of
a. $A \mid B$?
b. $A' \mid B'$?
c. $A \mid B'$?
d. Are events A and B independent?

5.18 If $P(A \text{ and } B) = 0.4$ and $P(B) = 0.8$, find $P(A \mid B)$.

5.19 If $P(A) = 0.7, P(B) = 0.6$, and A and B are independent, find $P(A \text{ and } B)$.

5.20 If $P(A) = 0.3, P(B) = 0.4$, and $P(A \text{ and } B) = 0.2$, are A and B independent?

APPLYING THE CONCEPTS

5.21 Does it take more time to be removed from an email list than it used to take? A study of 100 large online retailers revealed the following:

	NEED THREE OR MORE CLICKS TO BE REMOVED	
YEAR	**Yes**	**No**
2009	39	61
2008	7	93

Source: Data extracted from "More Clicks to Escape an Email List," *The New York Times*, March 29, 2010, p. B2.

a. Given that three or more clicks are needed to be removed from an email list, what is the probability that this occurred in 2009?

b. Given that the year 2009 is involved, what is the probability that three or more clicks are needed to be removed from an email list?
c. Explain the difference in the results in (a) and (b).
d. Are needing three or more clicks to be removed from an email list and the year independent?

5.22 Do people of different age groups differ in their response to email messages? A survey by the Center for the Digital Future of the University of Southern California (data extracted from A. Mindlin, "Older E-mail Users Favor Fast Replies," *The New York Times*, July 14, 2008, p. B3) reported that 70.7% of users over 70 years of age believe that email messages should be answered quickly, as compared to 53.6% of users 12 to 50 years old. Suppose that the survey was based on 1,000 users over 70 years of age and 1,000 users 12 to 50 years old. The following table summarizes the results:

	ANSWERS QUICKLY		
AGE OF RESPONDENTS	**12–50**	**Over 70**	**Total**
Yes	536	707	1,243
No	464	293	757
Total	1,000	1,000	2,000

a. Suppose you know that the respondent is between 12 and 50 years old. What is the probability that he or she answers quickly?
b. Suppose you know that the respondent is over 70 years old. What is the probability that he or she answers quickly?
c. Are the two events, answers quickly and age of respondents, independent? Explain.

5.23 What is the preferred way for people to order fast food? A survey was conducted in 2009, but the sample sizes were not reported. Suppose the results, based on a sample of 100 males and 100 females, were as follows:

	GENDER		
DINING PREFERENCE	**Male**	**Female**	**Total**
Dine inside	21	12	33
Order inside to go	19	10	29
Order at the drive-through	60	78	138
Total	100	100	200

Source: Data extracted from **www.qsrmagazine.com/reports/drive-thru_time_study/2009/2009_charts/whats_your_preferred_way_to_order_fast_food.html**.

a. Given that a respondent is a male, what is the probability that he prefers to order at the drive-through?
b. Given that a respondent is a female, what is the probability that she prefers to order at the drive-through?

c. Is dining preference independent of gender? Explain.

5.24 According to a Gallup Poll, the extent to which employees are engaged with their workplace varies from country to country. Gallup reports that the percentage of U.S. workers engaged with their workplace is more than twice as high as the percentage of German workers. The study also shows that having more engaged workers leads to increased innovation, productivity, and profitability, as well as reduced employee turnover. The results of the poll are summarized in the following table:

	COUNTRY		
ENGAGEMENT	United States	Germany	Total
Engaged	550	246	796
Not engaged	1,345	1,649	2,994
Total	1,895	1,895	3,790

Source: Data extracted from M. Nink, "Employee Disengagement Plagues Germany," *Gallup Management Journal*, **gmj.gallup.com**, April 9, 2009.

a. Given that a worker is from the United States, what is the probability that the worker is engaged?
b. Given that a worker is from the United States, what is the probability that the worker is not engaged?
c. Given that a worker is from Germany, what is the probability that the worker is engaged?
d. Given that a worker is from Germany, what is the probability that the worker is not engaged?

5.25 A survey of 1,085 adults asked "Do you enjoy shopping for clothing for yourself." The results (data extracted from "Split decision on clothes shopping," *USA Today*, January 28, 2011, p. 1B) indicated that 51% of the females enjoyed shopping for clothing for themselves as compared to 44% of the males. The sample sizes of males and females were not provided. Suppose that the results were as shown in the following table:

ENJOYS SHOPPING FOR CLOTHING	GENDER		
	Male	Female	Total
Yes	238	276	514
No	304	267	571
Total	542	543	1,085

a. Suppose that the respondent chosen is a female. What is the probability that she does not enjoy shopping for clothing?
b. Suppose that the respondent chosen enjoys shopping for clothing. What is the probability that the individual is a male?
c. Are enjoying shopping for clothing and the gender of the individual independent? Explain.

5.26 Each year, ratings are compiled concerning the performance of new cars during the first 90 days of use. Suppose that the cars have been categorized according to whether a car needs warranty-related repair (yes or no) and the country in which the company manufacturing a car is based (United States or not United States). Based on the data collected, the probability that the new car needs a warranty repair is 0.04, the probability that the car is manufactured by a U.S.-based company is 0.60, and the probability that the new car needs a warranty repair *and* was manufactured by a U.S.-based company is 0.025.

a. Suppose you know that a company based in the United States manufactured a particular car. What is the probability that the car needs warranty repair?
b. Suppose you know that a company based in the United States did not manufacture a particular car. What is the probability that the car needs warranty repair?
c. Are need for warranty repair and location of the company manufacturing the car independent?

5.27 In 39 of the 61 years from 1950 through 2010, the S&P 500 finished higher after the first five days of trading. In 34 of those 39 years, the S&P 500 finished higher for the year. Is a good first week a good omen for the upcoming year? The following table gives the first-week and annual performance over this 61-year period:

	S&P 500'S ANNUAL PERFORMANCE	
FIRST WEEK	Higher	Lower
Higher	34	5
Lower	11	11

a. If a year is selected at random, what is the probability that the S&P 500 finished higher for the year?
b. Given that the S&P 500 finished higher after the first five days of trading, what is the probability that it finished higher for the year?
c. Are the two events "first-week performance" and "annual performance" independent? Explain.
d. Look up the performance after the first five days of 2011 and the 2011 annual performance of the S&P 500 at **finance.yahoo.com**. Comment on the results.

5.28 A standard deck of cards is being used to play a game. There are four suits (hearts, diamonds, clubs, and spades), each having 13 faces (ace, 2, 3, 4, 5, 6, 7, 8, 9, 10, jack, queen, and king), making a total of 52 cards. This complete deck is thoroughly mixed, and you will receive the first 2 cards from the deck, without replacement (the first card is not returned to the deck after it is selected).

a. What is the probability that both cards are queens?
b. What is the probability that the first card is a 10 and the second card is a 5 or 6?

c. If you were sampling with replacement (the first card is returned to the deck after it is selected), what would be the answer in (a)?

d. In the game of blackjack, the face cards (jack, queen, king) count as 10 points, and the ace counts as either 1 or 11 points. All other cards are counted at their face value. Blackjack is achieved if 2 cards total 21 points. What is the probability of getting blackjack in this problem?

5.29 A box of nine gloves contains two left-handed gloves and seven right-handed gloves.

a. If two gloves are randomly selected from the box, without replacement (the first glove is not returned to the box after it is selected), what is the probability that both gloves selected will be right-handed?

b. If two gloves are randomly selected from the box, without replacement (the first glove is not returned to the box after it is selected), what is the probability that there will be one right-handed glove and one left-handed glove selected?

c. If three gloves are selected, with replacement (the gloves are returned to the box after they are selected), what is the probability that all three will be left-handed?

d. If you were sampling with replacement (the first glove is returned to the box after it is selected), what would be the answers to (a) and (b)?

5.3 Bayes' Theorem

Bayes' theorem is used to revise previously calculated probabilities based on new information. Developed by Thomas Bayes in the eighteenth century (see references 1, 2, and 7), Bayes' theorem is an extension of what you previously learned about conditional probability.

You can apply Bayes' theorem to the situation in which M&R Electronics World is considering marketing a new model of televisions. In the past, 40% of the new-model televisions have been successful, and 60% have been unsuccessful. Before introducing the new model television, the marketing research department conducts an extensive study and releases a report, either favorable or unfavorable. In the past, 80% of the successful new-model television(s) had received favorable market research reports, and 30% of the unsuccessful new-model television(s) had received favorable reports. For the new model of television under consideration, the marketing research department has issued a favorable report. What is the probability that the television will be successful?

Bayes' theorem is developed from the definition of conditional probability. To find the conditional probability of B given A, consider Equation (5.4b) (originally presented on page 213 and shown below):

$$P(B \mid A) = \frac{P(A \text{ and } B)}{P(A)} = \frac{P(A \mid B)P(B)}{P(A)}$$

Bayes' theorem is derived by substituting Equation (5.8) on page 218 for $P(A)$ in the denominator of Equation (5.4b).

BAYES' THEOREM

$$P(B_i \mid A) = \frac{P(A \mid B_i)P(B_i)}{P(A \mid B_1)P(B_1) + P(A \mid B_2)P(B_2) + \cdots + P(A \mid B_k)P(B_k)} \quad \textbf{(5.9)}$$

where B_i is the ith event out of k mutually exclusive and collectively exhaustive events.

To use Equation (5.9) for the television-marketing example, let

event S = successful television   event F = favorable report

event S' = unsuccessful television   event F' = unfavorable report

and

$$P(S) = 0.40 \quad P(F \mid S) = 0.80$$
$$P(S') = 0.60 \quad P(F \mid S') = 0.30$$

Then, using Equation (5.9),

$$P(S|F) = \frac{P(F|S)P(S)}{P(F|S)P(S) + P(F|S')P(S')}$$

$$= \frac{(0.80)(0.40)}{(0.80)(0.40) + (0.30)(0.60)}$$

$$= \frac{0.32}{0.32 + 0.18} = \frac{0.32}{0.50}$$

$$= 0.64$$

The probability of a successful television, given that a favorable report was received, is 0.64. Thus, the probability of an unsuccessful television, given that a favorable report was received, is $1 - 0.64 = 0.36$.

Table 5.4 summarizes the computation of the probabilities, and Figure 5.5 presents the decision tree.

TABLE 5.4

Bayes' Theorem Calculations for the Television-Marketing Example

Event S_i	Prior Probability $P(S_i)$	Conditional Probability $P(F|S_i)$	Joint Probability $P(F|S_i)P(S_i)$	Revised Probability $P(S_i|F)$
S = successful television	0.40	0.80	0.32	$P(S|F) = 0.32/0.50$ $= 0.64$
S' = unsuccessful television	0.60	0.30	$\dfrac{0.18}{0.50}$	$P(S'|F) = 0.18/0.50$ $= 0.36$

FIGURE 5.5

Decision tree for marketing a new television

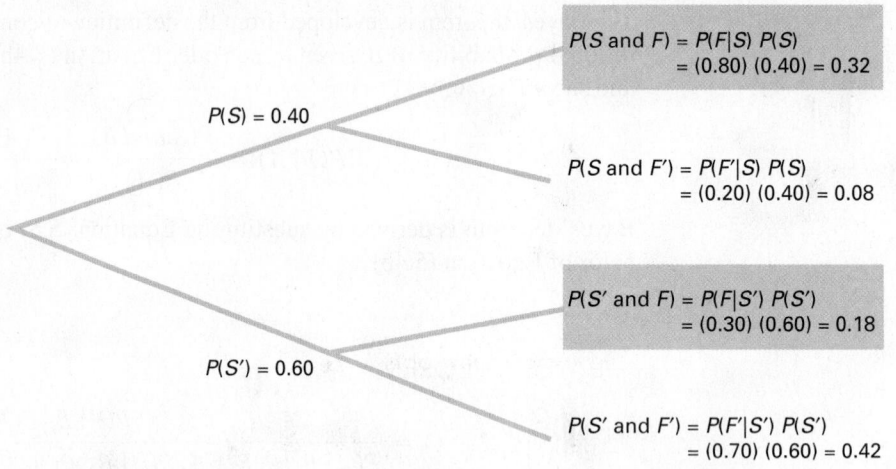

$P(S) = 0.40$

$P(S and F) = P(F|S) P(S)$
$= (0.80) (0.40) = 0.32$

$P(S and F') = P(F'|S) P(S)$
$= (0.20) (0.40) = 0.08$

$P(S' and F) = P(F|S') P(S')$
$= (0.30) (0.60) = 0.18$

$P(S') = 0.60$

$P(S' and F') = P(F'|S') P(S')$
$= (0.70) (0.60) = 0.42$

Example 5.10 applies Bayes' theorem to a medical diagnosis problem.

EXAMPLE 5.10

Using Bayes' Theorem in a Medical Diagnosis Problem

The probability that a person has a certain disease is 0.03. Medical diagnostic tests are available to determine whether the person actually has the disease. If the disease is actually present, the probability that the medical diagnostic test will give a positive result (indicating that the disease is present) is 0.90. If the disease is not actually present, the probability of a positive test result (indicating that the disease is present) is 0.02. Suppose that the medical diagnostic test has given a positive result (indicating that the disease is present). What is the probability that the disease is actually present? What is the probability of a positive test result?

SOLUTION Let

event D = has disease	event T = test is positive
event D' = does not have disease	event T' = test is negative

and

$$P(D) = 0.03 \quad P(T \mid D) = 0.90$$
$$P(D') = 0.97 \quad P(T \mid D') = 0.02$$

Using Equation (5.9) on page 221,

$$P(D \mid T) = \frac{P(T \mid D)P(D)}{P(T \mid D)P(D) + P(T \mid D')P(D')}$$

$$= \frac{(0.90)(0.03)}{(0.90)(0.03) + (0.02)(0.97)}$$

$$= \frac{0.0270}{0.0270 + 0.0194} = \frac{0.0270}{0.0464}$$

$$= 0.582$$

The probability that the disease is actually present, given that a positive result has occurred (indicating that the disease is present), is 0.582. Table 5.5 summarizes the computation of the probabilities, and Figure 5.6 presents the decision tree.

TABLE 5.5

Bayes' Theorem Calculations for the Medical Diagnosis Problem

Event D_i	Prior Probability $P(D_i)$	Conditional Probability $P(T \mid D_i)$	Joint Probability $P(T \mid D_i)P(D_i)$	Revised Probability $P(D_i \mid T)$
D = has disease	0.03	0.90	0.0270	$P(D \mid T) = 0.0270/0.0464$ $= 0.582$
D' = does not have disease	0.97	0.02	0.0194 0.0464	$P(D' \mid T) = 0.0194/0.0464$ $= 0.418$

FIGURE 5.6

Decision tree for the medical diagnosis problem

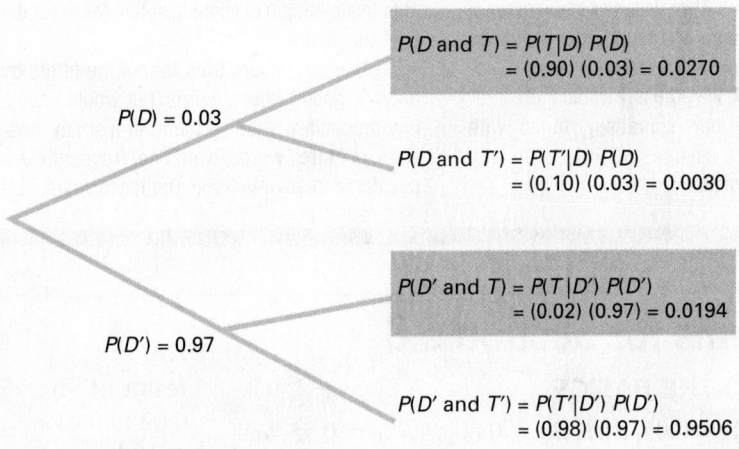

$P(D) = 0.03$

$P(D \text{ and } T) = P(T|D) \, P(D)$
$= (0.90) (0.03) = 0.0270$

$P(D \text{ and } T') = P(T'|D) \, P(D)$
$= (0.10) (0.03) = 0.0030$

$P(D' \text{ and } T) = P(T \mid D') \, P(D')$
$= (0.02) (0.97) = 0.0194$

$P(D') = 0.97$

$P(D' \text{ and } T') = P(T'|D') \, P(D')$
$= (0.98) (0.97) = 0.9506$

The denominator in Bayes' theorem represents $P(T)$, the probability of a positive test result, which in this case is 0.0464, or 4.64%.

THINK ABOUT THIS   Divine Providence and Spam

Would you ever guess that the essays *Divine Benevolence: Or, An Attempt to Prove That the Principal End of the Divine Providence and Government Is the Happiness of His Creatures* and *An Essay Towards Solving a Problem in the Doctrine of Chances* were written by the same person? Probably not, and in doing so, you illustrate a modern-day application of Bayesian statistics: spam, or junk mail filters.

In not guessing correctly, you probably looked at the words in the titles of the essays and concluded that they were talking about two different things. An implicit rule you used was that word frequencies vary by subject matter. A statistics essay would very likely contain the word *statistics* as well as words such as *chance*, *problem*, and *solving*. An eighteenth-century essay about theology and religion would be more likely to contain the uppercase forms of *Divine* and *Providence*.

Likewise, there are words you would guess to be very unlikely to appear in either book, such as technical terms from finance, and words that are most likely to appear in both—common words such as *a*, *and*, and *the*. That words would either be likely or unlikely suggests an application of probability theory. Of course, likely and unlikely are fuzzy concepts, and we might occasionally misclassify an essay if we kept things too simple, such as relying solely on the occurrence of the words *Divine* and *Providence*.

For example, a profile of the late Harris Milstead, better known as *Divine*, the star of *Hairspray* and other films, visiting Providence (Rhode Island), would most certainly not be an essay about theology. But if we widened the number of words we examined and found such words as *movie* or the name John Waters (Divine's director in many films), we probably would quickly realize the essay had something to do with twentieth-century cinema and little to do with theology and religion.

We can use a similar process to try to classify a new email message in your in-box as either spam or a legitimate message (called "ham," in this context). We would first need to add to your email program a "spam filter" that has the ability to track word frequencies associated with spam and ham messages as you identify them on a day-to-day basis. This would allow the filter to constantly update the prior probabilities necessary to use Bayes' theorem. With these probabilities, the filter can ask, "What is the probability that an email is spam, given the presence of a certain word?"

Applying the terms of Equation (5.9) on page 221, such a Bayesian spam filter would multiply the probability of finding the word in a spam email, $P(A|B)$, by the probability that the email is spam, $P(B)$, and then divide by the probability of finding the word in an email, the denominator in Equation (5.9). Bayesian spam filters also use shortcuts by focusing on a small set of words that have a high probability of being found in a spam message as well as on a small set of other words that have a low probability of being found in a spam message.

As spammers (people who send junk email) learned of such new filters, they tried to outfox them. Having learned that Bayesian filters might be assigning a high $P(A|B)$ value to words commonly found in spam, such as Viagra, spammers thought they could fool the filter by misspelling the word as Vi@gr@ or V1agra. What they overlooked was that the misspelled variants were even *more likely* to be found in a spam message than the original word. Thus, the misspelled variants made the job of spotting spam *easier* for the Bayesian filters.

Other spammers tried to fool the filters by adding "good" words, words that would have a low probability of being found in a spam message, or "rare" words, words not frequently encountered in any message. But these spammers

overlooked the fact that the conditional probabilities are constantly updated and that words once considered "good" would be soon discarded from the good list by the filter as their $P(A|B)$ value increased. Likewise, as "rare" words grew more common in spam and yet stayed rare in ham, such words acted like the misspelled variants that others had tried earlier.

Even then, and perhaps after reading about Bayesian statistics, spammers thought that they could "break" Bayesian filters by inserting random words in their messages. Those random words would affect the filter by causing it to see many words whose $P(A|B)$ value would be low. The Bayesian filter would begin to label many spam messages as ham and end up being of no practical use. Spammers again overlooked that conditional probabilities are constantly updated.

Other spammers decided to eliminate all or most of the words in their messages and replace them with graphics so that Bayesian filters would have very few words with which to form conditional probabilities. But this approach failed, too, as Bayesian filters were rewritten to consider things other than words in a message. After all, Bayes' theorem concerns *events*, and "graphics present with no text" is as valid an event as "some word, *X*, present in a message." Other future tricks will ultimately fail for the same reason. (By the way, spam filters use non-Bayesian techniques as well, which makes spammers' lives even more difficult.)

Bayesian spam filters are an example of the unexpected way that applications of statistics can show up in your daily life. You will discover more examples as you read the rest of this book. *By the way, the author of the two essays mentioned earlier was Thomas Bayes, who is a lot more famous for the second essay than the first essay, a failed attempt to use mathematics and logic to prove the existence of God.*

Problems for Section 5.3

LEARNING THE BASICS

5.30 If $P(B) = 0.05, P(A|B) = 0.80, P(B') = 0.95$, and $P(A|B') = 0.40$, find $P(B|A)$.

5.31 If $P(B) = 0.30, P(A|B) = 0.60, P(B') = 0.70$, and $P(A|B') = 0.50$, find $P(B|A)$.

APPLYING THE CONCEPTS

5.32 In Example 5.10 on page 222, suppose that the probability that a medical diagnostic test will give a positive

result if the disease is not present is reduced from 0.02 to 0.01.

a. If the medical diagnostic test has given a positive result (indicating that the disease is present), what is the probability that the disease is actually present?

b. If the medical diagnostic test has given a negative result (indicating that the disease is not present), what is the probability that the disease is not present?

5.33 An advertising executive is studying television viewing habits of married men and women during prime-time hours.

Based on past viewing records, the executive has determined that during prime time, husbands are watching television 60% of the time. When the husband is watching television, 40% of the time the wife is also watching. When the husband is not watching television, 30% of the time the wife is watching television.

a. Find the probability that if the wife is watching television, the husband is also watching television.

b. Find the probability that the wife is watching television during prime time.

5.34 Olive Construction Company is determining whether it should submit a bid for a new shopping center. In the past, Olive's main competitor, Base Construction Company, has submitted bids 70% of the time. If Base Construction Company does not bid on a job, the probability that Olive Construction Company will get the job is 0.50. If Base Construction Company bids on a job, the probability that Olive Construction Company will get the job is 0.25.

a. If Olive Construction Company gets the job, what is the probability that Base Construction Company did not bid?

b. What is the probability that Olive Construction Company will get the job?

5.35 Laid-off workers who become entrepreneurs because they cannot find meaningful employment with another company are known as *entrepreneurs by necessity*. *The Wall Street Journal* reports that these entrepreneurs by necessity are less likely to grow into large businesses than are *entrepreneurs by choice* (J. Bailey, "Desire—More Than Need— Builds a Business," *The Wall Street Journal*, May 21, 2001, p. B4). This article states that 89% of the entrepreneurs in the United States are entrepreneurs by choice and 11% are entrepreneurs by necessity. Only 2% of entrepreneurs by necessity expect their new business to employ 20 or more people within five years, whereas 14% of entrepreneurs by choice expect to employ at least 20 people within five years.

a. If an entrepreneur is selected at random and that individual expects that his or her new business will employ 20 or more people within five years, what is the probability that this individual is an entrepreneur by choice?

b. Discuss several possible reasons why entrepreneurs by choice are more likely than entrepreneurs by necessity to believe that they will grow their businesses.

5.36 The editor of a textbook publishing company is trying to decide whether to publish a proposed business statistics textbook. Information on previous textbooks published indicates that 10% are huge successes, 20% are modest successes, 40% break even, and 30% are losers. However, before a publishing decision is made, the book will be reviewed. In the past, 99% of the huge successes received favorable reviews, 70% of the moderate successes received favorable reviews, 40% of the break-even books received favorable reviews, and 20% of the losers received favorable reviews.

a. If the proposed textbook receives a favorable review, how should the editor revise the probabilities of the various outcomes to take this information into account?

b. What proportion of textbooks receives favorable reviews?

5.37 A municipal bond service has three rating categories (*A*, *B*, and *C*). Suppose that in the past year, of the municipal bonds issued throughout the United States, 70% were rated *A*, 20% were rated *B*, and 10% were rated *C*. Of the municipal bonds rated *A*, 50% were issued by cities, 40% by suburbs, and 10% by rural areas. Of the municipal bonds rated *B*, 60% were issued by cities, 20% by suburbs, and 20% by rural areas. Of the municipal bonds rated *C*, 90% were issued by cities, 5% by suburbs, and 5% by rural areas.

a. If a new municipal bond is to be issued by a city, what is the probability that it will receive an *A* rating?

b. What proportion of municipal bonds are issued by cities?

c. What proportion of municipal bonds are issued by suburbs?

5.4 Counting Rules

In Equation (5.1) on page 204, the probability of occurrence of an outcome was defined as the number of ways the outcome occurs, divided by the total number of possible outcomes. Often, there are a large number of possible outcomes, and determining the exact number can be difficult. In such circumstances, rules have been developed for counting the number of possible outcomes. This section presents five different counting rules.

Counting Rule 1

Counting rule 1 determines the number of possible outcomes for a set of mutually exclusive and collectively exhaustive events.

COUNTING RULE 1

If any one of k different mutually exclusive and collectively exhaustive events can occur on each of n trials, the number of possible outcomes is equal to

$$k^n \qquad \text{(5.10)}$$

For example, using Equation (5.10), the number of different possible outcomes from tossing a two-sided coin five times is $2^5 = 2 \times 2 \times 2 \times 2 \times 2 = 32$.

EXAMPLE 5.11

Rolling a Die Twice

Suppose you roll a die twice. How many different possible outcomes can occur?

SOLUTION If a six-sided die is rolled twice, using Equation (5.10), the number of different outcomes is $6^2 = 36$.

Counting Rule 2

The second counting rule is a more general version of the first and allows the number of possible events to differ from trial to trial.

COUNTING RULE 2

If there are k_1 events on the first trial, k_2 events on the second trial, ... , and k_n events on the nth trial, then the number of possible outcomes is

$$(k_1)(k_2) \ldots (k_n) \qquad \text{(5.11)}$$

For example, a state motor vehicle department would like to know how many license plate numbers are available if a license plate number consists of three letters followed by three numbers (0 through 9). Using Equation (5.11), if a license plate number consists of three letters followed by three numbers, the total number of possible outcomes is $(26)(26)(26)(10)(10)(10) = 17,576,000$.

EXAMPLE 5.12

Determining the Number of Different Dinners

A restaurant menu has a price-fixed complete dinner that consists of an appetizer, an entrée, a beverage, and a dessert. You have a choice of 5 appetizers, 10 entrées, 3 beverages, and 6 desserts. Determine the total number of possible dinners.

SOLUTION Using Equation (5.11), the total number of possible dinners is $(5)(10)(3)(6) = 900$.

Counting Rule 3

The third counting rule involves computing the number of ways that a set of items can be arranged in order.

> **COUNTING RULE 3**
>
> The number of ways that all n items can be arranged in order is
>
> $$n! = (n)(n-1)\ldots(1) \qquad (5.12)$$
>
> where $n!$ is called n factorial, and $0!$ is defined as 1.

EXAMPLE 5.13

Using Counting Rule 3

If a set of six books is to be placed on a shelf, in how many ways can the six books be arranged?

SOLUTION To begin, you must realize that any of the six books could occupy the first position on the shelf. Once the first position is filled, there are five books to choose from in filling the second position. You continue this assignment procedure until all the positions are occupied. The number of ways that you can arrange six books is

$$n! = 6! = (6)(5)(4)(3)(2)(1) = 720$$

Counting Rule 4

In many instances you need to know the number of ways in which a subset of an entire group of items can be arranged in *order*. Each possible arrangement is called a **permutation**.

> **COUNTING RULE 4: PERMUTATIONS**
>
> The number of ways of arranging x objects selected from n objects in order is
>
> $$_nP_x = \frac{n!}{(n-x)!} \qquad (5.13)$$
>
> where
>
> $n = $ total number of objects
>
> $x = $ number of objects to be arranged
>
> $n! = n$ factorial $= n(n-1)\ldots(1)$
>
> $P = $ symbol for permutations[1]

[1]On many scientific calculators, there is a button labeled nPr that allows you to compute permutations. The symbol r is used instead of x.

EXAMPLE 5.14

Using Counting Rule 4

Modifying Example 5.13, if you have six books, but there is room for only four books on the shelf, in how many ways can you arrange these books on the shelf?

SOLUTION Using Equation (5.13), the number of ordered arrangements of four books selected from six books is equal to

$$_nP_x = \frac{n!}{(n-x)!} = \frac{6!}{(6-4)!} = \frac{(6)(5)(4)(3)(2)(1)}{(2)(1)} = 360$$

Counting Rule 5

In many situations, you are not interested in the *order* of the outcomes but only in the number of ways that x items can be selected from n items, *irrespective of order*. Each possible selection is called a **combination**.

COUNTING RULE 5: COMBINATIONS

The number of ways of selecting x objects from n objects, irrespective of order, is equal to

$$_nC_x = \frac{n!}{x!(n-x)!} \qquad (5.14)$$

where

$$n = \text{total number of objects}$$

$$x = \text{number of objects to be arranged}$$

$$n! = n \text{ factorial} = n(n-1)\ldots(1)$$

$$C = \text{symbol for combinations}^2$$

[2]On many scientific calculators, there is a button labeled nCr that allows you to compute combinations. The symbol r is used instead of x.

If you compare this rule to counting rule 4, you see that it differs only in the inclusion of a term $x!$ in the denominator. When permutations were used, all of the arrangements of the x objects are distinguishable. With combinations, the $x!$ possible arrangements of objects are irrelevant.

EXAMPLE 5.15

Using Counting Rule 5

Modifying Example 5.14, if the order of the books on the shelf is irrelevant, in how many ways can you arrange these books on the shelf?

SOLUTION Using Equation (5.14), the number of combinations of four books selected from six books is equal to

$$_nC_x = \frac{n!}{x!(n-x)!} = \frac{6!}{4!(6-4)!} = \frac{(6)(5)(4)(3)(2)(1)}{(4)(3)(2)(1)(2)(1)} = 15$$

Problems for Section 5.4

APPLYING THE CONCEPTS

5.38 If there are 10 multiple-choice questions on an exam, each having three possible answers, how many different sequences of answers are there?

5.39 A lock on a bank vault consists of three dials, each with 30 positions. In order for the vault to open, each of the three dials must be in the correct position.
a. How many different possible dial combinations are there for this lock?
b. What is the probability that if you randomly select a position on each dial, you will be able to open the bank vault?
c. Explain why "dial combinations" are not mathematical combinations expressed by Equation (5.14).

5.40 a. If a coin is tossed seven times, how many different outcomes are possible?
b. If a die is tossed seven times, how many different outcomes are possible?
c. Discuss the differences in your answers to (a) and (b).

5.41 A particular brand of women's jeans is available in seven different sizes, three different colors, and three different styles. How many different women's jeans does the store manager need to order to have one pair of each type?

5.42 You would like to make a salad that consists of lettuce, tomato, cucumber, and peppers. You go to the supermarket, intending to purchase one variety of each of these ingredients. You discover that there are eight varieties of lettuce, four varieties of tomatoes, three varieties of cucumbers, and three varieties of peppers for sale at the supermarket. If you buy them all, how many different salads can you make?

5.43 A team is being formed that includes four different people. There are four different positions on the teams. How many different ways are there to assign the four people to the four positions?

5.44 In Major League Baseball, there are five teams in the Eastern Division of the National League: Atlanta, Florida,

New York, Philadelphia, and Washington. How many different orders of finish are there for these five teams? (Assume that there are no ties in the standings.) Do you believe that all these orders are equally likely? Discuss.

5.45 Referring to Problem 5.44, how many different orders of finish are possible for the first four positions?

5.46 A gardener has six rows available in his vegetable garden to place tomatoes, eggplant, peppers, cucumbers, beans, and lettuce. Each vegetable will be allowed one and only one row. How many ways are there to position these vegetables in this garden?

5.47 There are eight members of a team. How many ways are there to select a team leader, assistant team leader, and team coordinator?

5.48 Four members of a group of 10 people are to be selected to a team. How many ways are there to select these four members?

5.49 A student has seven books that she would like to place in her backpack. However, there is room for only four books. Regardless of the arrangement, how many ways are there of placing four books into the backpack?

5.50 A daily lottery is conducted in which 2 winning numbers are selected out of 100 numbers. How many different combinations of winning numbers are possible?

5.51 A reading list for a course contains 20 articles. How many ways are there to choose 3 articles from this list?

5.5 Ethical Issues and Probability

Ethical issues can arise when any statements related to probability are presented to the public, particularly when these statements are part of an advertising campaign for a product or service. Unfortunately, many people are not comfortable with numerical concepts (see reference 5) and tend to misinterpret the meaning of the probability. In some instances, the misinterpretation is not intentional, but in other cases, advertisements may unethically try to mislead potential customers.

One example of a potentially unethical application of probability relates to advertisements for state lotteries. When purchasing a lottery ticket, the customer selects a set of numbers (such as 6) from a larger list of numbers (such as 54). Although virtually all participants know that they are unlikely to win the lottery, they also have very little idea of how unlikely it is for them to select all 6 winning numbers from the list of 54 numbers. They have even less of an idea of the probability of winning a consolation prize by selecting either 4 or 5 winning numbers.

Given this background, you might consider a recent commercial for a state lottery that stated, "We won't stop until we have made everyone a millionaire" to be deceptive and possibly unethical. Do you think the state has any intention of ever stopping the lottery, given the fact that the state relies on it to bring millions of dollars into its treasury? Is it possible that the lottery can make everyone a millionaire? Is it ethical to suggest that the purpose of the lottery is to make everyone a millionaire?

Another example of a potentially unethical application of probability relates to an investment newsletter promising a 90% probability of a 20% annual return on investment. To make the claim in the newsletter an ethical one, the investment service needs to (a) explain the basis on which this probability estimate rests, (b) provide the probability statement in another format, such as 9 chances in 10, and (c) explain what happens to the investment in the 10% of the cases in which a 20% return is not achieved (e.g., is the entire investment lost?).

These are serious ethical issues. If you were going to write an advertisement for the state lottery that ethically describes the probability of winning a certain prize, what would you say? If you were going to write an advertisement for the investment newsletter that ethically states the probability of a 20% return on an investment, what would you say?

USING STATISTICS @ M&R Electronics World Revisited

© Alan Levenson / Corbis

As the marketing manager for M&R Electronics World, you analyzed the survey results of an intent-to-purchase study. This study asked the heads of 1,000 households about their intentions to purchase a big-screen television sometime during the next 12 months, and as a follow-up, M&R surveyed the same people 12 months later to see whether such a television was purchased. In addition, for households purchasing big-screen televisions, the survey asked whether the television they purchased had a faster refresh rate, whether they also purchased a Blu-ray disc (BD) player in the past 12 months, and whether they were satisfied with their purchase of the big-screen television.

By analyzing the results of these surveys, you were able to uncover many pieces of valuable information that will help you plan a marketing strategy to enhance sales and better target those households likely to purchase multiple or more expensive products. Whereas only 30% of the households actually purchased a big-screen television, if a household indicated that it planned to purchase a big-screen television in the next 12 months, there was an 80% chance that the household actually made the purchase. Thus the marketing strategy should target those households that have indicated an intention to purchase.

You determined that for households that purchased a television that had a faster refresh rate, there was a 47.5% chance that the household also purchased a Blu-ray disc player. You then compared this conditional probability to the marginal probability of purchasing a Blu-ray disc player, which was 36%. Thus, households that purchased televisions that had a faster refresh rate are more likely to purchase a Blu-ray disc player than are households that purchased big-screen televisions that have a standard refresh rate.

You were also able to apply Bayes' theorem to M&R Electronics World's market research reports. The reports investigate a potential new television model prior to its scheduled release. If a favorable report was received, then there was a 64% chance that the new television model would be successful. However, if an unfavorable report was received, there is only a 16% chance that the model would be successful. Therefore, the marketing strategy of M&R needs to pay close attention to whether a report's conclusion is favorable or unfavorable.

SUMMARY

This chapter began by developing the basic concepts of probability. You learned that probability is a numeric value from 0 to 1 that represents the chance, likelihood, or possibility that a particular event will occur. In addition to simple probability, you learned about conditional probabilities and independent events. Bayes' theorem was used to revise previously calculated probabilities based on new information. You also learned about several counting rules. Throughout the chapter, contingency tables and decision trees were used to display information. In the next chapter, important discrete probability distributions such as the binomial and Poisson distributions are developed.

KEY EQUATIONS

Probability of Occurrence

$$\text{Probability of occurrence} = \frac{X}{T}$$

Marginal Probability

$$P(A) = P(A \text{ and } B_1) + P(A \text{ and } B_2) \\ + \cdots + P(A \text{ and } B_k)$$

General Addition Rule

$$P(A \text{ or } B) = P(A) + P(B) - P(A \text{ and } B)$$

Conditional Probability

$$P(A|B) = \frac{P(A \text{ and } B)}{P(B)}$$

$$P(B|A) = \frac{P(A \text{ and } B)}{P(A)}$$

Independence

$$P(A|B) = P(A)$$

General Multiplication Rule

$$P(A \text{ and } B) = P(A|B)P(B)$$

Multiplication Rule for Independent Events

$$P(A \text{ and } B) = P(A)P(B)$$

Marginal Probability Using the General Multiplication Rule

$$P(A) = P(A|B_1)P(B_1) + P(A|B_2)P(B_2) + \cdots + P(A|B_k)P(B_k)$$

Bayes' Theorem

$$P(B_i|A) = \frac{P(A|B_i)P(B_i)}{P(A|B_1)P(B_1) + P(A|B_2)P(B_2) + \cdots + P(A|B_k)P(B_k)}$$

Counting Rule 1

$$k^n$$

Counting Rule 2

$$(k_1)(k_2)\ldots(k_n)$$

Counting Rule 3

$$n! = (n)(n-1)\ldots(1)$$

Counting Rule 4: Permutations

$$_nP_x = \frac{n!}{(n-x)!}$$

Counting Rule 5: Combinations

$$_nC_x = \frac{n!}{x!(n-x)!}$$

KEY TERMS

PROBLEMS

CHECKING YOUR UNDERSTANDING

5.52 What are the differences between *a priori* probability, empirical probability, and subjective probability?

5.53 What is the difference between a simple event and a joint event?

5.54 How can you use the general addition rule to find the probability of occurrence of event *A* or *B*?

5.55 What is the difference between mutually exclusive events and collectively exhaustive events?

5.56 How does conditional probability relate to the concept of independence?

5.57 How does the multiplication rule differ for events that are and are not independent?

5.58 How can you use Bayes' theorem to revise probabilities in light of new information?

5.59 In Bayes' theorem, how does the prior probability differ from the revised probability?

APPLYING THE CONCEPTS

5.60 A survey by the Pew Research Center ("Snapshots: Goals of 'Gen Next' vs. 'Gen X,'" *USA Today*, March 27, 2007, p. 1A) indicated that 81% of 18- to 25-year-olds had getting rich as a goal, as compared to 62% of 26- to 40-year-olds. Suppose that the survey was based on 500 respondents from each of the two groups.
a. Construct a contingency table.
b. Give an example of a simple event and a joint event.
c. What is the probability that a randomly selected respondent has a goal of getting rich?
d. What is the probability that a randomly selected respondent has a goal of getting rich *and* is in the 26- to 40-year-old group?
e. Are the events "age group" and "has getting rich as a goal" independent? Explain.

5.61 The owner of a restaurant serving Continental-style entrées was interested in studying ordering patterns of patrons for the Friday-to-Sunday weekend time period.

Records were maintained that indicated the demand for dessert during the same time period. The owner decided to study two other variables, along with whether a dessert was ordered: the gender of the individual and whether a beef entrée was ordered. The results are as follows:

	GENDER		
DESSERT ORDERED	Male	Female	Total
Yes	96	40	136
No	224	240	464
Total	320	280	600

	BEEF ENTRÉE		
DESSERT ORDERED	Yes	No	Total
Yes	71	65	136
No	116	348	464
Total	187	413	600

A waiter approaches a table to take an order for dessert. What is the probability that the first customer to order at the table

a. orders a dessert?
b. orders a dessert *or* has ordered a beef entrée?
c. is a female *and* does not order a dessert?
d. is a female *or* does not order a dessert?
e. Suppose the first person from whom the waiter takes the dessert order is a female. What is the probability that she does not order dessert?
f. Are gender and ordering dessert independent?
g. Is ordering a beef entrée independent of whether the person orders dessert?

5.62 Which meal are people most likely to order at a drive-through? A survey was conducted in 2009, but the sample sizes were not reported. Suppose the results, based on a sample of 100 males and 100 females, were as follows:

	GENDER		
MEAL	Male	Female	Total
Breakfast	18	10	28
Lunch	47	52	99
Dinner	29	29	58
Snack/beverage	6	9	15
Total	100	100	200

Source: Data extracted from **www.qsrmagazine.com/reports/drive-thru_time_study/2009/2009_charts/whats_your_preferred_way_to_order_fast_food.html**.

If a respondent is selected at random, what is the probability that he or she

a. prefers ordering lunch at the drive-through?
b. prefers ordering breakfast or lunch at the drive-through?
c. is a male *or* prefers ordering dinner at the drive-through?

d. is a male *and* prefers ordering dinner at the drive-through?
e. Given that the person selected is a female, what is the probability that she prefers ordering breakfast at the drive-through?

5.63 According to a Gallup Poll, companies with employees who are engaged with their workplace have greater innovation, productivity, and profitability, as well as less employee turnover. A survey of 1,895 workers in Germany found that 13% of the workers were engaged, 67% were not engaged, and 20% were actively disengaged. The survey also noted that 48% of engaged workers strongly agreed with the statement "My current job brings out my most creative ideas." Only 20% of the not engaged workers and 3% of the actively disengaged workers agreed with this statement (data extracted from M. Nink, "Employee Disengagement Plagues Germany," *Gallup Management Journal*, **gmj.gallup.com**, April 9, 2009). If a worker is known to strongly agree with the statement "My current job brings out my most creative ideas," what is the probability that the worker is engaged?

5.64 Sport utility vehicles (SUVs), vans, and pickups are generally considered to be more prone to roll over than cars. In 1997, 24.0% of all highway fatalities involved rollovers; 15.8% of all fatalities in 1997 involved SUVs, vans, and pickups, given that the fatality involved a rollover. Given that a rollover was not involved, 5.6% of all fatalities involved SUVs, vans, and pickups (data extracted from A. Wilde Mathews, "Ford Ranger, Chevy Tracker Tilt in Test," *The Wall Street Journal*, July 14, 1999, p. A2). Consider the following definitions:

A = fatality involved an SUV, van, or pickup
B = fatality involved a rollover

a. Use Bayes' theorem to find the probability that a fatality involved a rollover, given that the fatality involved an SUV, a van, or a pickup.
b. Compare the result in (a) to the probability that a fatality involved a rollover and comment on whether SUVs, vans, and pickups are generally more prone to rollover accidents than other vehicles.

5.65 Enzyme-linked immunosorbent assay (ELISA) is the most common type of screening test for detecting the HIV virus. A positive result from an ELISA indicates that the HIV virus is present. For most populations, ELISA has a high degree of sensitivity (to detect infection) and specificity (to detect noninfection). (See "HIV InSite Gateway to HIV and AIDS Knowledge" at **HIVInsite.ucsf.edu**.) Suppose the probability that a person is infected with the HIV virus for a certain population is 0.015. If the HIV virus is actually present, the probability that the ELISA test will give a positive result is 0.995. If the HIV virus is not actually present, the probability of a positive result from an ELISA is 0.01. If the ELISA has given a positive result, use

Bayes' theorem to find the probability that the HIV virus is actually present.

TEAM PROJECT

The file Bond Funds contains information regarding three categorical variables from a sample of 184 bond funds. The variables include

Type—Bond fund type (intermediate government or short-term corporate)

Fees—Sales charges (no or yes)

Risk—Risk-of-loss factor of the bond fund (below average, average, or above average)

5.66 Construct contingency tables of type and fees, type and risk, and fees and risk.

a. For each of these contingency tables, compute all the conditional and marginal probabilities.

b. Based on (a), what conclusions can you reach about whether these variables are independent?

STUDENT SURVEY DATABASE

5.67 Problem 1.21 on page 20 describes a survey of 62 undergraduate students (see the file UndergradSurvey). For these data, construct contingency tables of gender and major, gender and graduate school intention, gender and employment status, gender and computer preference, class and graduate school intention, class and employment status, major and graduate school intention, major and employment status, and major and computer preference.

a. For each of these contingency tables, compute all the conditional and marginal probabilities.

b. Based on (a), what conclusions can you reach about whether these variables are independent?

5.68 Problem 1.21 on page 20 describes a survey of 62 undergraduate students (stored in UndergradSurvey).

a. Select a sample of undergraduate students at your school and conduct a similar survey for those students.

b. For your data, construct contingency tables of gender and major, gender and graduate school intention, gender and employment status, gender and computer preference, class and graduate school intention, class and employment status, major and graduate school intention, major and employment status, and major and computer preference.

c. Based on (b), what conclusions can you reach about whether these variables are independent?

d. Compare the results of (c) to those of Problem 5.67 (b).

5.69 Problem 1.22 on page 21 describes a survey of 44 MBA students (stored in GradSurvey). For these data, construct contingency tables of gender and graduate major, gender and undergraduate major, gender and employment status, gender and computer preference, graduate major and undergraduate major, graduate major and employment status, and graduate major and computer preference.

a. For each of these contingency tables, compute all the conditional and marginal probabilities.

b. Based on (b), what conclusions can you reach about whether these variables are independent?

5.70 Problem 1.22 on page 21 describes a survey of 44 MBA students (stored in GradSurvey).

a. Select a sample of MBA students from your MBA program and conduct a similar survey for those students.

b. For your data, construct contingency tables of gender and graduate major, gender and undergraduate major, gender and employment status, gender and computer preference, graduate major and undergraduate major, graduate major and employment status, and graduate major and computer preference.

c. Based on (b), what conclusions can you reach about whether these variables are independent?

d. Compare the results of (c) to those of Problem 5.69 (b).

DIGITAL CASE

Apply your knowledge about contingency tables and the proper application of simple and joint probabilities in this continuing Digital Case from Chapter 4.

Open **EndRunGuide.pdf**, the EndRun Financial Services "Guide to Investing," and read the information about the Guaranteed Investment Package (GIP). Read the claims and examine the supporting data. Then answer the following questions:

1. How accurate is the claim of the probability of success for EndRun's GIP? In what ways is the claim misleading? How would you calculate and state the probability of having an annual rate of return not less than 15%?

2. Using the table found under the "Show Me The Winning Probabilities" subhead, compute the proper probabilities for the group of investors. What mistake was made in reporting the 7% probability claim?

3. Are there any probability calculations that would be appropriate for rating an investment service? Why or why not?

REFERENCES

1. Bellhouse, D. R., "The Reverend Thomas Bayes, FRS: A Biography to Celebrate the Tercentenary of His Birth," *Statistical Science*, 19 (2004), 3–43.

2. Lowd, D., and C. Meek, "Good Word Attacks on Statistical Spam Filters," presented at the Second Conference on Email and Anti-Spam, CEAS 2005.

3. *Microsoft Excel 2010* (Redmond, WA: Microsoft Corp., 2010).

4. *Minitab Release 16* (State College, PA.: Minitab, Inc., 2010).

5. Paulos, J. A., *Innumeracy* (New York: Hill and Wang, 1988).

6. Silberman, S., "The Quest for Meaning," *Wired 8.02*, February 2000.

7. Zeller, T., "The Fight Against V1@gra (and Other Spam)," *The New York Times*, May 21, 2006, pp. B1, B6.

CHAPTER 5 EXCEL GUIDE

EG5.1 Basic Probability Concepts

Simple and Joint Probability and the General Addition Rule

PHStat2 Use **Simple & Joint Probabilities** to compute basic probabilities. Select **PHStat → Probability & Prob. Distributions → Simple & Joint Probabilities**. The procedure inserts a worksheet similar to Figure EG5.1 into the current workbook. (Unlike with other procedures, no dialog box is first displayed.) To use the worksheet, fill in the **Sample Space** area with your data.

In-Depth Excel Use the **COMPUTE worksheet** of the **Probabilities workbook** as a template for computing basic probabilities (see Figure EG5.1, below). The worksheet contains the Table 5.1 purchase behavior data shown on page 206. Overwrite these values when you enter data for other problems.

Open to the **COMPUTE_FORMULAS worksheet** to examine the formulas used in the worksheet, many of which are shown in the inset to Figure EG5.1.

FIGURE EG5.1 COMPUTE worksheet of the Probabilities workbook

	A	B	C	D	E
1	Probabilities				
2					
3	Sample Space		ACTUALLY PURCHASED		
4			Yes	No	Totals
5	PLANNED TO PURCHASE	Yes	200	50	250
6		No	100	650	750
7		Totals	300	700	1000
8					
9	Simple Probabilities		Simple Probabilities		
10	P(Yes)	0.25	="P(" & B5 & ")"	=E5/E7	
11	P(No)	0.75	="P(" & B6 & ")"	=E6/E7	
12	P(Yes)	0.30	="P(" & C4 & ")"	=C7/E7	
13	P(No)	0.70	="P(" & D4 & ")"	=D7/E7	
14					
15	Joint Probabilities		Joint Probabilities		
16	P(Yes and Yes)	0.20	="P(" & B5 & " and " & C4 & ")"	=C5/E7	
17	P(Yes and No)	0.05	="P(" & B5 & " and " & D4 & ")"	=D5/E7	
18	P(No and Yes)	0.10	="P(" & B6 & " and " & C4 & ")"	=C6/E7	
19	P(No and No)	0.65	="P(" & B6 & " and " & D4 & ")"	=D6/E7	
20					
21	Addition Rule		Addition Rule		
22	P(Yes or Yes)	0.35	="P(" & B5 & " or " & C4 & ")"	=B10 + B12 - B16	
23	P(Yes or No)	0.90	="P(" & B5 & " or " & D4 & ")"	=B10 + B13 - B17	
24	P(No or Yes)	0.95	="P(" & B6 & " or " & C4 & ")"	=B11 + B12 - B18	
25	P(No or No)	0.80	="P(" & B6 & " or " & D4 & ")"	=B11 + B13 - B19	

EG5.2 Conditional Probability

There is no Excel material for this section.

EG5.3 Bayes' Theorem

In-Depth Excel Use the **COMPUTE worksheet** of the **Bayes workbook** as a template for computing basic probabilities (see Figure EG5.2, at right). The worksheet contains the television-marketing example of Table 5.4 on page 222. Overwrite these values when you enter data for other problems.

Open to the **COMPUTE_FORMULAS worksheet** to examine the simple arithmetic formulas that compute the probabilities which are also shown in the inset to Figure EG5.2.

	A	B	C	D	E
1	Bayes Theorem Calculations				
2					
3			Probabilities		
4	Event	Prior	Conditional	Joint	Revised
5	S	0.4	0.8	0.32	0.64
6	S'	0.6	0.3	0.18	0.36
7			Total:	0.5	

Joint	Revised
=B5 * C5	=D5/$D$7
=B6 * C6	=D6/$D$7
=D5 + D6	

FIGURE EG5.2 COMPUTE worksheet of the Bayes workbook

EG5.4 Counting Rules

Counting Rule 1

In-Depth Excel Use the **POWER(k, n)** worksheet function in a cell formula to compute the number of outcomes given k events and n trials. For example, the formula =**POWER(6, 2)** computes the answer for Example 5.11 on page 226.

Counting Rule 2

In-Depth Excel Use a formula that takes the product of successive **POWER(k, n)** functions to solve problems related to counting rule 2. For example, the formula =**POWER(26, 3) * POWER(10, 3)** computes the answer for the state motor vehicle department example on page 226.

Counting Rule 3

In-Depth Excel Use the **FACT(n)** worksheet function in a cell formula to compute how many ways n items can be arranged. For example, the formula =**FACT(6)** computes 6!.

Counting Rule 4

In-Depth Excel Use the **PERMUT(n, x)** worksheet function in a cell formula to compute the number of ways of arranging x objects selected from n objects in order. For example, the formula =**PERMUT(6, 4)** computes the answer for Example 5.14 on page 227.

Counting Rule 5

In-Depth Excel Use the **COMBIN(n, x)** worksheet function in a cell formula to compute the number of ways of arranging x objects selected from n objects, irrespective of order. For example, the formula =**COMBIN(6, 4)** computes the answer for Example 5.15 on page 228.

CHAPTER 5 MINITAB GUIDE

MG5.1 Basic Probability Concepts

There is no Minitab material for this section.

MG5.2 Conditional Probability

There is no Minitab material for this section.

MG5.3 Bayes' Theorem

There is no Minitab material for this section.

MG5.4 Counting Rules

Use **Calculator** to apply the counting rules. Select **Calc → Calculator**. In the Calculator dialog box (shown at right):

1. Enter the column name of an empty column in the **Store result in variable** box and then press **Tab**.
2. Build the appropriate expression (as discussed later in this section) in the **Expression** box. To apply counting rules 3 through 5, select **Arithmetic** from the **Functions** drop-down list to facilitate the function selection.

3. Click **OK**.

If you have previously used the Calculator during your Minitab session, you may have to clear the contents of the Expression box by selecting the contents and pressing **Del** before you begin step 2.

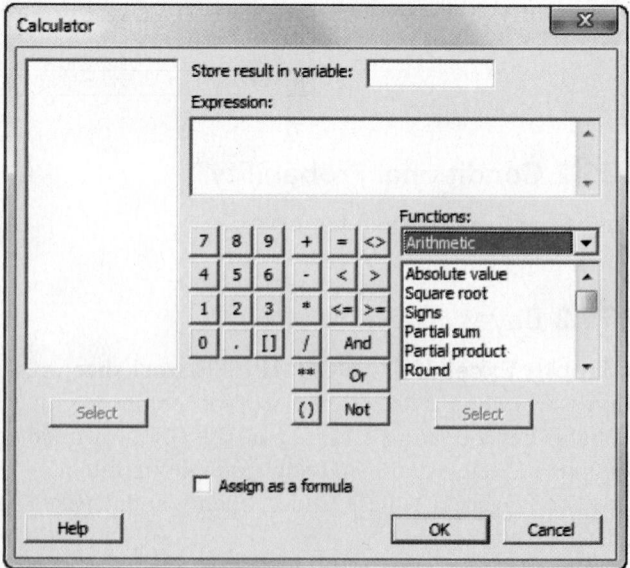

Counting Rule 1

Enter an expression that uses the exponential operator ******. For example, the expression **6 ** 2** computes the answer for Example 5.11 on page 226.

Counting Rule 2

Enter an expression that uses the exponential operator ******. For example, the expression **26 ** 3 * 10 ** 3** computes the answer for the state motor vehicle department example on page 226.

Counting Rule 3

Enter an expression that uses the **FACTORIAL(*n*)** function to compute how many ways *n* items can be arranged. For example, the expression **FACTORIAL(6)** computes 6!

Counting Rule 4

Enter an expression that uses the **PERMUTATIONS(*n*, *x*)** function to compute the number of ways of arranging *x* objects selected from *n* objects in order. For example, the expression **PERMUTATIONS(6, 4)** computes the answer for Example 5.14 on page 227.

Counting Rule 5

Enter an expression that uses the **COMBINATIONS(*n*, *x*)** function to compute the number of ways of arranging *x* objects selected from *n* objects, irrespective of order. For example, the expression **COMBINATIONS(6, 4)** computes the answer for Example 5.15 on page 228.

6 Discrete Probability Distributions

Learning Objectives

In this chapter, you learn:

- The properties of a probability distribution
- To compute the expected value and variance of a probability distribution
- To compute probabilities from the binomial and Poisson distributions
- How to use the binomial and Poisson distributions to solve business problems

@ Saxon Home Improvement, Part I

Y ou are an accountant for the Saxon Home Improvement Company, which uses a state-of-the-art accounting information system to manage its accounting and financial operations.

Accounting information systems collect, process, store, transform, and distribute financial information to decision makers both internal and external to a business organization. These systems continuously audit accounting information, looking for errors or incomplete or improbable information. For example, when customers of the Saxon Home Improvement Company submit online orders, the company's accounting information system reviews the order forms for possible mistakes. Any questionable invoices are *tagged* and included in a daily *exceptions report*. Recent data collected by the company show that the likelihood is 0.10 that an order form will be tagged. Saxon would like to determine the likelihood of finding a certain number of tagged forms in a sample of a specific size. For example, what would be the likelihood that none of the order forms is tagged in a sample of four forms? That one of the order forms is tagged?

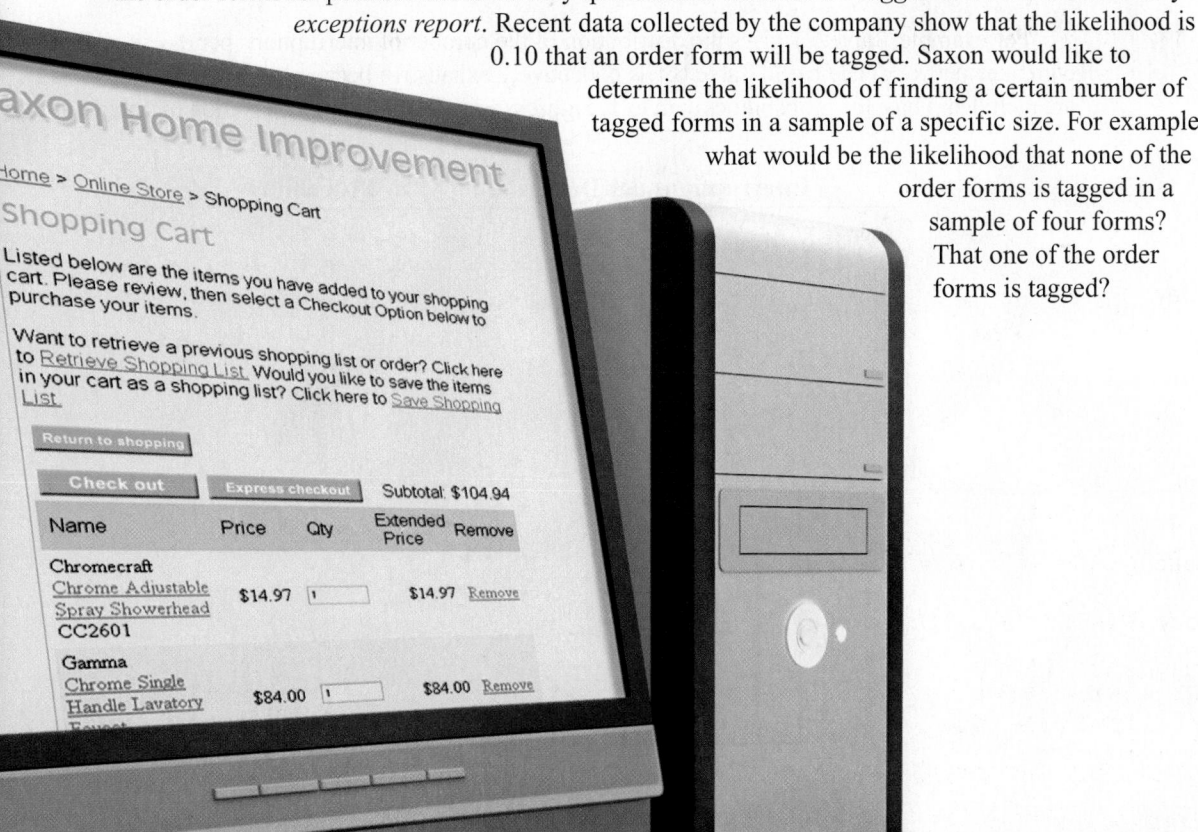

How could the Saxon Home Improvement Company determine the solution to this type of probability problem? One way is to use a model, or small-scale representation, that approximates the process. By using such an approximation, Saxon managers could make inferences about the actual order process. In this case, the Saxon managers can use *probability distributions*, mathematical models suited for solving the type of probability problems the managers are facing.

This chapter introduces you to the concept and characteristics of probability distributions. You will also learn how the binomial and Poisson distributions can be applied to help solve business problems.

6.1 The Probability Distribution for a Discrete Random Variable

In Section 1.3, a *numerical variable* was defined as a variable that yields numerical responses, such as the number of magazines you subscribe to or your height. Numerical variables are either *discrete* or *continuous*. Continuous numerical variables produce outcomes that come from a measuring process (e.g., your height). Discrete numerical variables produce outcomes that come from a counting process (e.g., the number of magazines you subscribe to). This chapter deals with probability distributions that represent discrete numerical variables.

> ### PROBABILITY DISTRIBUTION FOR A DISCRETE RANDOM VARIABLE
>
> A **probability distribution for a discrete random variable** is a mutually exclusive list of all the possible numerical outcomes along with the probability of occurrence of each outcome.

For example, Table 6.1 gives the distribution of the number of interruptions per day in a large computer network. The list in Table 6.1 is collectively exhaustive because all possible outcomes are included. Thus, the probabilities sum to 1. Figure 6.1 is a graphical representation of Table 6.1.

TABLE 6.1

Probability Distribution of the Number of Interruptions per Day

Interruptions per Day	Probability
0	0.35
1	0.25
2	0.20
3	0.10
4	0.05
5	0.05

FIGURE 6.1

Probability distribution of the number of interruptions per day

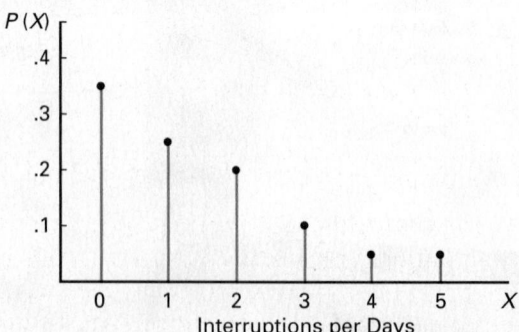

Definitions

Random Variable: A variable whose value is determined by the outcome of a random experiment. The symbol used is usually X.

Discrete Random Variable: A random variable whose possible values are discrete, that is, clearly separated individual values.

Discrete Probability Distribution: A table or formula that shows the probability associated with each possible value of a discrete random variable.

EXAMPLE 6.1

A study of the number of cars sold on Sunday at a particular dealership shows that the following probability distribution exists:

let X = # cars sold on Sunday

The probability distribution of X is

TABLE 6.2

X	P(X)
0	0.1
1	0.1
2	0.4
3	0.3
4	0.1
Total	1.0

EXAMPLE 6.2

A company is in the process of trying to decide whether or not to market a particular new product that it is considering. A market analysis has determined that the probabilities of various acceptance levels are as follows: high with a probability of 0.2, medium with a probability of 0.5, and low with a probability of 0.3. If the company decides to build a local manufacturing facility, the estimated profits over the life of the product if there is high acceptance is $10 million, if there is medium acceptance the profit should be around $3 million, and if there is low acceptance there will be a loss of $2 million.

let X = estimated profit over life of product ($ million)

The probability distribution of X is

TABLE 6.3

Product Acceptance	X	P(X)
High	10	0.2
Medium	3	0.5
Low	-2	0.3
Total		1.0

EXAMPLE 6.3

Toss a fair coin three times. The sample space is composed of eight equally likely outcomes, namely

S = {HHH, HHT, HTH, THH, TTH, THT, HTT, TTT}

let X = # tails

The probability distribution of X is

TABLE 6.4

X	P(X)
0	1/8 = 0.125
1	3/8 = 0.375
2	3/8 = 0.375
3	1/8 = 0.125
Total	1.000

EXAMPLE 6.4

Roll a fair die. The sample space is composed of six equally likely outcomes, namely:

S = {1, 2, 3, 4, 5, 6}

let X = # rolled

The probability distribution of X is

TABLE 6.5

X	P(X)
1	1/6 = 0.167
2	1/6 = 0.167
3	1/6 = 0.167
4	1/6 = 0.167
5	1/6 = 0.167
6	1/6 = 0.167
Total	6/6 = 1

EXAMPLE 6.5

Roll two fair dice. The sample space, as seen previously, is composed of 36 equally likely outcomes.

let X = total of the two dice

The probability distribution of X is

TABLE 6.6

X	P(X)
2	1/36 = 0.028
3	2/36 = 0.056
4	3/36 = 0.083
5	4/36 = 0.111
6	5/36 = 0.139
7	6/36 = 0.167
8	5/36 = 0.139
9	4/36 = 0.111
10	3/36 = 0.083
11	2/36 = 0.056
12	1/36 = 0.028
Total	36/36 = 1

Expected Value of a Discrete Random Variable

The mean, μ, of a probability distribution is the **expected value** of its random variable. To calculate the expected value, multiply each possible outcome, X, by its corresponding probability, $P(X)$, and then sum these products.

EXPECTED VALUE, μ, OF A DISCRETE RANDOM VARIABLE

$$\mu = E(X) = \sum_{i=1}^{N} X_i P(X_i) \qquad (6.1)$$

where

X_i = the ith outcome of the discrete random variable X

$P(X_i)$ = probability of occurrence of the ith outcome of X

For the probability distribution of the number of home mortgages approved per week (Table 6.2), the expected value is computed using Equation (6.1) and is also shown in Table 6.7.

$$\mu = E(X) = \sum_{i=1}^{N} X_i P(X_i)$$

$$= (0)(0.1) + (1)(0.1) + (2)(0.2) + (3)(0.3) + (4)(0.15) + (5)(0.1) + (6)(0.05)$$

$$= 0 + 0.1 + 0.4 + 0.9 + 0.6 + 0.5 + 0.3$$

$$= 2.8$$

SOLUTION

TABLE 6.7

Computing the Expected Value of the Number of Home Mortgages Approved per Week

By Formula			By Casio Calculator

Home Mortgages Approved per Week (X_i)	$P(X_i)$	**Formula:** $X_i P(X_i)$	Calculator instructions:
			 1. Enter the data in List 1 and List 2 where
			     List 1: 0, 1, 2, 3, 4, 5, 6
			     List 2: 0.10, 0.10, 0.20, 0.30, 0.15, 0.10, 0.05
			 2. Press **F2**(CALC)

0	0.10	$(0)(0.10) = 0.0$	3. Press **F6** (SET)
1	0.10	$(1)(0.10) = 0.1$	1Var XList : List 1
2	0.20	$(2)(0.20) = 0.4$	1Var Freq : List 2
3	0.30	$(3)(0.30) = 0.9$	EXE
4	0.15	$(4)(0.15) = 0.6$	4. To obtain results, press **F1**(1Var)
5	0.10	$(5)(0.10) = 0.5$	$\bar{x} = 2.8$
6	0.05	$(6)(0.05) = 0.3$	*Note: the calculator symbol is $\bar{x}$ but it*
	1.00	$\mu = E(X) = 2.8$	*should be* μ

The expected value is 2.8. The expected value of 2.8 for the number of mortgages approved is not a possible outcome because the actual number of mortgages approved in a given week must be an integer value. The expected value represents the *mean* number of mortgages approved per week.

Mean, Variance, and Standard Deviation

A discrete probability distribution is equivalent to a population of data. We can calculate any parameters that can be calculated for a population. However, the formulas will look a little different.

I. MEAN OR EXPECTED VALUE:

Formula: $\mu = E(X) = \sum XP(X)$

EXAMPLE 6.1

(Revisit)

A study of the number of cars sold on Sunday at a particular dealership shows that the following probability distribution exists:

let X = # cars sold on Sunday

The mean or expected number of cars that will be sold on Sunday can be calculated as follows:

SOLUTION

TABLE 6.8

By Formula			By Casio Calculator
X	P(X)	Formula: XP(X)	Calculator instructions:
0	0.1	(0)(0.1) = 0.0	1. Enter the data in List 1 and List 2 where
1	0.1	(1)(0.1) = 0.1	List 1: 0, 1, 2, 3, 4
2	0.4	(2)(0.4) = 0.8	List 2: 0.1, 0.1, 0.4, 0.3, 0.1
3	0.3	(3)(0.3) = 0.9	2. Press **F2**(CALC)
4	0.1	(4)(0.1) = 0.4	3. Press **F6** (SET)
Total	1.0	$\mu = E(X) = 2.2$	1Var XList : List 1
			1Var Freq : List 2
			EXE
			4. To obtain results, press **F1**(1Var)
			$\bar{x} = 2.2$
			Note: the calculator symbol is $\bar{x}$ but it should be μ

Therefore, the *average* number of cars sold on *infinite* Sundays is 2.2. Also, we can say that the number of cars the dealer expects to sell on Sunday is 2.2.

> **Notes: 1.** Calculating a mean for a discrete probability distribution is essentially the same as calculating a *weighted mean,* where the probabilities are the weights.

$$\bar{x}_w = \frac{\sum xw}{\sum w} = \frac{\sum xP(x)}{\sum P(x)} = \sum xP(x) \quad \text{since} \quad \sum P(x) = 1$$

> **2.** To calculate the mean on the Casio calculator, enter the data as follows and set up as if calculating a weighted mean of the X data.

Example 6.1:			Example 6.4:	
List 1	List 2		List 1	List 2
0	.1		1	1÷6
1	.1		2	1÷6
2	.4		3	1÷6
3	.3		4	1÷6
4	.1		5	1÷6
			6	1÷6

1 Var Xlist: List 1
1 Var Freq: List 2   yields E(X) = 2.2

1 Var Xlist: List 1
1 Var Freq: List 2   yields E(X) = 3.5

EXAMPLE 6.2

(Revisit)

Referring to the product marketing decision Example 6.2,

let X = estimated profit over the life of product ($ million)

SOLUTION

TABLE 6.9

By Formula				By Casio Calculator
Product Acceptance	**X**	**P(X)**	**Formula: XP(X)**	Calculator instructions:
High	10	0.2	(10)(0.2) = 2	1. Enter the data in List 1 and List 2 where
Medium	3	0.5	(3)(0.5) = 1.5	List 1: 10, 3, –2
Low	–2	0.3	(–2)(0.3) = –0.6	List 2: 0.2, 0.5, 0.3
Total		1.0	$\mu = E(X) = 2.9$	2. Press **F2**(CALC)

By Casio Calculator details:
Calculator instructions:
1. Enter the data in List 1 and List 2 where
   List 1: 10, 3, –2
   List 2: 0.2, 0.5, 0.3
2. Press **F2**(CALC)
3. Press **F6** (SET)
   1Var XList : List 1
   1Var Freq : List 2
   EXE
4. To obtain results, press **F1**(1Var)
   $\bar{x} = 2.9$
   Note: the calculator symbol is $\bar{x}$ but it should be μ

Therefore, the expected profit is $2.9 million.

EXAMPLE 6.3

(Revisit)

Toss a fair coin three times.

let X = # tails

SOLUTION

TABLE 6.10

By Formula			By Casio Calculator
X = Number of Tails	**P(X)**	**Formula: XP(X)**	Calculator instructions:
0	0.125	(0)(0.125) = 0.000	1. Enter the data in List 1 and List 2 where
1	0.375	(1)(0.375) = 0.375	List 1: 0, 1, 2, 3
2	0.375	(2)(0.375) = 0.750	List 2: 0.125, 0.375, 0.375, 0.125
3	0.125	(3)(0.125) = 0.375	2. Press **F2**(CALC)
	1.000	$\mu = E(X) = 1.5$	3. Press **F6** (SET)

By Casio Calculator details:
Calculator instructions:
1. Enter the data in List 1 and List 2 where
   List 1: 0, 1, 2, 3
   List 2: 0.125, 0.375, 0.375, 0.125
2. Press **F2**(CALC)
3. Press **F6** (SET)
   1Var XList : List 1
   1Var Freq : List 2
   EXE
4. To obtain results, press **F1**(1Var)
   $\bar{x} = 1.5$
   Note: the calculator symbol is $\bar{x}$ but it should be μ

The average number of tails when a coin is tossed three times, an *infinite* number of times, is 1.5. Also, the expected number of tails if you toss a coin three times is 1.5.

EXAMPLE 6.4
(Revisit)

Roll a fair die.   let X = # rolled

SOLUTION

TABLE 6.11

By Formula			By Casio Calculator

X =
Number
of rolled
	P(X)	Formula:
		XP(X)
			Calculator instructions:
			1. Enter the data in List 1 and List 2 where
			   List 1: 1/6, 1/6, 1/6, 1/6, 1/6, 1/6
			   List 2: 1/6, 2/6, 3/6, 4/6, 5/6, 6/6

1	1/6 = 0.167	(1)(1/6) = 1/6	2. Press **F2**(CALC)
2	1/6 = 0.167	(2)(1/6) = 2/6	3. Press **F6** (SET)
3	1/6 = 0.167	(3)(1/6) = 3/6	1Var XList : List 1
4	1/6 = 0.167	(4)(1/6) = 4/6	1Var Freq : List 2
5	1/6 = 0.167	(5)(1/6) = 5/6	EXE
6	1/6 = 0.167	(6)(1/6) = 6/6	4. To obtain results, press **F1**(1Var)
	6/6 = 1	$\mu = E(X) = 21/6 = 3.5$	$\bar{x} = 3.5$ *Note: the calculator symbol is $\bar{x}$ but it should be μ*

If you roll one die infinite times, the average number rolled will be 3.5. Therefore, if you roll a die once, the expected value is 3.5.

EXAMPLE 6.5
(Revisit)

Roll two fair dice.

let X = total of the two dice

SOLUTION

TABLE 6.12

By Formula			By Casio Calculator

X =
Total of
the two
dice
	P(X)	Formula:
		XP(X)
			Calculator instructions:
			1. Enter the data in List 1 and List 2 where
			   List 1: 0.028, 0.056, 0.083, . . . etc.
			   List 2: 2/36, 6/36, 12/36, . . . etc.

2	1/36 = 0.028	(2)(1/36) = 2/36	2. Press **F2**(CALC)
3	2/36 = 0.056	(3)(2/36) = 6/36	3. Press **F6** (SET)
4	3/36 = 0.083	(4)(3/36) = 12/36	1Var XList : List 1
5	4/36 = 0.111	(5)(4/36) = 20/36	1Var Freq : List 2
6	5/36 = 0.139	(6)(5/36) = 30/36	EXE
7	6/36 = 0.167	(7)(6/36) = 42/36	4. To obtain results, press **F1**(1Var)
8	5/36 = 0.139	(8)(5/36) = 40/36	$\bar{x} = 7$
9	4/36 = 0.111	(9)(4/36) = 36/36	*Note: the calculator symbol is $\bar{x}$*
10	3/36 = 0.083	(10)(3/36) = 30/36	*but it should be μ*
11	2/36 = 0.056	(11)(2/36) = 22/36	
12	1/36 = 0.028	(12)(1/36) = 12/36	
Total	36/36 = 1	$\mu = E(X) = 252/36 = 7$	

Therefore, if we roll two dice we can expect to get a total of 7.

II. VARIANCE

Formula: $$\sigma^2 = \sum (X - \mu)^2 P(X)$$ (6.2)

III. STANDARD DEVIATION

Formula: $$\sigma = \sqrt{\left(\sum (X - \mu)^2 P(X) \right)}$$ (6.3)

Note: We are not interested in showing the use of this formula manually, since if you need to calculate the standard deviation of a random variable you will use your calculator as illustrated earlier.

Expected Value Decision Making

EXAMPLE 6.6

A fast-food company plans to install a new ice-cream dispensing unit in one of two store locations. The company figures that the probability of a unit being successful in location A is 3/4, and the annual profit in this case is $150,000. If it is not successful there will be losses of $80,000. At location B the probability of succeeding is 1/2, but the potential profit and loss are $240,000 and $48,000, respectively.

a) Where should the company locate to maximize expected profit?

SOLUTION X = **Profit**

Location A		Location B	
Profit	Prob.	Profit	Prob.
$150,000	0.75	$240,000	0.5
–$80,000	0.25	–$48,000	0.5

Location A: E(X) = $92,500   Location B: E(X) = $96,000

b) Which location is less risky, that is, has the lowest relative variability?

$$\text{Location A: } CV = \frac{\sigma}{\mu} \times 100\% = \frac{\$99,593}{\$92,500} \times 100\% = 108\%$$

$$\text{Location B: } CV = \frac{\sigma}{\mu} \times 100\% = \frac{\$144,000}{\$96,000} \times 100\% = 150\%$$

Since $CV_{\text{Location}} = 150\%$ is greater than $CV_{\text{Location A}} = 108\%$, Location A is less risky than Location B.

*CASIO Calculator Instruction to Obtain μ and σ

Location A	**Location B**
Instructions:	Instructions:
1. Enter data in List 1 and List 2.	1. Enter data in List 1 and List 2.
List 1: 150,000; –80,000	List 1: 240,000; –48,000
List 2: 0.75; 0.25	List 2: 0.5; 0.5
2. Press F2 (CALC).	2. Press F2 (CALC).
3. Press F6 (SET).	3. Press F6 (SET).
1Var XList: List 1	1Var XList: List 1
1Var Freq: List 2	1Var Freq: List 2
4. To obtain result, press F1(1Var).	4. To obtain result, press F1(1Var).
$\bar{x}$ = 92,500 *and* σx = 99,592.9214	$\bar{x}$ = 96,000 *and* σx = 144,000

EXAMPLE 6.7

An investment advisor sends information to various clients via express delivery companies. In all cases it is important that the client receive the information on the day it is sent. Three companies are capable of providing the delivery service. The following information is available:

TABLE 6.13

Company	Cost	Probability of same day arrival
Can-Express	$22.00	0.99
Can-Parcel	14.00	0.97
Canada Mail	6.00	0.89

The average payoff is $200 when the information arrives on time, but there is no payoff if the delivery is late. Based on maximizing expected profit, which delivery service should be used?

SOLUTION let X = profit

TABLE 6.14

Can-Express		Can-Parcel		Canada Mail	
X	P(X)	X	P(X)	X	P(X)
178	0.99	186	0.97	194	0.89
−22	0.01	−14	0.03	−6	0.11

The expected values are as follows:

Can-Express: E(X) = $176

Can-Parcel: E(X) = $180

Canada Mail: E(X) = $172

Therefore, the company should choose **Can-Parcel** since it has the highest expected profit (value).

*CASIO Calculator Instruction to Obtain μ and σ

Can-Express

Instructions:
1. Enter data in List 1 and List 2.
   List 1: 178; −22
   List 2: 0.99; 0.01
2. Press F2 (CALC).
3. Press F6 (SET).
   1Var XList: List 1
   1Var Freq: List 2
4. To obtain result, press F1(1Var).
   $\bar{x} = 176$

Can-Parcel

Instructions:
1. Enter data in List 1 and List 2.
   List 1: 186; −14
   List 2: 0.97; 0.03
2. Press F2 (CALC).
3. Press F6 (SET).
   1Var XList: List 1
   1Var Freq: List 2
4. To obtain result, press F1(1Var).
   $\bar{x} = 180$

Canada Mail

Instructions:
1. Enter data in List 1 and List 2.
   List 1: 194; −6
   List 2: 0.89; 0.11
2. Press F2 (CALC).
3. Press F6 (SET).
   1Var XList: List 1
   1Var Freq: List 2
4. To obtain result, press F1(1Var).
   $\bar{x} = 172$

Variance and Standard Deviation of a Discrete Random Variable

You compute the variance of a probability distribution by multiplying each possible squared difference $[X_i - E(X)]^2$ by its corresponding probability, $P(X = x_i)$, and then summing the resulting products. Equation (6.4) defines the **variance of a discrete random variable**.

VARIANCE OF A DISCRETE RANDOM VARIABLE

$$\sigma^2 = \sum_{i=1}^{N}[X_i - E(X)]^2 P(X = x_i) \tag{6.4}$$

where

$$X_i = \text{the } i\text{th outcome of the discrete random variable } X$$
$$P(X = X_i) = \text{probability of occurrence of the } i\text{th outcome of } X$$

Equation (6.5) defines the **standard deviation of a discrete random variable**.

STANDARD DEVIATION OF A DISCRETE RANDOM VARIABLE

$$\sigma = \sqrt{\sigma^2} = \sqrt{\sum_{i=1}^{N}[X_i - E(X)]^2 P(X = x_i)} \tag{6.5}$$

The variance and the standard deviation of the number of interruptions per day are computed as follows and in Table 6.15, using Equations (6.4) and (6.5):

$$\sigma^2 = \sum_{i=1}^{N}[X_i - E(X)]^2 P(X = x_i)$$

$$= (0 - 1.4)^2(0.35) + (1 - 1.4)^2(0.25) + (2 - 1.4)^2(0.20) + (3 - 1.4)^2(0.10)$$
$$+ (4 - 1.4)^2(0.05) + (5 - 1.4)^2(0.05)$$

$$= 0.686 + 0.040 + 0.072 + 0.256 + 0.338 + 0.648$$

$$= 2.04$$

TABLE 6.15

Computing the Variance and Standard Deviation of the Number of Interruptions per Day

Interruptions per Day (x_i)	$P(X = x_i)$	$x_i P(X = x_i)$	$[x_i - E(X)]^2 P(X = x_i)$
0	0.35	$(0)(0.35) = 0.00$	$(0 - 1.4)^2(0.35) = 0.686$
1	0.25	$(1)(0.25) = 0.25$	$(1 - 1.4)^2(0.25) = 0.040$
2	0.20	$(2)(0.20) = 0.40$	$(2 - 1.4)^2(0.20) = 0.072$
3	0.10	$(3)(0.10) = 0.30$	$(3 - 1.4)^2(0.10) = 0.256$
4	0.05	$(4)(0.05) = 0.20$	$(4 - 1.4)^2(0.05) = 0.338$
5	0.05	$(5)(0.05) = 0.25$	$(5 - 1.4)^2(0.05) = 0.648$
	1.00	$\mu = E(X) = 1.40$	$\sigma^2 = 2.04$

and

$$\sigma = \sqrt{\sigma^2} = \sqrt{2.04} = 1.4283$$

Thus, the mean number of interruptions per day is 1.4, the variance is 2.04, and the standard deviation is approximately 1.43 interruptions per day.

Problems for Section 6.1

LEARNING THE BASICS

6.1 Given the following probability distributions:

Distribution A		Distribution B	
X	$P(X = x_i)$	X	$P(X = x_i)$
0	0.50	0	0.05
1	0.20	1	0.10
2	0.15	2	0.15
3	0.10	3	0.20
4	0.05	4	0.50

a. Compute the expected value for each distribution.
b. Compute the standard deviation for each distribution.
c. Compare the results of distributions A and B.

APPLYING THE CONCEPTS

✓ SELF Test **6.2** The following table contains the probability distribution for the number of traffic accidents daily in a small city:

Number of Accidents Daily (X)	$P(X = x_i)$
0	0.10
1	0.20
2	0.45
3	0.15
4	0.05
5	0.05

a. Compute the mean number of accidents per day.
b. Compute the standard deviation.

6.3 Recently, a regional automobile dealership sent out fliers to perspective customers, indicating that they had already won one of three different prizes: a Kia Optima valued at $15,000, a $500 gas card, or a $5 Walmart shopping card. To claim his or her prize, a prospective customer needed to present the flier at the dealership's showroom. The fine print on the back of the flier listed the probabilities of winning. The chance of winning the car was 1 out of 31,478, the chance of winning the gas card was 1 out of 31,478, and the chance of winning the shopping card was 31,476 out 31,478.
a. How many fliers do you think the automobile dealership sent out?
b. Using your answer to (a) and the probabilities listed on the flier, what is the expected value of the prize won by a prospective customer receiving a flier?
c. Using your answer to (a) and the probabilities listed on the flier, what is the standard deviation of the value of the prize won by a prospective customer receiving a flier?
d. Do you think this is an effective promotion? Why or why not?

6.4 In the carnival game Under-or-Over-Seven, a pair of fair dice is rolled once, and the resulting sum determines whether the player wins or loses his or her bet. For example, the player can bet $1 that the sum will be under 7—that is, 2, 3, 4, 5, or 6. For this bet, the player wins $1 if the result is under 7 and loses $1 if the outcome equals or is greater than 7. Similarly, the player can bet $1 that the sum will be over 7—that is, 8, 9, 10, 11, or 12. Here, the player wins $1 if the result is over 7 but loses $1 if the result is 7 or under. A third method of play is to bet $1 on the outcome 7. For this bet, the player wins $4 if the result of the roll is 7 and loses $1 otherwise.
a. Construct the probability distribution representing the different outcomes that are possible for a $1 bet on under 7.
b. Construct the probability distribution representing the different outcomes that are possible for a $1 bet on over 7.
c. Construct the probability distribution representing the different outcomes that are possible for a $1 bet on 7.
d. Show that the expected long-run profit (or loss) to the player is the same, no matter which method of play is used.

6.5 The number of arrivals per minute at a bank located in the central business district of a large city was recorded over a period of 200 minutes, with the following results:

Arrivals	Frequency
0	14
1	31
2	47
3	41
4	29
5	21
6	10
7	5
8	2

a. Compute the expected number of arrivals per minute.
b. Compute the standard deviation.

6.6 The manager of a commercial mortgage department of a large bank has collected data during the past two years concerning the number of commercial mortgages approved per week. The results from these two years (104 weeks) indicated the following:

Number of Commercial Mortgages Approved	Frequency
0	13
1	25
2	32
3	17
4	9
5	6
6	1
7	1

a. Compute the expected number of mortgages approved per week.
b. Compute the standard deviation.

6.7 You are trying to develop a strategy for investing in two different stocks. The anticipated annual return for a $1,000 investment in each stock under four different economic conditions has the following probability distribution:

		Returns	
Probability	Economic Condition	Stock X	Stock Y
0.1	Recession	−50	−100
0.3	Slow growth	20	50
0.4	Moderate growth	100	130
0.2	Fast growth	150	200

Compute the
a. expected return for stock X and for stock Y.
b. standard deviation for stock X and for stock Y.
c. Would you invest in stock X or stock Y? Explain.

6.8 You plan to invest $1,000 in a corporate bond fund or in a common stock fund. The following information about the annual return (per $1,000) of each of these investments under different economic conditions is available, along with the probability that each of these economic conditions will occur:

	Economic	Corporate	Common
Probability	Condition	Bond Fund	Stock Fund
0.01	Extreme recession	−200	−999
0.09	Recession	−70	−300
0.15	Stagnation	30	−100
0.35	Slow growth	80	100
0.30	Moderate growth	100	150
0.10	High growth	120	350

Compute the
a. expected return for the corporate bond fund and for the common stock fund.
b. standard deviation for the corporate bond fund and for the common stock fund.
c. Would you invest in the corporate bond fund or the common stock fund? Explain.
d. If you chose to invest in the common stock fund in (c), what do you think about the possibility of losing $999 of every $1,000 invested if there is an extreme recession?

6.9 After consulting the sales reps, a marketing manager has decided that the following table represents the potential profits they might make next year for one of the company's products.

Profit	Prob.
$50,000	0.02
35,000	0.12
20,000	0.50
10,000	0.25
0	0.08
−10,000	0.03

What is the expected profit?

6.10 The Chancit Marketing Company is considering the distribution of a new item. It thinks there is a 20% chance that the item will be successful, in which case the company will make $1,000,000 in revenue. There is a 40% chance that the company will break even, and the other possibility is that there will be virtually no revenues. The distribution expenses in all cases will be $200,000. What is the expected net profit from the distribution of this item?

6.11 A mail order magazine service has the exclusive subscription rights to a certain magazine. Subscriptions can be reserved for one, two, three, or five years. A study of the subscriber list for other similar magazines reveals that the following information regarding the probabilities of subscription length would be appropriate: there are five time as many one-year subscriptions as five-year subscriptions, and the number of two-year and three-year subscriptions are each one-fifth of the total.

The mail order service company receives a fee of $2.00 for a one-year subscription, $3.50 for each two-year subscriptions and an additional dollar for every year over two years.

a. What is the probability distribution of subscription fees?
b. What is the expected total fee revenue from 125 new subscriptions?

6.12 A financial analyst for Petrified Paper Products has submitted the following probability distributions of profit for three investment proposals. The company has sufficient funds to consider only one of the proposals.

Project 1		Project 2		Project 3	
Profit	Prob.	Profit	Prob.	Profit	Prob.
−5,000	0.1	−2,000	0.10	−3,000	0.10
0	0.1	0	0.15	2,000	0.20
2,000	0.2	2,000	0.30	4,000	0.40
4,000	0.3	4,000	0.30	6,000	0.25
6,000	0.3	7,000	0.15	8,000	0.05

a. Based on expected profit, which proposal should be selected?
b. Which proposal has the lowest relative variability (i.e., risk)?

6.13 An export company may ship goods to country A at a cost of $2,000; country B at a cost of $3,000; or country C at a cost of $5,000. The revenues earned by selling the goods in these countries are $5,000; $7,000; and $10,000, respectively. Currently the countries are all involved in wars, and only 70% of shipments have been arriving at the destination country. The remainder are being lost at sea.

Based on expected values, to which country would you ship the next shipment of goods?

6.14 B. F. Retread, a tire manufacturer, wants to select one of the feasible designs for a new longer-wearing radial tire. The manufacturing cost of each type of tire is shown next.

Tire Design	Fixed Cost/year	Variable Cost per Tire
A	$60,000	$30
B	90,000	20
C	120,000	15

There are 3 possible levels of annual demand: 4,000 tires; 7,000; tires and 10,000 tires. The respective probabilities are 0.3, 0.5, and 0.2. The selling price will be $80 for A, $75 for B, and $75 for C. Based on expected profit, which design should be produced?

6.15 The normal weekly demand of a certain perishable product sold by QMS Inc. is given by the following distribution:

Demand	Probability
8	0.1
9	0.2
10	0.3
11	0.3
12	0.1

The product costs QMS $3 each. The product sells for $10 each. If not sold by the end of the week, the leftover units must be scrapped.

The supplier only has 10 or 11 units available for QMS to purchase. How many would you recommend QMS purchase based on expected profit?

6.2 Binomial Distribution

The next two sections use mathematical models to solve business problems.

> MATHEMATICAL MODEL
> A **mathematical model** is a mathematical expression that represents a variable of interest.

When a mathematical expression is available, you can compute the exact probability of occurrence of any particular outcome of the variable.

The **binomial distribution** is one of the most useful mathematical models. You use the binomial distribution when the discrete random variable is the number of events of interest in a sample of *n* observations.

Characteristics of a Binomial Experiment

1. The experiment consists of *n* repetitions (trials) of some action.
   or
   A sample of *n* items are selected from a large population.
2. Each trial will result in one of two possible outcomes called *success* or *failure,* where success is when the outcome of interest occurs.
   or
   Each item in the sample will either possess a certain characteristic (success) or it will not (failure).

3. The probability of success on each trial or selection is constant and is given the symbol π. The probability of failure is therefore $(1 - \pi)$. Note that this condition implies that the trials are *independent*.

The random variable associated with a binomial experiment is

$$X = \text{Number of successes}$$

To calculate the probability that X takes on a specific value we use the

Binomial Probability Distribution Function:

$$P(X = x) = \frac{n!}{x!(n - x)!} \pi^x (1 - \pi)^{n - x}$$

where   n = # of trials or sample size

π = probability of success in each trial

n! = n factorial

= n(n-1)(n-2)(n-3) . . . 3•2•1

Example: 6! = 6•5•4•3•2•1 = 720

EXAMPLE 6.8

Toss a coin six times. Find the probability of getting two tails.

SOLUTION X = # of tails

n = 6

$\pi = 0.5$

$$P(X = 2) = \frac{6!}{2!(6 - 2)!}(0.5)^2(1 - 0.5)^{6-2} = 0.2344$$

Note: The part of the binomial formula $\frac{n!}{x!(n - x)!}$ calculates the number of outcomes where there are x successes in n trials. For example, if a coin is tossed 6 times, there will be $\frac{6!}{(2!(6 - 2)!}$ = 15 possible outcomes that have exactly 2 tails. These outcomes are the following:

TTHHHH	THTHHH	THHTHH	THHHTH	THHHHT
HTTHHH	HTHTHH	HTHHTH	HTHHHT	
HHTTHH	HHTHTH	HHTHHT		
HHHTTH	HHHTHT			
HHHHTT				

The factor $\frac{n!}{x!(n - x)!}$ is often given the shorthand symbol $_nC_x$.

CASIO CALCULATOR INSTRUCTION

Use the CASIO calculator to obtain the probability value (refer to Calculator Lesson 4).

Select **STAT F5**(DIST) **F5**(BINM) **F1**(Bpd), and then select the following options.

Data   : **F2**(Var)
x   : **2 EXE**
Numtrial : **6 EXE**
p   : **0.5**

Now key **EXE** or **F1**(Calc).

Results: Binomial P.D.

p(x = 2) = 0.23437

EXAMPLE 6.9   Roll a die 10 times. Find the probability of getting three 5s?

SOLUTION X = # of 5s
n = 10
$\pi = 1/6$

$$P(X = 3) = \frac{10!}{3!(10 - 3)!}\left(\frac{1}{6}\right)^3\left(1 - \frac{1}{6}\right)^{10-3} = 0.1550$$

CASIO CALCULATOR INSTRUCTION

Use the CASIO calculator to obtain the probability value.

Select **STAT F5**(DIST)   **F5**(BINM)   **F1**(Bpd), and then select the following options.

Data   : **F2**(Var)
x   : **3**
Numtrial : **10**
p   : **1 ÷ 6**

Results: Binomial P.D.

p(x = 3) = 0.15504

EXAMPLE 6.10   A survey of people in the 30–40 age bracket shows that 43 percent of them have investments in mutual funds. In a particular condominium there are 18 adults in this age bracket. What is the probability that

a. 5 of them will have investments in mutual funds?

SOLUTION X = # of people in their 30s with investments in mutual funds

n = 18

$\pi = 0.43$

$$P(X = 5) = \frac{18!}{5!(18 - 5)!}(0.43)^5(1 - 0.43)^{18-5} = 0.0845$$

CASIO CALCULATOR INSTRUCTION

Use the CASIO calculator to obtain the probability value.

Select **STAT F5**(DIST)   **F5**(BINM)   **F1**(Bpd), and then select the following options.

Data   : **F2**(Var)
x   : **5**
Numtrial : **18**
p   : **0.43**

Results: Binomial P.D.

p(x = 5) = 0.084449

b. at most 2 of these people will have investments in mutual funds?

SOLUTION $P(X \leq 2) = P(X = 0) + P(X = 1) + P(X = 2)$
$= 0.00004 + 0.00055 + 0.00351 = 0.0041$

CASIO CALCULATOR INSTRUCTION

Use the CASIO calculator to obtain the probability value.

Select **STAT F5**(DIST)   **F5**(BINM)   **F1**(Bcd), and then select the following options.

Data	: **F2**(Var)
x	: **2**
Numtrial	: **18**
p	: **0.43**

Results: Binomial C.D.

$$p(x \le 2) = 4.1007E.03$$

which is 0.0041007

c. more than 10 of these people will have investments in mutual funds?

SOLUTION $P(X > 10) = 1 - P(X \le 10)$
$$= 1 - 0.9049 = 0.0951$$

Explanation:

Variable X	Probability $P(X = x)$	Calculator Input	Probability Value	
0	$P(X = 0)$	Bpd(0, 18, 0.43)	0.0000403411	Add probabilities from $P(X = 0)$ to $p(X = 10)$ and you will obtain $p(X \le 10)$.
1	$P(X = 1)$	Bpd(1, 18, 0.43)	0.000547789	
2	$P(X = 2)$	Bpd(2, 18, 0.43)	0.003512578	
3	$P(X = 3)$	Bpd(3, 18, 0.43)	0.014132479	
4	$P(X = 4)$	Bpd(4, 18, 0.43)	0.03998004	
5	$P(X = 5)$	Bpd(5, 18, 0.43)	0.084449068	
6	$P(X = 6)$	Bpd(6, 18, 0.43)	0.138032248	
7	$P(X = 7)$	Bpd(7, 18, 0.43)	0.17850787	
8	$P(X = 8)$	Bpd(8, 18, 0.43)	0.185162768	
9	$P(X = 9)$	Bpd(9, 18, 0.43)	0.15520466	
10	$P(X = 10)$	Bpd(10, 18, 0.43)	0.105375795	
11	$P(X = 11)$	Bpd(11, 18, 0.43)	0.057813833	Add probabilities from $P(X = 11)$ to $p(X = 18)$ and you will obtain $p(X > 10)$ or $p(X \ge 11)$.
12	$P(X = 12)$	Bpd(12, 18, 0.43)	0.025441468	
13	$P(X = 13)$	Bpd(13, 18, 0.43)	0.008858163	
14	$P(X = 14)$	Bpd(14, 18, 0.43)	0.002386598	
15	$P(X = 15)$	Bpd(15, 18, 0.43)	0.000480111	
16	$P(X = 16)$	Bpd(16, 18, 0.43)	0.0000679104	
17	$P(X = 17)$	Bpd(17, 18, 0.43)	0.00000602714	
18	$P(X = 18)$	Bpd(18, 18, 0.43)	0.000000252599	
		Total	1	

Note : $p(X \le 10) + p(X > 10) = 1$
$p(X > 10) = 1 - p(X \le 10)$

d. from 3 to 9 of these people will have investments in mutual funds?

SOLUTION $P(3 \leq X \leq 9) = p(X = 3) + p(X = 4) + p(X = 5) + p(X = 6) +$
$p(X = 7) + p(X = 8) + p(X = 9)$

$P(X = 3)$	Bpd(3, 18, 0.43)	0.014132479
$P(X = 4)$	Bpd(4, 18, 0.43)	0.03998004
$P(X = 5)$	Bpd(5, 18, 0.43)	0.084449068
$P(X = 6)$	Bpd(6, 18, 0.43)	0.138032248
$P(X = 7)$	Bpd(7, 18, 0.43)	0.17850787
$P(X = 8)$	Bpd(8, 18, 0.43)	0.185162768
$P(X = 9)$	Bpd(9, 18, 0.43)	0.15520466
	TOTAL	**0.795469**

OR alternatively you may solve $P(3 \leq X \leq 9)$ in the following way.

$$P(3 \leq X \leq 9) = p(X \leq 9) - p(X \leq 2)$$
$$= \text{Bcd}(9, 18, 0.43) - \text{Bcd}(2, 18, 0.43)$$
$$= 0.7996 - 0.0041$$
$$= \textbf{0.7955}$$

Binomial Template

You will notice that a similar style is used to present all the answers to the sample examples above. You are *not* to follow this style exactly, however, since you will be using a calculator or computer to determine the probability value. Your answers should look like the following template:

X = # of _____
      (successes)

n = _____

π = _____
      (dec.)

P(_____) = P(X symbol #) = _____ = 0._ _ _ _
   (words*)   (calculator or SPSS input)   (4 dec.)

* if the question does not directly say what the number is

EXAMPLE 6.11

Determining
$P(X = 3)$, Given
$n = 4$ and $\pi = 0.1$

If the likelihood of a tagged order form is 0.1, what is the probability that there are three tagged order forms in the sample of four?

SOLUTION The probability of three tagged orders from a sample of four is

$$P(X = 3 | n = 4, \pi = 0.1) = \frac{4!}{3!(4 - 3)!}(0.1)^3(1 - 0.1)^{4-3}$$

$$= \frac{4!}{3!(1)!}(0.1)^3(0.9)^1$$

$$= 4(0.1)(0.1)(0.1)(0.9) = 0.0036$$

Examples 6.12 and 6.13 show the computations for other values of X.

EXAMPLE 6.12

Determining $P(X \geq 3)$, Given $n = 4$ and $\pi = 0.1$

If the likelihood of a tagged order form is 0.1, what is the probability that there are three or more (i.e., at least three) tagged order forms in the sample of four?

SOLUTION In Example 6.11, you found that the probability of *exactly* three tagged order forms from a sample of four is 0.0036. To compute the probability of *at least* three tagged order forms, you need to add the probability of three tagged order forms to the probability of four tagged order forms. The probability of four tagged order forms is

$$P(X = 4 | n = 4, \pi = 0.1) = \frac{4!}{4!(4 - 4)!}(0.1)^4(1 - 0.1)^{4-4}$$

$$= \frac{4!}{4!(0)!}(0.1)^4(0.9)^0$$

$$= 1(0.1)(0.1)(0.1)(0.1)(1) = 0.0001$$

Thus, the probability of at least three tagged order forms is

$$P(X \geq 3) = P(X = 3) + P(X = 4)$$

$$= 0.0036 + 0.0001$$

$$= 0.0037$$

There is a 0.37% chance that there will be at least three tagged order forms in a sample of four.

EXAMPLE 6.13

Determining $P(X < 3)$, Given $n = 4$ and $\pi = 0.1$

If the likelihood of a tagged order form is 0.1, what is the probability that there are fewer than three tagged order forms in the sample of four?

SOLUTION The probability that there are fewer than three tagged order forms is

$$P(X < 3) = P(X = 0) + P(X = 1) + P(X = 2)$$

These probabilities are

$$P(X = 0 | n = 4, \pi = 0.1) = \frac{4!}{0!(4 - 0)!}(0.1)^0(1 - 0.1)^{4-0} = 0.6561$$

$$P(X = 1 | n = 4, \pi = 0.1) = \frac{4!}{1!(4 - 1)!}(0.1)^1(1 - 0.1)^{4-1} = 0.2916$$

$$P(X = 2 | n = 4, \pi = 0.1) = \frac{4!}{2!(4 - 2)!}(0.1)^2(1 - 0.1)^{4-2} = 0.0486$$

Therefore, $P(X < 3) = 0.6561 + 0.2916 + 0.0486 = 0.9963$. $P(X < 3)$ could also be calculated from its complement, $P(X \geq 3)$, as follows:

$$P(X < 3) = 1 - P(X \geq 3)$$

$$= 1 - 0.0037 = 0.9963$$

Computing binomial probabilities become tedious as *n* gets large. Table 6.16 shows how binomial probabilities can be computed by Excel (left) and Minitab (right). Binomial probabilities can also be looked up in a table of probabilities, as discussed in the **Binomial** online topic available on this book's download page.

TABLE 6.16
Finding a Binomial
Probability for
$n = 4$, $X = 2$, and
$\pi = 0.1$

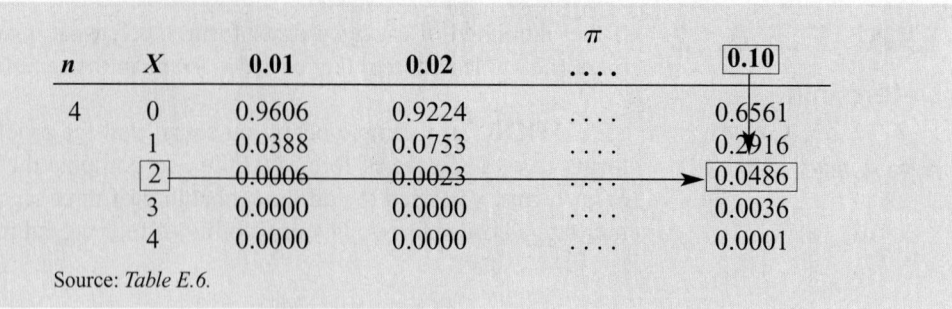

n	X	0.01	0.02	....	0.10
4	0	0.9606	0.9224	....	0.6561
	1	0.0388	0.0753	....	0.2916
	2	0.0006	0.0023	....	0.0486
	3	0.0000	0.0000	....	0.0036
	4	0.0000	0.0000	....	0.0001

Source: *Table E.6.*

You can also compute the binomial probabilities given in Table A.6 by using the Casio calculator as shown in Figures 6.2 and 6.3 (note that the Casio calculator uses the letter p instead of π to denote the probability of an event of interest).

FIGURE 6.2
CASIO calculator for
computing binomial
probabilities

Compute the binomial probabilities using the **Bpd** function.

Binomial Probabilities with n = 4 and π = 0.1

Variable X	Probability P(X = x)	Calculator Input	Probability Value
0	P(X = 0)	Bpd(0, 4, 0.1)	0.6561
1	P(X = 1)	Bpd(1, 4, 0.1)	0.2916
2	P(X = 2)	Bpd(2, 4, 0.1)	0.0486
3	P(X = 3)	Bpd(3, 4, 0.1)	0.0036
4	P(X = 4)	Bpd(4, 4, 0.1)	0.0001
		TOTAL	1

FIGURE 6.3
Minitab results for
computing binomial
probabilities

Compute the binomial probabilities using the LIST and **Bpd** function.

Binomial Probabilities with n = 4 and π = 0.1

Input the variable values (X=0,1,2,3,4) in **LIST 1**

Select **STAT F5**(DIST) **F5**(BINM) **F1**(Bpd) **F1**(List), and then select the following options.

Binomial P.D.
Data   : **List 1**
Numtrial : **4**
p   : **0.10**
Save Res : **None**
Execute

Now key **EXE** or **F1**(CALC).

The calculator will show the following result:

Binomial P.D.

0	0.6561
1	0.2916
2	0.0486
3	0.0036
4	0.0001

The shape of a binomial probability distribution depends on the values of n and π. Whenever $\pi = 0.5$, the binomial distribution is symmetrical, regardless of how large or small the value of n. When $\pi \neq 0.5$, the distribution is skewed. The closer π is to 0.5 and the larger the number of observations, n, the less skewed the distribution becomes. For example, the distribution of the number of tagged order forms is highly right skewed because $\pi = 0.1$ and $n = 4$ (see Figure 6.4).

FIGURE 6.4

Histogram of the binomial probability distribution with $n = 4$ and $\pi = 0.1$

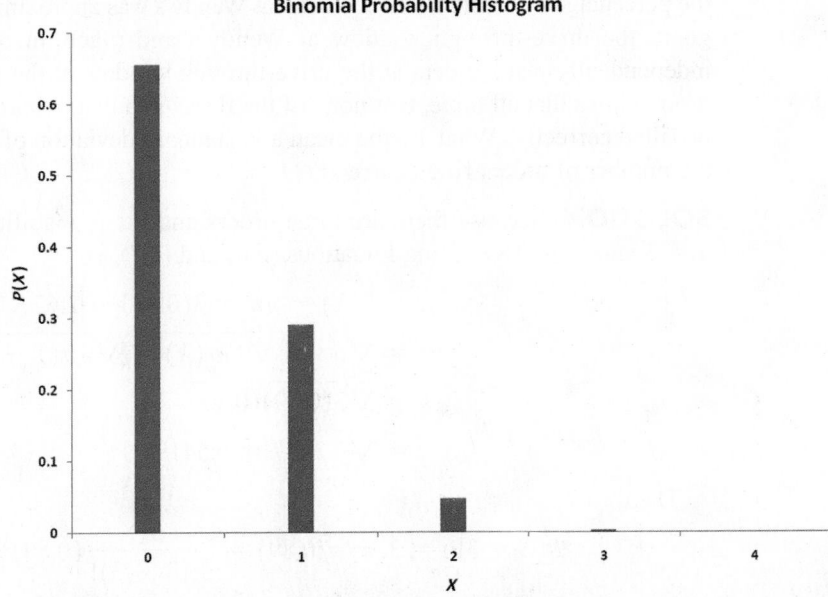

Observe from Figure 6.4 that unlike the histogram for continuous variables in Section 3.10, the bars for the values are very thin, and there is a large gap between each pair of values. That is because the histogram represents a discrete variable. (Theoretically, the bars should have no width. They should be vertical lines.)

The mean (or expected value) of the binomial distribution is equal to the product of n and π. Instead of using Equation (6.1) on page 242 to compute the mean of the probability distribution, you can also use Equation (6.6) to compute the mean for variables that follow the binomial distribution.

MEAN OF THE BINOMIAL DISTRIBUTION

The mean, μ, of the binomial distribution is equal to the sample size, n, multiplied by the probability of an event of interest, π.

$$\mu = E(X) = n\pi \qquad (6.6)$$

On the average, over the long run, you theoretically expect $\mu = E(X) = n\pi = (4)(0.1) = 0.4$ tagged order form in a sample of four orders.

The standard deviation of the binomial distribution can be calculated using Equation (6.7).

STANDARD DEVIATION OF THE BINOMIAL DISTRIBUTION

$$\sigma = \sqrt{\sigma^2} = \sqrt{Var(X)} = \sqrt{n\pi(1 - \pi)} \qquad (6.7)$$

The standard deviation of the number of tagged order forms is

$$\sigma = \sqrt{4(0.1)(0.9)} = 0.60$$

You get the same result if you use Equation (6.5) on page 249.

Example 6.14 applies the binomial distribution to service at a fast-food restaurant.

EXAMPLE 6.14

Computing Binomial Probabilities

Accuracy in taking orders at a drive-through window is important for fast-food chains. Periodically, *QSR Magazine*, (**http://www.qsrmagazine.com/**), publishes the results of its surveys. Accuracy is measured as the percentage of orders that are filled correctly. Recently, the percentage of orders filled correctly at Wendy's was approximately 89%. Suppose that you go to the drive-through window at Wendy's and place an order. Two friends of yours independently place orders at the drive-through window at the same Wendy's. What are the probabilities that all three, that none of the three, and that at least two of the three orders will be filled correctly? What are the mean and standard deviation of the binomial distribution for the number of orders filled correctly?

SOLUTION Because there are three orders and the probability of a correct order is 0.89, $n = 3$ and $\pi = 0.89$. Using Equations (6.6) and (6.7),

$$\mu = E(X) = n\pi = 3(0.89) = 2.67$$
$$\sigma = \sqrt{\sigma^2} = \sqrt{Var(X)} = \sqrt{n\pi(1-\pi)}$$
$$= \sqrt{3(0.89)(0.11)}$$
$$= \sqrt{0.2937} = 0.5419$$

Then,

$$P(X = 3 | n = 3, \pi = 0.89) = \frac{3!}{3!(3-3)!}(0.89)^3(1-0.89)^{3-3}$$

$$= \frac{3!}{3!(3-3)!}(0.89)^3(0.11)^0$$

$$= 1(0.89)(0.89)(0.89)(1) = 0.7050$$

$$P(X = 0 | n = 3, \pi = 0.89) = \frac{3!}{0!(3-0)!}(0.89)^0(1-0.89)^{3-0}$$

$$= \frac{3!}{0!(3-0)!}(0.89)^0(0.11)^3$$

$$= 1(1)(0.11)(0.11)(0.11) = 0.0013$$

$$P(X = 2 | n = 3, \pi = 0.89) = \frac{3!}{2!(3-2)!}(0.89)^2(1-0.89)^{3-2}$$

$$= \frac{3!}{2!(3-2)!}(0.89)^2(0.11)^1$$

$$= 3(0.89)(0.89)(0.11) = 0.2614$$

$$P(X \geq 2) = P(X = 2) + P(X = 3)$$

$$= 0.2614 + 0.7050$$

$$= 0.9664$$

The mean number of orders filled correctly in a sample of three orders is 2.67, and the standard deviation is 0.5419. The probability that all three orders are filled correctly is 0.7050, or 70.50%. The probability that none of the orders are filled correctly is 0.0013, or 0.13%. The probability that at least two orders are filled correctly is 0.9664, or 96.64%.

In this section, you have been introduced to the binomial distribution. The binomial distribution is an important mathematical model in many business situations.

CALCULATOR LESSON 5

CASIO FX-9750G, CFX-9850GB, OR FX-9750GII CALCULATOR

Lesson 5—Binomial Probabilities

Note: The following instructions refer to examples in the notes on the binomial probability distribution.

The Casio calculator has *two* binomial probability functions programmed into its memory. These are:

i. **Bpd**, which stands for **b**inomial **p**robability **d**istribution. This function calculates a binomial probability of the form

$$P(X = \#)$$

ii. **Bcd**, which stands for **b**inomial **c**umulative **d**istribution. This function calculates a Binomial probability of the form

$$P(X \leq \#)$$

A. Individual values of X—using the built-in **Bpd** distribution function

EXAMPLE 6.8
(Revisit)

$P(X = 2)$ where $n = 6$ and $\pi = 0.5$

Select **STAT F5**(DIST) **F5**(BINM) **F1**(Bpd), and then select the following options.

Data	: **F2**(Var) ▼ (Note: Do not key **EXE** now.)
x	: **2 EXE**
Numtrial	: **6 EXE**
p	: **.5 EXE**

Now key **EXE** or **F1**(Calc).

The calculator will show the result 0.23437.

To calculate another binomial probability, key **EXE** and enter new values where necessary.

B. Cumulative values of X—using the built-in **Bcd** distribution function

EXAMPLE 6.10a
(Revisit)

$P(X \leq 2)$ where $n = 18$ and $\pi = 0.43$

Select **STAT F5**(DIST) **F5**(BINM) **F2**(Bcd), and then select the following options.

Data	: **F2**(Var) ▼ (Note: Do not key **EXE** now.)
x	: **2 EXE**
Numtrial	: **18 EXE**
p	: **.43 EXE**

Now key **EXE** or **F1**(Calc).

The calculator will show the result 4.1007 E –03, which is scientific notation for the value 0.0041. E –03 means that you should move the decimal point 3 places to the left.

EXAMPLE 6.10c
(Revisit)

$P(X > 10) = 1 - P(X \leq 10)$ where $n = 18$ and $\pi = 0.43$

You must *first* calculate $P(X \leq 10)$.

Select **STAT F5**(DIST) **F5**(BINM) **F2**(Bcd), and then select the following options.

Data   : **F2**(Var) ▼ (Note: Do not key **EXE** now.)

x   : **10 EXE**

Numtrial   : **18 EXE**

p   : **.43 EXE**

Now key **EXE** or **F1**(Calc)

The calculator will show the result 0.90494.

Therefore, $P(X > 10) = 1 - P(X \leq 10) = 1 - 0.9049 = 0.0951$.

EXAMPLE 6.10d
(Revisit)

$P(3 \leq X \leq 9) = P(X \leq 9) - P(X \leq 2)$ where $n = 18$ and $\pi = 0.43$

You will have to calculate the two cumulative probabilities separately and then record the results and subtract the appropriate values to get the final result 0.7955.

Problems for Binomial Probabilities

APPLYING THE CONCEPTS

Binomial Template:

X = # of _____
                    (successes)

$n =$ _____

$\pi =$ _____
        (dec.)

$P(_____) = P(X$ symbol #$) =$
    (words)

_____ $= 0.\_\_\_\_$
    (calculator or SPSS input)   (4 dec.)

6.16 A new public school is presently being built in your community. The classrooms will include chairs that have a small table attached on the right or left side. The school is trying to determine how many left-handed tables should be included in each classroom. If only 7% of the population is left-handed, what is the probability that in a class of 25 students:

a. two will be left-handed?

b. more than three will be left-handed?

c. What is the expected number of left-handed children in a class of 25?

6.17 The quality inspector for a company that produces heptium computer chips has determined that 3% of the production is defective. The company does not perform final product inspection, but instead agrees to replace any defective chip found by any customer and will give the customer a $5 discount on their next order.

a. If a customer orders 30 heptium chips, what is the probability that 3 or more defective chips will be included in the order?

b. What is the expected number of defective chips in the above order?

c. Another customer assembles computer motherboards, each with 7 heptium chips. If any chip fails, then the motherboard fails. What is the probability that a motherboard will fail?

6.18 According to a well-known accounting firm, the chances of your tax return being audited by Revenue Canada are about 9 in 1000 if your income is less than $50,000. The chances increase to 22 in 1000 if your income is more than $50,000. You are presently employed by an accounting firm and have prepared tax returns for 58 clients with income under $50,000 and for 42 clients with income over $50,000.

a. What is the probability that at most 3 of the clients with incomes under $50,000 will be audited?

b. What is the probability that at least 4 of your clients that have incomes over $50,000 will be audited?

6.19 A salesperson has to sell a minimum of 50 cars in a month in order to get a bonus. One particular salesperson has sold 43 cars so far this month. Today he has appointments with 9 prospective customers. Based on past experience he has a 55% chance of selling a car to any customer. What is the probability that he will earn his bonus today?

6.20 A certain soft drink manufacturer believes that 40% of the people that drink cola prefer their brand. A random sample of 60 cola drinkers was surveyed. If the manufacturer is correct:
a. What is the probability that less than half of those surveyed will prefer the manufacturer's product?
b. What is the probability that at least the expected number of people will prefer the manufacturer's product?

6.21 The increase or decrease in the price of a stock between the beginning and the end of a trading day is assumed to be an equally likely random event. What is the probability that a stock will show an increase in its closing price on five consecutive days?

6.22 The U.S. Department of Transportation reported that in 2009, Southwest led all domestic airlines in on-time arrivals for domestic flights, with a rate of 0.825. Using the binomial distribution, what is the probability that in the next six flights
a. four flights will be on time?
b. all six flights will be on time?
c. at least four flights will be on time?
d. What are the mean and standard deviation of the number of on-time arrivals?
e. What assumptions do you need to make in (a) through (c)?

6.23 A student is taking a multiple-choice exam in which each question has four choices. Assume that the student has no knowledge of the correct answers to any of the questions. She has decided on a strategy in which she will place four balls (marked *A*, *B*, *C*, and *D*) into a box. She randomly selects one ball for each question and replaces the ball in the box. The marking on the ball will determine her answer to the question. There are five multiple-choice questions on the exam. What is the probability that she will get
a. five questions correct?
b. at least four questions correct?
c. no questions correct?
d. no more than two questions correct?

6.24 Investment advisors agree that near-retirees, defined as people aged 55 to 65, should have balanced portfolios. Most advisors suggest that the near-retirees have no more than 50% of their investments in stocks. However, during the huge decline in the stock market in 2008, 22% of near-retirees had 90% or more of their investments in stocks (P. Regnier, "What I Learned from the Crash," *Money*, May

2009, p. 114). Suppose you have a random sample of 10 people who would have been labeled as near-retirees in 2008. What is the probability that during 2008
a. none had 90% or more of their investment in stocks?
b. exactly one had 90% or more of his or her investment in stocks?
c. two or fewer had 90% or more of their investment in stocks?
d. three or more had 90% or more of their investment in stocks?

6.25 When a customer places an order with Rudy's On-Line Office Supplies, a computerized accounting information system (AIS) automatically checks to see if the customer has exceeded his or her credit limit. Past records indicate that the probability of customers exceeding their credit limit is 0.05. Suppose that, on a given day, 20 customers place orders. Assume that the number of customers that the AIS detects as having exceeded their credit limit is distributed as a binomial random variable.
a. What are the mean and standard deviation of the number of customers exceeding their credit limits?
b. What is the probability that zero customers will exceed their limits?
c. What is the probability that one customer will exceed his or her limit?
d. What is the probability that two or more customers will exceed their limits?

 6.26 In Example 6.14 on page 260, you and two friends decided to go to Wendy's. Now, suppose that instead you go to Popeye's, which last month filled approximately 84.8% of orders correctly. What is the probability that
a. all three orders will be filled correctly?
b. none of the three will be filled correctly?
c. at least two of the three will be filled correctly?
d. What are the mean and standard deviation of the binomial distribution used in (a) through (c)? Interpret these values.

6.27 In Example 6.14 on page 260, you and two friends decided to go to Wendy's. Now, suppose that instead you go to McDonald's, which last month filled approximately 90.1% of the orders correctly. What is the probability that
a. all three orders will be filled correctly?
b. none of the three will be filled correctly?
c. at least two of the three will be filled correctly?
d. What are the mean and standard deviation of the binomial distribution used in (a) through (c)? Interpret these values.
e. Compare the result of (a) through (d) with those of Popeye's in Problem 6.21 and Wendy's in Example 6.14 on page 260.

6.3 Poisson Probability Distribution

Many studies are based on counts of the times a particular event occurs in a given *area of opportunity*. An **area of opportunity** is a continuous unit or interval of time, volume, or any physical area in which there can be more than one occurrence of an event. Examples are the surface defects on a new refrigerator, the number of network failures in a day, the number of people arriving at a bank, and the number of fleas on the body of a dog.

Characteristics of a Poisson Experiment

1. The experiment consists of observing some situation for a period of *time*.
   or
   An *amount of space* is inspected or analyzed. Space may be length, area, volume or weight.
2. In each infinitesimally small amount of time or space there will either be one success or no successes, where success is when the outcome of interest occurs. The successes must occur *randomly*. Note that this condition implies that the successes are *independent* of each other.
3. The average rate of success for the amount of time or space we are interested in is given the symbol λ (lambda).

The **random variable** associated with a Poisson experiment is

$$X = \# \text{ of successes in a certain amount of time or space.}$$

To calculate the probability that X takes on a specific value we use the

Poisson Probability Distribution Function:

$$P(X = x) = \frac{e^{-\lambda}\lambda^{x}}{x!} \tag{6.8}$$

where $e = 2.718281828459\ldots$ (a mathematical constant)

Note: On your calculator there is an e^x key. Try calculating e^1.

EXAMPLE 6.15

Records have been kept for the past several months, and they show that customers arrive to use a certain banking machine at an average rate of 15 per hour.

a. What is the probability that 12 customers will use the machine in the next hour?

SOLUTION X = # of customers at the bank machine in 1 hour

$\lambda = 15$ / hour

$P(X = 12) =$ Ppd (12, 15) $= 0.0829$

b. What is the probability that there will be fewer than 3 customers in the next 10 minutes?

SOLUTION X = # of customers at the bank machine in 10 minutes

$\lambda = 15$ / hour = 2.5 / 10 minutes

$P(X < 3) = P(X \le 2)$

$= $ Pcd (2, 2.5) $= 0.5438$

a. What is the probability that there will be more than 40 customers in the next 2 hours?

SOLUTION X = # of customers at the bank machine in 2 hours

$\lambda = 15$ / hour = 30 / 2 hours

$P(X > 40) = 1 - P(X \le 40) = 1 - $ Pcd (40, 30)

$= 1 - 0.9677 = 0.0323$

EXAMPLE 6.16   It has been noted that potholes on the 401 highway occur randomly. An inspection of a 200 km stretch of the 401 indicated that there were 450 potholes. Today the pothole repair work crew will repair 3 km of the highway. What is the probability that the crew will repair at least 6 potholes?

SOLUTION X = # of potholes in 3 km

$$\lambda = 450 / 200 \text{ km} = 2.25 / \text{km} = 6.75 / 3 \text{ km}$$

$$P(X \geq 6) = 1 - P(X \leq 5) = 1 - \text{Pcd}(5, 6.75)$$

$$= 1 - 0.3338 = 0.6662$$

Consider the number of customers arriving during the lunch hour at a bank located in the central business district in a large city. You are interested in the number of customers who arrive each minute. Does this situation match the four properties of the Poisson distribution given earlier? First, the *event* of interest is a customer arriving, and the *given area of opportunity* is defined as a one-minute interval. Will zero customers arrive, one customer arrive, two customers arrive, and so on? Second, it is reasonable to assume that the probability that a customer arrives during a particular one-minute interval is the same as the probability for all the other one-minute intervals. Third, the arrival of one customer in any one-minute interval has no effect on (i.e., is independent of) the arrival of any other customer in any other one-minute interval. Finally, the probability that two or more customers will arrive in a given time period approaches zero as the time interval becomes small. For example, the probability is virtually zero that two customers will arrive in a time interval of 0.01 second. Thus, you can use the Poisson distribution to determine probabilities involving the number of customers arriving at the bank in a one-minute time interval during the lunch hour.

The Poisson distribution has one characteristic, called λ (the Greek lowercase letter *lambda*), which is the mean or expected number of events per unit. The variance of a Poisson distribution is also equal to λ, and the standard deviation is equal to $\sqrt{\lambda}$. The number of events, X, of the Poisson random variable ranges from 0 to infinity (∞).

Equation (6.9) is the mathematical expression for the Poisson distribution for computing the probability of $X = x$ events, given that λ events are expected.

POISSON DISTRIBUTION

$$P(X = x | \lambda) = \frac{e^{-\lambda} \lambda^x}{x!} \tag{6.9}$$

where

$P(X = x | \lambda) =$ the probability that $X = x$ events in an area of opportunity given λ

$\lambda =$ expected number of events

$e =$ mathematical constant approximated by 2.71828

$x =$ number of events ($x = 0, 1, 2, \ldots, \infty$)

To illustrate an application of the Poisson distribution, suppose that the mean number of customers who arrive per minute at the bank during the noon-to-1 P.M. hour is equal to 3.0. What is the probability that in a given minute, exactly two customers will arrive? And what is the probability that more than two customers will arrive in a given minute?

Using Equation (6.9) and $\lambda = 3$, the probability that in a given minute exactly two customers will arrive is

$$P(X = 2 | \lambda = 3) = \frac{e^{-3.0}(3.0)^2}{2!} = \frac{9}{(2.71828)^3(2)} = 0.2240$$

To determine the probability that in any given minute more than two customers will arrive,

$$P(X > 2) = P(X = 3) + P(X = 4) + \cdots + P(X = \infty)$$

Because in a probability distribution, all the probabilities must sum to 1, the terms on the right side of the equation $P(X > 2)$ also represent the complement of the probability that X is less than or equal to 2 [i.e., $1 - P(X \leq 2)$]. Thus,

$$P(X > 2) = 1 - P(X \leq 2) = 1 - [P(X = 0) + P(X = 1) + P(X = 2)]$$

Now, using Equation (6.9),

$$P(X > 2) = 1 - \left[\frac{e^{-3.0}(3.0)^0}{0!} + \frac{e^{-3.0}(3.0)^1}{1!} + \frac{e^{-3.0}(3.0)^2}{2!} \right]$$

$$= 1 - [0.0498 + 0.1494 + 0.2240]$$

$$= 1 - 0.4232 = 0.5768$$

You can also use the Bcd function to solve the above question, for example

$$P(X > 2) = 1 - P(X \leq 2)$$

$$= 1 - \text{Bcd}(2, 3)$$

$$= 1 - 0.4232 = 0.5768$$

Thus, there is a 57.68% chance that more than two customers will arrive in the same minute.

To avoid the drudgery involved in these computations, you can find Poisson probabilities directly from Table A.7 (in Appendix A), a portion of which is reproduced in Table 6.17. Table A.7 provides the probabilities that the Poisson random variable takes on values of $X = 0, 1, 2, \ldots$, for selected values of the parameter λ. To find the probability that exactly two customers will arrive in a given minute when the mean number of customers arriving is 3.0 per minute, you can read the probability corresponding to the row $X = 2$ and column $\lambda = 3.0$ from the table. The result is 0.2240, as demonstrated in Table 6.17.

TABLE 6.17

Finding a Poisson Probability for $\lambda = 3$

X	2.1	2.2	λ	3.0
0	.1225	.1108	....	.0498
1	.2572	.2438	....	.1494
2	.2700	.2681	....	.2240
3	.1890	.1966	....	.2240
4	.0992	.1082	....	.1680
5	.0417	.0476	....	.1008
6	.0146	.0174	....	.0504
7	.0044	.0055	....	.0216
8	.0011	.0015	....	.0081
9	.0003	.0004	....	.0027
10	.0001	.0001	....	.0008
11	.0000	.0000	....	.0002
12	.0000	.0000	....	.0001

Source: *Table A.7.*

You can also compute the Poisson probabilities given in Table A.7 by using the CASIO calculator, as illustrated in Figures 6.5 and 6.6.

FIGURE 6.5
CASIO calculator for computing Poisson probabilities with λ = 3

Compute the Poisson probabilities using the **Ppd** function.

Poisson Probabilities with λ = 3

Variable X	Probability $P(X = x)$	Calculator Input	Probability Value
0	$P(X = 0)$	Ppd(0, 3)	0.049787068
1	$P(X = 1)$	Ppd (1, 3)	0.149361205
2	$P(X = 2)$	Ppd (2, 3)	0.224041808
3	$P(X = 3)$	Ppd (3, 3)	0.224041808
4	$P(X = 4)$	Ppd (4, 3)	0.168031356
5	$P(X = 5)$	Ppd (5, 3)	0.100818813
6	$P(X = 6)$	Ppd (6, 3)	0.050409407
7	$P(X = 7)$	Ppd (7, 3)	0.021604031
8	$P(X = 8)$	Ppd (8, 3)	0.008101512
9	$P(X = 9)$	Ppd (9, 3)	0.002700504
10	$P(X = 10)$	Ppd (10, 3)	0.000810151
11	$P(X = 11)$	Ppd (11, 3)	0.00022095
12	$P(X = 12)$	Ppd (12, 3)	0.0000552376
13	$P(X = 13)$	Ppd (13, 3)	0.0000127471
14	$P(X = 14)$	Ppd (14, 3)	0.00000273153
15	$P(X = 15)$	Ppd (15, 3)	0.000000546306
16	$P(X = 16)$	Ppd (16, 3)	0.000000102432
17	$P(X = 17)$	Ppd (17, 3)	0.0000000180763
18	$P(X = 18)$	Ppd (18, 3)	0.00000000301272
19	$P(X = 19)$	Ppd (17, 3)	0.000000000475692
20	$P(X = 20)$	Ppd (18, 3)	0.0000000000713538
		Total	1

FIGURE 6.6
CASIO calculator results for computing Poisson probabilities with λ = 3

Compute the Poisson probabilities using the LIST and **Ppd** function.

Poisson Probabilities with λ = 3

Input the variable values ($X = 0,1,2, ..., 20$) in **LIST 1**.

Select **STAT F5**(DIST) **F1**(POISN) **F1**(Ppd) **F1**(List), and then select the following options.

Binomial P.D.
Data : **List**
List : **List 1**
μ : **3**
Save Res : **None**
Execute
Now key **EXE** or **F1**(CALC).

NOTE: The CASIO calculator uses the symbol μ instead of λ to denote the average rate of success.

The calculator will show the following result:

Poisson P.D.

0	0.049787068	7	0.021604031	14	0.00000273153
1	0.149361205	8	0.008101512	15	0.000000546306
2	0.224041808	9	0.002700504	16	0.000000102432
3	0.224041808	10	0.000810151	17	0.0000000180763
4	0.168031356	11	0.00022095	18	0.00000000301272
5	0.100818813	12	0.0000552376	19	0.000000000475692
6	0.050409407	13	0.0000127471	20	0.0000000000713538

EXAMPLE 6.17

Computing Poisson Probabilities

The number of work-related injuries per month in a manufacturing plant is known to follow a Poisson distribution with a mean of 2.5 work-related injuries a month. What is the probability that in a given month, no work-related injuries occur? That at least one work-related injury occurs?

SOLUTION Using Equation (6.9) on page 265 with $\lambda = 2.5$ (or Excel, Minitab, or a Poisson table lookup), the probability that in a given month no work-related injuries occur is

$$P(X = 0 | \lambda = 2.5) = \frac{e^{-2.5}(2.5)^0}{0!} = \frac{1}{(2.71828)^{2.5}(1)} = 0.0821$$

The probability that there will be no work-related injuries in a given month is 0.0821 or 8.21%. Thus,

$$P(X \geq 1) = 1 - P(X = 0)$$
$$= 1 - 0.0821$$
$$= 0.9179$$

The probability that there will be at least one work-related injury is 0.9179 or 91.79%.

CALCULATOR LESSON 6

CASIO FX-9750G, CFX-9850GB, OR FX-9750GII CALCULATOR

Lesson 6—Poisson Probabilities

Note: The following instructions refer to examples in the notes on the Poisson probability distribution.

The Casio calculator has *two* Poisson probability functions programmed into its memory. These are

i. **Ppd**, which stands for **P**oisson **p**robability **d**istribution. This function calculates a Poisson probability of the form

P(X = #)

ii. **Pcd**, which stands for **P**oisson **c**umulative **d**istribution. This function calculates a Poisson probability of the form

P(X ≤ #)

A. Individual values of X—using the built-in **Ppd** distribution function

P(X = 12)   where $\lambda = 15$

Select **STAT F5**(DIST) **F6**(✕) **F1**(POISN) **F1**(Ppd), and then select the following options.

Data   : **F2**(Var) ▼ (Note: Do not key **EXE** now.)
x   : **12 EXE**
μ   : **15 EXE**   (Note: the calculator uses the μ symbol instead of λ.)

Now key **EXE** or **F1**(Calc).

The calculator will show the result 0.082859.

To calculate another Poisson probability, key **EXE** and enter new values where necessary.

B. Cumulative values of X—using the built-in **Pcd** distribution function

$P(X < 3) = P(X \leq 2)$ where $\lambda = 2.5$

Select **STAT F5**(DIST) **F6**(×) **F1**(POISN) **F2**(Pcd), and then select the following options.

Data   : **F2**(Var) ▼ (Note: Do not key **EXE** now.)
x   : **2 EXE**
μ   : **2.5 EXE**

Now key **EXE** or **F1**(Calc).

The calculator will show the result 0.54381.

$P(X > 40) = 1 - P(X \leq 40)$ where $\lambda = 30$

You must *first* calculate $P(X \leq 40)$.

Select **STAT F5**(DIST) **F5**(BINM) **F2**(Bcd), and then select the following options.

Data   : **F2**(Var) ▼ (Note: Do not key **EXE** now.)
x   : **40 EXE**
μ   : **30 EXE**

Now key **EXE** or **F1**(Calc).

The calculator will show the result 0.96769.k

Therefore, $P(X > 40) = 1 - P(X \leq 40) = 1 - 0.9677 = 0.0323$.

Problems for Poisson Probabilities

APPLYING THE CONCEPTS

Poisson Template:

X = # of _____ IN _____
            (successes)   (time or space)

$\lambda = \underline{\quad\quad} = \underline{\quad\quad\quad\quad}$
      (given)   (new—if needed)

P(_____) = P(X symbol #) =
    (words)

$\underline{\quad\quad\quad\quad\quad\quad\quad\quad} = 0.\_\,\_\,\_\,\_$
(calculator or SPSS input)   (4 dec.)

6.28 A taxicab company has found that, on the average, two accidents occur in a month. The accidents appear to occur randomly. Find the probability of there being 5 or more accidents during a given month.

6.29 Customers arrive randomly at a service desk at an average rate of 2 every five minutes. Find the probability that:
a. None arrive in a five minute period.
b. More than four arrive in a ten minute period.

6.30 Bankruptcies of convenience stores in Toronto occur randomly at an average rate of 4.5 per year. Find the probability that:
a. there will be no corner store bankruptcies in the next four months.
b. there will be at most 3 corner store bankruptcies this year.

6.31 Flaws in plate glass used for large office buildings occur randomly at an average of 1 per 10 square feet. What is the probability that a 6 ft. by 10 ft. sheet of this type of glass will contain:
a. less than 2 flaws?
b. at least 1 flaw?

6.32 A data entry typist makes an average of 2 errors per page. If the errors occur randomly, what is the probability that:
a. there will be one error on the next page?
b. there will be more than 5 errors on the next 2 pages?

6.33 Two students have started a business to seal driveways during the summer months. They rent a pickup truck and a power sprayer. With this they will use a tar based spray to seal asphalt driveways. Past experience has shown that the

best time to sign up customers is to ring their doorbells between 5:00 and 8:00 p.m. on any weekday evening. Any jobs that they obtain will be completed the next day. In the months of June, July and August they find that they get an average 2 customers per hour ringing doorbells.
a. What is the probability that they will get from 5 to 9 jobs in an evening of soliciting?
b. They charge $25 per driveway. If the truck costs $50 per day, and the spraying equipment costs $20 per day and the material to seal one driveway costs $5, what is the probability that they will make a profit on any given day.

6.34 Assume that the number of network errors experienced in a day on a local area network (LAN) is distributed as a Poisson random variable. The mean number of network errors experienced in a day is 2.4. What is the probability that in any given day
a. zero network errors will occur?
b. exactly one network error will occur?
c. two or more network errors will occur?
d. fewer than three network errors will occur?

SELF Test **6.35** The quality control manager of Marilyn's Cookies is inspecting a batch of chocolate-chip cookies that has just been baked. If the production process is in control, the mean number of chip parts per cookie is 6.0. What is the probability that in any particular cookie being inspected
a. fewer than five chip parts will be found?
b. exactly five chip parts will be found?
c. five or more chip parts will be found?
d. either four or five chip parts will be found?

6.36 Refer to Problem 6.35. How many cookies in a batch of 100 should the manager expect to discard if company policy requires that all chocolate-chip cookies sold have at least four chocolate-chip parts?

6.37 The U.S. Department of Transportation maintains statistics for mishandled bags per 1,000 airline passengers. In the first nine months of 2010, Delta had mishandled 3.52 bags per 1,000 passengers. What is the probability that in the next 1,000 passengers, Delta will have
a. no mishandled bags?
b. at least one mishandled bag?
c. at least two mishandled bags?

6.38 The U.S. Department of Transportation maintains statistics for consumer complaints per 100,000 airline passengers. In the first nine months of 2009, consumer complaints were 0.99 per 100,000 passengers. What is the probability that in the next 100,000 passengers, there will be
a. no complaints?
b. at least one complaint?
c. at least two complaints?

6.39 Based on past experience, it is assumed that the number of flaws per foot in rolls of grade 2 paper follows a Poisson distribution with a mean of 1 flaw per 5 feet of paper (0.2 flaw per foot). What is the probability that in a
a. 1-foot roll, there will be at least 2 flaws?
b. 12-foot roll, there will be at least 1 flaw?
c. 50-foot roll, there will be more than or equal to 5 flaws and fewer than or equal to 15 flaws?

6.40 J.D. Power and Associates calculates and publishes various statistics concerning car quality. The initial quality score measures the number of problems per new car sold. For 2009 model cars, Ford had 1.02 problems per car and Dodge had 1.34 problems per car (data extracted from S. Carty, "U.S. Autos Power Forward with Gains in Quality Survey," *USA Today*, June 23, 2009, p. 3B). Let the random variable X be equal to the number of problems with a newly purchased 2009 Ford.
a. What assumptions must be made in order for X to be distributed as a Poisson random variable? Are these assumptions reasonable?
Making the assumptions as in (a), if you purchased a 2009 Ford, what is the probability that the new car will have
b. zero problems?
c. two or fewer problems?
d. Give an operational definition for *problem*. Why is the operational definition important in interpreting the initial quality score?

6.41 Refer to Problem 6.40. If you purchased a 2009 Dodge, what is the probability that the new car will have
a. zero problems?
b. two or fewer problems?
c. Compare your answers in (a) and (b) to those for the Ford in Problem 6.40 (b) and (c).

6.42 Refer to Problem 6.40. Another article reported that in 2008, Ford had 1.12 problems per car and Dodge had 1.41 problems per car (data extracted from S. Carty, "Ford Moves Up in Quality Survey," *USA Today*, June 5, 2008, p. 3B). If you purchased a 2008 Ford, what is the probability that the new car will have
a. zero problems?
b. two or fewer problems?
c. Compare your answers in (a) and (b) to those for the 2009 Ford in Problem 6.40 (b) and (c).

6.43 Refer to Problem 6.42. If you purchased a 2008 Dodge, what is the probability that the new car will have
a. zero problems?
b. two or fewer problems?
c. Compare your answers in (a) and (b) to those for the 2009 Dodge in Problem 6.41 (a) and (b).

6.44 A toll-free phone number is available from 9 A.M. to 9 P.M. for your customers to register complaints about a product purchased from your company. Past history indicates that an average of 0.8 calls is received per minute.

a. What properties must be true about the situation described here in order to use the Poisson distribution to calculate probabilities concerning the number of phone calls received in a one-minute period?

Assuming that this situation matches the properties discussed in (a), what is the probability that during a one-minute period

b. zero phone calls will be received?

c. three or more phone calls will be received?

d. What is the maximum number of phone calls that will be received in a one-minute period 99.99% of the time?

USING STATISTICS @ Saxon Home Improvement, Part I Revisited

Monkey Business Images / Shutterstock.com

I n the Saxon Home Improvement scenario at the beginning of this chapter, you were an accountant for the Saxon Home Improvement Company. The company's accounting information system automatically reviews order forms from online customers for possible mistakes. Any questionable invoices are tagged and included in a daily exceptions report. Knowing that the probability that an order will be tagged is 0.10, you were able to use the binomial distribution to determine the chance of finding a certain number of tagged forms in a sample of size four. There was a 65.6% chance that none of the forms would be tagged, a 29.2% chance that one would be tagged, and a 5.2% chance that two or more would be tagged. You were also able to determine that, on average, you would expect 0.4 forms to be tagged, and the standard deviation of the number of tagged order forms would be 0.6. Now that you have learned the mechanics of using the binomial distribution for a known probability of 0.10 and a sample size of four, you will be able to apply the same approach to any given probability and sample size. Thus, you will be able to make inferences about the online ordering process and, more importantly, evaluate any changes or proposed changes to the process.

SUMMARY

In this chapter, you have studied mathematical expectation and two important discrete probability distributions: the binomial and Poisson distributions. In the next chapter, you will study the most important continuous distribution, the normal distribution.

To help decide what probability distribution to use for a particular situation, you need to ask the following question:

- Is there a fixed number of observations, n, each of which is classified as an event of interest or not an event of interest? Or is there an area of opportunity?

- If there is a fixed number of observations, n, each of which is classified as an event of interest or not an event of interest, you use the binomial distribution. If there is an area of opportunity, you use the Poisson distribution.

KEY EQUATIONS

Expected Value, μ, of a Discrete Random Variable

$$\mu = E(X) = \sum_{i=1}^{N} x_i P(X = x_i)$$

Variance

$$\sigma^2 = \sum (X - \mu)^2 P(X)$$

Standard Deviation

$$\sigma = \sqrt{\left(\sum (X - \mu)^2 P(X) \right)}$$

Variance of a Discrete Random Variable

$$\sigma^2 = \sum_{i=1}^{N} [x_i - E(X)]^2 P(X = x_i)$$

Standard Deviation of a Discrete Random Variable

$$\sigma = \sqrt{\sigma^2} = \sqrt{\sum_{i=1}^{N} [x_i - E(X)]^2 P(X = x_i)}$$

Mean of the Binomial Distribution

$$\mu = E(X) = n\pi$$

Standard Deviation of the Binomial Distribution

$$\sigma = \sqrt{\sigma^2} = \sqrt{Var(X)} = \sqrt{n\pi(1 - \pi)}$$

Poisson Probability Distribution Function

$$P(X = x) = \frac{e^{-\lambda}\lambda^{x}}{x!}$$

Poisson Distribution

$$P(X = x|\lambda) = \frac{e^{-\lambda}\lambda^{x}}{x!}$$

KEY TERMS

area of opportunity 262	probability distribution for a discrete	standard deviation of a discrete
binomial distribution 250	random variable 238	random variable 247
expected value 240	random variable 238	variance of a discrete random
mathematical model 250		variable 247

PROBLEMS

CHECKING YOUR UNDERSTANDING

6.45 What is the meaning of the expected value of a probability distribution?

6.46 What are the four properties that must be present in order to use the binomial distribution?

6.47 What are the four properties that must be present in order to use the Poisson distribution?

APPLYING THE CONCEPTS

6.48 Darwin Head, a 35-year-old sawmill worker, won $1 million and a Chevrolet Malibu Hybrid by scoring 15 goals within 24 seconds at the Vancouver Canucks National Hockey League game (B. Ziemer, "Darwin Evolves into an Instant Millionaire," *Vancouver Sun*, February 28, 2008, p. 1). Head said he would use the money to pay off his mortgage and provide for his children, and he had no plans to quit his job. The contest was part of the Chevrolet Malibu Million Dollar Shootout, sponsored by General Motors Canadian Division. Did GM-Canada risk the $1 million? No! GM-Canada purchased event insurance from a company specializing in promotions at sporting events such as a half-court basketball shot or a hole-in-one giveaway at the local charity golf outing. The event insurance company estimates the probability of a contestant winning the contest, and for a modest charge, insures the event. The promoters pay the insurance premium but take on no added risk as the insurance company will make the large payout in the unlikely event that a contestant wins. To see how it works, suppose that the insurance company estimates that the probability a contestant would win a Million Dollar Shootout is 0.001, and that the insurance company charges $4,000.

a. Calculate the expected value of the profit made by the insurance company.

b. Many call this kind of situation a win–win opportunity for the insurance company and the promoter. Do you agree? Explain.

6.49 Between 1896 when the Dow Jones Index was created and 2009, the index rose in 64% of the years (data extracted from M. Hulbert, "What the Past Can't Tell Investors," *The New York Times*, January 3, 2010, p. BU2). Based on this information, and assuming a binomial distribution, what do you think is the probability that the stock market will rise

a. next year?

b. the year after next?

c. in four of the next five years?

d. in none of the next five years?

e. For this situation, what assumption of the binomial distribution might not be valid?

6.50 In late 2007, it was reported that 79% of U.S. adults owned a cell phone (data extracted from E. C. Baig, "Tips Help Navigate Tech-Buying Maze," *USA Today*, November 28, 2007, p. 5B). Suppose that by the end of 2010, that percentage was 85%. If a sample of 10 U.S. adults is selected, what is the probability that

a. 8 own a cell phone?

b. at least 8 own a cell phone?

c. all 10 own a cell phone?

d. If you selected the sample in a particular geographical area and found that none of the 10 respondents owned a cell phone, what conclusion might you reach about whether the percentage of cell phone owners in this area was 85%?

6.51 One theory concerning the Dow Jones Industrial Average is that it is likely to increase during U.S. presidential election years. From 1964 through 2008, the Dow Jones Industrial Average increased in 9 of the 12 U.S. presidential election years. Assuming that this indicator is a random event with no predictive value, you would expect that the indicator would be correct 50% of the time.

a. What is the probability of the Dow Jones Industrial Average increasing in 9 or more of the 12 U.S. presidential election years if the probability of an increase in the Dow Jones Industrial Average is 0.50?

b. What is the probability that the Dow Jones Industrial Average will increase in 9 or more of the 12 U.S. presidential election years if the probability of an increase in the Dow Jones Industrial Average in any year is 0.75?

6.52 Errors in a billing process often lead to customer dissatisfaction and ultimately hurt bottom-line profits. An article in *Quality Progress* (L. Tatikonda, "A Less Costly Billing Process," *Quality Progress*, January 2008, pp. 30–38) discussed a company where 40% of the bills prepared contained errors. If 10 bills are processed, what is the probability that

a. 0 bills will contain errors?

b. exactly 1 bill will contain an error?

c. 2 or more bills will contain errors?

d. What are the mean and the standard deviation of the probability distribution?

6.53 Refer to Problem 6.52. Suppose that a quality improvement initiative has reduced the percentage of bills containing errors to 20%. If 10 bills are processed, what is the probability that

a. 0 bills will contain errors?

b. exactly 1 bill will contain an error?

c. 2 or more bills will contain errors?

d. What are the mean and the standard deviation of the probability distribution?

e. Compare the results of (a) through (c) to those of Problem 6.41 (a) through (c).

6.54 Social log-ins involve recommending or sharing an article that you read online. According to Janrain ("T. Wayne, One Log-In Catches on for Many Sites," *Drilling Down, The New York Times*, May 2, 2011, p. B2) in the first quarter of 2011, 35% signed in via Facebook compared with 31% for Google.

If a sample of 10 social log-ins is selected, what is the probability that

a. more than 4 signed in using Facebook?

b. more than 4 signed in using Google?

c. none signed in using Facebook?

d. What assumptions did you have to make to answer (a) through (c)?

6.55 One of the biggest frustrations for the consumer electronics industry is that customers are accustomed to returning goods for any reason (C. Lawton, "The War on Returns," *The Wall Street Journal*, May 8, 2008, pp. D1, D6). Recently, it was reported that returns for "no trouble found" were 68% of all the returns. Consider a sample of 20 customers who returned consumer electronics purchases. Use the binomial model to answer the following questions:

a. What is the expected value, or mean, of the binomial distribution?

b. What is the standard deviation of the binomial distribution?

c. What is the probability that 15 of the 20 customers made a return for "no trouble found"?

d. What is the probability that no more than 10 of the customers made a return for "no trouble found"?

e. What is the probability that 10 or more of the customers made a return for "no trouble found"?

6.56 Refer to Problem 6.55. In the same time period, 27% of the returns were for "buyer's remorse."

a. What is the expected value, or mean, of the binomial distribution?

b. What is the standard deviation of the binomial distribution?

c. What is the probability that none of the 20 customers made a return for "buyer's remorse"?

d. What is the probability that no more than 2 of the customers made a return for "buyer's remorse"?

e. What is the probability that 3 or more of the customers made a return for "buyer's remorse"?

6.57 One theory concerning the S&P 500 Index is that if it increases during the first five trading days of the year, it is likely to increase during the entire year. From 1950 through 2010, the S&P 500 Index had these early gains in 39 years. In 34 of these 39 years, the S&P 500 Index increased for the entire year. Assuming that this indicator is a random event with no predictive value, you would expect that the indicator would be correct 50% of the time. What is the probability of the S&P 500 Index increasing in 34 or more years if the true probability of an increase in the S&P 500 Index is

a. 0.50?

b. 0.70?

c. 0.90?

d. Based on the results of (a) through (c), what do you think is the probability that the S&P 500 Index will increase if there is an early gain in the first five trading days of the year? Explain.

6.58 *Spurious correlation* refers to the apparent relationship between variables that either have no true relationship or are related to other variables that have not been measured. One widely publicized stock market indicator in the United States that is an example of spurious correlation is the relationship between the winner of the National Football League Super Bowl and the performance of the Dow Jones Industrial Average in that year. The "indicator" states that when a team that existed before the National Football League merged with the American Football League wins the Super Bowl, the Dow Jones Industrial Average will increase in that year. (Of course, any correlation between these is spurious as one thing has absolutely nothing to do with the other!) Since the first Super Bowl was held in 1967 through 2010, the indicator has been correct 35 out of 44 times (data extracted from W. Power, "The Bulls Want Jets Grounded," *The Wall Street Journal*, January 22, 2011, p. B2). Assuming that this indicator is a random event with no predictive value, you would expect that the indicator would be correct 50% of the time.

a. What is the probability that the indicator would be correct 35 or more times in 44 years?

b. What does this tell you about the usefulness of this indicator?

6.59 Approximately 300 million golf balls were lost in the United States in 2009. Assume that the number of golf balls lost in an 18-hole round is distributed as a Poisson random variable with a mean of 5 balls.

a. What assumptions need to be made so that the number of golf balls lost in an 18-hole round is distributed as a Poisson random variable?

Making the assumptions given in (a), what is the probability that

b. 0 balls will be lost in an 18-hole round?

c. 5 or fewer balls will be lost in an 18-hole round?

d. 6 or more balls will be lost in an 18-hole round?

6.60 According to a Virginia Tech survey, college students make an average of 11 cell phone calls per day. Moreover,

80% of the students surveyed indicated that their parents pay their cell phone expenses (J. Elliot, "Professor Researches Cell Phone Usage Among Students," **www .physorg.com**, February 26, 2007).

a. What distribution can you use to model the number of calls a student makes in a day?

b. If you select a student at random, what is the probability that he or she makes more than 10 calls in a day? More than 15? More than 20?

c. If you select a random sample of 10 students, what distribution can you use to model the proportion of students who have parents who pay their cell phone expenses?

d. Using the distribution selected in (c), what is the probability that all 10 have parents who pay their cell phone expenses? At least 9? At least 8?

MANAGING ASHLAND MULTICOMM SERVICES

The Ashland MultiComm Services (AMS) marketing department wants to increase subscriptions for its *3-For-All* telephone, cable, and Internet combined service. AMS marketing has been conducting an aggressive direct-marketing campaign that includes postal and electronic mailings and telephone solicitations. Feedback from these efforts indicates that including premium channels in this combined service is a very important factor for both current and prospective subscribers. After several brainstorming sessions, the marketing department has decided to add premium cable channels as a no-cost benefit of subscribing to the *3-For-All* service.

The research director, Mona Fields, is planning to conduct a survey among prospective customers to determine how many premium channels need to be added to the *3-For-All* service in order to generate a subscription to the service. Based on past campaigns and on industry-wide data, she estimates the following:

Number of Free Premium Channels	Probability of Subscriptions
0	0.02
1	0.04
2	0.06
3	0.07
4	0.08
5	0.085

1. If a sample of 50 prospective customers is selected and no free premium channels are included in the *3-For-All* service offer, given past results, what is the probability that

a. fewer than 3 customers will subscribe to the *3-For-All* service offer?

b. 0 customers or 1 customers will subscribe to the *3-For-All* service offer?

c. more than 4 customers will subscribe to the *3-For-All* service offer?

Suppose that in the actual survey of 50 prospective customers, 4 customers subscribe to the *3-For-All* service offer.

d. What does this tell you about the previous estimate of the proportion of customers who would subscribe to the *3-For-All* service offer?

2. Instead of offering no premium free channels as in Problem 1, suppose that two free premium channels are included in the *3-For-All* service offer, Given past results, what is the probability that

a. fewer than 3 customers will subscribe to the *3-For-All* service offer?

b. 0 customers or 1 customer will subscribe to the *3-For-All* service offer?

c. more than 4 customers will subscribe to the *3-For-All* service offer?

d. Compare the results of (a) through (c) to those of 1.

Suppose that in the actual survey of 50 prospective customers, 6 customers subscribe to the *3-For-All* service offer.

e. What does this tell you about the previous estimate of the proportion of customers who would subscribe to the *3-For-All* service offer?

f. What do the results in (e) tell you about the effect of offering free premium channels on the likelihood of obtaining subscriptions to the *3-For-All* service?

3. Suppose that additional surveys of 50 prospective customers were conducted in which the number of free premium channels was varied. The results were as follows:

Number of Free Premium Channels	Number of Subscriptions
1	5
3	6
4	6
5	7

How many free premium channels should the research director recommend for inclusion in the *3-For-All* service? Explain.

REFERENCES

1. Levine, D. M., P. Ramsey, and R. Smidt, *Applied Statistics for Engineers and Scientists Using Microsoft Excel and Minitab* (Upper Saddle River, NJ: Prentice Hall, 2001).
2. *Microsoft Excel 2010* (Redmond, WA: Microsoft Corp., 2010).
3. *Minitab Release* 16 (State College, PA.: Minitab, Inc., 2010).
4. Moscove, S. A., M. G. Simkin, and N. A. Bagranoff, *Core Concepts of Accounting Information Systems*, 11th ed. (New York: Wiley, 2010).

EG6.1 The Probability Distribution for a Discrete Random Variable

In-Depth Excel Use the **COMPUTE worksheet** of the **Discrete Random Variable workbook** (shown below) as a template for computing the expected value, variance, and standard deviation of a discrete random variable. The worksheet contains the data for the Section 6.1 example on page 240 involving the number of interruptions per day in a large computer network. For other problems, overwrite the X and $P(X)$ values in columns A and B, respectively. If a problem has more or fewer than six outcomes, select the cell range **A5:E5**. If the problem has more than six outcomes:

1. Right-click and click **Insert** from the shortcut menu.

2. If a dialog box appears, click **Shift cells down** and then click **OK**.

3. Repeat steps 1 and 2 as many times as necessary.

4. Select the formulas in cell range **C4:E4** and copy them down through the new table rows.

5. Enter the new X and $P(X)$ values in columns **A** and **B**.

If the problem has fewer than six outcomes, right-click and click **Delete** from the shortcut menu. If a dialog box appears, click **Shift cells up** and then click **OK**. Repeat as many times as necessary and then enter the new X and $P(X)$ values in columns **A** and **B**.

	A	B	C	D	E	F	G	H
1	Discrete Random Variable Probability Distribution							
2							**Statistics**	
3	X	P(X)	X*P(X)	[X-E(X)]^2	[X-E(X)]^2*P(X)		Expected value	1.4 =SUM(C:C)
4	0	0.35	0	1.96	0.686		Variance	2.04 =SUM(E:E)
5	1	0.25	0.25	0.16	0.04		Standard deviation	1.43 =SQRT(H4)
6	2	0.20	0.4	0.36	0.072			
7	3	0.10	0.3	2.56	0.256	X*P(X)	[X-E(X)]^2	[X-E(X)]^2*P(X)
8	4	0.05	0.2	6.76	0.338	=A4*B4	=(A4-$H$3)^2	=D4*B4
9	5	0.05	0.25	12.96	0.648	=A5*B5	=(A5-$H$3)^2	=D5*B5
						=A6*B6	=(A6-$H$3)^2	=D6*B6
						=A7*B7	=(A7-$H$3)^2	=D7*B7
						=A8*B8	=(A8-$H$3)^2	=D8*B8
						=A9*B9	=(A9-$H$3)^2	=D9*B9

EG6.2 Binomial Distribution

PHStat2 Use **Binomial** to compute binomial probabilities. For example, to create a binomial probabilities table and histogram for Example 6.13 on page 257, similar to those in Table 6.16 and Figure 6.4, select **PHStat → Probability & Prob. Distributions → Binomial**. In the procedure's dialog box (shown in next column):

1. Enter **4** as the **Sample Size**.

2. Enter **0.1** as the **Prob. of an Event of Interest**.

3. Enter **0** as the **Outcomes From** value and enter **4** as the (Outcomes) **To** value.

4. Enter a **Title**, check **Histogram**, and click **OK**.

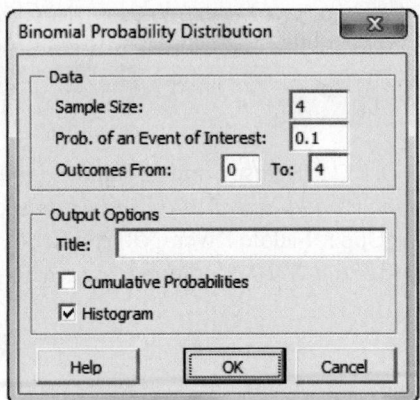

To add columns to the binomial probabilities table for $P(<= X), P(< X), P(> X)$, and $P(\geq X)$, check **Cumulative Probabilities** before clicking **OK** in step 4.

In-Depth Excel Use the **BINOMDIST** worksheet function to compute binomial probabilities. Enter the function as **BINOMDIST** (*X, sample size, π, cumulative*), where X is the number of events of interest, π is the probability of an event of interest, and *cumulative* is a **True** or **False** value. (When *cumulative* is **True**, the function computes the probability of X or fewer events of interest; when *cumulative* is **False**, the function computes the probability of exactly X events of interest.)

Use the **COMPUTE worksheet** of the **Binomial workbook**, shown in Table 6.16 on page 258, as a template for computing binomial probabilities. The worksheet contains the data for the Section 6.2 tagged orders example. Overwrite these values and adjust the table of probabilities for other problems. To create a histogram of the probability distribution, use the instructions in Appendix Section F.5.

EG6.3 Poisson Distribution

PHStat2 Use **Poisson** to compute Poisson probabilities. For example, to create a Poisson probabilities table similar to Table 6.17 on page 266, select **PHStat → Probability &**

Prob. Distributions → Poisson. In this procedure's dialog box (shown below):

1. Enter **3** as the **Mean/Expected No. of Events of Interest**.
2. Enter a **Title** and click **OK**.

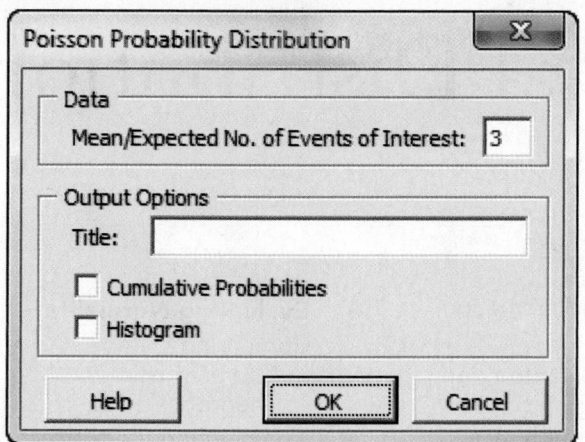

To add columns to the Poisson probabilities table for $P(<=X), P(<X), P(>X)$, and $P(\geq X)$, check **Cumulative**

Probabilities before clicking **OK** in step 2. To create a histogram of the probability distribution on a separate chart sheet, check **Histogram** before clicking **OK** in step 2.

In-Depth Excel Use the **POISSON** worksheet function to compute Poisson probabilities. Enter the function as **POISSON(X, *lambda, cumulative*)**, where X is the number of events of interest, *lambda* is the average or expected number of events of interest, and *cumulative* is a **True** or **False** value. (When *cumulative* is **True**, the function computes the probability of X or fewer events of interest; when *cumulative* is **False**, the function computes the probability of exactly X events of interest.)

Use the **COMPUTE worksheet** of the **Poisson workbook**, shown in Table 6.17 on page 266, as a template for computing Poisson probabilities. The worksheet contains the entries for the bank customer arrivals problem of Section 6.3. To adapt this worksheet to other problems, change the **Mean/Expected number of events of interest value** in cell **E4**. To create a histogram of the probability distribution, use the instructions in Appendix Section F.5.

7

The Normal Distribution

Learning Objectives
In this chapter, you learn:

- To compute probabilities from the normal distribution
- How to use the normal distribution to solve business problems
- To use the normal probability plot to determine whether a set of data is approximately normally distributed

Lee Morris / Shutterstock.com

USING STATISTICS

@ OurCampus!

You are a designer for the OurCampus! website, a social networking site that targets college students. To attract and retain visitors to the site, you need to make sure that the exclusive-content daily videos can be quickly downloaded and played in a user's browser. Download time, the amount of time, in seconds, that passes from first linking to the website home page until the first video is ready to play, is both a function of the streaming media technology used and the number of simultaneous users of the website.

To check how fast a video downloads, you open a web browser on a PC at the corporate offices of OurCampus! and measure the download time. Past data indicate that the mean download time is 7 seconds, and that the standard deviation is 2 seconds. Approximately two-thirds of the download times are between 5 and 9 seconds, and about 95% of the download times are between 3 and 11 seconds. In other words, the download times are distributed as a bell-shaped curve, with a clustering around the mean of 7 seconds. How could you use this information to answer questions about the download times of the first video?

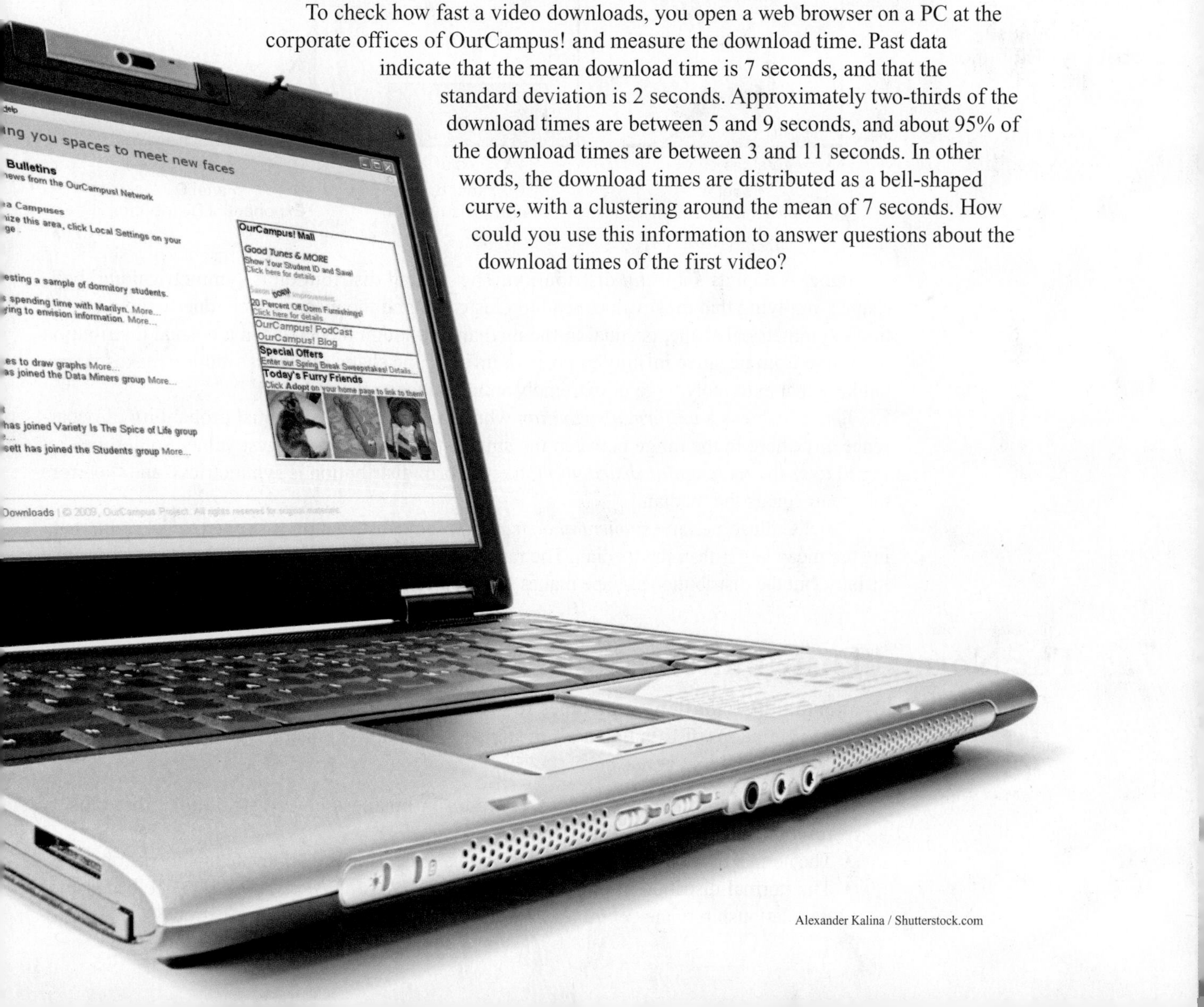

Alexander Kalina / Shutterstock.com

In Chapter 6, Saxon Home Improvement Company managers wanted to be able to answer questions about the number of tagged items in a given sample size. As an OurCampus! web designer, you face a different task, one that involves a continuous measurement because a download time could be any value and not just a whole number. How can you answer questions, such as the following, about this *continuous numerical variable*:

- What proportion of the video downloads take more than 9 seconds?
- How many seconds elapse before 10% of the downloads are complete?
- How many seconds elapse before 99% of the downloads are complete?
- How would enhancing the streaming media technology used affect the answers to these questions?

As in Chapter 6, you can use a probability distribution as a model. Reading this chapter will help you learn about characteristics of continuous probability distributions and how to use the normal distribution to solve business problems.

7.1 Continuous Probability Distributions

A **probability density function** is a mathematical expression that defines the distribution of the values for a continuous random variable. Figure 7.1 graphically displays three probability density functions.

FIGURE 7.1
Three continuous probability distributions

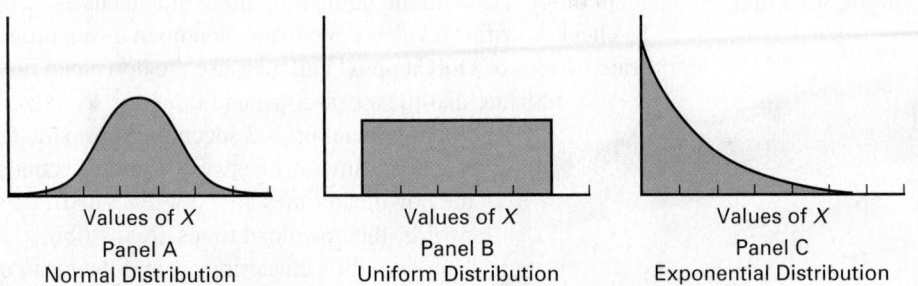

Values of *X*	Values of *X*	Values of *X*
Panel A	Panel B	Panel C
Normal Distribution	Uniform Distribution	Exponential Distribution

Panel A depicts a *normal* distribution. The normal distribution is symmetrical and bell-shaped, implying that most values tend to cluster around the mean, which, due to the distribution's symmetrical shape, is equal to the median. Although the values in a normal distribution can range from negative infinity to positive infinity, the shape of the distribution makes it very unlikely that extremely large or extremely small values will occur.

Panel B shows a *uniform distribution* where each value has an equal probability of occurrence anywhere in the range between the smallest value and the largest value. Sometimes referred to as the *rectangular distribution*, the uniform distribution is symmetrical, and therefore the mean equals the median.

Panel C illustrates an *exponential distribution*. This distribution is skewed to the right, making the mean larger than the median. The range for an exponential distribution is zero to positive infinity, but the distribution's shape makes the occurrence of extremely large values unlikely.

7.2 The Normal Distribution

The **normal distribution** (sometimes referred to as the *Gaussian distribution*) is the most common continuous distribution used in statistics. The normal distribution is vitally important in statistics for three main reasons:

- Numerous continuous variables common in business have distributions that closely resemble the normal distribution.
- The normal distribution can be used to approximate various discrete probability distributions.
- The normal distribution provides the basis for *classical statistical inference* because of its relationship to the *central limit theorem* (which is discussed in Section 8.4).

The normal distribution is represented by the classic bell shape shown in Panel A of Figure 7.1. In the normal distribution, you can calculate the probability that values occur within certain ranges or intervals. However, because probability for continuous variables is measured as an area under the curve, the *exact* probability of a *particular value* from a continuous distribution such as the normal distribution is zero. As an example, time (in seconds) is measured and not counted. Therefore, you can determine the probability that the download time for a video on a web browser is between 7 and 10 seconds, or the probability that the download time is between 8 and 9 seconds, or the probability that the download time is between 7.99 and 8.01 seconds. However, the probability that the download time is *exactly* 8 seconds is zero.

The normal distribution has several important theoretical properties:

- It is symmetrical, and its mean and median are therefore equal.
- It is bell-shaped in appearance.
- Its interquartile range is equal to 1.33 standard deviations. Thus, the middle 50% of the values are contained within an interval of two-thirds of a standard deviation below the mean and two-thirds of a standard deviation above the mean.
- It has an infinite range $(-\infty < X < \infty)$.

In practice, many variables have distributions that closely resemble the theoretical properties of the normal distribution. The data in Table 7.1 represent the amount of soft drink in 10,000 1-liter bottles filled on a recent day. The continuous variable of interest, the amount of soft drink filled, can be approximated by the normal distribution. The measurements of the amount of soft drink in the 10,000 bottles cluster in the interval 1.05 to 1.055 liters and distribute symmetrically around that grouping, forming a bell-shaped pattern.

TABLE 7.1

Amount of Fill in 10,000 Bottles of a Soft Drink

Amount of Fill (liters)	Relative Frequency
< 1.025	48/10,000 = 0.0048
1.025 < 1.030	122/10,000 = 0.0122
1.030 < 1.035	325/10,000 = 0.0325
1.035 < 1.040	695/10,000 = 0.0695
1.040 < 1.045	1,198/10,000 = 0.1198
1.045 < 1.050	1,664/10,000 = 0.1664
1.050 < 1.055	1,896/10,000 = 0.1896
1.055 < 1.060	1,664/10,000 = 0.1664
1.060 < 1.065	1,198/10,000 = 0.1198
1.065 < 1.070	695/10,000 = 0.0695
1.070 < 1.075	325/10,000 = 0.0325
1.075 < 1.080	122/10,000 = 0.0122
1.080 or above	48/10,000 = 0.0048
Total	1.0000

Figure 7.2 shows the relative frequency histogram and polygon for the distribution of the amount filled in 10,000 bottles.

FIGURE 7.2

Relative frequency histogram and polygon of the amount filled in 10,000 bottles of a soft drink

Source: Data are taken from Table 7.1.

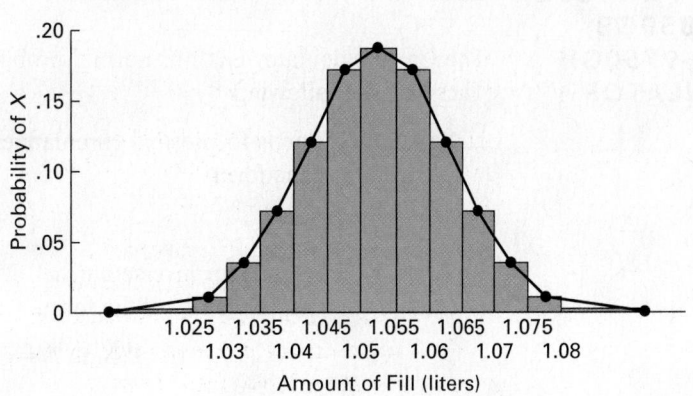

For these data, the first three theoretical properties of the normal distribution are approximately satisfied. However, the fourth one, having an infinite range, is not. The amount filled in a bottle cannot possibly be zero or below, nor can a bottle be filled beyond its capacity. From Table 7.1, you see that only 48 out of every 10,000 bottles filled are expected to contain 1.08 liters or more, and an equal number are expected to contain less than 1.025 liters.

The symbol $f(X)$ is used to represent a probability density function. The **probability density function for the normal distribution** is given in Equation (7.1).

NORMAL PROBABILITY DENSITY FUNCTION

$$f(X) = \frac{1}{\sqrt{2\pi}\sigma} e^{-(1/2)[(X-\mu)/\sigma]^2}$$ **(7.1)**

where

$e =$ mathematical constant approximated by 2.71828

$\pi =$ mathematical constant approximated by 3.14159

$\mu =$ mean

$\sigma =$ standard deviation

$X =$ any value of the continuous variable, where $-\infty < X < \infty$

Although Equation (7.1) may look complicated, because e and π are mathematical constants, the probabilities of the random variable X are dependent only on the two parameters of the normal distribution—the mean, μ, and the standard deviation, σ. Every time you specify particular values of μ and σ, a *different* normal probability distribution is generated. Figure 7.3 illustrates this principle. The distributions labeled A and B have the same mean (μ) but have different standard deviations. Distributions A and C have the same standard deviation (σ) but have different means. Distributions B and C have different values for both μ and σ.

FIGURE 7.3
Three normal distributions

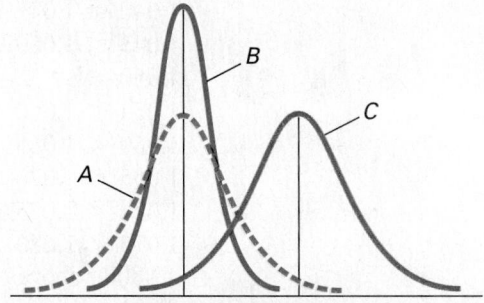

CALCULATOR LESSON 7

CASIO FX-9750G, CFX-9850GB, OR FX-9750GII CALCULATOR

Lesson 7—Normal Distribution

The Casio calculator has *two* normal probability functions programmed into its memory. These are the following:

i. **Ncd**, which stands for **n**ormal **c**umulative **d**istribution. This function calculates a normal probability of the form

$$P(X \leq \#)$$

ii. **InvN**, which stands for **inv**erse **n**ormal. This function calculates an "x" value (i.e., ?) for a known normal probability of the form

$$P(X \leq ?) = \text{given probability}$$

Suppose that the weights of adults are normally distributed with a mean of 170.0 lbs. and a standard deviation of 25.0 lbs.

a. What is the probability that a person weighs from 150 to 190 lbs.?

Solution: X = a person's weight
μ = 170.0 lbs.
σ = 25.0 lbs.

Select **STAT F5**(DIST) **F1**(NORM) **F2**(Ncd), and then select the following options:

Lower   : **150 EXE**
Upper   : **190 EXE**
σ : **25 EXE**
μ : **170 EXE**

Now key **EXE** or **F1**(Calc).

The calculator will now show the result 0.5762892.

(i.e., $P(150 \leq X \leq 190) = 0.5763$)

b. What is the probability that a person weighs less than 140 lbs.?

Lower   : **–100 EXE**
Upper   : **140 EXE**
σ : **25 EXE**
μ : **170 EXE**

Now key **EXE** or **F1**(Calc).

The calculator will now show the result 0.11506967.

(i.e., $P(X < 140) = 0.1151$)

Note: To represent $-\infty$ use any value less than $\mu - 6\sigma$.
To represent ∞ use any value more than $\mu + 6\sigma$.

c. What is the probability that a person weighs at least 160 lbs.?

Lower   : **160 EXE**
Upper   : **1000 EXE**
σ : **25 EXE**
μ : **170 EXE**

$P(X \geq 160) = 0.6554$

d. What is the maximum weight of the lightest 15% of the adult population?

$P(X \leq ?) = 0.15$

Select **STAT F5**(DIST) **F1**(NORM) **F3**(InvN), and then select the following options.

Area   : **.15 EXE**
σ : **25 EXE**
μ : **170 EXE**

Now key **EXE** or **F1**(Calc).   The calculator will now show the result 144.089165.

(i.e., The lightest 15% of adults weigh at most 144.1 lbs.)

e. What is the minimum weight to be in the heaviest 30% of the adult population?

$P(X \geq ?) = 0.3$

Select **STAT F5**(DIST) **F1**(NORM) **F3**(InvN), and then select the following options:

Area   : .7   **EXE**
σ : **25 EXE**
μ : **170 EXE**

Now key **EXE** or **F1**(Calc).   The calculator will now show the result 183.110013.

(i.e., The heaviest 30% weigh at least 183.1 lbs.)

Note: When using the InvN function, the *Area* value that is required is the area to the *left* of the desired X value.

Problems for Section 7.2

NORMAL PROBABILITY EXERCISES

Normal Template:

X = _____

μ =
          } Normal
σ =

P(_____) = P(X symbol #) =
   (words*)

_____ = 0._ _ _ _
   (calculator or SPSS input)   (4 dec.)

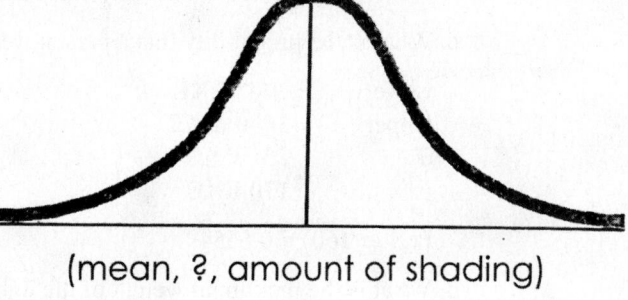

(mean, value, shading)

Inverse Normal Template:

X = _____

μ =
          } Normal
σ =

P(_____) = P(X symbol ?) = 0._____
   (words*)   (given)

? = _____ = _____
   (calculator or SPSS input)   (same dec. as μ)

Concluding statement.

(mean, ?, amount of shading)

7.1 The lifetime of a certain brand of tire is normally distributed with a mean of 90,000 km. and standard deviation of 8,000 km. The tire carries a warranty for 80,000 km.
a. What is the probability that the tire you recently purchased will last more than 100,000 km.?
b. What percent of this brand of tire will fail before the warranty expires?
c. What should the mileage warranty be so that only 4% of the tires need to be replaced under warranty?

7.2 A firm's marketing manager believes that total sales for next year can be represented by a normal distribution, with a mean of $2.5 million and a standard deviation of $300,000. The firm has fixed costs of $1.8 million.
a. What is the probability that the firm's sales will be less than $3.0 million?
b. What is the probability that the firm will have sufficient sales to cover fixed costs?

c. What is the probability that the firm's sales will be within $150,000 of the expected (i.e., mean) sales?

d. Determine the sales level that has only a 9% chance of being exceeded.

7.3 The owner of a convenience store has copies of the local newspaper delivered early each morning. The demand for papers is normally distributed with a mean of 75 and a standard deviation of 16.

a. What is the probability that the newspapers will be sold out if the owner orders 65 copies?

b. How many copies should be ordered so that the probability of selling out is at most 15%?

7.4 In the movie *Forest Gump*, the public school required an IQ of at least 80 for admittance.

a. If IQ test scores are normally distributed with a mean of 100 and a standard deviation of 16, what percent of children would qualify for admittance to the school?

b. If the public school wished to have only 5% of all children not qualify for admittance, what minimum IQ test score should be required for admittance?

7.5 An investment broker reports that the annual returns on common stock and municipal bonds are both normally distributed. The stocks have a mean return of 12.4% with a standard deviation of 20.6%. On the other hand, the bonds have a mean return of 5.2% with a standard deviation of 8.6%.

a. If you are a conservative investor and just don't like to lose money, which type of investment should you choose?

b. If you are a more ambitious investor and would like to have the best chance of making more than 15%, which investment should you choose?

c. What minimum return would a stock have to earn to be rated in the top 20% of stocks in terms of return?

7.6 At a certain university the cumulative grade point average (CGPA) of first year students usually averages 2.73 with a standard deviation of 0.37. It has been found that the marks are usually approximately normally distributed.

a. What is the probability that a student will have a CGPA that is between 2.00 and 3.00?

b. What percent of students will be on probation (i.e., their CGPA is less than 2.00)?

c. Academic scholarships are awarded to the top 1% of first year students. What minimum CGPA is needed to receive a scholarship?

APPLYING THE CONCEPTS

7.7 In 2008, the per capita consumption of coffee in the United States was reported to be 4.2 kg, or 9.24 pounds (data extracted from **en.wikipedia.org/wiki/List_of_countries_ by_coffee_consumption_per_capita**). Assume that the per capita consumption of coffee in the United States is approxi-

mately distributed as a normal random variable, with a mean of 9.24 pounds and a standard deviation of 3 pounds.

a. What is the probability that someone in the United States consumed more than 10 pounds of coffee in 2008?

b. What is the probability that someone in the United States consumed between 3 and 5 pounds of coffee in 2008?

c. What is the probability that someone in the United States consumed less than 5 pounds of coffee in 2008?

d. 99% of the people in the United States consumed less than how many pounds of coffee?

✓ SELF Test **7.8** Toby's Trucking Company determined that the distance traveled per truck per year is normally distributed, with a mean of 50 thousand miles and a standard deviation of 12 thousand miles.

a. What proportion of trucks can be expected to travel between 34 and 50 thousand miles in a year?

b. What percentage of trucks can be expected to travel either below 30 or above 60 thousand miles in a year?

c. How many miles will be traveled by at least 80% of the trucks?

d. What are your answers to (a) through (c) if the standard deviation is 10 thousand miles?

7.9 Consumers spend an average of $21 per week in cash without being aware of where it goes (data extracted from "Snapshots: A Hole in Our Pockets," *USA Today*, January 18, 2010, p. 1A). Assume that the amount of cash spent without being aware of where it goes is normally distributed and that the standard deviation is $5.

a. What is the probability that a randomly selected person will spend more than $25?

b. What is the probability that a randomly selected person will spend between $10 and $20?

c. Between what two values will the middle 95% of the amounts of cash spent fall?

7.10 A set of final examination grades in an introductory statistics course is normally distributed, with a mean of 73 and a standard deviation of 8.

a. What is the probability that a student scored below 91 on this exam?

b. What is the probability that a student scored between 65 and 89?

c. The probability is 5% that a student taking the test scores higher than what grade?

d. If the professor grades on a curve (i.e., gives A's to the top 10% of the class, regardless of the score), are you better off with a grade of 81 on this exam or a grade of 68 on a different exam, where the mean is 62 and the standard deviation is 3? Show your answer statistically and explain.

7.11 A statistical analysis of 1,000 long-distance telephone calls made from the headquarters of the Bricks and Clicks Computer Corporation indicates that the length of these calls is normally distributed, with $\mu = 240$ seconds and $\sigma = 40$ seconds.

a. What is the probability that a call lasted less than 180 seconds?
b. What is the probability that a call lasted between 180 and 300 seconds?
c. What is the probability that a call lasted between 110 and 180 seconds?
d. 1% of all calls will last less than how many seconds?

7.12 In 2008, the per capita consumption of coffee in Sweden was reported to be 8.2 kg, or 18.04 pounds (data extracted from **en.wikipedia.org/wiki/List_of_countries_ by_coffee_consumption_per_capita**). Assume that the per capita consumption of coffee in Sweden is approximately distributed as a normal random variable, with a mean of 18.04 pounds and a standard deviation of 5 pounds.

a. What is the probability that someone in Sweden consumed more than 10 pounds of coffee in 2008?
b. What is the probability that someone in Sweden consumed between 3 and 5 pounds of coffee in 2008?

c. What is the probability that someone in Sweden consumed less than 5 pounds of coffee in 2008?
d. 99% of the people in Sweden consumed less than how many pounds of coffee?

7.13 Many manufacturing problems involve the matching of machine parts, such as shafts that fit into a valve hole. A particular design requires a shaft with a diameter of 22.000 mm, but shafts with diameters between 21.990 mm and 22.010 mm are acceptable. Suppose that the manufacturing process yields shafts with diameters normally distributed, with a mean of 22.002 mm and a standard deviation of 0.005 mm. For this process, what is

a. the proportion of shafts with a diameter between 21.99 mm and 22.00 mm?
b. the probability that a shaft is acceptable?
c. the diameter that will be exceeded by only 2% of the shafts?
d. What would be your answers in (a) through (c) if the standard deviation of the shaft diameters were 0.004 mm?

7.3 Computing Z-Scores and Normal Probability

To compute normal probabilities, you first convert a normally distributed random variable, X, to a **standardized normal random variable**, Z, using the **transformation formula**, shown in Equation (7.2). Applying this formula allows you to look up values in a normal probability table and avoid the tedious and complex computations that Equation (7.1) would otherwise require.

THE TRANSFORMATION FORMULA

The Z value is equal to the difference between X and the mean, μ, divided by the standard deviation, σ.

$$Z = \frac{X - \mu}{\sigma} \qquad (7.2)$$

The transformation formula computes a Z value that expresses the difference of the X value from the mean, μ, in units of the standard deviation called *standardized units*. While a random variable, X, has mean, μ, and standard deviation, σ, the standardized random variable, Z, always has mean $\mu = 0$ and standard deviation $\sigma = 1$.

Then you can determine the probabilities by using Table E.2, the **cumulative standardized normal distribution**. For example, recall from the Using Statistics scenario on page 279 that past data indicate that the time to download a video is normally distributed, with a mean $\mu = 7$ seconds and a standard deviation $\sigma = 2$ seconds. From Figure 7.4, you see that every measurement X has a corresponding standardized measurement Z, computed from Equation (7.2), the transformation formula. Therefore, a download time of 9 seconds is equivalent to 1 standardized unit (1 standard deviation) above the mean because

$$Z = \frac{9 - 7}{2} = +1$$

Z Scores

An **extreme value** or **outlier** is a value located far away from the mean. Z scores are useful in identifying outliers. The larger the Z score, the greater the distance from the value to the mean. The **Z score** is the difference between the value and the mean, divided by the standard deviation.

Z SCORES		
	$$Z = \frac{X - \bar{X}}{S}$$	(7.3)

For the time-to-get-ready data, the mean is 39.6 minutes, and the standard deviation is 6.77 minutes. The time to get ready on the first day is 39.0 minutes. You compute the Z score for Day 1 by using Equation (4.7):

$$Z = \frac{X - \bar{X}}{S}$$

$$= \frac{39.0 - 39.6}{6.77}$$

$$= -0.09$$

Table 7.2 shows the Z scores for all 10 days. The largest Z score is 1.83 for Day 4, on which the time to get ready was 52 minutes. The lowest Z score was -1.57 for Day 2, on which the time to get ready was 29 minutes. As a general rule, a Z score is considered an outlier if it is less than -3.0 or greater than $+3.0$. None of the times met that criterion to be considered outliers.

TABLE 7.2

Z Scores for the 10 Getting-Ready Times

	Time (X)	Z Score
	39	−0.09
	29	−1.57
	43	0.50
	52	1.83
	39	−0.09
	44	0.65
	40	0.06
	31	−1.27
	44	0.65
	35	−0.68
Mean	39.6	
Standard deviation	6.77	

EXAMPLE 7.1

Computing the Z Scores of the Number of Calories in Iced Coffee Drinks

The data in the file `CoffeeDrink` represent the calories of 16-ounce iced coffee drinks at Dunkin' Donuts and Starbucks. Compute the Z scores of the calories of 16-ounce iced coffee drinks.

SOLUTION   Table 7.3 illustrates the Z scores of the calories of 16-ounce iced coffee drinks. The largest Z score is 1.33, for an iced coffee drink with 530 calories. The lowest Z score is -1.24, for an iced coffee drink with 240 calories. There are no apparent outliers in these data because none of the Z scores is less than -3.0 or greater than $+3.0$.

TABLE 7.3

Z Scores of the Number of Calories in Iced Coffee Drinks

	Calories	Z Scores
	240	−1.24
	260	−1.06
	350	−0.27
	350	−0.27
	420	0.35
	510	1.15
	530	1.33
Mean	380	
Standard Deviation	113.1371	

FIGURE 7.4
Transformation of scales

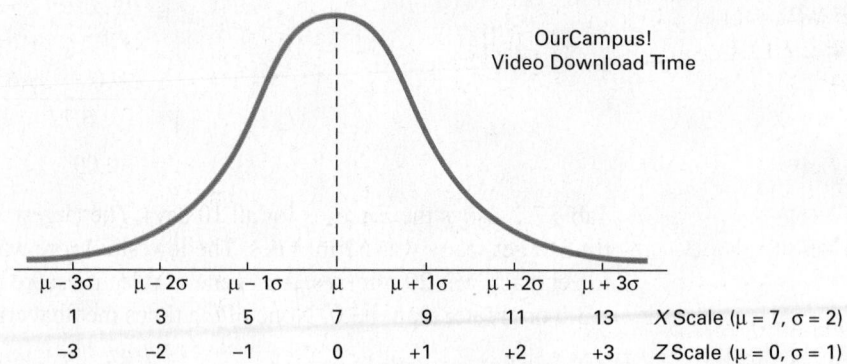

A download time of 1 second is equivalent to −3 standardized units (3 standard deviations) below the mean because

$$Z = \frac{1 - 7}{2} = -3$$

Figure 7.4 illustrates that the standard deviation is the unit of measurement. In other words, a time of 9 seconds is 2 seconds (1 standard deviation) higher, or *slower*, than the mean time of 7 seconds. Similarly, a time of 1 second is 6 seconds (3 standard deviations) lower, or *faster*, than the mean time.

To further illustrate the transformation formula, suppose that another website has a download time for a video that is normally distributed, with a mean $\mu = 4$ seconds and a standard deviation $\sigma = 1$ second. Figure 7.5 shows this distribution.

FIGURE 7.5
A different transformation of scales

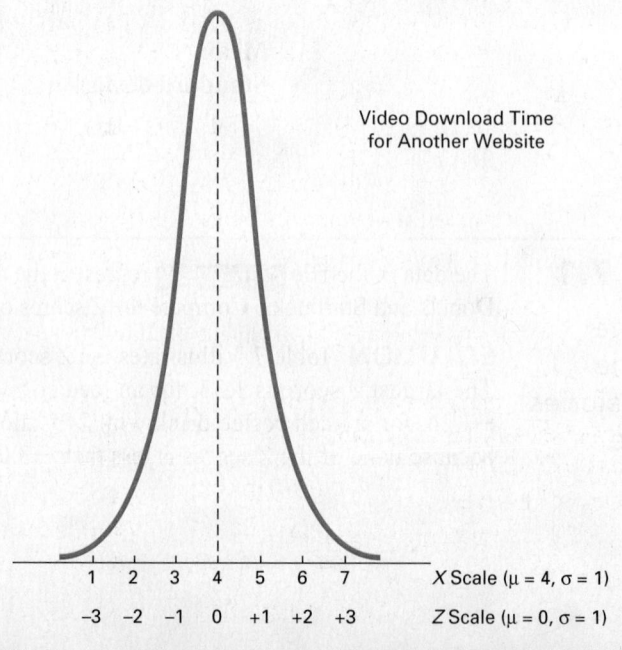

Comparing these results with those of the OurCampus! website, you see that a download time of 5 seconds is 1 standard deviation above the mean download time because

$$Z = \frac{5 - 4}{1} = +1$$

A time of 1 second is 3 standard deviations below the mean download time because

$$Z = \frac{1 - 4}{1} = -3$$

With the Z value computed, you look up the normal probability using a table of values from the cumulative standardized normal distribution, such as Table E.2 in Appendix E. Suppose you wanted to find the probability that the download time for the OurCampus! site is less than 9 seconds. Recall from page 288 that transforming $X = 9$ to standardized Z units, given a mean $\mu = 7$ seconds and a standard deviation $\sigma = 2$ seconds, leads to a Z value of +1.00.

With this value, you use Table E.2 to find the cumulative area under the normal curve less than (to the left of) $Z = +1.00$. To read the probability or area under the curve less than $Z = +1.00$, you scan down the Z column in Table E.2 until you locate the Z value of interest (in 10ths) in the Z row for 1.0. Next, you read across this row until you intersect the column that contains the 100ths place of the Z value. Therefore, in the body of the table, the probability for $Z = 1.00$ corresponds to the intersection of the row $Z = 1.0$ with the column $Z = .00$. Table 7.2, which reproduces a portion of Table E.2, shows this intersection. The probability listed at the intersection is 0.8413, which means that there is an 84.13% chance that the download time will be less than 9 seconds. Figure 7.6 graphically shows this probability.

TABLE 7.4

Finding a Cumulative Area Under the Normal Curve

					Cumulative Probabilities					
Z	.00	.01	.02	.03	.04	.05	.06	.07	.08	.09
0.0	.5000	.5040	.5080	.5120	.5160	.5199	.5239	.5279	.5319	.5359
0.1	.5398	.5438	.5478	.5517	.5557	.5596	.5636	.5675	.5714	.5753
0.2	.5793	.5832	.5871	.5910	.5948	.5987	.6026	.6064	.6103	.6141
0.3	.6179	.6217	.6255	.6293	.6331	.6368	.6406	.6443	.6480	.6517
0.4	.6554	.6591	.6628	.6664	.6700	.6736	.6772	.6808	.6844	.6879
0.5	.6915	.6950	.6985	.7019	.7054	.7088	.7123	.7157	.7190	.7224
0.6	.7257	.7291	.7324	.7357	.7389	.7422	.7454	.7486	.7518	.7549
0.7	.7580	.7612	.7642	.7673	.7704	.7734	.7764	.7794	.7823	.7852
0.8	.7881	.7910	.7939	.7967	.7995	.8023	.8051	.8078	.8106	.8133
0.9	.8159	.8186	.8212	.8238	.8264	.8289	.8315	.8340	.8365	.8389
1.0	.8413	.8438	.8461	.8485	.8508	.8531	.8554	.8577	.8599	.8621

Source: Extracted from Table E.2.

Finding Z Value Using the CASIO Calculator

To find a particular value, Z, associated with a known probability, mean and standard deviation, follow these calculator steps.

Select **STAT F5**(DIST) **F1**(NORM) **F3**(InvN) **F2**(Var), and then select the following options:

Inverse Normal
Data   : **Variable**
Tail   : **Left (F1)** OR **Right (F2)** OR **CNTR (F3)**
Area   :
σ :
μ :
Save Res : **None**
Execute
Now key **EXE** or **F1**(CALC).

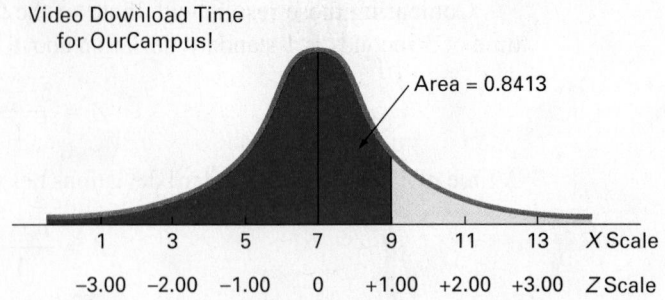

However, for the other website, you see that a time of 5 seconds is 1 standardized unit above the mean time of 4 seconds. Thus, the probability that the download time will be less than 5 seconds is also 0.8413. Figure 7.7 shows that regardless of the value of the mean, μ, and standard deviation, σ, of a normally distributed variable, Equation (7.2) can transform the X value to a Z value.

FIGURE 7.7
Demonstrating a transformation of scales for corresponding cumulative portions under two normal curves

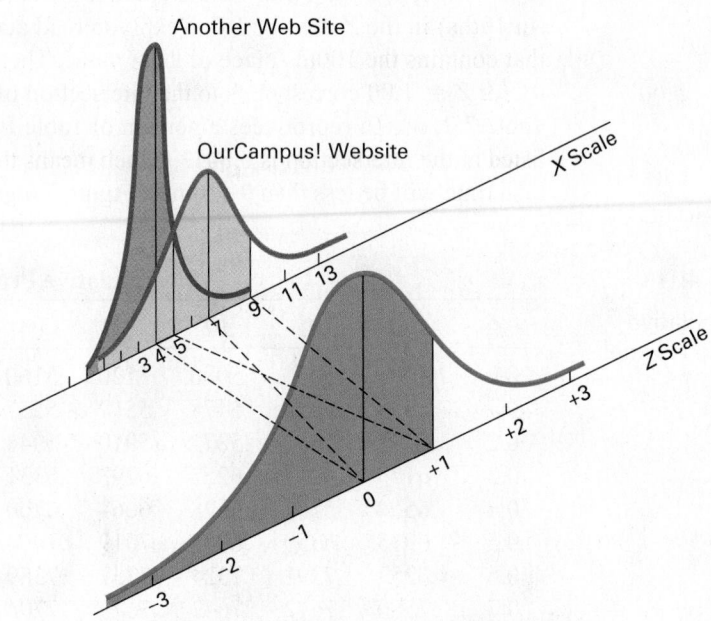

Now that you have learned to use Table E.2 with Equation (7.2), you can answer many questions related to the OurCampus! video download, using the normal distribution.

The Empirical Rule

In most data sets, a large portion of the values tend to cluster somewhere near the median. In right-skewed data sets, this clustering occurs to the left of the mean—that is, at a value less than the mean. In left-skewed data sets, the values tend to cluster to the right of the mean—that is, greater than the mean. In symmetrical data sets, where the median and mean are the same, the values often tend to cluster around the median and mean, producing a bell-shaped distribution. You can use the **empirical rule** to examine the variability in such distributions:

- Approximately 68% of the values are within a distance of ±1 standard deviation from the mean.
- Approximately 95% of the values are within a distance of ±2 standard deviations from the mean.
- Approximately 99.7% of the values are within a distance of ±3 standard deviations from the mean.

The empirical rule helps you measure how the values distribute above and below the mean and can help you identify outliers. The empirical rule implies that for bell-shaped distributions, only about 1 out of 20 values will be beyond two standard deviations from the mean in either direction. As a general rule, you can consider values not found in the interval $\mu \pm 2\sigma$ as potential outliers. The rule also implies that only about 3 in 1,000 will be beyond three standard deviations from the mean. Therefore, values not found in the interval $\mu \pm 3\sigma$ are almost always considered outliers.

EXAMPLE 7.2

Using the Empirical Rule

A population of 12-ounce cans of cola is known to have a mean fill-weight of 12.06 ounces and a standard deviation of 0.02. The population is known to be bell-shaped. Describe the distribution of fill-weights. Is it very likely that a can will contain less than 12 ounces of cola?

SOLUTION

$$\mu \pm \sigma = 12.06 \pm 0.02 = (12.04, 12.08)$$

$$\mu \pm 2\sigma = 12.06 \pm 2(0.02) = (12.02, 12.10)$$

$$\mu \pm 3\sigma = 12.06 \pm 3(0.02) = (12.00, 12.12)$$

Using the empirical rule, approximately 68% of the cans will contain between 12.04 and 12.08 ounces, approximately 95% will contain between 12.02 and 12.10 ounces, and approximately 99.7% will contain between 12.00 and 12.12 ounces. Therefore, it is highly unlikely that a can will contain less than 12 ounces.

For heavily skewed data sets, or those not appearing bell-shaped for any other reason, the Chebyshev rule discussed next should be applied instead of the empirical rule.

The Chebyshev Rule

The **Chebyshev rule** states that for any data set, regardless of shape, the percentage of values that are found within distances of k standard deviations from the mean must be at least

$$(1 - 1/k^2) \times 100\%$$

You can use this rule for any value of k greater than 1. Consider $k = 2$. The Chebyshev rule states that at least $[1 - (1/2)^2] \times 100\% = 75\%$ of the values must be found within ± 2 standard deviations of the mean.

The Chebyshev rule is very general and applies to any type of distribution. The rule indicates *at least* what percentage of the values fall within a given distance from the mean. However, if the data set is approximately bell-shaped, the empirical rule will more accurately reflect the greater concentration of data close to the mean. Table 7.5 compares the Chebyshev and empirical rules.

TABLE 7.5

How Data Vary Around the Mean

	% of Values Found in Intervals Around the Mean	
Interval	Chebyshev (any distribution)	Empirical Rule (bell-shaped distribution)
$(\mu - \sigma, \mu + \sigma)$	At least 0%	Approximately 68%
$(\mu - 2\sigma, \mu + 2\sigma)$	At least 75%	Approximately 95%
$(\mu - 3\sigma, \mu + 3\sigma)$	At least 88.89%	Approximately 99.7%

EXAMPLE 7.3

Using the Chebyshev Rule

A population of 12-ounce cans of cola is known to have a mean fill-weight of 12.06 ounces and a standard deviation of 0.02. However, the shape of the population is unknown, and you cannot assume that it is bell-shaped. Describe the distribution of fill-weights. Is it very likely that a can will contain less than 12 ounces of cola?

SOLUTION

$$\mu \pm \sigma = 12.06 \pm 0.02 = (12.04, 12.08)$$

$$\mu \pm 2\sigma = 12.06 \pm 2(0.02) = (12.02, 12.10)$$

$$\mu \pm 3\sigma = 12.06 \pm 3(0.02) = (12.00, 12.12)$$

Because the distribution may be skewed, you cannot use the empirical rule. Using the Chebyshev rule, you cannot say anything about the percentage of cans containing between 12.04 and 12.08 ounces. You can state that at least 75% of the cans will contain between 12.02 and 12.10 ounces and at least 88.89% will contain between 12.00 and 12.12 ounces. Therefore, between 0 and 11.11% of the cans will contain less than 12 ounces.

You can use these two rules for understanding how data are distributed around the mean when you have sample data. In each case, you use the value you calculated for $\overline{X}$ in place of μ and the value you calculated for S in place of σ. The results you compute using the sample statistics are *approximations* because you used sample statistics $(\overline{X}, S)$ and not population parameters (μ, σ).

EXAMPLE 7.4

Finding $P(X > 9)$

What is the probability that the video download time for the OurCampus! website will be at least 9 seconds?

SOLUTION The probability that the download time will be less than 9 seconds is 0.8413 (see Figure 7.6 on page 290). Thus, the probability that the download time will be at least 9 seconds is the *complement* of less than 9 seconds, $1 - 0.8413 = 0.1587$. Figure 7.8 illustrates this result.

FIGURE 7.8
Finding $P(X > 9)$

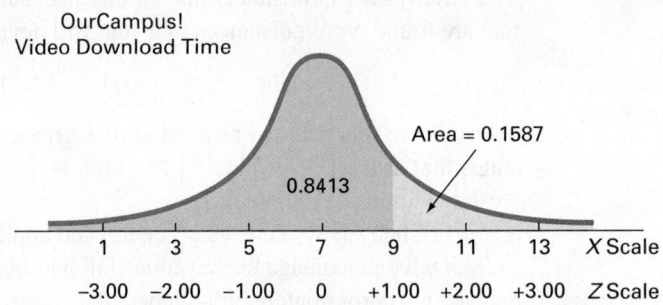

CASIO Calculator Instruction

Use the Casio calculator to find $P(X > 9)$.

Select **STAT F5**(DIST) **F1**(NORM) **F2**(Ncd) **F2**(Var), and then select the following options:

Normal C.D.
Data   : **Variable**
Lower   : 9
Upper   : **10000** (Note: The calculator will not accept "+ ∞." Therefore, you input a large positive number relative to its mean value.)
σ : 2
μ : 7
Save Res : **None**
Execute
Now key **EXE** or **F1**(CALC).

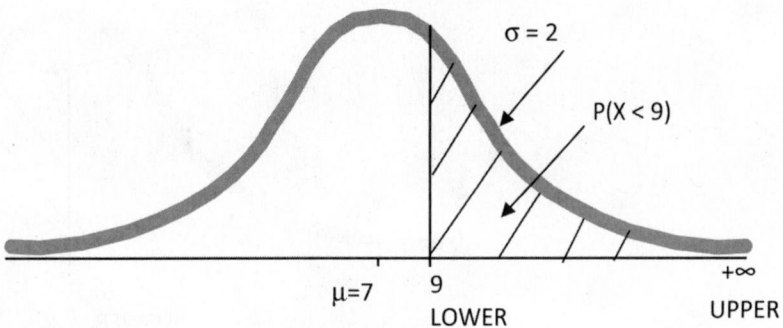

The calculator will now show the following result:

Normal C.D.
p = 0.15865525
z: Low = 1
z: Up   = 4996.5

Answer: The probability that the download time will be more than 9 seconds is 0.1587.

EXAMPLE 7.5
Finding
$P(X < 7$ or $X > 9)$

What is the probability that the video download time for the OurCampus! website will be under 7 seconds or over 9 seconds?

SOLUTION To find this probability, you separately calculate the probability of a download time less than 7 seconds and the probability of a download time greater than 9 seconds and then add these two probabilities together. Figure 7.9 illustrates this result. Because the mean is 7 seconds, 50% of download times are under 7 seconds. From Example 7.4, you know that the probability that the download time is greater than 9 seconds is 0.1587. Therefore, the probability that a download time is under 7 or over 9 seconds, $P(X < 7$ or $X > 9)$, is $0.5000 + 0.1587 = 0.6587$.

FIGURE 7.9
Finding
$P(X < 7$ or $X > 9)$

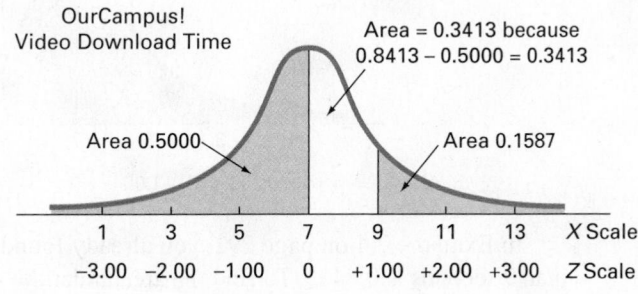

CASIO Calculator Instruction

Use the Casio calculator to find $P(7 < X < 9)$.

Select **STAT F5**(DIST) **F1**(NORM) **F2**(Ncd) **F2**(Var), and then select the following options:

Normal C.D.
Data   : **Variable**
Lower   : **7**
Upper   : **9**
σ : **2**
μ : **7**
Save Res : **None**
Execute
Now key **EXE** or **F1**(CALC).

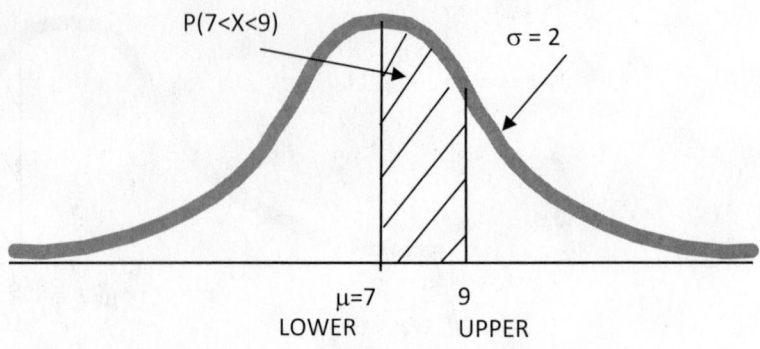

The calculator will now show the following result:

Normal C.D.
p = 0.34134474
z: Low = 0
z : Up = 1

Answer: The probability that the download time will be between 7 and 9 seconds is 0.3413.

EXAMPLE 7.6

Finding
$P(5 < X < 9)$

What is the probability that video download time for the OurCampus! website will be between 5 and 9 seconds—that is, $P(5 < X < 9)$?

SOLUTION In Figure 7.10, you can see that the area of interest is located between two values, 5 and 9.

FIGURE 7.10
Finding $P(5 < X < 9)$

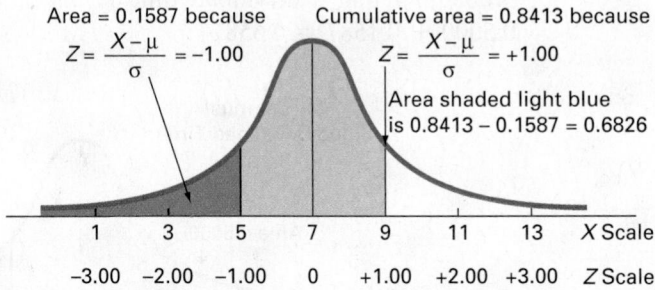

In Example 7.4 on page 292, you already found that the area under the normal curve less than 9 seconds is 0.8413. To find the area under the normal curve less than 5 seconds,

$$Z = \frac{5 - 7}{2} = -1.00$$

Using Table E.2, you look up $Z = -1.00$ and find 0.1587. Therefore, the probability that the download time will be between 5 and 9 seconds is $0.8413 - 0.1587 = 0.6826$, as displayed in Figure 7.10.

CASIO Calculator Instruction

Use the Casio calculator to find $P(X < 7)$ or $P(X > 9)$. You have to solve this problem in two stages. In stage 1 you solve for $P(X < 7)$, and in stage 2 you solve for $P(X > 9)$.

Stage 1: Solve for $P(X < 7)$.

Select **STAT F5**(DIST) **F1**(NORM) **F2**(Ncd) **F2**(Var), and then select the following options:

Normal C.D.
Data   : **Variable**
Lower   : **−10000** (Note: The calculator will not accept "- ∞." Therefore, you input a large negative number relative to its mean value.)
Upper   : **7**
σ   : 2
μ   : 7
Save Res : **None**
Execute
Now key **EXE** or **F1**(CALC).

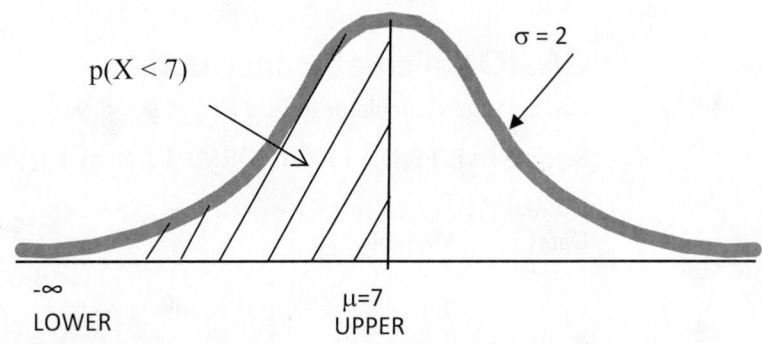

The calculator will now show the following result:

Normal C.D.
p = 0.5
z: Low = −5003.5
z : Up = 0

Answer: The probability that the download time is under 7 seconds is 0.5.

Stage 2: Solve for $P(X > 9)$.

Select **STAT F5**(DIST) **F1**(NORM) **F2**(Ncd) **F2**(Var), and then select the following options:

Normal C.D.
Data   : **Variable**
Lower   : 9
Upper   : **10000** (Note: The calculator will not accept "+ ∞." Therefore, you input a large positive number relative to its mean value.)
σ   : 2
μ   : **7**
Save Res : **None**
Execute
Now key **EXE** or **F1**(CALC).

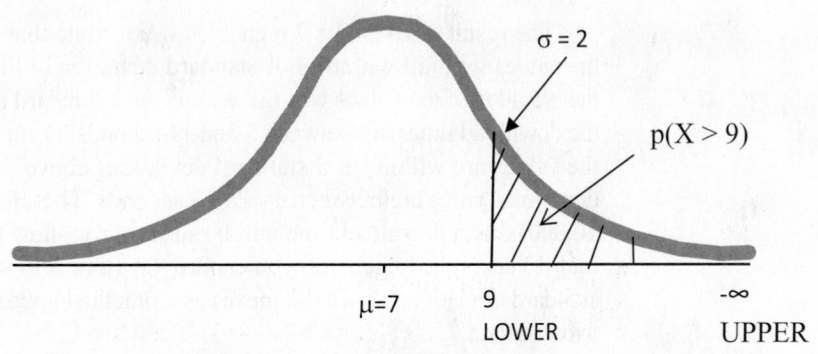

The calculator will now show the following result:

Normal C.D.
p = 0.15865525
z: Low = 1
z: Up   = 4996.5

Answer: The probability that the download time is over 9 seconds is 0.1587.

Hence, the probability that a download time is under 7 or over 9 seconds is 0.5 + 0.1587 = 0.6587.

CASIO Calculator Instruction

Use the Casio calculator to find $P(5 < X < 9)$.

Select **STAT F5**(DIST) **F1**(NORM) **F2**(Ncd) **F2**(Var), and then select the following options:

Normal C.D.
Data   : **Variable**
Lower   : **5**
Upper   : **9**
σ : **2**
μ : **7**
Save Res : **None**
Execute
Now key **EXE** or **F1**(CALC).

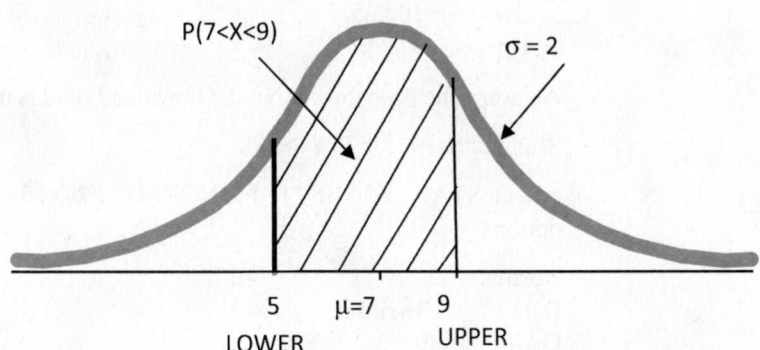

The calculator will now show the following result:

Normal C.D.
p = 0.68268949
z: Low = −1
z : Up = 1

Answer: The probability that the download time will be between 5 and 9 seconds is 0.6827.

   The result of Example 7.6 enables you to state that for any normal distribution, 68.26% of the values will fall within ± 1 standard deviation of the mean. From Figure 7.11, you can see that 95.44% of the values will fall within ± 2 standard deviations of the mean. Thus, 95.44% of the download times are between 3 and 11 seconds. From Figure 7.12, you can see that 99.73% of the values are within ± 3 standard deviations above or below the mean. Thus, 99.73% of the download times are between 1 and 13 seconds. Therefore, it is unlikely (0.0027, or only 27 in 10,000) that a download time will be so fast or so slow that it will take under 1 second or more than 13 seconds. In general, you can use 6σ (that is, 3 standard deviations below the mean to 3 standard deviations above the mean) as a practical approximation of the range for normally distributed data.

FIGURE 7.11
Finding $P(3 < X < 11)$

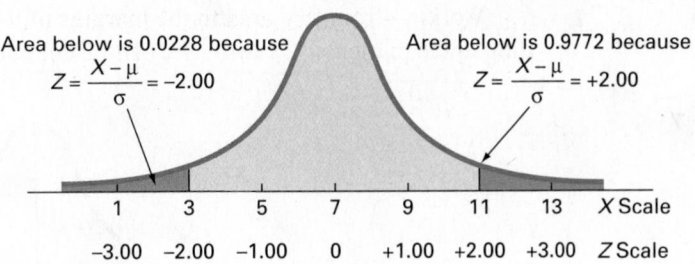

FIGURE 7.12
Finding $P(1 < X < 13)$

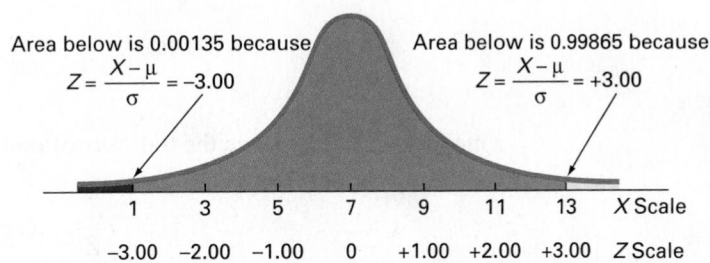

Figures 7.10, 7.11, and 7.12 illustrate that for any normal distribution,

- Approximately 68.26% of the values fall within ±1 standard deviation of the mean.
- Approximately 95.44% of the values fall within ±2 standard deviations of the mean.
- Approximately 99.73% of the values fall within ±3 standard deviations of the mean.

This result is the justification for the empirical rule. The accuracy of the empirical rule improves as a data set follows the normal distribution more closely.

Examples 7.4 through 7.6 require you to use the normal distribution Table E.2 to find an area under the normal curve that corresponds to a specific X value. There are many circumstances in which you want to find the X value that corresponds to a specific area. Examples 7.7 and 7.8 illustrate such situations.

Inverse Normal

Find x given the probability.

EXAMPLE 7.7

Finding the X Value for a Cumulative Probability of 0.10

How much time (in seconds) will elapse before the fastest 10% of the downloads of an Our-Campus! video are complete?

SOLUTION Because 10% of the videos are expected to download in under X seconds, the area under the normal curve less than this value is 0.1000. Using the body of Table E.2, you search for the area or probability of 0.1000. The closest result is 0.1003, as shown in Table 7.6 (which is extracted from Table E.2).

TABLE 7.6

Finding a Z Value Corresponding to a Particular Cumulative Area (0.10) Under the Normal Curve

				Cumulative Probabilities					
Z	.00	.01	.02	.03	.04	.05	.06	.07	.08	.09
⋮	⋮	⋮	⋮	⋮	⋮	⋮	⋮	⋮	⋮
−1.5	.0668	.0655	.0643	.0630	.0618	.0606	.0594	.0582	.0571	.0559
−1.4	.0808	.0793	.0778	.0764	.0749	.0735	.0721	.0708	.0694	.0681
−1.3	.0968	.0951	.0934	.0918	.0901	.0885	.0869	.0853	.0838	.0823
−1.2	.1151	.1131	.1112	.1093	.1075	.0156	.0138	.1020	.1003	.0985

Source: Extracted from Table E.2.

Working from this area to the margins of the table, you find that the Z value corresponding to the particular Z row (-1.2) and Z column ($.08$) is -1.28 (see Figure 7.13).

FIGURE 7.13

Finding Z to
determine X

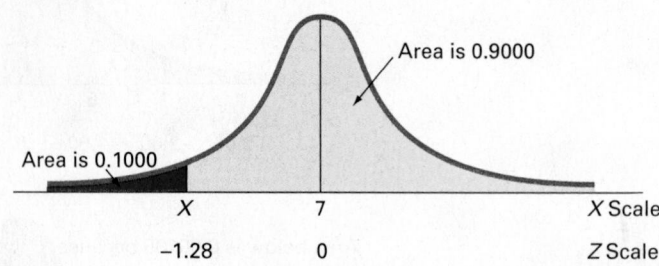

Once you find Z, you use the transformation formula Equation (7.2) on page 290 to determine the X value. Because

$$Z = \frac{X - \mu}{\sigma}$$

then

$$X = \mu + Z\sigma$$

Substituting $\mu = 7$, $\sigma = 2$, and $Z = -1.28$,

$$X = 7 + (-1.28)(2) = 4.44 \text{ seconds}$$

Thus, 10% of the download times are 4.44 seconds or less.

CASIO Calculator Instruction

Use the Casio calculator to obtain the inverse normal probability (i.e., find X given the probability).

Select **STAT F5**(DIST) **F1**(NORM) **F3**(InvN) **F2**(Var), and then select the following options:

Inverse Normal
Data   : **Variable**
Tail   : **Left (F1)** (Note: Left (F1), Right (F2), CNTR (F3))
Area   : **0.1**
σ : 2
μ : 7
Save Res   : **None**
Execute
Now key **EXE** or **F1**(CALC).

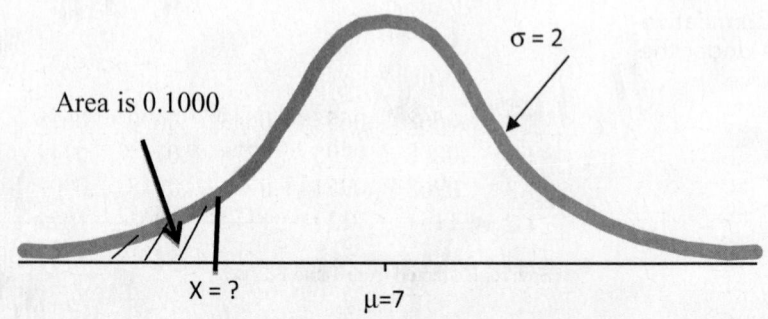

The calculator will now show the following result:

Inverse Normal
XInv= 4.43689687

Answer: 10% of the download times are 4.44 seconds or less.

Finding an X Value Associated with Known Probability Using the CASIO Calculator

To find a particular value, X, associated with a known probability, mean and standard deviation, follow these calculator steps.

Select **STAT F5**(DIST) **F1**(NORM) **F3**(InvN) **F2**(Var), and then select the following options:

Inverse Normal
Data   : **Variable**
Tail   : **Left (F1)** OR **Right (F2)** OR **CNTR (F3)**
Area   :
σ :
μ :
Save Res : **None**
Execute
Now key **EXE** or **F1**(CALC).

What are the lower and upper values of X, symmetrically distributed around the mean, that include 95% of the download times for a video at the OurCampus! website?

SOLUTION First, you need to find the lower value of X (called X_L). Then, you find the upper value of X (called X_U). Because 95% of the values are between X_L and X_U, and because X_L and X_U are equally distant from the mean, 2.5% of the values are below X_L (see Figure 7.14).

FIGURE 7.14

Finding Z to determine X_L

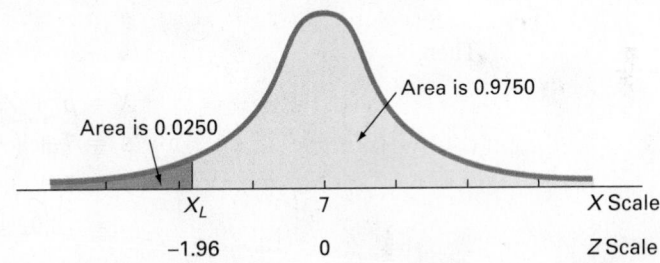

Although X_L is not known, you can find the corresponding Z value because the area under the normal curve less than this Z is 0.0250. Using the body of Table 7.7, you search for the probability 0.0250.

TABLE 7.7

Finding a Z Value Corresponding to a Cumulative Area of 0.025 Under the Normal Curve

					Cumulative Area					
Z	.00	.01	.02	.03	.04	.05	.06	.07	.08	.09
⋮	⋮	⋮	⋮	⋮	⋮	⋮	⋮	⋮	⋮	⋮
−2.0	.0228	.0222	.0217	.0212	.0207	.0202	.0197	.0192	.0188	.0183
−1.9	.0287	.0281	.0274	.0268	.0262	.0256	.0250	.0244	.0239	.0233
−1.8	.0359	.0351	.0344	.0336	.0329	.0232	.0314	.0307	.0301	.0294

Source: Extracted from Table E.2.

Working from the body of the table to the margins of the table, you see that the Z value corresponding to the particular Z row (-1.9) and Z column $(.06)$ is -1.96.

Once you find Z, the final step is as follows:

$$X = \mu + Z\sigma$$
$$= 7 + (-1.96)(2)$$
$$= 7 - 3.92$$
$$= 3.08 \text{ seconds}$$

You use a similar process to find X_U. Because only 2.5% of the video downloads take longer than X_U seconds, 97.5% of the video downloads take less than X_U seconds. From the symmetry of the normal distribution, you find that the desired Z value, as shown in Figure 7.15, is $+1.96$ (because Z lies to the right of the standardized mean of 0). You can also extract this Z value from Table 7.8. You can see that 0.975 is the area under the normal curve less than the Z value of $+1.96$.

FIGURE 7.15

Finding Z
to determine X_U

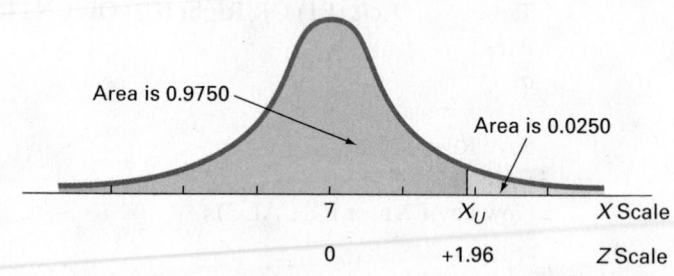

TABLE 7.8

Finding a Z Value
Corresponding to a
Cumulative Area
of 0.975 Under the
Normal Curve

					Cumulative Area					
Z	.00	.01	.02	.03	.04	.05	.06	.07	.08	.09
$\vdots$	$\vdots$	$\vdots$	$\vdots$	$\vdots$	$\vdots$	$\vdots$	$\vdots$	$\vdots$	$\vdots$	$\vdots$
+1.8	.9641	.9649	.9656	.9664	.9671	.9678	.9686	.9693	.9699	.9706
+1.9	.9713	.9719	.9726	.9732	.9738	.9744	.9750	.9756	.9761	.9767
+2.0	.9772	.9778	.9783	.9788	.9793	.9798	.9803	.9808	.9812	.9817

Source: Extracted from Table E.2.

Then,

$$X = \mu + Z\sigma$$
$$= 7 + (+1.96)(2)$$
$$= 7 + 3.92$$
$$= 10.92 \text{ seconds}$$

Therefore, 95% of the download times are between 3.08 and 10.92 seconds. Using Example 7.8, illustrate the calculator steps to obtain the lower and upper values of X.

FIGURE 7.16

Calculator steps for
computing inverse
normal probability

Question: What are the lower and upper values of X, symmetrically distributed around the mean, that include 95% of the download times?

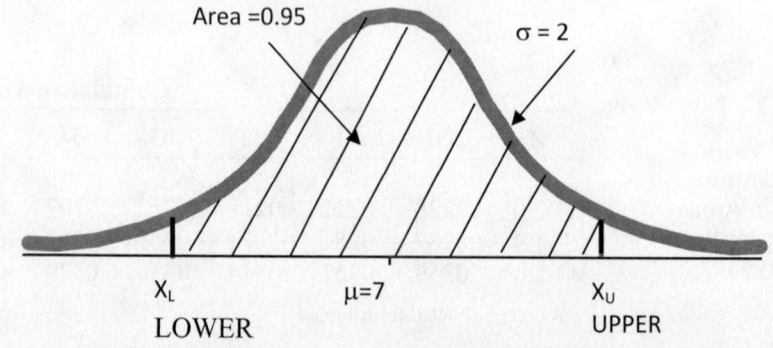

To find the values X_L and X_U associated with a known probability, $\mu = 7$ and $\sigma = 2$, follow these calculator steps.

Select **STAT** **F5**(DIST) **F1**(NORM) **F3**(InvN) **F2**(Var), and then select the following options:

Inverse Normal
Data   : **Variable**
Tail   : **CNTR (F3)**
Area   : **0.95**
σ : 2
μ : 7
Save Res : **None**
Execute
Now key **EXE** or **F1**(CALC).

The calculator will now show the following result:

Inverse Normal
X1 Inv = 3.08007203
X2 Inv = 10.919928

Answer: 95% of the download times are between 3.08 and 10.92 seconds.

Instead of looking up cumulative probabilities in a table, you can use Excel or Minitab to compute normal probabilities. Figure 7.17 is an Excel worksheet that computes normal probabilities for problems similar to Examples 7.4 through 7.7. Figure 7.18 shows Minitab results for Examples 7.4 and 7.7.

FIGURE 7.17
Excel worksheet for computing normal probabilities

	A	B	
1	**Normal Probabilities**		
3	**Common Data**		
4	Mean	7	
5	Standard Deviation	2	
7	**Probability for X <=**		
8	X Value	7	
9	Z Value	0	=STANDARDIZE(B8,B4,B5)
10	P(X<=7)	0.5000	=NORMDIST(B8,B4,B5,TRUE)
12	**Probability for X >**		
13	X Value	9	
14	Z Value	1	=STANDARDIZE(B13,B4,B5)
15	P(X>9)	0.1587	=1-NORMDIST(B13,B4,B5,TRUE)
17	**Probability for X<7 or X >9**		
18	P(X<7 or X >9)	0.6587	=B10+B15

	D	E	
6	**Probability for a Range**		
7	From X Value	5	
8	To X Value	9	
9	Z Value for 5	-1	=STANDARDIZE(E7,B4,B5)
10	Z Value for 9	1	=STANDARDIZE(E8,B4,B5)
11	P(X<=5)	0.1587	=NORMDIST(E7,B4,B5,TRUE)
12	P(X<=9)	0.8413	=NORMDIST(E8,B4,B5,TRUE)
13	P(5<=X<=9)	0.6827	=ABS(E12-E11)
15	**Find X and Z Given Cum. Pctage.**		
16	Cumulative Percentage	10.00%	
17	Z Value	-1.2816	=NORMSINV(E16)
18	X Value	4.4369	=NORMINV(E16,B4,B5)

FIGURE 7.18
Minitab results for Examples 7.4 and 7.7

Cumulative Distribution Function
Normal with mean = 7 and standard deviation = 2
x   P(X <= x)
9   0.841345

Inverse Cumulative Distribution Function
Normal with mean = 7 and standard deviation = 2
P(X <= x)   x
0.1   4.43690

THINK ABOUT THIS   What Is Normal?

Ironically, the statistician who popularized the use of "normal" to describe the distribution discussed in Section 7.2 was someone who saw the distribution as anything but the everyday, anticipated occurrence that the adjective *normal* usually suggests.

Starting with an 1894 paper, Karl Pearson argued that measurements of phenomena do not naturally, or "normally," conform to the classic bell shape. While this principle underlies statistics today, Pearson's point of view was radical to contemporaries who saw the world as standardized and normal. Pearson changed minds by showing that some populations are naturally *skewed* (coining that term in passing), and he helped put to rest the notion that the normal distribution underlies all phenomena.

Today, unfortunately, people still make the type of mistake that Pearson refuted. As a student, you are probably familiar with discussions about grade inflation, a real phenomenon at many schools. But, have you ever realized that a "proof" of this inflation—that there are "too few" low grades because grades are skewed toward A's and B's—wrongly implies that grades should be "normally" distributed. By the time you finish reading this book, you may realize that because college students represent small nonrandom samples, there are plenty of reasons to suspect that the distribution of grades would not be "normal."

Misunderstandings about the normal distribution have occurred both in business and in the public sector through the years. These misunderstandings have caused a number of business blunders and have sparked several public policy debates, including the causes of the collapse of large financial institutions in 2008. According to one theory, the investment banking industry's application of the normal distribution to assess risk may have contributed to the global collapse (see "A Finer Formula for Assessing Risks," *The New York Times*, May 11, 2010, p. B2). Using the normal distribution led these banks to overestimate the probability of having stable market conditions and underestimate the chance of unusually large market losses. According to this theory, the use of other distributions that have less area in the middle of their curves, and, therefore, more in the "tails" that represent unusual market outcomes, may have led to less serious losses.

As you study this chapter, make sure you understand the assumptions that must hold for the proper use of the "normal" distribution, assumptions that were not explicitly verified by the investment bankers. And, most importantly, always remember that the name *normal* distribution does not mean normal in the everyday sense of the word.

VISUAL EXPLORATIONS   Exploring the Normal Distribution

Use the Visual Explorations Normal Distribution procedure to see the effects of changes in the mean and standard deviation on the area under a normal distribution curve. Open the **Visual Explorations add-in workbook** (see Appendix Section D.4). Select **Add-ins → VisualExplorations → Normal Distribution.**

The add-in displays a normal curve for the OurCampus! download example and a floating control panel (see illustration at right). Use the control panel spinner buttons to change the values for the mean, standard deviation, and X value and note the effects of these changes on the probability of $X <$ value and the corresponding shaded area under the curve (see illustration at right). If you prefer to see the normal curve labeled with Z values, click **Z Values.**

Click the **Reset** button to reset the control panel values or click **Help** for additional information about the problem. Click **Finish** when you are done exploring.

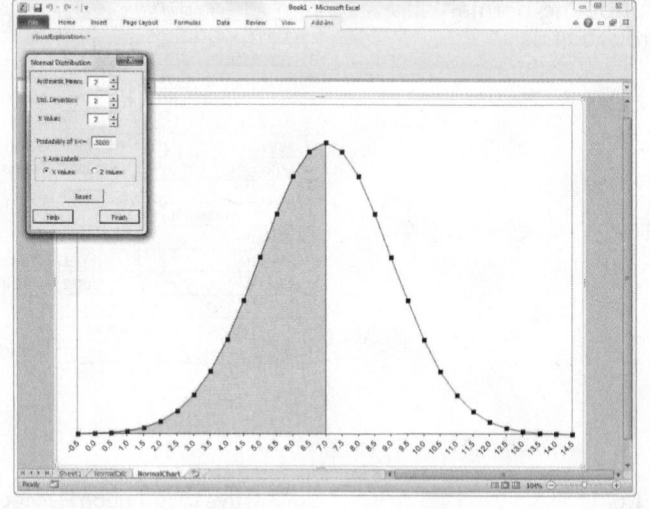

Problems for Section 7.3

LEARNING THE BASICS

7.14 Given a standardized normal distribution (with a mean of 0 and a standard deviation of 1, as in Table E.2), what is the probability that
a. Z is less than 1.57?
b. Z is greater than 1.84?
c. Z is between 1.57 and 1.84?
d. Z is less than 1.57 or greater than 1.84?

7.15 Given a standardized normal distribution (with a mean of 0 and a standard deviation of 1, as in Table E.2), what is the probability that
a. Z is between -1.57 and 1.84?
b. Z is less than -1.57 or greater than 1.84?
c. What is the value of Z if only 2.5% of all possible Z values are larger?
d. Between what two values of Z (symmetrically distributed around the mean) will 68.26% of all possible Z values be contained?

7.16 Given a standardized normal distribution (with a mean of 0 and a standard deviation of 1, as in Table E.2), what is the probability that
a. Z is less than 1.08?
b. Z is greater than -0.21?
c. Z is less than -0.21 or greater than the mean?
d. Z is less than -0.21 or greater than 1.08?

7.17 Given a standardized normal distribution (with a mean of 0 and a standard deviation of 1, as in Table E.2), determine the following probabilities:
a. $P(Z > 1.08)$
b. $P(Z < -0.21)$
c. $P(-1.96 < Z < -0.21)$
d. What is the value of Z if only 15.87% of all possible Z values are larger?

7.18 Given a normal distribution with $\mu = 100$ and $\sigma = 10$, what is the probability that
a. $X > 75$?
b. $X < 70$?
c. $X < 80$ or $X > 110$?
d. Between what two X values (symmetrically distributed around the mean) are 80% of the values?

7.19 Given a normal distribution with $\mu = 50$ and $\sigma = 4$, what is the probability that
a. $X > 43$?
b. $X < 42$?
c. 5% of the values are less than what X value?
d. Between what two X values (symmetrically distributed around the mean) are 60% of the values?

APPLYING THE CONCEPTS

7.20 In 2008, the per capita consumption of coffee in the United States was reported to be 4.2 kg, or 9.24 pounds (data extracted from **en.wikipedia.org/wiki/List_of_countries_by_coffee_consumption_per_capita**). Assume that the per capita consumption of coffee in the United States is approximately distributed as a normal random variable, with a mean of 9.24 pounds and a standard deviation of 3 pounds.
a. What is the probability that someone in the United States consumed more than 10 pounds of coffee in 2008?
b. What is the probability that someone in the United States consumed between 3 and 5 pounds of coffee in 2008?
c. What is the probability that someone in the United States consumed less than 5 pounds of coffee in 2008?
d. 99% of the people in the United States consumed less than how many pounds of coffee?

SELF Test **7.21** Toby's Trucking Company determined that the distance traveled per truck per year is normally distributed, with a mean of 50 thousand miles and a standard deviation of 12 thousand miles.
a. What proportion of trucks can be expected to travel between 34 and 50 thousand miles in a year?
b. What percentage of trucks can be expected to travel either below 30 or above 60 thousand miles in a year?
c. How many miles will be traveled by at least 80% of the trucks?
d. What are your answers to (a) through (c) if the standard deviation is 10 thousand miles?

7.22 Consumers spend an average of $21 per week in cash without being aware of where it goes (data extracted from "Snapshots: A Hole in Our Pockets," *USA Today*, January 18, 2010, p. 1A). Assume that the amount of cash spent without being aware of where it goes is normally distributed and that the standard deviation is $5.
a. What is the probability that a randomly selected person will spend more than $25?
b. What is the probability that a randomly selected person will spend between $10 and $20?
c. Between what two values will the middle 95% of the amounts of cash spent fall?

7.23 A set of final examination grades in an introductory statistics course is normally distributed, with a mean of 73 and a standard deviation of 8.
a. What is the probability that a student scored below 91 on this exam?
b. What is the probability that a student scored between 65 and 89?
c. The probability is 5% that a student taking the test scores higher than what grade?

d. If the professor grades on a curve (i.e., gives A's to the top 10% of the class, regardless of the score), are you better off with a grade of 81 on this exam or a grade of 68 on a different exam, where the mean is 62 and the standard deviation is 3? Show your answer statistically and explain.

7.24 A statistical analysis of 1,000 long-distance telephone calls made from the headquarters of the Bricks and Clicks Computer Corporation indicates that the length of these calls is normally distributed, with $\mu = 240$ seconds and $\sigma = 40$ seconds.
a. What is the probability that a call lasted less than 180 seconds?
b. What is the probability that a call lasted between 180 and 300 seconds?
c. What is the probability that a call lasted between 110 and 180 seconds?
d. 1% of all calls will last less than how many seconds?

7.25 In 2008, the per capita consumption of coffee in Sweden was reported to be 8.2 kg, or 18.04 pounds (data extracted from **en.wikipedia.org/wiki/List_of_countries_by_coffee_consumption_per_capita**). Assume that the per capita consumption of coffee in Sweden is approximately distributed as a normal random variable, with a mean of 18.04 pounds and a standard deviation of 5 pounds.
a. What is the probability that someone in Sweden consumed more than 10 pounds of coffee in 2008?
b. What is the probability that someone in Sweden consumed between 3 and 5 pounds of coffee in 2008?
c. What is the probability that someone in Sweden consumed less than 5 pounds of coffee in 2008?
d. 99% of the people in Sweden consumed less than how many pounds of coffee?

7.26 Many manufacturing problems involve the matching of machine parts, such as shafts that fit into a valve hole. A particular design requires a shaft with a diameter of 22.000 mm, but shafts with diameters between 21.990 mm and 22.010 mm are acceptable. Suppose that the manufacturing process yields shafts with diameters normally distributed, with a mean of 22.002 mm and a standard deviation of 0.005 mm. For this process, what is
a. the proportion of shafts with a diameter between 21.99 mm and 22.00 mm?
b. the probability that a shaft is acceptable?
c. the diameter that will be exceeded by only 2% of the shafts?
d. What would be your answers in (a) through (c) if the standard deviation of the shaft diameters were 0.004 mm?

7.4 Evaluating Normality

As discussed in Section 7.3, many continuous variables used in business closely follow a normal distribution. To determine whether a set of data can be approximated by the normal distribution, you either compare the characteristics of the data with the theoretical properties of the normal distribution or construct a normal probability plot.

Comparing Data Characteristics to Theoretical Properties

The normal distribution has several important theoretical properties:

- It is symmetrical; thus, the mean and median are equal.
- It is bell-shaped; thus, the empirical rule applies.
- The interquartile range equals 1.33 standard deviations.
- The range is approximately equal to 6 standard deviations.

Many continuous variables have characteristics that approximate these theoretical properties. However, other continuous variables are often neither normally distributed nor approximately normally distributed. For such variables, the descriptive characteristics of the data are inconsistent with the properties of a normal distribution. One approach that you can use to determine whether a variable follows a normal distribution is to compare the observed characteristics of the variable with what would be expected if the variable followed a normal distribution. To do so, you can

- Construct charts and observe their appearance. For small- or moderate-sized data sets, create a stem-and-leaf display or a boxplot. For large data sets, in addition, plot a histogram or polygon.
- Compute descriptive statistics and compare these statistics with the theoretical properties of the normal distribution. Compare the mean and median. Is the interquartile range

approximately 1.33 times the standard deviation? Is the range approximately 6 times the standard deviation?

- Evaluate how the values are distributed. Determine whether approximately two-thirds of the values lie between the mean and ±1 standard deviation. Determine whether approximately four-fifths of the values lie between the mean and ±1.28 standard deviations. Determine whether approximately 19 out of every 20 values lie between the mean and ±2 standard deviations.

For example, you can use these techniques to determine whether the returns in 2009 (stored in Bond Funds) follow a normal distribution. Figures 7.19 and 7.20 display relevant Excel results for these data, and Figure 7.21 displays a Minitab boxplot for the same data.

FIGURE 7.19

Descriptive statistics for the 2009 returns

Return 2009	
Mean	7.1641
Standard Error	0.4490
Median	6.4000
Mode	6.0000
Standard Deviation	6.0908
Sample Variance	37.0984
Kurtosis	2.4560
Skewness	0.9085
Range	40.8000
Minimum	-8.8000
Maximum	32.0000
Sum	1318.2000
Count	184

FIGURE 7.20

Five-number summary and boxplot for the 2009 returns

Five-Number Summary	
Minimum	-8.8
First Quartile	3.4
Median	6.4
Third Quartile	10.8
Maximum	32

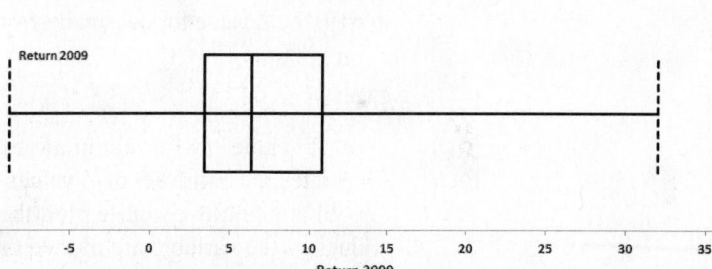

FIGURE 7.21

Minitab boxplot

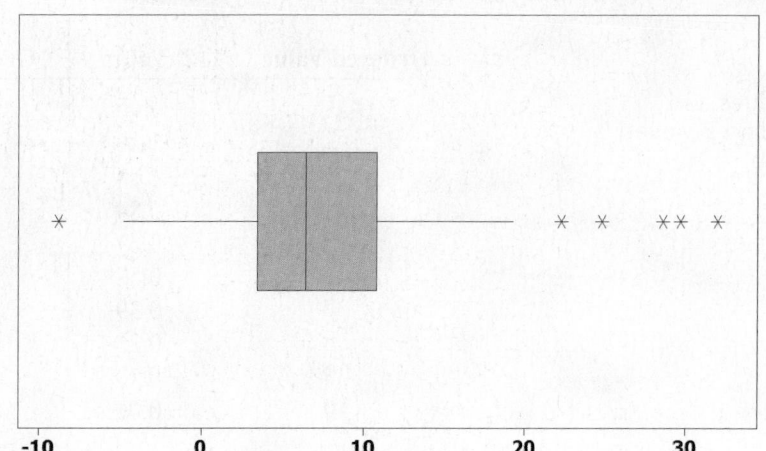

Boxplot for Bond Funds 2009 Returns

From Figures 7.19 through 7.21, and from an ordered array of the returns (not shown here), you can make the following statements:

- The mean of 7.1641 is greater than the median of 6.4. (In a normal distribution, the mean and median are equal.)
- The boxplot is very right-skewed, with a long tail on the right. (The normal distribution is symmetrical.)
- The interquartile range of 7.4 is approximately 1.21 standard deviations. (In a normal distribution, the interquartile range is 1.33 standard deviations.)
- The range of 40.8 is equal to 6.70 standard deviations. (In a normal distribution, the range is approximately 6 standard deviations.)
- 73.91% of the returns are within ±1 standard deviation of the mean. (In a normal distribution, 68.26% of the values lie within ±1 standard deviation of the mean.)
- 85.33% of the returns are within ±1.28 standard deviations of the mean. (In a normal distribution, 80% of the values lie within ±1.28 standard deviations of the mean.)
- 96.20% of the returns are within ±2 standard deviations of the mean. (In a normal distribution, 95.44% of the values lie within ±2 standard deviations of the mean.)
- The skewness statistic is 0.9085 and the kurtosis statistic is 2.456. (In a normal distribution, each of these statistics equals zero.)

Based on these statements and the criteria given on pages 304–305, you can conclude that the 2009 returns are highly right-skewed and have somewhat more values within ±1 standard deviation of the mean than expected. The range is higher than what would be expected in a normal distribution, but this is mostly due to the single outlier at 32. Primarily because of the skewness, you can conclude that the data characteristics of the 2009 returns differ from the theoretical properties of a normal distribution.

Constructing the Normal Probability Plot

A **normal probability plot** is a visual display that helps you evaluate whether the data are normally distributed. One common plot is called the **quantile–quantile plot**. To create this plot, you first transform each ordered value to a Z value. For example, if you have a sample of $n = 19$, the Z value for the smallest value corresponds to a cumulative area of

$$\frac{1}{n+1} = \frac{1}{19+1} = \frac{1}{20} = 0.05.$$

The Z value for a cumulative area of 0.05 (from Table E.2) is -1.65. Table 7.9 illustrates the entire set of Z values for a sample of $n = 19$.

In a quantile–quantile plot, the Z values are plotted on the X axis, and the corresponding values of the variable are plotted on the Y axis. If the data are normally distributed, the values will plot along an approximately straight line.

TABLE 7.9

Ordered Values and Corresponding Z Values for a Sample of $n = 19$

Ordered Value	Z Value	Ordered Value	Z Value
1	−1.65	11	0.13
2	−1.28	12	0.25
3	−1.04	13	0.39
4	−0.84	14	0.52
5	−0.67	15	0.67
6	−0.52	16	0.84
7	−0.39	17	1.04
8	−0.25	18	1.28
9	−0.13	19	1.65
10	−0.00		

Figure 7.22 illustrates the typical shape of the quantile–quantile normal probability plot for a left-skewed distribution (Panel A), a normal distribution (Panel B), and a right-skewed distribution (Panel C). If the data are left-skewed, the curve will rise more rapidly at first and then level off. If the data are normally distributed, the points will plot along an approximately straight line. If the data are right-skewed, the data will rise more slowly at first and then rise at a faster rate for higher values of the variable being plotted.

FIGURE 7.22

Normal probability plots for a left-skewed distribution, a normal distribution, and a right-skewed distribution

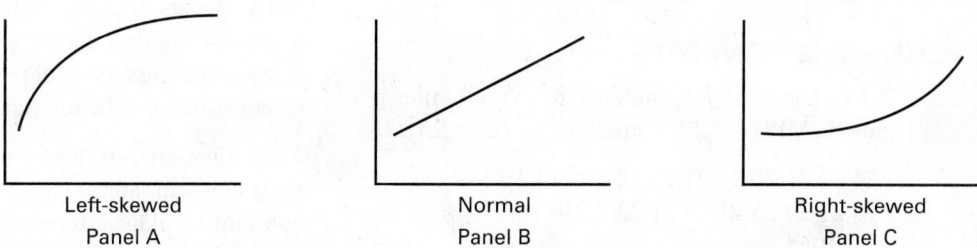

| Left-skewed | Normal | Right-skewed |
| Panel A | Panel B | Panel C |

Figure 7.23 shows a normal probability plot for the 2009 returns as created using Excel (left results, a quantile–quantile plot) and Minitab (right results). The Excel quantile–quantile plot shows that the 2009 returns rise slowly at first and then rise more rapidly. Therefore, you can conclude that the 2009 returns are right-skewed.

The Minitab normal probability plot has the Return 2009 variable on the X axis and the cumulative percentage for a normal distribution on the Y axis. As is the case with the quantile–quantile plot, if the data are normally distributed, the points will plot along an approximately

FIGURE 7.23

Excel (quantile–quantile) and Minitab normal probability plots for 2009 returns

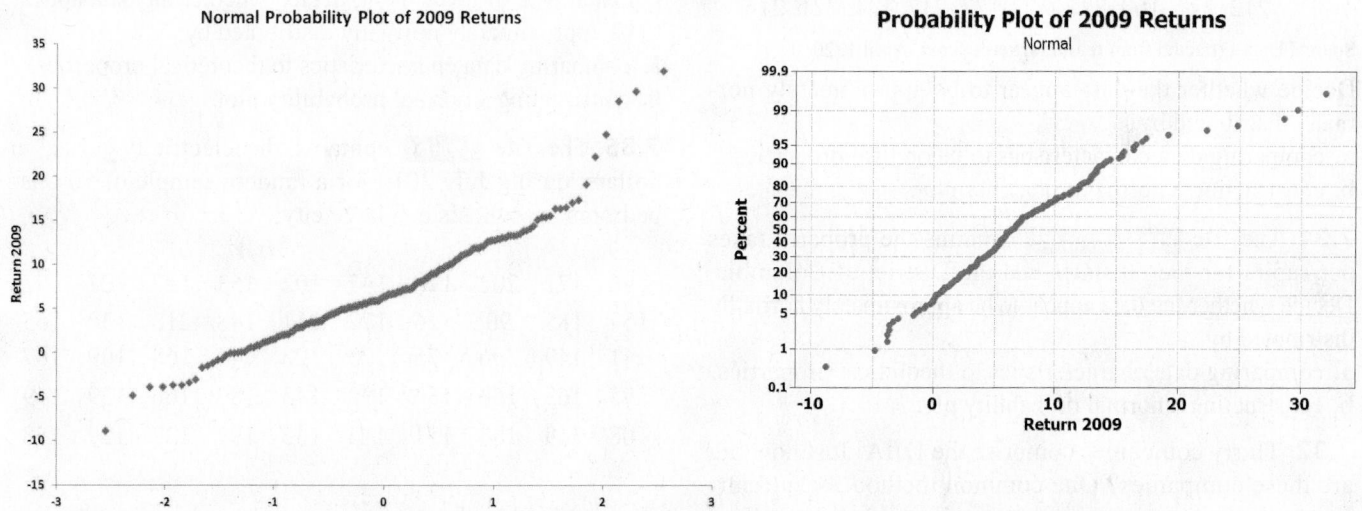

straight line. However, if the data are right-skewed, the curve will rise more rapidly at first and then level off. If the data are left-skewed, the data will rise more slowly at first and then rise at a faster rate for higher values of the variable being plotted. Observe that the values rise more rapidly at first and then level off, indicating a right-skewed distribution.

Problems for Section 7.4

LEARNING THE BASICS

7.27 Show that for a sample of $n = 39$, the smallest and largest Z values are -1.96 and $+1.96$, and the middle (i.e., 20th) Z value is 0.00.

7.28 For a sample of $n = 6$, list the six Z values.

APPLYING THE CONCEPTS

 7.29 The file **SUV** contains the overall miles per gallon (MPG) of 2011 small SUVs ($n = 25$):

> 20 24 22 23 20 22 21 22 22 19 22 22 26
> 19 19 23 24 21 21 19 21 22 22 16 16

Source: Data extracted from "Ratings," *Consumer Reports,* April 2011, pp. 35–36.

Decide whether the data appear to be approximately normally distributed by
a. comparing data characteristics to theoretical properties.
b. constructing a normal probability plot.

7.30 As player salaries have increased, the cost of attending baseball games has increased dramatically. The file **BBCost 2010** contains the cost of four tickets, two beers, four soft drinks, four hot dogs, two game programs, two baseball caps, and the parking fee for one car for each of the 30 Major League Baseball teams in 2010:

> 172, 335, 250, 180, 173, 162, 132, 207, 316, 178,
> 184, 141, 168, 208, 115, 158, 330, 151, 161, 170,
> 212, 222, 160, 227, 227, 127, 217, 121, 221, 216

Source: Data extracted from **teammarketing.com**, April 1, 2010.

Decide whether the data appear to be approximately normally distributed by
a. comparing data characteristics to theoretical properties.
b. constructing a normal probability plot.

7.31 The file **PropertyTaxes** contains the property taxes per capita for the 50 states and the District of Columbia. Decide whether the data appear to be approximately normally distributed by
a. comparing data characteristics to theoretical properties.
b. constructing a normal probability plot.

7.32 Thirty companies comprise the DJIA. Just how big are these companies? One common method for measuring the size of a company is to use its market capitalization, which is computed by multiplying the number of stock shares by the price of a share of stock. On April 8, 2011, the market capitalization of these companies ranged from Alcoa's \$19.2 billion to ExxonMobil's \$426.4 billion. The entire population of market capitalization values is stored in **DowMarketCap**.

Source: Data extracted from **money.cnn.com**, April 8, 2011.

Decide whether the market capitalization of companies in the DJIA appears to be approximately normally distributed by
a. comparing data characteristics to theoretical properties.
b. constructing a normal probability plot.
c. constructing a histogram.

7.33 One operation of a mill is to cut pieces of steel into parts that will later be used as the frame for front seats in an automotive plant. The steel is cut with a diamond saw, and the resulting parts must be within ± 0.005 inch of the length specified by the automobile company. The data come from a sample of 100 steel parts and are stored in **Steel**. The measurement reported is the difference, in inches, between the actual length of the steel part, as measured by a laser measurement device, and the specified length of the steel part. Determine whether the data appear to be approximately normally distributed by
a. comparing data characteristics to theoretical properties.
b. constructing a normal probability plot.

7.34 The file **CDRate** contains the yields for a one-year certificate of deposit (CD) and a five-year certificate of deposit (CD) for 23 banks in the United States, as of April 4, 2011.

Source: Data extracted from **www.Bankrate.com**, April 4, 2011.

For each type of investment, decide whether the data appear to be approximately normally distributed by
a. comparing data characteristics to theoretical properties.
b. constructing a normal probability plot.

7.35 The file **Utility** contains the electricity costs, in dollars, during July 2010 for a random sample of 50 one-bedroom apartments in a large city:

96	171	202	178	147	102	153	197	127	82
157	185	90	116	172	111	148	213	130	165
141	149	206	175	123	128	144	168	109	167
95	163	150	154	130	143	187	166	139	149
108	119	183	151	114	135	191	137	129	158

Decide whether the data appear to be approximately normally distributed by
a. comparing data characteristics to theoretical properties.
b. constructing a normal probability plot.

USING STATISTICS @ OurCampus! Revisited

Lee Morris / Shutterstock.com

In the OurCampus! scenario, you were a designer for a social networking website. You sought to ensure that a video could be downloaded quickly for playback in the web browsers of site visitors. (Quick playback of videos would help attract and retain those visitors.) By running experiments in the corporate offices, you determined that the amount of time, in seconds, that passes from first linking to the website until a video is fully displayed is a bell-shaped distribution with a mean download time of 7 seconds and standard deviation of 2 seconds. Using the normal distribution, you were able to calculate that approximately 84% of the download times are 9 seconds or less, and 95% of the download times are between 3.08 and 10.92 seconds.

Now that you understand how to calculate probabilities from the normal distribution, you can evaluate download times of a video using different web page designs. For example, if the standard deviation remained at 2 seconds, lowering the mean to 6 seconds would shift the entire distribution lower by 1 second. Thus, approximately 84% of the download times would be 8 seconds or less, and 95% of the download times would be between 2.08 and 9.92 seconds. Another change that could reduce long download times would be reducing the variation. For example, consider the case where the mean remained at the original 7 seconds but the standard deviation was reduced to 1 second. Again, approximately 84% of the download times would be 8 seconds or less, and 95% of the download times would be between 5.04 and 8.96 seconds.

SUMMARY

In this and the previous chapter, you have learned about mathematical models called probability distributions and how they can be used to solve business problems. In Chapter 6, you used discrete probability distributions in situations where the outcomes come from a counting process (e.g., the number of courses you are enrolled in, the number of tagged order forms in a report generated by an accounting information system). In this chapter, you learned about continuous probability distributions where the outcomes come from a measuring process (e.g., your height, the download time of a video). Continuous probability distributions come in various shapes, but the most common and most important in business is the normal distribution. The normal distribution is symmetrical; thus, its mean and median are equal. It is also bell-shaped, and approximately 68.26% of its observations are within 1 standard deviation of the mean, approximately 95.44% of its observations are within 2 standard deviations of the mean, and approximately 99.73% of its observations are within 3 standard deviations of the mean. Although many data sets in business are closely approximated by the normal distribution, do not think that all data can be approximated using the normal distribution. In Section 7.4, you learned about various methods for evaluating normality in order to determine whether the normal distribution is a reasonable mathematical model to use in specific situations.

Chapter 8 uses the normal distribution to develop the subject of statistical inference.

KEY EQUATIONS

Normal Probability Density Function

$$f(X) = \frac{1}{\sqrt{2\pi\sigma}} e^{-(1/2)[(X-\mu)/\sigma]^2}$$

Transformation Formula

$$Z = \frac{X - \mu}{\sigma}$$

Finding an X Value Associated with a Known Probability

$$X = \mu + Z\sigma$$

KEY TERMS

Chebyshev Rule   291
cumulative standardized normal
    distribution   286
empirical rule   290
normal distribution   280

normal probability plot   306
probability density function   280
probability density function for the
    normal distribution   282

quantile–quantile plot   306
standardized normal random
    variable   286
transformation formula   286

PROBLEMS

CHECKING YOUR UNDERSTANDING

7.36 Why is only one normal distribution table such as Table E.2 needed to find any probability under the normal curve?

7.37 How do you find the area between two values under the normal curve?

7.38 How do you find the X value that corresponds to a given percentile of the normal distribution?

7.39 What are some of the distinguishing properties of a normal distribution?

7.40 How does the shape of the normal distribution differ from the shapes of the uniform and exponential distributions?

7.41 How can you use the normal probability plot to evaluate whether a set of data is normally distributed?

APPLYING THE CONCEPTS

7.42 An industrial sewing machine uses ball bearings that are targeted to have a diameter of 0.75 inch. The lower and upper specification limits under which the ball bearings can operate are 0.74 inch and 0.76 inch, respectively. Past experience has indicated that the actual diameter of the ball bearings is approximately normally distributed, with a mean of 0.753 inch and a standard deviation of 0.004 inch. What is the probability that a ball bearing is
a. between the target and the actual mean?
b. between the lower specification limit and the target?
c. above the upper specification limit?
d. below the lower specification limit?
e. Of all the ball bearings, 93% of the diameters are greater than what value?

7.43 The fill amount in 2-liter soft drink bottles is normally distributed, with a mean of 2.0 liters and a standard deviation of 0.05 liter. If bottles contain less than 95% of the listed net content (1.90 liters, in this case), the manufacturer may be subject to penalty by the state office of consumer affairs. Bottles that have a net content above 2.10 liters may cause excess spillage upon opening. What proportion of the bottles will contain
a. between 1.90 and 2.0 liters?
b. between 1.90 and 2.10 liters?
c. below 1.90 liters or above 2.10 liters?
d. At least how much soft drink is contained in 99% of the bottles?
e. 99% of the bottles contain an amount that is between which two values (symmetrically distributed) around the mean?

7.44 In an effort to reduce the number of bottles that contain less than 1.90 liters, the bottler in Problem 6.43 sets the filling machine so that the mean is 2.02 liters. Under these circumstances, what are your answers in Problem 6.43 (a) through (e)?

7.45 An orange juice producer buys all his oranges from a large orange grove. The amount of juice squeezed from each of these oranges is approximately normally distributed, with a mean of 4.70 ounces and a standard deviation of 0.40 ounce.
a. What is the probability that a randomly selected orange will contain between 4.70 and 5.00 ounces of juice?
b. What is the probability that a randomly selected orange will contain between 5.00 and 5.50 ounces of juice?
c. At least how many ounces of juice will 77% of the oranges contain?
d. 80% of the oranges contain between what two values (in ounces of juice), symmetrically distributed around the population mean?

7.46 The file **DomesticBeer** contains the percentage alcohol, number of calories per 12 ounces, and number of carbohydrates (in grams) per 12 ounces for 145 of the best-selling domestic beers in the United States. For each of the three variables, decide whether the data appear to be approximately normally distributed. Support your decision through the use of appropriate statistics and graphs.
Source: Data extracted from **www.Beer100.com**, April 1, 2011.

7.47 The evening manager of a restaurant was very concerned about the length of time some customers were waiting in line to be seated. She also had some concern about the seating times—that is, the length of time between when a customer is seated and the time he or she leaves the restaurant. Over the course of one week, 100 customers (no more than 1 per party) were randomly selected, and their waiting and seating times (in minutes) were recorded in **Wait**.
a. Think about your favorite restaurant. Do you think waiting times more closely resemble a uniform, an exponential, or a normal distribution?
b. Again, think about your favorite restaurant. Do you think seating times more closely resemble a uniform, an exponential, or a normal distribution?
c. Construct a histogram and a normal probability plot of the waiting times. Do you think these waiting times more closely resemble a uniform, an exponential, or a normal distribution?
d. Construct a histogram and a normal probability plot of the seating times. Do you think these seating times more closely resemble a uniform, an exponential, or a normal distribution?

7.48 All the major stock market indexes posted gains in 2010. The mean one-year return for stocks in the S&P 500, a group of 500 very large companies, was 12.8%. The mean one-year return for the NASDAQ, a group of 3,200 small and medium-sized companies, was 16.9%. Historically, the one-year returns are approximately normally distributed, the standard deviation in the S&P 500 is approximately 20%, and the standard deviation in the NASDAQ is approximately 30%.

a. What is the probability that a stock in the S&P 500 gained value in 2010?

b. What is the probability that a stock in the S&P 500 gained 10% or more in 2010?

c. What is the probability that a stock in the S&P 500 lost 20% or more in 2010?

d. What is the probability that a stock in the S&P 500 lost 40% or more in 2010?

e. Repeat (a) through (d) for a stock in the NASDAQ.

f. Write a short summary on your findings. Be sure to include a discussion of the risks associated with a large standard deviation.

7.49 The speed in which the home page of a website is downloaded is an important quality characteristic of that website. Suppose that the mean time to download the home page for the Internal Revenue Service is 1.2 seconds. Suppose that the download time is normally distributed, with a standard deviation of 0.2 second. What is the probability that a download time is

a. less than 2 seconds?

b. between 1.5 and 2.5 seconds?

c. above 1.8 seconds?

d. 99% of the download times are slower (higher) than how many seconds?

e. 95% of the download times are between what two values, symmetrically distributed around the mean?

7.50 Suppose that the mean download time for a commercial tax preparation site is 2.0 seconds. Suppose that the download time is normally distributed, with a standard deviation of 0.5 second. What is the probability that a download time is

a. less than 2 seconds?

b. between 1.5 and 2.5 seconds?

c. above 1.8 seconds?

d. 99% of the download times are slower (higher) than how many seconds ?

e. Compare the results for the IRS site computed in Problem 7.49 to those of the commercial site.

7.51 (Class Project) One theory about the daily changes in the closing price of stock is that these changes follow a *random walk*—that is, these daily events are independent of each other and move upward or downward in a random manner—and can be approximated by a normal distribution. To test this theory, use either a newspaper or the Internet to select one company traded on the NYSE, one company traded on the American Stock Exchange, and one company traded on the NASDAQ and then do the following:

1. Record the daily closing stock price of each of these companies for six consecutive weeks (so that you have 30 values per company).

2. Compute the daily changes in the closing stock price of each of these companies for six consecutive weeks (so that you have 30 values per company).

For each of your six data sets, decide whether the data are approximately normally distributed by

a. constructing the stem-and-leaf display, histogram or polygon, and boxplot.

b. comparing data characteristics to theoretical properties.

c. constructing a normal probability plot.

d. Discuss the results of (a) through (c). What can you say about your three stocks with respect to daily closing prices and daily changes in closing prices? Which, if any, of the data sets are approximately normally distributed?

Note: *The random-walk theory pertains to the daily changes in the closing stock price, not the daily closing stock price.*

TEAM PROJECT

The file Bond Funds contains information regarding eight variables from a sample of 184 bond mutual funds:

Type—Type of bonds comprising the bond mutual fund (intermediate government or short-term corporate)

Assets—In millions of dollars

Fees—Sales charges (no or yes)

Expense ratio—Ratio of expenses to net assets in percentage

Return 2009—Twelve-month return in 2009

Three-year return—Annualized return, 2007–2009

Five-year return—Annualized return, 2005–2009

Risk—Risk-of-loss factor of the mutual fund (below average, average, or above average)

7.52 For the expense ratio, three-year return, and five-year return, decide whether the data are approximately normally distributed by

a. comparing data characteristics to theoretical properties.

b. constructing a normal probability plot.

STUDENT SURVEY DATABASE

7.53 Problem 1.21 on page 20 describes a survey of 62 undergraduate students (stored in UndergradSurvey). For these data, for each numerical variable, decide whether the data are approximately normally distributed by

a. comparing data characteristics to theoretical properties.

b. constructing a normal probability plot.

7.54 Problem 1.21 on page 20 describes a survey of 62 undergraduate students (stored in UndergradSurvey).

a. Select a sample of undergraduate students and conduct a similar survey for those students.

b. For the data collected in (a), repeat (a) and (b) of Problem 7.53.

c. Compare the results of (b) to those of Problem 7.53.

7.55 Problem 1.22 on page 21 describes a survey of 44 MBA students (stored in GradSurvey). For these data, for

each numerical variable, decide whether the data are approximately normally distributed by
a. comparing data characteristics to theoretical properties.
b. constructing a normal probability plot.

7.56 Problem 1.22 on page 21 describes a survey of 44 MBA students (stored in GradSurvey).

a. Select a sample of graduate students and conduct a similar survey for those students.
b. For the data collected in (a), repeat (a) and (b) of Problem 7.55.
c. Compare the results of (b) to those of Problem 7.55.

MANAGING ASHLAND MULTICOMM SERVICES

The AMS technical services department has embarked on a quality improvement effort. Its first project relates to maintaining the target upload speed for its Internet service subscribers. Upload speeds are measured on a standard scale in which the target value is 1.0. Data collected over the past year indicate that the upload speed is approximately normally distributed, with a mean of 1.005 and a standard deviation of 0.10. Each day, one upload speed is measured. The upload speed is considered acceptable if the measurement on the standard scale is between 0.95 and 1.05.

Exercises

1. Assuming that the distribution has not changed from what it was in the past year, what is the probability that the upload speed is
   a. less than 1.0?
   b. between 0.95 and 1.0?
   c. between 1.0 and 1.05?
   d. less than 0.95 or greater than 1.05?
2. The objective of the operations team is to reduce the probability that the upload speed is below 1.0. Should the team focus on process improvement that increases the mean upload speed to 1.05 or on process improvement that reduces the standard deviation of the upload speed to 0.075? Explain.

DIGITAL CASE

Apply your knowledge about the normal distribution in this Digital Case, which extends the Using Statistics scenario from this chapter.

To satisfy concerns of potential customers, the management of OurCampus! has undertaken a research project to learn the amount of time it takes users to load a complex video features page. The research team has collected data and has made some claims based on the assertion that the data follow a normal distribution.

Open **OC_QRTStudy.pdf**, which documents the work of a quality response team at OurCampus! Read the internal report that documents the work of the team and their conclusions. Then answer the following:

1. Can the collected data be approximated by the normal distribution?
2. Review and evaluate the conclusions made by the OurCampus! research team. Which conclusions are correct? Which ones are incorrect?
3. If OurCampus! could improve the mean time by five seconds, how would the probabilities change?

REFERENCES

1. Gunter, B., "Q-Q Plots," *Quality Progress* (February 1994), 81–86.
2. Levine, D. M., P. Ramsey, and R. Smidt, *Applied Statistics for Engineers and Scientists Using Microsoft Excel and Minitab* (Upper Saddle River, NJ: Prentice Hall, 2001).
3. *Microsoft Excel 2010* (Redmond, WA: Microsoft Corp., 2010).
4. Miller, J., "Earliest Known Uses of Some of the Words of Mathematics," **http://jeff560.tripod.com/mathword.html**.
5. *Minitab Release 16* (State College, PA: Minitab Inc., 2010).
6. Pearl, R., "Karl Pearson, 1857–1936," *Journal of the American Statistical Association*, 31 (1936), 653–664.
7. Pearson, E. S., "Some Incidents in the Early History of Biometry and Statistics, 1890–94," *Biometrika*, 52 (1965), 3–18.
8. Walker, H., "The Contributions of Karl Pearson," *Journal of the American Statistical Association*, 53 (1958), 11–22.

CHAPTER 7 EXCEL GUIDE

EG7.1 Continuous Probability Distributions

There are no Excel Guide instructions for this section.

EG7.2 The Normal Distribution

PHStat2 Use **Normal** to compute normal probabilities. For example, to create the Figure 7.17 worksheet (see page 301) that computes probabilities for several Chapter 7 examples, select **PHStat → Probability & Prob. Distributions → Normal**. In this procedure's dialog box (shown below):

1. Enter **7** as the **Mean** and **2** as the **Standard Deviation**.
2. Check **Probability for:** X< = and enter **7** in its box.
3. Check **Probability for:** X > and enter **9** in its box.
4. Check **X for Cumulative Percentage** and enter **10** in its box.
5. Enter a **Title** and click **OK**.

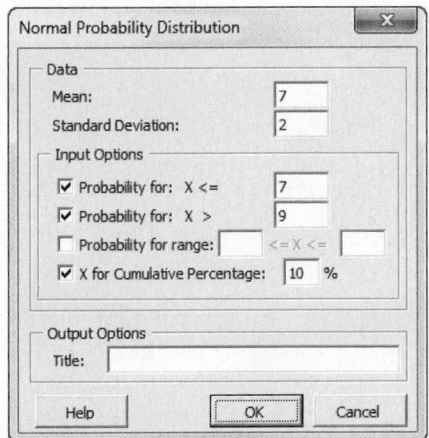

In-Depth Excel Use the **NORMDIST** worksheet function to compute normal probabilities. Enter the function as **NORMDIST(X value, mean, standard deviation, True)** to return the cumulative probability for less than or equal to the specified X value.

Use the **COMPUTE worksheet** of the **Normal workbook**, shown in Figure 7.17 on page 301, as a template for computing normal probabilities. The worksheet contains the data for solving the problems in Examples 7.4 through 7.7. Change the values for the **Mean, Standard Deviation, X Value, From X Value, To X Value**, and/or **Cumulative Percentage** to solve similar problems. To solve a problem that is similar to Example 7.8 on page 299, change the **Cumulative Percentage** cell twice, once to determine the lower value of X and the other time to determine the upper value of X.

The COMPUTE worksheet also uses the **STANDARDIZE** worksheet function to compute Z values, **NORMDIST** to

compute the probability of less than or equal to the X value given, **NORMSINV** to compute the Z value for the cumulative percentage, and **NORMINV** to compute the X value for the given cumulative probability, mean, and standard deviation.

The worksheet also includes formulas that update probability labels when an X value is changed. Open to the **COMPUTE_FORMULAS worksheet** to examine all formulas.

EG7.3 Evaluating Normality

Comparing Data Characteristics to Theoretical Properties

Use instructions in Sections EG3.1 through EG3.3 in the Chapter 3 Excel Guide to compare data characteristics to theoretical properties.

Constructing the Normal Probability Plot

PHStat2 Use **Normal Probability Plot** to create a normal probability plot. For example, to create the Figure 7.23 normal probability plot for the 2009 returns on page 307, open to the **DATA worksheet** of the **Bond Funds workbook**. Select **PHStat → Probability & Prob. Distributions → Normal Probability Plot**. In the procedure's dialog box (shown below):

1. Enter **F1:F185** as the **Variable Cell Range**.
2. Check **First cell contains label**.
3. Enter a **Title** and click **OK**.

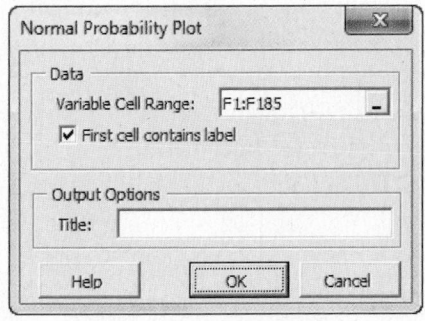

In addition to the chart sheet containing the normal probability plot, the procedure creates a worksheet of plot data that uses the **NORMSINV** function to compute the Z values used in the plot.

In-Depth Excel Create a normal probability plot in a two-step process. First create a worksheet that computes Z values for the data to be plotted. Then create a chart from that worksheet. Use the **PLOT_DATA worksheet** of the **NPP workbook** as a model for computing Z values. This worksheet contains columns for the rank, proportion, Z value, and the **Return 2009** variable and is the source of the data for the **NORMAL_PLOT chart sheet** that contains the Figure 7.23 normal probability plot (see page 307). For other problems, paste sorted variable data in column D, update the number of ranks in column A, and adjust the formulas in columns B and C. Column B formulas divide the column A cell by the quantity $n + 1$ (185 for the 2009 returns data) to compute cumulative percentages and column C formulas use the NORMSINV function to compute the Z values for those cumulative percentages. (Open to the **PLOT_FORMULAS worksheet** in the same workbook to examine these formulas.)

If you have fewer than 184 values, delete rows from the bottom up. If you have more than 184 values, insert rows from somewhere inside the body of the table to ensure that the normal probability plot is properly updated. To create your own normal probability plot for the Return 2009 variable, select the cell range **C1:D185**. Then select **Insert → Scatter** and select the first **Scatter** gallery choice (**Scatter with only Markers**). Relocate the chart to a chart sheet and adjust the chart formatting by using the instructions in Appendix F.

8 Sampling and Sampling Distributions

Learning Objectives
In this chapter, you learn:

- About different sampling methods
- The concept of the sampling distribution
- To compute probabilities related to the sample mean and the sample proportion
- The importance of the Central Limit Theorem

© Corbis

@ Oxford Cereals, Part I

Oxford Cereals fills thousands of boxes of cereal during an eight-hour shift. As the plant operations manager, you are responsible for monitoring the amount of cereal placed in each box. To be consistent with package labeling, boxes should contain a mean of 368 grams of cereal. Because of the speed of the process, the cereal weight varies from box to box, causing some boxes to be underfilled and others overfilled. If the process is not working properly, the mean weight in the boxes could vary too much from the label weight of 368 grams to be acceptable.

Because weighing every single box is too time-consuming, costly, and inefficient, you must take a sample of boxes. For each sample you select, you plan to weigh the individual boxes and calculate a sample mean. You need to determine the probability that such a sample mean could have been randomly selected from a population whose mean is 368 grams. Based on your analysis, you will have to decide whether to maintain, alter, or shut down the cereal-filling process.

R. MACKAY PHOTOGRAPHY / Shutterstock.com

In Chapter 7, you used the normal distribution to study the distribution of video download times from the OurCampus! website. In this chapter, you need to make a decision about the cereal-filling process, based on the weights of a sample of cereal boxes packaged at Oxford cereals. You will learn different methods of sampling and about sampling distributions and how to use them to solve business problems.

8.1 Types of Sampling Methods

In Section 1.4, a sample is defined as the portion of a population that has been selected for analysis. Rather than selecting every item in the population, statistical sampling procedures focus on collecting a small representative portion of the larger population. The results of the sample are then used to estimate characteristics of the entire population. There are three main reasons for selecting a sample:

- Selecting a sample is less time-consuming than selecting every item in the population.
- Selecting a sample is less costly than selecting every item in the population.
- Analyzing a sample is less cumbersome and more practical than analyzing the entire population.

The sampling process begins by defining the **frame**, a listing of items that make up the population. Frames are data sources such as population lists, directories, or maps. Samples are drawn from frames. Inaccurate or biased results can occur if a frame excludes certain portions of the population. Using different frames to generate data can lead to different conclusions.

After you select a frame, you draw a sample from the frame. As illustrated in Figure 8.1, there are two types of samples: nonprobability samples and probability samples.

FIGURE 8.1

Types of samples

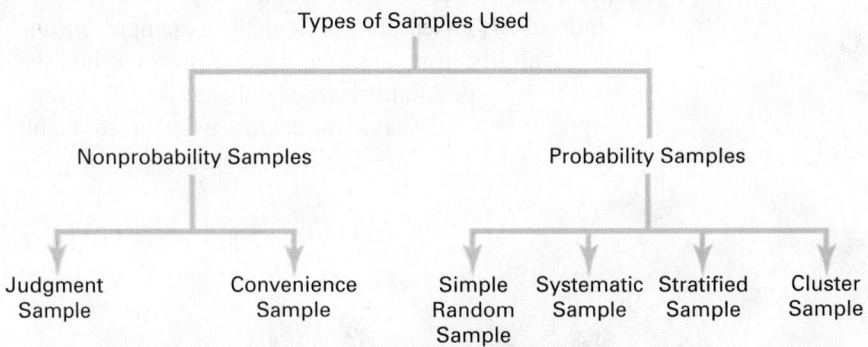

In a **nonprobability sample**, you select the items or individuals without knowing their probabilities of selection. Because of this, the theory of statistical inference that has been developed for probability sampling cannot be applied to nonprobability samples. A common type of nonprobability sampling is **convenience sampling**. In convenience sampling, items selected are easy, inexpensive, or convenient to sample. For example, if you were sampling tires stacked in a warehouse, it would be much more convenient to sample tires at the top of a stack than tires at the bottom of a stack. In many cases, participants in the sample select themselves. For example, many companies conduct surveys by giving visitors to their website the opportunity to complete survey forms and submit them electronically. The responses to these surveys can provide large amounts of data quickly and inexpensively, but the sample consists of self-selected web users. For many studies, only a nonprobability sample such as a judgment sample is available. In a **judgment sample**, you get the opinions of preselected experts in the subject matter. Although the experts may be well informed, you cannot generalize their results to the population.

Nonprobability samples can have certain advantages, such as convenience, speed, and low cost. However, their lack of accuracy due to selection bias and the fact that the results cannot be used for statistical inference more than offset these advantages.

In a **probability sample**, you select items based on known probabilities. Whenever possible, you should use probability sampling methods. Probability samples allow you to make inferences about the population of interest. The four types of probability samples most commonly used are simple random, systematic, stratified, and cluster samples. These sampling methods vary in their cost, accuracy, and complexity.

Simple Random Samples

In a **simple random sample**, every item from a frame has the same chance of selection as every other item. In addition, every sample of a fixed size has the same chance of selection as every other sample of that size. Simple random sampling is the most elementary random sampling technique. It forms the basis for the other random sampling techniques.

With simple random sampling, you use n to represent the sample size and N to represent the frame size. You number every item in the frame from 1 to N. The chance that you will select any particular member of the frame on the first selection is $1/N$.

You select samples with replacement or without replacement. **Sampling with replacement** means that after you select an item, you return it to the frame, where it has the same probability of being selected again. Imagine that you have a fishbowl containing N business cards, one card for each person. On the first selection, you select the card for Judy Craven. You record pertinent information and replace the business card in the bowl. You then mix up the cards in the bowl and select a second card. On the second selection, Judy Craven has the same probability of being selected again, $1/N$. You repeat this process until you have selected the desired sample size, n.

However, usually you do not want the same item to be selected again. **Sampling without replacement** means that once you select an item, you cannot select it again. The chance that you will select any particular item in the frame—for example, the business card for Judy Craven—on the first selection is $1/N$. The chance that you will select any card not previously chosen on the second selection is now 1 out of $N - 1$. This process continues until you have selected the desired sample of size n.

Regardless of whether you have sampled with or without replacement, "fishbowl" methods of sample selection have a major drawback—the ability to thoroughly mix the cards and randomly select the sample. As a result, fishbowl methods are not very useful. You need to use less cumbersome and more scientific methods of selection.

One such method uses a **table of random numbers** (see Table E.1 in Appendix E) for selecting the sample. A table of random numbers consists of a series of digits listed in a randomly generated sequence (see reference 8). Because the numeric system uses 10 digits $(0, 1, 2, \ldots, 9)$, the chance that you will randomly generate any particular digit is equal to the probability of generating any other digit. This probability is 1 out of 10. Hence, if you generate a sequence of 800 digits, you would expect about 80 to be the digit 0, 80 to be the digit 1, and so on. Because every digit or sequence of digits in the table is random, the table can be read either horizontally or vertically. The margins of the table designate row numbers and column numbers. The digits themselves are grouped into sequences of five in order to make reading the table easier.

To use Table E.1 instead of a fishbowl for selecting the sample, you first need to assign code numbers to the individual items of the frame. Then you generate the random sample by reading the table of random numbers and selecting those individuals from the frame whose assigned code numbers match the digits found in the table. You can better understand the process of sample selection by studying Example 8.1.

EXAMPLE 8.1

Selecting a Simple Random Sample by Using a Table of Random Numbers

A company wants to select a sample of 32 full-time workers from a population of 800 full-time employees in order to collect information on expenditures concerning a company-sponsored dental plan. How do you select a simple random sample?

SOLUTION The company decides to conduct an e-mail survey. Assuming that not everyone will respond to the survey, you need to send more than 32 surveys to get the necessary 32 responses. Assuming that 8 out of 10 full-time workers will respond to such a survey (i.e., a response rate of 80%), you decide to send 40 surveys. Because you want to send the 40 surveys to 40 different individuals, you should sample without replacement.

The frame consists of a listing of the names and e-mail addresses of all $N = 800$ full-time employees taken from the company personnel files. Thus, the frame is a complete listing of the population. To select the random sample of 40 employees from this frame, you use a table of random numbers. Because the frame size (800) is a three-digit number, each assigned code number must also be three digits so that every full-time worker has an equal chance of selection. You assign a code of 001 to the first full-time employee in the population listing, a code of 002 to the second full-time employee in the population listing, and so on, until a code of 800 is assigned to the *N*th full-time worker in the listing. Because $N = 800$ is the largest possible coded value, you discard all three-digit code sequences greater than 800 (i.e., 801 through 999 and 000).

To select the simple random sample, you choose an arbitrary starting point from the table of random numbers. One method you can use is to close your eyes and strike the table of random numbers with a pencil. Suppose you used this procedure and you selected row 06, column 05 of Table 8.1 (which is extracted from Table E.1) as the starting point. Although you can go in any direction, in this example you read the table from left to right, in sequences of three digits, without skipping.

TABLE 8.1

Using a Table of Random Numbers

	Column							
	00000	00001	11111	11112	22222	22223	33333	33334
Row	12345	67890	12345	67890	12345	67890	12345	67890
01	49280	88924	35779	00283	81163	07275	89863	02348
02	61870	41657	07468	08612	98083	97349	20775	45091
03	43898	65923	25078	86129	78496	97653	91550	08078
04	62993	93912	30454	84598	56095	20664	12872	64647
05	33850	58555	51438	85507	71865	79488	76783	31708
06	97340	03364	88472	04334	63919	36394	11095	92470
07	70543	29776	10087	10072	55980	64688	68239	20461
08	89382	93809	00796	95945	34101	81277	66090	88872
09	37818	72142	67140	50785	22380	16703	53362	44940
10	60430	22834	14130	96593	23298	56203	92671	15925
11	82975	66158	84731	19436	55790	69229	28661	13675
12	39087	71938	40355	54324	08401	26299	49420	59208
13	55700	24586	93247	32596	11865	63397	44251	43189
14	14756	23997	78643	75912	83832	32768	18928	57070
15	32166	53251	70654	92827	63491	04233	33825	69662
16	23236	73751	31888	81718	06546	83246	47651	04877
17	45794	26926	15130	82455	78305	55058	52551	47182
18	09893	20505	14225	68514	46427	56788	96297	78822
19	54382	74598	91499	14523	68479	27686	46162	83554
20	94750	89923	37089	20048	80336	94598	26940	36858
21	70297	34135	53140	33340	42050	82341	44104	82949
22	85157	47954	32979	26575	57600	40881	12250	73742
23	11100	02340	12860	74697	96644	89439	28707	25815
24	36871	50775	30592	57143	17381	68856	25853	35041
25	23913	48357	63308	16090	51690	54607	72407	55538

Begin selection (row 06, column 05) — labels at rows 06–09.

Source: Data extracted from Rand Corporation, *A Million Random Digits with 100,000 Normal Deviates* (Glencoe, IL: The Free Press, 1955) and contained in Table E.1.

The individual with code number 003 is the first full-time employee in the sample (row 06 and columns 05–07), the second individual has code number 364 (row 06 and columns 08–10), and the third individual has code number 884. Because the highest code for any employee is 800, you discard the number 884. Individuals with code numbers 720, 433, 463, 363, 109, 592, 470, and 705 are selected third through tenth, respectively.

You continue the selection process until you get the required sample size of 40 full-time employees. If any three-digit sequence repeats during the selection process, you discard the repeating sequence because you are sampling without replacement.

Systematic Samples

In a **systematic sample**, you partition the N items in the frame into n groups of k items, where

$$k = \frac{N}{n}$$

You round k to the nearest integer. To select a systematic sample, you choose the first item to be selected at random from the first k items in the frame. Then, you select the remaining $n - 1$ items by taking every kth item thereafter from the entire frame.

If the frame consists of a listing of prenumbered checks, sales receipts, or invoices, taking a systematic sample is faster and easier than taking a simple random sample. A systematic sample is also a convenient mechanism for collecting data from telephone books, class rosters, and consecutive items coming off an assembly line.

To take a systematic sample of $n = 40$ from the population of $N = 800$ full-time employees, you partition the frame of 800 into 40 groups, each of which contains 20 employees. You then select a random number from the first 20 individuals and include every twentieth individual after the first selection in the sample. For example, if the first random number you select is 008, your subsequent selections are 028, 048, 068, 088, 108, ..., 768, and 788.

Simple random sampling and systematic sampling are simpler than other, more sophisticated, probability sampling methods, but they generally require a larger sample size. In addition, systematic sampling is prone to selection bias. When using systematic sampling, if there is a pattern in the frame, you could have severe selection biases. To overcome the inefficiency of simple random sampling and the potential selection bias involved with systematic sampling, you can use either stratified sampling methods or cluster sampling methods.

Stratified Samples

In a **stratified sample**, you first subdivide the N items in the frame into separate subpopulations, or **strata**. A stratum is defined by some common characteristic, such as gender or year in school. You select a simple random sample within each of the strata and combine the results from the separate simple random samples. Stratified sampling is more efficient than either simple random sampling or systematic sampling because you are ensured of the representation of items across the entire population. The homogeneity of items within each stratum provides greater precision in the estimates of underlying population parameters.

EXAMPLE 8.2

Selecting a
Stratified Sample

A company wants to select a sample of 32 full-time workers from a population of 800 full-time employees in order to estimate expenditures from a company-sponsored dental plan. Of the full-time employees, 25% are managers and 75% are nonmanagerial workers. How do you select the stratified sample in order for the sample to represent the correct percentage of managers and nonmanagerial workers?

SOLUTION If you assume an 80% response rate, you need to send 40 surveys to get the necessary 32 responses. The frame consists of a listing of the names and e-mail addresses of all $N = 800$ full-time employees included in the company personnel files. Because 25% of the full-time employees are managers, you first separate the frame into two strata: a subpopulation listing of all 200 managerial-level personnel and a separate subpopulation listing of all 600 full-time nonmanagerial workers. Because the first stratum consists of a listing of 200 managers, you assign three-digit code numbers from 001 to 200. Because the second stratum contains a listing of 600 nonmanagerial workers, you assign three-digit code numbers from 001 to 600.

To collect a stratified sample proportional to the sizes of the strata, you select 25% of the overall sample from the first stratum and 75% of the overall sample from the second stratum. You take two separate simple random samples, each of which is based on a distinct random starting point from a table of random numbers (Table E.1). In the first sample, you select 10 managers from the listing of 200 in the first stratum, and in the second sample, you select 30 nonmanagerial workers from the listing of 600 in the second stratum. You then combine the results to reflect the composition of the entire company.

Cluster Samples

In a **cluster sample**, you divide the N items in the frame into clusters that contain several items. **Clusters** are often naturally occurring designations, such as counties, election districts, city blocks, households, or sales territories. You then take a random sample of one or more clusters and study all items in each selected cluster.

Cluster sampling is often more cost-effective than simple random sampling, particularly if the population is spread over a wide geographic region. However, cluster sampling often requires a larger sample size to produce results as precise as those from simple random sampling or stratified sampling. A detailed discussion of systematic sampling, stratified sampling, and cluster sampling procedures can be found in reference 1.

Problems for Section 8.1

LEARNING THE BASICS

8.1 For a population containing $N = 902$ individuals, what code number would you assign for
a. the first person on the list?
b. the fortieth person on the list?
c. the last person on the list?

8.2 For a population of $N = 902$, verify that by starting in row 05, column 01 of the table of random numbers (Table E.1), you need only six rows to select a sample of $N = 60$ *without* replacement.

8.3 Given a population of $N = 93$, starting in row 29, column 01 of the table of random numbers (Table E.1), and reading across the row, select a sample of $N = 15$
a. *without* replacement.
b. *with* replacement.

APPLYING THE CONCEPTS

8.4 For a study that consists of personal interviews with participants (rather than mail or phone surveys), explain why simple random sampling might be less practical than some other sampling methods.

8.5 You want to select a random sample of $n = 1$ from a population of three items (which are called A, B, and C). The rule for selecting the sample is as follows: Flip a coin; if it is heads, pick item A; if it is tails, flip the coin again; this time, if it is heads, choose B; if it is tails, choose C. Explain why this is a probability sample but not a simple random sample.

8.6 A population has four members (called A, B, C, and D). You would like to select a random sample of $n = 2$, which you decide to do in the following way: Flip a coin; if it is heads, the sample will be items A and B; if it is tails, the sample will be items C and D. Although this is a random sample, it is not a simple random sample. Explain why. (Compare the procedure described in Problem 8.5 with the procedure described in this problem.)

8.7 The registrar of a college with a population of $N = 4,000$ full-time students is asked by the president to conduct a survey to measure satisfaction with the quality of life on campus.

The following table contains a breakdown of the 4,000 registered full-time students, by gender and class designation:

	Class Designation				
Gender	Fr.	So.	Jr.	Sr.	Total
Female	700	520	500	480	2,200
Male	560	460	400	380	1,800
Total	1,260	980	900	860	4,000

The registrar intends to take a probability sample of $n = 200$ students and project the results from the sample to the entire population of full-time students.
a. If the frame available from the registrar's files is an alphabetical listing of the names of all $N = 4,000$ registered full-time students, what type of sample could you take? Discuss.
b. What is the advantage of selecting a simple random sample in (a)?
c. What is the advantage of selecting a systematic sample in (a)?
d. If the frame available from the registrar's files is a listing of the names of all $N = 4,000$ registered full-time students compiled from eight separate alphabetical lists, based on the gender and class designation breakdowns shown in the class designation table, what type of sample should you take? Discuss.
e. Suppose that each of the $N = 4,000$ registered full-time students lived in one of the 10 campus dormitories. Each dormitory accommodates 400 students. It is college policy to fully integrate students by gender and class designation in each dormitory. If the registrar is able to compile a listing of all students by dormitory, explain how you could take a cluster sample.

8.8 Prenumbered sales invoices are kept in a sales journal. The invoices are numbered from 0001 to 5000.
a. Beginning in row 16, column 01, and proceeding horizontally in Table E.1, select a simple random sample of 50 invoice numbers.
b. Select a systematic sample of 50 invoice numbers. Use the random numbers in row 20, columns 05–07, as the starting point for your selection.

c. Are the invoices selected in (a) the same as those selected in (b)? Why or why not?

8.9 Suppose that 5,000 sales invoices are separated into four strata. Stratum 1 contains 50 invoices, stratum 2 contains 500 invoices, stratum 3 contains 1,000 invoices, and stratum 4 contains 3,450 invoices. A sample of 500 sales invoices is needed.
a. What type of sampling should you do? Why?
b. Explain how you would carry out the sampling according to the method stated in (a).
c. Why is the sampling in (a) not simple random sampling?

8.2 Evaluating Survey Worthiness

Surveys are used to collect data. Nearly every day, you read or hear about survey or opinion poll results in newspapers, on the Internet, or on radio or television. To identify surveys that lack objectivity or credibility, you must critically evaluate what you read and hear by examining the worthiness of the survey. First, you must evaluate the purpose of the survey, why it was conducted, and for whom it was conducted.

The second step in evaluating the worthiness of a survey is to determine whether it was based on a probability or nonprobability sample (as discussed in Section 8.1). You need to remember that the only way to make valid statistical inferences from a sample to a population is through the use of a probability sample. Surveys that use nonprobability sampling methods are subject to serious, perhaps unintentional, biases that may make the results meaningless.

Survey Error

Even when surveys use random probability sampling methods, they are subject to potential errors. There are four types of survey errors:

- Coverage error
- Nonresponse error
- Sampling error
- Measurement error

Well-designed surveys reduce or minimize these four types of errors, often at considerable cost.

Coverage Error The key to proper sample selection is having an adequate frame. Remember that a frame is an up-to-date list of all the items from which you will select the sample. **Coverage error** occurs if certain groups of items are excluded from the frame so that they have no chance of being selected in the sample. Coverage error results in a **selection bias**. If the frame is inadequate because certain groups of items in the population were not properly included, any random probability sample selected will provide only an estimate of the characteristics of the frame, not the *actual* population.

Nonresponse Error Not everyone is willing to respond to a survey. In fact, research has shown that individuals in the upper and lower economic classes tend to respond less frequently to surveys than do people in the middle class. **Nonresponse error** arises from failure to collect data on all items in the sample and results in a **nonresponse bias**. Because you cannot always assume that persons who do not respond to surveys are similar to those who do, you need to follow up on the nonresponses after a specified period of time. You should make several attempts to convince such individuals to complete the survey. The follow-up responses are then compared to the initial responses in order to make valid inferences from the survey (see reference 1). The mode of response you use affects the rate of response. Personal interviews and telephone interviews usually produce a higher response rate than do mail surveys—but at a higher cost.

Sampling Error As discussed earlier, a sample is selected because it is simpler, less costly, and more efficient to examine than an entire population. However, chance dictates which individuals or items will or will not be included in the sample. **Sampling error** reflects the variation, or "chance differences," from sample to sample, based on the probability of particular individuals or items being selected in the particular samples.

When you read about the results of surveys or polls in newspapers or magazines, there is often a statement regarding a margin of error, such as "the results of this poll are expected to be within ±4 percentage points of the actual value." This **margin of error** is the sampling error. You can reduce sampling error by using larger sample sizes, although doing so increases the cost of conducting the survey.

Measurement Error   In the practice of good survey research, you design a questionnaire with the intention of gathering meaningful information. But you have a dilemma here: Getting meaningful measurements is often easier said than done. Consider the following proverb:

A person with one watch always knows what time it is;

A person with two watches always searches to identify the correct one;

A person with ten watches is always reminded of the difficulty in measuring time.

Unfortunately, the process of measurement is often governed by what is convenient, not what is needed. The measurements you get are often only a proxy for the ones you really desire. Much attention has been given to measurement error that occurs because of a weakness in question wording (see reference 2). A question should be clear, not ambiguous. Furthermore, in order to avoid *leading questions*, you need to present questions in a neutral manner.

Three sources of **measurement error** are ambiguous wording of questions, the Hawthorne effect, and respondent error. As an example of ambiguous wording, several years ago, the U.S. Department of Labor reported that the unemployment rate in the United States had been underestimated for more than a decade because of poor questionnaire wording in the Current Population Survey. In particular, the wording had led to a significant undercount of women in the labor force. Because unemployment rates are tied to benefit programs such as state unemployment compensation, survey researchers had to rectify the situation by adjusting the questionnaire wording.

The *Hawthorne effect* occurs when a respondent feels obligated to please the interviewer. Proper interviewer training can minimize the Hawthorne effect.

Respondent error occurs as a result of an overzealous or underzealous effort by the respondent. You can minimize this error in two ways: (1) by carefully scrutinizing the data and then recontacting those individuals whose responses seem unusual and (2) by establishing a program of recontacting a small number of randomly chosen individuals in order to determine the reliability of the responses.

Ethical Issues

Ethical considerations arise with respect to coverage error, nonresponse error, sampling error, and measurement error. Coverage error can result in selection bias and becomes an ethical issue if particular groups or individuals are *purposely* excluded from the frame so that the survey results are more favorable to the survey's sponsor. Nonresponse error can lead to nonresponse bias and becomes an ethical issue if the sponsor knowingly designs the survey so that particular groups or individuals are less likely than others to respond. Sampling error becomes an ethical issue if the findings are purposely presented without reference to sample size and margin of error so that the sponsor can promote a viewpoint that might otherwise be inappropriate. Measurement error becomes an ethical issue in one of three ways: (1) a survey sponsor chooses leading questions that guide the responses in a particular direction; (2) an interviewer, through mannerisms and tone, purposely creates a Hawthorne effect or otherwise guides the responses in a particular direction; or (3) a respondent willfully provides false information.

Ethical issues also arise when the results of nonprobability samples are used to form conclusions about the entire population. When you use a nonprobability sampling method, you need to explain the sampling procedures and state that the results cannot be generalized beyond the sample.

THINK ABOUT THIS   New Media Surveys/Old Sampling Problems

Imagine that you are a software distributor and you decide to create a "customer experience improvement program" that records how your customers are using your products, with the goal of using the collected data to improve your products. Or say that you're the moderator of an opinion blog who decides to create an instant poll to ask your readers about important political issues. Or you're a marketer of products aimed at a specific demographic and decide to create a page in a social networking site through which you plan to collect consumer feedback. What might you have in common with a *dead-tree* publication that went out of business over 70 years ago?

By 1932, before there was ever an Internet—or even commercial television—a "straw poll" conducted by the magazine *Literary Digest* had successfully predicted five U.S. presidential elections in a row. For the 1936 election, the magazine promised its largest poll ever and sent about 10 million ballots to people all across the country. After receiving and tabulating more than 2.3 million ballots, the *Digest* confidently proclaimed that Alf Landon would be an easy winner over Franklin D. Roosevelt. As things turned out, FDR won in a landslide, with Landon receiving the fewest electoral votes in U.S. history. The reputation of the *Literary Digest* was ruined; the magazine would cease publication less than two years later.

The failure of the *Literary Digest* poll was a watershed event in the history of sample surveys and polls. This failure refuted the notion that the larger the sample is, the better. (Remember this the next time someone complains about a political survey's "small" sample size.) The failure opened the door to new and more modern methods of sampling—the theory and concepts this book discusses in Sections 8.1 and 8.2. Today's Gallup polls of political opinion (**www.gallup.com**) or Roper (now GfK Roper) Reports about consumer behavior (**www.gfkamerica.com/practice_areas/roper_consulting/roper_reports**) arose,

in part, due to this failure. George Gallup, the "Gallup" of the poll, and Elmo Roper, of the eponymous reports, both first gained widespread public notice for their correct "scientific" predictions of the 1936 election.

The failed *Literary Digest* poll became fodder for several postmortems, and the reason for the failure became almost an urban legend. Typically, the explanation is coverage error: The ballots were sent mostly to "rich people," and this created a frame that excluded poorer citizens (presumably more inclined to vote for the Democrat Roosevelt than the Republican Landon). However, later analyses suggest that this was not true; instead, low rates of response (2.3 million ballots represented less than 25% of the ballots distributed) and/or nonresponse error (Roosevelt voters were less likely to mail in a ballot than Landon voters) were significant reasons for the failure (see reference 9).

When Microsoft introduced its new Office Ribbon interface with Office 2007, a program manager explained how Microsoft had applied data collected from its "Customer Experience Improvement Program" to the redesign of the user interface. This led others to speculate that the data were biased toward beginners—who might be less likely to *decline* participation in the

program—and that, in turn, had led Microsoft to make decisions that ended up perplexing more experienced users. This was another case of nonresponse error!

The blog moderator's instant poll mentioned earlier is targeted to the moderator's community, and the social network–based survey is aimed at "friends" of a product; such polls can also suffer from nonresponse error, and this fact is often overlooked by users of these new media. Often, marketers extol how much they "know" about survey respondents, thanks to information that can be "mined" from a social network community. But no amount of information about the respondents can tell marketers who the nonresponders are. Therefore, new media surveys fall prey to the same old type of error that may have been fatal to *Literary Digest* way back when.

Today, companies establish formal surveys based on probability sampling and go to great lengths—and spend large sums—to deal with coverage error, nonresponse error, sampling error, and measurement error. Instant polling and tell-a-friend surveys can be interesting and fun, but they are not replacements for the methods discussed in this chapter.

Problems for Section 8.2

APPLYING THE CONCEPTS

8.10 A survey indicates that the vast majority of college students own their own personal computers. What information would you want to know before you accepted the results of this survey?

8.11 A simple random sample of $n = 300$ full-time employees is selected from a company list containing the names of all $N = 5,000$ full-time employees in order to evaluate job satisfaction.
a. Give an example of possible coverage error.
b. Give an example of possible nonresponse error.
c. Give an example of possible sampling error.
d. Give an example of possible measurement error.

SELF Test **8.12** Business Professor Thomas Callarman traveled to China more than a dozen times from 2000 to 2005. He warns people about believing everything they read about surveys conducted in China and gives two specific reasons: "First, things are changing so rapidly that what you hear today may not be true tomorrow. Second, the people who answer the surveys may tell you what they think you want to hear, rather than what they really believe" (T. E. Callarman, "Some Thoughts on China," *Decision Line*, March 2006, pp. 1, 43–44).
a. List the four types of survey error discussed in the paragraph above.

b. Which of the types of survey error in (a) are the basis for Professor Callarman's two reasons to question the surveys being conducted in China?

8.13 A recent survey of college freshmen investigated the amount of involvement their parents have with decisions concerning their education. When asked about the decision to go to college, 84% said their parents' involvement was about right, 10.3% said it was too much, and 5.7% said it was too little. When it came to selecting individual courses, 72.5% said their parents' involvement was about right, 3.5% said it was too much, and 24.0% said it was too little (M. B. Marklein, "Study: Colleges Shouldn't Fret Over Hands-on Parents," **www.usatoday.com**, January 23, 2008). What additional information would you want to know about the survey before you accepted the results of the study?

8.14 Recruiters are finding a wealth of unfiltered information about candidates on social-networking websites. A recent survey found that 83% of recruiters use search engines to learn more about candidates, and 43% eliminated candidates based on information they found (I. Phaneuf, "Who's Googling You?" *Job Postings*, Spring 2009, pp. 12–13). What additional information would you want to know about a survey before you accepted the results of the study?

8.3 Sampling Distributions

In many applications, you want to make inferences that are based on statistics calculated from samples to estimate the values of population parameters. In the next two sections, you will learn about how the sample mean (a statistic) is used to estimate the population mean (a parameter) and how the sample proportion (a statistic) is used to estimate the population proportion (a parameter). Your main concern when making a statistical inference is reaching conclusions about a population, *not* about a sample. For example, a political pollster is interested in the sample results only as a way of estimating the actual proportion of the votes that each candidate will receive from the population of voters. Likewise, as plant operations manager for Oxford Cereals, you are only interested in using the sample mean weight calculated from a sample of cereal boxes for estimating the mean weight of a population of boxes.

In practice, you select a single random sample of a predetermined size from the population. Hypothetically, to use the sample statistic to estimate the population parameter, you could examine *every* possible sample of a given size that could occur. A **sampling distribution** is the distribution of the results if you actually selected all possible samples. The single result you obtain in practice is just one of the results in the sampling distribution.

8.4 Sampling Distribution of the Mean

In Chapter 4, several measures of central tendency, including the mean, median, and mode, were discussed. Undoubtedly, the mean is the most widely used measure of central tendency. The sample mean is often used to estimate the population mean. The **sampling distribution of the mean** is the distribution of all possible sample means if you select all possible samples of a given size.

The Unbiased Property of the Sample Mean

The sample mean is **unbiased** because the mean of all the possible sample means (of a given sample size, n) is equal to the population mean, μ. A simple example concerning a population of four administrative assistants demonstrates this property. Each assistant is asked to apply the same set of updates to a human resources database. Table 8.2 presents the number of errors made by each of the administrative assistants. This population distribution is shown in Figure 8.2.

TABLE 8.2

Number of Errors Made by Each of Four Administrative Assistants

Administrative Assistant	Number of Errors
Ann	$X_1 = 3$
Bob	$X_2 = 2$
Carla	$X_3 = 1$
Dave	$X_4 = 4$

FIGURE 8.2

Number of errors made by a population of four administrative assistants

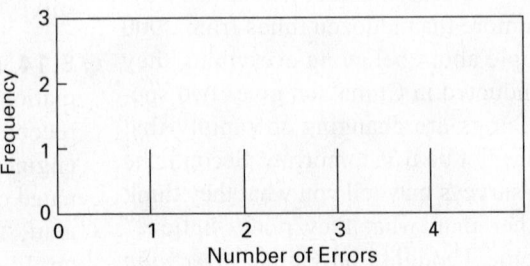

When you have the data from a population, you compute the mean by using Equation (8.1).

POPULATION MEAN

The population mean is the sum of the values in the population divided by the population size, N.

$$\mu = \frac{\sum_{i=1}^{N} X_i}{N} \tag{8.1}$$

You compute the population standard deviation, σ, by using Equation (8.2).

POPULATION STANDARD DEVIATION

$$\sigma = \sqrt{\frac{\sum_{i=1}^{N} (X_i - \mu)^2}{N}} \tag{8.2}$$

Thus, for the data of Table 8.2,

$$\mu = \frac{3 + 2 + 1 + 4}{4} = 2.5 \text{ errors}$$

and

$$\sigma = \sqrt{\frac{(3 - 2.5)^2 + (2 - 2.5)^2 + (1 - 2.5)^2 + (4 - 2.5)^2}{4}} = 1.12 \text{ errors}$$

If you select samples of two administrative assistants *with* replacement from this population, there are 16 possible samples ($N^n = 4^2 = 16$). Table 8.3 lists the 16 possible sample outcomes. If you average all 16 of these sample means, the mean of these values, is equal to 2.5, which is also the mean of the population, μ.

TABLE 8.3

All 16 Samples of $n = 2$ Administrative Assistants from a Population of $N = 4$ Administrative Assistants When Sampling with Replacement

Sample	Administrative Assistants	Sample Outcomes	Sample Mean
1	Ann, Ann	3, 3	$\bar{X}_1 = 3$
2	Ann, Bob	3, 2	$\bar{X}_2 = 2.5$
3	Ann, Carla	3, 1	$\bar{X}_3 = 2$
4	Ann, Dave	3, 4	$\bar{X}_4 = 3.5$
5	Bob, Ann	2, 3	$\bar{X}_5 = 2.5$
6	Bob, Bob	2, 2	$\bar{X}_6 = 2$
7	Bob, Carla	2, 1	$\bar{X}_7 = 1.5$
8	Bob, Dave	2, 4	$\bar{X}_8 = 3$
9	Carla, Ann	1, 3	$\bar{X}_9 = 2$
10	Carla, Bob	1, 2	$\bar{X}_{10} = 1.5$
11	Carla, Carla	1, 1	$\bar{X}_{11} = 1$
12	Carla, Dave	1, 4	$\bar{X}_{12} = 2.5$
13	Dave, Ann	4, 3	$\bar{X}_{13} = 3.5$
14	Dave, Bob	4, 2	$\bar{X}_{14} = 3$
15	Dave, Carla	4, 1	$\bar{X}_{15} = 2.5$
16	Dave, Dave	4, 4	$\bar{X}_{16} = 4$
			$\mu_{\bar{X}} = 2.5$

Because the mean of the 16 sample means is equal to the population mean, the sample mean is an unbiased estimator of the population mean. Therefore, although you do not know how close the sample mean of any particular sample selected comes to the population mean, you are assured that the mean of all the possible sample means that could have been selected is equal to the population mean.

Standard Error of the Mean

Figure 8.3 illustrates the variation in the sample means when selecting all 16 possible samples.

FIGURE 8.3

Sampling distribution of the mean, based on all possible samples containing two administrative assistants

Source: Data are from Table 8.3.

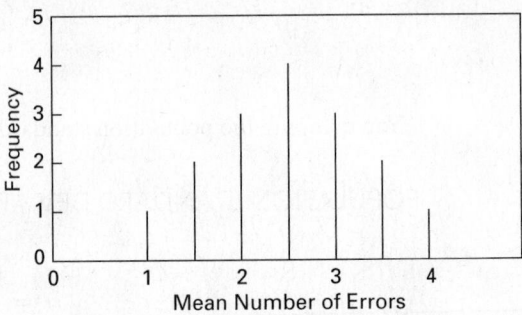

In this small example, although the sample means vary from sample to sample, depending on which two administrative assistants are selected, the sample means do not vary as much as the individual values in the population. That the sample means are less variable than the individual values in the population follows directly from the fact that each sample mean averages together all the values in the sample. A population consists of individual outcomes that can take on a wide range of values, from extremely small to extremely large. However, if a sample contains an extreme value, although this value will have an effect on the sample mean, the effect is reduced because the value is averaged with all the other values in the sample. As the sample size increases, the effect of a single extreme value becomes smaller because it is averaged with more values.

The value of the standard deviation of all possible sample means, called the **standard error of the mean**, expresses how the sample means vary from sample to sample. As the sample size increases, the standard error of the mean decreases by a factor equal to the square root of the sample size.

STANDARD ERROR OF THE MEAN

The standard error of the mean, $\sigma_{\bar{X}}$, is equal to the standard deviation in the population, σ, divided by the square root of the sample size, n.

$$\sigma_{\bar{X}} = \frac{\sigma}{\sqrt{n}}$$ (8.3)

Equation (8.3) defines the standard error of the mean when sampling *with* replacement or sampling *without* replacement from large or infinite populations.

Example 8.3 computes the standard error of the mean when the sample selected without replacement contains less than 5% of the entire population.

EXAMPLE 8.3

Computing the Standard Error of the Mean

Returning to the cereal-filling process described in the Using Statistics scenario on page 317, if you randomly select a sample of 25 boxes without replacement from the thousands of boxes filled during a shift, the sample contains much less than 5% of the population. Given that the standard deviation of the cereal-filling process is 15 grams, compute the standard error of the mean.

SOLUTION Using Equation (8.3) with $n = 25$ and $\sigma = 15$, the standard error of the mean is

$$\sigma_{\bar{X}} = \frac{\sigma}{\sqrt{n}} = \frac{15}{\sqrt{25}} = \frac{15}{5} = 3$$

The variation in the sample means for samples of $n = 25$ is much less than the variation in the individual boxes of cereal (i.e., $\sigma_{\bar{X}} = 3$, while $\sigma = 15$).

Sampling from Normally Distributed Populations

Now that the concept of a sampling distribution has been introduced and the standard error of the mean has been defined, what distribution will the sample mean, $\overline{X}$, follow? If you are sampling from a population that is normally distributed with mean, μ, and standard deviation, σ, then regardless of the sample size, n, the sampling distribution of the mean is normally distributed, with mean, $\mu_{\overline{X}} = \mu$, and standard error of the mean, $\sigma_{\overline{X}} = \sigma/\sqrt{n}$.

In the simplest case, if you take samples of size $n = 1$, each possible sample mean is a single value from the population because

$$\overline{X} = \frac{\sum_{i=1}^{n} X_i}{n} = \frac{X_1}{1} = X_1$$

Therefore, if the population is normally distributed, with mean μ and standard deviation σ, the sampling distribution $\overline{X}$ for samples of $n = 1$ must also follow the normal distribution, with mean $\mu_{\overline{X}} = \mu$ and standard error of the mean $\sigma_{\overline{X}} = \sigma/\sqrt{1} = \sigma$. In addition, as the sample size increases, the sampling distribution of the mean still follows a normal distribution, with $\mu_{\overline{X}} = \mu$, but the standard error of the mean decreases, so that a larger proportion of sample means are closer to the population mean. Figure 8.4 illustrates this reduction in variability. Note that 500 samples of size 1, 2, 4, 8, 16, and 32 were randomly selected from a normally distributed population. From the polygons in Figure 8.4, you can see that, although the sampling distribution of the mean is approximately[1] normal for each sample size, the sample means are distributed more tightly around the population mean as the sample size increases.

[1]Remember that "only" 500 samples out of an infinite number of samples have been selected, so that the sampling distributions shown are only approximations of the population distributions.

FIGURE 8.4

Sampling distributions of the mean from 500 samples of sizes $n = 1, 2, 4, 8, 16,$ and 32 selected from a normal population

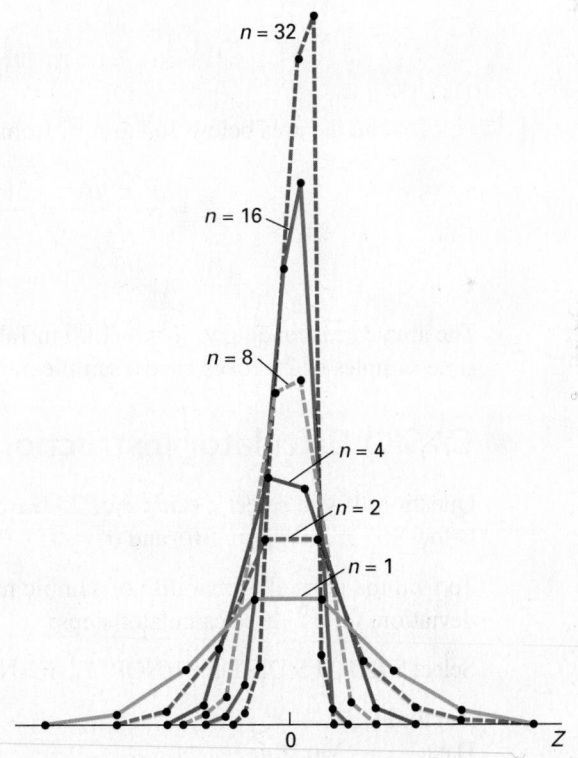

To further examine the concept of the sampling distribution of the mean, consider the Using Statistics scenario described on page 317. The packaging equipment that is filling 368-gram boxes of cereal is set so that the amount of cereal in a box is normally distributed, with a mean of 368 grams. From past experience, you know the population standard deviation for this filling process is 15 grams.

If you randomly select a sample of 25 boxes from the many thousands that are filled in a day and the mean weight is computed for this sample, what type of result could you expect? For example, do you think that the sample mean could be 368 grams? 200 grams? 365 grams?

The sample acts as a miniature representation of the population, so if the values in the population are normally distributed, the values in the sample should be approximately normally distributed. Thus, if the population mean is 368 grams, the sample mean has a good chance of being close to 368 grams.

How can you determine the probability that the sample of 25 boxes will have a mean below 365 grams? From the normal distribution (Section 7.2), you know that you can find the area below any value X by converting to standardized Z values:

$$Z = \frac{X - \mu}{\sigma}$$

In the examples in Section 7.2, you studied how any single value, X, differs from the population mean. Now, in this example, you want to study how a sample mean, $\bar{X}$, differs from the population mean. Substituting $\bar{X}$ for X, $\mu_{\bar{X}}$ for μ, and $\sigma_{\bar{X}}$ for σ in the equation above results in Equation (8.4).

FINDING Z FOR THE SAMPLING DISTRIBUTION OF THE MEAN

The Z value is equal to the difference between the sample mean, $\bar{X}$, and the population mean, μ, divided by the standard error of the mean, $\sigma_{\bar{X}}$.

$$Z = \frac{\bar{X} - \mu_{\bar{X}}}{\sigma_{\bar{X}}} = \frac{\bar{X} - \mu}{\frac{\sigma}{\sqrt{n}}} \tag{8.4}$$

To find the area below 365 grams, from Equation (8.4),

$$Z = \frac{\bar{X} - \mu_{\bar{X}}}{\sigma_{\bar{X}}} = \frac{365 - 368}{\frac{15}{\sqrt{25}}} = \frac{-3}{3} = -1.00$$

The area corresponding to $Z = -1.00$ in Table E.2 is 0.1587. Therefore, 15.87% of all the possible samples of 25 boxes have a sample mean below 365 grams.

CASIO Calculator Instruction

Question: If you select a sample of 25 boxes, what is the probability that the sample mean is below 365 grams? $\mu = 368$ and $\sigma = 15$

To find the normal probability of sample mean, associated with a known mean and standard deviation, follow these calculator steps:

Select **STAT**, **F5**(DIST), **F1**(NORM), **F2**(Ncd), and **F2**(Var). Then select the following options.

Normal C.D.
Data   : **Variable**
Lower   : **−10000** (Note: The calculator would not accept "- ∞. Therefore, you input a large negative number relative to its mean value.)
Upper   : **365**
σ : $\frac{15}{\sqrt{25}}$
μ : **368**
Save Res : **None**
Execute
Now press **EXE** or **F1**(CALC).

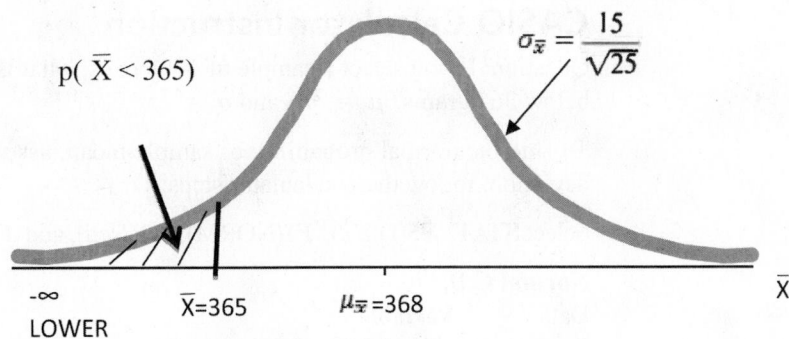

The calculator will now show the result:

Normal C.D.
p = 0.15865525
z: Low = −3456
z : Up = −1

Answer: 15.87% of the samples of 25 boxes have means below 365 grams.

The preceding statement is not the same as saying that a certain percentage of *individual* boxes will contain less than 365 grams of cereal. You compute that percentage as follows:

$$Z = \frac{X - \mu}{\sigma} = \frac{365 - 368}{15} = \frac{-3}{15} = -0.20$$

The area corresponding to $Z = -0.20$ in Table E.2 is 0.4207. Therefore, 42.07% of the *individual* boxes are expected to contain less than 365 grams. Comparing these results, you see that many more *individual boxes* than *sample means* are below 365 grams. This result is explained by the fact that each sample consists of 25 different values, some small and some large. The averaging process dilutes the importance of any individual value, particularly when the sample size is large. Thus, the chance that the sample mean of 25 boxes is far away from the population mean is less than the chance that a *single* box is far away.

Examples 8.4 and 8.5 show how these results are affected by using different sample sizes.

EXAMPLE 8.4

The Effect of Sample Size, *n*, on the Computation of $\sigma_{\bar{X}}$

How is the standard error of the mean affected by increasing the sample size from 25 to 100 boxes?

SOLUTION If n = 100 boxes, then using Equation (8.3) on page 328:

$$\sigma_{\bar{X}} = \frac{\sigma}{\sqrt{n}} = \frac{15}{\sqrt{100}} = \frac{15}{10} = 1.5$$

The fourfold increase in the sample size from 25 to 100 reduces the standard error of the mean by half—from 3 grams to 1.5 grams. This demonstrates that taking a larger sample results in less variability in the sample means from sample to sample.

EXAMPLE 8.5

The Effect of Sample Size, *n*, on the Clustering of Means in the Sampling Distribution

If you select a sample of 100 boxes, what is the probability that the sample mean is below 365 grams?

SOLUTION Using Equation (8.4) on page 330,

$$Z = \frac{\bar{X} - \mu_{\bar{X}}}{\sigma_{\bar{X}}} = \frac{365 - 368}{\dfrac{15}{\sqrt{100}}} = \frac{-3}{1.5} = -2.00$$

From Table E.2, the area less than $Z = -2.00$ is 0.0228. Therefore, 2.28% of the samples of 100 boxes have means below 365 grams, as compared with 15.87% for samples of 25 boxes.

CASIO Calculator Instruction

Question: If you select a sample of 100 boxes, what is the probability that the sample mean is below 365 grams? $\mu = 368$ and $\sigma = 15$

To find the normal probability of sample mean, associated with a known mean and standard deviation, follow these calculator steps:

Select **STAT**, **F5**(DIST), **F1**(NORM), **F2**(Ncd), and **F2**(Var). Then select the following options.

Normal C.D.
Data   : **Variable**
Lower   : **−10000** (Note: The calculator would not accept "- ∞. Therefore, you input a large negative number relative to its mean value.)
Upper   : **365**
σ : $\dfrac{15}{\sqrt{100}}$
μ : **368**
Save Res : **None**
Execute
Now press **EXE** or **F1**(CALC).

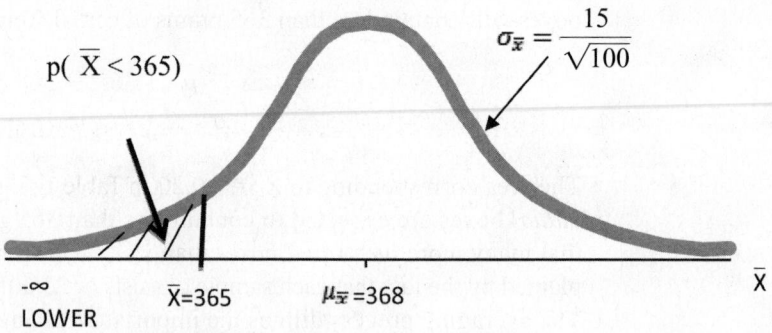

The calculator will now show the result:

Normal C.D.
p = 0.02275013
z: Low = −6912
z : Up = −2

Answer: 2.28% of the samples of 100 boxes have means below 365 grams.

Note: If everything else remains the same, as n increases, the probability decreases.

Sometimes you need to find the interval that contains a fixed proportion of the sample means. To do so, determine a distance below and above the population mean containing a specific area of the normal curve. From Equation (8.4) on page 330,

$$Z = \frac{\overline{X} - \mu}{\dfrac{\sigma}{\sqrt{n}}}$$

Solving for $\overline{X}$ results in Equation (8.5).

> ### FINDING $\overline{X}$ FOR THE SAMPLING DISTRIBUTION OF THE MEAN
>
> $$\overline{X} = \mu + Z\frac{\sigma}{\sqrt{n}} \qquad\qquad \textbf{(8.5)}$$

Example 8.6 illustrates the use of Equation (8.5).

Inverse Normal

Find $\bar{x}$ (sample mean) given the probability.

EXAMPLE 8.6

Determining the Interval That Includes a Fixed Proportion of the Sample Means

In the cereal-filling example, find an interval symmetrically distributed around the population mean that will include 95% of the sample means, based on samples of 25 boxes.

SOLUTION If 95% of the sample means are in the interval, then 5% are outside the interval. Divide the 5% into two equal parts of 2.5%. The value of Z in Table E.2 corresponding to an area of 0.0250 in the lower tail of the normal curve is -1.96, and the value of Z corresponding to a cumulative area of 0.9750 (i.e., 0.0250 in the upper tail of the normal curve) is $+1.96$. The lower value of $\bar{X}$ (called $\bar{X}_L$) and the upper value of $\bar{X}$ (called $\bar{X}_U$) are found by using Equation (8.5):

$$\bar{X}_L = 368 + (-1.96)\frac{15}{\sqrt{25}} = 368 - 5.88 = 362.12$$

$$\bar{X}_U = 368 + (1.96)\frac{15}{\sqrt{25}} = 368 + 5.88 = 373.88$$

Therefore, 95% of all sample means, based on samples of 25 boxes, are between 362.12 and 373.88 grams.

CASIO Calculator Instruction

Use the Casio calculator to obtain the inverse normal probability (i.e., find $\bar{X}$ given the probability).

Select **STAT**, **F5**(DIST), **F1**(NORM), **F3**(InvN), and **F2**(Var). Then select the following options.

Inverse Normal
Data   : **Variable**
Tail   : **CNTR (F3)**
Area   : **0.95**
σ : $\dfrac{15}{\sqrt{25}}$
μ : **368**
Save Res : **None**
Execute
Now press **EXE** or **F1**(CALC).

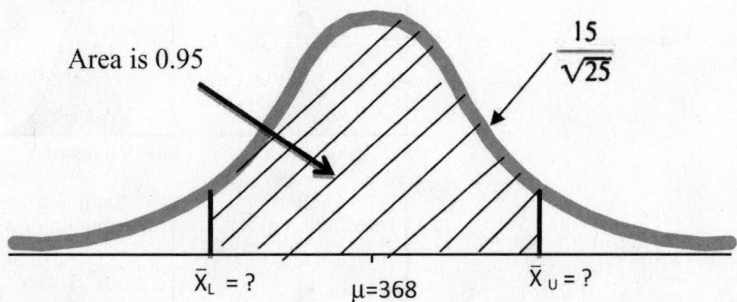

The calculator will now show the result:

Inverse Normal
X_1Inv   = 362.120108
X_2Inv   = 373.879892

Answer: 95% of all sample means based on samples of 25 boxes are between 362.12 and 373.88 grams.

Sampling from Non-Normally Distributed Populations—The Central Limit Theorem

Thus far in this section, only the sampling distribution of the mean for a normally distributed population has been considered. However, in many instances, either you know that the population is not normally distributed or it is unrealistic to assume that the population is normally distributed. An important theorem in statistics, the Central Limit Theorem, deals with this situation.

> ### THE CENTRAL LIMIT THEOREM
> The **Central Limit Theorem** states that as the sample size (i.e., the number of values in each sample) gets *large enough*, the sampling distribution of the mean is approximately normally distributed. This is true regardless of the shape of the distribution of the individual values in the population.

What sample size is large enough? A great deal of statistical research has gone into this issue. As a general rule, statisticians have found that for many population distributions, when the sample size is at least 30, the sampling distribution of the mean is approximately normal. However, you can apply the Central Limit Theorem for even smaller sample sizes if the population distribution is approximately bell-shaped. In the case in which the distribution of a variable is extremely skewed or has more than one mode, you may need sample sizes larger than 30 to ensure normality in the sampling distribution of the mean.

Figure 8.5 illustrates the application of the Central Limit Theorem to different populations. The sampling distributions from three different continuous distributions (normal, uniform, and exponential) for varying sample sizes ($n = 2, 5, 30$) are displayed.

FIGURE 8.5

Sampling distribution of the mean for different populations for samples of $n = 2, 5,$ and 30

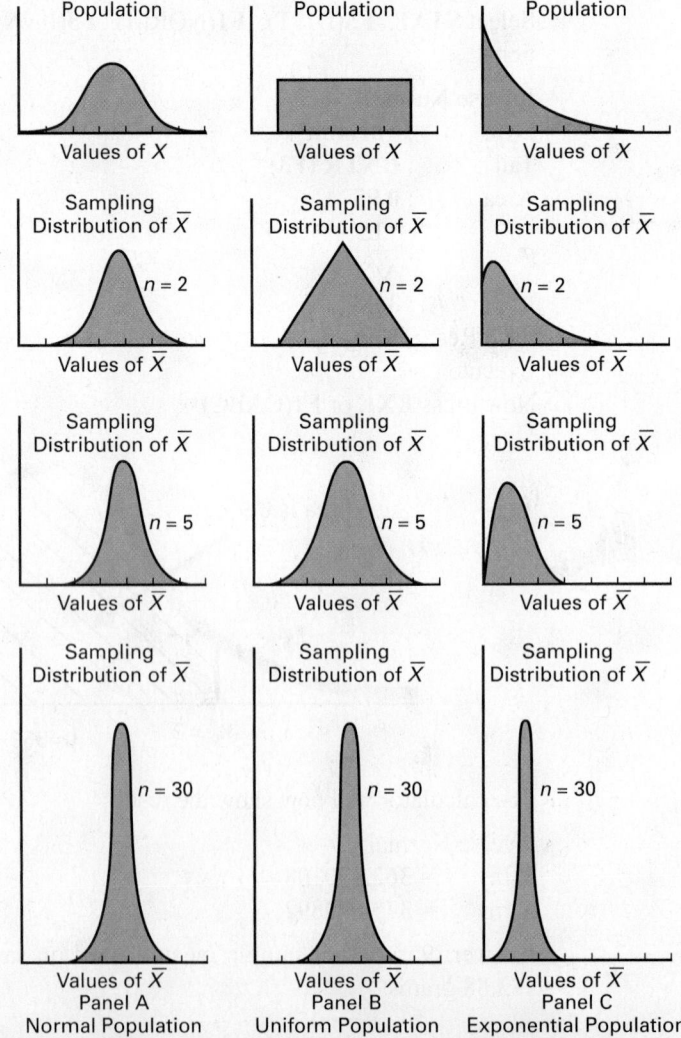

In each of the panels, because the sample mean is an unbiased estimator of the population mean, the mean of any sampling distribution is always equal to the mean of the population.

Panel A of Figure 8.5 shows the sampling distribution of the mean selected from a normal population. As mentioned earlier in this section, when the population is normally distributed, the sampling distribution of the mean is normally distributed for any sample size. [You can measure the variability by using the standard error of the mean, Equation (8.3), on page 328.]

Panel B of Figure 8.5 depicts the sampling distribution from a population with a uniform (or rectangular) distribution (see Section 7.1). When samples of size $n = 2$ are selected, there is a peaking, or *central limiting*, effect already working. For $n = 5$, the sampling distribution is bell-shaped and approximately normal. When $n = 30$, the sampling distribution looks very similar to a normal distribution. In general, the larger the sample size, the more closely the sampling distribution will follow a normal distribution. As with all other cases, the mean of each sampling distribution is equal to the mean of the population, and the variability decreases as the sample size increases.

Panel C of Figure 8.5 presents an exponential distribution (see Section 7.1). This population is extremely right-skewed. When $n = 2$, the sampling distribution is still highly right-skewed but less so than the distribution of the population. For $n = 5$, the sampling distribution is slightly right-skewed. When $n = 30$, the sampling distribution looks approximately normal. Again, the mean of each sampling distribution is equal to the mean of the population, and the variability decreases as the sample size increases.

Using the results from the normal, uniform, and exponential distributions, you can reach the following conclusions regarding the Central Limit Theorem:

- For most population distributions, regardless of shape, the sampling distribution of the mean is approximately normally distributed if samples of at least size 30 are selected.
- If the population distribution is fairly symmetrical, the sampling distribution of the mean is approximately normal for samples as small as size 5.
- If the population is normally distributed, the sampling distribution of the mean is normally distributed, regardless of the sample size.

The Central Limit Theorem is of crucial importance in using statistical inference to reach conclusions about a population. It allows you to make inferences about the population mean without having to know the specific shape of the population distribution.

VISUAL EXPLORATIONS   Exploring Sampling Distributions

Use the Visual Explorations **Two Dice Probability** procedure to observe the effects of simulated throws on the frequency distribution of the sum of the two dice. Open the **Visual Explorations add-in workbook** (see Appendix Section D.4) and:

1. Select **Add-Ins → VisualExplorations → Two Dice Probability**.
2. Click the **Tally** button to tally a set of throws in the frequency distribution table and histogram. Optionally, click the spinner buttons to adjust the number of throws per tally (round).
3. Repeat step 2 as many times as necessary.
4. Click **Finish** to end the simulation.

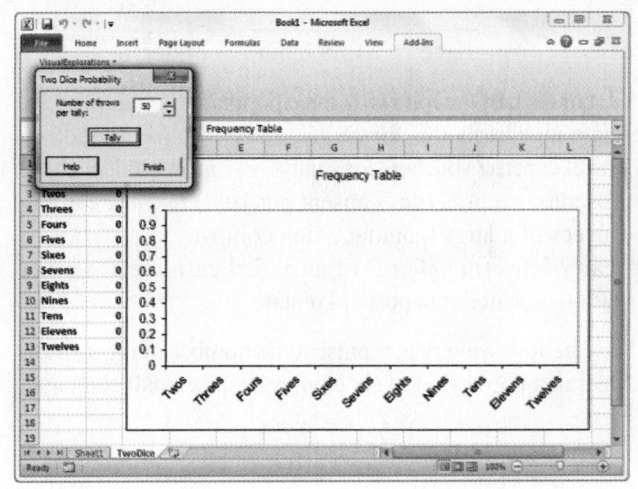

Problems for Section 8.4

LEARNING THE BASICS

8.15 Given a normal distribution with $\mu = 100$ and $\sigma = 10$, if you select a sample of $n = 25$, what is the probability that $\bar{X}$ is
a. less than 95?
b. between 95 and 97.5?
c. above 102.2?
d. There is a 65% chance that $\bar{X}$ is above what value?

8.16 Given a normal distribution with $\mu = 50$ and $\sigma = 5$, if you select a sample of $n = 100$, what is the probability that $\bar{X}$ is
a. less than 47?
b. between 47 and 49.5?
c. above 51.1?
d. There is a 35% chance that $\bar{X}$ is above what value?

APPLYING THE CONCEPTS

Central Limit Theorem Template:

$X =$ _____

$\left.\begin{array}{l} \mu = \\ \\ \sigma = \\ \\ n = \end{array}\right\}$ Normal or blank

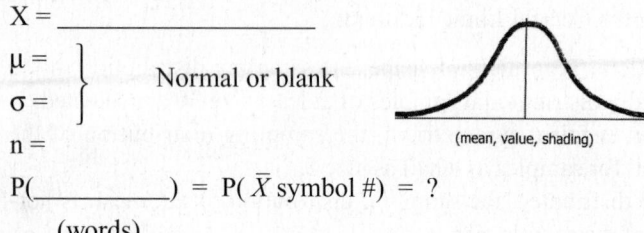
(mean, value, shading)

P(_____) = P($\bar{X}$ symbol #) = ?
    (words)

Info about $\bar{X}$

1. $\mu_{\bar{x}} = \mu =$

2. $\sigma_{\bar{x}} = \dfrac{\sigma}{\sqrt{n}} =$

3. a) The original population is normal; therefore, $\bar{X}$ is normal.

   OR

   b) The original population is not normal, but $\bar{X}$ is normal because n ≥ 30.

P($\bar{X}$ symbol #) = _____ = 0._ _ _ _
         (calc. or SPSS input)   (4 dec.)

8.17 For each of the following three populations, indicate what the sampling distribution for samples of 25 would consist of:
a. Travel expense vouchers for a university in an academic year
b. Absentee records (days absent per year) in 2011 for employees of a large manufacturing company.
c. Yearly sales (in gallons) of unleaded gasoline at service stations located in a particular state.

8.18 The following data represent the number of days absent per year in a population of six employees of a small company:

1 3 6 7 9 10

a. Assuming that you sample without replacement, select all possible samples of $n = 2$ and construct the sampling distribution of the mean. Compute the mean of all the sample means and also compute the population mean. Are they equal? What is this property called?
b. Repeat (a) for all possible samples of $n = 3$.
c. Compare the shape of the sampling distribution of the mean in (a) and (b). Which sampling distribution has less variability? Why?
d. Assuming that you sample with replacement, repeat (a) through (c) and compare the results. Which sampling distributions have the least variability—those in (a) or (b)? Why?

8.19 The diameter of a brand of Ping-Pong balls is approximately normally distributed, with a mean of 1.30 inches and a standard deviation of 0.04 inch. If you select a random sample of 16 Ping-Pong balls,
a. what is the sampling distribution of the mean?
b. what is the probability that the sample mean is less than 1.28 inches?
c. what is the probability that the sample mean is between 1.31 and 1.33 inches?
d. The probability is 60% that the sample mean will be between what two values, symmetrically distributed around the population mean?

8.20 The U.S. Census Bureau announced that the median sales price of new houses sold in 2010 was \$221,000, and the mean sales price was \$272,400 (**www.census.gov/newhomesales**, April 1, 2011). Assume that the standard deviation of the prices is \$90,000.
a. If you select samples of $n = 2$, describe the shape of the sampling distribution of $\bar{X}$.
b. If you select samples of $n = 100$, describe the shape of the sampling distribution of $\bar{X}$.
c. If you select a random sample of $n = 100$, what is the probability that the sample mean will be less than \$300,000?
d. If you select a random sample of $n = 100$, what is the probability that the sample mean will be between \$275,000 and \$290,000?

8.21 Time spent using e-mail per session is normally distributed, with $\mu = 8$ minutes and $\sigma = 2$ minutes. If you select a random sample of 25 sessions,
a. what is the probability that the sample mean is between 7.8 and 8.2 minutes?
b. what is the probability that the sample mean is between 7.5 and 8 minutes?
c. If you select a random sample of 100 sessions, what is the probability that the sample mean is between 7.8 and 8.2 minutes?
d. Explain the difference in the results of (a) and (c).

SELF **Test** **8.22** The amount of time a bank teller spends with each customer has a population mean $\mu = 3.10$ minutes and a standard deviation $\sigma = 0.40$ minute. If you select a random sample of 16 customers,
a. what is the probability that the mean time spent per customer is at least 3 minutes?
b. there is an 85% chance that the sample mean is less than how many minutes?
c. What assumption must you make in order to solve (a) and (b)?
d. If you select a random sample of 64 customers, there is an 85% chance that the sample mean is less than how many minutes?

PROBABILITY DISTRIBUTIONS—REVIEW EXERCISES

8.23 A manufacturing company anticipates that its daily demand for electric power during the next few months will fluctuate around a mean of 100.0 kilowatts. Based on past results, the daily power usage distribution should be normally distributed, with a standard deviation of 10.0 kilowatts.
a. What is the probability that the demand for electric power on a given day will range from 90.0 to 125.0 kilowatts?
b. What is the level of usage that will be exceeded only 20 percent of the time?

8.24 The defects in an automatic weaving process occur randomly at an average rate of 0.0025 per square metre and a standard deviation of 0.05 per square metre. The process has just been set up to run 1,000 square metres of fabric. What is the probability that there will be at least four defects in this fabric?

8.25 The occurrence of the first breakdown of an automatic washing machine is normally distributed, with a mean of 5.9 years and a standard deviation of 1.5 years. How long (full years) should these washing machines be guaranteed so that no more than 10% would require repairs during the warrantee period?

8.26 A large company is currently evaluating 14 cost-reducing proposals submitted by employees. Past experience has shown that 30 percent of such proposals are implemented by the company.
a. What is the probability that more than five proposals will be implemented?
b. What is the probability that at least half of the proposals will be implemented?
c. What is the expected number of proposals implemented?

8.27 The manufacturer of a quartz travel clock claims that, on average, its clocks deviate from perfect time by an average of 30 seconds in a month, with a standard deviation of 10 seconds. The test group that works for a consumer magazine purchased 40 of these clocks and found that the average deviation from perfect time was 35 seconds after one month.

a. If the manufacturer's claim is correct, what is the probability that the average deviation from perfect time for the 40 clocks would be 35 seconds or more?
b. If the average clock deviates by 33 seconds from perfect in one month, what is the probability that the average deviation from perfect time for the 40 clocks would be 35 seconds or more?

8.28 The Executours Corp. offers tours of the city to visiting businesspersons and uses a 12-passenger luxury bus. From past experience 10% of the people who make advance reservations will cancel at the last minute, therefore, Executours usually takes 13 reservations. For what percent of tours will they have enough seats for the passengers who show up for the tour?

8.29 The number of man-hours required by the Victory Construction Co. to assemble its prefabricated two-bedroom house is normally distributed, with a mean of 400 man-hours and a standard deviation of 40 man-hours.
a. The probability is 0.9 that the assembly of a house will take less than how many hours?
b. What is the probability that assembly of a house will take more than 420 man-hours?

8.30 There are two major steps in the production of solar covers for swimming pools. First, a 1-metre wide continuous strip of plastic air bubble material is produced. Then the material is cut to the required length (in this case 10 metres) and an appropriate number of these strips are sewn together to produce a solar cover.

Records kept by the quality control department indicate that on average:
i. there is one puncture in every 1,000 m^2 of plastic material.
ii. there is one sewing defect for every 1,500 m of sewing.

For a 4 m by 10 m solar cover:
a. What is the probability that the cover will not have a puncture?
b. What is the probability that the cover will not have a sewing defect?

8.31 In an attempt to improve sales, the management of a large chain of fast-food restaurants has decided to implement a reward/reprimand system based on monthly sales figures. The initial standards have been set up as follows:
i. Reward the managers of restaurants that have placed in the top 15% of sales for the month.
ii. Reprimand managers with sales less than $180,000 for the month.

For the month just past, the sales figures for the 4,350 restaurants were normally distributed, with a mean of $230,000 and a standard deviation of $22,000.
a. How many managers will be reprimanded?
b. What will be the minimum sales that will qualify for a reward?

8.32 A checkout counter is considered 'over-occupied' if more than eight customers arrive within a five-minute period. The average number of customers per hour is 78.
a. What is the probability that in one minute at most two customers arrive?
b. What is the probability that the counter is 'over-occupied' in a five-minute period?

8.33A From past experience, an airline has found that the luggage weight for individual air travelers on their trans-Atlantic route averages 40 kg, with a standard deviation of 10 kg. The plane consistently is booked with 100 passengers. The pilot insists on loading an extra 500 litres of fuel whenever the total luggage weight exceeds 4,200 kg. On what percent of the flights will the extra fuel be required?

8.33B The manufacturing process for automobile windshields involves placing a plastic adhesive film between two panes of glass. Then high pressure is applied to bond the three layers. The glass is then cut and bent to the required shape.

Quality standards require that there be no bubbles in order for a windshield to be considered suitable for installation into an automobile. Also, the glass must withstand an impact of 10 kg dropped from a height of 3 metres. The thickness of the finished windshield must be from 3.2 to 3.4 mm.

The High-Lite Glass Company makes rectangular windshield glass in sheets that are 2 metres wide by 1.5 metres high. The process usually averages 0.39 bubbles per sheet. Usually, only 3% of the windshields made from this company's glass fail the impact test.

One particular auto manufacturer just ordered 20 sheets of glass, which will be enough to make 60 windshields that are 2 metres wide by 0.5 metres high.
a. What is the probability that a finished windshield will have no bubbles?
b. What is the probability that at least 57 of the windshields will be able to withstand the impact test?

8.34 The Long-Life Tire Co. claims that its Super-All-Season tire lasts an average of 110,000 km. It is known that the tire life is normally distributed, with a standard deviation of 2800 km. Your company has just purchased all new tires for its fleet of 10 cars. Assuming that the manufacturer's claim is true, answer the following questions
a. What is the probability that a tire will last longer than 112,000 km?
b. What is the probability that the tires for your company car will last an average of at least 112,000 km?
c. What is the probability that the average life of all the tires purchased by your company will be at least 112,000 km?
d. What is the probability that all the tires of your car will last more than 112,000 km?

8.35 A sand and gravel dealer has received an order for five hundred 10.0 kg. bags of sand. Currently, the company has 5,150 kg of sand available.

A specialized sand-bag filling machine will be used to fill the bags. The machine can fill 100 bags per hour. The weight of sand in each bag will be normally distributed, with a standard deviation of 0.3 kg. The sand bags' mean weight can be adjusted by the filling machine operator.

If the mean weight is set at 10.25 kg, how many of the 500 bags are expected to meet the customer's expectations?

8.36 An automobile battery has a mean life of 1,200 days, with a standard deviation of 100 days. If the battery lifetimes are normally distributed, how long should the manufacturer make the guarantee in order to replace at most 10% of the batteries under warranty?

8.37 A hardware store chain has just received a truckload of 5,000 electric drills. Before accepting the shipment, the purchasing manager will test a random selection of 10 drills. The drills will be tested for maximum power consumption and the shipment will be rejected if the mean consumption is more than the 300 watts indicated on the product label. Suppose that the maximum power consumption of the drills in the shipment is normally distributed and averages only 295 watts, with a standard deviation of 12 watts.
a. What is the probability that the shipment will be rejected?
b. How many of the drills in the shipment are expected to exceed the maximum power consumption indicated on the label?

8.38 The quality control manager of Marilyn's Cookies is inspecting a batch of chocolate-chip cookies that has just been baked. If the production process is operating properly, the average number of chocolate chips per cookie is 6.76, with a standard deviation of 2.6 chocolate chips. What percent of the cookies will have fewer than four chocolate chips?

8.39 A student is about to write his marketing final exam that consists of 30 multiple-choice questions, each of which has five possible answers. If he has not studied, has no common sense regarding marketing, and thus has to guess the answer to each question, what is the probability that he will pass the exam?

8.40 The time to get an oil change at a certain car dealership averages 42.3 minutes, with a standard deviation of 8.6 minutes.
a. There are 45 cars booked for oil changes today. What is the probability that the jobs can be done in an average of 38 minutes or less?
b. Suppose 90 oil changes were done in one particular week. There is a 95% chance that the mean time was more than _____ minutes.

8.41 Table A at the bottom of this page appeared in the November 2000 issue of *Quality Progress* magazine. Assume that the salary distributions for all categories of analysts are normal.

a. What is the probability that an analyst with 3.1 to 6 years experience in the quality field will earn more than $60,000?

b. What is the third quartile salary of analysts with 10.1 to 20 years experience in the quality field?

8.42 The following table appeared in the Autumn 2003 issue of *Canadian Social Trends*.

	Total '000	Too many demands/ hours	Risk of accident/ injury	Poor interpersonal relations	Threat of layoff/ job loss	Having to learn computer skills	Other
					%		
Work arrangements							
Class of worker							
All workers	16,800	34	13	15	13	11	6
Self-employed	2,800	37	12	10	8	11	10
Employees	14,000	34	13	16	14	11	6
Employees only							
Hours of work							
All employees[1]	14,000	34	13	16	14	11	6
Full-time	11,500	37	14	17	15	12	6
30-35 hours/week	1,900	29	11	15	15	11	6
36-40 hours/week	6,100	33	14	17	16	12	6
41 or more hours/week	3,600	47	16	18	13	13	6
Part-time	2,300	20	9	11	10	7	5
1-15 hours/week	900	16	6	10	8	4E	4E
16-29 hours/week	1,400	22	11	12	11	9	5
Work schedules							
Regular daytime	9,500	35	11	15	14	12	6
Rotating shift	1,800	35	24	20	16	11	5
Regular evening or night	1,400	27	16	16	12	5	4
Irregular/split shift	900	35	17	16	13	11	5E
Other/on call	300	21	11E	15E	13E	F	9E

CST One in four rotating shift employees worry about the risk of accident or injury

1. Full-time and part-time employees.
E High sampling variability.
F Sample too small to provide reliable estimate.
Source: Statistics Canada, General Social Survey, 2000.

Living in one particular neighbourhood are 183 full-time workers that work 36–40 hours per week.

a. What is the probability that more than 15% of them worry about the risk of accident or injury?

b. In a sample of 120 rotating shift workers, what is the relative variability of the number who worry about the threat of layoff or job loss?

PROBABILITY DISTRIBUTIONS—COMBINATION QUESTIONS

8.43 In the 1840, Lambert Quetelet recorded data on an entire regiment of 5,732 soldiers. According to the records of Monsieur Quetelet,

- soldiers' chest measurements were normal, with a mean of 39.80 inches and a standard deviation of 2.05 inches;
- 12% of soldiers reported that they suffered from skin rash; and
- on average, 25 soldiers reported to Sick Bay each day.

a. What percentage of the soldiers in this regiment could be expected to have had chest measurements less than 38.5 inches?

b. Twenty-five percent of the soldiers had a chest measurement below what size?

c. In a group of 50 soldiers, what is the probability that more than four of them suffered from skin rash?

d. In a group of 40 soldiers, what is the probability that no more than eight of them suffered from skin rash?

e. What is the probability that exactly 30 soldiers reported to Sick Bay on a particular day?

f. What is the probability that a maximum of 200 soldiers reported to Sick Bay in a week?

g. In a sample of 35 randomly selected soldiers, what is the probability that the average chest measurement of the soldiers in this sample was at least 40.5 inches?

8.44 There are 12 agents in one office of a certain real estate firm. Much of the business in this office is conducted by taking a prospective customer out to view a particular property. The time to drive to and view a property is normally distributed and averages 47.3 minutes, with a standard deviation of 11.7 minutes. Past studies have shown that 26 percent of customers who visit properties with an agent will eventually buy a property being shown by that agent. On average, each agent visits 3.6 properties a day, with a standard deviation of 1.9 visits. All these activities are independent of each other.

a. What is the probability that an agent will visit at least seven properties over the next three days?

Table A. Salary by Job Title and Number of Years' Experience in the Quality Field for Respondents Who Work in the United States

	Minimum	Maximum	Standard deviation	Count	Mean	Median
Analyst						
Less than 1 year	$50,000	$64,000	$ 7,095	3	$56,333	$55,000
1 to 3 years	22,000	70,000	13,414	29	43,835	42,300
3.1 to 6 years	28,500	85,000	14,148	34	48,351	45,000
6.1 to 10 years	30,000	98,000	16,221	26	50,438	44,000
10.1 to 20 years	26,800	85,000	14,780	36	50,733	53,000
More than 20 years	21,000	83,000	18,851	9	54,111	55,000
No experience	42,000	77,000	11,404	6	58,731	58,000

b. What is the probability that the average time of the next 50 property viewings will be less than 45 minutes?

c. A particular agent currently has 17 prospective customers that are being shown properties for sale. What is the probability that fewer than four of these customers will eventually buy a property being shown by the agent?

d. Eighty-two (82) percent of property visits will take what range of time, centered at the mean?

8.45 For the Seashell gas station in your neighbourhood, records indicate that the number of customers arriving in any five-minute interval averages 0.94 customers, with a standard deviation of 0.97 customers. Sixty-five (65) percent of the customers use a credit card to pay for their purchase. There are eight pumps at this service station. The time that a car is parked at a pump is normally distributed, with a mean of 6.35 minutes and a standard deviation of 2.10 minutes. All these activities are independent of each other.

a. Ninety-four (94) percent of the customers will be parked for what maximum amount of time?

b. For 12 randomly selected customers, what is the probability that at least 10 of them will pay using a credit card?

c. What is the probability that more than five customers will arrive in a 15-minute period?

d. What is the probability that the average parked time for the next 40 customers will be less than six minutes?

8.46 There are 12 brokers in one office of a certain brokerage firm. Much of the business in this office is conducted by telephone. The duration of a telephone call is normally distributed and averages 7.45 minutes, with a standard deviation of 1.7 minutes. Past studies have shown that 57 percent of telephone calls result in a buy or sell order. On average, each broker receives 1.6 calls every 20 minutes, with a standard deviation of 1.3 calls. All these activities are independent of each other.

a. What is the probability that a broker will receive at least four calls in the next hour?

b. What is the probability that the average duration of the next 40 calls will be less than seven minutes?

c. For nine randomly selected calls, what is the probability that at least seven of them will result in a buy or sell order?

d. Ninety-two (92) percent of the calls will last for what minimum amount of time?

8.47 During the month of December, the average number of customers entering Reader's Bookstore is 7.84 every 20 minutes, with a standard deviation of 2.8 customers. The time to get through the check-out counter is approximately normally distributed, with a mean of 5.6 minutes and a standard deviation of 1.9 minutes. Fifteen percent of customers are first-time shoppers and 25% of all customers use their debit card to pay for their books.

a. Currently, there are 40 customers in the store. What is the probability that more than three-quarters of them will have shopped at Reader's before?

b. What is the probability that a customer will take less than four minutes to check-out?

c. What is the probability that more than 10 customers will enter the store in the next half-hour?

d. Ten percent of the customers will take longer than _____ to check out.

8.48 New houses are being built and sold at record paces in the GTA this year. It was reported on the radio last week that, on average, one new home was sold every six minutes. In February, 3,215 new houses were sold in the GTA region, of which 80% were located in the 905 area code municipalities.

The prices of new homes being built and sold this year are also at record high levels. The average price of a two-bedroom home was $212,000, with a standard deviation of $5,300. The mean and standard deviation of the prices of three-bedroom homes were $276,000 and $10,700, respectively. For four-bedroom homes, the corresponding figures were $328,000 and $24,800. All the price data sets were normally distributed.

The figures also showed that 32% of homes being built this year had two bedrooms, 45% had three bedrooms, 15% had four bedrooms, and the remainder were equal numbers of five- and six-bedroom homes. The time to build a three-bedroom home averaged 205 days, with a standard deviation of 12 days. The sizes of three-bedroom homes were normally distributed, with a mean of 2,540 ft^2 and a standard deviation of 175 ft^2.

In Mississauga, just west of Winston Churchill Blvd., a large new community of 2,400 houses is being built on a 3-square-kilometre (3,000,000 m^2) area. Only 10% of the houses will be bungalows—that is, one-storey. All others will be two-storey houses. The bungalows are to be randomly distributed throughout the community.

(Note: All figures above, except those in the first paragraph, also apply to the Mississauga community.)

a. What is the probability that a two-bedroom home will cost more than $225,000?

b. On one street in the Mississauga development, there are 23 houses. What is the probability that at most five of them have four bedrooms?

c. One developer is building 53 three-bedroom homes in the new Mississauga community. What is the probability that the mean time to construct these homes will be less than 200 days?

d. What is the probability that 12 new homes will be sold in an hour?

e. One developer in the new Mississauga community has a special deal this weekend on three-bedroom houses. There will be a $20,000 price discount on the largest 15% of houses. How big a three-bedroom house do you have to buy to get this discount?

f. What is the expected number of bedrooms in new homes being built this year?

g. What is the probability that there would be at least three bungalows in a 10,000 m² area in the new development in Mississauga?

8.49 The production process used to produce 500-ft spools of electrical cable operates continuously, 24 hours a day, and is capable of producing approximately six spools per day. The time required to produce one spool is normally distributed, with a mean of 4.23 hours and a standard deviation of 0.45 hours. Defects occur in the wire at an average rate of 1 per 1,000 feet. As a result, 61% of all spools have no defects. The machine used to produce the wire, needs to be adjusted an average of four times per day, with a standard deviation of two times per day.

a. What is the probability that in a week's production, i.e. (i.e., 42 spools) there will be at least 35 spools without defects?

b. What is the probability that a spool can be produced in less than four hours?

c. What is the probability that the wire-producing machine will need to be adjusted at most once in an eight-hour shift?

d. What is the probability that the average time to produce the next 15 spools will be more than 4.1 hours?

e. Seventy-eight (78) percent of the spools will be produced within what range of time, centered at the mean?

8.5 Sampling Distribution of the Proportion

Consider a categorical variable that has only two categories, such as the customer prefers your brand or the customer prefers the competitor's brand. You are interested in the proportion of items belonging to one of the categories—for example, the proportion of customers that prefer your brand. The population proportion, represented by π, is the proportion of items in the entire population with the characteristic of interest. The sample proportion, represented by p, is the proportion of items in the sample with the characteristic of interest. The sample proportion, a statistic, is used to estimate the population proportion, a parameter. To calculate the sample proportion, you assign one of two possible values, 1 or 0, to represent the presence or absence of the characteristic. You then sum all the 1 and 0 values and divide by n, the sample size. For example, if, in a sample of five customers, three preferred your brand and two did not, you have three 1s and two 0s. Summing the three 1s and two 0s and dividing by the sample size of 5 results in a sample proportion of 0.60.

SAMPLE PROPORTION

$$p = \frac{X}{n} = \frac{\text{Number of items having the characteristic of interest}}{\text{Sample size}} \quad (8.6)$$

The sample proportion, p, will be between 0 and 1. If all items have the characteristic, you assign each a score of 1, and p is equal to 1. If half the items have the characteristic, you assign half a score of 1 and assign the other half a score of 0, and p is equal to 0.5. If none of the items have the characteristic, you assign each a score of 0, and p is equal to 0.

In Section 8.4, you learned that the sample mean, $\bar{X}$ is an unbiased estimator of the population mean, μ. Similarly, the statistic p is an unbiased estimator of the population proportion, π. By analogy to the sampling distribution of the mean, whose standard error is $\sigma_{\bar{X}} = \frac{\sigma}{\sqrt{n}}$, the **standard error of the proportion**, σ_p, is given in Equation (8.7).

STANDARD ERROR OF THE PROPORTION

$$\sigma_p = \sqrt{\frac{\pi(1-\pi)}{n}} \quad (8.7)$$

The **sampling distribution of the proportion** follows the binomial distribution, as discussed in Section 6.2 when sampling with replacement (or without replacement from extremely large populations). However, you can use the normal distribution to approximate the binomial distribution when $n\pi$ and $n(1-\pi)$ are each at least 5. In most cases in which inferences are made about the proportion, the sample size is substantial enough to meet the conditions for using the normal approximation (see reference 1). Therefore, in many instances, you can use the normal distribution to estimate the sampling distribution of the proportion.

Substituting p for $\bar{X}$, π for μ, and $\sqrt{\dfrac{\pi(1-\pi)}{n}}$ for $\dfrac{\sigma}{\sqrt{n}}$ in Equation (8.4) on page 330 results in Equation (8.8).

FINDING Z FOR THE SAMPLING DISTRIBUTION OF THE PROPORTION

$$Z = \frac{p - \pi}{\sqrt{\dfrac{\pi(1-\pi)}{n}}} \qquad (8.8)$$

To illustrate the sampling distribution of the proportion, suppose that the manager of the local branch of a bank determines that 40% of all depositors have multiple accounts at the bank. If you select a random sample of 200 depositors, because $n\pi = 200(0.40) = 80 \geq 5$ and $n(1 - \pi) = 200(0.60) = 120 \geq 5$, the sample size is large enough to assume that the sampling distribution of the proportion is approximately normally distributed. Then, you can calculate the probability that the sample proportion of depositors with multiple accounts is less than 0.30 by using Equation (8.8):

$$Z = \frac{p - \pi}{\sqrt{\dfrac{\pi(1-\pi)}{n}}}$$

$$= \frac{0.30 - 0.40}{\sqrt{\dfrac{(0.40)(0.60)}{200}}} = \frac{-0.10}{\sqrt{\dfrac{0.24}{200}}} = \frac{-0.10}{0.0346}$$

$$= -2.89$$

Using Table E.2, the area under the normal curve less than -2.89 is 0.0019. Therefore, if the population proportion of items of interest is 0.40, only 0.19% of the samples of $n = 200$ would be expected to have sample proportions less than 0.30.

Problems for Section 8.5

LEARNING THE BASICS

8.50 In a random sample of 64 people, 48 are classified as "successful."

a. Determine the sample proportion, p, of "successful" people.
b. If the population proportion is 0.70, determine the standard error of the proportion.

8.51 A random sample of 50 households was selected for a telephone survey. The key question asked was, "Do you or any member of your household own a cellular telephone that you can use to access the Internet?" Of the 50 respondents, 20 said yes and 30 said no.

a. Determine the sample proportion, p, of households with cellular telephones that can be used to access the Internet.

b. If the population proportion is 0.45, determine the standard error of the proportion.

8.52 The following data represent the responses (Y for yes and N for no) from a sample of 40 college students to the question "Do you currently own shares in any stocks?"

N N Y N N Y N Y N Y N N Y N Y Y N N N Y
N Y N N N N Y N N Y Y N N N Y N N Y N N

a. Determine the sample proportion, p, of college students who own shares of stock.
b. If the population proportion is 0.30, determine the standard error of the proportion.

APPLYING THE CONCEPTS

✓SELF Test 8.53 A political pollster is conducting an analysis of sample results in order to make predictions on election night. Assuming a two-candidate election, if a specific candidate receives at least 55% of the vote in the sample, that candidate will be forecast as the winner of the election. If you select a random sample of 100 voters, what is the probability that a candidate will be forecast as the winner when

a. the population percentage of her vote is 50.1%?
b. the population percentage of her vote is 60%?
c. the population percentage of her vote is 49% (and she will actually lose the election)?
d. If the sample size is increased to 400, what are your answers to (a) through (c)? Discuss.

8.54 You plan to conduct a marketing experiment in which students are to taste one of two different brands of soft drink. Their task is to correctly identify the brand tasted. You select a random sample of 200 students and assume that the students have no ability to distinguish between the two brands. (Hint: If an individual has no ability to distinguish between the two soft drinks, then the two brands are equally likely to be selected.)

a. What is the probability that the sample will have between 50% and 60% of the identifications correct?
b. The probability is 90% that the sample percentage is contained within what symmetrical limits of the population percentage?
c. What is the probability that the sample percentage of correct identifications is greater than 65%?
d. Which is more likely to occur—more than 60% correct identifications in the sample of 200 or more than 55% correct identifications in a sample of 1,000? Explain.

8.55 In a recent survey of full-time female workers ages 22 to 35 years, 46% said that they would rather give up some of their salary for more personal time. (Data extracted from "I'd Rather Give Up," *USA Today*, March 4, 2010, p. 1B.) Suppose you select a sample of 100 full-time female workers 22 to 35 years old.

a. What is the probability that in the sample, fewer than 50% would rather give up some of their salary for more personal time?
b. What is the probability that in the sample, between 40% and 50% would rather give up some of their salary for more personal time?
c. What is the probability that in the sample, more than 40% would rather give up some of their salary for more personal time?
d. If a sample of 400 is taken, how does this change your answers to (a) through (c)?

8.56 Companies often make flextime scheduling available to help recruit and keep female employees who have chil-

dren. Other workers sometimes view these flextime schedules as unfair. An article in *USA Today* indicates that 25% of male employees state that they have to pick up the slack for moms working flextime schedules. (Data extracted from D. Jones, "Poll Finds Resentment of Flextime," **www.usa today.com**, May 11, 2007.) Suppose you select a random sample of 100 male employees working for companies offering flextime.

a. What is the probability that 25% or fewer male employees will indicate that they have to pick up the slack for moms working flextime?
b. What is the probability that 20% or fewer male employees will indicate that they have to pick up the slack for moms working flextime?
c. If a random sample of 500 is taken, how does this change your answers to (a) and (b)?

8.57 According to Gallup's poll on consumer behavior, 36% of Americans say they will consider only cars manufactured by an American company when purchasing a new car. (Data extracted from *The Gallup Poll*, **www.gallup.com**, March 31, 2010.) If you select a random sample of 200 Americans,

a. what is the probability that the sample will have between 30% and 40% who say they will consider only cars manufactured by an American company when purchasing a new car?
b. the probability is 90% that the sample percentage will be contained within what symmetrical limits of the population percentage?
c. the probability is 95% that the sample percentage will be contained within what symmetrical limits of the population percentage?

8.58 The Agency for Healthcare Research and Quality reports that medical errors are responsible for injury to 1 out of every 25 hospital patients in the United States. (Data extracted from M. Ozan-Rafferty, "Hospitals: Never Have a Never Event," *The Gallup Management Journal*, **gmj .gallup.com**, May 7, 2009.) These errors are tragic and expensive. Preventable health care–related errors cost an estimated $29 billion each year in the United States. Suppose that you select a sample of 100 U.S. hospital patients.

a. What is the probability that the sample percentage reporting injury due to medical errors will be between 5% and 10%?
b. The probability is 90% that the sample percentage will be within what symmetrical limits of the population percentage?
c. The probability is 95% that the sample percentage will be within what symmetrical limits of the population percentage?
d. Suppose you selected a sample of 400 U.S. hospital patients. How does this change your answers in (a) through (c)?

8.59 A survey of 2,250 American adults reported that 59% got news both online and offline in a typical day. (Data extracted from "How Americans Get News in a Typical Day," *USA Today*, March 10, 2010, p. 1A.)

a. Suppose that you take a sample of 100 American adults. If the population proportion of American adults who get news both online and offline in a typical day is 0.59, what is the probability that fewer than half in your sample will get news both online and offline in a typical day?

b. Suppose that you take a sample of 500 American adults. If the population proportion of American adults who get news both online and offline in a typical day is 0.59, what is the probability that fewer than half in your sample will get news both online and offline in a typical day?

c. Discuss the effect of sample size on the sampling distribution of the proportion in general and the effect on the probabilities in (a) and (b).

USING STATISTICS @ Oxford Cereals, Part I Revisited

© Corbis

As the plant operations manager for Oxfords Cereals, you were responsible for monitoring the amount of cereal placed in each box. To be consistent with package labeling, boxes should contain a mean of 368 grams of cereal. Thousands of boxes are produced during a shift, and weighing every single box was determined to be too time-consuming, costly, and inefficient. Instead, a sample of boxes was selected. Based on your analysis of the sample, you had to decide whether to maintain, alter, or shut down the process.

Using the concept of the sampling distribution of the mean, you were able to determine probabilities that such a sample mean could have been randomly selected from a population with a mean of 368 grams. Specifically, if a sample of size $n = 25$ is selected from a population with a mean of 368 and standard deviation of 15, you calculated the probability of selecting a sample with a mean of 365 grams or less to be 15.87%. If a larger sample size is selected, the sample mean should be closer to the population mean. This result was illustrated when you calculated the probability if the sample size were increased to $n = 100$. Using the larger sample size, you determined the probability of selecting a sample with a mean of 365 grams or less to be 2.28%.

SUMMARY

You have learned that in many business situations, the population is so large that you cannot gather information on every item. Instead, statistical sampling procedures focus on selecting a small representative group of the larger population. The results of the sample are then used to estimate characteristics of the entire population. Selecting a sample is less time-consuming, less costly, and more practical than analyzing the entire population.

In this chapter, you studied four common probability sampling methods—simple random, systematic, stratified, and cluster sampling. You also studied the sampling distribution of the sample mean and the sampling distribution of the sample proportion and their relationship to the Central Limit Theorem. You learned that the sample mean is an unbiased estimator of the population mean, and the sample proportion is an unbiased estimator of the population proportion. In the next five chapters, the techniques of confidence intervals and tests of hypotheses commonly used for statistical inference are discussed.

KEY EQUATIONS

Population Mean

$$\mu = \frac{\sum_{i=1}^{N} X_i}{N}$$

Population Standard Deviation

$$\sigma = \sqrt{\frac{\sum_{i=1}^{N} (X_i - \mu)^2}{N}}$$

Standard Error of the Mean

$$\sigma_{\bar{X}} = \frac{\sigma}{\sqrt{n}}$$

Finding Z for the Sampling Distribution of the Mean

$$Z = \frac{\bar{X} - \mu_{\bar{X}}}{\sigma_{\bar{X}}} = \frac{\bar{X} - \mu}{\frac{\sigma}{\sqrt{n}}}$$

Finding $\bar{X}$ for the Sampling Distribution of the Mean

$$\bar{X} = \mu + Z \frac{\sigma}{\sqrt{n}}$$

Sample Proportion

$$p = \frac{X}{n}$$

Standard Error of the Proportion

$$\sigma_p = \sqrt{\frac{\pi(1 - \pi)}{n}}$$

Finding Z for the Sampling Distribution of the Proportion

$$Z = \frac{p - \pi}{\sqrt{\frac{\pi(1 - \pi)}{n}}}$$

KEY TERMS

Central Limit Theorem   334
cluster   322
cluster sample   322
convenience sampling   318
coverage error   323
frame   318
judgment sample   318
margin of error   324
measurement error   324
nonprobability sample   318

nonresponse bias   323
nonresponse error   323
probability sample   318
sampling distribution   326
sampling distribution of the mean   326
sampling distribution of the
   proportion   342
sampling error   323
sampling with replacement   319
sampling without replacement   319

selection bias   323
simple random sample   319
standard error of the mean   328
standard error of the proportion   321
strata   321
stratified sample   321
systematic sample   321
table of random numbers   319
unbiased   326

PROBLEMS

CHECKING YOUR UNDERSTANDING

8.60 Why is the sample mean an unbiased estimator of the population mean?

8.61 Why does the standard error of the mean decrease as the sample size, n, increases?

8.62 Why does the sampling distribution of the mean follow a normal distribution for a large enough sample size, even though the population may not be normally distributed?

8.63 What is the difference between a population distribution and a sampling distribution?

8.64 Under what circumstances does the sampling distribution of the proportion approximately follow the normal distribution?

8.65 What is the difference between probability sampling and nonprobability sampling?

8.66 What are some potential problems with using "fishbowl" methods to select a simple random sample?

8.67 What is the difference between sampling *with* replacement versus sampling *without* replacement?

8.68 What is the difference between a simple random sample and a systematic sample?

8.69 What is the difference between a simple random sample and a stratified sample?

8.70 What is the difference between a stratified sample and a cluster sample?

APPLYING THE CONCEPTS

8.71 An industrial sewing machine uses ball bearings that are targeted to have a diameter of 0.75 inch. The lower and upper specification limits under which the ball bearing can operate are 0.74 inch (lower) and 0.76 inch (upper). Past experience has indicated that the actual diameter of the ball bearings is approximately normally distributed, with a mean of 0.753 inch and a standard deviation of 0.004 inch. If you select a random sample of 25 ball bearings, what is the probability that the sample mean is
a. between the target and the population mean of 0.753?
b. between the lower specification limit and the target?
c. greater than the upper specification limit?
d. less than the lower specification limit?
e. The probability is 93% that the sample mean diameter will be greater than what value?

8.72 The fill amount of bottles of a soft drink is normally distributed, with a mean of 2.0 liters and a standard deviation of 0.05 liter. If you select a random sample of 25 bottles, what is the probability that the sample mean will be
a. between 1.99 and 2.0 liters?
b. below 1.98 liters?
c. greater than 2.01 liters?
d. The probability is 99% that the sample mean amount of soft drink will be at least how much?
e. The probability is 99% that the sample mean amount of soft drink will be between which two values (symmetrically distributed around the mean)?

8.73 An orange juice producer buys oranges from a large orange grove that has one variety of orange. The amount of juice squeezed from these oranges is approximately normally distributed, with a mean of 4.70 ounces and a standard deviation of 0.40 ounce. Suppose that you select a sample of 25 oranges.
a. What is the probability that the sample mean amount of juice will be at least 4.60 ounces?
b. The probability is 70% that the sample mean amount of juice will be contained between what two values symmetrically distributed around the population mean?
c. The probability is 77% that the sample mean amount of juice will be greater than what value?

8.74 In Problem 8.73, suppose that the mean amount of juice squeezed is 5.0 ounces.
a. What is the probability that the sample mean amount of juice will be at least 4.60 ounces?
b. The probability is 70% that the sample mean amount of juice will be contained between what two values symmetrically distributed around the population mean?

c. The probability is 77% that the sample mean amount of juice will be greater than what value?

8.75 The stock market in Chile reported strong returns in 2010. The population of stocks earned a mean return of 49.6% in 2010. (Data extracted from *The Wall Street Journal*, January 3, 2011, p. R7.) Assume that the returns for stocks on the Chilean stock market were distributed as a normal random variable, with a mean of 49.6 and a standard deviation of 20. If you selected a random sample of 16 stocks from this population, what is the probability that the sample would have a mean return
a. less than 50?
b. between 40 and 60?
c. greater than 40?

8.76 The article mentioned in Problem 8.75 reported that the stock market in France had a mean return of −5.7% in 2010. Assume that the returns for stocks on the French stock market were distributed as a normal random variable, with a mean of −5.7 and a standard deviation of 10. If you select an individual stock from this population, what is the probability that it would have a return
a. less than 0 (i.e., a loss)?
b. between −10 and −20?
c. greater than 5?
If you selected a random sample of four stocks from this population, what is the probability that the sample would have a mean return
d. less than 0—that is, a loss?
e. between −10 and −20?
f. greater than 5?
g. Compare your results in parts (d) through (f) to those in (a) through (c).

8.77 (Class Project) The table of random numbers is an example of a uniform distribution because each digit is equally likely to occur. Starting in the row corresponding to the day of the month in which you were born, use the table of random numbers (Table E.1) to take one digit at a time.

Select five different samples each of $n = 2, n = 5$, and $n = 10$. Compute the sample mean of each sample. Develop a frequency distribution of the sample means for the results of the entire class, based on samples of sizes $n = 2, n = 5$, and $n = 10$.

What can be said about the shape of the sampling distribution for each of these sample sizes?

8.78 (Class Project) Toss a coin 10 times and record the number of heads. If each student performs this experiment five times, a frequency distribution of the number of heads can be developed from the results of the entire class. Does this distribution seem to approximate the normal distribution?

8.79 (Class Project) The number of cars waiting in line at a car wash is distributed as follows:

Number of Cars	Probability
0	0.25
1	0.40
2	0.20
3	0.10
4	0.04
5	0.01

You can use the table of random numbers (Table E.1) to select samples from this distribution by assigning numbers as follows:
1. Start in the row corresponding to the day of the month in which you were born.
2. Select a two-digit random number.
3. If you select a random number from 00 to 24, record a length of 0; if from 25 to 64, record a length of 1; if from 65 to 84, record a length of 2; if from 85 to 94, record a length of 3; if from 95 to 98, record a length of 4; if 99, record a length of 5.

   Select samples of $n = 2, n = 5$, and $n = 10$. Compute the mean for each sample. For example, if a sample of size 2 results in the random numbers 18 and 46, these would correspond to lengths 0 and 1, respectively, producing a sample mean of 0.5. If each student selects five different samples for each sample size, a frequency distribution of the sample means (for each sample size) can be developed from the results of the entire class. What conclusions can you reach

concerning the sampling distribution of the mean as the sample size is increased?

8.80 (Class Project) Using Table E.1, simulate the selection of different-colored balls from a bowl, as follows:
1. Start in the row corresponding to the day of the month in which you were born.
2. Select one-digit numbers.
3. If a random digit between 0 and 6 is selected, consider the ball white; if a random digit is a 7, 8, or 9, consider the ball red.

   Select samples of $n = 10, n = 25$, and $n = 50$ digits. In each sample, count the number of white balls and compute the proportion of white balls in the sample. If each student in the class selects five different samples for each sample size, a frequency distribution of the proportion of white balls (for each sample size) can be developed from the results of the entire class. What conclusions can you reach about the sampling distribution of the proportion as the sample size is increased?

8.81 (Class Project) Suppose that step 3 of Problem 8.80 uses the following rule: "If a random digit between 0 and 8 is selected, consider the ball to be white; if a random digit of 9 is selected, consider the ball to be red." Compare and contrast the results in this problem and those in Problem 8.80.

MANAGING ASHLAND MULTICOMM SERVICES

Continuing the quality improvement effort first described in the Chapter 6 Managing Ashland MultiComm Services case, the target upload speed for AMS Internet service subscribers has been monitored. As before, upload speeds are measured on a standard scale in which the target value is 1.0. Data collected over the past year indicate that the upload speeds are approximately normally distributed, with a mean of 1.005 and a standard deviation of 0.10.

Exercise

1. Each day, at 25 random times, the upload speed is measured. Assuming that the distribution has not changed

from what it was in the past year, what is the probability that the upload speed is
   a. less than 1.0?
   b. between 0.95 and 1.0?
   c. between 1.0 and 1.05?
   d. less than 0.95 or greater than 1.05?
   e. Suppose that the mean upload speed of today's sample of 25 is 0.952. What conclusion can you reach about the upload speed today based on this result? Explain.
2. Compare the results of AMS1 (a) through (d) to those of AMS1 in Chapter 7 on page 312. What conclusions can you reach concerning the differences?

DIGITAL CASE

Apply your knowledge about sampling distributions in this Digital Case, which reconsiders the Oxford Cereals Using Statistics scenario.

The advocacy group Consumers Concerned About Cereal Cheaters (CCACC) suspects that cereal companies, including Oxford Cereals, are cheating consumers by packaging cereals at less than labeled weights. Recently, the group investigated the package weights of two popular Oxford brand cereals. Open **CCACC.pdf** to examine the group's claims and supporting data, and then answer the following questions:

1. Are the data collection procedures that the CCACC uses to form its conclusions flawed? What procedures could the group follow to make its analysis more rigorous?

2. Assume that the two samples of five cereal boxes (one sample for each of two cereal varieties) listed on the CCACC website were collected randomly by organization members. For each sample, do the following:

a. Calculate the sample mean.

b. Assume that the standard deviation of the process is 15 grams and the population mean is 368 grams. Calculate the percentage of all samples for each process that have a sample mean less than the value you calculated in (a).

c. Again, assuming that the standard deviation is 15 grams, calculate the percentage of individual boxes of cereal that have a weight less than the value you calculated in (a).

3. What, if any, conclusions can you form by using your calculations about the filling processes for the two different cereals?

4. A representative from Oxford Cereals has asked that the CCACC take down its page discussing shortages in Oxford Cereals boxes. Is that request reasonable? Why or why not?

5. Can the techniques discussed in this chapter be used to prove cheating in the manner alleged by the CCACC? Why or why not?

REFERENCES

1. Cochran, W. G., *Sampling Techniques*, 3rd ed. (New York: Wiley, 1977).
2. Gallup, G. H., *The Sophisticated Poll-Watcher's Guide* (Princeton, NJ: Princeton Opinion Press, 1972).
3. Goleman, D., "Pollsters Enlist Psychologists in Quest for Unbiased Results," *The New York Times*, September 7, 1993, pp. C1, C11.
4. Hahn, G., and W. Meeker, *Statistical Intervals: A Guide for Practitioners* (New York: John Wiley and Sons, Inc., 1991).
5. "Landon in a Landslide: The Poll That Changed Polling," *History Matters: The U.S. Survey Course on the Web*, New York: American Social History Productions, 2005, downloaded at **http://historymatters.gmu.edu/d/5168/**.
6. *Microsoft Excel 2010* (Redmond, WA: Microsoft Corp., 2010).
7. *Minitab Release 16* (State College, PA: Minitab, Inc., 2010).
8. Rand Corporation, *A Million Random Digits with 100,000 Normal Deviates* (New York: The Free Press, 1955).
9. Squire, P., "Why the 1936 *Literary Digest* Poll Failed," *Public Opinion Quarterly 52*, 1988, pp.125–133.

CHAPTER 8 EXCEL GUIDE

EG8.1 Types of Sampling Methods

Simple Random Samples

PHStat2 Use **Random Sample Generation** to create a random sample *without replacement*. For example, to select the Example 8.1 sample of 40 workers on page 319, select **PHStat → Sampling → Random Sample Generation**. In the procedure's dialog box (shown below):

1. Enter **40** as the **Sample Size**.
2. Click **Generate list of random numbers** and enter **800** as the **Population Size**.
3. Enter a **Title** and click **OK**.

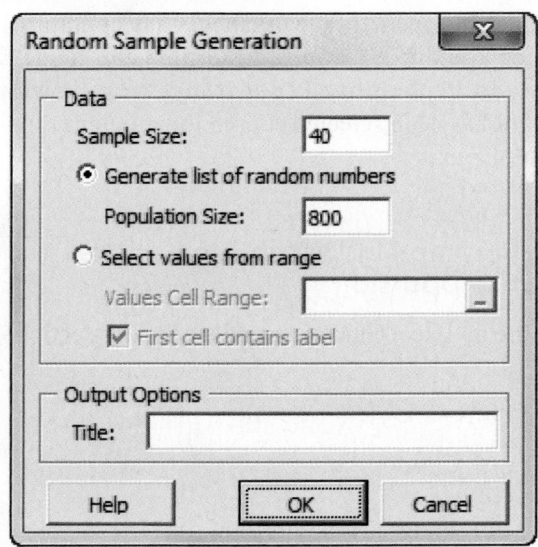

In-Depth Excel Use the **RANDBETWEEN** worksheet function to select a random integer that can be used to select an item from a frame. Enter the function as **RANDBETWEEN(1,** *population size*).

Use the **COMPUTE worksheet** of the **Random workbook** as a template for creating a random sample. This worksheet contains 40 copies of the formula **=RANDBETWEEN(1, 800)** in column B and provides an alternative way of selecting the sample desired in Example 8.1 on page 319. Because the RANDBETWEEN function samples *with replacement*, add additional copies of the formula in new column B rows until you have the sample size *without replacement* that Example 8.1 needs.

Analysis ToolPak Use **Sampling** to create a random sample *with replacement*. For example, to select a random sample of $n = 20$ from a cell range A1:A201 of 200 values that

contains a column heading in cell A1, select **Data → Data Analysis**. In the Data Analysis dialog box, select **Sampling** from the **Analysis Tools** list and then click **OK**. In the procedure's dialog box (see below):

1. Enter **A1:A201** as the **Input Range** and check **Labels**.
2. Click **Random** and enter **20** as the **Number of Samples**.
3. Click **New Worksheet Ply** and then click **OK**.

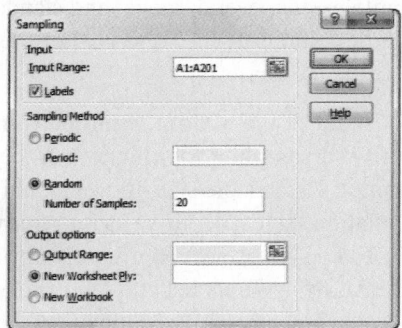

EG8.2 Evaluating Survey Worthiness

There are no Excel Guide instructions for this section.

EG8.3 Sampling Distributions

There are no Excel Guide instructions for this section.

EG8.4 Sampling Distribution of the Mean

PHStat2 Use **Sampling Distributions Simulation** to create a simulated sampling distribution. For example, to create 100 samples of $n = 30$ from a uniformly distributed population, select **PHStat → Sampling → Sampling Distributions Simulation**. In the procedure's dialog box (shown at the top of page 350):

1. Enter **100** as the **Number of Samples**.
2. Enter **30** as the **Sample Size**.
3. Click **Uniform**.
4. Enter a **Title** and click **OK**.

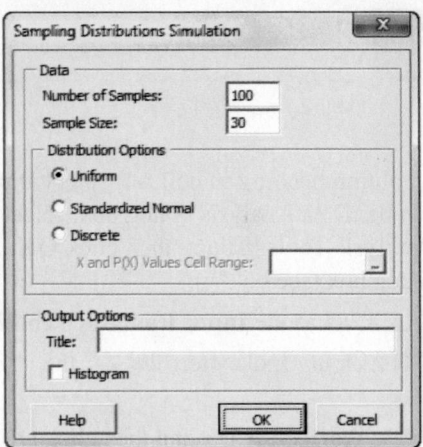

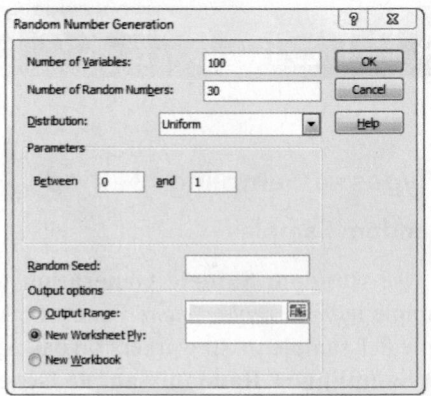

The sample means, overall mean, and standard error of the mean can be found starting in row 34 of the worksheet that the procedure creates.

Analysis ToolPak Use **Random Number Generation** to create a simulated sampling distribution. For example, to create 100 samples of sample size 30 from a uniformly distributed population, select **Data → Data Analysis**. In the Data Analysis dialog box, select **Random Number Generation** from the **Analysis Tools** list and then click **OK**. In the procedure's dialog box (shown at the top of the next column):

1. Enter **100** as the **Number of Variables**
2. Enter **30** as the **Number of Random Numbers**.
3. Select **Uniform** from the **Distribution** drop-down list.
4. Keep the **Parameters** values as is.
5. Click **New Worksheet Ply** and then click **OK**.

Use the formulas that appear in rows 35 through 39 in the **SDS_FORMULAS worksheet** of the **SDS workbook** as models if you want to compute sample means, the overall mean, and the standard error of the mean.

If, for other problems, you select **Discrete** in step 3, you must be open to a worksheet that contains a cell range of X and $P(X)$ values. Enter this cell range as the **Value and Probability Input Range** (not shown when **Uniform** has been selected) in the **Parameters** section of the dialog box.

EG8.5 Sampling Distribution of the Proportion

There are no Excel Guide instructions for this section.

9 Statistical Applications in Quality Management

Learning Objectives

In this chapter, you learn:

- How to construct various control charts
- Which control chart to use for a particular type of data
- The basic themes of total quality management and Deming's 14 points
- The basic aspects of Six Sigma

USING STATISTICS

@ Beachcomber Hotel

You find yourself managing the Beachcomber Hotel, one of the resorts owned by T.C. Resort Properties (see Chapter 14). Your business objective is to continually improve the quality of service that your guests receive so that overall guest satisfaction increases. To help you achieve this improvement, T.C. Resort Properties has provided its managers with training in Six Sigma. In order to meet the business objective of increasing the return rate of guests at your hotel, you have decided to focus on the critical first impressions of the service that your hotel provides. Is the assigned hotel room ready when a guest checks in? Are all expected amenities, such as extra towels and a complimentary guest basket, in the room when the guest first walks in? Are the video-entertainment center and high-speed Internet access working properly? And do guests receive their luggage in a reasonable amount of time?

To study these guest satisfaction issues, you have embarked on an improvement project that focuses on the readiness of the room and the time it takes to deliver luggage. You would like to learn the following:

- Are the proportion of rooms ready and the time required to deliver luggage to the rooms acceptable?
- Are the proportion of rooms ready and the luggage delivery time consistent from day to day, or are they increasing or decreasing?
- On the days when the proportion of rooms that are not ready or the time to deliver luggage is greater than normal, are these fluctuations due to a chance occurrence, or are there fundamental flaws in the processes used to make rooms ready and to deliver luggage?

Ian Logan / Getty Images

All companies, whether they manufacture products or provide services, as T.C. Resort Properties does in the Beachcomber Hotel scenario, understand that quality is essential for survival in the global economy. Quality has an impact on our everyday work and personal lives in many ways: in the design, production, and reliability of our automobiles; in the services provided by hotels, banks, schools, retailers, and telecommunications companies; in the continuous improvement in integrated circuits that makes for more capable consumer electronics and computers; and in the availability of new technology and equipment that has led to improved diagnosis of illnesses and improved delivery of health care services.

In this chapter you will learn how to develop and analyze control charts, a statistical tool that is widely used for quality improvement. You will then learn how businesses and organizations around the world are using control charts as part of two important quality improvement approaches: total quality management (TQM) and Six Sigma.

9.1 The Theory of Control Charts

A **process** is the value-added transformation of inputs to outputs. The inputs and outputs of a process can involve machines, materials, methods, measurement, people, and the environment. Each of the inputs is a source of variability. Variability in the output can result in poor service and poor product quality, both of which often decrease customer satisfaction.

Control charts, developed by Walter Shewhart in the 1920s (see reference 16), are commonly used statistical tools for monitoring and improving processes. A **control chart** analyzes a process in which data are collected sequentially over time. You use a control chart to study past performance, to evaluate present conditions, or to predict future outcomes. You use control charts at the beginning of quality improvement efforts to study an existing process (such charts are called *Phase 1 control charts*). Information gained from analyzing Phase 1 control charts forms the basis for process improvement. After improvements to the process are implemented, you then use control charts to monitor the process to ensure that the improvements continue (these charts are called *Phase 2 control charts*).

Different types of control charts allow you to analyze different types of **critical-to-quality** (*CTQ* in Six Sigma lingo—see Section 9.4) variables—for categorical variables, such as the proportion of hotel rooms that are nonconforming in terms of the availability of amenities and the working order of all appliances in the room; for discrete variables such as the number of hotel guests registering complaints in a week; and for continuous variables, such as the length of time required for delivering luggage to the room.

In addition to providing a visual display of data representing a process, a principal focus of a control chart is the attempt to separate special causes of variation from common causes of variation.

THE TWO TYPES OF CAUSES OF VARIATION

Special causes of variation represent large fluctuations or patterns in data that are not part of a process. These fluctuations are often caused by unusual events and represent either problems to correct or opportunities to exploit. Some organizations refer to special causes of variation as **assignable causes of variation**.

Common causes of variation represent the inherent variability that exists in a process. These fluctuations consist of the numerous small causes of variability that operate randomly or by chance. Some organizations refer to common causes of variation as **chance causes of variation**.

Walter Shewhart (see reference 16) developed an experiment that illustrates the distinction between common and special causes of variation. The experiment asks you to repeatedly write the letter A in a horizontal line across a piece of paper:

AAAAAAAAAAAAAAAAAA

When you do this, you immediately notice that the A's are all similar but not exactly the same. In addition, you may notice some difference in the size of the A's from letter to letter. This difference is due to common cause variation. Nothing special happened that caused the differences in the size of the A. You probably would have a hard time trying to explain why the largest A is bigger than the smallest A. These types of differences almost certainly represent common cause variation.

However, if you did the experiment over again but wrote half of the A's with your right hand and the other half of the A's with your left hand, you would almost certainly see a very big difference in the A's written with each hand. In this case, the hand that you used to write the A's is the source of the special cause variation.

Common and special cause variation have a crucial difference. Common causes of variation can be reduced only by changing the process. (Such systemic changes are the responsibility of management.) In contrast, because special causes of variation are not part of a process, special causes are correctable or exploitable without changing the process. (In the example, changing the hand to write the A's corrects the special cause variation but does nothing to change the underlying process of handwriting.)

Control charts allow you to monitor a process and identify the presence or absence of special causes. By doing so, control charts help prevent two types of errors. The first type of error involves the belief that an observed value represents special cause variation when it is due to the common cause variation of the process. Treating common cause variation as special cause variation often results in overadjusting a process. This overadjustment, known as **tampering**, increases the variation in the process. The second type of error involves treating special cause variation as common cause variation. This error results in not taking immediate corrective action when necessary. Although both of these types of errors can occur even when using a control chart, they are far less likely.

To construct a control chart, you collect samples from the output of a process over time. The samples used for constructing control charts are known as **subgroups**. For each subgroup (i.e., sample), you calculate a sample statistic. Commonly used statistics include the sample proportion for a categorical variable and the mean and range of a numerical variable. You then plot the values over time and add control limits around the center line of the chart. The most typical form of a control chart sets control limits that are within ± 3 standard deviations[1] of the statistical measure of interest. Equation (9.1) defines, in general, the upper and lower control limits for control charts.

[1]Recall from Section 7.2 that in the normal distribution, $\mu \pm 3\sigma$ includes almost all (99.73%) of the values in the population.

CONSTRUCTING CONTROL LIMITS

$$\text{Process mean} \pm 3 \text{ standard deviations} \qquad (9.1)$$

so that

Upper control limit (UCL) = Process mean $+3$ standard deviations

Lower control limit (LCL) = Process mean -3 standard deviations

---

When these control limits are set, you evaluate the control chart by trying to find whether any pattern exists in the values over time and by determining whether any points fall outside the control limits. Figure 9.1 illustrates three different patterns.

FIGURE 9.1

Three control chart patterns

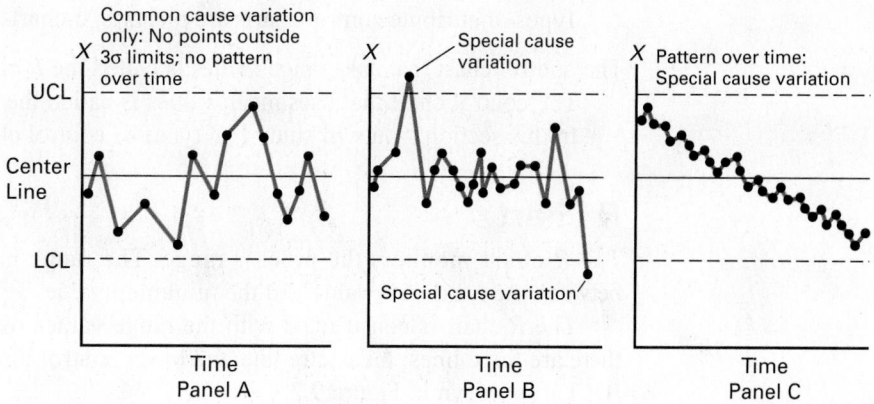

In Panel A of Figure 9.1, there is no apparent pattern in the values over time and there are no points that fall outside the 3 standard deviation control limits. The process appears stable and contains only common cause variation. Panel B, on the contrary, contains two points that fall outside the 3 standard deviation control limits. You should investigate these points to try to determine the special causes that led to their occurrence. Although Panel C does not have any points outside the control limits, it has a series of consecutive points above the mean value (the center line) as well as a series of consecutive points below the mean value. In addition, a long-term overall downward trend is clearly visible. You should investigate the situation to try to determine what may have caused this pattern.

Detecting a pattern is not always so easy. The following simple rule (see references 8, 12, and 18) can help you to detect a trend or a shift in the mean level of a process:

Eight or more *consecutive* points that lie above the center line or eight or more *consecutive* points that lie below the center line.[2]

[2]This rule is often referred to as the *runs rule*. A similar rule that some companies use is called the *trend rule*: eight or more consecutive points that increase in value or eight or more consecutive points that decrease in value. Some statisticians (see reference 4) have criticized the trend rule. It should be used only with extreme caution.

A process whose control chart indicates an out-of-control condition (i.e., a point outside the control limits or a series of points that exhibits a pattern) is said to be out of control. An **out-of-control process** contains both common causes of variation and special causes of variation. Because special causes of variation are not part of the process design, an out-of-control process is unpredictable. When you determine that a process is out of control, you must identify the special causes of variation that are producing the out-of-control conditions. If the special causes are detrimental to the quality of the product or service, you need to implement plans to eliminate this source of variation. When a special cause increases quality, you should change the process so that the special cause is incorporated into the process design. Thus, this beneficial special cause now becomes a common cause source of variation, and the process is improved.

A process whose control chart does not indicate any out-of-control conditions is said to be in control. An **in-control process** contains only common causes of variation. Because these sources of variation are inherent to the process itself, an in-control process is predictable. In-control processes are sometimes said to be in a **state of statistical control**. When a process is in control, you must determine whether the amount of common cause variation in the process is small enough to satisfy the customers of the products or services. If the common cause variation is small enough to consistently satisfy the customers, you then use control charts to monitor the process on a continuing basis to make sure the process remains in control. If the common cause variation is too large, you need to alter the process itself.

9.2 Types of Control Charts

There are two types of control charts:

1. A control chart that uses a quantitative measurement is called a **variable control chart**. Types of variable control charts are R charts, $\overline{X}$ charts (also called X-bar charts), and S charts.
2. A control chart that uses a qualitative measurement is called an **attribute control chart**. Types of attribute control charts are p charts, c-charts, np-charts, and u-charts.

The control chart that uses range values is called the R chart.

The control chart that uses mean values is called the X-bar chart.

In this section, you will study two types of control charts, namely X-bar and R charts.

R Chart

The **R chart** monitors the process range. The range is measured by taking the difference between the maximum value and the minimum value.

The R chart is constructed with the range values over a period of time. On the R chart, there are three lines: the centre line, the lower control limit (LCL), and the upper control limit (UCL), as shown in Figure 9.2.

FIGURE 9.2

R chart

NOTE: "Std dev" denotes standard deviation.

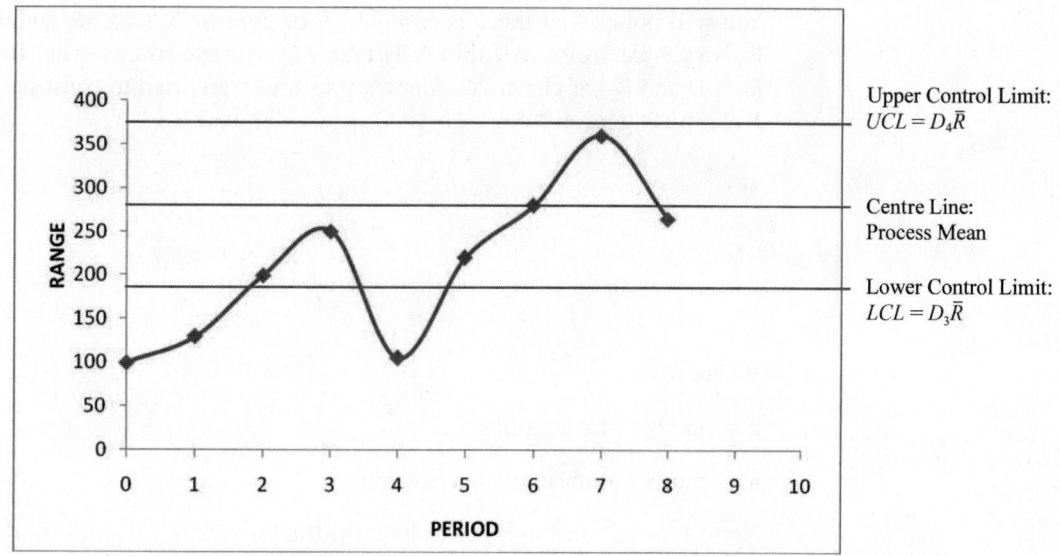

The formulas used to construct the three lines are as follows:

a) The plotted points on the graph (see Figure 9.2) are the range (R) values.

b) Range (R) = Maximum Value − Minimum Value

c) Central Line: Average Range, denoted as $\overline{R} = \dfrac{\sum_{i=1}^{k} R_i}{k}$

d) Upper Control Limit: $UCL = D_4 \overline{R}$

e) Lower Control Limit: $LCL = D_3 \overline{R}$

Note that

i. the values of D_3 and D_4 are obtained from Table A.9 in Appendix A. The values of D_3 and D_4 depend on the number of observations in the sample.

ii. all the formulas are based on the assumption that the population of measurements follows a normal distribution.

TABLE A.9

Control Chart Factors

Number of Observations in Sample	d_2	d_3	D_3	D_4	A_2
2	1.128	0.853	0	3.267	1.880
3	1.693	0.888	0	2.575	1.023
4	2.059	0.880	0	2.282	0.729
5	2.326	0.864	0	2.114	0.577
6	2.534	0.848	0	2.004	0.483
7	2.704	0.833	0.076	1.924	0.419
8	2.847	0.820	0.136	1.864	0.373
9	2.970	0.808	0.184	1.816	0.337
10	3.078	0.797	0.223	1.777	0.308
11	3.173	0.787	0.256	1.744	0.285
12	3.258	0.778	0.283	1.717	0.266
13	3.336	0.770	0.307	1.693	0.249
14	3.407	0.763	0.328	1.672	0.235
15	3.472	0.756	0.347	1.653	0.223
16	3.532	0.750	0.363	1.637	0.212
17	3.588	0.744	0.378	1.622	0.203
18	3.640	0.739	0.391	1.609	0.194
19	3.689	0.733	0.404	1.596	0.187
20	3.735	0.729	0.415	1.585	0.180
21	3.778	0.724	0.425	1.575	0.173
22	3.819	0.720	0.435	1.565	0.167
23	3.858	0.716	0.443	1.557	0.162
24	3.895	0.712	0.452	1.548	0.157
25	3.931	0.708	0.459	1.541	0.153

You will notice that there is another set of control factors, d_2 and d_3, in the Control Chart Factors table (refer to Table A.9) that you can use to construct the control limits for the R chart and X-bar chart. The following formulas are used to construct the control limits for an R chart using d_2 and d_3.

$$LCL = \bar{R} - \frac{3\bar{R}d_3}{d_2}$$

$$UCL = \bar{R} + \frac{3\bar{R}d_3}{d_2}$$

Where $\bar{R} = \dfrac{\sum_{i=1}^{k}R_i}{k}$

k = number of subgroups

n = number of observations in sample

Note: Use "n" and not "k" to look up the factors D_3, D_4 and d_2, d_3.

X-bar Chart

The **X-bar chart** monitors the process sample means.

The X-bar chart is constructed with the mean values over a period of time. On the X-bar chart, there are three lines: the centre line, the lower control limit (LCL), and the upper control limit (UCL).

FIGURE 9.3

X-bar chart

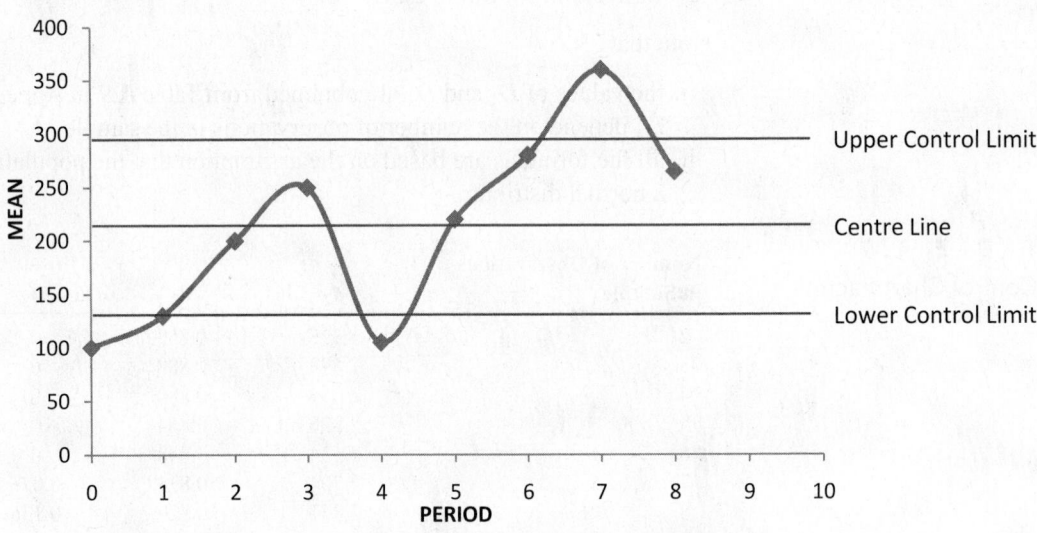

The formulas used to construct the three lines are as follows:

a) The plotted points on the graph (see Figure 9.3) are the sample mean ($\bar{X}$) values.

b) Mean $(\bar{x}) = \dfrac{\sum_{i=1}^{n}x_i}{n}$

c) Central Line: Average of means, denoted as $(\bar{\bar{x}}) = \dfrac{\sum_{i=1}^{k}\bar{X}_i}{k}$ where $\bar{x}_i$ is the sample mean at time i.

d) Upper Control Limit: $UCL = \bar{\bar{x}} + A_2\bar{R}$

e) Lower Control Limit: $LCL = \bar{\bar{x}} - A_2\bar{R}$

Note that

i. the value of A_2 is obtained from Table A.9 in Appendix A. The value of A_2 depends on the number of samples (denoted as k).
ii. all the formulas are based on the assumption that the population of measurements follows a normal distribution.

You will notice that there is another set of control factors, d_2 and d_3, in the Control Chart Factors table (refer to Table A.9) that you can use to construct the control limits for the R chart and X-bar chart. The following formulas are used to construct the control limits for the X-bar chart using d_2 and d_3.

$$UCL = \overline{\overline{X}} + 3\frac{\overline{R}}{d_2\sqrt{n}}$$

$$LCL = \overline{\overline{X}} - 3\frac{\overline{R}}{d_2\sqrt{n}}$$

Where $\overline{R} = \dfrac{\sum_{i=1}^{k}R_i}{k}$, $\overline{\overline{X}} = \dfrac{\sum_{i=1}^{k}\bar{x}_i}{k}$

k = number of subgroups

n = number of observations in sample

Note: Use "n" and not "k" to look up the factors D_3, D_4 and d_2, d_3.

TABLE 9.1

Summary of Equations for Control Chart Limits for Mean and Range using factors D_3, D_4 and d_2, d_3

	Control Limits for		Control Limits for	
	Range	**Mean**	**Range**	**Mean**
	Using the D_3, D_4 factors		Using the d_2, d_3 factors	
Upper Control Limit	$D_4\overline{R}$	$\overline{\overline{x}} + A_2\overline{R}$	$\overline{R} + \dfrac{3\overline{R}d_3}{d_2}$	$\overline{\overline{X}} + 3\dfrac{\overline{R}}{d_2\sqrt{n}}$
Centre Line (Process mean)	$\overline{R} = \dfrac{\sum_{i=1}^{k}R_i}{k}$	$\overline{\overline{X}} = \dfrac{\sum_{i=1}^{k}\bar{x}_i}{k}$	$\overline{R} = \dfrac{\sum_{i=1}^{k}R_i}{k}$	$\overline{\overline{X}} = \dfrac{\sum_{i=1}^{k}\bar{x}_i}{k}$
Lower Control Limit	$D_3\overline{R}$	$\overline{\overline{x}} - A_2\overline{R}$	$\overline{R} - \dfrac{3\overline{R}d_3}{d_2}$	$\overline{\overline{X}} - 3\dfrac{\overline{R}}{d_2\sqrt{n}}$

Quality Control Charts

We will only be studying two charts, X-bars and R charts. Also, the only out-of-control indications that we will be concerned with are the following:

a. A point above the UCL on the range chart
b. A point above the UCL or a point below the LCL on the X-bar chart

In a real-life setting, if there is an indication that the process is out of control, the people monitoring the process will find a "special cause" for the situation. They will then take appropriate steps to make changes in the process so that this instability does not occur again in the future. It is these changes that will result in the improvement of quality.

In order to establish the centre-lines and the upper and lower control limits for the X-bar charts and R charts we need some initial sample data. Usually the results from 10 to 30 samples are used. The following two examples will illustrate the formulas and techniques for setting up X-bar chart and R chart limits. It should be noted that all the formulas shown are based on the assumption that the population of measurements would fit a *normal* distribution.

EXAMPLE 9.1

A chocolate company monitors the weights of its chocolate bars. One particular bar will have a label indicating that it is a 60-gram bar. In order to monitor the bar weights, every hour a sample of 4 bars is taken and the bars are weighed. The results of the first 15 samples are shown in Table 9.2.

TABLE 9.2

Weight of a bar (grams)						
Sample	Bar 1	Bar 2	Bar 3	Bar 4	Mean	Range
1	60.2	60.4	60.1	60.5	60.300	0.4
2	60.6	60.2	60.7	60.6	60.525	0.5
3	60.2	60.2	60.5	60.7	60.400	0.5
4	60.1	60.1	60.6	60.4	60.300	0.5
5	60.3	60.6	60.3	60.1	60.325	0.5
6	60.5	60.4	60.3	60.1	60.325	0.4
7	60.5	60.4	60.5	60.2	60.400	0.3
8	60.3	60.5	60.2	60.3	60.325	0.3
9	60.5	60.1	60.0	60.5	60.275	0.5
10	60.7	60.4	60.4	60.5	60.500	0.3
11	60.0	60.3	60.7	60.3	60.325	0.7
12	60.2	60.7	60.3	60.6	60.450	0.5
13	60.6	60.0	60.6	60.2	60.350	0.6
14	59.9	60.1	60.3	60.6	60.225	0.7
15	60.5	60.2	60.5	60.5	60.425	0.3

First you calculate the R chart values using the control factors as follows:

$$\bar{R} = 0.47$$
$$UCL_R = D_4\bar{R} = 2.282(0.47) = 1.064933333333333 = 1.07$$
$$LCL_R = D_3\bar{R} = 0(0.47) = 0$$

Then you check the sample ranges to see if any range values are higher than 1.07. There are none. You can now proceed to calculate the X-bar chart values.

$$\bar{\bar{X}} = 60.36333333$$
$$UCL_{\bar{X}} = \bar{\bar{X}} + A_2\bar{R} = 60.36333333 + (0.729)(0.47) = 60.7059$$
$$LCL_{\bar{X}} = \bar{\bar{X}} - A_2\bar{R} = 60.36333333 - (0.729)(0.47) = 60.0207$$

Now you check the sample means to see if any values are higher than 60.7059 or lower than 60.0207. There are none. This process is in control (i.e., stable), and you have established the control chart limits for future samples of this product.

    If in the initial samples used to set up the control charts points are found to be out of control, then you will assume that a special cause can be found to account for this problem. In the meantime, the sample data for any point that is out of control is removed from the calculations, and the control chart values are recalculated. The following example will illustrate the appropriate procedure to follow.

EXAMPLE 9.2

A company is concerned about a particular measurement. The results of 24 samples of 5 items are shown in Table 9.3.

TABLE 9.3

			Sample results				
Sample	Item 1	Item 2	Item 3	Item 4	Item 5	Mean	Range
1	10.65	10.70	10.65	10.65	10.85	10.70	0.20
2	10.75	10.85	10.75	10.85	10.65	10.77	0.20
3	10.75	10.80	10.80	10.70	10.75	10.76	0.10
4	10.60	10.70	10.70	10.75	10.65	10.68	0.15
5	10.70	10.75	10.65	10.85	10.80	10.75	0.20
6	10.60	10.75	10.75	10.85	10.70	10.73	0.25
7	10.60	10.80	10.70	10.75	10.75	10.72	0.20
8	10.75	10.80	10.65	10.75	10.70	10.73	0.15
9	10.65	10.80	10.85	10.85	10.75	10.78	0.20
10	10.60	10.70	10.60	10.80	10.65	10.67	0.20
11	10.80	10.75	10.90	10.50	10.85	10.76	0.40
12	10.85	10.75	10.85	10.65	10.70	10.76	0.20
13	10.70	10.70	10.75	10.75	10.70	10.72	0.05
14	10.65	10.70	10.85	10.75	10.60	10.71	0.25
15	10.75	10.80	10.75	10.80	10.65	10.75	0.15
16	10.90	10.80	10.80	10.75	10.85	10.82	0.15
17	10.75	10.70	10.85	10.70	10.80	10.76	0.15
18	10.75	10.70	10.60	10.70	10.60	10.67	0.15
19	10.65	10.65	10.85	10.65	10.70	10.70	0.20
20	10.55	10.55	10.60	10.50	10.60	10.56	0.10
21	10.50	10.55	10.65	10.80	10.80	10.66	0.30
22	10.80	10.65	10.75	10.65	10.65	10.70	0.15
23	10.65	10.60	10.65	10.60	10.70	10.64	0.10
24	10.65	10.70	10.70	10.60	10.65	10.66	0.10

First you calculate the R chart values:

$$\bar{R} = 0.179$$
$$UCL_R = D_4\bar{R} = 2.114(0.179) = 0.378$$
$$LCL_R = D_3\bar{R} = 0(0.179) = 0$$

Then you look at the sample ranges and find that sample 11 with R = 0.40 is out of control. You can assume that a special cause can be found, and proceed to **remove** sample 11 and recalculate the R chart values.

$$\bar{R} = 0.170$$
You now get: $\quad UCL_R = D_4\bar{R} = 2.114(0.170) = 0.359$
$$LCL_R = D_3\bar{R} = 0(0.170) = 0$$

Once again you check the sample ranges, and this time there are no range values that are out of control.

Now you calculate the $\bar{X}$ bar chart values (with sample 11 having been removed from the data).

$$\overline{\overline{X}} = 10.713$$

You get
$$UCL_{\overline{X}} = \overline{\overline{X}} + A_2\overline{R} = 10.713 + (0.577)(0.170) = 10.811$$
$$LCL_{\overline{X}} = \overline{\overline{X}} - A_2\overline{R} = 10.713 - (0.577)(0.170) = 10.615$$

You now check the sample means and find that sample 16 with $\overline{X} = 10.82$ and sample 20 with $\overline{X} = 10.56$ are out of control. Once again you assume that special causes can be found to account for these out of control results, and proceed to **remove** samples 16 and 20.

Since the R chart values have been calculated including samples 16 and 20, these results are no longer valid. We must calculate new R chart values before calculating new X-bar chart values.

$$\overline{R} = 0.174$$

You now get
$$UCL_R = D_4\overline{R} = 2.114(0.174) = 0.368$$
$$LCL_R = D_3\overline{R} = 0(0.174) = 0$$

Now check again the sample ranges for any out-of-control points. There are none. You therefore proceed to calculate the X-bar chart values.

$$\overline{\overline{X}} = 10.715$$

You get
$$UCL_{\overline{X}} = \overline{\overline{X}} + A_2\overline{R} = 10.715 + (0.577)(0.174) = 10.815$$
$$LCL_{\overline{X}} = \overline{\overline{X}} - A_2\overline{R} = 10.715 - (0.577)(0.174) = 10.615$$

Once again you check the sample means and find that none of the remaining samples is out of control. You now have determined the appropriate X-bar chart and R chart control limits.

Problems for Section 9.2

(Note: Some of these exercises may not be indicative of real world processes, but are intended to demonstrate the correct procedures for establishing control chart limits.)

9.1 The following results came from samples of size 4. Determine the X-bar and R chart control limits. If any sample results are out-of-control assume an assignable cause can be found and make the necessary adjustments to the control chart values.

Sample	Mean	Range	Sample	Mean	Range
1	75.72	1.0	11	75.80	0.6
2	75.24	0.9	12	75.22	0.2
3	75.18	0.8	13	75.56	1.5
4	75.44	0.4	14	75.22	0.5
5	75.46	0.5	15	75.04	0.8
6	75.32	1.2	16	75.62	1.1
7	75.40	0.9	17	75.92	0.6
8	75.44	0.3	18	75.46	0.5
9	75.08	0.2	19	75.60	0.4
10	75.50	0.6	20	75.74	0.3

9.2 The following results came from samples of size 6. Determine the X-bar and R chart control limits. If any sample results are out-of-control assume an assignable cause can be found and make the necessary adjustments to the control chart values.

Sample	Mean	Range	Sample	Mean	Range
1	35.35	0.34	14	35.41	0.36
2	35.40	0.36	15	35.45	0.24
3	35.36	0.32	16	35.34	0.36
4	35.65	0.26	17	35.42	0.37
5	35.20	0.46	18	35.50	0.58
6	35.40	0.35	19	35.36	0.35
7	35.43	0.31	20	35.31	0.18
8	35.37	0.34	21	35.39	0.73
9	35.48	0.30	22	35.39	0.33
10	35.42	0.37	23	35.40	0.32
11	35.39	0.19	24	35.41	0.34
12	35.38	0.50	25	35.40	0.30
13	35.40	0.33			

9.3 The following results came from samples of size 5. Use the first 20 samples to determine the X-bar and R chart control limits. If any sample results are out-of-control assume an assignable cause can be found and make the necessary adjustments to the control chart values. Are any of the samples 21 to 30 out of control? Explain.

Sample	Mean	Range	Sample	Mean	Range
1	101	22	16	109	12
2	104	17	17	111	38
3	109	36	18	100	30
4	98	19	19	97	19
5	105	23	20	89	31
6	107	16	21	103	27
7	109	16	22	97	36
8	115	30	23	92	25
9	99	20	24	89	23
10	119	29	25	98	18
11	91	14	26	108	24
12	99	20	27	114	19
13	115	39	28	117	51
14	100	30	29	110	21
15	103	26	30	99	30

9.4 The following results came from samples of size 4. Determine the X-bar and R chart control limits. If any sample results are out-of-control assume an assignable cause can be found and make the necessary adjustments to the control chart values.

Sample	Mean	Range	Sample	Mean	Range
1	376.2	32	14	382.7	22
2	366.7	24	15	406.3	23
3	384.3	32	16	396.4	23
4	366.7	26	17	378.7	25
5	370.1	24	18	384.2	24
6	394.2	24	19	406.9	23
7	386.9	28	20	376.4	25
8	396.4	23	21	385.8	29
9	388.0	24	22	390.2	25
10	382.3	26	23	363.5	22
11	398.8	25	24	363.1	27
12	364.6	24	25	374.8	22
13	384.5	24			

9.5 Motel Inn plans to improve service by reducing the mean and variation in time it takes to clean and prepare rooms. In order to study the situation 5 rooms are randomly selected each day and the time required to clean and prepare each room is recorded. The data for the first 10 days is given below.

	Cleaning and Preparation time (minutes)				
Day	Room 1	Room 2	Room 3	Room 4	Room 5
1	14.0	17.7	16.9	14.0	14.9
2	17.6	16.5	15.3	14.5	15.1
3	14.6	14.0	14.7	16.9	14.2
4	14.0	15.5	16.5	15.4	14.7
5	15.3	15.3	15.9	15.0	17.8
6	21.4	14.9	17.7	16.6	13.8
7	18.9	19.9	18.6	17.2	17.9
8	14.8	15.1	16.6	16.3	14.5
9	16.1	14.6	17.5	16.9	17.7
10	14.2	14.7	15.3	15.7	14.3

Determine the X-bar and R chart control limits, assuming that any out-of-control results have assignable causes.

9.6 A chemical company has collected 15 daily samples of measurements of an important chemical property called 'acid value' for one of its products. Each sample consists of six acid value readings, where a single reading is taken every 4 hours during the day. The measurements are shown in the table below.

	Acid Value measurements					
Day	1	2	3	4	5	6
1	202.1	201.2	196.2	201.6	201.6	201.6
2	202.4	201.9	202.0	201.8	201.9	201.8
3	200.4	200.0	200.8	200.1	198.7	200.4
4	200.4	200.4	200.4	200.8	200.4	201.2
5	203.4	201.6	203.9	201.6	201.4	202.0
6	200.0	200.4	200.8	200.8	199.5	200.4
7	200.4	200.0	200.4	200.4	200.4	200.4
8	200.0	200.8	200.0	200.4	200.0	200.0
9	199.1	200.1	200.4	200.4	200.4	200.0
10	201.2	195.3	197.4	201.2	200.0	201.6
11	201.6	200.8	200.4	201.2	200.4	199.5
12	200.0	199.5	200.4	200.8	200.4	200.8
13	201.2	201.6	200.8	201.2	200.8	200.8
14	200.4	200.0	202.5	200.4	201.2	201.2
15	200.0	200.0	201.6	200.8	200.4	200.0

Determine the X-bar and R chart control limits, assuming that any out-of-control results have assignable causes.

LEARNING THE BASICS

9.7 The following data were collected on nonconformances for a period of 10 days:

Day	Sample Size	Nonconformances
1	100	12
2	100	14
3	100	10
4	100	18
5	100	22
6	100	14
7	100	15
8	100	13
9	100	14
10	100	16

a. On what day is the proportion of nonconformances largest? Smallest?
b. What are the LCL and UCL?
c. Are there any special causes of variation?

9.8 The following data were collected on nonconformances for a period of 10 days:

Day	Sample Size	Nonconformances
1	111	12
2	93	14
3	105	10
4	92	18
5	117	22
6	88	14
7	117	15
8	87	13
9	119	14
10	107	16

a. On what day is the proportion of nonconformances largest? Smallest?
b. What are the LCL and UCL?
c. Are there any special causes of variation?

APPLYING THE CONCEPTS

9.9 A medical transcription service enters medical data on patient files for hospitals. The service has the business objective of improving the turnaround time (defined as the time between sending data and the time the client receives completed files). After studying the process, it was determined that turnaround time was increased by transmission errors. A transmission error was defined as data transmitted that did not go through as planned and needed to be retrans-

mitted. Data were collected for a period of 31 days from a daily random sample of 125 transmissions and stored in **Transmit**. The following table presents the number and proportion of transmissions with errors:

Day (i)	Number of Errors (X_i)	Proportion of Errors (p_i)	Day (i)	Number of Errors (X_i)	Proportion of Errors (p_i)
1	6	0.048	17	4	0.032
2	3	0.024	18	6	0.048
3	4	0.032	19	3	0.024
4	4	0.032	20	5	0.040
5	9	0.072	21	1	0.008
6	0	0.000	22	3	0.024
7	0	0.000	23	14	0.112
8	8	0.064	24	6	0.048
9	4	0.032	25	7	0.056
10	3	0.024	26	3	0.024
11	4	0.032	27	10	0.080
12	1	0.008	28	7	0.056
13	10	0.080	29	5	0.040
14	9	0.072	30	0	0.000
15	3	0.024	31	3	0.024
16	1	0.008			

a. Construct an R-chart and X-bar chart.
b. Is the process in a state of statistical control? Why?

SELF Test **9.10** A manufacturer of film canisters has the business objective of reducing the number of nonconforming film canisters. During each day of a 32-day study, 500 film canisters were sampled and inspected. The following table (stored in **Canister**) lists the number of defective film canisters (the nonconforming items) for each day (the subgroup):

Day	Number Nonconforming	Day	Number Nonconforming
1	26	17	23
2	25	18	19
3	23	19	18
4	24	20	27
5	26	21	28
6	20	22	24
7	21	23	26
8	27	24	23
9	23	25	27
10	25	26	28
11	22	27	24
12	26	28	22
13	25	29	20
14	29	30	25
15	20	31	27
16	19	32	19

a. Construct an *R*-chart and X-bar chart.

b. Is the process in a state of statistical control? Why?

9.11 A hospital administrator has the business objective of reducing the time to process patients' medical records after discharge. She determined that all records should be processed within 5 days of discharge. Thus, any record not processed within 5 days of a patient's discharge is nonconforming. The administrator recorded the number of patients discharged and the number of records not processed within the 5-day standard for a 30-day period and stored in MedRec.

a. Construct an *R*-chart and X-bar chart for these data.

b. Does the process give an out-of-control signal? Explain.

c. If the process is out of control, assume that special causes were subsequently identified and corrective action was taken to keep them from happening again. Then eliminate the data causing the out-of-control signals and recalculate the control limits.

9.12 The bottling division of Sweet Suzy's Sugarless Cola has the business objective of reducing the occurrence of unacceptable cans flowing from the filling and sealing machine. Data are collected and stored in Colaspc from a sample of cans filled for one month (based on a five-day workweek).

a. Construct an *R*-chart and X-bar chart for the proportion of unacceptable cans for the month. Does the process give an out-of-control signal?

b. If you want to develop a process for reducing the proportion of unacceptable cans, how should you proceed?

9.13 The manager of the accounting office of a large hospital has the business objective of reducing the number of incorrect account numbers entered into the computer system. Data are collected from a subgroup of 200 account numbers selected from each day's output, and each account number is inspected to determine whether it is nonconforing. The results for a period of 39 days are stored in Errorspc.

a. Construct an *R*-chart and X-bar chart for the proportion of nonconforming items. Does the process give an out-of-control signal?

b. Based on your answer in (a), if you were the manager of the accounting office, what would you do to improve the process of account number entry?

9.14 A regional manager of a telephone company is responsible for processing requests concerning additions, changes, and deletions of telephone service. She has the business objective of reducing the number of orders that need correction. Data are collected over a period of 30 days and are stored in Telespc.

a. Construct an *R*-chart and X-bar chart for the proportion of corrections. Does the process give an out-of-control signal?

b. What should the regional manager do to improve the processing of requests for changes in telephone service?

9.3 Total Quality Management

An increased interest in improving the quality of products and services in the United States occurred as a reaction to improvements of Japanese industry that began as early as 1950. Individuals such as W. Edwards Deming, Joseph Juran, and Kaoru Ishikawa developed an approach that focuses on continuous improvement of products and services through an increased emphasis on statistics, process improvement, and optimization of the total system. This approach, widely known as **total quality management (TQM)**, is characterized by these themes:

- The primary focus is on process improvement.
- Most of the variation in a process is due to the system and not the individual.
- Teamwork is an integral part of a quality management organization.
- Customer satisfaction is a primary organizational goal.
- Organizational transformation must occur in order to implement quality management.
- Fear must be removed from organizations.
- Higher quality costs less, not more, but requires an investment in training.

In the 1980s, the federal government of the United States increased its efforts to encourage the improvement of quality in American business. Congress passed the Malcolm Baldrige National Improvement Act of 1987 and began awarding the Malcolm Baldrige Award to companies making the greatest strides in improving quality and customer satisfaction. Deming became a prominent consultant to many Fortune 500 companies, including Ford Motor Company, and Procter & Gamble. Many companies adopted some or all the basic themes of TQM.

Today, quality improvement systems have been implemented in many organizations world-wide. Although most organizations no longer use the name TQM, the underlying philosophy and statistical methods used in today's quality improvement systems are consistent with TQM, as reflected by **Deming's 14 points for management**:

1. Create constancy of purpose for improvement of product and service.
2. Adopt the new philosophy.
3. Cease dependence on inspection to achieve quality.
4. End the practice of awarding business on the basis of price tag alone. Instead, minimize total cost by working with a single supplier.
5. Improve constantly and forever every process for planning, production, and service.
6. Institute training on the job.
7. Adopt and institute leadership.
8. Drive out fear.
9. Break down barriers between staff areas.
10. Eliminate slogans, exhortations, and targets for the workforce.
11. Eliminate numerical quotas for the workforce and numerical goals for management.
12. Remove barriers that rob people of pride of workmanship. Eliminate the annual rating or merit system.
13. Institute a vigorous program of education and self-improvement for everyone.
14. Put everyone in the company to work to accomplish the transformation.

Points 1, 2, 5, 7, and 14 focus on the need for organizational transformation and the responsibility of top management to assert leadership in committing to the transformation. Without this commitment, any improvements obtained will be limited.

One aspect of the improvement process is illustrated by the **Shewhart–Deming cycle**, shown in Figure 9.4. The Shewhart–Deming cycle represents a continuous cycle of "plan, do, study, and act." The first step, planning, represents the initial design phase for planning a change in a manufacturing or service process. This step involves teamwork among individuals from different areas within an organization. The second step, doing, involves implementing the change, preferably on a small scale. The third step, studying, involves analyzing the results, using statistical methods to determine what was learned. The fourth step, acting, involves the acceptance of the change, its abandonment, or further study of the change under different conditions.

FIGURE 9.4
Shewhart–Deming cycle

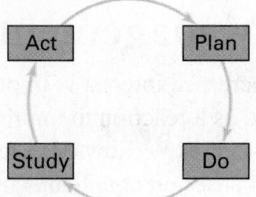

Point 3, cease dependence on inspection to achieve quality, implies that any inspection whose purpose is to improve quality is too late because the quality is already built into the product. It is better to focus on making it right the first time. Among the difficulties involved in inspection (besides high costs) are the failure of inspectors to agree on the operational definitions for nonconforming items and the problem of separating good and bad items. The following example illustrates the difficulties inspectors face.

Suppose your job involves proofreading the sentence in Figure 9.5, with the objective of counting the number of occurrences of the letter F. Perform this task and record the number of occurrences of the letter F that you discover.

FINISHED FILES ARE THE RESULT OF YEARS OF SCIENTIFIC STUDY COMBINED WITH THE EXPERIENCE OF MANY YEARS

People usually see either three *F*s or six *F*s. The correct number is six *F*s. The number you see depends on the method you use to examine the sentence. You are likely to find three *F*s if you read the sentence phonetically and six *F*s if you count the number of *F*s carefully. If such a simple process as counting *F*s leads to inconsistency of inspectors' results, what will happen when a much more complicated process fails to provide clear operational definitions?

Point 4, end the practice of awarding business on the basis of price tag alone, focuses on the idea that there is no real long-term meaning to price without knowledge of the quality of the product. In addition, minimizing the number of entities in the supply chain will reduce the variation involved.

Points 6 and 13 refer to training and reflect the needs of all employees. Continuous learning is critical for quality improvement within an organization. In particular, management needs to understand the differences between special causes and common causes of variation so that proper action is taken in each circumstance.

Points 8 through 12 relate to the evaluation of employee performance. Deming believed that an emphasis on targets and exhortations places an improper burden on the workforce. Workers cannot produce beyond what the system allows. It is management's job to *improve* the system, not to raise the expectations on workers beyond the system's capability.

Although Deming's points are thought provoking, some have criticized his approach for lacking a formal, objective accountability (see reference 11). Many managers of large organizations, used to seeing financial analyses of policy changes, need a more prescriptive approach.

9.4 Six Sigma

Six Sigma is a quality improvement system originally developed by Motorola in the mid-1980s. After seeing the huge financial successes at Motorola, GE, and other early adopters of Six Sigma, many companies worldwide have now instituted Six Sigma to improve efficiency, cut costs, eliminate defects, and reduce product variation (see references 1, 3, 10, and 17). Six Sigma offers a more prescriptive and systematic approach to process improvement than TQM. It is also distinguished from other quality improvement systems by its clear focus on achieving bottom-line results in a relatively short three- to six-month period of time.

The name *Six Sigma* comes from the fact that it is a managerial approach designed to create processes that result in no more than 3.4 defects per million. The Six Sigma approach assumes that processes are designed so that the upper and lower specification limits are each six standard deviations away from the mean. Then, if the processes are monitored correctly with control charts, the worst possible scenario is for the mean to shift to within 4.5 standard deviations from the nearest specification limit. The area under the normal curve less than 4.5 standard deviations below the mean is approximately 3.4 out of 1 million. (Table E.2 reports this probability as 0.000003398.)

The DMAIC Model

To guide managers in their task of improving short-term and long-term results, Six Sigma uses a five-step process known as the **DMAIC model**—named for the five steps in the process:

- **Define** The problem is defined, along with the costs, the benefits, and the impact on the customer.
- **Measure** Important characteristics related to the quality of the service or product are identified and discussed. Variables measuring these characteristics are defined and called *critical-to-quality (CTQ)* variables. Operational definitions for all the CTQ variables are then developed. In addition, the measurement procedure is verified so that it is consistent over repeated measurements.
- **Analyze** The root causes of *why* defects occur are determined, and variables in the process causing the defects are identified. Data are collected to determine benchmark values for each process variable. This analysis often uses control charts.
- **Improve** The importance of each process variable on the CTQ variable is studied using designed experiments (see Chapter 12 and references 8, 9, and 12). The objective is to determine the best level for each variable.
- **Control** The objective is to maintain the benefits for the long term by avoiding potential problems that can occur when a process is changed.

The *Define* phase of a Six Sigma project consists of the development of a project charter, performing a SIPOC analysis, and identifying the customers for the output of the process. The development of a project charter involves forming a table of business objectives and indicators for all potential Six Sigma projects. Importance ratings are assigned by top management, projects are prioritized, and the most important project is selected. A **SIPOC analysis** is used to identify the **S**uppliers to the process, list the **I**nputs provided by the suppliers, flowchart the **P**rocess, list the process **O**utputs, and identify the **C**ustomers of the process. This is followed by a Voice of the Customer analysis that involves market segmentation in which different types of users of the process are identified and the circumstances of their use of the process are identified. Statistical methods used in the *Define* phase include tables and charts, descriptive statistics, and control charts.

In the *Measure* phase of a Six Sigma project, members of a team identify the CTQ variables that measure important quality characteristics. Next, operational definitions (see Section 1.3) of each CTQ variable are developed so that everyone will have a firm understanding of the CTQ. Then studies are undertaken to ensure that there is a valid measurement system for the CTQ that is consistent across measurements. Finally, baseline data are collected to determine the capability and stability of the current process. Statistical methods used in the *Measure* phase include tables and charts, descriptive statistics, the normal distribution, the Analysis of Variance, and control charts.

The *Analyze* phase of a Six Sigma project focuses on the factors that affect the central tendency, variation, and shape of each CTQ variable. Factors are identified, and the relationships between the factors and the CTQs are analyzed. Statistical methods used in the *Analyze* phase include tables and charts, descriptive statistics, the Analysis of Variance, regression analysis, and control charts.

In the *Improve* phase of a Six Sigma project, team members carry out designed experiments to actively intervene in a process. The objective of the experiments is to determine the settings of the factors that will optimize the central tendency, variation, and shape of each CTQ variable. Statistical methods used in the *Improve* phase include tables and charts, descriptive statistics, regression analysis, hypothesis testing, the Analysis of Variance, and designed experiments.

The *Control* phase of a Six Sigma project focuses on the maintenance of improvements that have been made in the *Improve* phase. A risk abatement plan is developed to identify elements that can cause damage to a process. Statistical methods used in the *Control* phase include tables and charts, descriptive statistics, and control charts.

Roles in a Six Sigma Organization

Six Sigma requires that the employees of an organization have well-defined roles. The roles senior executive (CEO or president), executive committee, champion, process owner, master black belt, black belt, and green belt are critical to Six Sigma. More importantly, everyone must be properly trained in order to successfully fulfill their roles' tasks and responsibilities.

The role of the **senior executive** is critical for Six Sigma's ultimate success. The most successful, highly publicized Six Sigma efforts have all had unwavering, clear, and committed leadership from top management. Although Six Sigma concepts and processes can be initiated at lower levels, high-level success cannot be achieved without the leadership of the senior executive.

The members of the **executive committee** consist of the top management of an organization. They need to operate at the same level of commitment to Six Sigma as the senior executive.

Champions take a strong sponsorship and leadership role in conducting and implementing Six Sigma projects. They work closely with the executive committee, the black belt assigned to their project, and the master black belt overseeing their project. A champion should be a member of the executive committee, or at least someone who reports directly to a member of the executive committee. He or she should have enough influence to remove obstacles or provide resources without having to go higher in the organization.

A **process owner** is the manager of a process. He or she has responsibility for the process and has the authority to change the process on her or his signature. The process owner should be identified and involved immediately in all Six Sigma projects related to his or her own area.

A **master black belt** takes on a leadership role in the implementation of the Six Sigma process and as an advisor to senior executives. The master black belt must use his or her skills while working on projects that are led by black belts and green belts. A master black belt has successfully led many teams through complex Six Sigma projects. He or she is a proven change agent, leader, facilitator, and technical expert in Six Sigma.

A **black belt** works full time on Six Sigma projects. A black belt is mentored by a master black belt but may report to a manager for his or her tour of duty as a black belt. Ideally, a black belt works well in a team format, can manage meetings, is familiar with statistics and systems theory, and has a focus on the customer.

A **green belt** is an individual who works on Six Sigma projects part time (approximately 25%), either as a team member for complex projects or as a project leader for simpler projects. Most managers in a mature Six Sigma organization are green belts. Green belt certification is a critical prerequisite for advancement into upper management in a Six Sigma organization.

Recent research (see reference 3) indicates that more than 80% of the top 100 publicly traded companies in the United States use Six Sigma. So, you do need to be aware of the distinction between master black belt, black belt, and green belt if you are to function effectively in a Six Sigma organization.

In a Six Sigma organization, 25% to 50% of the organization will be green belts, only 6% to 12% of the organization will be black belts, and only 1% of the organization will be master black belts (reference 8). Individual companies, professional organizations such as the American Society for Quality, and universities such as the University of Miami offer certification programs for green belt, black belt, and master black belt. For more information on certification and other aspects of Six Sigma, see references 8, 9, and 12.

USING STATISTICS @ Beachcomber Hotel Revisited

I n the Using Statistics scenario, you were the manager of the Beach-comber Hotel. After being trained in Six Sigma, you decided to fo-cus on two critical first impressions: Is the room ready when a guest checks in? And, do guests receive their luggage in a reasonable amount of time?

You constructed a p chart of the proportion of rooms not ready at check-in. The p chart indicated that the check-in process was in control and that, on average, the pro-portion of rooms not ready was approximately 0.08 (i.e., 8%). You then constructed $\bar{X}$ and R charts for the amount of time required to deliver luggage. Although there was a considerable amount of variability around the overall mean of approximately 9.5 minutes, you determined that the luggage delivery process was also in control.

You have learned that an in-control process contains common causes of variation but no spe-cial causes of variation. Improvements in the outcomes of in-control processes must come from changes in the actual processes. Thus, if you want to reduce the proportion of rooms not ready at check-in and/or lower the mean luggage delivery time, you will need to change the check-in process and/or the luggage delivery process. From your knowledge of Six Sigma and statistics, you know that during the *Improve* phase of the DMAIC model, you will be able to perform and analyze experiments using different process designs. Hopefully you will discover better process designs that will lead to a higher percentage of rooms being ready on time and/or quicker luggage delivery times. These improvements should ultimately lead to greater guest satisfaction.

SUMMARY

In this chapter you have learned how to use control charts to distinguish between common causes and special causes of variation. For categorical variables, you learned how to construct and analyze p charts. For numerically measured variables, you learned how to construct and analyze $\bar{X}$ and R charts. The chapter also discussed managerial approaches such as TQM and Six Sigma that improve the quality of products and services.

KEY EQUATIONS

Constructing Control Limits

Process mean ± 3 standard deviations

Upper control limit (UCL) = process mean
$+3$ standard deviations

Lower control limit (LCL) = process mean
-3 standard deviations

KEY TERMS

PROBLEMS

CHECKING YOUR UNDERSTANDING

9.15 What is the difference between common cause variation and special cause variation?

9.16 What should you do to improve a process when special causes of variation are present?

9.17 What should you do to improve a process when only common causes of variation are present?

9.18 Under what circumstances do you use a p chart?

9.19 What is the difference between attribute control charts and variables control charts?

9.20 Why are $\overline{X}$ and R charts used together?

APPLYING THE CONCEPTS

9.21 According to the American Society for Quality, customers in the United States consistently rate service quality lower than product quality (American Society for Quality, *The Quarterly Quality Report*, **www.asq.org**, May 16, 2006). For example, products in the beverage, personal care, and cleaning industries, as well as the major appliance sector all received very high customer satisfaction ratings. At the other extreme, services provided by airlines, banks, and insurance companies all received low customer satisfaction ratings.
a. Why do you think service quality consistently rates lower than product quality?
b. What are the similarities and differences between measuring service quality and product quality?
c. Do Deming's 14 points apply to both products and services?
d. Can Six Sigma be used for both products and services?

9.22 Suppose that you have been hired as a summer intern at a large amusement park. Every day, your task is to conduct 200 exit interviews in the parking lot when customers leave. You need to construct questions to address the cleanliness of the park and the customers' intent to return. When you begin to construct a short questionnaire, you remember the control charts you learned in a statistics course, and you decide to write questions that will provide you with data to graph on control charts. After collecting data for 30 days, you plan to construct the control charts.
a. Write a question that will allow you to develop a control chart of customers' perceptions of cleanliness of the park.
b. Give examples of common cause variation and special cause variation for the control chart.
c. If the control chart is in control, what does that indicate and what do you do next?
d. If the control chart is out of control, what does this indicate and what do you do next?
e. Repeat (a) through (d), this time addressing the customers' intent to return to the park.
f. After the initial 30 days, assuming that the charts indicate in-control processes or that the root sources of special cause variation have been corrected, explain how the charts can be used on a daily basis to monitor and improve the quality in the park.

9.23 Researchers at Miami University in Oxford, Ohio, investigated the use of p charts to monitor the market share of a product and to document the effectiveness of marketing promotions. Market share is defined as the company's proportion of the total number of products sold in a category. If a p chart based on a company's market share indicates an in-control process, then the company's share in the marketplace is deemed to be stable and consistent over time. In the example given in the article, the RudyBird Disk Company collected daily sales data from a nationwide retail audit service. The first 30 days of data in the accompanying table (stored in RudyBird) indicate the total number of cases of computer disks sold and the number of RudyBird disks sold. The final 7 days of data were taken after Rudy-Bird launched a major in-store promotion. A control chart was used to see if the in-store promotion would result in special cause variation in the marketplace.

Cases Sold Before the Promotion

Day	Total	RudyBird	Day	Total	RudyBird
1	154	35	16	177	56
2	153	43	17	143	43
3	200	44	18	200	69
4	197	56	19	134	38
5	194	54	20	192	47
6	172	38	21	155	45
7	190	43	22	135	36
8	209	62	23	189	55
9	173	53	24	184	44
10	171	39	25	170	47
11	173	44	26	178	48
12	168	37	27	167	42
13	184	45	28	204	71
14	211	58	29	183	64
15	179	35	30	169	43

Cases Sold After the Promotion

Day	Total	RudyBird
31	201	92
32	177	76
33	205	85
34	199	90
35	187	77
36	168	79
37	198	97

Source: Data extracted from C. T. Crespy, T. C. Krehbiel, and J. M. Stearns, "Integrating Analytic Methods into Marketing Research Education: Statistical Control Charts as an Example," *Marketing Education Review*, 5 (Spring 1995), 11–23.

a. Construct a p chart, using data from the first 30 days (prior to the promotion) to monitor the market share for RudyBird disks.
b. Is the market share for RudyBird in control before the start of the in-store promotion?
c. On your control chart, extend the control limits generated in (b) and plot the proportions for days 31 through 37.

What effect, if any, did the in-store promotion have on RudyBird's market share?

9.24 The manufacturer of Boston and Vermont asphalt shingles constructed control charts and analyzed several quality characteristics. One characteristic of interest is the strength of the sealant on the shingle. During each day of production, three shingles are tested for their sealant strength. (Thus, a subgroup is operationally defined as one day of production, and the sample size for each subgroup is 3.) Separate pieces are cut from the upper and lower portions of a shingle and then reassembled to simulate shingles on a roof. A timed heating process is used to simulate the sealing process. The sealed shingle pieces are pulled apart, and the amount of force (in pounds) required to break the sealant bond is measured and recorded. This variable is called the *sealant strength*. The file Sealant contains sealant strength measurements on 25 days of production for Boston shingles and 19 days for Vermont shingles.

For the 25 days of production for Boston shingles,
a. construct a control chart for the range.
b. construct a control chart for the mean.
c. is the process in control?
d. Repeat (a) through (c), using the 19 production days for Vermont shingles.

9.25 A professional basketball player has embarked on a program to study his ability to shoot foul shots. On each day in which a game is not scheduled, he intends to shoot 100 foul shots. He maintains records over a period of 40 days of practice, with the results stored in Foulspc :
a. Construct a p chart for the proportion of successful foul shots. Do you think that the player's foul-shooting process is in statistical control? If not, why not?
b. What if you were told that the player used a different method of shooting foul shots for the last 20 days? How might this information change your conclusions in (a)?
c. If you knew the information in (b) prior to doing (a), how might you do the analysis differently?

9.26 The funds-transfer department of a bank has the business objective of reducing the turnaround time for investigations of funds-transfer payments. A payment may involve the bank as a remitter of funds, a beneficiary of funds, or an intermediary in the payment. An investigation is initiated by a payment inquiry or a query by a party involved in the payment or any department affected by the flow of funds. When a query is received, an investigator reconstructs the transaction trail of the payment and verifies that the information is correct and that the proper payment is transmitted. The investigator then reports the results of the investigation, and the transaction is considered closed. It is important that investigations be closed rapidly, preferably within the same day. The number of new investigations and the number and proportion closed on the same day that the inquiry was made are stored in FundTran .
a. Construct a control chart for these data.
b. Is the process in a state of statistical control? Explain.
c. Based on the results of (a) and (b), what should management do next to improve the process?

9.27 A branch manager of a brokerage company has the business objective of reducing the number of undesirable trades made by her sales staff. A trade is considered undesirable if there is an error on the trade ticket. Trades with errors are canceled and resubmitted. The cost of correcting errors is billed to the brokerage company. The branch manager wants to know whether the proportion of undesirable trades is in a state of statistical control so she can plan the next step in a quality improvement process. Data were collected for a 30-day period and stored in Trade .
a. Construct a control chart for these data.
b. Is the process in control? Explain.
c. Based on the results of (a) and (b), what should the manager do next to improve the process?

9.28 As chief operating officer of a local community hospital, you have just returned from a three-day seminar on quality and productivity. It is your intention to implement many of the ideas that you learned at the seminar. You have decided to construct control charts for the upcoming month for the proportion of rework in the laboratory (based on 1,000 daily samples) and time (in hours) between receipt of a specimen at the laboratory and completion of the work (based on a subgroup of 10 specimens per day). The data collected are summarized and stored in HospAdm . You are to make a presentation to the chief executive officer of the hospital and the board of directors. Prepare a report that summarizes the conclusions drawn from analyzing control charts for these variables. In addition, recommend additional variables to measure and monitor by using control charts.

9.29 A team working at a cat food company had the business objective of reducing nonconformance in the cat food canning process. As the team members began to investigate the current process, they found that, in some instances, production needed expensive overtime costs to meet the requirements requested by the market forecasting team. They also realized that data were not available concerning the stability and magnitude of the rate of nonconformance and the production volume throughout the day. Their previous study of the process indicated that output could be nonconforming for a variety of reasons. The reasons broke down into two categories: quality characteristics due to the can and characteristics concerning the fill weight of the container. Because these nonconformities stemmed from different sets of underlying causes, they decided to study them separately. The group assigned to study and reduce the nonconformities due to the

can decided that at 15-minute intervals during each shift the number of nonconforming cans would be determined along with the total number of cans produced during the time period. The results for a single day's production of kidney cat food and a single day's production of shrimp cat food for each shift are stored in CatFood3 . You want to study the process of producing cans of cat food for the two shifts and the two types of food. Completely analyze the data.

9.30 Refer to Problem 9.29. The production team at the cat food company investigating nonconformities due to the fill weight of the cans determined that at 15-minute intervals during each shift, a subgroup of five cans would be selected, and the contents of the selected cans would be weighed. The results for a single day's production of kidney cat food and a single day's production of shrimp cat food are stored in CatFood4 . You want to study the process of producing cans of cat food for the two shifts and the two types of food. Completely analyze the data.

9.31 For a period of four weeks, record your pulse rate (in beats per minute) just after you get out of bed in the morning and then again before you go to sleep at night. Construct $\overline{X}$ and R charts and determine whether your pulse rate is in a state of statistical control. Discuss.

9.32 **(Class Project)** Use the table of random numbers (Table E.1) to simulate the selection of different-colored balls from an urn, as follows:
1. Start in the row corresponding to the day of the month in which you were born plus the last two digits of the year in which you were born. For example, if you were born October 3, 1990, you would start in row 93 (3 + 90). If your total exceeds 100, subtract 100 from the total.
2. Select two-digit random numbers.
3. If you select a random number from 00 to 94, consider the ball to be white; if the random number is from 95 to 99, consider the ball to be red.

Each student is to select 100 two-digit random numbers and report the number of "red balls" in the sample. Construct a control chart for the proportion of red balls. What conclusions can you draw about the system of selecting red balls? Are all the students part of the system? Is anyone outside the system? If so, what explanation can you give for someone who has too many red balls? If a bonus were paid to the top 10% of the students (the 10% with the fewest red balls), what effect would that have on the rest of the students? Discuss.

THE HARNSWELL SEWING MACHINE COMPANY CASE

Phase 1

For more than 40 years, the Harnswell Sewing Machine Company has manufactured industrial sewing machines. The company specializes in automated machines called pattern tackers that sew repetitive patterns on such mass-produced products as shoes, garments, and seat belts. Aside from the sales of machines, the company sells machine parts. Because the company's products have a reputation for being superior, Harnswell is able to command a price premium for its product line.

Recently, the operations manager, Natalie York, purchased several books related to quality. After reading them, she considered the feasibility of beginning a quality program at the company. At the current time, the company has no formal quality program. Parts are 100% inspected at the time of shipping to a customer or installation in a machine, yet Natalie has always wondered why inventory of certain parts (in particular, the half-inch cam rollers) invariably falls short before a full year lapses, even though 7,000 pieces have been produced for a demand of 5,000 pieces per year.

After a great deal of reflection and with some apprehension, Natalie has decided that she will approach John Harnswell, the owner of the company, about the possibility of beginning a program to improve quality in the company, starting with a trial project in the machine parts area. As she is walking to Mr. Harnswell's office for the meeting, she has second thoughts about whether this is such a good idea. After all, just last month, Mr. Harnswell told her, "Why do you need to go to graduate school for your master's degree in business? That is a waste of your time and will not be of any value to the Harnswell Company. All those professors are just up in their ivory towers and don't know a thing about running a business, like I do."

As she enters his office, Mr. Harnswell invites Natalie to sit down across from him. "Well, what do you have on your mind this morning?" Mr. Harnswell asks her in an inquisitive tone. She begins by starting to talk about the books that she has just completed reading and about how she has some interesting ideas for making production even better than it is now and improving profits. Before she can finish, Mr. Harnswell has started to answer: "Look, everything has been fine since I started this company in 1968. I have built this company up from nothing to one that employs more than 100 people. Why do you want to make waves? Remember, if it ain't broke, don't fix it." With that, he ushers her from his office with the admonishment of, "What am I going to do with you if you keep coming up with these ridiculous ideas?"

EXERCISES

1. Based on what you have read, which of Deming's 14 points of management are most lacking at the Harnswell Sewing Machine Company? Explain.
2. What changes, if any, do you think that Natalie York might be able to institute in the company? Explain.

Phase 2

Natalie slowly walks down the hall after leaving Mr. Harnswell's office, feeling rather downcast. He just won't listen to anyone, she thinks. As she walks, Jim Murante, the shop foreman, comes up beside her. "So," he says, "did you really think that he would listen to you? I've been here more than 25 years. The only way he listens is if he is shown something that worked after it has already been done. Let's see what we can plan together."

Natalie and Jim decide to begin by investigating the production of the cam rollers, which are precision-ground parts. The last part of the production process involves the grinding of the outer diameter. After grinding, the part mates with the cam groove of the particular sewing pattern. The half-inch rollers technically have an engineering specification for the outer diameter of the roller of 0.5075 inch (the specifications are actually metric, but in factory floor jargon, they are referred to as half-inch), plus a tolerable error of 0.0003 inch on the lower side. Thus, the outer diameter is allowed to be between 0.5072 and 0.5075 inch. Anything larger is reclassified into a different and less costly category, and anything smaller is unusable for anything other than scrap.

The grinding of the cam roller is done on a single machine with a single tool setup and no change in the grinding wheel after initial setup. The operation is done by Dave Martin, the head machinist, who has 30 years of experience in the trade and specific experience producing the cam roller part. Because production occurs in batches, Natalie and Jim sample five parts produced from each batch. Table HS9.1 presents data collected over 30 batches (stored in Harnswell).

EXERCISE

3. **a.** Is the process in control? Why?
   b. What recommendations do you have for improving the process?

Phase 3

Natalie examines the $\bar{X}$ and R charts developed from the data presented in Table HS9.1. The R chart indicates that the process is in control, but the $\bar{X}$ chart reveals that the

TABLE HS9.1

Diameter of Cam Rollers (in Inches)

	Cam Roller				
Batch	1	2	3	4	5
1	.5076	.5076	.5075	.5077	.5075
2	.5075	.5077	.5076	.5076	.5075
3	.5075	.5075	.5075	.5075	.5076
4	.5075	.5076	.5074	.5076	.5073
5	.5075	.5074	.5076	.5073	.5076
6	.5076	.5075	.5076	.5075	.5075
7	.5076	.5076	.5076	.5075	.5075
8	.5075	.5076	.5076	.5075	.5074
9	.5074	.5076	.5075	.5075	.5076
10	.5076	.5077	.5075	.5075	.5075
11	.5075	.5075	.5075	.5076	.5075
12	.5075	.5076	.5075	.5077	.5075
13	.5076	.5076	.5073	.5076	.5074
14	.5075	.5076	.5074	.5076	.5075
15	.5075	.5075	.5076	.5074	.5073
16	.5075	.5074	.5076	.5075	.5075
17	.5075	.5074	.5075	.5074	.5072
18	.5075	.5075	.5076	.5075	.5076
19	.5076	.5076	.5075	.5075	.5076
20	.5075	.5074	.5077	.5076	.5074
21	.5075	.5074	.5075	.5075	.5075
22	.5076	.5076	.5075	.5076	.5074
23	.5076	.5076	.5075	.5075	.5076
24	.5075	.5076	.5075	.5076	.5075
25	.5075	.5075	.5075	.5075	.5074
26	.5077	.5076	.5076	.5074	.5075
27	.5075	.5075	.5074	.5076	.5075
28	.5077	.5076	.5075	.5075	.5076
29	.5075	.5075	.5074	.5075	.5075
30	.5076	.5075	.5075	.5076	.5075

mean for batch 17 is outside the LCL. This immediately gives her cause for concern because low values for the roller diameter could mean that parts have to be scrapped. Natalie goes to see Jim Murante, the shop foreman, to try to find out what had happened to batch 17. Jim looks up the production records to determine when this batch was produced. "Aha!" he exclaims. "I think I've got the answer! This batch was produced on that really cold morning we had last month. I've been after Mr. Harnswell for a long time to let us install an automatic thermostat here in the shop so that the place doesn't feel so cold when we get here in the morning. All he ever tells me is that people aren't as tough as they used to be."

Natalie is almost in shock. She realizes that what happened is that, rather than standing idle until the environment and the equipment warmed to acceptable

temperatures, the machinist opted to manufacture parts that might have to be scrapped. In fact, Natalie recalls that a major problem occurred on that same day, when several other expensive parts had to be scrapped. Natalie says to Jim, "We just have to do something. We can't let this go on now that we know what problems it is potentially causing." Natalie and Jim decide to take enough money out of petty cash to get the thermostat without having to fill out a requisition requiring Mr. Harnswell's signature. They install the thermostat and set the heating control so that the heat turns on a half hour before the shop opens each morning.

EXERCISES

4. What should Natalie do now concerning the cam roller data? Explain.
5. Explain how the actions of Natalie and Jim to avoid this particular problem in the future have resulted in quality improvement.

PHASE 4

Because corrective action was taken to eliminate the special cause of variation, Natalie removes the data for batch 17 from the analysis. The control charts for the remaining days indicate a stable system, with only common causes of variation operating on the system. Then, Natalie and Jim sit down with Dave Martin and several other machinists to try to determine all the possible causes for the existence of oversized and scrapped rollers. Natalie is still troubled by the data. After all, she wants to find out whether the process is giving oversizes (which are downgraded) and undersizes (which are scrapped). She thinks about which tables and charts might be most helpful.

EXERCISE

6. a. Construct a frequency distribution and a stem-and-leaf display of the cam roller diameters. Which do you prefer in this situation?
   b. Based on your results in (a), construct all appropriate charts of the cam roller diameters.
   c. Write a report, expressing your conclusions concerning the cam roller diameters. Be sure to discuss the diameters as they relate to the specifications.

PHASE 5

Natalie notices immediately that the overall mean diameter with batch 17 eliminated is 0.507527, which is higher than the specification value. Thus, the mean diameter of the rollers produced is so high that many will be downgraded in value. In fact, 55 of the 150 rollers sampled (36.67%) are above the specification value. If this percentage is extrapolated to the full year's production, 36.67% of the 7,000 pieces manufactured, or 2,567, could not be sold as half-inch rollers, leaving only 4,433 available for sale. "No wonder we often have shortages that require costly emergency runs," she thinks. She also notes that not one diameter is below the lower specification of 0.5072, so not one of the rollers had to be scrapped.

Natalie realizes that there has to be a reason for all this. Along with Jim Murante, she decides to show the results to Dave Martin, the head machinist. Dave says that the results don't surprise him that much. "You know," he says, "there is only 0.0003 inch variation in diameter that I'm allowed. If I aim for exactly halfway between 0.5072 and 0.5075, I'm afraid that I'll make a lot of short pieces that will have to be scrapped. I know from way back when I first started here that Mr. Harnswell and everybody else will come down on my head if they start seeing too many of those scraps. I figure that if I aim at 0.5075, the worst thing that will happen will be a bunch of downgrades, but I won't make any pieces that have to be scrapped."

EXERCISES

7. What approach do you think the machinist should take in terms of the diameter he should aim for? Explain.
8. What do you think that Natalie should do next? Explain.

MANAGING ASHLAND MULTICOMM SERVICES

The AMS technical services team has embarked on a quality improvement effort. Its first project relates to maintaining the target upload speed for its Internet service subscribers. Upload speeds are measured on a device that records the results on a standard scale in which the target value is 1.0. Each day five uploads are randomly selected, and the speed of each upload is measured. Table AMS9.1 below presents the results for 25 days (stored in AMS9).

EXERCISE

1. a. Construct the appropriate control charts for these data.
   b. Is the process in a state of statistical control? Explain.
   c. What should the team recommend as the next step to improve the process?

TABLE AMS9.1

Upload Speeds for 25 Consecutive Days

Day	1	2	3	4	5
1	0.96	1.01	1.12	1.07	0.97
2	1.06	1.00	1.02	1.16	0.96
3	1.00	0.90	0.98	1.18	0.96
4	0.92	0.89	1.01	1.16	0.90
5	1.02	1.16	1.03	0.89	1.00
6	0.88	0.92	1.03	1.16	0.91
7	1.05	1.13	1.01	0.93	1.03
8	0.95	0.86	1.14	0.90	0.95
9	0.99	0.89	1.00	1.15	0.92
10	0.89	1.18	1.03	0.96	1.04
11	0.97	1.13	0.95	0.86	1.06
12	1.00	0.87	1.02	0.98	1.13
13	0.96	0.79	1.17	0.97	0.95
14	1.03	0.89	1.03	1.12	1.03
15	0.96	1.12	0.95	0.88	0.99
16	1.01	0.87	0.99	1.04	1.16
17	0.98	0.85	0.99	1.04	1.16
18	1.03	0.82	1.21	0.98	1.08
19	1.02	0.84	1.15	0.94	1.08
20	0.90	1.02	1.10	1.04	1.08
21	0.96	1.05	1.01	0.93	1.01
22	0.89	1.04	0.97	0.99	0.95
23	0.96	1.00	0.97	1.04	0.95
24	1.01	0.98	1.04	1.01	0.92
25	1.01	1.00	0.92	0.90	1.11

REFERENCES

1. Arndt, M., "Quality Isn't Just for Widgets," *Business-Week*, July 22, 2002, pp. 72–73.
2. Automotive Industry Action Group (AIAG), *Statistical Process Control Reference Manual* (Chrysler, Ford, and General Motors Quality and Supplier Assessment Staff, 1995).
3. Cyger, M., "The Last Word—Riding the Bandwagon," *iSixSigma Magazine*, November/December 2006.
4. Davis, R. B., and T. C. Krehbiel, "Shewhart and Zone Control Charts Under Linear Trend," *Communications in Statistics: Simulation and Computation*, 31 (2002), 91–96.

5. Deming, W. E., *The New Economics for Business, Industry, and Government* (Cambridge, MA: MIT Center for Advanced Engineering Study, 1993).

6. Deming, W. E., *Out of the Crisis* (Cambridge, MA: MIT Center for Advanced Engineering Study, 1986).

7. Gabor, A., *The Man Who Discovered Quality* (New York: Time Books, 1990).

8. Gitlow, H., and D. Levine, *Six Sigma for Green Belts and Champions* (Upper Saddle River, NJ: Financial Times/Prentice Hall, 2005).

9. Gitlow, H., D. Levine, and E. Popovich, *Design for Six Sigma for Green Belts and Champions* (Upper Saddle River, NJ: Financial Times/Prentice Hall, 2006).

10. Hahn, G. J., N. Doganaksoy, and R. Hoerl, "The Evolution of Six Sigma," *Quality Engineering*, 12 (2000), 317–326.

11. Lemak, D. L., N. P. Mero, and R. Reed, "When Quality Works: A Premature Post-Mortem on TQM," *Journal of Business and Management*, 8 (2002), 391–407.

12. Levine, D. M., *Statistics for Six Sigma for Green Belts with Minitab and JMP* (Upper Saddle River, NJ: Financial Times/Prentice Hall, 2006).

13. *Microsoft Excel 2010* (Redmond, WA: Microsoft Corp., 2010).

14. *Minitab Release 16* (State College, PA: Minitab Inc., 2010).

15. Scherkenbach, W. W., *The Deming Route to Quality and Productivity: Road Maps and Roadblocks* (Washington, DC: CEEP Press, 1987).

16. Shewhart, W. A., *Economic Control of the Quality of Manufactured Product* (New York: Van Nostrand-Reinhard, 1931, reprinted by the American Society for Quality Control, Milwaukee, 1980).

17. Snee, R. D., "Impact of Six Sigma on Quality," *Quality Engineering*, 12 (2000), ix–xiv.

18. Vardeman, S. B., and J. M. Jobe, *Statistical Methods for Quality Assurance: Basics, Measurement, Control, Capability and Improvement* (New York: Springer-Verlag, 2009).

19. Walton, M., *The Deming Management Method* (New York: Perigee Books, 1986).

CHAPTER 9 EXCEL GUIDE

EG9.1 The Theory of Control Charts

There are no Excel Guide instructions for this section.

EG9.2 Type of Control Charts

PHStat2 Use **p Chart** to create a *p* chart and supporting worksheets that compute the control limits and plot points. For example, to create the Figure 9.2 *p* chart for the Table 9.1 nonconforming hotel room data, open to the **DATA worksheet** of the **Hotel1 workbook**. Select **PHStat → Control Charts → p Chart** and in the procedure's dialog box (shown at right):

1. Enter **C1:C29** as the **Nonconformances Cell Range.**
2. Check **First cell contains label.**
3. Click **Size does not vary** and enter **200** as the **Sample/Subgroup Size.**
4. Enter a **Title** and click **OK.**

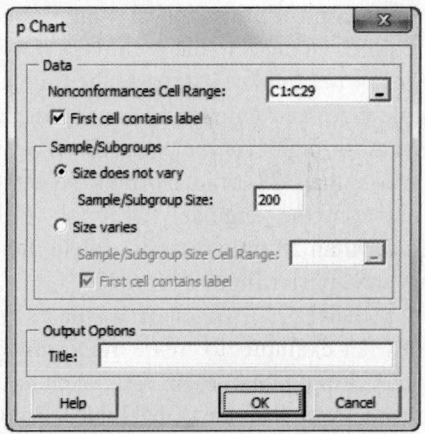

The procedure creates a *p* chart on its own chart sheet and two supporting worksheets: one that computes the control limits and one that computes the values to be plotted. For more information about these two worksheets, read the following *In-Depth Excel* instructions.

For problems in which the sample/subgroup sizes vary, replace step 3 with this step: Click **Size varies**, enter the cell range that contains the sample/subgroup sizes as the **Sample/ Subgroup Cell Range**, and click **First cell contain label**.

In-Depth Excel Use the **pChartDATA** and **COMPUTE worksheets** of the **p Chart workbook** as a template for computing control limits and plot points. The pChartDATA worksheet uses formulas in column D that divide the column C number of nonconformances value by the column B subgroup/sample size value to compute the proportion (p_i) and uses formulas in columns E through G to display the values for the LCL, $\bar{p}$, and UCL that are computed in cells B12 through B14 of the COMPUTE worksheet. In turn, the COMPUTE worksheet (shown below) uses the subgroup sizes and the proportion values found in the pChartDATA worksheet to compute the control limits.

	A	B	
1	p Chart Summary		
2			
3	Intermediate Calculations		
4	Sum of Subgroup Sizes	5600	=SUM(pChartDATA!B:B)
5	Number of Subgroups Taken	28	=COUNT(pChartDATA!B:B)
6	Average Sample/Subgroup Size	200	=B4/B5
7	Average Proportion of Nonconforming Items	0.0827	=SUM(pChartDATA!C:C)/B4
8	Three Standard Deviations	0.0584	=3 * SQRT(B7 * (1 - B7)/B6)
9	Preliminary Lower Control Limit	0.0243	=B7 - B8
10			
11	p Chart Control Limits		
12	Lower Control Limit	0.0243	=IF(B9 > 0, B9, 0)
13	Center	0.0827	=B7
14	Upper Control Limit	0.1411	=B7 + B8

Computing control limits and plotting points for other problems requires changes to the **pChartDATA worksheet** of the **p Chart workbook**. First, paste the time period, subgroup/sample size, and number of nonconformances data into columns A through C of the pChartDATA worksheet. If there are more than 28 time periods, select cell range **D29:G29** and copy the range down through all the rows. If there are fewer than 28 time periods, delete the extra rows from the bottom up, starting with row 29.

Use the pChartDATA worksheet as the basis for creating a p chart. For example, to create the Figure 9.2 p chart for the nonconforming hotel room data, open to the pChartDATA worksheet which contains the Table 9.1 nonconforming hotel room data. Select the cell range **A1:A29** and while holding down the **Ctrl** key, select the cell range **D1:G29**. (This operation selects the cell range **A1:A29, D1:G29**.) Then:

1. Select **Insert → Scatter** and select the fourth choice from the **Scatter** gallery **(Scatter with Straight Lines and Markers)**.
2. Relocate the chart to a chart sheet and adjust chart formatting by using the instructions in Appendix Section F.4.

At this point, a recognizable chart begins to take shape, but the control limit and center lines are improperly formatted and are not properly labeled. Use the following three sets of instructions to correct these formatting errors:

To reformat each control limit line:

1. Right-click the control limit line and select **Format Data Series** from the shortcut menu.
2. In the Format Data Series dialog box left pane, click **Marker Options** and in the **Marker Options** right panel, click **None**.
3. In the left pane, click **Line Style** and in the **Line Style** right panel, select the sixth choice (a dashed line) from the **Dash type** drop-down gallery list.
4. In the left pane, click **Line Color** and in the **Line Color** right panel, select the black color from the **Color** drop-down gallery list.
5. Click **Close**.

To reformat the center line:

1. Right-click the center line and select **Format Data Series** from the shortcut menu.
2. In the Format Data Series dialog box left pane, click **Marker Options** and in the **Marker Options** right panel, click **None**.
3. In the left pane, click **Line Color** and in the **Line Color** right panel, click **Solid line** and then select a red color from the **Color** drop-down gallery.
4. Click **Close**.

To label a control limit line or the center line:

1. Select **Layout → Text Box** (in Insert group) and starting slightly above and to the right of the line, drag the special cursor diagonally to form a new text box.
2. Enter the line label in the text box and then click on the chart background.

EG9.4 Control Charts for the Range and the Mean

The R Chart and the X Chart

PHStat2 Use **R and XBar Charts** to create R and $\bar{X}$ charts and supporting worksheets that compute the control limits and plot points. For example, to create the Figure 9.5 R chart and the Figure 14.6 $\bar{X}$ chart for the Table 14.4 luggage delivery times, open to the **DATA worksheet** of the **Hotel2 workbook**. Because the PHStat2 procedure requires column cell ranges that contain either means or ranges, first add two columns that compute the mean and ranges on this worksheet. Enter the column heading **Mean** in cell **G1** and the heading **Range** in cell **H1**. Enter the formula **=AVERAGE(B2:F2)** in cell **G2** and the formula **=MAX(B2:F2) - MIN(B2:F2)** in cell **H2**. Select the cell range **G2:H2** and copy the range down through row 29.

With the two columns created, select **PHStat → Control Charts → R and XBar Charts**. In the procedure's dialog box (shown below):

1. Enter **5** as the **Subgroup/Sample Size**.
2. Enter **H1:H29** as the **Subgroup Ranges Cell Range**.
3. Check **First cell contains label**.
4. Click **R and XBar Charts**. Enter **G1:G29** as the **Subgroup Means Cell Range** and check **First cell contains label**.
5. Enter a **Title** and click **OK**.

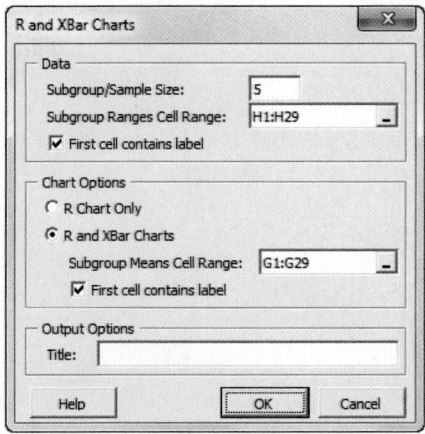

The procedure creates the two charts on separate chart sheets and two supporting worksheets: one that computes the control limits and one that computes the values to be plotted. For more information about these two worksheets, read the following *In-Depth Excel* section.

In-Depth Excel Use the **DATA**, **RXChartDATA**, and **COMPUTE worksheets** of the **R and XBar Chart workbook** as a template for computing control limits and plotting points. The RXChartDATA worksheet uses formulas in columns B and C to compute the mean and range values for the Table 14.4 luggage delivery times stored in the DATA worksheet. The worksheet uses formulas in columns D through I to display the values for the control limit and center lines, using values that are computed in the COMPUTE worksheet. Formulas in columns D and G use IF functions that will omit the lower control limit if the LCL value computed is less than 0. (To examine the formulas used in the worksheet, open to the **RXChartDATA_FORMULAS worksheet**.)

The COMPUTE worksheet (shown below) uses the computed means and ranges to compute $\bar{R}$ and $\bar{\bar{X}}$, the mean of the subgroup means. Unlike the COMPUTE worksheets for other control charts, you must manually enter the **Sample/Subgroup Size** in cell **B4** (**5**, as shown below) in addition to the D_3, D_4, and A_2 factors in cells **B8**, **B9**, and **B18** (**0**, **2.114**, and **0.577**, as shown).

Use Table E.8 to look up the values for the D_3, D_4, and A_2 factors.

▲	A	B	
1	**R and XBar Chart Summary**		
2			
3	**Data**		
4	Sample/Subgroup Size	5	
5			
6	R Chart Intermediate Calculations		
7	RBar	3.4821	=AVERAGE(RXChartDATA!C:C)
8	D_3 Factor	0	
9	D_4 Factor	2.114	
10			
11	**R Chart Control Limits**		
12	Lower Control Limit	0.0000	=B8 * B7
13	Center	3.4821	=B7
14	Upper Control Limit	7.3613	=B9 * B7
15			
16	XBar Chart Intermediate Calculations		
17	Average of Subgroup Averages	9.4779	=AVERAGE(RXChartDATA!B:B)
18	A_2 Factor	0.577	
19	A_2 Factor * RBar	2.0092	=B18 * B7
20			
21	**XBar Chart Control Limits**		
22	Lower Control Limit	7.4687	=B17- B19
23	Center	9.4779	=B17
24	Upper Control Limit	11.4871	=B17 + B19

Computing control limits and plotting points for other problems requires changes to the RXChartDATA or the DATA worksheet, depending on whether means and ranges have been previously computed. If the means and ranges have been previously computed, paste these values into column B and C of the RXChartDATA worksheet. If there are more than 28 time periods, select cell range **D29:I29** and copy the range down through all the rows. If there are fewer than 28 time periods, delete the extra rows from the bottom up, starting with row 29.

If the means and ranges have not been previously computed, changes must be made to the DATA worksheet. First, determine the subgroup size. If the subgroup size is less than 5, delete the extra columns, right-to-left, starting with column F. If the subgroup size is greater than 5, select column F, right-click, and click **Insert** from the short-cut menu. (Repeat as many times as necessary.) With the DATA worksheet so adjusted, paste the time and subgroup data into the worksheet, starting with cell A1. Then open to the RXChartDATA worksheet, and if the number of time periods is not equal to 28, adjust the number of rows using the instructions of the previous paragraph.

Use the RXChartDATA worksheet as the basis for creating R and $\bar{X}$ charts. For example, open to the **RXChartDATA worksheet** of the **R and XBar Chart workbook** which contains Table 14.4 luggage delivery times data. To create the Figure 14.5 R chart for Excel, select the cell range **C1:F29**. To create the Figure 14.6 $\bar{X}$ chart, select the cell range **B1:B29, G1:I29** (while holding down the **Ctrl key**, select the cell range **B1:B29** and then the cell range **G1:I29**). In either case:

1. Select **Insert → Scatter** and select the fourth choice from the **Scatter** gallery **(Scatter with Straight Lines and Markers)**.

2. Relocate the chart to a chart sheet and adjust the chart formatting by using the instructions in Appendix Section F.4.

At this point, a recognizable chart begins to take shape, but the control limit and center lines are improperly formatted and are not properly labeled. To correct these formatting errors, use the three sets of instructions given in the Section EG9.2 *In-Depth Excel* instructions.

10 Confidence Interval Estimation

Learning Objectives

In this chapter, you learn:

- To construct and interpret confidence interval estimates for the mean and the proportion
- How to determine the sample size necessary to develop a confidence interval estimate for the mean or proportion

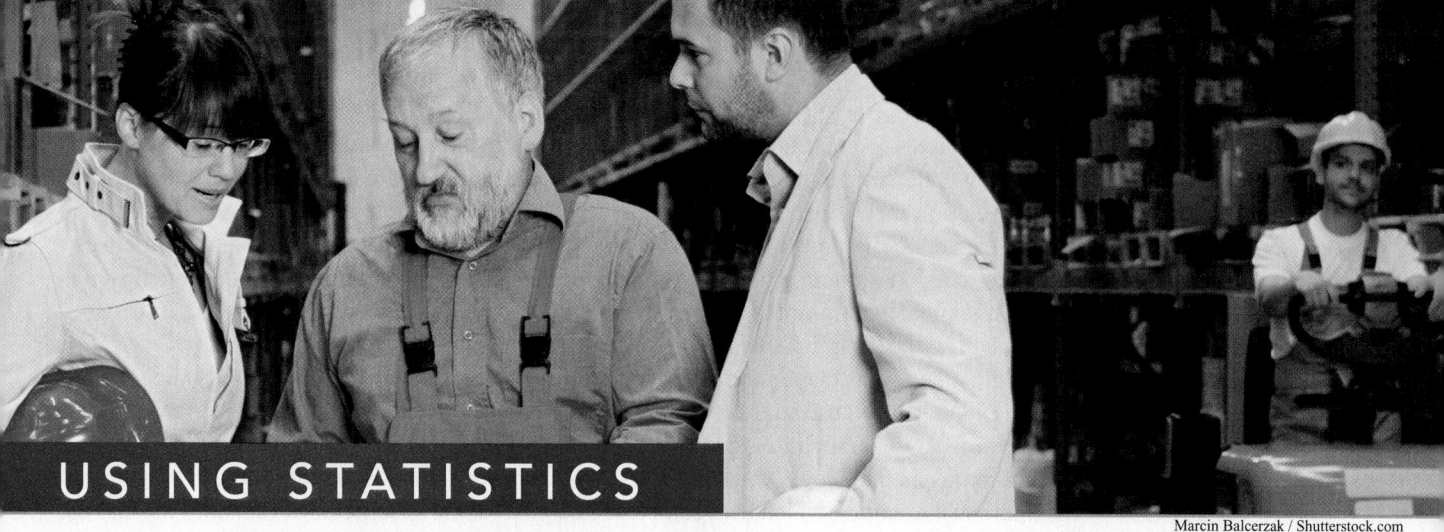

Marcin Balcerzak / Shutterstock.com

USING STATISTICS

@ Saxon Home Improvement, Part II

Saxon Home Improvement distributes home improvement supplies in the northeastern United States. As a company accountant, you are responsible for the accuracy of the integrated inventory management and sales information system. You could review the contents of each and every record to check the accuracy of this system, but such a detailed review would be time-consuming and costly. A better approach is to use statistical inference techniques to draw conclusions about the population of all records from a relatively small sample collected during an audit. At the end of each month, you could select a sample of the sales invoices to estimate the following:

- The mean dollar amount listed on the sales invoices for the month
- The proportion of invoices that contain errors that violate the internal control policy of the warehouse

How accurate are the results from the sample, and how do you use this information? Is the sample size large enough to give you the information you need?

Kristy Pargeter / Shutterstock.com

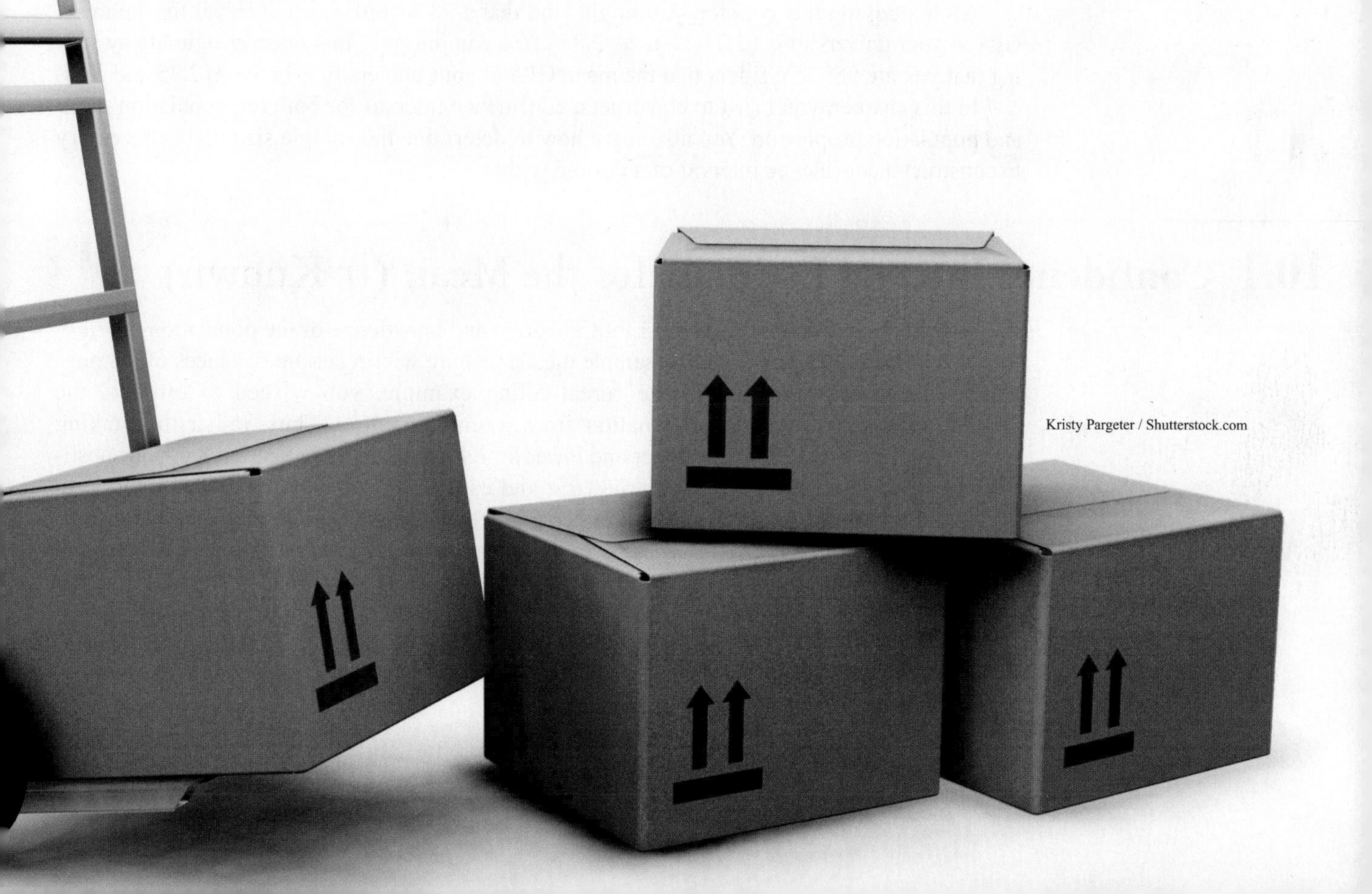

I n Section 8.4, you used the Central Limit Theorem and knowledge of the population distribution to determine the percentage of sample means that are within certain distances of the population mean. For instance, in the cereal-filling example used throughout Chapter 8 (see Example 8.6 on page 333), you can conclude that 95% of all sample means are between 362.12 and 373.88 grams. This is an example of *deductive* reasoning because the conclusion is based on taking something that is true in general (for the population) and applying it to something specific (the sample means).

Getting the results that Saxon Home Improvement needs requires *inductive* reasoning. Inductive reasoning lets you use some specifics to make broader generalizations. You cannot guarantee that the broader generalizations are absolutely correct, but with a careful choice of the specifics and a rigorous methodology, you can get useful conclusions. As a Saxon accountant, you need to use inferential statistics, which uses sample results (the "some specifics") to *estimate* (the making of "broader generalizations") unknown population parameters such as a population mean or a population proportion. Note that statisticians use the word *estimate* in the same sense of the everyday usage: something you are reasonably certain about but cannot flatly say is absolutely correct.

You estimate population parameters by using either point estimates or interval estimates. A **point estimate** is the value of a single sample statistic, such as a sample mean. A **confidence interval estimate** is a range of numbers, called an *interval*, constructed around the point estimate. The confidence interval is constructed such that the probability that the interval includes the population parameter is known.

Suppose you want to estimate the mean GPA of all the students at your university. The mean GPA for all the students is an unknown population mean, denoted by μ. You select a sample of students and compute the sample mean, denoted by $\bar{X}$, to be 2.80. As a *point estimate* of the population mean, μ, you ask how accurate is the 2.80 value as an estimate of the population mean, μ? By taking into account the variability from sample to sample (see Section 8.4, concerning the sampling distribution of the mean), you can construct a confidence interval estimate for the population mean to answer this question.

When you construct a confidence interval estimate, you indicate the confidence of correctly estimating the value of the population parameter, μ. This allows you to say that there is a specified confidence that μ is somewhere in the range of numbers defined by the interval.

After studying this chapter, you might find that a 95% confidence interval for the mean GPA at your university is $(2.75 \leq \mu \leq 2.85)$. You can interpret this interval estimate by stating that you are 95% confident that the mean GPA at your university is between 2.75 and 2.85.

In this chapter, you learn to construct a confidence interval for both the population mean and population proportion. You also learn how to determine the sample size that is necessary to construct a confidence interval of a desired width.

10.1 Confidence Interval Estimate for the Mean (σ Known)

In Section 8.4, you used the Central Limit Theorem and knowledge of the population distribution to determine the percentage of sample means that are within certain distances of the population mean. Suppose that in the cereal-filling example, you wished to estimate the population mean, using the information from a single sample. Thus, rather than taking $\mu \pm (1.96)(\sigma/\sqrt{n})$ to find the upper and lower limits around μ, as in Section 8.4, you substitute the sample mean, $\bar{X}$, for the unknown μ and use $\bar{X} \pm (1.96)(\sigma/\sqrt{n})$ as an interval to estimate the unknown μ. Although in practice you select a single sample of n values and compute the mean, $\bar{X}$, in order to understand the full meaning of the interval estimate, you need to examine a hypothetical set of all possible samples of n values.

Suppose that a sample of $n = 25$ boxes has a mean of 362.3 grams and a standard deviation of 15 grams. The interval developed to estimate μ is $362.3 \pm (1.96)(15)/(\sqrt{25})$ or 362.3 ± 5.88. The estimate of μ is

$$356.42 \leq \mu \leq 368.18$$

FLOWCHART FOR CONFIDENCE INTERVAL ESTIMATE

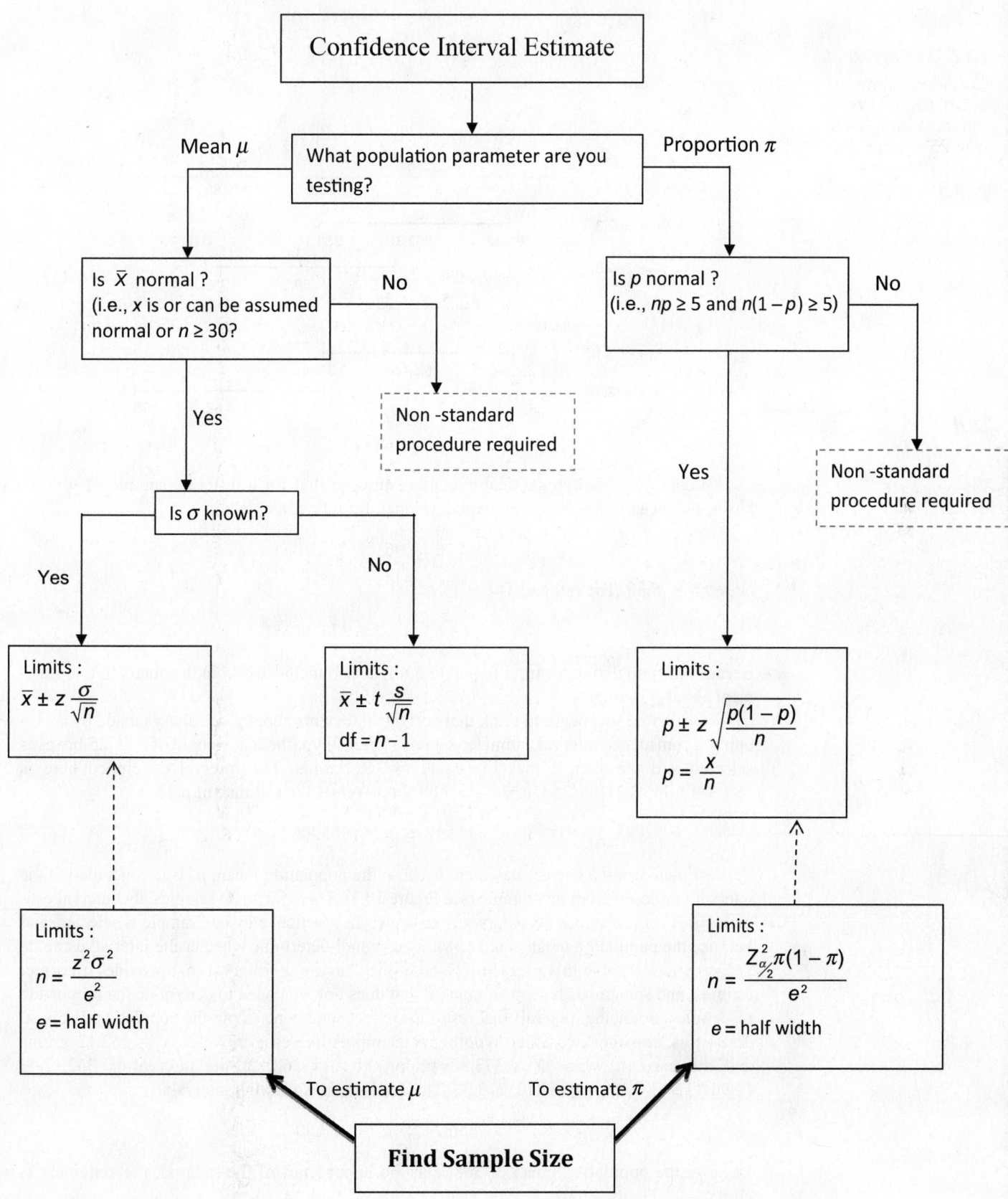

Because the population mean, μ (equal to 366), is included within the interval, this sample results in a correct statement about μ (see Figure 10.1).

FIGURE 10.1
Confidence interval estimates for five different samples of $n = 25$ taken from a population where $\mu = 368$ and $\sigma = 15$

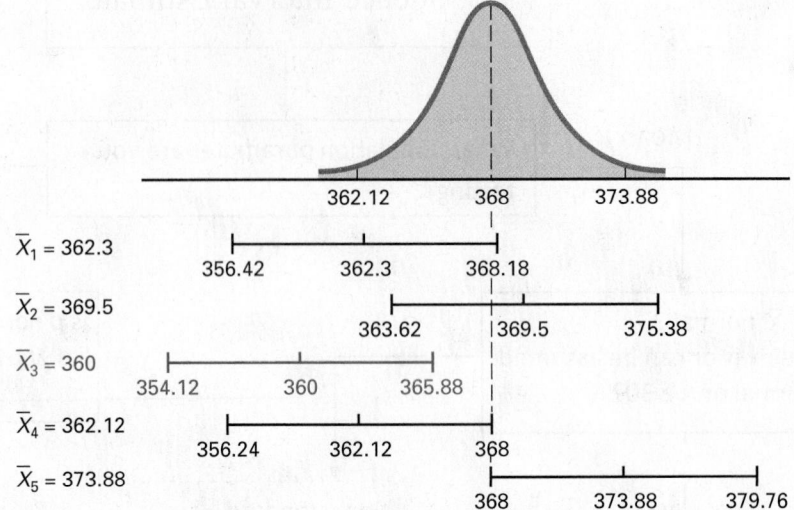

To continue this hypothetical example, suppose that for a different sample of $n = 25$ boxes, the mean is 369.5. The interval developed from this sample is

$$369.5 \pm (1.96)(15)/(\sqrt{25})$$

or 369.5 ± 5.88. The estimate is

$$363.62 \le \mu \le 375.38$$

Because the population mean, μ (equal to 368), is also included within this interval, this statement about μ is correct.

Now, before you begin to think that correct statements about μ are always made by developing a confidence interval estimate, suppose a third hypothetical sample of $n = 25$ boxes is selected and the sample mean is equal to 360 grams. The interval developed here is $360 \pm (1.96)(15)/(\sqrt{25})$, or 360 ± 5.88. In this case, the estimate of μ is

$$354.12 \le \mu \le 365.88$$

This estimate is *not* a correct statement because the population mean, μ, is not included in the interval developed from this sample (see Figure 10.1). Thus, for some samples, the interval estimate for μ is correct, but for others it is incorrect. In practice, only one sample is selected, and because the population mean is unknown, you cannot determine whether the interval estimate is correct. To resolve this problem of sometimes having an interval that provides a correct estimate and sometimes having an interval that does not, you need to determine the proportion of samples producing intervals that result in correct statements about the population mean, μ. To do this, consider two other hypothetical samples: the case in which $\bar{X} = 362.12$ grams and the case in which $\bar{X} = 373.88$ grams. If $\bar{X} = 362.12$, the interval is $362.12 \pm (1.96)(15)/(\sqrt{25})$, or 362.12 ± 5.88. This leads to the following interval:

$$356.24 \le \mu \le 368.00$$

Because the population mean of 368 is at the upper limit of the interval, the statement is correct (see Figure 10.1).

When $\bar{X} = 373.88$, the interval is $373.88 \pm (1.96)(15)/(\sqrt{25})$, or 373.88 ± 5.88. The interval estimate for the mean is

$$368.00 \le \mu \le 379.76$$

In this case, because the population mean of 368 is included at the lower limit of the interval, the statement is correct.

In Figure 10.1, you see that when the sample mean falls somewhere between 362.12 and 373.88 grams, the population mean is included *somewhere* within the interval. In Example 8.6 on page 337, you found that 95% of the sample means are between 362.12 and 373.88 grams. Therefore, 95% of all samples of $n = 25$ boxes have sample means that will result in intervals that include the population mean.

Because, in practice, you select only one sample of size n, and μ is unknown, you never know for sure whether your specific interval includes the population mean. However, if you take all possible samples of n and compute their 95% confidence intervals, 95% of the intervals will include the population mean, and only 5% of them will not. In other words, you have 95% confidence that the population mean is somewhere in your interval.

Consider once again the first sample discussed in this section. A sample of $n = 25$ boxes had a sample mean of 362.3 grams. The interval constructed to estimate μ is

$$362.3 \pm (1.96)(15)/(\sqrt{25})$$

$$362.3 \pm 5.88$$

$$356.42 \le \mu \le 368.18$$

The interval from 356.42 to 368.18 is referred to as a *95% confidence interval*. The following contains an interpretation of the interval that most business professionals will understand. (For a technical discussion of different ways to interpret confidence intervals, see reference 3.)

> "I am 95% confident that the mean amount of cereal in the population of boxes is somewhere between 356.42 and 368.18 grams."

To assist in your understanding of the meaning of the confidence interval, the following example concerns the order-filling process at a website. Filling orders consists of several steps, including receiving an order, picking the parts of the order, checking the order, packing, and shipping the order. The file **Order** contains the time, in minutes, to fill orders for a population of $N = 200$ orders on a recent day. Although in practice the population characteristics are rarely known, for this population of orders, the mean, μ, is known to be equal to 69.637 minutes, and the standard deviation, σ, is known to be equal to 10.411 minutes and the population is normally distributed. To illustrate how the sample mean and sample standard deviation can vary from one sample to another, 20 different samples of $n = 10$ were selected from the population of 200 orders, and the sample mean and sample standard deviation (and other statistics) were calculated for each sample. Figure 10.2 shows these results.

FIGURE 10.2

Sample statistics and 95% confidence intervals for 20 samples of $n = 10$ randomly selected from the population of $N = 200$ orders

Variable	Count	Mean	StDev	Minimum	Median	Maximum	Range	95% CI
Sample 1	10	74.15	13.39	56.10	76.85	97.70	41.60	(67.6973, 80.6027)
Sample 2	10	61.10	10.60	46.80	61.35	79.50	32.70	(54.6473, 67.5527)
Sample 3	10	74.36	6.50	62.50	74.50	84.00	21.50	(67.9073, 80.8127)
Sample 4	10	70.40	12.80	47.20	70.95	84.00	36.80	(63.9473, 76.8527)
Sample 5	10	62.18	10.85	47.10	59.70	84.00	36.90	(55.7273, 68.6327)
Sample 6	10	67.03	9.68	51.10	69.60	83.30	32.20	(60.5773, 73.4827)
Sample 7	10	69.03	8.81	56.60	68.85	83.70	27.10	(62.5773, 75.4827)
Sample 8	10	72.30	11.52	54.20	71.35	87.00	32.80	(65.8473, 78.7527)
Sample 9	10	68.18	14.10	50.10	69.95	86.20	36.10	(61.7273, 74.6327)
Sample 10	10	66.67	9.08	57.10	64.65	86.10	29.00	(60.2173, 73.1227)
Sample 11	10	72.42	9.76	59.60	74.65	86.10	26.50	(65.9673, 78.8727)
Sample 12	10	76.26	11.69	50.10	80.60	87.00	36.90	(69.8073, 82.7127)
Sample 13	10	65.74	12.11	47.10	62.15	86.10	39.00	(59.2873, 72.1927)
Sample 14	10	69.99	10.97	51.00	73.40	84.60	33.60	(63.5373, 76.4427)
Sample 15	10	75.76	8.60	61.10	75.05	87.80	26.70	(69.3073, 82.2127)
Sample 16	10	67.94	9.19	56.70	67.70	87.80	31.10	(61.4873, 74.3927)
Sample 17	10	71.05	10.48	50.10	71.15	86.20	36.10	(64.5973, 77.5027)
Sample 18	10	71.68	7.96	55.60	72.35	82.60	27.00	(65.2273, 78.1327)
Sample 19	10	70.97	9.83	54.40	70.05	84.60	30.20	(64.5173, 77.4227)
Sample 20	10	74.48	8.80	62.00	76.25	85.70	23.70	(68.0273, 80.9327)

From Figure 10.2, you can see the following:

- The sample statistics differ from sample to sample. The sample means vary from 61.10 to 76.26 minutes, the sample standard deviations vary from 6.50 to 14.10 minutes, the sample medians vary from 59.70 to 80.60 minutes, and the sample ranges vary from 21.50 to 41.60 minutes.
- Some of the sample means are greater than the population mean of 69.637 minutes, and some of the sample means are less than the population mean.
- Some of the sample standard deviations are greater than the population standard deviation of 10.411 minutes, and some of the sample standard deviations are less than the population standard deviation.
- The variation in the sample ranges is much more than the variation in the sample standard deviations.

The variation of sample statistics from sample to sample is called *sampling error*. Sampling error is the variation that occurs due to selecting a single sample from the population. The size of the sampling error is primarily based on the amount of variation in the population and on the sample size. Large samples have less sampling error than small samples, but large samples cost more to select.

The last column of Figure 10.2 contains 95% confidence interval estimates of the population mean order-filling time, based on the results of those 20 samples of $n = 10$. Begin by examining the first sample selected. The sample mean is 74.15 minutes, and the interval estimate for the population mean is 67.6973 to 80.6027 minutes. In a typical study, you would not know for sure whether this interval estimate is correct because you rarely know the value of the population mean. However, for this example *concerning the order-filling times*, the population mean is known to be 69.637 minutes. If you examine the interval 67.6973 to 80.6027 minutes, you see that the population mean of 69.637 minutes is located *between* these lower and upper limits. Thus, the first sample provides a correct estimate of the population mean in the form of an interval estimate. Looking over the other 19 samples, you see that similar results occur for all the other samples *except* for samples 2, 5, and 12. For each of the intervals generated (other than samples 2, 5, and 12), the population mean of 69.637 minutes is located *somewhere* within the interval.

For sample 2, the sample mean is 61.10 minutes, and the interval is 54.6473 to 67.5527 minutes; for sample 5, the sample mean is 62.18, and the interval is between 55.7273 and 68.6327; for sample 12, the sample mean is 76.26, and the interval is between 69.8073 and 82.7127 minutes. The population mean of 69.637 minutes is *not* located within any of these intervals, and the estimate of the population mean made using these intervals is incorrect. Although 3 of the 20 intervals did not include the population mean, if you had selected all the possible samples of $n = 10$ from a population of $N = 200$, 95% of the intervals would include the population mean.

In some situations, you might want a higher degree of confidence of including the population mean within the interval (such as 99%). In other cases, you might accept less confidence (such as 90%) of correctly estimating the population mean. In general, the **level of confidence** is symbolized by $(1 - \alpha) \times 100\%$, where α is the proportion in the tails of the distribution that is outside the confidence interval. The proportion in the upper tail of the distribution is $\alpha/2$, and the proportion in the lower tail of the distribution is $\alpha/2$. You use Equation (10.1) to construct a $(1 - \alpha) \times 100\%$ confidence interval estimate for the mean with σ known.

CONFIDENCE INTERVAL FOR THE MEAN (σ KNOWN)

$$\bar{X} \pm Z_{\alpha/2} \frac{\sigma}{\sqrt{n}}$$

or

$$\bar{X} - Z_{\alpha/2} \frac{\sigma}{\sqrt{n}} \leq \mu \leq \bar{X} + Z_{\alpha/2} \frac{\sigma}{\sqrt{n}} \qquad (10.1)$$

where $Z_{\alpha/2}$ is the value corresponding to an upper-tail probability of $\alpha/2$ from the standardized normal distribution (i.e., a cumulative area of $1 - \alpha/2$).

The value of $Z_{\alpha/2}$ needed for constructing a confidence interval is called the **critical value** for the distribution. 95% confidence corresponds to an α value of 0.05. The critical Z value corresponding to a cumulative area of 0.975 is 1.96 because there is 0.025 in the upper tail of the distribution, and the cumulative area less than $Z = 1.96$ is 0.975.

There is a different critical value for each level of confidence, $1 - \alpha$. A level of confidence of 95% leads to a Z value of 1.96 (see Figure 10.3). 99% confidence corresponds to an α value of 0.01. The Z value is approximately 2.58 because the upper-tail area is 0.005 and the cumulative area less than $Z = 2.58$ is 0.995 (see Figure 10.4).

FIGURE 10.3

Normal curve for determining the Z value needed for 95% confidence

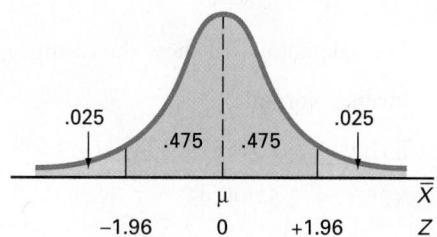

FIGURE 10.4

Normal curve for determining the Z value needed for 99% confidence

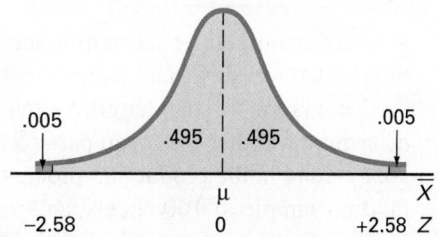

Now that various levels of confidence have been considered, why not make the confidence level as close to 100% as possible? Before doing so, you need to realize that any increase in the level of confidence is achieved only by widening (and making less precise) the confidence interval. There is no "free lunch" here. You would have more confidence that the population mean is within a broader range of values; however, this might make the interpretation of the confidence interval less useful. The trade-off between the width of the confidence interval and the level of confidence is discussed in greater depth in the context of determining the sample size in Section 10.4. Example 10.1 illustrates the application of the confidence interval estimate.

Using CASIO Calculator to Determine the Z Value for 99% Confidence

To find the Z-value associated with 99% confidence (i.e., probability = 0.99), mean = 0, and standard deviation = 1, follow these calculator steps:

Select **STAT F5**(DIST) **F1**(NORM) **F3**(InvN) **F2**(Var). Then select the following options.

Inverse Normal
Data   : **Variable**
Tail   : **CNTR (F3)**
Area   : **0.99**
σ : 1
μ : 0
Save Res : **None**
Execute
Now press **EXE** or **F1**(CALC).

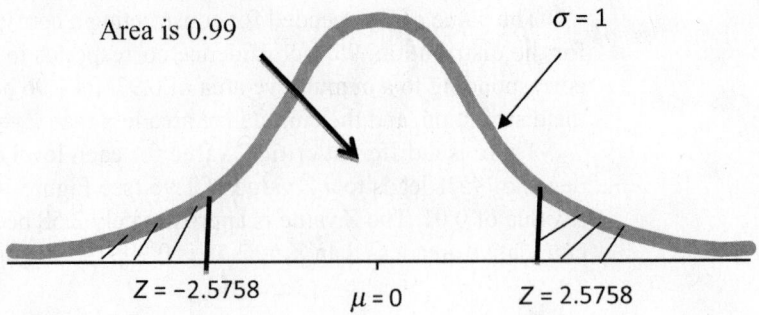

The calculator will show the results:

Inverse Normal

X1Inv = −2.5758293

X2Inv = 2.5758293

EXAMPLE 10.1

Estimating the Mean Paper Length with 95% Confidence

A paper manufacturer has a production process that operates continuously throughout an entire production shift. The paper is expected to have a mean length of 11 inches, and the standard deviation of the length is 0.02 inch. At periodic intervals, a sample is selected to determine whether the mean paper length is still equal to 11 inches or whether something has gone wrong in the production process to change the length of the paper produced. You select a random sample of 100 sheets, and the mean paper length is 10.998 inches. Construct a 95% confidence interval estimate for the population mean paper length.

SOLUTION Using Equation (10.1) on page 390, with $Z_{\alpha/2} = 1.96$ for 95% confidence,

$$\bar{X} \pm Z_{\alpha/2}\frac{\sigma}{\sqrt{n}} = 10.998 \pm (1.96)\frac{0.02}{\sqrt{100}}$$

$$= 10.998 \pm 0.0039$$

$$10.9941 \le \mu \le 11.0019$$

Thus, with 95% confidence, you conclude that the population mean is between 10.9941 and 11.0019 inches. Because the interval includes 11, the value indicating that the production process is working properly, you have no reason to believe that anything is wrong with the production process.

CASIO Calculator Instruction

Refer to Example 10.1: Construct a 95% confidence interval estimate for the population mean paper length. Use $\bar{X} = 10.998$, $\sigma = 0.02$, and $n = 100$.

To find the confidence interval for the population mean associated with a known population standard deviation, follow these calculator steps:

Select **STAT F4**(INTR) **F1**(Z) **F1**(1-S). Then select the following options.

(Note: Use the **EXE** key only after a new data entry. Otherwise, use the cursor ▼ arrow. If you accidentally hit the wrong key, use **AC/ON** or **EXIT** to go back.)

1-Sample zInterval

Data	: F2(Var)	▼
C-Level	: 0.95	**EXE**
σ	: 0.02	**EXE**
$\bar{x}$	: 10.998	**EXE**
n	: 100	**EXE**
Save Res	: None	

Now press **EXE** or **F1**(Calc).

The calculator will show the results:

1-Sample ZInterval

Left	= 10.9940801
Right	= 11.0019199
$\bar{x}$	= 10.998
n	= 100

As you can see, the 95% confidence interval estimate for the population mean is 10.9940801 to 11.0019199 inches. The calculator displays the numerical result only; you must remember to write up the complete answer as shown in class.

To see the effect of using a 99% confidence interval, examine Example 10.2.

EXAMPLE 10.2

Estimating the Mean Paper Length with 99% Confidence

Construct a 99% confidence interval estimate for the population mean paper length.

SOLUTION Using Equation (10.1) on page 388, with $Z_{\alpha/2} = 2.58$ for 99% confidence,

$$\bar{X} \pm Z_{\alpha/2}\frac{\sigma}{\sqrt{n}} = 10.998 \pm (2.58)\frac{0.02}{\sqrt{100}}$$

$$= 10.998 \pm 0.00516$$

$$10.9928 \leq \mu \leq 11.0032$$

Once again, because 11 is included within this wider interval, you have no reason to believe that anything is wrong with the production process.

CASIO Calculator Instruction

Refer to Example 10.2: Construct a 99% confidence interval estimate for the population mean paper length. Use $\bar{X} = 10.998$, $\sigma = 0.02$, and $n = 100$.

To find the confidence interval for the population mean associated with a known population standard deviation, follow these calculator steps:

Select **STAT F4**(INTR) **F1**(Z) **F1**(1-S). Then select the following options.

(Note: Use the **EXE** key only after a new data entry. Otherwise, use the cursor ▼ arrow. If you accidentally hit the wrong key, use **AC/ON** or **EXIT** to go back.)

1-Sample zInterval

Data	: F2(Var)	▼
C-Level	: 0.99	**EXE**
σ	: 0.02	**EXE**
$\bar{x}$	: 10.998	**EXE**
n	: 100	**EXE**
Save Res	: None	

Now press **EXE** or **F1**(Calc).

The calculator will show the results:

1-Sample zInterval
Left   = 10.9928483
Right   = 11.0031517
$\bar{x}$ = 10.998
n = 100

As you can see, the 99% confidence interval estimate for the population mean is 10.9928483 to 11.0031517 inches. The calculator displays the numerical result only; you must remember to write up the complete answer as shown in class.

As discussed in Section 8.4, the sampling distribution of the sample mean, $\bar{X}$, is normally distributed if the population for your characteristic of interest, X, follows a normal distribution. And, if the population of X does not follow a normal distribution, the Central Limit Theorem almost always ensures that $\bar{X}$ is approximately normally distributed when n is large. However, when dealing with a small sample size and a population that does not follow a normal distribution, the sampling distribution of $\bar{X}$ is not normally distributed, and therefore the confidence interval discussed in this section is inappropriate. In practice, however, as long as the sample size is large enough and the population is not very skewed, you can use the confidence interval defined in Equation (10.1) to estimate the population mean when σ is known. To assess the assumption of normality, you can evaluate the shape of the sample data by constructing a histogram, stem-and-leaf display, boxplot, or normal probability plot.

Can You Ever Know the Population Standard Deviation?

To solve Equation 10.1, you must know the value for σ, the population standard deviation. To know σ implies that you know all the values in the entire population. (How else would you know the value of this population parameter?) If you knew all the values in the entire population, you could directly compute the population mean. There would be no need to use the *inductive* reasoning of inferential statistics to *estimate* the population mean. In other words, if you knew σ, you really do not have a need to use Equation 10.1 to construct a "confidence interval estimate of the mean (σ known)."

More significantly, in virtually all real-world business situations, you would never know the standard deviation of the population. In business situations, populations are often too large to examine all the values. So why study the confidence interval estimate of the mean (σ known) at all? This method serves as an important introduction to the concept of a confidence interval because it uses the normal distribution, which has already been thoroughly discussed in Chapters 7 and 8. In the next section, you will see that constructing a confidence interval estimate when σ is not known requires another distribution (the t distribution) not previously mentioned in this book.

Because the confidence interval concept is a very important concept to understand when reading the rest of this book, review this section carefully to understand the underlying concept—even if you never have a practical reason to use the confidence interval estimate of the mean (σ known).

Problems for Section 10.1

LEARNING THE BASICS

10.1 If $\bar{X} = 85$, $\sigma = 8$, and $n = 64$, construct a 95% confidence interval estimate for the population mean, μ.

10.2 If $\bar{X} = 125$, $\sigma = 24$, and $n = 36$, construct a 99% confidence interval estimate for the population mean, μ.

10.3 Why is it not possible in Example 10.1 on page 390 to have 100% confidence? Explain.

10.4 Is it true in Example 10.1 on page 390 that you do not know for sure whether the population mean is between 10.9941 and 11.0019 inches? Explain.

APPLYING THE CONCEPTS

10.5 A market researcher selects a simple random sample of $n = 100$ customers from a population of 2 million customers. After analyzing the sample, she states that she has 95% confidence that the mean annual income of the 2 million customers is between $70,000 and $85,000. Explain the meaning of this statement.

10.6 Suppose that you are going to collect a set of data, either from an entire population or from a random sample taken from that population.
a. Which statistical measure would you compute first: the mean or the standard deviation? Explain.
b. What does your answer to (a) tell you about the "practicality" of using the confidence interval estimate formula given in Equation (10.1)?

10.7 Consider the confidence interval estimate discussed in Problem 10.5. Suppose that the population mean annual income is $71,000. Is the confidence interval estimate stated in Problem 10.5 correct? Explain.

10.8 You are working as an assistant to the dean of institutional research at your university. The dean wants to survey members of the alumni association who obtained their baccalaureate degrees 5 years ago to learn what their starting salaries were in their first full-time job after receiving their degrees. A sample of 100 alumni is to be randomly selected from the list of 2,500 graduates in that class. If the dean's goal is to construct a 95% confidence interval estimate for the population mean starting salary, why is it not possible that you will be able to use Equation (10.1) on page 388 for this purpose? Explain.

10.9 The manager of a paint supply store wants to estimate the actual amount of paint contained in 1-gallon cans purchased from a nationally known manufacturer. The manufacturer's specifications state that the standard deviation of the amount of paint is equal to 0.02 gallon. A random sample of 50 cans is selected, and the sample mean amount of paint per 1-gallon can is 0.995 gallon.
a. Construct a 99% confidence interval estimate for the population mean amount of paint included in a 1-gallon can.
b. On the basis of these results, do you think that the manager has a right to complain to the manufacturer? Why?
c. Must you assume that the population amount of paint per can is normally distributed here? Explain.
d. Construct a 95% confidence interval estimate. How does this change your answer to (b)?

SELF Test **10.10** The quality control manager at a light bulb factory needs to estimate the mean life of a large shipment of light bulbs. The standard deviation is 100 hours. A random sample of 64 light bulbs indicated a sample mean life of 350 hours.
a. Construct a 95% confidence interval estimate for the population mean life of light bulbs in this shipment.
b. Do you think that the manufacturer has the right to state that the light bulbs have a mean life of 400 hours? Explain.
c. Must you assume that the population light bulb life is normally distributed? Explain.
d. Suppose that the standard deviation changes to 80 hours. What are your answers in (a) and (b)?

10.2 Confidence Interval Estimate for the Mean (σ Unknown)

In the previous section, you learned that in most business situations, you do not know σ, the population standard deviation. This section discusses a method of constructing a confidence interval estimate of μ that uses the sample statistic S as an estimate of the population parameter σ.

Student's t Distribution

[1] Guinness considered all research conducted to be proprietary and a trade secret. The firm prohibited its employees from publishing their results. Gosset circumvented this ban by using the pen name "Student" to publish his findings.

At the start of the twentieth century, William S. Gosset was working at Guinness in Ireland, trying to help brew better beer less expensively (see reference 4). As he had only small samples to study, he needed to find a way to make inferences about means without having to know σ. Writing under the pen name "Student,"[1] Gosset solved this problem by developing what today is known as the **Student's t distribution**, or the t distribution.

If the random variable X is normally distributed, then the following statistic:

$$t = \frac{\bar{X} - \mu}{\frac{S}{\sqrt{n}}}$$

has a t distribution with $n - 1$ **degrees of freedom**. This expression has the same form as the Z statistic in Equation (8.4) on page 330, except that S is used to estimate the unknown σ.

Properties of the *t* Distribution

The *t* distribution is very similar in appearance to the standardized normal distribution. Both distributions are symmetrical and bell-shaped, with the mean and the median equal to zero. However, the *t* distribution has more area in the tails and less in the center than does the standardized normal distribution (see Figure 10.5). This is due to the fact that because *S* is used to estimate the unknown σ, the values of *t* are more variable than those for *Z*.

FIGURE 10.5

Standardized normal distribution and *t* distribution for 5 degrees of freedom

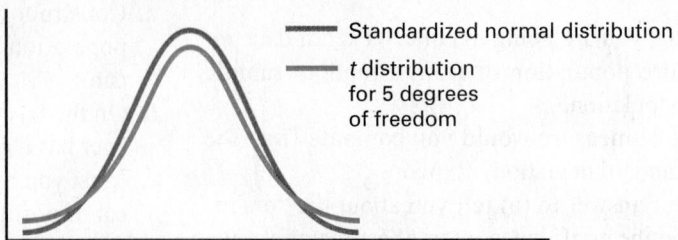

The degrees of freedom, $n - 1$, are directly related to the sample size, *n*. The concept of *degrees of freedom* is discussed further on page 398. As the sample size and degrees of freedom increase, *S* becomes a better estimate of σ, and the *t* distribution gradually approaches the standardized normal distribution, until the two are virtually identical. With a sample size of about 120 or more, *S* estimates σ closely enough so that there is little difference between the *t* and *Z* distributions.

As stated earlier, the *t* distribution assumes that the random variable *X* is normally distributed. In practice, however, when the sample size is large enough and the population is not very skewed, in most cases you can use the *t* distribution to estimate the population mean when σ is unknown. When dealing with a small sample size and a skewed population distribution, the confidence interval estimate may not provide a valid estimate of the population mean. To assess the assumption of normality, you can evaluate the shape of the sample data by constructing a histogram, stem-and-leaf display, boxplot, or normal probability plot. However, the ability of any of these graphs to help you evaluate normality is limited when you have a small sample size.

You find the critical values of *t* for the appropriate degrees of freedom from the table of the *t* distribution (see Table E.3). The columns of the table present the most commonly used cumulative probabilities and corresponding upper-tail areas. The rows of the table represent the degrees of freedom. The critical *t* values are found in the cells of the table. For example, with 99 degrees of freedom, if you want 95% confidence, you find the appropriate value of *t*, as shown in Table 10.1. The 95% confidence level means that 2.5% of the values (an area of 0.025) are in

TABLE 10.1

Determining the Critical Value from the *t* Table for an Area of 0.025 in Each Tail with 99 Degrees of Freedom

	Cumulative Probabilities					
	.75	.90	.95	.975	.99	.995
	Upper-Tail Areas					
Degrees of Freedom	.25	.10	.05	.025	.01	.005
1	1.0000	3.0777	6.3138	12.7062	31.8207	63.6574
2	0.8165	1.8856	2.9200	4.3027	6.9646	9.9248
3	0.7649	1.6377	2.3534	3.1824	4.5407	5.8409
4	0.7407	1.5332	2.1318	2.7764	3.7469	4.6041
5	0.7267	1.4759	2.0150	2.5706	3.3649	4.0322
.	.	.	.	.	.	.
.	.	.	.	.	.	.
.	.	.	.	.	.	.
96	0.6771	1.2904	1.6609	1.9850	2.3658	2.6280
97	0.6770	1.2903	1.6607	1.9847	2.3654	2.6275
98	0.6770	1.2902	1.6606	1.9845	2.3650	2.6269
99	0.6770	1.2902	1.6604	1.9842	2.3646	2.6264
100	0.6770	1.2901	1.6602	1.9840	2.3642	2.6259

Source: Extracted from Table E.3.

each tail of the distribution. Looking in the column for a cumulative probability of 0.975 and an upper-tail area of 0.025 in the row corresponding to 99 degrees of freedom gives you a critical value for t of 1.9842 (see Figure 10.6). Because t is a symmetrical distribution with a mean of 0, if the upper-tail value is $+1.9842$, the value for the lower-tail area (lower 0.025) is -1.9842. A t value of -1.9842 means that the probability that t is less than -1.9842 is 0.025, or 2.5%.

FIGURE 10.6

t distribution with 99 degrees of freedom

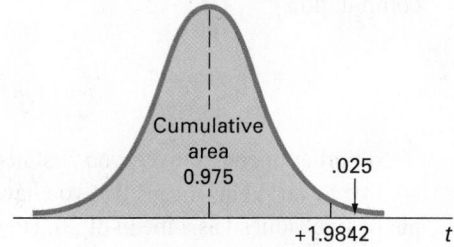

CASIO Calculator Model fx-9750GII Instruction

Question: Determine the critical value using the calculator for an area of 0.025 in each tail with 99 degrees of freedom (df = 99).

To determine the t critical value(s), follow these calculator steps:

Select **STAT F5**(DIST) **F2**(t) **F3**(Invt) **F2**(Var). Then select the following options.

Inverse Normal
Data   : **Variable**
Area   : **0.025**
df   : **99**
Save Res : **None**
Execute

Now press **EXE** or **F1**(CALC).

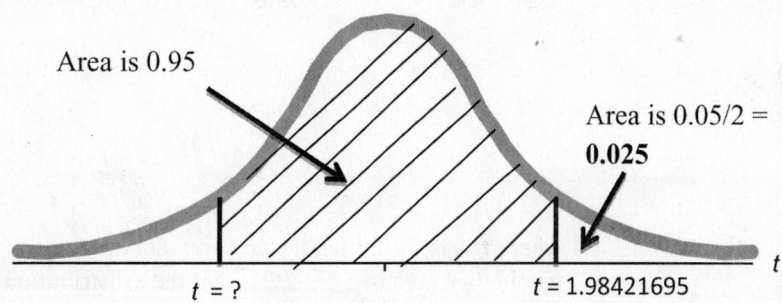

The calculator will show the result:

Inverse Normal
XInv = 1.98421695

The calculator gives you an upper-tail value of 1.98421695. The value for the lower-tail area (lower 0.025) is -1.98421695 because the t-distribution is symmetrical.

Answer: The critical values for a 95% confidence interval with df = 99 are -1.98421695 and 1.98421695.

Note that for a 95% confidence interval, you will always have a cumulative probability of 0.975 and an upper-tail area of 0.025. Similarly, for a 99% confidence interval, you will have 0.995 and 0.005, and for a 90% confidence interval you will have 0.95 and 0.05.

The Concept of Degrees of Freedom

In Chapter 4, you learned that the numerator of the sample variance, S^2 requires the computation

$$\sum_{i=1}^{n}(X_i - \bar{X})^2$$

In order to compute S^2, you first need to know $\bar{X}$. Therefore, only $n - 1$ of the sample values are free to vary. This means that you have $n - 1$ degrees of freedom. For example, suppose a sample of five values has a mean of 20. How many values do you need to know before you can determine the remainder of the values? The fact that $n = 5$ and $\bar{X} = 20$ also tells you that

$$\sum_{i=1}^{n} X_i = 100$$

because

$$\frac{\sum_{i=1}^{n} X_i}{n} = \bar{X}$$

Thus, when you know four of the values, the fifth one is *not* free to vary because the sum must be 100. For example, if four of the values are 18, 24, 19, and 16, the fifth value must be 23 so that the sum is 100.

The Confidence Interval Statement

Equation (10.2) defines the $(1 - \alpha) \times 100\%$ confidence interval estimate for the mean with σ unknown.

> CONFIDENCE INTERVAL FOR THE MEAN (σ UNKNOWN)
>
> $$\bar{X} \pm t_{\alpha/2}\frac{S}{\sqrt{n}}$$
>
> or
>
> $$\bar{X} - t_{\alpha/2}\frac{S}{\sqrt{n}} \leq \mu \leq \bar{X} + t_{\alpha/2}\frac{S}{\sqrt{n}} \qquad (10.2)$$
>
> where $t_{\alpha/2}$ is the critical value corresponding to an upper-tail probability of $\alpha/2$ (i.e., a cumulative area of $1 - \alpha/2$) from the t distribution with $n - 1$ degrees of freedom.

To illustrate the application of the confidence interval estimate for the mean when the standard deviation is unknown, recall the Saxon Home Improvement scenario presented on page 383. You define the variable of interest as the dollar amount listed on the sales invoices for the month. Your business objective is to estimate the mean dollar amount. Then, you collect the data by selecting a sample of 100 sales invoices from the population of sales invoices during the month. Once you have collected the data, you organize the data in a worksheet. You can construct various graphs (not shown here) to better visualize the distribution of the dollar amounts. To analyze the data, you compute the sample mean of the 100 sales invoices to be equal to $110.27 and the sample standard deviation to be equal to $28.95. For 95% confidence, the critical value from the t distribution (as shown in Table 10.1 on page 394) is 1.9842. Using Equation (10.2),

$$\bar{X} \pm t_{\alpha/2}\frac{S}{\sqrt{n}}$$

$$= 110.27 \pm (1.9842)\frac{28.95}{\sqrt{100}}$$

$$= 110.27 \pm 5.74$$

$$104.53 \le \mu \le 116.01$$

Use the CASIO Calculator to obtain 95% confidence interval when x is unknown, confidence level is 95%, $\bar{x}$ is 110.27, and s is 28.95.

FIGURE 10.7

Estimate for the mean sales invoice amount

From the **Main Menu**, select the following:

STAT F4(INTR) **F2**(t) **F1**(1-S). Then enter the following items:

1-Sample tInterval
Data	: **F2(Var)**	▼
C-Level	: **0.95**	**EXE**
$\bar{x}$	: **110.27**	**EXE**
sx	: **28.95**	**EXE**
n	: **100**	**EXE**
Save Res	: **None**	

Now press **EXE** or **F1**(Calc).

The calculator will show the results:

1-Sample tInterval
Left	= 104.525692
Right	= 116.014308
$\bar{x}$	= 110.27
sx	= 28.95
n	= 100

The 95% confidence interval is $104.525692 \le \mu \le 116.014308$

Thus, with 95% confidence, you conclude that the mean amount of all the sales invoices is between \$104.53 and \$116.01. The 95% confidence level indicates that if you selected all possible samples of 100 (something that is never done in practice), 95% of the intervals developed would include the population mean somewhere within the interval. The validity of this confidence interval estimate depends on the assumption of normality for the distribution of the amount of the sales invoices. With a sample of 100, the normality assumption is not overly restrictive (see the Central Limit Theorem on page 334), and the use of the t distribution is likely appropriate. Example 10.3 further illustrates how you construct the confidence interval for a mean when the population standard deviation is unknown.

EXAMPLE 10.3

Estimating the Mean Force Required to Break Electric Insulators

A manufacturing company produces electric insulators. You define the variable of interest as the strength of the insulators. If the insulators break when in use, a short circuit is likely. To test the strength of the insulators, you carry out destructive testing to determine how much force is required to break the insulators. You measure force by observing how many pounds are applied to the insulator before it breaks. You collect the data by selecting 30 insulators to be used in the experiment. You organize the data collected in a worksheet. Table 10.2 lists 30 values from this experiment, which are stored in Force . To analyze the data, you need to construct a 95% confidence interval estimate for the population mean force required to break the insulator.

TABLE 10.2

Force (in Pounds) Required to Break Insulators

1,870	1,728	1,656	1,610	1,634	1,784	1,522	1,696	1,592	1,662
1,866	1,764	1,734	1,662	1,734	1,774	1,550	1,756	1,762	1,866
1,820	1,744	1,788	1,688	1,810	1,752	1,680	1,810	1,652	1,736

SOLUTION To visualize the data, you construct a boxplot of the force, as displayed in Figure 10.8, and a normal probability plot, as shown in Figure 10.9. To analyze the data, you construct the confidence interval estimate shown in Figure 10.10.

FIGURE 10.8

Excel and Minitab boxplots for the amount of force required to break electric insulators

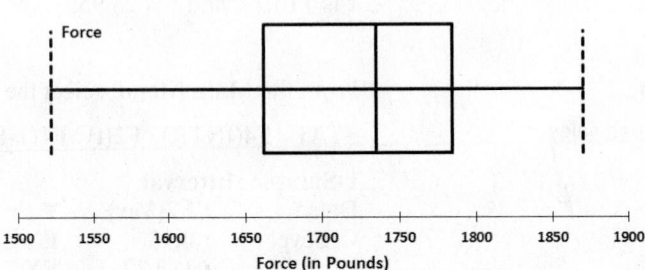

FIGURE 10.9

Excel and Minitab normal probability plots for the amount of force required to break electric insulators

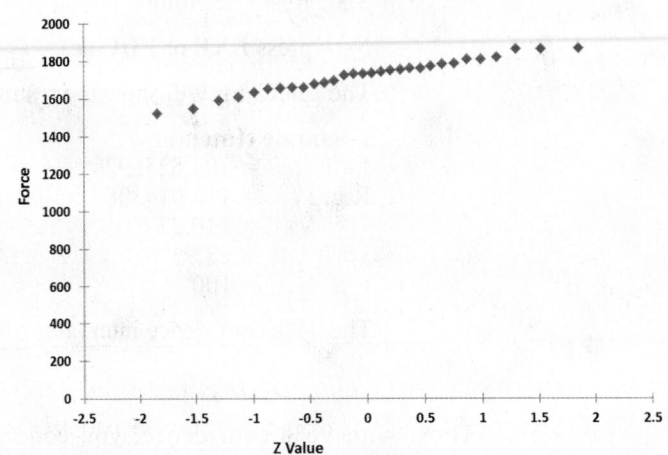

FIGURE 10.10

Excel and Minitab confidence interval estimate for the mean amount of force required to break electric insulators

	A	B	
1	Estimate for the Mean Amount of Force Required		
2			
3	**Data**		
4	Sample Standard Deviation	89.55	
5	Sample Mean	1723.4	
6	Sample Size	30	
7	Confidence Level	95%	
8			
9	**Intermediate Calculations**		
10	Standard Error of the Mean	16.3495	=B4/SQRT(B6)
11	Degrees of Freedom	29	=B6 - 1
12	t Value	2.0452	=TINV(1 - B7, B11)
13	Interval Half Width	33.4385	=B12 * B10
14			
15	**Confidence Interval**		
16	Interval Lower Limit	1689.96	=B5 - B13
17	Interval Upper Limit	1756.84	=B5 + B13

One-Sample T: Force

Variable	N	Mean	StDev	SE Mean	95% CI
Force	30	1723.4	89.6	16.3	(1690.0, 1756.8)

Figure 10.10 shows that the sample mean is $\bar{X} = 1{,}723.4$ pounds and the sample standard deviation is $S = 89.55$ pounds. Using Equation (10.2) on page 396 to construct the confidence interval, you need to determine the critical value from the t table, using the row for 29 degrees of freedom. For 95% confidence, you use the column corresponding to an upper-tail area of 0.025 and a cumulative probability of 0.975. From Table E.3, you see that $t_{\alpha/2} = 2.0452$. Thus, using $\bar{X} = 1{,}723.4$, $S = 89.55$, $n = 30$, and $t_{\alpha/2} = 2.0452$,

$$\bar{X} \pm t_{\alpha/2}\frac{S}{\sqrt{n}}$$

$$= 1{,}723.4 \pm (2.0452)\frac{89.55}{\sqrt{30}}$$

$$= 1{,}723.4 \pm 33.44$$

$$1{,}689.96 \le \mu \le 1{,}756.84$$

You conclude with 95% confidence that the mean breaking force required for the population of insulators is between 1,689.96 and 1,756.84 pounds. The validity of this confidence interval estimate depends on the assumption that the force required is normally distributed. Remember, however, that you can slightly relax this assumption for large sample sizes. Thus, with a sample of 30, you can use the t distribution even if the amount of force required is only slightly left-skewed. From the boxplot displayed in Figure 10.8 and the normal probability plot shown in Figure 10.9, the amount of force required appears only slightly left-skewed. Thus, the t distribution is appropriate for these data.

CASIO Calculator Instruction

Refer to Example 10.3: Construct a 95% confidence interval estimate for the population mean force required to break the insulator. Use $\bar{X} = 1723.4$, $s = 89.55$, and $n = 30$.

To find the confidence interval for the population mean associated with an unknown population standard deviation, follow these calculator steps:

From the **Main Menu** select **STAT**.

Enter the data into **List 1**.

        LIST 1
        1,870
        1,866
        1,820
        :
        :
        1,736

Now, from the **STAT mode**, select the following:

F4(INTR) **F2**(t) **F1**(1-S). Then enter the following items:

1-Sample tInterval
Data   : **F1**(List)   ▼
C-Level   : **0.95**   **EXE**
List   : **List1**   ▼
Freq   : **1**   **EXE**
Save Res : None

Now key **EXE** or **F1**(Calc)

The calculator will show the results:

1-Sample tInterval
Left   = 1689.96117
Right   = 1756.83883
$\bar{x}$ = 1723.4
sx = 89.5508332
n = 30

As you can see, the 95% confidence interval estimate for the population mean is 1689.96117 to 1756.83883 pounds. The calculator will display the numerical result only; you must remember to write up the complete answer as shown in class.

The interpretation of the confidence interval when σ is unknown is the same as when σ is known. To illustrate the fact that the confidence interval for the mean varies more when σ is unknown, return to the example concerning the order-filling times discussed in Section 10.1 on pages 387–388. Suppose that, in this case, you do *not* know the population standard deviation and instead use the sample standard deviation to construct the confidence interval estimate of the mean. Figure 10.11 shows the results for each of 20 samples of $n = 10$ orders.

In Figure 10.11, observe that the standard deviation of the samples varies from 6.25 (sample 17) to 14.83 (sample 3). Thus, the width of the confidence interval developed varies from 8.94 in sample 17 to 21.22 in sample 3. Because you know that the population mean order time $\mu = 69.637$ minutes, you can see that the interval for sample 8(69.68 − 85.48) and the interval for sample 10(56.41 − 68.69) do not correctly estimate the population mean. All the other intervals correctly estimate the population mean. Once again, remember that in practice you select only one sample, and you are unable to know for sure whether your one sample provides a confidence interval that includes the population mean.

FIGURE 10.11
Confidence interval estimates of the mean for 20 samples of $n = 10$, randomly selected from the population of $N = 200$ orders with σ unknown

Variable	n	Mean	Std Dev	SE Mean	95% CI
Sample 1	10	71.64	7.58	2.40	(66.22, 77.06)
Sample 2	10	67.22	10.95	3.46	(59.39, 75.05)
Sample 3	10	67.97	14.83	4.69	(57.36, 78.58)
Sample 4	10	73.90	10.59	3.35	(66.33, 81.47)
Sample 5	10	67.11	11.12	3.52	(59.15, 75.07)
Sample 6	10	68.12	10.83	3.43	(60.37, 75.87)
Sample 7	10	65.80	10.85	3.43	(58.03, 73.57)
Sample 8	10	77.58	11.04	3.49	(69.68, 85.48)
Sample 9	10	66.69	11.45	3.62	(58.50, 74.88)
Sample 10	10	62.55	8.58	2.71	(56.41, 68.69)
Sample 11	10	71.12	12.82	4.05	(61.95, 80.29)
Sample 12	10	70.55	10.52	3.33	(63.02, 78.08)
Sample 13	10	65.51	8.16	2.58	(59.67, 71.35)
Sample 14	10	64.90	7.55	2.39	(59.50, 70.30)
Sample 15	10	66.22	11.21	3.54	(58.20, 74.24)
Sample 16	10	70.43	10.21	3.23	(63.12, 77.74)
Sample 17	10	72.04	6.25	1.96	(67.57, 76.51)
Sample 18	10	73.91	11.29	3.57	(65.83, 81.99)
Sample 19	10	71.49	9.76	3.09	(64.51, 78.47)
Sample 20	10	70.15	10.84	3.43	(62.39, 77.91)

Problems for Section 10.2

LEARNING THE BASICS

10.11 If $\overline{X} = 75$, $S = 24$, and $n = 36$, and assuming that the population is normally distributed, construct a 95% confidence interval estimate for the population mean, μ.

10.12 Determine the critical value of t in each of the following circumstances:
a. $1 - \alpha = 0.95, n = 10$
b. $1 - \alpha = 0.99, n = 10$
c. $1 - \alpha = 0.95, n = 32$
d. $1 - \alpha = 0.95, n = 65$
e. $1 - \alpha = 0.90, n = 16$

10.13 Assuming that the population is normally distributed, construct a 95% confidence interval estimate for the population mean for each of the following samples:

    Sample A: 1 1 1 1 8 8 8 8
    Sample B: 1 2 3 4 5 6 7 8

Explain why these two samples produce different confidence intervals even though they have the same mean and range.

10.14 Assuming that the population is normally distributed, construct a 95% confidence interval for the population mean, based on the following sample of size $n = 7$:

    1, 2, 3, 4, 5, 6, 20

Change the number 20 to 7 and recalculate the confidence interval. Using these results, describe the effect of an outlier (i.e., an extreme value) on the confidence interval.

APPLYING THE CONCEPTS

10.15 A stationery store wants to estimate the mean retail value of greeting cards that it has in its inventory. A random sample of 100 greeting cards indicates a mean value of $2.55 and a standard deviation of $0.44.
a. Assuming a normal distribution, construct a 95% confidence interval estimate for the mean value of all greeting cards in the store's inventory.
b. Suppose there are 2,500 greeting cards in the store's inventory. How are the results in (a) useful in assisting the store owner to estimate the total value of the inventory?

SELF Test **10.16** Southside Hospital in Bay Shore, New York, commonly conducts stress tests to study the heart muscle after a person has a heart attack. Members of the diagnostic imaging department conducted a quality improvement project with the objective of reducing the turnaround time for stress tests. Turnaround time is defined as the time from when a test is ordered to when the radiologist signs off on the test results. Initially, the mean turnaround time for a stress test was 68 hours. After incorporating changes into the stress-test process, the quality improvement team collected a sample of 50 turnaround times. In this sample, the mean turnaround time was 32 hours, with a standard deviation of 9 hours. (Data extracted from E. Godin, D. Raven, C. Sweet-

apple, and F. R. Del Guidice, "Faster Test Results," *Quality Progress*, January 2004, 37(1), pp. 33–39.)
a. Construct a 95% confidence interval estimate for the population mean turnaround time.
b. Interpret the interval constructed in (a).
c. Do you think the quality improvement project was a success?

10.17 The U.S. Department of Transportation requires tire manufacturers to provide tire performance information on the sidewall of a tire to better inform prospective customers as they make purchasing decisions. One very important measure of tire performance is the tread wear index, which indicates the tire's resistance to tread wear compared with a tire graded with a base of 100. A tire with a grade of 200 should last twice as long, on average, as a tire graded with a base of 100. A consumer organization wants to estimate the actual tread wear index of a brand name of tires that claims "graded 200" on the sidewall of the tire. A random sample of $n = 18$ indicates a sample mean tread wear index of 195.3 and a sample standard deviation of 21.4.
a. Assuming that the population of tread wear indexes is normally distributed, construct a 95% confidence interval estimate for the population mean tread wear index for tires produced by this manufacturer under this brand name.
b. Do you think that the consumer organization should accuse the manufacturer of producing tires that do not meet the performance information provided on the sidewall of the tire? Explain.
c. Explain why an observed tread wear index of 210 for a particular tire is not unusual, even though it is outside the confidence interval developed in (a).

10.18 The file **FastFood** contains the amount that a sample of nine customers spent for lunch ($) at a fast-food restaurant

    4.20 5.03 5.86 6.45 7.38 7.54 8.46 8.47 9.87

a. Construct a 95% confidence interval estimate for the population mean amount spent for lunch ($) at a fast-food restaurant, assuming a normal distribution.
b. Interpret the interval constructed in (a).

10.19 The file **Sedans** contains the overall miles per gallon (MPG) of 2011 family sedans.

    24 21 25 22 23 34 34 20 20 22
    44 32 20 20

Source: Data extracted from "Ratings," *Consumer Reports*, April 2011, pp. 30–31.

a. Construct a 95% confidence interval estimate for the population mean MPG of 2011 family sedans, assuming a normal distribution.
b. Interpret the interval constructed in (a).
c. Compare the results in (a) to those in Problem 10.20(a).

10.20 The file SUV contains the overall miles per gallon (MPG) of 2011 small SUVs.

```
20 24 22 23 20 22 21 22 22 19 22 22 26
19 19 23 24 21 21 19 21 22 22 16 16
```

Source: Data extracted from "Ratings," *Consumer Reports*, April 2011, pp. 35–36.

a. Construct a 95% confidence interval estimate for the population mean MPG of 2011 small SUVs, assuming a normal distribution.
b. Interpret the interval constructed in (a).
c. Compare the results in (a) to those in Problem 10.19(a).

10.21 Is there a difference in the yields of different types of investments? The file CDRate contains the yields for a one-year certificate of deposit (CD) and a five-year certificate of deposit (CD) for 23 banks in the United States, as of April 4, 2011.

Source: Data extracted from **www.Bankrate.com**, April 4, 2011.

a. Construct a 95% confidence interval estimate for the mean yield of one-year certificates of deposit.
b. Construct a 95% confidence interval estimate for the mean yield of five-year certificates of deposit.
c. Compare the results of (a) and (b).

10.22 One of the major measures of the quality of service provided by any organization is the speed with which it responds to customer complaints. A large family-held department store selling furniture and flooring, including carpet, had undergone a major expansion in the past several years. In particular, the flooring department had expanded from 2 installation crews to an installation supervisor, a measurer, and 15 installation crews. The store had the business objective of improving its response to complaints. The variable of interest was defined as the number of days between when the complaint was made and when it was resolved. Data were collected from 50 complaints that were made in the last year. The data were stored in Furniture, and are as follows:

```
54   5   35 137   31 27 152   2 123 81  74 27
11  19 126 110  110 29   61 35  94 31  26  5
12   4 165  32   29 28   29 26  25  1  14 13
13  10   5  27    4 52   30 22  36 26  20 23
33  68
```

a. Construct a 95% confidence interval estimate for the population mean number of days between the receipt of a complaint and the resolution of the complaint.
b. What assumption must you make about the population distribution in order to construct the confidence interval estimate in (a)?
c. Do you think that the assumption needed in order to construct the confidence interval estimate in (a) is valid? Explain.
d. What effect might your conclusion in (c) have on the validity of the results in (a)?

10.23 In New York State, savings banks are permitted to sell a form of life insurance called savings bank life insurance (SBLI). The approval process consists of underwriting, which includes a review of the application, a medical information bureau check, possible requests for additional medical information and medical exams, and a policy compilation stage in which the policy pages are generated and sent to the bank for delivery. The ability to deliver approved policies to customers in a timely manner is critical to the profitability of this service to the bank. During a period of one month, a random sample of 27 approved policies was selected, and the total processing time, in days, was as shown below and stored in Insurance:

```
73  19  16  64  28  28  31  90  60  56  31  56  22  18
45  48  17  17  17  91  92  63  50  51  69  16  17
```

a. Construct a 95% confidence interval estimate for the population mean processing time.
b. What assumption must you make about the population distribution in order to construct the confidence interval estimate in (a)?
c. Do you think that the assumption needed in order to construct the confidence interval estimate in (a) is valid? Explain.

10.24 The file DarkChocolate contains the cost per ounce ($) for a sample of 14 dark chocolate bars:

```
0.68  0.72  0.92  1.14  1.42  0.94  0.77
0.57  1.51  0.57  0.55  0.86  1.41  0.90
```

Source: Data extracted from "Dark Chocolate: Which Bars Are Best?" *Consumer Reports*, September 2007, p. 8.

a. Construct a 95% confidence interval estimate for the population cost per ounce ($) of dark chocolate bars.
b. What assumption do you need to make about the population distribution to construct the interval in (a)?
c. Given the data presented, do you think the assumption needed in (a) is valid? Explain.

10.25 One operation of a mill is to cut pieces of steel into parts that are used in the frame for front seats in an automobile. The steel is cut with a diamond saw, and the resulting parts must be cut to be within ± 0.005 inch of the length specified by the automobile company. The measurement reported from a sample of 100 steel parts (stored in Steel) is the difference, in inches, between the actual length of the steel part, as measured by a laser measurement device, and the specified length of the steel part. For example, the first observation, -0.002, represents a steel part that is 0.002 inch shorter than the specified length.

a. Construct a 95% confidence interval estimate for the population mean difference between the actual length of the steel part and the specified length of the steel part.
b. What assumption must you make about the population distribution in order to construct the confidence interval estimate in (a)?
c. Do you think that the assumption needed in order to construct the confidence interval estimate in (a) is valid? Explain.

10.3 Confidence Interval Estimate for the Proportion

The concept of a confidence interval also applies to categorical data. With categorical data, you want to estimate the proportion of items in a population having a certain characteristic of interest. The unknown population proportion is represented by the Greek letter π. The point estimate for π is the sample proportion, $p = X/n$, where n is the sample size and X is the number of items in the sample having the characteristic of interest. Equation (10.3) defines the confidence interval estimate for the population proportion.

CONFIDENCE INTERVAL ESTIMATE FOR THE PROPORTION

$$p \pm Z_{\alpha/2}\sqrt{\frac{p(1-p)}{n}}$$

or

$$p - Z_{\alpha/2}\sqrt{\frac{p(1-p)}{n}} \le \pi \le p + Z_{\alpha/2}\sqrt{\frac{p(1-p)}{n}} \qquad \textbf{(10.3)}$$

where

$$p = \text{sample proportion} = \frac{X}{n} = \frac{\text{Number of items having the characteristic}}{\text{sample size}}$$

π = population proportion

$Z_{\alpha/2}$ = critical value from the standardized normal distribution

n = sample size

Note: To use this equation for the confidence interval, the sample size n must be large enough to ensure that both X and $n - X$ are greater than 5.

You can use the confidence interval estimate for the proportion defined in Equation (10.3) to estimate the proportion of sales invoices that contain errors (see the Saxon Home Improvement scenario on page 383). Using the Define, Collect, Organize, Visualize, and Analyze steps, you define the variable of interest as whether the invoice contains errors (yes or no). Then, you collect the data from a sample of 100 sales invoices. The results, which you organize and store in a worksheet, show that 10 invoices contain errors. To analyze the data, you compute, for these data, $p = X/n = 10/100 = 0.10$. Since both X and $n - X$ are > 5, using Equation (10.3) and $Z_{\alpha/2} = 1.96$, for 95% confidence,

$$p \pm Z_{\alpha/2}\sqrt{\frac{p(1-p)}{n}}$$

$$= 0.10 \pm (1.96)\sqrt{\frac{(0.10)(0.90)}{100}}$$

$$= 0.10 \pm (1.96)(0.03)$$

$$= 0.10 \pm 0.0588$$

$$0.0412 \le \pi \le 0.1588$$

Therefore, you have 95% confidence that the population proportion of all sales invoices containing errors is between 0.0412 and 0.1588. This means that between 4.12% and 15.88% of all the sales invoices contain errors. Figure 10.12 shows a Casio calculator worksheet for these data.

FIGURE 10.12

Casio calculator FX-9750G or FX-9750GII worksheet to construct a confidence interval estimate for the proportion of sales invoices that contain errors

From the **Main Menu** select the following:

STAT F4(INTR) **F1**(z) **F3**(1-p). Then enter the following items:

1-Prop ZInterval
C-Level	: **0.95**	**EXE**
x	: **10**	**EXE**
n	: **100**	**EXE**
Save Res	: None	

Now press **EXE** or **F1**(Calc).

The calculator will show the results:

1-Prop ZInterval
Left	= 0.04120108
Right	= 0.15879892
p	= 0.1
n	= 100

The 95% confidence interval is $0.04120108 \le \pi \le 0.15879892$.

Example 10.4 illustrates another application of a confidence interval estimate for the proportion.

EXAMPLE 10.4

Estimating the Proportion of Nonconforming Newspapers Printed

The operations manager at a large newspaper wants to estimate the proportion of newspapers printed that have a nonconforming attribute. Using the Define, Collect, Organize, Visualize, and Analyze steps, you define the variable of interest as whether the newspaper has excessive ruboff, improper page setup, missing pages, or duplicate pages. You collect the data by selecting a random sample of $n = 200$ newspapers from all the newspapers printed during a single day. You organize the results, which show that 35 newspapers contain some type of nonconformance, in a worksheet. To analyze the data, you need to construct and interpret a 90% confidence interval for the proportion of newspapers printed during the day that have a nonconforming attribute.

SOLUTION Using Equation (10.3),

$$p = \frac{X}{n} = \frac{35}{200} = 0.175, \text{ and with a 90\% level of confidence } Z_{\alpha/2} = 1.645$$

$$p \pm Z_{\alpha/2}\sqrt{\frac{p(1-p)}{n}}$$

$$= 0.175 \pm (1.645)\sqrt{\frac{(0.175)(0.825)}{200}}$$

$$= 0.175 \pm (1.645)(0.0269)$$

$$= 0.175 \pm 0.0442$$

$$0.1308 \le \pi \le 0.2192$$

You conclude with 90% confidence that the population proportion of all newspapers printed that day with nonconformities is between 0.1308 and 0.2192. This means that between 13.08% and 21.92% of the newspapers printed on that day have some type of nonconformance.

CASIO Calculator Instruction

Refer to Example 10.4: Construct a 90% confidence interval estimate for the population proportion of newspapers printed during the day that have a nonconforming attribute.

To find the confidence interval for population proportion with a 90% level of confidence, follow these calculator steps:

Select **STAT** **F4**(INTR) **F1**(Z) **F3**(1-P). Then select the following items:

1-Prop ZInterval
C-Level	: **0.90**	**EXE**
x	: **35**	**EXE**
n	: **200**	**EXE**
Save Res	: None	

Now press **EXE** or **F1**(Calc).

The calculator will show the results:

1-Prop ZInterval
Left	= 0.13080651
Right	= 0.21919348
$\hat{p}$	= 0.175
n	= 200

As you can see, the 90% confidence interval estimate for the population proportion is 0.13080651 to 0.21919348. The calculator will display the numerical result only; you must remember to write up the complete answer as shown in class.

Equation (10.3) contains a Z statistic because you can use the normal distribution to approximate the binomial distribution when the sample size is sufficiently large. In Example 10.4, the confidence interval using Z provides an excellent approximation for the population proportion because both X and $n - X$ are greater than 5. However, if you do not have a sufficiently large sample size, you should use the binomial distribution rather than Equation (10.3) (see references 1, 2, and 7). The exact confidence intervals for various sample sizes and proportions of successes have been tabulated by Fisher and Yates (reference 2).

Problems for Section 10.3

LEARNING THE BASICS

10.26 If $n = 200$ and $X = 50$, construct a 95% confidence interval estimate for the population proportion.

10.27 If $n = 400$ and $X = 25$, construct a 99% confidence interval estimate for the population proportion.

APPLYING THE CONCEPTS

10.28 The telephone company has the business objective of wanting to estimate the proportion of households that would purchase an additional telephone line if it were made available at a substantially reduced installation cost. Data are collected from a random sample of 500 households. The results indicate that 135 of the households would purchase the additional telephone line at a reduced installation cost.

a. Construct a 99% confidence interval estimate for the population proportion of households that would purchase the additional telephone line.

b. How would the manager in charge of promotional programs concerning residential customers use the results in (a)?

10.29 In a survey of 1,200 social media users, 76% said it is okay to friend co-workers, but 56% said it is not okay to friend your boss. (Data extracted from "Facebook Etiquette at Work," *USA Today*, March 24, 2010, p. 1B.)

a. Construct a 95% confidence interval estimate for the population proportion of social media users who would say it is okay to friend co-workers.

b. Construct a 95% confidence interval estimate for the population proportion of social media users who would say it is not okay to friend their boss.

c. Write a short summary of the information derived from (a) and (b).

10.30 Have you ever negotiated a pay raise? According to an Accenture survey, 52% of U.S. workers have (J. Yang and K. Carter, "Have You Ever Negotiated a Pay Raise?" **www.usatoday.com**, May 22, 2009).

a. Suppose that the survey had a sample size of $n = 500$. Construct a 95% confidence interval for the proportion of all U.S. workers who have negotiated a pay raise.

b. Based on (a), can you claim that more than half of all U.S. workers have negotiated a pay raise?

c. Repeat parts (a) and (b), assuming that the survey had a sample size of $n = 5,000$.

d. Discuss the effect of sample size on confidence interval estimation.

10.31 In a survey of 1,000 airline travelers, 760 responded that the airline fee that is most unreasonable is additional charges to redeem points/miles. (Data extracted from "Which Airline Fee Is Most Unreasonable?" *USA Today*, December 2, 2008, p. B1.) Construct a 95% confidence interval estimate for the population proportion of airline travelers who think that the airline fee that is most unreasonable is additional charges to redeem points/miles.

10.32 In a survey of 2,395 adults, 1,916 reported that e-mails are easy to misinterpret, but only 1,269 reported that telephone conversations are easy to misinterpret. (Data extracted from "Open to Misinterpretation," *USA Today*, July 17, 2007, p. 1D.)

a. Construct a 95% confidence interval estimate for the population proportion of adults who report that e-mails are easy to misinterpret.

b. Construct a 95% confidence interval estimate for the population proportion of adults who report that telephone conversations are easy to misinterpret.

c. Compare the results of (a) and (b).

10.33 What are the most preferred forms of recognition in the workplace? In a survey by Office Arrow, 163 of 388 administrative professionals responded that verbal recognition is the most preferred form of recognition, and 74 responded that cash bonuses are most preferred. (Data extracted from "Most Preferred Forms of Recognition at Workplace," *USA Today*, May 4, 2009, p. 1B.)

a. Construct a 95% confidence interval estimate for the population proportion of administrative professionals who prefer verbal recognition.

b. Construct a 95% confidence interval estimate for the population proportion of administrative professionals who prefer cash bonuses.

c. Interpret the intervals in (a) and (b).

d. Explain the difference in the results in (a) and (b).

10.4 Determining Sample Size

In each confidence interval developed so far in this chapter, the sample size was reported along with the results, with little discussion of the width of the resulting confidence interval. In the business world, sample sizes are determined prior to data collection to ensure that the confidence interval is narrow enough to be useful in making decisions. Determining the proper sample size is a complicated procedure, subject to the constraints of budget, time, and the amount of acceptable sampling error. In the Saxon Home Improvement example, if you want to estimate the mean dollar amount of the sales invoices, you must determine in advance how large a sampling error to allow in estimating the population mean. You must also determine, in advance, the level of confidence (i.e., 90%, 95%, or 99%) to use in estimating the population parameter.

Sample Size Determination for the Mean

To develop an equation for determining the appropriate sample size needed when constructing a confidence interval estimate for the mean, recall Equation (10.1) on page 388:

$$\bar{X} \pm Z_{\alpha/2}\frac{\sigma}{\sqrt{n}}$$

The amount added to or subtracted from $\bar{X}$ is equal to half the width of the interval. This quantity represents the amount of imprecision in the estimate that results from sampling error.[2] The **sampling error**, e, is defined as

$$e = Z_{\alpha/2}\frac{\sigma}{\sqrt{n}}$$

[2]In this context, some statisticians refer to e as the **margin of error**.

Solving for n gives the sample size needed to construct the appropriate confidence interval estimate for the mean. "Appropriate" means that the resulting interval will have an acceptable amount of sampling error.

SAMPLE SIZE DETERMINATION FOR THE MEAN

The sample size, n, is equal to the product of the $Z_{\alpha/2}$ value squared and the standard deviation, σ, squared, divided by the square of the sampling error, e.

$$n = \frac{Z_{\alpha/2}^2 \sigma^2}{e^2}$$

(10.4)

To compute the sample size, you must know three factors:

1. The desired confidence level, which determines the value of $Z_{\alpha/2}$, the critical value from the standardized normal distribution[3]
2. The acceptable sampling error, e
3. The standard deviation, σ

[3]You use Z instead of t because, to determine the critical value of t, you need to know the sample size, but you do not know it yet. For most studies, the sample size needed is large enough that the standardized normal distribution is a good approximation of the t distribution.

In some business-to-business relationships that require estimation of important parameters, legal contracts specify acceptable levels of sampling error and the confidence level required. For companies in the food and drug sectors, government regulations often specify sampling errors and confidence levels. In general, however, it is usually not easy to specify the three factors needed to determine the sample size. How can you determine the level of confidence and sampling error? Typically, these questions are answered only by a subject matter expert (i.e., an individual very familiar with the variables under study). Although 95% is the most common confidence level used, if more confidence is desired, then 99% might be more appropriate; if less confidence is deemed acceptable, then 90% might be used. For the sampling error, you should think not of how much sampling error you would like to have (you really do not want any error) but of how much you can tolerate when reaching conclusions from the confidence interval.

In addition to specifying the confidence level and the sampling error, you need an estimate of the standard deviation. Unfortunately, you rarely know the population standard deviation, σ. In some instances, you can estimate the standard deviation from past data. In other situations, you can make an educated guess by taking into account the range and distribution of the variable. For example, if you assume a normal distribution, the range is approximately equal to 6σ (i.e., $\pm 3\sigma$ around the mean) so that you estimate σ as the range divided by 6. If you cannot estimate σ in this way, you can conduct a small-scale study and estimate the standard deviation from the resulting data.

To explore how to determine the sample size needed for estimating the population mean, consider again the audit at Saxon Home Improvement. In Section 10.2, you selected a sample of 100 sales invoices and constructed a 95% confidence interval estimate for the population mean sales invoice amount. How was this sample size determined? Should you have selected a different sample size?

Suppose that, after consulting with company officials, you determine that a sampling error of no more than $\pm\$5$ is desired, along with 95% confidence. Past data indicate that the standard deviation of the sales amount is approximately \$25. Thus, $e = \$5, \sigma = \$25$, and $Z_{\alpha/2} = 1.96$ (for 95% confidence). Using Equation (10.4),

$$n = \frac{Z_{\alpha/2}^2 \sigma^2}{e^2} = \frac{(1.96)^2(25)^2}{(5)^2}$$

$$= 96.04$$

Because the general rule is to slightly oversatisfy the criteria by rounding the sample size up to the next whole integer, you should select a sample of size 97. Thus, the sample of size $n = 100$ used on page 241 is slightly more than what is necessary to satisfy the needs of the company, based on the estimated standard deviation, desired confidence level, and sampling error. Because the calculated sample standard deviation is slightly higher than expected, $28.95 compared to $25.00, the confidence interval is slightly wider than desired. Figure 10.13 shows an Excel worksheet for determining the sample size.

FIGURE 10.13

Excel worksheet for determining sample size for estimating the mean sales invoice amount for the Saxon Home Improvement Company

	A	B	
1	For the Mean Sales Invoice Amount		
2			
3	Data		
4	Population Standard Deviation	25	
5	Sampling Error	5	
6	Confidence Level	95%	
7			
8	Intemediate Calculations		
9	Z Value	-1.9600	=NORMSINV((1 - B6)/2)
10	Calculated Sample Size	96.0365	=((B9 * B4)/B5)^2
11			
12	Result		
13	Sample Size Needed	97	=ROUNDUP(B10, 0)

Example 10.5 illustrates another application of determining the sample size needed to develop a confidence interval estimate for the mean.

EXAMPLE 10.5

Determining the Sample Size for the Mean

Returning to Example 10.3 on page 397, suppose you want to estimate, with 95% confidence, the population mean force required to break the insulator to within ±25 pounds. On the basis of a study conducted the previous year, you believe that the standard deviation is 100 pounds. Determine the sample size needed.

SOLUTION Using Equation (10.4) on page 409 and $e = 25$, $\sigma = 100$, and $Z_{\alpha/2} = 1.96$ for 95% confidence,

$$n = \frac{Z_{\alpha/2}^2 \sigma^2}{e^2} = \frac{(1.96)^2 (100)^2}{(25)^2}$$

$$= 61.47$$

Therefore, you should select a sample of 62 insulators because the general rule for determining sample size is to always round up to the next integer value in order to slightly oversatisfy the criteria desired. An actual sampling error slightly larger than 25 will result if the sample standard deviation calculated in this sample of 62 is greater than 100 and slightly smaller if the sample standard deviation is less than 100.

Sample Size Determination for the Proportion

So far in this section, you have learned how to determine the sample size needed for estimating the population mean. Now suppose that you want to determine the sample size necessary for estimating a population proportion.

To determine the sample size needed to estimate a population proportion, π, you use a method similar to the method for a population mean. Recall that in developing the sample size for a confidence interval for the mean, the sampling error is defined by

$$e = Z_{\alpha/2} \frac{\sigma}{\sqrt{n}}$$

When estimating a proportion, you replace σ with $\sqrt{\pi(1 - \pi)}$. Thus, the sampling error is

$$e = Z_{\alpha/2}\sqrt{\frac{\pi(1 - \pi)}{n}}$$

Solving for n, you have the sample size necessary to develop a confidence interval estimate for a proportion.

SAMPLE SIZE DETERMINATION FOR THE PROPORTION

The sample size n is equal to the product of $Z_{\alpha/2}$ squared, the population proportion, π, and 1 minus the population proportion, π, divided by the square of the sampling error, e.

$$n = \frac{Z_{\alpha/2}^2\pi(1 - \pi)}{e^2} \tag{10.5}$$

To determine the sample size, you must know three factors:

1. The desired confidence level, which determines the value of $Z_{\alpha/2}$, the critical value from the standardized normal distribution
2. The acceptable sampling error (or margin of error), e
3. The population proportion, π

In practice, selecting these quantities requires some planning. Once you determine the desired level of confidence, you can find the appropriate $Z_{\alpha/2}$ value from the standardized normal distribution. The sampling error, e, indicates the amount of error that you are willing to tolerate in estimating the population proportion. The third quantity, π, is actually the population parameter that you want to estimate! Thus, how do you state a value for what you are trying to determine?

Here you have two alternatives. In many situations, you may have past information or relevant experience that provides an educated estimate of π. Or, if you do not have past information or relevant experience, you can try to provide a value for π that would never *underestimate* the sample size needed. Referring to Equation (10.5), you can see that the quantity $\pi(1 - \pi)$ appears in the numerator. Thus, you need to determine the value of π that will make the quantity $\pi(1 - \pi)$ as large as possible. When $\pi = 0.5$, the product $\pi(1 - \pi)$ achieves its maximum value. To show this result, consider the following values of π, along with the accompanying products of $\pi(1 - \pi)$:

When $\pi = 0.9$, then $\pi(1 - \pi) = (0.9)(0.1) = 0.09$.

When $\pi = 0.7$, then $\pi(1 - \pi) = (0.7)(0.3) = 0.21$.

When $\pi = 0.5$, then $\pi(1 - \pi) = (0.5)(0.5) = 0.25$.

When $\pi = 0.3$, then $\pi(1 - \pi) = (0.3)(0.7) = 0.21$.

When $\pi = 0.1$, then $\pi(1 - \pi) = (0.1)(0.9) = 0.09$.

Therefore, when you have no prior knowledge or estimate for the population proportion, π, you should use $\pi = 0.5$ for determining the sample size. Using $\pi = 0.5$ produces the largest possible sample size and results in the narrowest and most precise confidence interval. This increased precision comes at the cost of spending more time and money for an increased sample size. Also, note that if you use $\pi = 0.5$ and the proportion is different from 0.5, you will overestimate the sample size needed, because you will get a confidence interval narrower than originally intended.

Returning to the Saxon Home Improvement scenario on page 383, suppose that the auditing procedures require you to have 95% confidence in estimating the population proportion of sales invoices with errors to within ±0.07. The results from past months indicate that the largest proportion has been no more than 0.15. Thus, using Equation (10.5) with $e = 0.07$, $\pi = 0.15$, and $Z_{\alpha/2} = 1.96$ for 95% confidence,

$$n = \frac{Z_{\alpha/2}^2 \pi(1 - \pi)}{e^2}$$

$$= \frac{(1.96)^2(0.15)(0.85)}{(0.07)^2}$$

$$= 99.96$$

Because the general rule is to round the sample size up to the next whole integer to slightly oversatisfy the criteria, a sample size of 100 is needed. Thus, the sample size needed to satisfy the requirements of the company, based on the estimated proportion, desired confidence level, and sampling error, is equal to the sample size taken on page 403. The actual confidence interval is narrower than required because the sample proportion is 0.10, whereas 0.15 was used for π in Equation (10.5). Figure 10.14 shows an Excel worksheet for determining the sample size.

FIGURE 10.14

Excel worksheet for determining sample size for estimating the proportion of sales invoices with errors for the Saxon Home Improvement Company

	A	B	
1	For the Proportion of In-Error Sales Invoices		
2			
3	Data		
4	Estimate of True Proportion	0.15	
5	Sampling Error	0.07	
6	Confidence Level	95%	
7			
8	Intermediate Calculations		
9	Z Value	-1.9600	=NORMSINV((1 - B6)/2)
10	Calculated Sample Size	99.9563	=(B9^2 * B4 * (1 - B4))/B5^2
11			
12	Result		
13	Sample Size Needed	100	=ROUNDUP(B10, 0)

Example 10.6 provides another application of determining the sample size for estimating the population proportion.

EXAMPLE 10.6

Determining the Sample Size for the Population Proportion

You want to have 90% confidence of estimating the proportion of office workers who respond to e-mail within an hour to within ±0.05. Because you have not previously undertaken such a study, there is no information available from past data. Determine the sample size needed.

SOLUTION Because no information is available from past data, assume that $\pi = 0.50$. Using Equation (10.5) on page 409 and $e = 0.05$, $\pi = 0.50$, and $Z_{\alpha/2} = 1.645$ for 90% confidence,

$$n = \frac{Z_{\alpha/2}^2 \pi(1 - \pi)}{e^2}$$

$$= \frac{(1.645)^2(0.50)(0.50)}{(0.05)^2}$$

$$= 270.6$$

Therefore, you need a sample of 271 office workers to estimate the population proportion to within ±0.05 with 90% confidence.

Problems for Section 10.4

LEARNING THE BASICS

10.34 If you want to be 95% confident of estimating the population mean to within a sampling error of ± 5 and the standard deviation is assumed to be 15, what sample size is required?

10.35 If you want to be 99% confident of estimating the population mean to within a sampling error of ± 20 and the standard deviation is assumed to be 100, what sample size is required?

10.36 If you want to be 99% confident of estimating the population proportion to within a sampling error of ± 0.04, what sample size is needed?

10.37 If you want to be 95% confident of estimating the population proportion to within a sampling error of ± 0.02 and there is historical evidence that the population proportion is approximately 0.40, what sample size is needed?

APPLYING THE CONCEPTS

✓ **SELF Test** **10.38** A survey is planned to determine the mean annual family medical expenses of employees of a large company. The management of the company wishes to be 95% confident that the sample mean is correct to within $\pm\$50$ of the population mean annual family medical expenses. A previous study indicates that the standard deviation is approximately $400.
a. How large a sample is necessary?
b. If management wants to be correct to within $\pm\$25$, how many employees need to be selected?

10.39 If the manager of a paint supply store wants to estimate, with 95% confidence, the mean amount of paint in a 1-gallon can to within ± 0.004 gallon and also assumes that the standard deviation is 0.02 gallon, what sample size is needed?

10.40 If a quality control manager wants to estimate, with 95% confidence, the mean life of light bulbs to within ± 20 hours and also assumes that the population standard deviation is 100 hours, how many light bulbs need to be selected?

10.41 If the inspection division of a county weights and measures department wants to estimate the mean amount of soft-drink fill in 2-liter bottles to within ± 0.01 liter with 95% confidence and also assumes that the standard deviation is 0.05 liter, what sample size is needed?

10.42 A consumer group wants to estimate the mean electric bill for the month of July for single-family homes in a large city. Based on studies conducted in other cities, the standard deviation is assumed to be $25. The group wants to estimate, with 99% confidence, the mean bill for July to within $\pm\$5$.

a. What sample size is needed?
b. If 95% confidence is desired, how many homes need to be selected?

10.43 An advertising agency that serves a major radio station wants to estimate the mean amount of time that the station's audience spends listening to the radio daily. From past studies, the standard deviation is estimated as 45 minutes.
a. What sample size is needed if the agency wants to be 90% confident of being correct to within ± 5 minutes?
b. If 99% confidence is desired, how many listeners need to be selected?

10.44 A growing niche in the restaurant business is gourmet-casual breakfast, lunch, and brunch. Chains in this group include EggSpectation and Panera Bread. Suppose that the mean per-person check for EggSpectation is approximately $12.50, and the mean per-person check for Panera Bread is $7.50.
a. Assuming a standard deviation of $2.00, what sample size is needed to estimate, with 95% confidence, the mean per-person check for EggSpectation to within $\pm\$0.25$?
b. Assuming a standard deviation of $2.50, what sample size is needed to estimate, with 95% confidence, the mean per-person check for EggSpectation to within $\pm\$0.25$?
c. Assuming a standard deviation of $3.00, what sample size is needed to estimate, with 95% confidence, the mean per-person check for EggSpectation to within $\pm\$0.25$?
d. Discuss the effect of variation on the sample size needed.

10.45 What proportion of Americans get most of their news from the Internet? According to a poll conducted by Pew Research Center, 40% get most of their news from the Internet. (Data extracted from "Drill Down," *The New York Times*, January 5, 2009, p. B3.)
a. To conduct a follow-up study that would provide 95% confidence that the point estimate is correct to within ± 0.04 of the population proportion, how large a sample size is required?
b. To conduct a follow-up study that would provide 99% confidence that the point estimate is correct to within ± 0.04 of the population proportion, how many people need to be sampled?
c. To conduct a follow-up study that would provide 95% confidence that the point estimate is correct to within ± 0.02 of the population proportion, how large a sample size is required?
d. To conduct a follow-up study that would provide 99% confidence that the point estimate is correct to within ± 0.02 of the population proportion, how many people need to be sampled?
e. Discuss the effects on sample size requirements of changing the desired confidence level and the acceptable sampling error.

10.46 A survey of 1,000 adults was conducted in March 2009 concerning "green practices." In response to the question of what was the most beneficial thing to do for the environment, 28% said buying renewable energy, 19% said using greener transportation, and 7% said selecting minimal or reduced packaging. (Data extracted from "Environmentally Friendly Choices," *USA Today*, March 31, 2009, p. D1.) Construct a 95% confidence interval estimate of the population proportion of adults who said that the most beneficial thing to do for the environment was
a. buy renewable energy.
b. use greener transportation.
c. select minimal or reduced packaging.
d. You have been asked to update the results of this study. Determine the sample size necessary to estimate, with 95% confidence, the population proportions in (a) through (c) to within ±0.02.

10.47 In a study of 500 executives, 315 stated that their company informally monitored social networking sites to stay on top of information related to their company. (Data extracted from "Checking Out the Buzz," *USA Today*, June 26, 2009, p. 1B.)
a. Construct a 95% confidence interval for the proportion of companies that informally monitored social networking sites to stay on top of information related to their company.
b. Interpret the interval constructed in (a).
c. If you wanted to conduct a follow-up study to estimate the population proportion of companies that informally monitored social networking sites to stay on top of

information related to their company to within ±0.01 with 95% confidence, how many executives would you survey?

10.48 In response to the question "How do you judge a company?" 84% said the most important way was how a company responded to a crisis. (Data extracted from "How Do You Judge a Company?" *USA Today*, December 22, 2008, p. 1B.)
a. If you conduct a follow-up study to estimate the population proportion of individuals who said that the most important way to judge a company was how the company responded to a crisis, would you use a π of 0.84 or 0.50 in the sample size formula? Discuss.
b. Using your answer to (a), find the sample size necessary to estimate, with 95% certainty, the population proportion to within ±0.03.

10.49 Do you use the same password for all your social-network sites? A recent survey (*USA Today*, July 22, 2010, p. 1B) found that 32% of social-network users use the same password for all their social-network sites.
a. To conduct a follow-up study that would provide 99% confidence that the point estimate is correct to within ±0.03 of the population proportion, how many people need to be sampled?
b. To conduct a follow-up study that would provide 99% confidence that the point estimate is correct to within ±0.05 of the population proportion, how many people need to be sampled?
c. Compare the results of (a) and (b).

10.5 Confidence Interval Estimation and Ethical Issues

Ethical issues related to the selection of samples and the inferences that accompany them can occur in several ways. The major ethical issue relates to whether confidence interval estimates are provided along with the point estimates. Providing a point estimate without also including the confidence interval limits (typically set at 95%), the sample size used, and an interpretation of the meaning of the confidence interval in terms that a person untrained in statistics can understand raises ethical issues. Failure to include a confidence interval estimate might mislead the user of the results into thinking that the point estimate is all that is needed to predict the population characteristic with certainty.

When media outlets publicize the results of a political poll, they often overlook including this information. Sometimes, the results of a poll include the sampling error, but the sampling error is often presented in fine print or as an afterthought to the story being reported. A fully ethical presentation of poll results would give equal prominence to the confidence levels, sample size, sampling error, and confidence limits of the poll.

When you prepare your own point estimates, always state the interval estimate in a prominent place and include a brief explanation of the meaning of the confidence interval. In addition, make sure you highlight the sample size and sampling error.

USING STATISTICS @ Saxon Home Improvement, Part II Revisited

Marcin Balcerzak / Shutterstock.com

In the Saxon Home Improvement scenario, you were an accountant for a distributor of home improvement supplies in the northeastern United States. You were responsible for the accuracy of the integrated inventory management and sales information system. You used confidence interval estimation techniques to draw conclusions about the population of all records from a relatively small sample collected during an audit.

At the end of the month, you collected a random sample of 100 sales invoices and made the following inferences:

- With 95% confidence, you concluded that the mean amount of all the sales invoices is between $104.53 and $116.01.
- With 95% confidence, you concluded that between 4.12% and 15.88% of all the sales invoices contain errors.

These estimates provide an interval of values that you believe contain the true population parameters. If these intervals are too wide (i.e., the sampling error is too large) for the types of decisions Saxon Home Improvement needs to make, you will need to take a larger sample. You can use the sample size formulas in Section 10.4 to determine the number of sales invoices to sample to ensure that the size of the sampling error is acceptable.

SUMMARY

This chapter discusses confidence intervals for estimating the characteristics of a population, along with how you can determine the necessary sample size. You learned how to apply these methods to numerical and categorical data. Table 10.3 provides a list of topics covered in this chapter.

To determine what equation to use for a particular situation, you need to answer these questions:

- Are you constructing a confidence interval, or are you determining sample size?
- Do you have a numerical variable, or do you have a categorical variable?

The next three chapters develop a hypothesis-testing approach to making decisions about population parameters.

TABLE 10.3

Summary of Topics in Chapter 10

Type of Analysis	Type of Data	
	Numerical	Categorical
Confidence interval for a population parameter	Confidence interval estimate for the mean (Sections 10.1 and 10.2)	Confidence interval estimate for the proportion (Section 10.3)
Determining sample size	Sample size determination for the mean (Section 10.4)	Sample size determination for the proportion (Section 10.4)

KEY EQUATIONS

Confidence Interval for the Mean (σ Known)

$$\bar{X} \pm Z_{\alpha/2}\frac{\sigma}{\sqrt{n}}$$

or

$$\bar{X} - Z_{\alpha/2}\frac{\sigma}{\sqrt{n}} \le \mu \le \bar{X} + Z_{\alpha/2}\frac{\sigma}{\sqrt{n}}$$

Confidence Interval for the Mean (σ Unknown)

$$\bar{X} \pm t_{\alpha/2}\frac{S}{\sqrt{n}}$$

or

$$\bar{X} - t_{\alpha/2}\frac{S}{\sqrt{n}} \le \mu \le \bar{X} + t_{\alpha/2}\frac{S}{\sqrt{n}}$$

Confidence Interval Estimate for the Proportion

$$p \pm Z_{\alpha/2}\sqrt{\frac{p(1-p)}{n}}$$

or

$$p - Z_{\alpha/2}\sqrt{\frac{p(1-p)}{n}} \le \pi \le p + Z_{\alpha/2}\sqrt{\frac{p(1-p)}{n}}$$

Sample Size Determination for the Mean

$$n = \frac{Z_{\alpha/2}^2\sigma^2}{e^2}$$

Sample Size Determination for the Proportion

$$n = \frac{Z_{\alpha/2}^2\pi(1-\pi)}{e^2}$$

KEY TERMS

confidence interval estimate   384
critical value   389
degrees of freedom   393

level of confidence   388
margin of error   406
point estimate   384

sampling error   406
Student's t distribution   393

PROBLEMS

CHECKING YOUR UNDERSTANDING

10.50 Why can you never really have 100% confidence of correctly estimating the population characteristic of interest?

10.51 When should you use the t distribution to develop the confidence interval estimate for the mean?

10.52 Why is it true that for a given sample size, n, an increase in confidence is achieved by widening (and making less precise) the confidence interval?

10.53 Why is the sample size needed to determine the proportion smaller when the population proportion is 0.20 than when the population proportion is 0.50?

APPLYING THE CONCEPTS

10.54 You work in the corporate office for a nationwide convenience store franchise that operates nearly 10,000 stores. The per-store daily customer count has been steady, at 900, for some time (i.e., the mean number of customers in a store in one day is 900). To increase the customer count, the franchise is considering cutting coffee prices. The 12-ounce

size will now be $0.59 instead of $0.99, and the 16-ounce size will be $0.69 instead of $1.19. Even with this reduction in price, the franchise will have a 40% gross margin on coffee. To test the new initiative, the franchise has reduced coffee prices in a sample of 34 stores, where customer counts have been running almost exactly at the national average of 900. After four weeks, the sample stores stabilize at a mean customer count of 974 and a standard deviation of 96. This increase seems like a substantial amount to you, but it also seems like a pretty small sample. Is there some way to get a feel for what the mean per-store count in all the stores will be if you cut coffee prices nationwide? Do you think reducing coffee prices is a good strategy for increasing the mean customer count?

10.55 What do Americans do to conserve energy? A survey of 500 adults (data extracted from "Going on an Energy Diet," *USA Today*, April 16, 2009, p. 1A) found the following percentages:
  Turn off lights, power strips, unplug things: 73%
  Recycle aluminum, plastic, newspapers, cardboard: 47%
  Recycle harder-to-recycle products: 36%

Buy products with least packaging: 34%
Ride a bike or walk: 23%
a. Construct 95% confidence interval estimates for the population proportion of what adults do to conserve energy.
b. What conclusions can you reach concerning what adults do to conserve energy?

10.56 A market researcher for a consumer electronics company wants to study the television viewing habits of residents of a particular area. A random sample of 40 respondents is selected, and each respondent is instructed to keep a detailed record of all television viewing in a particular week. The results are as follows:
- Viewing time per week: $\bar{X} = 15.3$ hours, $S = 3.8$ hours.
- 27 respondents watch the evening news on at least three weeknights.
a. Construct a 95% confidence interval estimate for the mean amount of television watched per week in this area.
b. Construct a 95% confidence interval estimate for the population proportion who watch the evening news on at least three weeknights per week.
Suppose that the market researcher wants to take another survey in a different location. Answer these questions:
c. What sample size is required to be 95% confident of estimating the population mean viewing time to within ±2 hours assuming that the population standard deviation is equal to five hours?
d. How many respondents need to be selected to be 95% confident of being within ±0.035 of the population proportion who watch the evening news on at least three weeknights if no previous estimate is available?
e. Based on (c) and (d), how many respondents should the market researcher select if a single survey is being conducted?

10.57 The real estate assessor for a county government wants to study various characteristics of single-family houses in the county. A random sample of 70 houses reveals the following:
- Heated area of the houses (in square feet): $\bar{X} = 1,759, S = 380$.
- 42 houses have central air-conditioning.
a. Construct a 99% confidence interval estimate for the population mean heated area of the houses.
b. Construct a 95% confidence interval estimate for the population proportion of houses that have central air-conditioning.

10.58 The personnel director of a large corporation wishes to study absenteeism among clerical workers at the corporation's central office during the year. A random sample of 25 clerical workers reveals the following:
- Absenteeism: $\bar{X} = 9.7$ days, $S = 4.0$ days.
- 12 clerical workers were absent more than 10 days.
a. Construct a 95% confidence interval estimate for the mean number of absences for clerical workers during the year.

b. Construct a 95% confidence interval estimate for the population proportion of clerical workers absent more than 10 days during the year.
Suppose that the personnel director also wishes to take a survey in a branch office. Answer these questions:
c. What sample size is needed to have 95% confidence in estimating the population mean absenteeism to within ±1.5 days if the population standard deviation is estimated to be 4.5 days?
d. How many clerical workers need to be selected to have 90% confidence in estimating the population proportion to within ±0.075 if no previous estimate is available?
e. Based on (c) and (d), what sample size is needed if a single survey is being conducted?

10.59 The market research director for Dotty's Department Store wants to study women's spending on cosmetics. A survey of the store's customers is designed in order to estimate the proportion of women who purchase their cosmetics primarily from Dotty's Department Store and the mean yearly amount that women spend on cosmetics. A previous survey found that the standard deviation of the amount women spend on cosmetics in a year is approximately $18.
a. What sample size is needed to have 99% confidence of estimating the population mean amount spent to within ±$5?
b. How many of the store's credit card holders need to be selected to have 90% confidence of estimating the population proportion to within ±0.045?

10.60 The branch manager of a nationwide bookstore chain (located near a college campus) wants to study characteristics of her store's customers. She decides to focus on two variables: the amount of money spent by customers (on items other than textbooks) and whether the customers would consider purchasing educational DVDs related to graduate preparation exams, such as the GMAT, GRE, or LSAT. The results from a sample of 70 customers are as follows:
- Amount spent: $\bar{X} = \$28.52, S = \$11.39$.
- 28 customers stated that they would consider purchasing the educational DVDs.
a. Construct a 95% confidence interval estimate for the population mean amount spent in the bookstore.
b. Construct a 90% confidence interval estimate for the population proportion of customers who would consider purchasing educational DVDs.
Assume that the branch manager of another store in the chain (also located close to a college campus) wants to conduct a similar survey in his store. Answer the following questions:
c. What sample size is needed to have 95% confidence of estimating the population mean amount spent in this store to within ±$2 if the standard deviation is assumed to be $10?
d. How many customers need to be selected to have 90% confidence of estimating the population proportion who

would consider purchasing the educational DVDs to within ±0.04?

e. Based on your answers to (c) and (d), how large a sample should the manager take?

10.61 The branch manager of an outlet (Store 1) of a nationwide chain of pet supply stores wants to study characteristics of her customers. In particular, she decides to focus on two variables: the amount of money spent by customers and whether the customers own only one dog, only one cat, or more than one dog and/or cat. The results from a sample of 70 customers are as follows:

- Amount of money spent: $\bar{X} = \$21.34, S = \$9.22$.
- 37 customers own only a dog.
- 26 customers own only a cat.
- 7 customers own more than one dog and/or cat.

a. Construct a 95% confidence interval estimate for the population mean amount spent in the pet supply store.

b. Construct a 90% confidence interval estimate for the population proportion of customers who own only a cat.

The branch manager of another outlet (Store 2) wishes to conduct a similar survey in his store. The manager does not have access to the information generated by the manager of Store 1. Answer the following questions:

c. What sample size is needed to have 95% confidence of estimating the population mean amount spent in this store to within ±$1.50 if the standard deviation is estimated to be $10?

d. How many customers need to be selected to have 90% confidence of estimating the population proportion of customers who own only a cat to within ±0.045?

e. Based on your answers to (c) and (d), how large a sample should the manager take?

10.62 Scarlett and Heather, the owners of an upscale restaurant in Dayton, Ohio, want to study the dining characteristics of their customers. They decide to focus on two variables: the amount of money spent by customers and whether customers order dessert. The results from a sample of 60 customers are as follows:

- Amount spent: $\bar{X} = \$38.54, S = \$7.26$.
- 18 customers purchased dessert.

a. Construct a 95% confidence interval estimate for the population mean amount spent per customer in the restaurant.

b. Construct a 90% confidence interval estimate for the population proportion of customers who purchase dessert.

Jeanine, the owner of a competing restaurant, wants to conduct a similar survey in her restaurant. Jeanine does not have access to the information that Scarlett and Heather have obtained from the survey they conducted. Answer the following questions:

c. What sample size is needed to have 95% confidence of estimating the population mean amount spent in her restaurant to within ±$1.50, assuming that the standard deviation is estimated to be $8?

d. How many customers need to be selected to have 90% confidence of estimating the population proportion of customers who purchase dessert to within ±0.04?

e. Based on your answers to (c) and (d), how large a sample should Jeanine take?

10.63 The manufacturer of Ice Melt claims that its product will melt snow and ice at temperatures as low as 0° Fahrenheit. A representative for a large chain of hardware stores is interested in testing this claim. The chain purchases a large shipment of 5-pound bags for distribution. The representative wants to know, with 95% confidence and within ±0.05, what proportion of bags of Ice Melt perform the job as claimed by the manufacturer.

a. How many bags does the representative need to test? What assumption should be made concerning the population proportion? (This is called *destructive testing*; i.e., the product being tested is destroyed by the test and is then unavailable to be sold.)

b. Suppose that the representative tests 50 bags, and 42 of them do the job as claimed. Construct a 95% confidence interval estimate for the population proportion that will do the job as claimed.

c. How can the representative use the results of (b) to determine whether to sell the Ice Melt product?

10.64 A home furnishings store that sells bedroom furniture is conducting an end-of-month inventory of the beds (mattress, bed spring, and frame) in stock. An auditor for the store wants to estimate the mean value of the beds in stock at that time. She wants to have 99% confidence that her estimate of the mean value is correct to within ±$100. On the basis of past experience, she estimates that the standard deviation of the value of a bed is $200.

a. How many beds should she select?

b. Using the sample size selected in (a), an audit was conducted, with the following results:

$$\bar{X} = \$1,654.27 \qquad S = \$184.62$$

Construct a 99% confidence interval estimate for the mean value of the beds in stock at the end of the month.

10.65 A quality characteristic of interest for a tea-bag-filling process is the weight of the tea in the individual bags. In this example, the label weight on the package indicates that the mean amount is 5.5 grams of tea in a bag. If the bags are underfilled, two problems arise. First, customers may not be able to brew the tea to be as strong as they wish. Second, the company may be in violation of the truth-in-labeling laws. On the other hand, if the mean amount of tea in a bag exceeds the label weight, the company is giving away product. Getting an exact amount of tea in a bag is problematic because of variation in the temperature and humidity inside the factory, differences in the density of the tea, and the extremely fast filling operation of the machine (approximately 170 bags per minute). The following data (stored in Teabags) are the weights, in grams, of a sample of 50 tea bags produced in one hour by a single machine:

```
5.65 5.44 5.42 5.40 5.53 5.34 5.54 5.45 5.52 5.41
5.57 5.40 5.53 5.54 5.55 5.62 5.56 5.46 5.44 5.51
5.47 5.40 5.47 5.61 5.53 5.32 5.67 5.29 5.49 5.55
5.77 5.57 5.42 5.58 5.58 5.50 5.32 5.50 5.53 5.58
5.61 5.45 5.44 5.25 5.56 5.63 5.50 5.57 5.67 5.36
```

a. Construct a 99% confidence interval estimate for the population mean weight of the tea bags.
b. Is the company meeting the requirement set forth on the label that the mean amount of tea in a bag is 5.5 grams?
c. Do you think the assumption needed to construct the confidence interval estimate in (a) is valid?

10.66 A manufacturing company produces steel housings for electrical equipment. The main component part of the housing is a steel trough that is made from a 14-gauge steel coil. It is produced using a 250-ton progressive punch press with a wipe-down operation that puts two 90-degree forms in the flat steel to make the trough. The distance from one side of the form to the other is critical because of weatherproofing in outdoor applications. The widths (in inches), shown below and stored in Trough, are from a sample of 49 troughs:

```
8.312 8.343 8.317 8.383 8.348 8.410 8.351 8.373 8.481 8.422
8.476 8.382 8.484 8.403 8.414 8.419 8.385 8.465 8.498 8.447
8.436 8.413 8.489 8.414 8.481 8.415 8.479 8.429 8.458 8.462
8.460 8.444 8.429 8.460 8.412 8.420 8.410 8.405 8.323 8.420
8.396 8.447 8.405 8.439 8.411 8.427 8.420 8.498 8.409
```

a. Construct a 95% confidence interval estimate for the mean width of the troughs.
b. Interpret the interval developed in (a).
c. Do you think the assumption needed to construct the confidence interval estimate in (a) in valid?

10.67 The manufacturer of Boston and Vermont asphalt shingles knows that product weight is a major factor in a customer's perception of quality. The last stage of the assembly line packages the shingles before they are placed on wooden pallets. Once a pallet is full (a pallet for most brands holds 16 squares of shingles), it is weighed, and the measurement is recorded. The file Pallet contains the weight (in pounds) from a sample of 368 pallets of Boston shingles and 330 pallets of Vermont shingles.

a. For the Boston shingles, construct a 95% confidence interval estimate for the mean weight.
b. For the Vermont shingles, construct a 95% confidence interval estimate for the mean weight.
c. Do you think the assumption needed to construct the confidence interval estimates in (a) and (b) is valid?
d. Based on the results of (a) and (b), what conclusions can you reach concerning the mean weight of the Boston and Vermont shingles?

10.68 The manufacturer of Boston and Vermont asphalt shingles provides its customers with a 20-year warranty on most of its products. To determine whether a shingle will last the entire warranty period, accelerated-life testing is conducted at the manufacturing plant. Accelerated-life testing exposes the shingle to the stresses it would be subject to in a lifetime of normal use via a laboratory experiment that takes only a few minutes to conduct. In this test, a shingle is repeatedly scraped with a brush for a short period of time, and the shingle granules removed by the brushing are weighed (in grams). Shingles that experience low amounts of granule loss are expected to last longer in normal use than shingles that experience high amounts of granule loss. In this situation, a shingle should experience no more than 0.8 grams of granule loss if it is expected to last the length of the warranty period. The file Granule contains a sample of 170 measurements made on the company's Boston shingles and 140 measurements made on Vermont shingles.

a. For the Boston shingles, construct a 95% confidence interval estimate for the mean granule loss.
b. For the Vermont shingles, construct a 95% confidence interval estimate for the mean granule loss.
c. Do you think the assumption needed to construct the confidence interval estimates in (a) and (b) is valid?
d. Based on the results of (a) and (b), what conclusions can you reach concerning the mean granule loss of the Boston and Vermont shingles?

REPORT WRITING EXERCISE

10.69 Referring to the results in Problem 10.66 concerning the width of a steel trough, write a report that summarizes your conclusions.

TEAM PROJECT

10.70 Refer to the team project on page 126 that uses the data in Bond Funds. Construct all appropriate confidence interval estimates of the population characteristics of below-average-risk, average-risk, and above-average-risk bond funds. Include these estimates in a report to the vice president for research at the financial investment service.

STUDENT SURVEY DATABASE

10.71 Problem 1.21 on page 20 describes a survey of 62 undergraduate students (stored in UndergradSurvey).
a. For these data, for each variable, construct a 95% confidence interval estimate for the population characteristic.
b. Write a report that summarizes your conclusions.

10.72 Problem 1.21 on page 20 describes a survey of 62 undergraduate students (stored in UndergradSurvey).
a. Select a sample of undergraduate students at your school and conduct a similar survey for those students.
b. For the data collected in (a), repeat (a) and (b) of Problem 10.71.
c. Compare the results of (b) to those of Problem 10.71.

10.73 Problem 1.22 on page 21 describes a survey of 44 MBA students (stored in GradSurvey).
a. For these data, for each variable, construct a 95% confidence interval estimate for the population characteristic.
b. Write a report that summarizes your conclusions.

10.74 Problem 1.22 on page 21 describes a survey of 44 MBA students (stored in `GradSurvey`).

a. Select a sample of graduate students in your MBA program and conduct a similar survey for those students.

b. For the data collected in (a), repeat (a) and (b) of Problem 10.73.

c. Compare the results of (b) to those of Problem 10.73.

MANAGING ASHLAND MULTICOMM SERVICES

The marketing department has been considering ways to increase the number of new subscriptions to the *3-For-All* cable/phone/Internet service. Following the suggestion of Assistant Manager Lauren Adler, the department staff designed a survey to help determine various characteristics of households who subscribe to cable television service from Ashland. The survey consists of the following 10 questions:

1. Does your household subscribe to telephone service from Ashland?
   (1) Yes   (2) No
2. Does your household subscribe to Internet service from Ashland?
   (1) Yes   (2) No
3. What type of cable television service do you have?
   (1) Basic
   (2) Enhanced
   (If Basic, skip to question 5.)
4. How often do you watch the cable television stations that are only available with enhanced service?
   (1) Every day
   (2) Most days
   (3) Occasionally or never
5. How often do you watch premium or on-demand services that require an extra fee?
   (1) Almost every day
   (2) Several times a week
   (3) Rarely
   (4) Never
6. Which method did you use to obtain your current AMS subscription?
   (1) AMS toll-free phone number
   (2) AMS website
   (3) Direct mail reply card
   (4) Good Tunes & More promotion
   (5) Other
7. Would you consider subscribing to the *3-For-All* cable/phone/Internet service for a trial period if a discount were offered?
   (1) Yes   (2) No
   (If no, skip to question 9.)
8. If purchased separately, cable, Internet, and phone services would currently cost $24.99 per week. How much would you be willing to pay per week for the *3-For-All* cable/phone/Internet service?

9. Does your household use another provider of telephone service?
   (1) Yes   (2) No
10. AMS may distribute Ashland Gold Cards that would provide discounts at selected Ashland-area restaurants for subscribers who agree to a two-year subscription contract to the *3-For-All* service. Would being eligible to receive a Gold Card cause you to agree to the two-year term?
    (1) Yes   (2) No

Of the 500 households selected that subscribe to cable television service from Ashland, 82 households either refused to participate, could not be contacted after repeated attempts, or had telephone numbers that were not in service. The summary results are as follows:

Household has AMS Telephone Service	Frequency
Yes	83
No	335

Household has AMS Internet Service	Frequency
Yes	262
No	156

Type of Cable Service	Frequency
Basic	164
Enhanced	254

Watches Enhanced Programming	Frequency
Every day	50
Most days	144
Occasionally or never	60

Watches Premium or On-Demand Services	Frequency
Almost every day	14
Several times a week	35
Almost never	313
Never	56

Method Used to Obtain Current AMS Subscription	Frequency
Toll-free phone number	230
AMS website	106
Direct mail	46
Good Tunes & More	10
Other	26

Would Consider Discounted Trial Offer	Frequency
Yes	40
No	378

Trial Weekly Rate (\$) Willing to Pay (stored in AMS8)									
23.00	20.00	22.75	20.00	20.00	24.50	17.50	22.25	18.00	21.00
18.25	21.00	18.50	20.75	21.25	22.25	22.75	21.75	19.50	20.75
16.75	19.00	22.25	21.00	16.75	19.00	22.25	21.00	19.50	22.75
23.50	19.50	21.75	22.00	24.00	23.25	19.50	20.75	18.25	21.50

Uses Another Phone Service Provider	Frequency
Yes	354
No	64

Gold Card Leads to Two-Year Agreement	Frequency
Yes	38
No	380

EXERCISE

1. Analyze the results of the survey of Ashland households that receive AMS cable television service. Write a report that discusses the marketing implications of the survey results for Ashland MultiComm Services.

DIGITAL CASE

Apply your knowledge about confidence interval estimation in this Digital Case, which extends the OurCampus! Digital Case from Chapter 7.

Among its other features, the OurCampus! website allows customers to purchase OurCampus! LifeStyles merchandise online. To handle payment processing, the management of OurCampus! has contracted with the following firms:

- **PayAFriend (PAF)** This is an online payment system with which customers and businesses such as OurCampus! register in order to exchange payments in a secure and convenient manner, without the need for a credit card.
- **Continental Banking Company (Conbanco)** This processing services provider allows OurCampus! customers to pay for merchandise using nationally recognized credit cards issued by a financial institution.

To reduce costs, management is considering eliminating one of these two payment systems. However, Lorraine Hildick of the sales department suspects that customers use the two forms of payment in unequal numbers and that customers display different buying behaviors when using the two forms of payment. Therefore, she would like to first determine the following:

- The proportion of customers using PAF and the proportion of customers using a credit card to pay for their purchases.
- The mean purchase amount when using PAF and the mean purchase amount when using a credit card.

Assist Ms. Hildick by preparing an appropriate analysis. Open **PaymentsSample.pdf**, read Ms. Hildick's comments, and use her random sample of 50 transactions as the basis for your analysis. Summarize your findings to determine whether Ms. Hildick's conjectures about OurCampus! customer purchasing behaviors are correct. If you want the sampling error to be no more than \$3 when estimating the mean purchase amount, is Ms. Hildick's sample large enough to perform a valid analysis?

REFERENCES

1. Cochran, W. G., *Sampling Techniques*, 3rd ed. (New York: Wiley, 1977).
2. Fisher, R. A., and F. Yates, *Statistical Tables for Biological, Agricultural and Medical Research*, 5th ed. (Edinburgh: Oliver & Boyd, 1957).
3. Hahn, G., and W. Meeker, *Statistical Intervals, A Guide for Practitioners* (New York: John Wiley and Sons, Inc., 1991).
4. Kirk, R. E., ed., *Statistical Issues: A Reader for the Behavioral Sciences* (Belmont, CA: Wadsworth, 1972).
5. Larsen, R. L., and M. L. Marx, *An Introduction to Mathematical Statistics and Its Applications*, 4th ed. (Upper Saddle River, NJ: Prentice Hall, 2006).
6. *Microsoft Excel 2010* (Redmond, WA: Microsoft Corp., 2010).
7. *Minitab Release16* (State College, PA.: Minitab Inc., 2010).
8. Snedecor, G. W., and W. G. Cochran, *Statistical Methods*, 7th ed. (Ames, IA: Iowa State University Press, 1980).

APPENDIX 10.1

CALCULATOR LESSON 8

CASIO FX-9750GII CALCULATOR EXAMPLE 10.7

Lesson 8—Confidence Interval

1-Sample Z Interval (Using sample statistics)

A certain population is known to have a standard deviation of 4.0. A sample of 40 has been chosen and the mean is 9.7. Construct a 95% confidence interval estimate for the mean.

Solution: From the **Main Menu** select the following:

STAT   F4(INTR)   **F1**(Z)   **F1**(1-S). Then enter the following items:

(Note: Use the **EXE** key only after a new data entry. Otherwise, use the cursor ▼ arrow. If you accidentally hit the wrong key, use **AC/ON** or **EXIT** to go back.)

1-Sample ZInterval

Data	: **F2**(Var)	▼
C-Level	: .95	EXE
σ	: 4	EXE
$\bar{x}$	: 9.7	EXE
n	: 40	EXE
Save Res	: None(press **F1**)	

Now press **EXE** or **F1**(Calc).

The calculator will show the results:

1-Sample ZInterval

Left	=8.46040994
Right	=10.9395901
$\bar{x}$	=9.7
n	=40

As you can see, the 95% confidence interval estimate for the population mean is 8.46 to 10.94. The calculator will display the numerical result only; you must remember to write up the complete answer as shown in class.

EXAMPLE 10.8

1-Sample Z Interval (Using raw data)

A random survey of eight dry-cleaning outlets indicated that the amounts of GST collected from the outlets on the previous day were $70, $65, $76, $53, $75, $71, $59, and $67. Use this information to estimate the mean daily amount of GST collected by all dry-cleaning outlets if the amounts are known to be normally distributed, with a standard deviation of $5. Determine the 90% confidence interval estimate.

Solution:

First enter the data into **List 1**.

Now, from the **Main Menu** select the following:

STAT   F4(INTR)   **F1**(Z)   **F1**(1-S). Then enter the following items:

1-Sample ZInterval

Data	: F1(List)	▼
C-Level	: .90	EXE
σ	: 5	EXE
List	: List1	EXE (Press F1 and answer the question.)
Freq	: 1 (F1)	EXE Note: If the data given are a weighted data, then enter the weight values in a list–in that case, you would select list (F2).

Save Res   : None

Now press **EXE** or **F1**(Calc).

The calculator will show the results:

1-Sample ZInterval

Left	=64.0922821
Right	=69.9077179
$\bar{x}$	=67
sx	=9.13392421
n	=8

As you can see, the 90% confidence interval estimate for the population mean is $64.09 to $69.91. The calculator will display the numerical result only; you must remember to write up the complete answer as shown in class.

EXAMPLE 10.9   **1-Sample *t* Interval** (Using sample statistics)

Management at a bank wishes to estimate the mean amount of time customers spend at the automated teller machine (ATM). It believes the times to be normally distributed. A random sample of 20 customers has been selected and the sample mean time was 255 seconds, with a standard deviation of 33 seconds. Construct a 95% confidence interval estimate for the mean time at the ATM machine per customer.

Solution: From the **Main Menu** select the following:

STAT   F4(INTR)   **F2**(t)   **F1**(1-S). Then enter the following items:

(Note: Use the **EXE** key only after a new data entry. Otherwise, use the cursor ▼ arrow. If you accidentally hit the wrong key, use **AC/ON** or **EXIT** to go back.)

1-Sample tInterval

Data	: F2(Var)	▼
C-Level	: 0.95	EXE
$\bar{x}$	: 255	EXE
sx	: 33	EXE
n	: 20	EXE
Save Res	: None	

Now press **EXE** or **F1**(Calc).

The calculator will show the results:

1-Sample tInterval

Left	=239.555525
Right	=270.444475
$\bar{x}$	=255
sx	=33
n	=20

As you can see, the 95% confidence interval estimate for the population mean is 240 to 270 seconds. The calculator will display the numerical result only; you must remember to write up the complete answer as shown in class.

EXAMPLE 10.10   **1-Sample *t* Interval** (Using raw data)

A random survey of eight dry-cleaning outlets indicated that the amounts of GST collected from the outlets on the previous day were $70, $65, $76, $53, $75, $71, $59, and $67. Use this information to estimate the mean daily amount of GST collected by all dry-cleaning outlets if the amounts are known to be normally distributed. Determine the 90% confidence interval estimate.

Solution:

First enter the data into **List 1**.

Now, from the **Main Menu** select the following:

STAT   F4(INTR)   **F2**(t)   **F1**(1-S). Then enter the following items:

1-Sample tInterval
Data	: **F1**(List)	▼
C-Level	: **0.90**	**EXE**
List	: **List1**	▼
Freq	: **1**	**EXE**
Save Res	: None	

Now press **EXE** or **F1**(Calc).

The calculator will show the results:

1-Sample tInterval
Left	=61.7257164
Right	=72.2742836
$\bar{x}$	=67
sx	=9.13392421
n	=8

As you can see, the 90% confidence interval estimate for the population mean is $60.88 to $73.12. The calculator will display the numerical result only; you must remember to write up the complete answer as shown in class.

EXAMPLE 10.11   **1-Proportion *Z* Interval**

A bank manager wants to estimate the proportion of all the bank's customers who use the ATM to pay bills. A random sample of 80 customers has been selected and it was found that 43 of those customers use the ATM to pay bills. Determine the 99% confidence interval estimate for the proportion of all the bank's customers who use the ATM to pay bills.

Solution: From the **Main Menu** select:

STAT   F4(INTR)   **F1**(Z)   **F3**(1-P). Then enter the following items:

1-Prop ZInterval
C-Level	: **0.99**	**EXE**
x	: **43**	**EXE**
n	: **80**	**EXE**
Save Res	: None	

Now press **EXE** or **F1**(Calc).

The calculator will show the results:

1-Prop ZInterval

Left	=0.39391231
Right	=0.68108768
$\hat{p}$	=0.5375
n	=80

As you can see, the 99% confidence interval estimate for the population proportion is 0.394 to 0.681. The calculator will display the numerical result only; you must remember to write up the complete answer as shown in class.

CHAPTER 10 EXCEL GUIDE

EG10.1 Confidence Interval Estimate for the Mean (σ Known)

PHStat2 Use **Estimate for the Mean, sigma known** to compute the confidence interval estimate for the mean when σ is known. For example, to compute the estimate for the Example 10.1 mean paper length problem on page 390, select **PHStat → Confidence Intervals → Estimate for the Mean, sigma known**. In the procedure's dialog box (shown below):

1. Enter **0.02** as the **Population Standard Deviation**.
2. Enter **95** as the **Confidence Level** percentage.
3. Click **Sample Statistics Known** and enter **100** as the **Sample Size** and **10.998** as the **Sample Mean**.
4. Enter a **Title** and click **OK**.

For problems that use unsummarized data, click **Sample Statistics Unknown** and enter the **Sample Cell Range** in step 3.

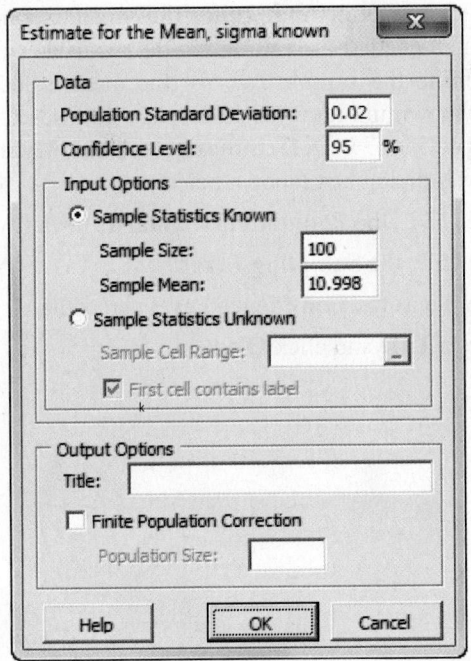

In-Depth Excel Use the **CONFIDENCE** worksheet function to compute the half-width of a confidence interval. Enter the function as **CONFIDENCE(1 – *confidence level*, *population standard deviation*, *sample size*)**.

Use the **COMPUTE worksheet** of the **CIE sigma known workbook** as a template for computing confidence interval estimates when σ is known. The worksheet also uses **NORMSINV(*cumulative percentage*)** to compute the Z value in cell B11 for one-half of the $(1 - \alpha)$ value.

The worksheet contains the data for the Example 10.1 mean paper length problem on page 390. To compute confidence interval estimates for other problems, change the **Population Standard Deviation, Sample Mean, Sample Size,** and **Confidence Level** values in cells B4 through B7, respectively. To examine all the formulas in the worksheet, open to the **COMPUTE_FORMULAS worksheet**.

EG10.2 Confidence Interval Estimate for the Mean (σ Unknown)

PHStat2 Use **Estimate for the Mean, sigma unknown** to compute the confidence interval estimate for the mean when σ is unknown. For example, to compute the Figure 10.7 estimate for the mean sales invoice amount (see page 397), select **PHStat → Confidence Intervals → Estimate for the Mean, sigma unknown**. In the procedure's dialog box (shown below):

1. Enter **95** as the **Confidence Level** percentage.
2. Click **Sample Statistics Known** and enter **100** as the **Sample Size, 110.27** as the **Sample Mean**, and **28.95** as the **Sample Std. Deviation**.
3. Enter a **Title** and click **OK**.

For problems that use unsummarized data, click **Sample Statistics Unknown** and enter the **Sample Cell Range** in step 2.

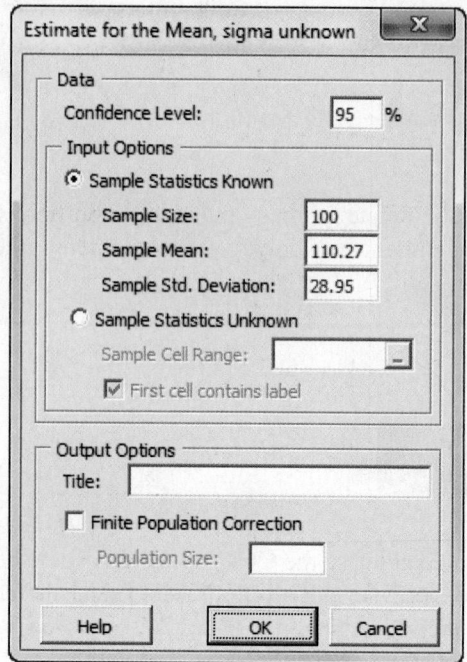

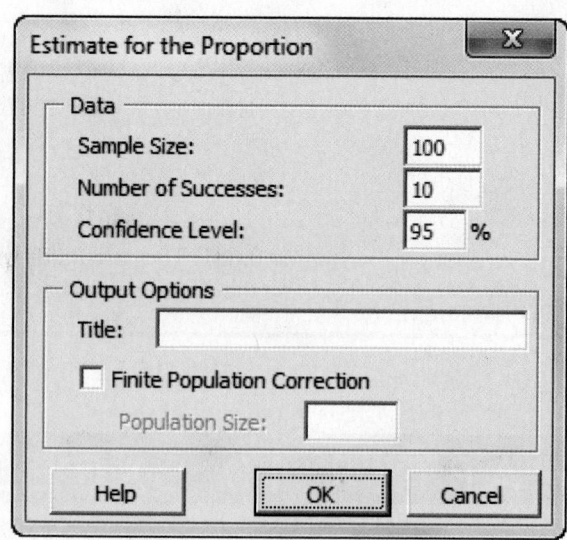

In-Depth Excel Use the **COMPUTE worksheet** of the **CIE sigma unknown workbook**, shown in Figure 10.7 on page 397, as a template for computing confidence interval estimates when σ is unknown. The worksheet contains the data for the Section 10.2 example for estimating the mean sales invoice amount. In cell B12, the worksheet uses **TINV(1 – *confidence level*, *degrees of freedom*)** to determine the critical value from the *t* distribution.

To compute confidence interval estimates for other problems, change the **Sample Standard Deviation**, **Sample Mean**, **Sample Size**, and **Confidence Level** values in cells B4 through B7, respectively.

EG10.3 Confidence Interval Estimate for the Proportion

PHStat2 Use **Estimate for the Proportion** to compute the confidence interval estimate for the proportion. For example, to compute the Figure 10.12 estimate for the proportion of in-error sales invoices (see page 404), select **PHStat →Confidence Intervals → Estimate for the Proportion**. In the procedure's dialog box (shown below):

1. Enter **100** as the **Sample Size**.
2. Enter **10** as the **Number of Successes**.
3. Enter **95** as the **Confidence Level** percentage.
4. Enter a **Title** and click **OK**.

In-Depth Excel Use the **COMPUTE worksheet** of the **CIE Proportion workbook**, shown in Figure 10.12 on page 404, as a template for computing confidence interval estimates for the proportion. The worksheet contains the data for the Figure 10.12 estimate for the proportion of in-error sales invoices. In cell B10, the worksheet uses **NORMSINV((1 – *confidence level*) / 2)** to compute the *Z* value and, in cell B11, uses **SQRT(*sample proportion* * (1 – *sample proportion*) / *sample size*)** to compute the standard error of the proportion.

To compute confidence interval estimates for other problems, change the **Sample Size**, **Number of Successes**, and **Confidence Level** values in cells B4 through B6.

EG10.4 Determining Sample Size

Sample Size Determination for the Mean

PHStat2 Use **Determination for the Mean** to compute the sample size needed for estimating the mean. For example, to determine the sample size for the mean sales invoice amount, shown in Figure 10.13 on page 408, select **PHStat → Sample Size → Determination for the Mean.** In the procedure's dialog box (shown below):

1. Enter **25** as the **Population Standard Deviation**.
2. Enter **5** as the **Sampling Error**.
3. Enter **95** as the **Confidence Level** percentage.
4. Enter a **Title** and click **OK**.

In-Depth Excel Use the **COMPUTE worksheet** of the **Sample Size Mean workbook**, shown in Figure 10.13 on page 408, as a template for determining the sample size needed for estimating the mean. The worksheet contains the data for the Section 10.4 mean sales invoice amount problem. In cell B9, the worksheet uses **NORMSINV((1 – confidence level) / 2)** to compute the Z value and, in cell B13, uses **ROUNDUP(calculated sample size, 0)** to round up the calculated sample size to the next higher integer. To compute confidence interval estimates for other problems, change the **Population Standard Deviation**, **Sampling Error**, and **Confidence Level** values in cells B4 through B6.

Sample Size Determination for the Proportion

PHStat2 Use **Determination for the Proportion** to compute the sample size needed for estimating the proportion. For example, to determine the sample size for the proportion of in-error sales invoices, shown in Figure 10.14 on page 410, select **PHStat → Sample Size → Determination for the Proportion**. In the procedure's dialog box (shown below):

1. Enter **0.15** as the **Estimate of True Proportion**.
2. Enter **0.07** as the **Sampling Error**.
3. Enter **95** as the **Confidence Level** percentage.
4. Enter a **Title** and click **OK**.

In-Depth Excel Use the **NORMSINV** and **ROUNDUP** functions to help determine the sample size needed for estimating the proportion. Enter **NORMSINV((1 – confidence level) / 2)** to compute the Z value and enter **ROUNDUP(calculated sample size, 0)** to round up the calculated sample size to the next higher integer.

Use the **COMPUTE worksheet** of the **Sample Size Proportion workbook**, shown in Figure 10.14 on page 410, as a template for determining the sample size needed for estimating the proportion. The worksheet contains the data for the Section 10.4 in-error sales invoice problem. The worksheet uses the **NORMSINV** and **ROUNDUP** functions in the same way as discussed in the "Sample Size Determination for the Mean" *In-Depth Excel* instructions. To compute confidence interval estimates for other problems, change the **Estimate of True Proportion**, **Sampling Error**, and **Confidence Level** in cells B4 through B6.

11 Fundamentals of Hypothesis Testing: One-Sample Tests

Learning Objectives

In this chapter, you learn:

- The basic principles of hypothesis testing
- How to use hypothesis testing to test a mean or proportion
- The assumptions of each hypothesis-testing procedure, how to evaluate them, and the consequences if they are seriously violated
- How to avoid the pitfalls involved in hypothesis testing
- Ethical issues involved in hypothesis testing

USING STATISTICS

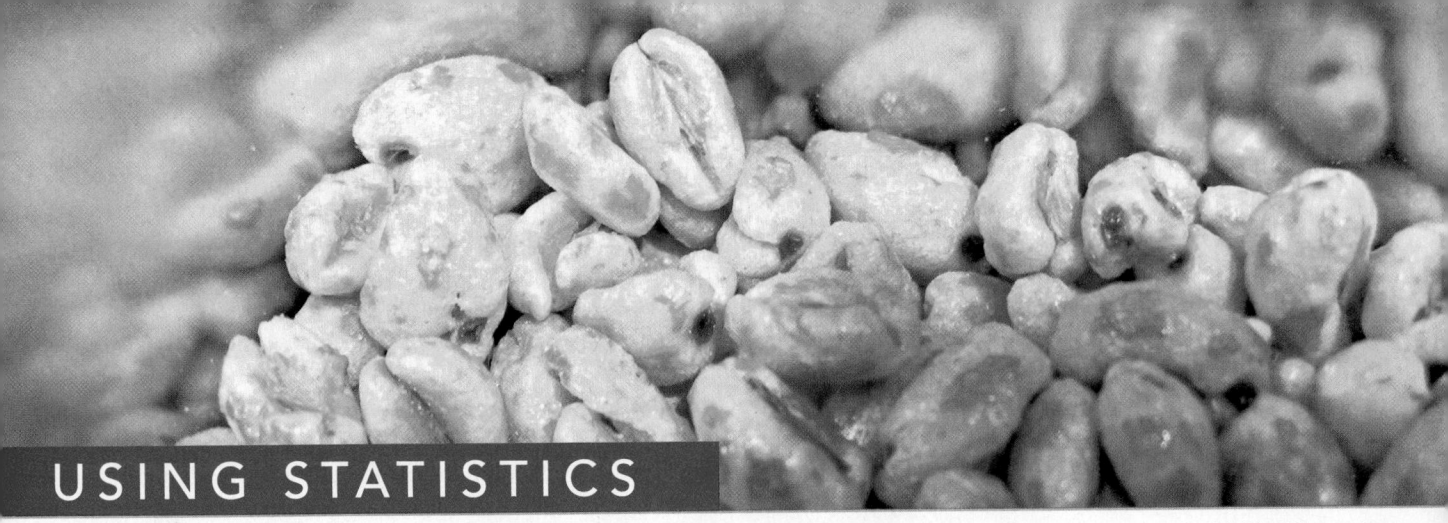

Maja Schon / Shutterstock.com

@ Oxford Cereals, Part II

As in Chapter 8, you again find yourself as plant operations manager for Oxford Cereals. You are responsible for monitoring the amount in each cereal box filled. Company specifications require a mean weight of 368 grams per box. It is your responsibility to adjust the process when the mean fill weight in the population of boxes differs from 368 grams. How can you make the decision about whether to adjust the process when you are unable to weigh every single box as it is being filled? You begin by selecting and weighing a random sample of 25 cereal boxes. After computing the sample mean, how do you proceed?

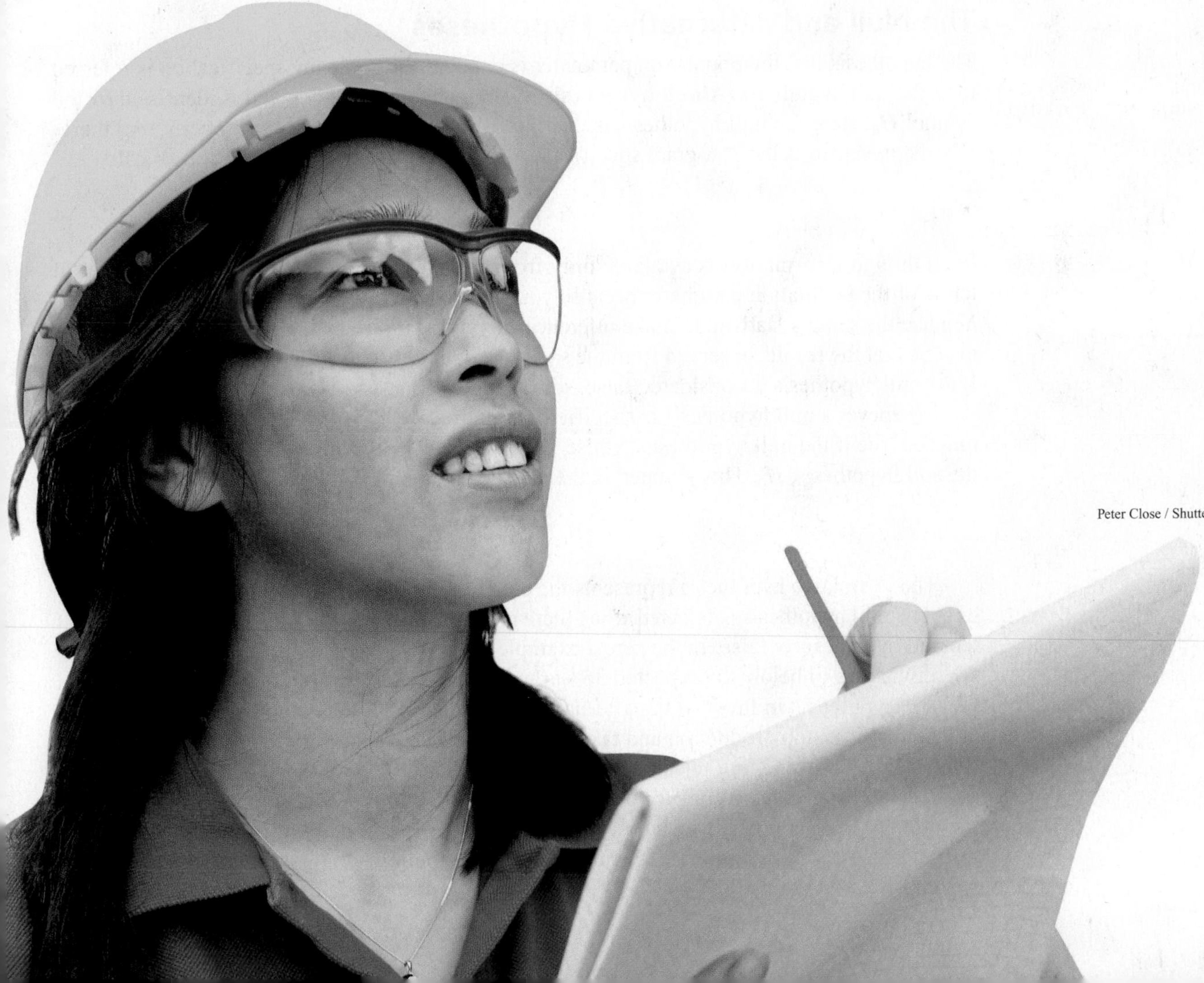

Peter Close / Shutterstock.com

I n Chapter 8, you learned methods to determine whether the value of a sample mean is consistent with a known population mean. In this Oxford Cereals scenario, you want to use a sample mean to validate a claim about the population mean, a somewhat different problem. For this type of problem, you use an inferential method called **hypothesis testing**. Hypothesis testing requires that you state a claim unambiguously. In this scenario, the claim is that the population mean is 368 grams. You examine a sample statistic to see if it better supports the stated claim, called the *null hypothesis*, or the mutually exclusive alternative hypothesis (for this scenario, that the population mean is not 368 grams).

In this chapter, you will learn several applications of hypothesis testing. You will learn how to make inferences about a population parameter by *analyzing differences* between the results observed, the sample statistic, and the results you would expect to get if an underlying hypothesis were actually true. For the Oxford Cereals scenario, hypothesis testing allows you to infer one of the following:

- The mean weight of the cereal boxes in the sample is a value consistent with what you would expect if the mean of the entire population of cereal boxes is 368 grams.
- The population mean is not equal to 368 grams because the sample mean is significantly different from 368 grams.

11.1 Fundamentals of Hypothesis-Testing Methodology

Hypothesis testing typically begins with a theory, a claim, or an assertion about a particular parameter of a population. For example, your initial hypothesis in the cereal example is that the process is working properly, so the mean fill is 368 grams, and no corrective action is needed.

The Null and Alternative Hypotheses

The hypothesis that the population parameter is equal to the company specification is referred to as the null hypothesis. A **null hypothesis** is often one of status quo and is identified by the symbol H_0. Here the null hypothesis is that the filling process is working properly, and therefore the mean fill is the 368-gram specification provided by Oxford Cereals. This is stated as

$$H_0 : \mu = 368$$

Even though information is available only from the sample, the null hypothesis is stated in terms of the population parameter because your focus is on the population of all cereal boxes. You use the sample statistic to make inferences about the entire filling process. One inference may be that the results observed from the sample data indicate that the null hypothesis is false. If the null hypothesis is considered false, something else must be true.

Whenever a null hypothesis is specified, an alternative hypothesis is also specified, and it must be true if the null hypothesis is false. The **alternative hypothesis, H_1**, is the opposite of the null hypothesis, H_0. This is stated in the cereal example as

$$H_1 : \mu \neq 368$$

The alternative hypothesis represents the conclusion reached by rejecting the null hypothesis. The null hypothesis is rejected when there is sufficient evidence from the sample data that the null hypothesis is false. In the cereal example, if the weights of the sampled boxes are sufficiently above or below the expected 368-gram mean specified by Oxford Cereals, you reject the null hypothesis in favor of the alternative hypothesis that the mean fill is different from 368 grams. You stop production and take whatever action is necessary to correct the problem. If the null hypothesis is not rejected, you should continue to believe that the process is working correctly and therefore no corrective action is necessary. In this second circumstance, you have not proven that the process is working correctly. Rather, you have failed to prove that it is working incorrectly, and therefore you continue your belief (although unproven) in the null hypothesis.

In hypothesis testing, you reject the null hypothesis when the sample evidence suggests that it is far more likely that the alternative hypothesis is true. However, failure to reject the null hypothesis is not proof that it is true. You can never prove that the null hypothesis is correct because the decision is based only on the sample information, not on the entire population. Therefore, if you fail to reject the null hypothesis, you can only conclude that there is insufficient evidence to warrant its rejection. The following key points summarize the null and alternative hypotheses:

- The null hypothesis, H_0, represents the current belief in a situation.
- The alternative hypothesis, H_1, is the opposite of the null hypothesis and represents a research claim or specific inference you would like to prove.
- If you reject the null hypothesis, you have statistical proof that the alternative hypothesis is correct.
- If you do not reject the null hypothesis, you have failed to prove the alternative hypothesis. The failure to prove the alternative hypothesis, however, does not mean that you have proven the null hypothesis.
- The null hypothesis, H_0, always refers to a specified value of the population parameter (such as μ), not a sample statistic (such as $\overline{X}$).
- The statement of the null hypothesis always contains an equal sign regarding the specified value of the population parameter (e.g., $H_0 : \mu = 368$ grams).
- The statement of the alternative hypothesis never contains an equal sign regarding the specified value of the population parameter (e.g., $H_1 : \mu \neq 368$ grams).

EXAMPLE 11.1

The Null and Alternative Hypotheses

You are the manager of a fast-food restaurant. You want to determine whether the waiting time to place an order has changed in the past month from its previous population mean value of 4.5 minutes. State the null and alternative hypotheses.

SOLUTION The null hypothesis is that the population mean has not changed from its previous value of 4.5 minutes. This is stated as

$$H_0 : \mu = 4.5$$

The alternative hypothesis is the opposite of the null hypothesis. Because the null hypothesis is that the population mean is 4.5 minutes, the alternative hypothesis is that the population mean is not 4.5 minutes. This is stated as

$$H_1 : \mu \neq 4.5$$

The Critical Value of the Test Statistic

The logic of hypothesis testing involves determining how likely the null hypothesis is to be true by considering the data collected in a sample. In the Oxford Cereal Company scenario, the null hypothesis is that the mean amount of cereal per box in the entire filling process is 368 grams (the population parameter specified by the company). You select a sample of boxes from the filling process, weigh each box, and compute the sample mean. This statistic is an estimate of the corresponding parameter (the population mean, μ). Even if the null hypothesis is true, the statistic (the sample mean, $\overline{X}$) is likely to differ from the value of the parameter (the population mean, μ) because of variation due to sampling. However, you expect the sample statistic to be close to the population parameter if the null hypothesis is true. If the sample statistic is close to the population parameter, you have insufficient evidence to reject the null hypothesis. For example, if the sample mean is 367.9, you might conclude that the population mean has not changed (i.e., $\mu = 368$) because a sample mean of 367.9 is very close to the hypothesized value of 368. Intuitively, you think that it is likely that you could get a sample mean of 367.9 from a population whose mean is 368.

However, if there is a large difference between the value of the statistic and the hypothesized value of the population parameter, you might conclude that the null hypothesis is false. For example, if the sample mean is 320, you might conclude that the population mean is not 368 (i.e., $\mu \neq 368$) because the sample mean is very far from the hypothesized value of 368.

In such a case, you conclude that it is very unlikely to get a sample mean of 320 if the population mean is really 368. Therefore, it is more logical to conclude that the population mean is not equal to 368. Here you reject the null hypothesis.

However, the decision-making process is not always so clear-cut. Determining what is "very close" and what is "very different" is arbitrary without clear definitions. Hypothesis-testing methodology provides clear definitions for evaluating differences. Furthermore, it enables you to quantify the decision-making process by computing the probability of getting a certain sample result if the null hypothesis is true. You calculate this probability by determining the sampling distribution for the sample statistic of interest (e.g., the sample mean) and then computing the particular **test statistic** based on the given sample result. Because the sampling distribution for the test statistic often follows a well-known statistical distribution, such as the standardized normal distribution or t distribution, you can use these distributions to help determine whether the null hypothesis is true.

Regions of Rejection and Nonrejection

The sampling distribution of the test statistic is divided into two regions, a **region of rejection** (sometimes called the critical region) and a **region of nonrejection** (see Figure 11.1). If the test statistic falls into the region of nonrejection, you do not reject the null hypothesis. In the Oxford Cereals scenario, you conclude that there is insufficient evidence that the population mean fill is different from 368 grams. If the test statistic falls into the rejection region, you reject the null hypothesis. In this case, you conclude that the population mean is not 368 grams.

FIGURE 11.1

Regions of rejection and nonrejection in hypothesis testing

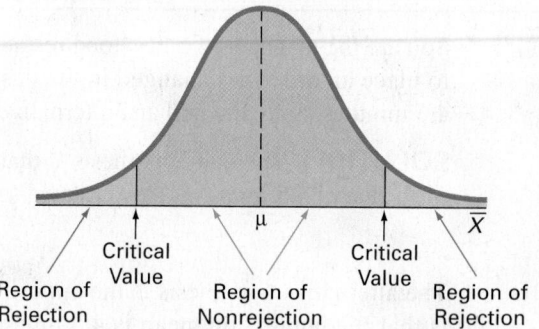

The region of rejection consists of the values of the test statistic that are unlikely to occur if the null hypothesis is true. These values are much more likely to occur if the null hypothesis is false. Therefore, if a value of the test statistic falls into this rejection region, you reject the null hypothesis because that value is unlikely if the null hypothesis is true.

To make a decision concerning the null hypothesis, you first determine the **critical value** of the test statistic. The critical value divides the nonrejection region from the rejection region. Determining the critical value depends on the size of the rejection region. The size of the rejection region is directly related to the risks involved in using only sample evidence to make decisions about a population parameter.

Risks in Decision Making Using Hypothesis Testing

Using hypothesis testing involves the risk of reaching an incorrect conclusion. You might wrongly reject a true null hypothesis, H_0, or, conversely, you might wrongly *not* reject a false null hypothesis, H_0. These types of risk are called Type I and Type II errors.

TYPE I AND TYPE II ERRORS

A **Type I error** occurs if you reject the null hypothesis, H_0, when it is true and should not be rejected. A Type I error is a "false alarm." The probability of a Type I error occurring is α. A **Type II error** occurs if you do not reject the null hypothesis, H_0, when it is false and should be rejected. A Type II error represents a "missed opportunity" to take some corrective action. The probability of a Type II error occurring is β.

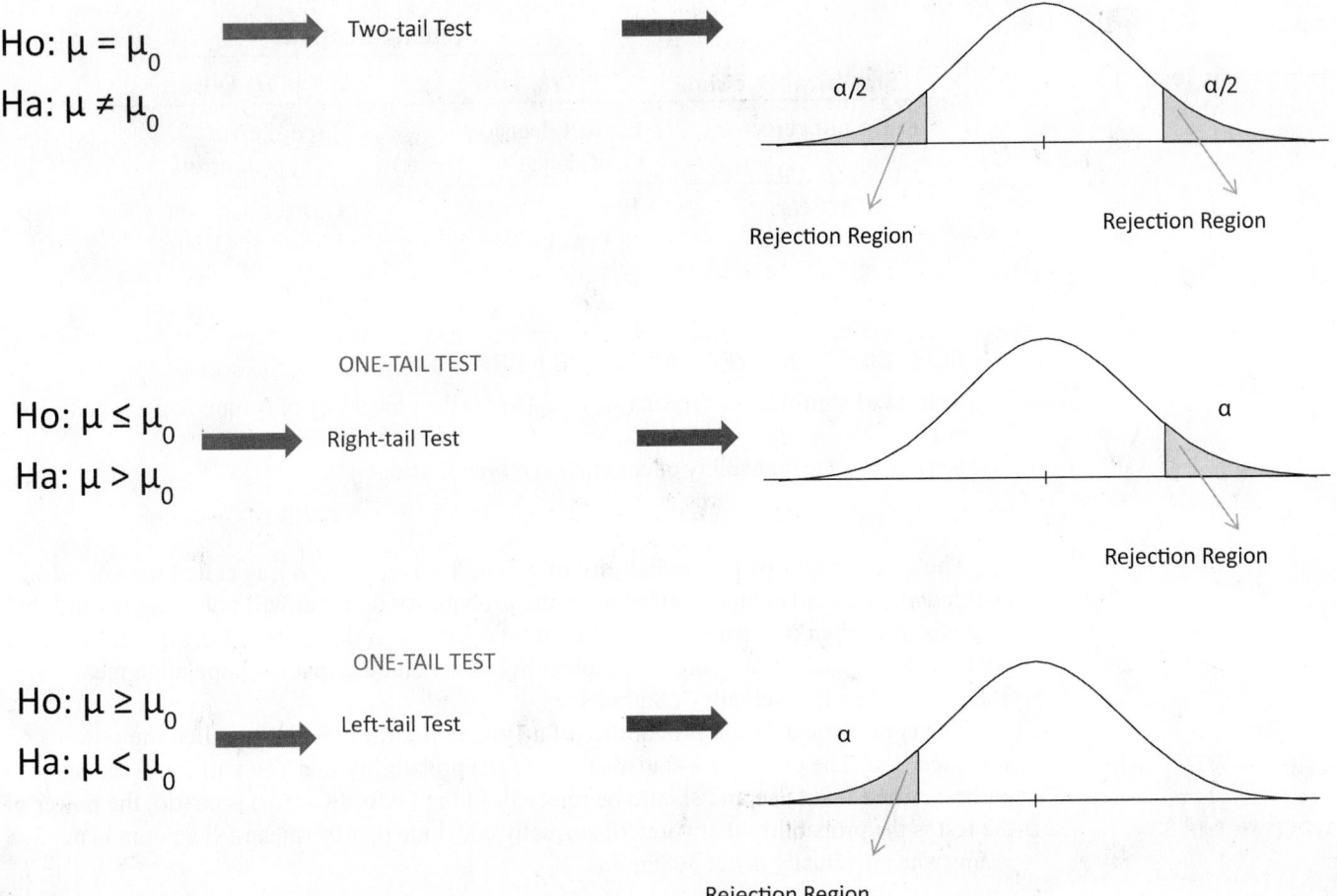

$H_0: \mu = \mu_0$
$H_a: \mu \neq \mu_0$

Two-tail Test

$\alpha/2$ $\alpha/2$

Rejection Region   Rejection Region

ONE-TAIL TEST

$H_0: \mu \leq \mu_0$
$H_a: \mu > \mu_0$

Right-tail Test

α

Rejection Region

ONE-TAIL TEST

$H_0: \mu \geq \mu_0$
$H_a: \mu < \mu_0$

Left-tail Test

α

Rejection Region

In the Oxford Cereals scenario, you would make a Type I error if you concluded that the population mean fill is *not* 368 when it *is* 368. This error causes you to needlessly adjust the filling process (the "false alarm") even though the process is working properly. In the same scenario, you would make a Type II error if you concluded that the population mean fill *is* 368 when it is *not* 368. In this case, you would allow the process to continue without adjustment, even though an adjustment is needed (the "missed opportunity").

Traditionally, you control the Type I error by determining the risk level, α (the lowercase Greek letter *alpha*) that you are willing to have of rejecting the null hypothesis when it is true. This risk, or probability, of committing a Type I error is called the *level of significance* (α). Because you specify the level of significance before you perform the hypothesis test, you directly control the risk of committing a Type I error. Traditionally, you select a level of 0.01, 0.05, or 0.10. The choice of a particular risk level for making a Type I error depends on the cost of making a Type I error. After you specify the value for α, you can then determine the critical values that divide the rejection and nonrejection regions. You know the size of the rejection region because α is the probability of rejection when the null hypothesis is true. From this, you can then determine the critical value or values that divide the rejection and nonrejection regions.

The probability of committing a Type II error is called the β *risk*. Unlike a Type I error, which you control through the selection of α, the probability of making a Type II error depends on the difference between the hypothesized and actual values of the population parameter. Because large differences are easier to find than small ones, if the difference between the hypothesized and actual value of the population parameter is large, β is small. For example, if the population mean is 330 grams, there is a small chance (β) that you will conclude that the mean has not changed from 368. However, if the difference between the hypothesized and actual value of the parameter is small, β is large. For example, if the population mean is actually 367 grams, there is a large chance (β) that you will conclude that the mean is still 368 grams.

TABLE 11.1

Hypothesis Testing and
Decision Making

	Actual Situation	
Statistical Decision	**H_0 True**	**H_0 False**
Do not reject H_0	Correct decision Confidence $= (1 - \alpha)$	Type II error $P(\text{Type II error}) = \beta$
Reject H_0	Type I error $P(\text{Type I error}) = \alpha$	Correct decision Power $= (1 - \beta)$

PROBABILITY OF TYPE I AND TYPE II ERRORS

The **level of significance (α)** of a statistical test is the probability of committing a Type I error.

The **β risk** is the probability of committing a Type II error.

The complement of the probability of a Type I error, $(1 - \alpha)$, is called the *confidence coefficient*. The confidence coefficient is the probability that you will not reject the null hypothesis, H_0, when it is true and should not be rejected. In the Oxford Cereals scenario, the confidence coefficient measures the probability of concluding that the population mean fill is 368 grams when it is actually 368 grams.

The complement of the probability of a Type II error, $(1 - \beta)$, is called the *power of a statistical test*. The power of a statistical test is the probability that you will reject the null hypothesis when it is false and should be rejected. In the Oxford Cereals scenario, the power of the test is the probability that you will correctly conclude that the mean fill amount is not 368 grams when it actually is not 368 grams.

COMPLEMENTS OF TYPE I AND TYPE II ERRORS

The **confidence coefficient**, $(1 - \alpha)$, is the probability that you will not reject the null hypothesis, H_0, when it is true and should not be rejected.

The **power of a statistical test**, $(1 - \beta)$, is the probability that you will reject the null hypothesis when it is false and should be rejected.

Risks in Decision Making: A Delicate Balance Table 11.1 illustrates the results of the two possible decisions (do not reject H_0 or reject H_0) that you can make in any hypothesis test. You can make a correct decision or make one of two types of errors.

One way to reduce the probability of making a Type II error is by increasing the sample size. Large samples generally permit you to detect even very small differences between the hypothesized values and the actual population parameters. For a given level of α, increasing the sample size decreases β and therefore increases the power of the statistical test to detect that the null hypothesis, H_0, is false.

However, there is always a limit to your resources, and this affects the decision of how large a sample you can select. For any given sample size, you must consider the trade-offs between the two possible types of errors. Because you can directly control the risk of Type I error, you can reduce this risk by selecting a smaller value for α. For example, if the negative consequences associated with making a Type I error are substantial, you could select $\alpha = 0.01$ instead of 0.05. However, when you decrease α, you increase β, so reducing the risk of a Type I error results in an increased risk of a Type II error. However, to reduce β, you could select a larger value for α. Therefore, if it is important to try to avoid a Type II error, you can select α of 0.05 or 0.10 instead of 0.01.

In the Oxford Cereals scenario, the risk of a Type I error occurring involves concluding that the mean fill amount has changed from the hypothesized 368 grams when it actually has not changed. The risk of a Type II error occurring involves concluding that the mean fill amount has not changed from the hypothesized 368 grams when it actually has changed. The

Flow chart for hypothesis test of one population parameter

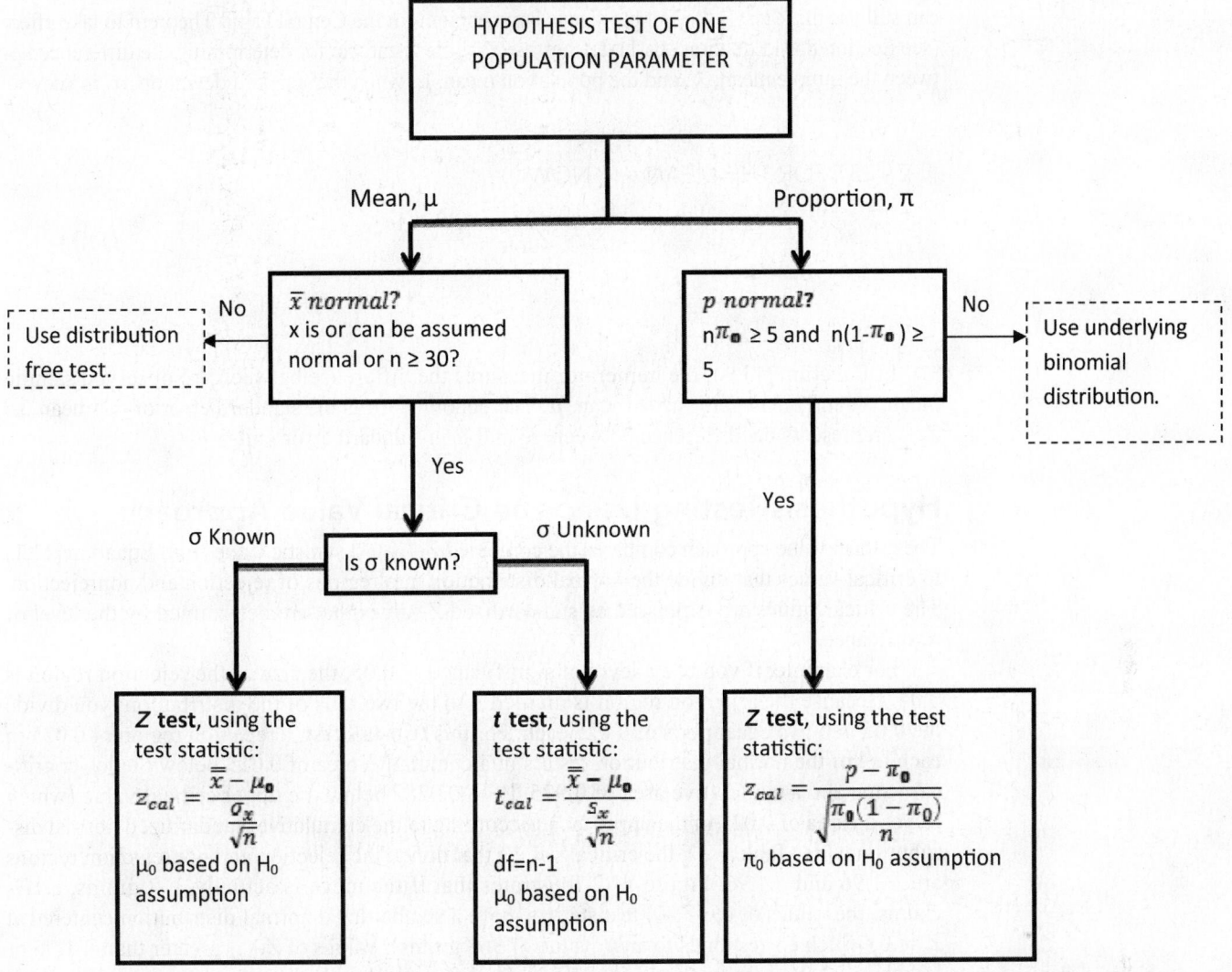

choice of reasonable values for α and β depends on the costs inherent in each type of error. For example, if it is very costly to change the cereal-filling process, you would want to be very confident that a change is needed before making any changes. In this case, the risk of a Type I error occurring is more important, and you would choose a small α. However, if you want to be very certain of detecting changes from a mean of 368 grams, the risk of a Type II error occurring is more important, and you would choose a higher level of α.

11.2 *Z* Test of Hypothesis for the Mean (σ Known)

Now that you have been introduced to hypothesis testing, recall that in the Using Statistics scenario on page 427, the business problem facing Oxford Cereals is to determine whether the cereal-filling process is working properly (i.e., whether the mean fill throughout the entire packaging process remains at the specified 368 grams, and no corrective action is needed). To evaluate the 368-gram requirement, you select a random sample of 25 boxes, weigh each box, compute the sample mean, $\overline{X}$, and then evaluate the difference between this sample statistic and the hypothesized population parameter by comparing the sample mean weight (in grams) to the expected population mean of 368 grams specified by the company. The null and alternative hypotheses are

$$H_0 : \mu = 368$$
$$H_1 : \mu \neq 368$$

When the standard deviation, σ, is known (which rarely occurs), you use the **Z test for the mean** if the population is normally distributed. If the population is not normally distributed, you can still use the Z test if the sample size is large enough for the Central Limit Theorem to take effect (see Section 8.4). Equation (11.1) defines the Z_{STAT} test statistic for determining the difference between the sample mean, $\overline{X}$, and the population mean, μ, when the standard deviation, σ, is known.

Z TEST FOR THE MEAN (σ KNOWN)

$$Z_{STAT} = \frac{\overline{X} - \mu}{\dfrac{\sigma}{\sqrt{n}}}$$

(11.1)

In Equation (11.1), the numerator measures the difference between the observed sample mean, $\overline{X}$, and the hypothesized mean, μ. The denominator is the standard error of the mean, so Z_{STAT} represents the difference between $\overline{X}$ and μ in standard error units.

Hypothesis Testing Using the Critical Value Approach

The critical value approach compares the computed Z_{STAT} test statistic value from Equation (11.1) to critical values that divide the normal distribution into regions of rejection and nonrejection. The critical values are expressed as standardized Z values that are determined by the level of significance.

For example, if you use a level of significance of 0.05, the size of the rejection region is 0.05. Because the rejection region is divided into the two tails of the distribution, you divide the 0.05 into two equal parts of 0.025 each. For this **two-tail test**, a rejection region of 0.025 in each tail of the normal distribution results in a cumulative area of 0.025 below the lower critical value and a cumulative area of $0.975 \, [1 - 0.025]$ below the upper critical value (which leaves an area of 0.025 in the upper tail). According to the cumulative standardized normal distribution table (Table E.2), the critical values that divide the rejection and nonrejection regions are -1.96 and $+1.96$. Figure 11.2 illustrates that if the mean is actually 368 grams, as H_0 claims, the values of the Z_{STAT} test statistic have a standardized normal distribution centered at $Z = 0$ (which corresponds to an $\overline{X}$ value of 368 grams). Values of Z_{STAT} greater than $+1.96$ or less than -1.96 indicate that $\overline{X}$ is sufficiently different from the hypothesized $\mu = 368$ that it is unlikely that such an $\overline{X}$ value would occur if H_0 were true.

FIGURE 11.2

Testing a hypothesis about the mean (σ known) at the 0.05 level of significance

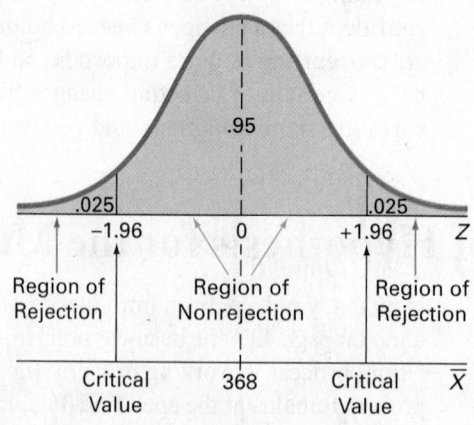

Therefore, the decision rule is

Reject H_0 if $Z_{STAT} > +1.96$

or if $Z_{STAT} < -1.96$;

otherwise, do not reject H_0.

Suppose that the sample of 25 cereal boxes indicates a sample mean, $\overline{X}$, of 372.5 grams, and the population standard deviation, σ, is 15 grams. Using Equation (11.1) on page 434,

$$Z_{STAT} = \frac{\overline{X} - \mu}{\dfrac{\sigma}{\sqrt{n}}} = \frac{372.5 - 368}{\dfrac{15}{\sqrt{25}}} = +1.50$$

Because $Z_{STAT} = +1.50$ is between -1.96 and $+1.96$, you do not reject H_0 (see Figure 11.3). You continue to believe that the mean fill amount is 368 grams. To take into account the possibility of a Type II error, you state the conclusion as "there is insufficient evidence that the mean fill is different from 368 grams."

Exhibit 11.1 summarizes the critical value approach to hypothesis testing. Steps 1 though 4 correspond to the Define task, step 5 combines the Collect and Organize tasks, and step 6 corresponds to the Visualize and Analyze tasks of the business problem-solving methodology.

FIGURE 11.3

Testing a hypothesis about the mean cereal weight (σ known) at the 0.05 level of significance

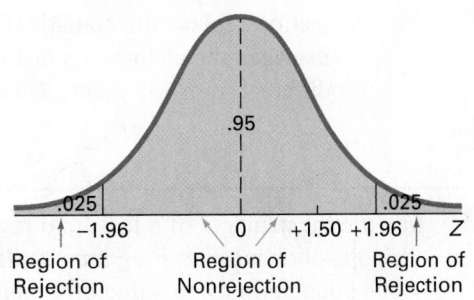

EXHIBIT 11.1 THE CRITICAL VALUE APPROACH TO HYPOTHESIS TESTING

1. State the null hypothesis, H_0, and the alternative hypothesis, H_1.
2. Choose the level of significance, α, and the sample size, n. The level of significance is based on the relative importance of the risks of committing Type I and Type II errors in the problem.
3. Determine the appropriate test statistic and sampling distribution.
4. Determine the critical values that divide the rejection and nonrejection regions.
5. Collect the sample data, organize the results, and compute the value of the test statistic.
6. Make the statistical decision and state the managerial conclusion. If the test statistic falls into the nonrejection region, you do not reject the null hypothesis. If the test statistic falls into the rejection region, you reject the null hypothesis. The managerial conclusion is written in the context of the real-world problem.

EXAMPLE 11.2

Applying the Critical Value Approach to Hypothesis Testing at Oxford Cereals

State the critical value approach to hypothesis testing at Oxford Cereals.

SOLUTION

Step 1: State the null and alternative hypotheses. The null hypothesis, H_0, is always stated as a mathematical expression, using population parameters. In testing whether the mean fill is 368 grams, the null hypothesis states that μ equals 368. The alternative hypothesis, H_1, is also stated as a mathematical expression, using population parameters. Therefore, the alternative hypothesis states that μ is not equal to 368 grams.

Step 2: Choose the level of significance and the sample size. You choose the level of significance, α, according to the relative importance of the risks of committing Type I and Type II errors in the problem. The smaller the value of α, the less risk there is of making a Type I error. In this example, making a Type I error means that you conclude that the population mean is not 368 grams when it is 368 grams. Thus, you will take corrective action on the filling process even though the process is working properly. Here, $\alpha = 0.05$ is selected. The sample size, n, is 25.

Step 3: Select the appropriate test statistic. Because σ is known from information about the filling process, you use the normal distribution and the Z_{STAT} test statistic.

Step 4: Determine the rejection region. Critical values for the appropriate test statistic are selected so that the rejection region contains a total area of α when H_0 is true and the nonrejection region contains a total area of $1 - \alpha$ when H_0 is true. Because $\alpha = 0.05$ in the cereal example, the critical values of the Z_{STAT} test statistic are -1.96 and $+1.96$. The rejection region is therefore $Z_{STAT} < -1.96$ or $Z_{STAT} > +1.96$. The nonrejection region is $-1.96 \leq Z_{STAT} \leq +1.96$.

Step 5: Collect the sample data and compute the value of the test statistic. In the cereal example, $\overline{X} = 372.5$, and the value of the test statistic is $Z_{STAT} = +1.50$.

Step 6: State the statistical decision and the managerial conclusion. First, determine whether the test statistic has fallen into the rejection region or the nonrejection region. For the cereal example, $Z_{STAT} = +1.50$ is in the region of nonrejection because $-1.96 \leq Z_{STAT} = +1.50 \leq +1.96$. Because the test statistic falls into the nonrejection region, the statistical decision is to not reject the null hypothesis, H_0. The managerial conclusion is that insufficient evidence exists to prove that the mean fill is different from 368 grams. No corrective action on the filling process is needed.

EXAMPLE 11.3

Testing and Rejecting a Null Hypothesis

You are the manager of a fast-food restaurant. The business problem is to determine whether the population mean waiting time to place an order has changed in the past month from its previous population mean value of 4.5 minutes. From past experience, you can assume that the population is normally distributed, with a population standard deviation of 1.2 minutes. You select a sample of 25 orders during a one-hour period. The sample mean is 5.1 minutes. Use the six-step approach listed in Exhibit 11.1 on page 435 to determine whether there is evidence at the 0.05 level of significance that the population mean waiting time to place an order has changed in the past month from its previous population mean value of 4.5 minutes.

SOLUTION

Step 1: The null hypothesis is that the population mean has not changed from its previous value of 4.5 minutes:

$$H_0 : \mu = 4.5$$

The alternative hypothesis is the opposite of the null hypothesis. Because the null hypothesis is that the population mean is 4.5 minutes, the alternative hypothesis is that the population mean is not 4.5 minutes:

$$H_1 : \mu \neq 4.5$$

Step 2: You have selected a sample of $n = 25$. The level of significance is 0.05 (i.e., $\alpha = 0.05$).

Step 3: Because σ is assumed known, you use the normal distribution and the Z_{STAT} test statistic.

Step 4: Because $\alpha = 0.05$, the critical values of the Z_{STAT} test statistic are -1.96 and $+1.96$. The rejection region is $Z_{STAT} < -1.96$ or $Z_{STAT} > +1.96$. The nonrejection region is $-1.96 \leq Z_{STAT} \leq +1.96$

Step 5: You collect the sample data and compute $\overline{X} = 5.1$. Using Equation (11.1) on page 434, you compute the test statistic:

$$Z_{STAT} = \frac{\overline{X} - \mu}{\dfrac{\sigma}{\sqrt{n}}} = \frac{5.1 - 4.5}{\dfrac{1.2}{\sqrt{25}}} = +2.50$$

Step 6: Because $Z_{STAT} = +2.50 > +1.96$, you reject the null hypothesis. You conclude that there is evidence that the population mean waiting time to place an order has changed from its previous value of 4.5 minutes. The mean waiting time for customers is longer now than it was last month. As the manager, you would now want to determine how waiting time could be reduced to improve service.

You can use the calculator to find the **z critical value** in **Step 4.**

Perform the following calculator instructions to obtain z critical value.

From the **Main Menu** select:

STAT F5 (DIST) **F1** (NORM) **F3**(InvN)   then enter the following items:

Inverse Normal

Data	: F2(Var)	▼	
Tail	: CNTR	EXE	**(Note: Since this is a two-tail test, select center area)**
Area	: **0.95**	EXE	**(Note: For the center area, take 1–α=1–0.05=0.95)**
σ	: **1**	EXE	
μ	; **0**		
Save Res	: None		

Execute

Now key **EXE** or **F1**(CALC)

The calculator will now show the results:

Inverse Normal
x_1Inv $= -1.959964$
x_2Inv $= 1.959964$

You can use the calculator to find the **test statistic, Z_{calc}** in **Step 5.**

Perform the following calculator instructions to obtain Z_{calc}.

From the **Main Menu** select:

STAT F3(TEST) **F1**(Z) **F1**(1-S)   then enter the following items:

1-Sample ZTest

Data	: F2(Var)		
μ	: $\neq \mu_0$	EXE	**(Note: The alternative hypothesis is $\mu \neq 4.5$)**
μ_0	: 4.5		
σ	: **1.2**	EXE	
$\bar{x}$	: **5.1**	EXE	
n	: **25**	EXE	
Save Res	: None		

Now key **EXE** or **F1**(Calc)

The calculator will now show the results:

1-Sample ZTest

μ	$\neq 4.5$	
z	$= 2.5$	**(Note: This is Z_{calc}=2.5)**
p	$= 0.01241933$	
$\bar{x}$	$= 5.1$	
n	$= 25$	

Hypothesis Testing Using the *p*-Value Approach

Using the *p*-value to determine rejection and nonrejection is another approach to hypothesis testing.

> ### *p*-VALUE
>
> The ***p*-value** is the probability of getting a test statistic equal to or more extreme than the sample result, given that the null hypothesis, H_0, is true. The *p*-value is also known as the *observed level of significance*.

The decision rules for rejecting H_0 in the *p*-value approach are

- If the *p*-value is greater than or equal to α, do not reject the null hypothesis.
- If the *p*-value is less than α, reject the null hypothesis.

Many people confuse these rules, mistakenly believing that a high p-value is reason for rejection. You can avoid this confusion by remembering the following:

> If the p-value is low, then H_0 must go.

To understand the p-value approach, consider the Oxford Cereals scenario. You tested whether the mean fill was equal to 368 grams. The test statistic resulted in a Z_{STAT} value of +1.50, and you did not reject the null hypothesis because +1.50 was less than the upper critical value of +1.96 and greater than the lower critical value of -1.96.

To use the p-value approach for the *two-tail test*, you find the probability of getting a test statistic Z_{STAT} that is equal to or *more extreme than* 1.50 standard error units from the center of a standardized normal distribution. In other words, you need to compute the probability of a Z_{STAT} value greater than +1.50, along with the probability of a Z_{STAT} value less than -1.50. Table E.2 shows that the probability of a Z_{STAT} value below -1.50 is 0.0668. The probability of a value below +1.50 is 0.9332, and the probability of a value above +1.50 is $1 - 0.9332 = 0.0668$. Therefore, the p-value for this two-tail test is $0.0668 + 0.0668 = 0.1336$ (see Figure 11.4). Thus, the probability of a test statistic equal to or more extreme than the sample result is 0.1336. Because 0.1336 is greater than $\alpha = 0.05$, you do not reject the null hypothesis.

FIGURE 11.4

Finding a p-value for a two-tail test

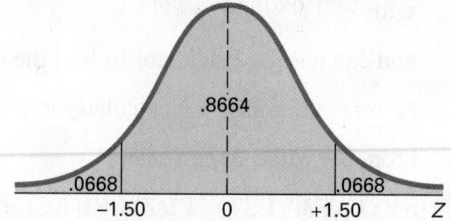

In this example, the observed sample mean is 372.5 grams, 4.5 grams above the hypothesized value, and the p-value is 0.1336. Thus, if the population mean is 368 grams, there is a 13.36% chance that the sample mean differs from 368 grams by at least 4.5 grams (i.e., is ≥ 372.5 grams or ≤ 363.5 grams). Therefore, even though 372.5 is above the hypothesized value of 368, a result as extreme as or more extreme than 372.5 is not highly unlikely when the population mean is 368.

Unless you are dealing with a test statistic that follows the normal distribution, you will only be able to approximate the p-value from the tables of the distribution. However, Excel and Minitab can compute the p-value for any hypothesis test, and this allows you to substitute the p-value approach for the critical value approach when you conduct hypothesis testing.

Figure 11.5 shows the results for the cereal-filling example discussed in this section, as computed by Excel and Minitab. These results include the Z_{STAT} test statistic and the critical values.

FIGURE 11.5

Casio Calculator FX-9750GII results for the cereal-fill example

Cereal-Filling Process Hypothesis Test

CALCULATOR SOLUTION

From the **Main Menu** select

STAT   F3(TEST)   **F1**(Z)   **F1**(1-S), and then enter the following items.

(**Note:** Only use the **EXE** key after a new entry. Otherwise, use the cursor ▼ arrow. If you accidentally hit the wrong key, use **AC/ON** or **EXIT** to go back.)

1-Sample ZTest

Data	: **F2**(Var)	▼
μ	: **F1**($\neq\mu$0)	▼
μ0	: **368**	**EXE**
σ	: **15**	**EXE**
$\bar{x}$	: **372.5**	**EXE**
n	: **25**	**EXE**
Save Res	: None	

Now press **EXE** or **F1**(CALC) or **F6**(DRAW).

If you select **F6**(DRAW), you will see a normal distribution.

If you select either **EXE** or **F1**(Calc), the calculator will show the following results:

1-Sample ZTest

μ	≠368
z	=1.5
p	=0.1336144
$\bar{x}$	=372.5
n	=25

Statistical Decision: Do not reject the null hypothesis because *p*-value is greater than $\alpha = 0.05$.

To find *Z* critical values:

From the **Main Menu** select

STAT   F5(dist)   **F1**(Norm)   **F3**(InvN), and then enter the following items.

Using calculator fx-9750GII

Inverse Normal

Data	: F2(Var)	▼
Tail	: F3(CNTR)	▼
Area	: 1–0.05	**EXE**
σ	: 1	**EXE**
μ	: 0	**EXE**
Save Res	: None	**EXE**

Now press **EXE** or **F1**(CALC).

The calculator will now show the following results:

Inverse Normal:
X_1 Inv = −1.959964
X_2 Inv = 1.95996398

Using calculator fx-9750G Plus

Inverse Normal

Area	: 0.05 ÷ 2	**EXE**
σ	: 1	**EXE**
μ	: 0	**EXE**

Now press **EXE** or **F1**(CALC).

The calculator will now show the following results:

Inverse Normal:
X = −1.959964
Note: For this model, when using the InvN function, the *Area* value that is required is the area to the *left* of the desired X value.

Exhibit 11.2 summarizes the *p*-value approach to hypothesis testing.

EXHIBIT 11.2 THE *p*-VALUE APPROACH TO HYPOTHESIS TESTING

1. State the null hypothesis, H_0, and the alternative hypothesis, H_1.
2. Choose the level of significance, α, and the sample size, *n*. The level of significance is based on the relative importance of the risks of committing Type I and Type II errors in the problem.
3. Determine the appropriate test statistic and the sampling distribution.
4. Collect the sample data, compute the value of the test statistic, and compute the *p*-value.
5. Make the statistical decision and state the managerial conclusion. If the *p*-value is greater than or equal to α, do not reject the null hypothesis. If the *p*-value is less than α, reject the null hypothesis. The managerial conclusion is written in the context of the real-world problem.

EXAMPLE 11.4

Testing and Rejecting a Null Hypothesis Using the *p*-Value Approach

You are the manager of a fast-food restaurant. The business problem is to determine whether the population mean waiting time to place an order has changed in the past month from its previous value of 4.5 minutes. From past experience, you can assume that the population standard deviation is 1.2 minutes and the population waiting time is normally distributed. You select a sample of 25 orders during a one-hour period. The sample mean is 5.1 minutes. Use the five-step *p*-value approach of Exhibit 11.2 to determine whether there is evidence that the population mean waiting time to place an order has changed in the past month from its previous population mean value of 4.5 minutes.

SOLUTION

Step 1: The null hypothesis is that the population mean has not changed from its previous value of 4.5 minutes:

$$H_0 : \mu = 4.5$$

The alternative hypothesis is the opposite of the null hypothesis. Because the null hypothesis is that the population mean is 4.5 minutes, the alternative hypothesis is that the population mean is not 4.5 minutes:

$$H_1 : \mu \neq 4.5$$

Step 2: You have selected a sample of $n = 25$, and you have chosen a 0.05 level of significance (i.e., $\alpha = 0.05$).

Step 3: Select the appropriate test statistic. Because σ is assumed known, you use the normal distribution and the Z_{STAT} test statistic.

Step 4: You collect the sample data and compute $\overline{X} = 5.1$. Using Equation (11.1) on page 438, you compute the test statistic as follows:

$$Z_{STAT} = \frac{\overline{X} - \mu}{\dfrac{\sigma}{\sqrt{n}}} = \frac{5.1 - 4.5}{\dfrac{1.2}{\sqrt{25}}} = +2.50$$

To find the probability of getting a Z_{STAT} test statistic that is equal to or more extreme than 2.50 standard error units from the center of a standardized normal distribution, you compute the probability of a Z_{STAT} value greater than +2.50 along with the probability of a Z_{STAT} value less than −2.50. From Table E.2, the probability of a Z_{STAT} value below −2.50 is 0.0062. The probability of a value below +2.50 is 0.9938. Therefore, the probability of a value above +2.50 is $1 - 0.9938 = 0.0062$. Thus, the *p*-value for this two-tail test is $0.0062 + 0.0062 = 0.0124$.

Step 5: Because the *p*-value $= 0.0124 < \alpha = 0.05$, you reject the null hypothesis. You conclude that there is evidence that the population mean waiting time to place an order has changed from its previous population mean value of 4.5 minutes. The mean waiting time for customers is longer now than it was last month.

A Connection Between Confidence Interval Estimation and Hypothesis Testing

This chapter and Chapter 10 discuss confidence interval estimation and hypothesis testing, the two major elements of statistical inference. Although confidence interval estimation and hypothesis testing share the same conceptual foundation, they are used for different purposes. In Chapter 10, confidence intervals estimated parameters. In this chapter, hypothesis testing makes decisions about specified values of population parameters. Hypothesis tests are used when trying to determine whether a parameter is less than, more than, or not equal to a specified value. Proper interpretation of a confidence interval, however, can also indicate whether a parameter is less than, more than, or not equal to a specified value. For example, in this section, you tested whether the population mean fill amount was different from 368 grams by using Equation (11.1) on page 434:

$$Z_{STAT} = \frac{\overline{X} - \mu}{\dfrac{\sigma}{\sqrt{n}}}$$

Instead of testing the null hypothesis that $\mu = 368$ grams, you can reach the same conclusion by constructing a confidence interval estimate of μ. If the hypothesized value of $\mu = 368$ is contained within the interval, you do not reject the null hypothesis because 368 would not be considered an unusual value. However, if the hypothesized value does not fall into the interval, you reject the null hypothesis because $\mu = 368$ grams is then considered an unusual value. Using Equation (10.1) on page 388 and the following data:

$$n = 25, \overline{X} = 372.5 \text{ grams}, \sigma = 15 \text{ grams}$$

for a confidence level of 95% (i.e., $\alpha = 0.05$),

$$\overline{X} \pm Z_{\alpha/2}\frac{\sigma}{\sqrt{n}}$$

$$372.5 \pm (1.96)\frac{15}{\sqrt{25}}$$

$$372.5 \pm 5.88$$

so that

$$366.62 \leq \mu \leq 378.38$$

Because the interval includes the hypothesized value of 368 grams, you do not reject the null hypothesis. There is insufficient evidence that the mean fill amount over the entire filling process is not 368 grams. You reached the same decision by using two-tail hypothesis testing.

Can You Ever Know the Population Standard Deviation?

The end of Section 10.1 on page 392 discussed how learning a confidence interval estimation method that required knowing σ, the population standard deviation, served as an effective introduction to the concept of a confidence interval. That passage then revealed that you would be unlikely to use that procedure for most practical applications for several reasons.

Likewise, for most practical applications, you are unlikely to use a hypothesis-testing method that requires knowing σ. If you knew the population standard deviation, you would also know the population mean and would not need to form a hypothesis about the mean and then test that hypothesis. So why study a hypothesis testing of the mean that requires that σ is known? Using such a test makes it much easier to explain the fundamentals of hypothesis testing. With a known population standard deviation, you can use the normal distribution and compute *p*-values using the tables of the normal distribution.

Because it is important that you understand the concept of hypothesis testing when reading the rest of this book, review this section carefully—even if you anticipate never having a practical reason to use the test represented by Equation (11.1).

CALCULATOR LESSON 9A

CFX-9850GB CALCULATOR

Lesson 9A—Z Test of a Single Mean

EXAMPLE 11.5

A company that makes batteries for computers needs to make sure that the voltage of these batteries is not too low or too high. The ideal voltage for the QMS model battery, which is used in many computers, is 5.60 volts. The process that is used to make these batteries is also used to make many other models of batteries with different voltages. It is known that the standard deviation of the process is 0.18 volts and that the voltages will fit a normal distribution. The process has just been set up to produce 1 million QMS batteries. Before too many are produced the batteries need to be checked to see if the average voltage is close to 5.60 volts. A sample of 25 QMS batteries is tested, and the average voltage is 5.65 volts. Should the process be allowed to continue production of the QMS battery, or should it be adjusted? Use a 5% level of significance.

Solution: From the **Main Menu** select

STAT F3(TEST) **F1**(Z) **F1**(1-S), and then enter the following items.

(Note: Only use the **EXE** key after a new entry. Otherwise, use the cursor ▼ arrow. If you accidentally hit the wrong key, use **AC/^{ON}** or **EXIT** to go back.)

1-Sample ZTest
Data	: F2(Var)	▼
μ	: F1($\neq\mu0$)	▼
$\mu0$	: 5.60	EXE
σ	: .18	EXE
$\bar{x}$	: 5.65	EXE
n	: 25	EXE

Now press **EXE** or **F1**(Calc).

The calculator will show the following results:

1-Sample ZTest
μ	$\neq 5.6$
z	=1.3888
p	=0.16486
x	=5.65
n	=25

Since the *p*-value > 0.05, the conclusion is to not reject the null hypothesis. In other words, the process does not need to be adjusted.

EXAMPLE 11.6

A company that sells a brand of soft drink with a label of 355 ml is suspected of cheating its purchasers. The consumers understand that it is not necessary that every can contain 355 ml, but the average should be at least 355 ml. They believe that the average amount in the cans is less than 355 ml. A group of concerned consumers has approached a consumer advocate who has found out that the bottling process that fills this type of can has a standard deviation of 2 ml and that the volume of soft drink in the cans will fit a normal distribution. To obtain evidence, a sample of 4 cases of 24 cans was measured carefully and the mean volume was found to be 354.5 ml. At the 5% level of significance, does this evidence support the claim of the consumers?

Solution: From the **Main Menu** select

STAT F3(TEST) **F1**(Z) **F1**(1-S), and then enter the following items.

1-Sample ZTest
Data	: F2(Var)	▼
μ	: F2($<\mu0$)	▼
$\mu0$	: 355	EXE
σ	: 2	EXE
$\bar{x}$	: 354.5	EXE
n	: 96	EXE

Now press **EXE** or **F1**(Calc).

The calculator will show the following results:

1-Sample ZTest
    μ <355
    z = −2.4495
    p =7.1529E-03 (=0.0071529)
    $\bar{x}$ =354.5
    n =96

Since the *p*-value < 0.05, the conclusion is to *reject* the null hypothesis. In other words the evidence supports the consumers' claim.

EXAMPLE 11.7

In the past an automobile manufacturer has been using seatbelts that could withstand a breaking force of 1000 kgs. New legislation has dictated that seatbelts should be able to withstand an average of at least 1500 kgs. One supplier has approached the manufacturer with a claim that its seatbelts have an average breaking strength that is significantly higher than 1500 kgs. The standard deviation of its process is known to be 48 kgs. In order to test the claim, the automobile manufacturer has purchased 60 of these seatbelts and has determined that their mean breaking strength is 1517 kgs. At the 1% level of significance, should the auto company accept the seatbelt manufacturer's claim?

Solution: From the **Main Menu** select

STAT F3(TEST) **F1**(Z) **F1**(1-S), and then enter the following items.

Data	: F2(Var) ▼	
μ	: F3(>μ0) ▼	
μ0	: 1500	**EXE**
σ	: 48	**EXE**
$\bar{x}$	: 1517	**EXE**
n	: 60	**EXE**

Now press **EXE** or **F1**(Calc).

The calculator will show the following results:

1-Sample ZTest
    μ >1500
    z   =2.7434
    p   =3.0407E-03 (=.0030407)
    $\bar{x}$ =1517
    n   =60

Since the *p*-value < 0.01, the conclusion is to *reject* the null hypothesis. In other words, the evidence supports the seatbelt manufacturer's claim.

EXAMPLE 11.8

A researcher is asked to test the hypothesis that the average price of a 2-star (CAA rating) motel room has decreased since last year. Last year a study showed that the prices of all rooms were normally distributed with an average of $89.50 and a standard deviation of $2.80. A random sample of twelve 2-star motels has yielded the following information on room prices: $85.00, 92.50, 87.50, 89.90, 90.00, 82.50, 87.50, 90.00, 85.00, 89.00, 91.50 and $87.50. If it is believed that the standard deviation of the population of room prices has not changed since last year and the prices are still normally distributed, at the 5% level of significance, what conclusion should the researcher make?

Solution:

First enter the data into **List 1.**

Now, from the **Main Menu** select

STAT F3(TEST) F1(Z) **F1**(1-S), and then enter the following items:

Data	: F1(List) ▼	
μ	: F2(<μ0) ▼	
μ0	: 89.50	EXE
σ	: 2.80	EXE
List	: List1	EXE
Freq	: 1	EXE

Now press **EXE** or **F1**(Calc).

The calculator will show the following results:

1-Sample ZTest

μ	<89.5
z	= −1.6599
p	=0.048469
$\bar{x}$	=88.158
xσn-1	=2.9203
n	=12

Since the *p*-value < 0.05, the conclusion is to *reject* the null hypothesis. In other words, the evidence indicates that the mean price of a 2-star motel room has decreased this year and is lower than last year's mean of $89.50.

CALCULATOR LESSON 9B

CASIO FX-9750GII CALCULATOR

Lesson 9B—Z Test of a Single Mean

EXAMPLE 11.9

A company that makes batteries for computers needs to make sure that the voltage of these batteries is not too low or too high. The ideal voltage for the QMS model battery, which is used in many computers, is 5.60 volts. The process that is used to make these batteries is also used to make many other models of batteries with different voltages. It is known that the standard deviation of the process is 0.18 volts and that the voltages will fit a normal distribution. The process has just been set up to produce 1 million QMS batteries. Before too many are produced the batteries need to be checked to see if the average voltage is close to 5.60 volts. A sample of 25 QMS batteries is tested, and the average voltage was 5.65 volts. Should the process be allowed to continue production of the QMS battery, or should it be adjusted? Use a 5% level of significance.

Solution: From the **Main Menu** select

STAT   F3(TEST)   **F1**(Z)   **F1**(1-S), and then enter the following items.

(Note: Only use the **EXE** key after a new entry. Otherwise, use the cursor ▼ arrow. If you accidentally hit the wrong key, use **AC/ON** or **EXIT** to go back.)

1-Sample ZTest

Data	: F2(Var) ▼	
μ	: F1(≠μ0) ▼	
μ0	: 5.60	EXE
σ	: 0.18	EXE
$\bar{x}$	: 5.65	EXE
n	: 25	EXE
Save Res	: None	

Now press **EXE** or **F1**(Calc) or **F6**(DRAW).

If you select **F6**(DRAW), you will see a normal distribution.

If you select either **EXE** or **F1**(Calc), the calculator will show the following results:

1-Sample ZTest
μ 5.6
z   =1.38888889
p   =0.16486654
$\bar{x}$ =5.65
n   =25

Since the *p*-value > 0.05, the conclusion is to *not reject* the null hypothesis. In other words, the process does not need to be adjusted.

EXAMPLE 11.10   A company that sells a brand of soft drink with a label of 355 ml is suspected of cheating its purchasers. The consumers understand that it is not necessary that every can contain 355 ml, but the average should be at least 355 ml. They believe that the average amount in the cans is less than 355 ml. A group of concerned consumers has approached a consumer advocate who has found out that the bottling process that fills this type of can has a standard deviation of 2 ml and that the volume of soft drink in the cans will fit a normal distribution. To obtain evidence, a sample of 4 cases of 24 cans was measured carefully and the mean volume was found to be 354.5 ml. At the 5% level of significance, does this evidence support the claim of the consumers?

Solution: From the **Main Menu** select

STAT F3(TEST) **F1**(Z) **F1**(1-S), and then enter the following items:

1-Sample ZTest
Data   : **F2**(Var)   ▼
μ : **F2**($<\mu0$)   ▼
$\mu0$: **355**   **EXE**
σ : **2**   **EXE**
$\bar{x}$: **354.5**   **EXE**
n   : **96**   **EXE**
Save Res   : None

Now press **EXE** or **F1**(Calc) or **F6**(DRAW).

If you select **F6**(DRAW), you will see a normal distribution.

If you select either **EXE** or **F1**(Calc), the calculator will show the following results:

1-Sample ZTest
μ <355
z   =−2.4494897
p   =7.1529E-03 (=0.0071529)
$\bar{x}$ =354.5
n   =25

Since the *p*-value < 0.05, the conclusion is to *reject* the null hypothesis. In other words, the evidence supports the consumers claim.

EXAMPLE 11.11   In the past an automobile manufacturer has been using seatbelts that could withstand a breaking force of 1000 kgs. New legislation has dictated that seatbelts should be able to withstand an average of at least 1500 kgs. One supplier has approached the manufacturer with a claim that its seatbelts have an average breaking strength that is significantly higher than 1500 kgs. The standard deviation of its process is known to be 48 kgs. In order to test the claim, the automobile manufacturer has purchased 60 of these seatbelts and has determined that their mean breaking strength is 1517 kgs. At the 1% level of significance, should the auto company accept the seatbelt manufacturer's claim?

Solution: From the **Main Menu** select

STAT F3(TEST) **F1**(Z) **F1**(1-S), and then enter the following items:

Data	: F2(Var)	▼
μ	: F3(>μ0)	▼
μ0	: 1500	EXE
σ	: 48	EXE
$\bar{x}$	: 1517	EXE
n	: 60	EXE
Save Res	: None	

Now press **EXE** or **F1**(Calc) or **F6**(DRAW).

If you select **F6**(DRAW), you will see a normal distribution.

If you select either **EXE** or **F1**(Calc), the calculator will show the following results:

1-Sample ZTest

μ	>1500
z	=2.7433632
p	=3.0406E-03 (=.0030406)
$\bar{x}$	=1517
n	=60

Since the *p*-value < 0.01, the conclusion is to *reject* the null hypothesis. In other words, the evidence supports the seatbelt manufacturer's claim.

EXAMPLE 11.12   A researcher is asked to test the hypothesis that the average price of a 2-star (CAA rating) motel room has decreased since last year. Last year a study showed that the prices were normally distributed with an average of $89.50 and a standard deviation of $2.80. A random sample of twelve 2-star motels has yielded the following information on room prices: $85.00, 92.50, 87.50, 89.90, 90.00, 82.50, 87.50, 90.00, 85.00, 89.00, 91.50 and $87.50. If it is believed that the standard deviation of room prices has not changed since last year and the prices are still normally distributed, at the 5% level of significance, what conclusion should the researcher make?

Solution:

First enter the data into **List 1**.

Now, from the **Main Menu** select

STAT F3(TEST) **F1**(Z) **F1**(1-S), and then enter the following items:

Data	: F1(List)	▼
μ	: F2(<μ0)	▼
μ0	: 89.50	EXE
σ	: 2.80	EXE
List	: List1	EXE
Freq	: 1	EXE
Save Res	: None	

Now press **EXE** or **F1**(Calc) or **F6**(DRAW).

If you select **F6**(DRAW), you will see a normal distribution.

If you select either **EXE** or **F1**(Calc), the calculator will show the following results:

1-Sample ZTest

μ	<89.5
z	=−1.659882
p	=0.04846909
$\bar{x}$	=88.1583333
sx	=2.92029212
n	=12

Since the *p*-value < 0.05, the conclusion is to *reject* the null hypothesis. In other words, the evidence indicates that the mean price of a 2-star motel room has decreased this year and is lower than last year's mean of $89.50.

Problems for Sections 11.1 and 11.2

LEARNING THE BASICS

11.1 If you use a 0.05 level of significance in a two-tail *Accept* hypothesis test, what will you decide if $Z_{STAT} = -0.76$?

11.2 If you use a 0.05 level of significance in a two-tail *Reject* hypothesis test, what will you decide if $Z_{STAT} = +2.21$?

11.3 If you use a 0.10 level of significance in a two-tail hypothesis test, what is your decision rule for rejecting a null hypothesis that the population mean is 500 if you use the *Z* test?

11.4 If you use a 0.01 level of significance in a two-tail hypothesis test, what is your decision rule for rejecting $H_0 : \mu = 12.5$ if you use the *Z* test?

11.5 What is your decision in Problem 11.4 if $Z_{STAT} = -2.61$?

11.6 What is the *p*-value if, in a two-tail hypothesis test, $Z_{STAT} = +2.00$?

11.7 In Problem 11.6, what is your statistical decision if you test the null hypothesis at the 0.10 level of significance?

11.8 What is the *p*-value if, in a two-tail hypothesis test, $Z_{STAT} = -1.38$?

APPLYING THE CONCEPTS

11.9 In the U.S. legal system, a defendant is presumed innocent until proven guilty. Consider a null hypothesis, H_0, that the defendant is innocent, and an alternative hypothesis, H_1, that the defendant is guilty. A jury has two possible decisions: Convict the defendant (i.e., reject the null hypothesis) or do not convict the defendant (i.e., do not reject the null hypothesis). Explain the meaning of the risks of committing either a Type I or Type II error in this example.

11.10 Suppose the defendant in Problem 11.9 is presumed guilty until proven innocent, as in some other judicial systems. How do the null and alternative hypotheses differ from those in Problem 11.9? What are the meanings of the risks of committing either a Type I or Type II error here?

11.11 Many consumer groups feel that the U.S. Food and Drug Administration (FDA) drug approval process is too easy and, as a result, too many drugs are approved that are later found to be unsafe. On the other hand, a number of industry lobbyists have pushed for a more lenient approval process so that pharmaceutical companies can get new drugs approved more easily and quickly. Consider a null hypothesis that a new, unapproved drug is unsafe and an alternative hypothesis that a new, unapproved drug is safe.

a. Explain the risks of committing a Type I or Type II error.

b. Which type of error are the consumer groups trying to avoid? Explain.

c. Which type of error are the industry lobbyists trying to avoid? Explain.

d. How would it be possible to lower the chances of both Type I and Type II errors?

11.12 As a result of complaints from both students and faculty about lateness, the registrar at a large university wants to determine whether the scheduled break between classes should be changed and, therefore, is ready to undertake a study. Until now, the registrar has believed that there should be 20 minutes between scheduled classes. State the null hypothesis, H_0, and the alternative hypothesis, H_1.

11.13 Do students at your school study more than, less than, or about the same as students at other business schools? *BusinessWeek* reported that at the top 50 business schools, students studied an average of 14.6 hours per week. (Data extracted from "Cracking the Books," Special Report/Online Extra, **www.businessweek.com**, March 19, 2007.) Set up a hypothesis test to try to prove that the mean number of hours studied at your school is different from the 14.6-hour-per-week benchmark reported by *BusinessWeek*.

a. State the null and alternative hypotheses.

b. What is a Type I error for your test?

c. What is a Type II error for your test?

✓ SELF **11.14** The quality-control manager at a light bulb
Test factory needs to determine whether the mean life of a large shipment of light bulbs is equal to 375 hours. The population standard deviation is 100 hours. A random sample of 64 light bulbs indicates a sample mean life of 350 hours.

a. At the 0.05 level of significance, is there evidence that the mean life is different from 375 hours?

b. Compute the *p*-value and interpret its meaning.

c. Construct a 95% confidence interval estimate of the population mean life of the light bulbs.

d. Compare the results of (a) and (c). What conclusions do you reach?

11.15 Suppose that in Problem 11.14, the standard deviation is 120 hours.

a. Repeat (a) through (d) of Problem 11.14, assuming a standard deviation of 120 hours.

b. Compare the results of (a) to those of Problem 11.14.

11.16 The manager of a paint supply store wants to determine whether the mean amount of paint contained in 1-gallon cans purchased from a nationally known manufacturer is actually 1 gallon. You know from the manufacturer's specifications that the standard deviation of the amount of paint is 0.02 gallon. You select a random sample of 50 cans, and the mean amount of paint per 1-gallon can is 0.995 gallon.

a. Is there evidence that the mean amount is different from 1.0 gallon? (Use $\alpha = 0.01$.)

b. Compute the p-value and interpret its meaning.

c. Construct a 99% confidence interval estimate of the population mean amount of paint.

d. Compare the results of (a) and (c). What conclusions do you reach?

11.17 Suppose that in Problem 11.16, the standard deviation is 0.012 gallon.

a. Repeat (a) through (d) of Problem 11.16, assuming a standard deviation of 0.012 gallon.

b. Compare the results of (a) to those of Problem 11.16.

11.3 *t* Test of Hypothesis for the Mean (σ Unknown)

In virtually all hypothesis-testing situations concerning the population mean, you do not know the population standard deviation, σ. Instead, you use the sample standard deviation, S. If you assume that the population is normally distributed, the sampling distribution of the mean follows a *t* distribution with $n - 1$ degrees of freedom, and you use the **t test for the mean**. If the population is not normally distributed, you can still use the *t* test if the sample size is large enough for the Central Limit Theorem to take effect (see Section 8.4). Equation (11.2) defines the test statistic for determining the difference between the sample mean, $\overline{X}$, and the population mean, μ, when using the sample standard deviation, S.

---

t TEST FOR THE MEAN (σ UNKNOWN)

$$t_{STAT} = \frac{\overline{X} - \mu}{\dfrac{S}{\sqrt{n}}} \qquad (11.2)$$

where the t_{STAT} test statistic follows a *t* distribution having $n - 1$ degrees of freedom.

To illustrate the use of the *t* test for the mean, return to the Chapter 10 Saxon Home Improvement scenario on page 383. The business objective is to determine whether the mean amount per sales invoice is unchanged from the $120 of the past five years. As an accountant for the company, you need to determine whether this amount changes. In other words, the hypothesis test is used to try to determine whether the mean amount per sales invoice is increasing or decreasing.

The Critical Value Approach

To perform this two-tail hypothesis test, you use the six-step method listed in Exhibit 11.1 on page 435.

Step 1   You define the following hypotheses:

$$H_0: \mu = \$120$$
$$H_1: \mu \neq \$120$$

The alternative hypothesis contains the statement you are trying to prove. If the null hypothesis is rejected, then there is statistical evidence that the population mean amount per sales invoice is no longer $120. If the statistical conclusion is "do not reject H_0," then you will conclude that there is insufficient evidence to prove that the mean amount differs from the long-term mean of $120.

Step 2   You collect the data from a sample of $n = 12$ sales invoices. You decide to use $\alpha = 0.05$.

Step 3   Because σ is unknown, you use the *t* distribution and the t_{STAT} test statistic. You must assume that the population of sales invoices is normally distributed because the sample size of 12 is too small for the Central Limit Theorem to take effect. This assumption is discussed on page 450.

Step 4   For a given sample size, n, the test statistic t_{STAT} follows a *t* distribution with $n - 1$ degrees of freedom. The critical values of the *t* distribution with $12 - 1 = 11$ degrees of freedom are found in Table E.3, as illustrated in Table 11.2 and Figure 11.6. The alternative hypothesis, $H_1 : \mu \neq \$120$, has two tails. The area in the rejection region of the *t* distribution's left (lower) tail is 0.025, and the area in the rejection region of the *t* distribution's right (upper) tail is also 0.025.

From the *t* table as given in Table E.3, a portion of which is shown in Table 11.2, the critical values are ±2.2010. The decision rule is

$$\text{Reject } H_0 \text{ if } t_{STAT} < -2.2010$$

$$\text{or if } t_{STAT} > +2.2010;$$

$$\text{otherwise, do not reject } H_0.$$

TABLE 11.2

Determining the Critical Value from the *t* Table for an Area of 0.025 in Each Tail, with 11 Degrees of Freedom

	Cumulative Probabilities					
	.75	.90	.95	.975	.99	.995
	Upper-Tail Areas					
Degrees of Freedom	.25	.10	.05	.025	.01	.005
1	1.0000	3.0777	6.3138	12.7062	31.8207	63.6574
2	0.8165	1.8856	2.9200	4.3027	6.9646	9.9248
3	0.7649	1.6377	2.3534	3.1824	4.5407	5.8409
4	0.7407	1.5332	2.1318	2.7764	3.7469	4.6041
5	0.7267	1.4759	2.0150	2.5706	3.3649	4.0322
6	0.7176	1.4398	1.9432	2.4469	3.1427	3.7074
7	0.7111	1.4149	1.8946	2.3646	2.9980	3.4995
8	0.7064	1.3968	1.8595	2.3060	2.8965	3.3554
9	0.7027	1.3830	1.8331	2.2622	2.8214	3.2498
10	0.6998	1.3722	1.8125	2.2281	2.7638	3.1693
11	0.6974	1.3634	1.7959	2.2010	2.7181	3.1058

Source: Extracted from Table E.3.

FIGURE 11.6

Testing a hypothesis about the mean (σ unknown) at the 0.05 level of significance with 11 degrees of freedom

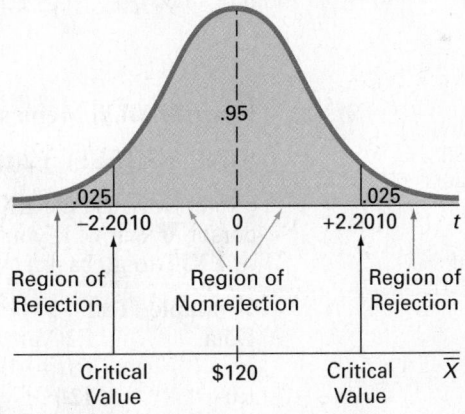

Step 5 You organize and store the data from a random sample of 12 sales invoices in Invoices :

108.98 152.22 111.45 110.59 127.46 107.26

93.32   91.97 111.56   75.71 128.58 135.11

Then,

$$\bar{X} = \$112.85 \text{ and } S = \$20.80$$

From Equation (11.2) on page 448,

$$t_{STAT} = \frac{\bar{X} - \mu}{\dfrac{S}{\sqrt{n}}} = \frac{112.85 - 120}{\dfrac{20.80}{\sqrt{12}}} = -1.1908$$

Figure 11.7 shows the results for this test of hypothesis, as computed by Excel and Minitab.

FIGURE 11.7

Excel and Minitab results for the t test of sales invoices

	A	B	
1	t Test for the Hypothesis of the Mean		
2			
3	**Data**		
4	Null Hypothesis μ=	120	
5	Level of Significance	0.05	
6	Sample Size	12	
7	Sample Mean	112.85	
8	Sample Standard Deviation	20.8	
9			
10	**Intermediate Calculations**		
11	Standard Error of the Mean	6.0044	=B8/SQRT(B6)
12	Degrees of Freedom	11	=B6 - 1
13	t Test Statistic	-1.1908	=(B7 - B4)/B11
14			
15	**Two-Tail Test**		
16	Lower Critical Value	-2.2010	=-TINV(B5, B12)
17	Upper Critical Value	2.2010	=TINV(B5, B12)
18	p -Value	0.2588	=TDIST(ABS(B13), B12, 2)
19	Do not reject the null hypothesis		=IF(B18 < B5, "Reject the null hypothesis", "Do not reject the null hypothesis")

One-Sample T

Test of mu = 120 vs not = 120

N	Mean	StDev	SE Mean	95% CI	T	P
12	112.85	20.80	6.00	(99.63, 126.07)	-1.19	0.259

Step 6   Because $-2.2010 < t_{STAT} = -1.1908 < 2.2010$, you do not reject H_0. You have insufficient evidence to conclude that the mean amount per sales invoice differs from \$120. The audit suggests that the mean amount per invoice has not changed.

The p-Value Approach

To perform this two-tail hypothesis test, you use the five-step method listed in Exhibit 11.2 on page 439.

Step 1–3   These steps are the same as in the critical value approach.

Step 4:   From the Casio calculator worksheet of Figure 11.8 or from the SPSS results of Figure 11.9, $t_{CALC} = -1.19$ and the p-value $= 0.259$.

FIGURE 11.8

Casio calculator FX 9750GII results for the t test of sales invoices

t-Test for the hypothesis of the mean

From the **Main Menu** select

STAT   F3(TEST)   **F2**(t)   **F1**(1-S), and then enter the following items:

(Note: Only use the **EXE** key after a new entry. Otherwise, use the cursor ▼ arrow. If you accidentally hit the wrong key, use **AC/ON** or **EXIT** to go back.)

1-Sample tTest

Data	: F2(Var)	▼
μ	: F1($\neq \mu 0$)	▼
μ0	: 120	EXE
$\bar{x}$	: 112.85	EXE
sx	: 20.8	EXE
n	: 12	EXE
Save Res	: None	

Now press **EXE** or **F1**(CALC) or **F6**(DRAW).

If you select **F6**(DRAW), you will see a normal distribution.

If you select either **EXE** or **F1**(Calc), the calculator will show the following results:

1-Sample tTest

μ	$\neq 120$
t	$= -1.1907849$
p	$= 0.25880033$
$\bar{x}$	$= 112.85$
n	$= 12$

Statistical Decision: Do not reject the null hypothesis.

To find the *t* critical value:

Two ways of finding the *t* critical value:

(1) Using the Casio calculator fx-9750GII
Note: fx-9750G Plus does not have this option; therefore, you have to use the *t* table.

From the **Main Menu** select

STAT   F5(DIST)   **F2**(t)   **F3**(Invt), and then enter the following items.

Inverse Student-t

Data	: F2(Var) ▼
Area	: 0.05 ÷ 2
df	: 12–1 EXE
Save Res	: None

Now press **EXE** or **F1**(CALC).

The calculator will show the following results:

Inverse Student-t
x-Inv = 2.20098516

(2) Using the *t* table.

	T Table			**Upper Tail Areas**		
df	**0.25**	**0.1**	**0.05**	**(0.025)**	**0.01**	**0.005**
1	1.000	3.078	6.314	12.706	31.821	63.657
2	0.816	1.886	2.920	4.303	6.965	9.925
3	0.765	1.638	2.353	3.182	4.541	5.841
4	0.741	1.533	2.132	2.776	3.747	4.604
5	0.727	1.476	2.015	2.571	3.365	4.032
6	0.718	1.440	1.943	2.447	3.143	3.707
7	0.711	1.415	1.895	2.365	2.998	3.499
8	0.706	1.397	1.860	2.306	2.896	3.355
9	0.703	1.383	1.833	2.262	2.821	3.250
10	0.700	1.372	1.812	2.228	2.764	3.169
(11)	0.697	1.363	1.796	(2.201)	2.718	3.106

Step 5: The Casio calculator results in Figure 11.9 give the *p*-value for this two-tail test as 0.259. Because the *p*-value of 0.259 is greater than $\alpha = 0.05$, you do not reject H_0. The data provide insufficient evidence to conclude that the mean amount per sales invoice differs from $120. You should inform the finance department that the audit suggests that the mean amount per invoice has not changed. The *p*-value indicates that if the null hypothesis is true, the probability that a sample of 12 invoices could have a sample mean that differs by $7.15 or more from the stated $120 is 0.259. In other words, if the mean amount per sales invoice is truly $120, then there is a 25.9% chance of observing a sample mean below $112.85 or above $127.15.

In the preceding example, it is incorrect to state that there is a 25.88% chance that the null hypothesis is true. Remember that the p-value is a conditional probability, calculated by *assuming* that the null hypothesis is true. In general, it is proper to state the following:

If the null hypothesis is true, there is a (p-value) $\times$ 100% chance of observing a test statistic at least as contradictory to the null hypothesis as the sample result.

Checking the Normality Assumption

You use the t test when the population standard deviation, σ, is not known and is estimated using the sample standard deviation, S. To use the t test, you assume that the data represent a random sample from a population that is normally distributed. In practice, as long as the sample size is not very small and the population is not very skewed, the t distribution provides a good approximation of the sampling distribution of the mean when σ is unknown.

There are several ways to evaluate the normality assumption necessary for using the t test. You can examine how closely the sample statistics match the normal distribution's theoretical properties. You can also construct a histogram, stem-and-leaf display, boxplot, or normal probability plot to visualize the distribution of the sales invoice amounts. For details on evaluating normality, see Section 7.4 on pages 304–307.

Figures 11.9 through 11.11 show the descriptive statistics, boxplot, and normal probability plot for the sales invoice data.

FIGURE 11.9

SPSS descriptive statistics for the sales invoice data

SPSS output

Statistics		
Sales Invoice		
N	Valid	12
Mean		112.8508
Median		111.0200
Mode		75.71[a]
Std. Deviation		20.79799
Variance		432.556
Skewness		.134
Std. Error of Skewness		.637
Kurtosis		.173
Std. Error of Kurtosis		1.232
Range		76.51
Minimum		75.71
Maximum		152.22
Sum		1354.21
Percentiles	25	96.8050
	50	111.0200
	75	128.3000

a. *Multiple modes exist. The smallest value is shown.*

The mean is very close to the median, and the points on the normal probability plots on page 453 appear to be increasing approximately in a straight line. The boxplots appear to be approximately symmetrical. Thus, you can assume that the population of sales invoices is approximately normally distributed. The normality assumption is valid, and therefore the auditor's results are valid.

FIGURE 11.10

Excel and Minitab boxplots for the sales invoice data

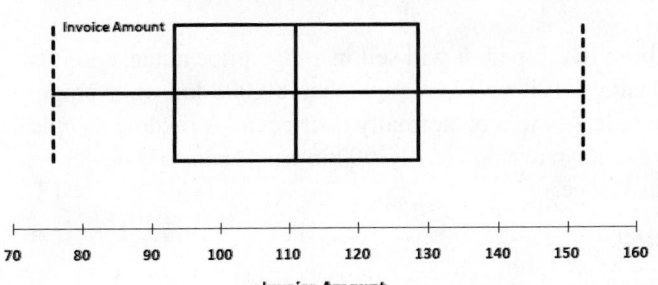

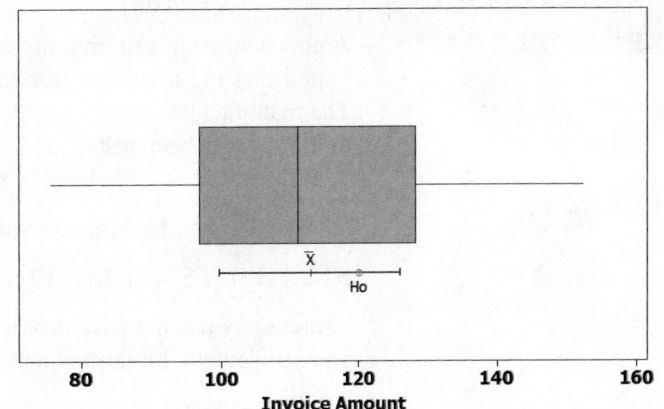

FIGURE 11.11

Excel and Minitab normal probability plots for the sales invoice data

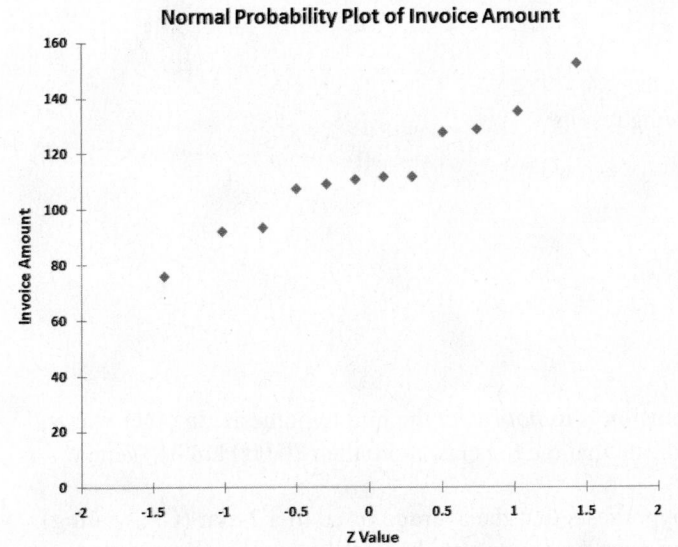

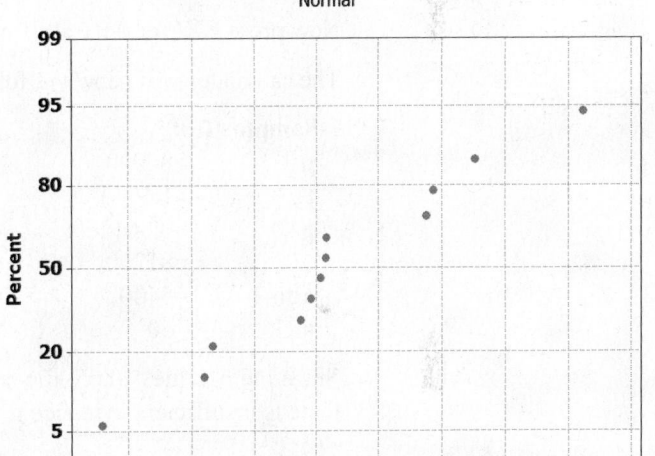

The *t* test is a **robust** test. A robust test does not lose power if the shape of the population departs somewhat from a normal distribution, particularly when the sample size is large enough to enable the test statistic *t* to be influenced by the Central Limit Theorem (see Section 8.4). However, you can reach erroneous conclusions and can lose statistical power if you use the *t* test incorrectly. If the sample size, *n*, is small (i.e., less than 30) and you cannot easily make the assumption that the underlying population is at least approximately normally distributed, then *nonparametric* testing procedures are more appropriate (see references 1 and 2).

CALCULATOR LESSON 10A

**CFX-9850GB
CALCULATOR**

EXAMPLE 11.13

Lesson 10A—t Test of a Single Mean

A new winter ice-gripping tire has been developed. It will sell in a high price range, and it is hoped that the manufacturer can claim that it will last more than 80,000 km on average. The manufacturer is certain that the mileages will be normally distributed. A random sample of 50 tires has been tested, and they lasted an average of 81,200 km with a standard deviation of 5,400 km. Use a 5% level of significance.

Solution: From the **Main Menu** select

STAT F3(TEST) **F2**(t) **F1**(1-S), and then enter the following items.

(Note: Only use the **EXE** key after a new data entry. Otherwise, use the cursor ▼ arrow. If you accidentally hit the wrong key, use **AC/ON** or **EXIT** to go back.)

1-Sample tTest

Data	: **F2**(Var)	▼
μ	: **F3**(>)	▼
μ_0	: **80000**	**EXE**
$\bar{x}$	: **81200**	**EXE**
xσn-1	: **5400**	**EXE**
n	: **50**	**EXE**

Now press **EXE** or **F1**(Calc).

The calculator will show the following results:

1-Sample tTest

μ	>80000
t	=1.5713
p	=0.061269
$\bar{x}$	=81200
xσn-1	=5400
n	=50

Since the *p*-value > 0.05, the conclusion is to *not reject* the null hypothesis. In other words, there is insufficient evidence to indicate that the tires last more then 80,000 km on average.

EXAMPLE 11.14

A researcher is asked to test the hypothesis that the average price of a 2-star (CAA rating) motel room has decreased since last year. Last year a study showed that the prices were normally distributed with an average of $89.50. A random sample of twelve 2-star motels has yielded the following information on room prices: $85.00, 92.50, 87.50, 89.90, 90.00, 82.50, 87.50, 90.00, 85.00, 89.00, 91.50 and $87.50. If it is believed that the distribution of room prices is normal, at the 5% level of significance, what conclusion should the researcher make?

Solution:

First enter the data into **List 1.**

Now, from the **Main Menu** select

STAT F3(TEST) **F2**(t) **F1**(1-S), and then enter the following items.

1-Sample tTest

Data	: **F1**(List)	▼
μ	: **F2**(<)	▼
μ_0	: **89.50**	**EXE**

List   : **List1**   ▼
Freq   : F1(1)   ▼

Now press **EXE** or **F1**(Calc).

The calculator will show the following results:

1-Sample tTest
μ   <89.5
t   = −1.5915
p   =0.069901
$\bar{x}$ =88.158
xσn-1   =2.9203
n   =12

Since the *p*-value > 0.05, the conclusion is to *not reject* the null hypothesis. In other words, the evidence does not indicate that the mean price of a 2-star motel room has decreased this year.

CALCULATOR LESSON 10B

CASIO FX-9750GII CALCULATOR

EXAMPLE 11.15

Lesson 10B—*t* Test of a Single Mean

A new winter ice-gripping tire has been developed. It will sell in a high price range, and the manufacturer hopes to claim that they will last more than 80,000 km on average. The manufacturer is certain that the mileages will be normally distributed. A random sample of 50 tires has been tested, and they lasted an average of 81,200 km with a standard deviation of 5,400 km. Use a 5% level of significance.

Solution: From the **Main Menu** select,

STAT   F3(TEST)   **F2**(t)   **F1**(1-S), and then enter the following items.

(Note: Only use the **EXE** key after a new data entry. Otherwise, use the cursor ▼ arrow. If you accidentally hit the wrong key, use **AC/ON** or **EXIT** to go back.)

1-Sample tTest
Data   : **F2**(Var)   ▼
μ   : **F3**(>)   ▼
μ_0 : **80000**   **EXE**
$\bar{x}$: **81200**   **EXE**
sx   : **5400**   **EXE**
n   : **50**   **EXE**
Save Res   : None   ▼

Now press **EXE** or **F1**(Calc) or **F6**(DRAW).

If you select **F6**(DRAW), you will see a normal distribution.

If you select either **EXE** or **F1**(Calc), the calculator will show the following results:

1-Sample tTest
μ   >80000
t   =1.5713484
p   =0.06126869
$\bar{x}$ =81200
Sx   =5400
n   =50

Since the *p*-value > 0.05, the conclusion is to *not reject* the null hypothesis. In other words, the tires do not average more than 80,000 km.

EXAMPLE 11.16   A researcher is asked to test the hypothesis that the average price of a 2-star (CAA rating) motel room has decreased since last year. Last year a study showed that the prices were normally distributed with an average of $89.50. A random sample of twelve 2-star motels has yielded the following information on room prices: $85.00, 92.50, 87.50, 89.90, 90.00, 82.50, 87.50, 90.00, 85.00, 89.00, 91.50 and $87.50. If it is believed that the distribution of room prices is normal, at the 5% level of significance, what conclusion should the researcher make?

Solution:

First enter the data into **List 1**.

Now, from the **Main Menu** select,

STAT   F3(TEST)   **F2**(t)   **F1**(1-S), and then enter the following items.

1-Sample tTest
Data	: **F1**(List) ▼
μ	: **F2**(<) ▼
μ_0	: **89.50** **EXE**
List	: **List1** (**Press F1 to enter list number.**)
Freq	: **1** ▼
Save Res	: None

Now press **EXE** or **F1**(Calc) or **F6**(DRAW).

If you select **F6**(DRAW), you will see a normal distribution.

If you select either **EXE** or **F1**(Calc), the calculator will show the following results:

1-Sample tTest
μ	<89.5
t	=-1.5915085
p	=0.06990119
$\bar{x}$	=88.1583333
sx	=2.92029212
n	=12

Since the *p*-value > 0.05, the conclusion is to *not reject* the null hypothesis. In other words, the evidence does not indicate that the mean price of a 2-star motel room has decreased this year.

Problems for Section 11.3

LEARNING THE BASICS

11.18 If, in a sample of $n = 16$ selected from a normal population, $\bar{X} = 56$ and $S = 12$, what is the value of t_{STAT} if you are testing the null hypothesis $H_0 : \mu = 50$?

11.19 In Problem 11.18, how many degrees of freedom does the *t* test have?

11.20 In Problems 11.18 and 11.19, what are the critical values of *t* if the level of significance, α, is 0.05 and the alternative hypothesis, H_1, is $\mu \neq 50$?

11.21 In Problems 11.18, 11.19, and 11.20, what is your statistical decision if the alternative hypothesis, H_1, is $\mu \neq 50$?

11.22 If, in a sample of $n = 16$ selected from a left-skewed population, $\bar{X} = 65$, and $S = 21$, would you use the *t* test to test the null hypothesis $H_0 : \mu = 60$? Discuss.

11.23 If, in a sample of $n = 160$ selected from a left-skewed population, $\bar{X} = 65$, and $S = 21$, would you use the *t* test to test the null hypothesis $H_0 : \mu = 60$? Discuss.

APPLYING THE CONCEPTS

✓SELF Test 11.24 You are the manager of a restaurant for a fast-food franchise. Last month, the mean waiting time at the drive-through window for branches in your geographical region, as measured from the time a customer places an order until the time the customer receives the order, was 3.7 minutes. You select a random sample of 64 orders. The sample mean waiting time is 3.57 minutes, with a sample standard deviation of 0.8 minute.

a. At the 0.05 level of significance, is there evidence that the population mean waiting time is different from 3.7 minutes?

b. Because the sample size is 64, do you need to be concerned about the shape of the population distribution when conducting the *t* test in (a)? Explain.

11.25 A manufacturer of chocolate candies uses machines to package candies as they move along a filling line. Although the packages are labeled as 8 ounces, the company wants the packages to contain a mean of 8.17 ounces so that virtually none of the packages contain less than 8 ounces. A sample of 50 packages is selected periodically, and the packaging process is stopped if there is evidence that the mean amount packaged is different from 8.17 ounces. Suppose that in a particular sample of 50 packages, the mean amount dispensed is 8.159 ounces, with a sample standard deviation of 0.051 ounce.

a. Is there evidence that the population mean amount is different from 8.17 ounces? (Use a 0.05 level of significance.)

b. Determine the *p*-value and interpret its meaning.

11.26 A stationery store wants to estimate the mean retail value of greeting cards that it has in its inventory. A random sample of 100 greeting cards indicates a mean value of $2.55 and a standard deviation of $0.44.

a. Is there evidence that the population mean retail value of the greeting cards is different from $2.50? (Use a 0.05 level of significance.)

b. Determine the *p*-value and interpret its meaning.

11.27 The U.S. Department of Transportation requires tire manufacturers to provide performance information on tire sidewalls to help prospective buyers make their purchasing decisions. One very important piece of information is the tread wear index, which indicates the tire's resistance to tread wear. A tire with a grade of 200 should last twice as long, on average, as a tire with a grade of 100.

A consumer organization wants to test the actual tread wear index of a brand name of tires that claims "graded 200" on the sidewall of the tire. A random sample of $n = 18$ indicates a sample mean tread wear index of 195.3 and a sample standard deviation of 21.4.

a. Is there evidence that the population mean tread wear index is different from 200? (Use a 0.05 level of significance.)

b. Determine the *p*-value and interpret its meaning.

11.28 The file **FastFood** contains the amount that a sample of nine customers spent for lunch ($) at a fast-food restaurant:

4.20   5.03   5.86   6.45   7.38   7.54   8.46   8.47   9.87

a. At the 0.05 level of significance, is there evidence that the mean amount spent for lunch is different from $6.50?

b. Determine the *p*-value in (a) and interpret its meaning.

c. What assumption must you make about the population distribution in order to conduct the *t* test in (a) and (b)?

d. Because the sample size is 9, do you need to be concerned about the shape of the population distribution when conducting the *t* test in (a)? Explain.

11.29 In New York State, savings banks are permitted to sell a form of life insurance called savings bank life insurance (SBLI). The approval process consists of underwriting, which includes a review of the application, a medical information bureau check, possible requests for additional medical information and medical exams, and a policy compilation stage in which the policy pages are generated and sent to the bank for delivery. The ability to deliver approved policies to customers in a timely manner is critical to the profitability of this service. During a period of one month, a random sample of 27 approved policies is selected, and the total processing time, in days, is recorded (and stored in **Insurance**):

73   19   16   64   28   28   31   90   60   56   31   56   22   18
45   48   17   17   17   91   92   63   50   51   69   16   17

a. In the past, the mean processing time was 45 days. At the 0.05 level of significance, is there evidence that the mean processing time has changed from 45 days?

b. What assumption about the population distribution is needed in order to conduct the *t* test in (a)?

c. Construct a boxplot or a normal probability plot to evaluate the assumption made in (b).

d. Do you think that the assumption needed in order to conduct the *t* test in (a) is valid? Explain.

11.30 The following data (in **Drink**) represent the amount of soft-drink filled in a sample of 50 consecutive 2-liter bottles. The results, listed horizontally in the order of being filled, were

2.109 2.086 2.066 2.075 2.065 2.057 2.052 2.044 2.036 2.038
2.031 2.029 2.025 2.029 2.023 2.020 2.015 2.014 2.013 2.014
2.012 2.012 2.012 2.010 2.005 2.003 1.999 1.996 1.997 1.992
1.994 1.986 1.984 1.981 1.973 1.975 1.971 1.969 1.966 1.967
1.963 1.957 1.951 1.951 1.947 1.941 1.941 1.938 1.908 1.894

a. At the 0.05 level of significance, is there evidence that the mean amount of soft drink filled is different from 2.0 liters?

b. Determine the *p*-value in (a) and interpret its meaning.

c. In (a), you assumed that the distribution of the amount of soft drink filled was normally distributed. Evaluate this assumption by constructing a boxplot or a normal probability plot.

d. Do you think that the assumption needed in order to conduct the *t* test in (a) is valid? Explain.

e. Examine the values of the 50 bottles in their sequential order, as given in the problem. Does there appear to be a pattern to the results? If so, what impact might this pattern have on the validity of the results in (a)?

11.31 One of the major measures of the quality of service provided by any organization is the speed with which it responds to customer complaints. A large family-held department store selling furniture and flooring, including carpet, had undergone a major expansion in the past several years. In particular, the flooring department had expanded from 2 installation crews to an installation supervisor, a measurer, and 15 installation crews. The store had the business objective of improving its response to complaints. The variable of interest was defined as the number of days between when the complaint was made and when it was resolved. Data were collected from 50 complaints that were made in the past year. The data, stored in Furniture , are as follows:

54	5	35	137	31	27	152	2	123	81	74	27
11	19	126	110	110	29	61	35	94	31	26	5
12	4	165	32	29	28	29	26	25	1	14	13
13	10	5	27	4	52	30	22	36	26	20	23
33	68										

a. The installation supervisor claims that the mean number of days between the receipt of a complaint and the resolution of the complaint is 20 days. At the 0.05 level of significance, is there evidence that the claim is not true (i.e., that the mean number of days is different from 20)?

b. What assumption about the population distribution is needed in order to conduct the t test in (a)?

c. Construct a boxplot or a normal probability plot to evaluate the assumption made in (b).

d. Do you think that the assumption needed in order to conduct the t test in (a) is valid? Explain.

11.32 A manufacturing company produces steel housings for electrical equipment. The main component part of the housing is a steel trough that is made out of a 14-gauge steel coil. It is produced using a 250-ton progressive punch press with a wipe-down operation that puts two 90-degree forms in the flat steel to make the trough. The distance from one side of the form to the other is critical because of weatherproofing in outdoor applications. The company requires that the width of the trough be between 8.31 inches and 8.61 inches. The file Trough contains the widths of the troughs, in inches, for a sample of $n = 49$:

8.312 8.343 8.317 8.383 8.348 8.410 8.351 8.373 8.481 8.422

8.476 8.382 8.484 8.403 8.414 8.419 8.385 8.465 8.498 8.447

8.436 8.413 8.489 8.414 8.481 8.415 8.479 8.429 8.458 8.462

8.460 8.444 8.429 8.460 8.412 8.420 8.410 8.405 8.323 8.420

8.396 8.447 8.405 8.439 8.411 8.427 8.420 8.498 8.409

a. At the 0.05 level of significance, is there evidence that the mean width of the troughs is different from 8.46 inches?

b. What assumption about the population distribution is needed in order to conduct the t test in (a)?

c. Evaluate the assumption made in (b).

d. Do you think that the assumption needed in order to conduct the t test in (a) is valid? Explain.

11.33 One operation of a steel mill is to cut pieces of steel into parts that are used in the frame for front seats in an automobile. The steel is cut with a diamond saw and requires the resulting parts must be cut to be within ± 0.005 inch of the length specified by the automobile company. The file Steel contains a sample of 100 steel parts. The measurement reported is the difference, in inches, between the actual length of the steel part, as measured by a laser measurement device, and the specified length of the steel part. For example, a value of -0.002 represents a steel part that is 0.002 inch shorter than the specified length.

a. At the 0.05 level of significance, is there evidence that the mean difference is not equal to 0.0 inches?

b. Construct a 95% confidence interval estimate of the population mean. Interpret this interval.

c. Compare the conclusions reached in (a) and (b).

d. Because $n = 100$, do you have to be concerned about the normality assumption needed for the t test and t interval?

11.34 In Problem 4.102 on page 188, you were introduced to a tea-bag-filling operation. An important quality characteristic of interest for this process is the weight of the tea in the individual bags. The file Teabags contains an ordered array of the weight, in grams, of a sample of 50 tea bags produced during an eight-hour shift.

a. Is there evidence that the mean amount of tea per bag is different from 5.5 grams? (Use $\alpha = 0.01$.)

b. Construct a 99% confidence interval estimate of the population mean amount of tea per bag. Interpret this interval.

c. Compare the conclusions reached in (a) and (b).

11.35 Although many people think they can put a meal on the table in a short period of time, an article reported that they end up spending about 40 minutes doing so. (Data extracted from N. Hellmich, "Americans Go for the Quick Fix for Dinner," *USA Today*, February 14, 2006.) Suppose another study is conducted to test the validity of this statement. A sample of 25 people is selected, and the length of time to prepare and cook dinner (in minutes) is recorded, with the following results (in Dinner):

44.0 51.9 49.7 40.0 55.5 33.0 43.4 41.3 45.2 40.7 41.1 49.1 30.9

45.2 55.3 52.1 55.1 38.8 43.1 39.2 58.6 49.8 43.2 47.9 46.6

a. Is there evidence that the population mean time to prepare and cook dinner is different from 40 minutes? Use the p-value approach and a level of significance of 0.05.

b. What assumption about the population distribution is needed in order to conduct the t test in (a)?

c. Make a list of the various ways you could evaluate the assumption noted in (b).

d. Evaluate the assumption noted in (b) and determine whether the t test in (a) is valid.

11.4 One-Tail Tests

In Section 11.1, hypothesis testing was used to examine the question of whether the population mean amount of cereal filled is 368 grams. The alternative hypothesis $1H_1 : \mu \neq 3682$ contains two possibilities: Either the mean is less than 368 grams or the mean is more than 368 grams. For this reason, the rejection region is divided into the two tails of the sampling distribution of the mean. In Section 11.2, a two-tail test was used to determine whether the mean amount per invoice had changed from $120.

In contrast to these two examples, many situations require an alternative hypothesis that focuses on a *particular direction*. For example, the population mean is *less than* a specified value. One such situation involves the business problem concerning the service time at the drive-through window of a fast-food restaurant. The speed with which customers are served is of critical importance to the success of the service (see **www.qsrmagazine.com/reports/drive-thru_time_study**). In one past study, McDonald's had a mean service time of 174.22 seconds, which was only ninth best in the industry. Suppose that McDonald's began a quality improvement effort to reduce the service time by deploying an improved drive-through service process in a sample of 25 stores. Because McDonald's would want to institute the new process in all of its stores only if the test sample saw a *decreased* drive-through time, the entire rejection region is located in the lower tail of the distribution.

The Critical Value Approach

You wish to determine whether the new drive-through process has a mean that is less than 174.22 seconds. To perform this one-tail hypothesis test, you use the six-step method listed in Exhibit 11.1 on page 435.

Step 1   You define the null and alternative hypotheses:

$$H_0 : \mu \geq 174.22$$

$$H_1 : \mu < 174.22$$

The alternative hypothesis contains the statement for which you are trying to find evidence. If the conclusion of the test is "reject H_0," there is statistical evidence that the mean drive-through time is less than the drive-through time in the old process. This would be reason to change the drive-through process for the entire population of stores. If the conclusion of the test is "do not reject H_0," then there is insufficient evidence that the mean drive-through time in the new process is significantly less than the drive-through time in the old process. If this occurs, there would be insufficient reason to institute the new drive-through process in the population of stores.

Step 2   You collect the data by selecting a sample of $n = 25$ stores. You decide to use $\alpha = 0.05$.

Step 3   Because σ is unknown, you use the t distribution and the t_{STAT} test statistic. You need to assume that the drive-through time is normally distributed because only a sample of 25 drive-through times is selected.

Step 4   The rejection region is entirely contained in the lower tail of the sampling distribution of the mean because you want to reject H_0 only when the sample mean is significantly less than 174.22 seconds. When the entire rejection region is contained in one tail of the sampling distribution of the test statistic, the test is called a **one-tail test**, or **directional test**. If the alternative hypothesis includes the *less than* sign, the critical value of t is negative. As shown in Table 11.3 and Figure 11.12, because the entire rejection region is in the lower tail of the t distribution and contains an area of 0.05, due to the symmetry of the t distribution, the critical value of the t test statistic with $25 - 1 = 24$ degrees of freedom is -1.7109. The decision rule is

$$\text{Reject } H_0 \text{ if } t_{STAT} < -1.7109;$$

$$\text{otherwise, do not reject } H_0.$$

TABLE 11.3

Determining the Critical Value from the t Table for an Area of 0.05 in the Lower Tail, with 24 Degrees of Freedom

	Cumulative Probabilities					
	.75	.90	.95	.975	.99	.995
	Upper-Tail Areas					
Degrees of Freedom	.25	.10	.05	.025	.01	.005
1	1.0000	3.0777	6.3138	12.7062	31.8207	63.6574
2	0.8165	1.8856	2.9200	4.3027	6.9646	9.9248
3	0.7649	1.6377	2.3534	3.1824	4.5407	5.8409
.	.	.	.	.	.	.
.	.	.	.	.	.	.
.	.	.	.	.	.	.
23	0.6853	1.3195	1.7139	2.0687	2.4999	2.8073
24	0.6848	1.3178 →	1.7109	2.0639	2.4922	2.7969
25	0.6844	1.3163	1.7081	2.0595	2.4851	2.7874

Source: Extracted from Table E.3.

FIGURE 11.12

One-tail test of hypothesis for a mean (σ unknown) at the 0.05 level of significance

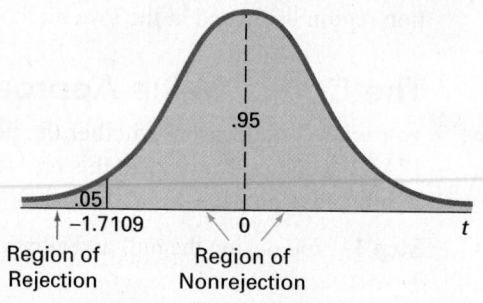

.95

.05
↑ −1.7109
Region of Rejection

0
Region of Nonrejection

t

Step 5 From the sample of 25 stores you selected, you find that the sample mean service time at the drive-through equals 162.96 seconds and the sample standard deviation equals 20.2 seconds. Using $n = 25$, $\overline{X} = 162.96$, $S = 20.2$, and Equation (11.2) on page 448,

$$t_{STAT} = \frac{\overline{X} - \mu}{\dfrac{S}{\sqrt{n}}} = \frac{162.96 - 174.22}{\dfrac{20.2}{\sqrt{25}}} = -2.7871$$

Step 6 Because $t_{STAT} = -2.7871 < -1.7109$, you reject the null hypothesis (see Figure 11.12). You conclude that the mean service time at the drive-through is less than 174.22 seconds. There is sufficient evidence to change the drive-through process for the entire population of stores.

The p-Value Approach

Use the five steps listed in Exhibit 11.2 on page 439 to illustrate the t test for the drive-through time study using the p-value approach.

Step 1–3 These steps are the same as in the critical value approach on page 459.

Step 4 $t_{STAT} = -2.7871$ (see step 5 of the critical value approach). Because the alternative hypothesis indicates a rejection region entirely in the lower tail of the sampling distribution, to compute the p-value, you need to find the probability that the t_{STAT} test statistic will be less than −2.7871. Figure 11.13 shows that the p-value is 0.0051.

FIGURE 11.13

Casio calculator FX-9750GII *t* test results for the drive-through time study

t test for the hypothesis of the mean service time at drive through study

From the **Main Menu** select

STAT F3(TEST) **F2**(t) **F1**(1-S), and then enter the following items.

(Note: Only use the **EXE** key after a new entry. Otherwise, use the cursor ▼ arrow. If you accidentally hit the wrong key, use **AC/ON** or **EXIT** to go back.)

1-Sample tTest

Data	: **F2**(Var)	▼
μ	: **F2**($<\mu 0$)	▼
μ0	: **163.9**	**EXE**
$\bar{x}$	: **152.7**	**EXE**
sx	: **20**	**EXE**
n	: **25**	**EXE**
Save Res	: None	

Now press **EXE** or **F1**(CALC) or **F6**(DRAW).

If you select **F6**(DRAW), you will see a normal distribution.

If you select either **EXE** or **F1**(Calc), the calculator will show the following results:

1-Sample tTest

μ	<163.9
t	$=-2.8$
p	$=4.9646\text{E-}03$ (which is 0.004946)
$\bar{x}$	$=152.7$
sx	$=20$
n	$=25$

Statistical Decision: Reject the null hypothesis.

Two ways of finding the *t* critical value:

(1)   Using the Casio calculator fx-9750GII
Note: Fx-9750G Plus does not have this option; therefore, you have to use the *t* table.

From the **Main Menu** select

STAT F6(DIST) **F2**(t) **F3**(Invt), and then enter the following items.

Inverse Student-t

Data	: **F2**(Var)	▼
Area	: **0.05**	
df	: **25–1**	**EXE**
Save Res	: None	

Now press **EXE** or **F1**(CALC).

The calculator will show the following results:

Inverse Student-t
x-Inv $= 1.71088208$

(2) Using the *t* table.

df	T Table		Upper Tail Areas			
	0.25	0.1	0.05	0.025	0.01	0.005
1	1.000	3.078	6.314	12.706	31.821	63.657
2	0.816	1.886	2.920	4.303	6.965	9.925
3	0.765	1.638	2.353	3.182	4.541	5.841
4	0.741	1.533	2.132	2.776	3.747	4.604
5	0.727	1.476	2.015	2.571	3.365	4.032
6	0.718	1.440	1.943	2.447	3.143	3.707
7	0.711	1.415	1.895	2.365	2.998	3.499
8	0.706	1.397	1.860	2.306	2.896	3.355
9	0.703	1.383	1.833	2.262	2.821	3.250
10	0.700	1.372	1.812	2.228	2.764	3.169
11	0.697	1.363	1.796	2.201	2.718	3.106
12	0.695	1.356	1.782	2.179	2.681	3.055
13	0.694	1.350	1.771	2.160	2.650	3.012
14	0.692	1.345	1.761	2.145	2.624	2.977
15	0.691	1.341	1.753	2.131	2.602	2.947
16	0.690	1.337	1.746	2.120	2.583	2.921
17	0.689	1.333	1.740	2.110	2.567	2.898
18	0.688	1.330	1.734	2.101	2.552	2.878
19	0.688	1.328	1.729	2.093	2.539	2.861
20	0.687	1.325	1.725	2.086	2.528	2.845
21	0.686	1.323	1.721	2.080	2.518	2.831
22	0.686	1.321	1.717	2.074	2.508	2.819
23	0.685	1.319	1.714	2.069	2.500	2.807
24	0.685	1.318	1.711	2.064	2.492	2.797

Step 5 The *p*-value of 0.0051 is less than $\alpha = 0.05$ (see Figure 11.14). You reject H_0 and conclude that the mean service time at the drive-through is less than 174.22 seconds. There is sufficient evidence to change the drive-through process for the entire population of stores.

FIGURE 11.14

Determining the *p*-value for a one-tail test

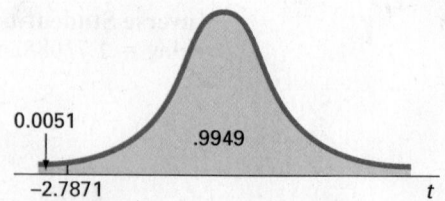

0.0051

.9949

−2.7871   *t*

EXAMPLE 11.17

A One-Tail Test for the Mean

A company that manufactures chocolate bars is particularly concerned that the mean weight of a chocolate bar is not greater than 6.03 ounces. A sample of 50 chocolate bars is selected; the sample mean is 6.034 ounces, and the sample standard deviation is 0.02 ounces. Using the $\alpha = 0.01$ level of significance, is there evidence that the population mean weight of the chocolate bars is greater than 6.03 ounces?

SOLUTION Using the critical value approach, listed in Exhibit 11.1 on page 435,

Step 1 First, you define your hypotheses:

$$H_0: \mu \le 6.03$$
$$H_1: \mu > 6.03$$

Step 2 You collect the data from a sample of $n = 50$. You decide to use $\alpha = 0.01$.

Step 3 Because σ is unknown, you use the t distribution and the t_{STAT} test statistic.

Step 4 The rejection region is entirely contained in the upper tail of the sampling distribution of the mean because you want to reject H_0 only when the sample mean is significantly greater than 6.03 ounces. Because the entire rejection region is in the upper tail of the t distribution and contains an area of 0.01, the critical value of the t distribution with $50 - 1 = 49$ degrees of freedom is 2.4049 (see Table E.3).

The decision rule is

$$\text{Reject } H_0 \text{ if } t_{STAT} > 2.4049;$$

$$\text{otherwise, do not reject } H_0.$$

Step 5 From your sample of 50 chocolate bars, you find that the sample mean weight is 6.034 ounces, and the sample standard deviation is 0.02 ounces. Using $n = 50$, $\overline{X} = 6.034$, $S = 0.02$, and Equation (11.2) on page 448,

$$t_{STAT} = \frac{\overline{X} - \mu}{\dfrac{S}{\sqrt{n}}} = \frac{6.034 - 6.03}{\dfrac{0.02}{\sqrt{50}}} = 1.414$$

Step 6 Because $t_{STAT} = 1.414 < 2.4049$, or using Microsoft Excel or Minitab, the p-value is $0.0818 > 0.01$, you do not reject the null hypothesis. There is insufficient evidence to conclude that the population mean weight is greater than 6.03 ounces.

CASIO Calculator Instruction

Refer to Example 11.17. At the 0.01 level of significance, is there evidence that the population mean weight of the chocolate bars is greater than 6.03 ounces?

t test for the hypothesis of the mean

From the **Main Menu** select

STAT F3(TEST) **F2**(t) **F1**(1-S), and then enter the following items.

(Note: Only use the **EXE** key after a new entry. Otherwise, use the cursor ▼ arrow. If you accidentally hit the wrong key, use **AC$^{/ON}$** or **EXIT** to go back.)

1-Sample tTest

Data	: F2(Var) ▼	
μ	: F3 ($> \mu$0) ▼	
μ0	: **6.03**	**EXE**
x	: **6.034**	**EXE**
sx	: **0.02**	**EXE**
n	: **50**	**EXE**
Save Res	: None	

Now press **EXE** or **F1**(CALC) or **F6** (DRAW).

If you select **F6** (DRAW), you will see a normal distribution.

If you select either **EXE** or **F1**(Calc), the calculator will show the following results:

1-Sample tTest
μ	> 6.03
t	= 1.41421356
p	=0.081811
x	=6.034
sx	=0.02
n	=50

Statistical Decision: Do not reject the null hypothesis because the *p*-value (0.0818) is greater than α (0.01) or t_{cal} (1.414) is less than the *t* critical value (2.4049).

To find the *t* critical value:

To find the *t* critical value using the Casio calculator fx-9750GII, follow the following calculator steps.

Note: Fx-9750G Plus does not have this option; therefore, you have to use the *t* table.

From the **Main Menu** select

STAT   F5(DIST)   **F2**(t)   **F3**(Invt), and then enter the following items:

Inverse Student-t
Data	: **F2**(Var) ▼
Area	: **0.01**
df	: **50-1** **EXE**
Save Res	: None

Now press **EXE** or **F1**(CALC).

The calculator will show the following results:

Inverse Student-t
x-Inv = 2.40489176

To perform one-tail tests of hypotheses, you must properly formulate H_0 and H_1. A summary of the null and alternative hypotheses for one-tail tests is as follows:

- The null hypothesis, H_0, represents the status quo or the current belief in a situation.
- The alternative hypothesis, H_1, is the opposite of the null hypothesis and represents a research claim or specific inference you would like to prove.
- If you reject the null hypothesis, you have statistical proof that the alternative hypothesis is correct.
- If you do not reject the null hypothesis, you have failed to prove the alternative hypothesis. The failure to prove the alternative hypothesis, however, does not mean that you have proven the null hypothesis.
- The null hypothesis always refers to a specified value of the *population parameter* (such as μ), not to a *sample statistic* (such as $\overline{X}$).
- The statement of the null hypothesis *always* contains an equal sign regarding the specified value of the parameter (e.g., $H_0 : \mu \geq 174.22$).
- The statement of the alternative hypothesis *never* contains an equal sign regarding the specified value of the parameter (e.g., $H_1 : \mu < 174.22$).

Problems for Section 11.4

LEARNING THE BASICS

11.36 In a one-tail hypothesis test where you reject H_0 only in the *upper* tail, what is the *p*-value if $Z_{STAT} = +2.00$?

11.37 In Problem 11.36, what is your statistical decision if you test the null hypothesis at the 0.05 level of significance?

11.38 In a one-tail hypothesis test where you reject H_0 only in the *lower* tail, what is the *p*-value if $Z_{STAT} = -1.38$?

11.39 In Problem 11.38, what is your statistical decision if you test the null hypothesis at the 0.01 level of significance?

11.40 In a one-tail hypothesis test where you reject H_0 only in the *lower* tail, what is the *p*-value if $Z_{STAT} = +1.38$?

11.41 In Problem 11.40, what is the statistical decision if you test the null hypothesis at the 0.01 level of significance?

11.42 In a one-tail hypothesis test where you reject H_0 only in the *upper* tail, what is the critical value of the *t*-test statistic with 10 degrees of freedom at the 0.01 level of significance?

11.43 In Problem 11.42, what is your statistical decision if $t_{STAT} = +2.39$?

11.44 In a one-tail hypothesis test where you reject H_0 only in the *lower* tail, what is the critical value of the t_{STAT} test statistic with 20 degrees of freedom at the 0.01 level of significance?

11.45 In Problem 11.44, what is your statistical decision if $t_{STAT} = -1.15$?

APPLYING THE CONCEPTS

11.46 In a recent year, the Federal Communications Commission reported that the mean wait for repairs for Verizon customers was 36.5 hours. In an effort to improve this service, suppose that a new repair service process was developed. This new process, used for a sample of 100 repairs, resulted in a sample mean of 34.5 hours and a sample standard deviation of 11.7 hours.

a. Is there evidence that the population mean amount is less than 36.5 hours? (Use a 0.05 level of significance.)

b. Determine the *p*-value and interpret its meaning.

11.47 In a recent year, the Federal Communications Commission reported that the mean wait for repairs for AT&T customers was 25.3 hours. In an effort to improve this service, suppose that a new repair service process was developed. This new process, used for a sample of 100 repairs, resulted in a sample mean of 22.3 hours and a sample standard deviation of 8.3 hours.

a. Is there evidence that the population mean amount is less than 25.3 hours? (Use a 0.05 level of significance.)

b. Determine the *p*-value and interpret its meaning.

SELF **Test** **11.48** Southside Hospital in Bay Shore, New York, commonly conducts stress tests to study the heart muscle after a person has a heart attack. Members of the diagnostic imaging department conducted a quality improvement project with the objective of reducing the turnaround time for stress tests. Turnaround time is defined as the time from when a test is ordered to when the radiologist signs off on the test results. Initially, the mean turnaround time for a stress test was 68 hours. After incorporating changes into the stress-test process, the quality improvement team collected a sample of 50 turnaround times. In this sample, the mean turnaround time was 32 hours, with a standard deviation of 9 hours. (Data extracted from E. Godin, D. Raven, C. Sweetapple, and F. R. Del Guidice, "Faster Test Results," *Quality Progress*, January 2004, 37(1), pp. 33–39.)

a. If you test the null hypothesis at the 0.01 level of significance, is there evidence that the new process has reduced turnaround time?

b. Interpret the meaning of the *p*-value in this problem.

11.49 You are the manager of a restaurant that delivers pizza to college dormitory rooms. You have just changed your delivery process in an effort to reduce the mean time between the order and completion of delivery from the current 25 minutes. A sample of 36 orders using the new delivery process yields a sample mean of 22.4 minutes and a sample standard deviation of 6 minutes.

a. Using the six-step critical value approach, at the 0.05 level of significance, is there evidence that the population mean delivery time has been reduced below the previous population mean value of 25 minutes?

b. At the 0.05 level of significance, use the five-step *p*-value approach.

c. Interpret the meaning of the *p*-value in (b).

d. Compare your conclusions in (a) and (b).

11.50 The per-store daily customer count (i.e., the mean number of customers in a store in one day) for a nationwide convenience store chain that operates nearly 10,000 stores has been steady, at 900, for some time. To increase the customer count, the chain is considering cutting prices for coffee beverages. The small size will now be $0.59 instead of $0.99, and the medium size will be $0.69 instead of $1.19. Even with this reduction in price, the chain will have a 40% gross margin on coffee. To test the new initiative, the chain has reduced coffee prices in a sample of 34 stores, where customer counts have been running almost exactly at the national average of 900. After four weeks, the sample stores stabilize at a mean customer count of 974 and a standard deviation of 96. This increase seems like a substantial amount to you, but it also seems like a pretty small sample. Do you think reducing coffee prices is a good strategy for increasing the mean customer count?

a. State the null and alternative hypotheses.
b. Explain the meaning of the Type I and Type II errors in the context of this scenario.
c. At the 0.01 level of significance, is there evidence that reducing coffee prices is a good strategy for increasing the mean customer count?
d. Interpret the meaning of the p-value in (c).

11.51 The population mean waiting time to check out of a supermarket has been 10.73 minutes. Recently, in an ef-

fort to reduce the waiting time, the supermarket has experimented with a system in which there is a single waiting line with multiple checkout servers. A sample of 100 customers was selected, and their mean waiting time to check out was 9.52 minutes, with a sample standard deviation of 5.8 minutes.

a. At the 0.05 level of significance, using the critical value approach to hypothesis testing, is there evidence that the population mean waiting time to check out is less than 10.73 minutes?
b. At the 0.05 level of significance, using the p-value approach to hypothesis testing, is there evidence that the population mean waiting time to check out is less than 10.73 minutes?
c. Interpret the meaning of the p-value in this problem.
d. Compare your conclusions in (a) and (b).

11.5 Z Test of Hypothesis for the Proportion

In some situations, you want to test a hypothesis about the proportion of events of interest in the population, π, rather than test the population mean. To begin, you select a random sample and compute the **sample proportion**, $p = X/n$. You then compare the value of this statistic to the hypothesized value of the parameter, π, in order to decide whether to reject the null hypothesis. If the number of events of interest (X) and the number of events that are not of interest ($n - X$) are each at least five, the sampling distribution of a proportion approximately follows a normal distribution. You use the **Z test for the proportion** given in Equation (11.3) to perform the hypothesis test for the difference between the sample proportion, p, and the hypothesized population proportion, π.

Z TEST FOR THE PROPORTION

$$Z_{STAT} = \frac{p - \pi}{\sqrt{\dfrac{\pi(1 - \pi)}{n}}} \qquad (11.3)$$

where

$$p = \text{Sample proportion} = \frac{X}{n} = \frac{\text{Number of events of interest in the sample}}{\text{Sample size}}$$

$$\pi = \text{Hypothesized proportion of events of interest in the population}$$

The Z_{STAT} test statistic approximately follows a standardized normal distribution when X and $(n - X)$ are each at least 5.

Alternatively, by multiplying the numerator and denominator by n, you can write the Z_{STAT} test statistic in terms of the number of events of interest, X, as shown in Equation (11.4).

Z TEST FOR THE PROPORTION IN TERMS OF THE NUMBER OF EVENTS OF INTEREST

$$Z_{STAT} = \frac{X - n\pi}{\sqrt{n\pi(1 - \pi)}} \qquad (11.4)$$

The Critical Value Approach

To illustrate the *Z* test for a proportion, consider a survey conducted for American Express that sought to determine the reasons adults wanted Internet access while on vacation. (Data extracted from "Wired Vacationers," *USA Today*, June 4, 2010, p. 1A.) Of 2,000 adults, 1,540 said that they wanted Internet access so they could check personal e-mail while on vacation. A survey conducted in the previous year indicated that 75% of adults wanted Internet access so they could check personal e-mail while on vacation. Is there evidence that the percentage of adults who wanted Internet access to check personal e-mail while on vacation has changed from the previous year? To investigate this question, the null and alternative hypotheses are follows:

$H_0: \pi = 0.75$ (i.e., the proportion of adults who want Internet access to check personal email while on vacation has not changed from the previous year)

$H_1: \pi \neq 0.75$ (i.e., the proportion of adults who want Internet access to check personal email while on vacation has changed from the previous year)

Because you are interested in determining whether the population proportion of adults who want Internet access to check personal email while on vacation has changed from 0.75 in the previous year, you use a two-tail test. If you select the $\alpha = 0.05$ level of significance, the rejection and nonrejection regions are set up as in Figure 11.15, and the decision rule is

Reject H_0 if $Z_{STAT} < -1.96$ or if $Z_{STAT} > +1.96$;

otherwise, do not reject H_0.

FIGURE 11.15

Two-tail test of hypothesis for the proportion at the 0.05 level of significance

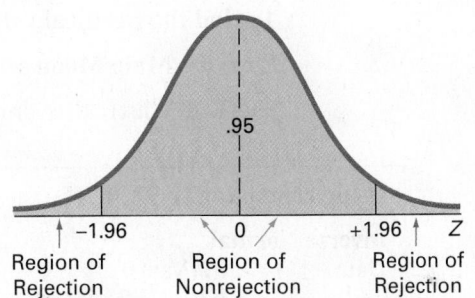

Because 1,540 of the 2,000 adults stated that they wanted Internet access to check personal email while on vacation,

$$p = \frac{1,540}{2,000} = 0.77$$

Since $X = 1,540$ and $n - X = 460$, each > 5, using Equation (11.3),

$$Z_{STAT} = \frac{p - \pi}{\sqrt{\dfrac{\pi(1 - \pi)}{n}}} = \frac{0.77 - 0.75}{\sqrt{\dfrac{0.75(1 - 0.75)}{2,000}}} = \frac{0.02}{0.0097} = 2.0656$$

or, using Equation (11.4),

$$Z_{STAT} = \frac{X - n\pi}{\sqrt{n\pi(1 - \pi)}} = \frac{1,540 - (2,000)(0.75)}{\sqrt{2,000(0.75)(0.25)}} = \frac{40}{19.3649} = 2.0656$$

Because $Z_{STAT} = 2.0656 > 1.96$, you reject H_0. There is evidence that the population proportion of all adults who want Internet access to check personal e-mail while on vacation has changed from 0.75 in the previous year. Figure 11.16 presents results for these data, as computed by Excel and Minitab.

FIGURE 11.16

Casio calculator
FX-9750GII results for
the survey of whether
customer service is
better or worse at e-
commerce sites than it is
at physical stores

Z test for the hypothesis
for the proportion

From the **Main Menu** select

STAT F3(TEST) **F1**(Z) **F3**(1-p), and then enter the following items.

(**Note:** Only use the **EXE** key after a new entry. Otherwise, use the cursor ▼ arrow. If you accidentally hit the wrong key, use **AC/ON** or **EXIT** to go back.)

1-Prop ZTest

Prop	: **F1**($\neq$p0)	▼
p0	: **0.5**	EXE
x	: **561**	EXE
n	: **1100**	EXE
Save Res	: None	

Now press **EXE** or **F1**(CALC) or **F6**(DRAW).

If you select **F6** (DRAW), you will see a normal distribution.

If you select either **EXE** or **F1**(Calc), the calculator will show the following results:

1-Prop ZTest

Prop	$\neq$0.5
z	=0.66332495
p	=0.50712245
$\bar{p}$	=0.51
n	=1100

Statistical Decision: Do not reject the null hypothesis.

To find the z critical value:

From the **Main Menu** select

STAT F5(dist) **F1**(Norm) **F3**(InvN), and then enter the following items.

Using calculator fx-9750GII	Using calculator fx-9750G Plus
Inverse Normal	**Inverse Normal**
Data : **F2**(Var) ▼	Area : **0.05** $\div$ **2** EXE
Tail : **F3**(CNTR) ▼	σ : **1** EXE
Area : **1–0.05** EXE	μ : **0** EXE
σ : **1** EXE	
μ : **0** EXE	Now press **EXE** or **F1**(CALC).
Save Res : **None** EXE	
	The calculator will show the following results:
Now press **EXE** or **F1**(CALC).	
	Inverse Normal:
The calculator will show the following results:	X = −1.959964
	Note: For this model, when using the InvN function, the *Area* value that is required is the area to the *left* of the desired X value.
Inverse Normal:	
X_1 Inv = −1.959964	
X_2 Inv = 1.95996398	

The *p*-Value Approach

As an alternative to the critical value approach, you can compute the *p*-value. For this two-tail test in which the rejection region is located in the lower tail and the upper tail, you need to find the area below a Z value of −2.0656 and above a Z value of +2.0656. Figure 11.16 reports a *p*-value of 0.0389. Because this value is less than the selected level of significance ($\alpha = 0.05$), you reject the null hypothesis.

EXAMPLE 11.18

Testing a Hypothesis for a Proportion

A fast-food chain has developed a new process to ensure that orders at the drive-through are filled correctly. The business problem is defined as determining whether the new process can increase the percentage of orders processed correctly. The previous process filled orders correctly 85% of the time. Data are collected from a sample of 100 orders using the new process. The results indicate that 94 orders were filled correctly. At the 0.01 level of significance, can you conclude that the new process has increased the proportion of orders filled correctly?

SOLUTION The null and alternative hypotheses are

$H_0 : \pi \leq 0.85$ (i.e., the population proportion of orders filled correctly using the new process is less than or equal to 0.85)

$H_1 : \pi > 0.85$ (i.e., the population proportion of orders filled correctly using the new process is greater than 0.85)

Since $X = 94$ and $n - X = 6$, both > 5, using Equation (11.3) on page 466,

$$p = \frac{X}{n} = \frac{94}{100} = 0.94$$

$$Z_{STAT} = \frac{p - \pi}{\sqrt{\dfrac{\pi(1 - \pi)}{n}}} = \frac{0.94 - 0.85}{\sqrt{\dfrac{0.85(1 - 0.85)}{100}}} = \frac{0.09}{0.0357} = 2.52$$

The *p*-value for $Z_{STAT} > 2.52$ is 0.0059.

Using the critical value approach, you reject H_0 if $Z_{STAT} > 2.33$. Using the *p*-value approach, you reject H_0 if *p*-value < 0.01. Because $Z_{STAT} = 2.52 > 2.33$ or the *p-value* $= 0.0059 < 0.01$, you reject H_0. You have evidence that the new process has increased the proportion of correct orders above 0.85.

CASIO Calculator Instruction

Refer to Example 11.18. At the 0.01 level of significance, can you conclude that the new process has increased the proportion of orders filled correctly?

Z test for the hypothesis for the proportion

From the **Main Menu** select

STAT F3(test) **F1**(Z) **F3**(1-p), and then enter the following items.

(Note: Only use the **EXE** key after a new entry. Otherwise, use the cursor ▼ arrow. If you accidentally hit the wrong key, use **AC/ON** or **EXIT** to go back.)

1-Prop ZTest

Prop	: F3 (>p0)	▼
p0	: 0.85	**EXE**
x	: 94	**EXE**
n	: 100	**EXE**
Save Res	: None	

Now press **EXE** or **F1**(CALC) or **F6** (DRAW).

If you select **F6** (DRAW), you will see a normal distribution.

If you select either **EXE** or **F1**(Calc), the calculator will show the following results:

1-Prop ZTest
Prop > 0.85
z $= 2.52050415$
p $= 5.8593E{-}03$
$\bar{p}$ $= 0.94$
n $= 100$

Statistical Decision: Reject the null hypothesis.

To find the z critical value:

From the **Main Menu** select

STAT F5(dist) **F1**(Norm) **F3**(InvN), and then enter the following items:

Using Calculator fx-9750GII	Using Calculator fx-9750G Plus
Inverse Normal	**Inverse Normal**
Data : **F2**(Var) ▼	Area : **0.01** **EXE**
Tail : **F2** (Right) ▼	σ : **1** **EXE**
Area : **0.01** **EXE**	μ : **0** **EXE**
σ : **1** **EXE**	Now press **EXE** or **F1**(CALC)
μ : **0** **EXE**	
Save Res : **None** **EXE**	The calculator will show the following results:
Now press **EXE** or F1(CALC)	**Inverse Normal:**
	X = −2.3263
The calculator will show the following results:	**Note: For this model, when using the**
Inverse Normal:	**InvN function, the *Area* value that is**
X Inv = 2.32634787	**required is the area to the *LEFT* of the**
	desired X value.

SUMMARY

	Hypothesis Testing for Mean		Hypothesis Testing for Proportion
	σ is known	σ is not known	
	Z test	*t* test	*Z* test
Standardized test statistics	Z_{CALC}	t_{CALC}	Z_{CALC}
Critical value	Z_{cv}	t_{cv}	Z_{cv}

Note: Z_{CALC} indicates calculated the Z value. Z_{cv} indicates the Z critical value.

CALCULATOR LESSON 11A

CFX-9850GB
CALCULATOR

Lesson 10A—*Z* Test of a Single Proportion

EXAMPLE 11.19

A bank manager wants to test the hypothesis that less than 60% of all the bank's customers use the ATM to pay some of their bills. A random sample of 80 customers was selected and it was found that 43 of those customers use the ATM to pay some bills. Use the 10% significance level.

Solution: From the **Main Menu** select

STAT **F3**(test) **F1**(Z) **F3**(1-P), and then enter the following items:

(Note: Only use the **EXE** key after a new data entry. Otherwise, use the cursor ▼ arrow. If you accidentally hit the wrong key, use **AC/ON** or **EXIT** to go back.)

1-Prop ZTest
Prop	: **F2**(<)	▼
p0	: **0.6**	**EXE**
x	: **43**	**EXE**
n	: **80**	**EXE**

Now press **EXE** or **F1**(Calc).

The calculator will show the following results:

1-Prop ZTest
μ <0.6
z = −1.141
p = 0.12692
$\hat{p}$ = 0.5375
n = 80

1 tail test

Since the *p*-value > 0.05, the conclusion is to *not reject* the null hypothesis. In other words, the bank manager cannot say that less than 60% of the bank's customers use the ATM to pay some bills.

CALCULATOR LESSON 11B

CASIO FX9750GII
CALCULATOR

Lesson 11B—*Z* Test of a Single Proportion

EXAMPLE 11.20

A bank manager wants to test the hypothesis that less than 60% of all the bank's customers use the ATM to pay some of their bills. A random sample of 80 customers was selected and it was found that 43 of the customers use the ATM to pay some bills. Use the 10% significance level.

Solution: From the **Main Menu** select

STAT **F3**(test) **F1**(Z) **F3**(1-P), and then enter the following items.

(Note: Only use the **EXE** key after a new data entry. Otherwise, use the cursor ▼ arrow. If you accidentally hit the wrong key, use **AC/ON** or **EXIT** to go back.)

1-Prop ZTest

Prop	: F2(<)	▼
p0	: 0.6	EXE
x	: 43	EXE
n	: 80	EXE

Save Res   : None

Now press **EXE** or **F1**(Calc) or **F6**(DRAW).

If you select **F6**(DRAW), you will see a normal distribution.

If you select either **EXE** or **F1**(Calc), the calculator will show the following results:

1-Prop ZTest

μ	<0.6
z	=−1.1410887
p	=0.12691651
$\hat{p}$	=0.5375
n	=80

Since the p-value > 0.05, the conclusion is to *not reject* the null hypothesis. In other words, the bank manager cannot say that less than 60% of the bank's customers use the ATM to pay some bills.

Problems for Section 11.5

LEARNING THE BASICS

11.52 If, in a random sample of 400 items, 88 are defective, what is the sample proportion of defective items?

11.53 In Problem 11.52, if the null hypothesis is that 20% of the items in the population are defective, what is the value of Z_{STAT}?

11.54 In Problems 11.52 and 11.53, suppose you are testing the null hypothesis $H_0 : \pi = 0.20$ against the two-tail alternative hypothesis $H_1 : \pi \neq 0.20$ and you choose the level of significance $\alpha = 0.05$. What is your statistical decision?

APPLYING THE CONCEPTS

11.55 The U.S. Department of Education reports that 46% of full-time college students are employed while attending college. (Data extracted from "The Condition of Education 2009," *National Center for Education Statistics*, **nces.ed .gov**.) A recent survey of 60 full-time students at Miami University found that 29 were employed.
a. Use the five-step p-value approach to hypothesis testing and a 0.05 level of significance to determine whether the proportion of full-time students at Miami University is different from the national norm of 0.46.
b. Assume that the study found that 36 of the 60 full-time students were employed and repeat (a). Are the conclusions the same?

11.56 The worldwide market share for the Mozilla Firefox web browser was 19.2% in a recent month. Suppose that you decided to select a sample of 100 students at your university and you found that 25 used the Mozilla Firefox web browser. (Data extracted from J. Swartz, "Race is On in Browser Wars as Users' Habits Shift," *USA Today*, December 1, 2010, pp. 1B, 2B.)
a. Use the five-step p-value approach to try to determine whether there is evidence that the market share for the Mozilla Firefox web browser at your university is greater than the worldwide market share of 19.2%. (Use the 0.05 level of significance.)
b. Suppose that the sample size was $n = 400$, and you found that 25% of the sample of students at your university (100 out of 400) used the Mozilla Firefox web browser. Use the five-step p-value approach to try to determine whether there is evidence that the market share for the Mozilla Firefox web browser at your university is greater than the worldwide market share of 19.2%. (Use the 0.05 level of significance.)
c. Discuss the effect that sample size has on hypothesis testing.
d. What do you think are your chances of rejecting any null hypothesis concerning a population proportion if a sample size of $n = 20$ is used?

11.57 One of the issues facing organizations is increasing diversity throughout the organization. One of the ways to evaluate an organization's success at increasing diversity is to compare the percentage of employees in the organization in a particular position with a specific background to the percentage in a particular position with that specific background in the general workforce. Recently, a large academic medical center determined that 9 of 17 employees in a particular position were female, whereas 55% of the employees for this position in the general workforce were female. At the 0.05 level of significance, is there evidence that the proportion of females in this position at this medical center is different from what would be expected in the general workforce?

SELF Test **11.58** Of 1,000 respondents aged 24 to 35, 65% reported that they preferred to "look for a job in a place where I would like to live" rather than "look for the best job I can find, the place where I live is secondary." (Data extracted from L. Belkin, "What Do Young Jobseekers Want? (Something Other Than a Job)," *The New York Times*, September 6, 2007, p. G2.) At the 0.05 level of significance, is there evidence that the proportion of all young jobseekers aged 24 to 35 who preferred to "look for a job in a place where I would like to live" rather than "look for the best job I can find, the place where I live is secondary" is different from 60%?

11.59 The telephone company wants to investigate the desirability of beginning a marketing campaign that would offer customers the right to purchase an additional telephone line at a substantially reduced installation cost. The campaign will be initiated if there is evidence that more than 20% of the customers would consider purchasing an additional telephone line

if it were made available at a substantially reduced installation cost. A random sample of 500 households is selected. The results indicate that 135 of the households would purchase the additional telephone line at a reduced installation cost.
a. At the 0.05 level of significance, is there evidence that more than 20% of the customers would purchase the additional telephone line?
b. How would the manager in charge of promotional programs concerning residential customers use the results in (a)?

11.60 A study by the Pew Internet and American Life Project (**pewinternet.org**) found that Americans had a complex and ambivalent attitude toward technology. (Data extracted from M. Himowitz, "How to Tell What Kind of Tech User You Are," *Newsday*, May 27, 2007, p. F6.) The study reported that 8% of the respondents were "Omnivores" who are gadget lovers, text messengers, and online gamers (often with their own blogs or web pages), video makers, and YouTube posters. You believe that the percentage of students at your school who are Omnivores is greater than 8%, and you plan to carry out a study to prove that this is so.
a. State the null and alternative hypotheses.
b. You select a sample of 200 students at your school and find that 30 students can be classified as Omnivores. Use either the six-step critical value hypothesis-testing approach or the five-step *p*-value approach to determine at the 0.05 level of significance whether there is evidence that the percentage of Omnivores at your school is greater than 8%.

11.6 Potential Hypothesis-Testing Pitfalls and Ethical Issues

To this point, you have studied the fundamental concepts of hypothesis testing. You have used hypothesis testing to analyze differences between sample statistics and hypothesized population parameters in order to make business decisions concerning the underlying population characteristics. You have also learned how to evaluate the risks involved in making these decisions.

When planning to carry out a hypothesis test based on a survey, research study, or designed experiment, you must ask several questions to ensure that you use proper methodology. You need to raise and answer questions such as the following in the planning stage:

- What is the goal of the survey, study, or experiment? How can you translate the goal into a null hypothesis and an alternative hypothesis?
- Is the hypothesis test a two-tail test or one-tail test?
- Can you select a random sample from the underlying population of interest?
- What types of data will you collect in the sample? Are the variables numerical or categorical?
- At what level of significance should you conduct the hypothesis test?
- Is the intended sample size large enough to achieve the desired power of the test for the level of significance chosen?
- What statistical test procedure should you use and why?
- What conclusions and interpretations can you reach from the results of the hypothesis test?

Failing to consider these questions early in the planning process can lead to biased or incomplete results. Proper planning can help ensure that the statistical study will provide objective information needed to make good business decisions.

Statistical Significance Versus Practical Significance

You need to make a distinction between the existence of a statistically significant result and its practical significance in a field of application. Sometimes, due to a very large sample size, you may get a result that is statistically significant but has little practical significance. For example, suppose that prior to a national marketing campaign focusing on a series of expensive television commercials, you believe that the proportion of people who recognize your brand is 0.30. At the completion of the campaign, a survey of 20,000 people indicates that 6,168 recognized your brand. A one-tail test trying to prove that the proportion is now greater than 0.30 results in a p-value of 0.0047, and the correct statistical conclusion is that the proportion of consumers recognizing your brand name has now increased. Was the campaign successful? The result of the hypothesis test indicates a statistically significant increase in brand awareness, but is this increase practically important? The population proportion is now estimated at $6{,}168/20{,}000 = 0.3084$, or 30.84%. This increase is less than 1% more than the hypothesized value of 30%. Did the large expenses associated with the marketing campaign produce a result with a meaningful increase in brand awareness? Because of the minimal real-world impact that an increase of less than 1% has on the overall marketing strategy and the huge expenses associated with the marketing campaign, you should conclude that the campaign was not successful. On the other hand, if the campaign increased brand awareness from 30% to 50%, you would be inclined to conclude that the campaign was successful.

Reporting of Findings

In conducting research, you should document both good and bad results. You should not just report the results of hypothesis tests that show statistical significance but omit those for which there is insufficient evidence in the findings. In instances in which there is insufficient evidence to reject H_0, you must make it clear that this does not prove that the null hypothesis is true. What the result does indicate is that with the sample size used, there is not enough information to *disprove* the null hypothesis.

Ethical Issues

You need to distinguish between poor research methodology and unethical behavior. Ethical considerations arise when the hypothesis-testing process is manipulated. Some of the areas where ethical issues can arise include the use of human subjects in experiments, the data collection method, the type of test (one-tail or two-tail test), the choice of the level of significance, the cleansing and discarding of data, and the failure to report pertinent findings.

USING STATISTICS @ Oxford Cereals, Part II Revisited

Maja Schon / Shutterstock.com

As the plant operations manager for Oxford Cereals, you were responsible for the cereal-filling process. It was your responsibility to adjust the process when the mean fill weight in the population of boxes deviated from the company specification of 368 grams. Because weighing all the cereal boxes would be too time-consuming and impractical, you needed to select and weigh a sample of boxes and conduct a hypothesis test.

You determined that the null hypothesis should be that the population mean fill was 368 grams. If the mean weight of the sampled boxes were sufficiently above or below the expected 368-gram mean specified by Oxford Cereals, you would reject the null hypothesis in favor of the alternative hypothesis that the mean fill was different from 368 grams. If this happened, you would stop production and take whatever action is necessary to correct the problem. If the null hypothesis was not rejected, you would continue to believe in the status quo—that the process was working correctly—and therefore take no corrective action.

Before proceeding, you considered the risks involved with hypothesis tests. If you rejected a true null hypothesis, you would make a Type I error and conclude that the population mean fill was not 368 when it actually was 368. This error would result in adjusting the filling process even though the process was working properly. If you did not reject a false null hypothesis, you would make a Type II error and conclude that the population mean fill was 368 when it actually was not 368. Here, you would allow the process to continue without adjustment even though the process was not working properly.

After collecting a random sample of 25 cereal boxes, you used the six-step critical value approach to hypothesis testing. Because the test statistic fell into the nonrejection region, you did not reject the null hypothesis. You concluded that there was insufficient evidence to prove that the mean fill differed from 368 grams. No corrective action on the filling process was needed.

SUMMARY

This chapter presented the foundation of hypothesis testing. You learned how to perform tests on the population mean and on the population proportion. The chapter developed both the critical value approach and the p-value approach to hypothesis testing.

In deciding which test to use, you should ask the following question: Does the test involve a numerical variable or a categorical variable? If the test involves a numerical variable, use the t test for the mean. If the test involves a categorical variable, use the Z test for the proportion. Table 11.4 lists the hypothesis tests covered in the chapter.

TABLE 11.4

Summary of Topics in Chapter 11

	Type of Data	
Type of Analysis	**Numerical**	**Categorical**
Hypothesis test concerning a single parameter	Z test of hypothesis for the mean (Section 11.1)	Z test of hypothesis for the proportion (Section 11.5)
	t test of hypothesis for the mean (Section 11.3)	

KEY EQUATIONS

Z Test for the Mean (σ Known)

$$Z_{STAT} = \frac{\bar{X} - \mu}{\dfrac{\sigma}{\sqrt{n}}}$$

t Test for the Mean (σ Unknown)

$$t_{STAT} = \frac{\bar{X} - \mu}{\dfrac{S}{\sqrt{n}}}$$

Z Test for the Proportion

$$Z_{STAT} = \frac{p - \pi}{\sqrt{\dfrac{\pi(1 - \pi)}{n}}}$$

Z Test for the Proportion in Terms of the Number of Events of Interest

$$Z_{STAT} = \frac{X - n\pi}{\sqrt{n\pi(1 - \pi)}}$$

KEY TERMS

alternative hypothesis (H_1) 428	one-tail test 459	test statistic 430
β risk 432	p-value 437	two-tail test 434
confidence coefficient 432	power of a statistical test 432	Type I error 430
critical value 430	region of nonrejection 430	Type II error 430
directional test 459	region of rejection 430	Z test for the mean 434
hypothesis testing 428	robust 453	Z test for the proportion 466
level of significance (α) 432	sample proportion 466	
null hypothesis (H_0) 428	t test for the mean 448	

PROBLEMS

CHECKING YOUR UNDERSTANDING

11.61 What is the difference between a null hypothesis, H_0, and an alternative hypothesis, H_1?

11.62 What is the difference between a Type I error and a Type II error?

11.63 What is meant by the power of a test?

11.64 What is the difference between a one-tail test and a two-tail test?

11.65 What is meant by a p-value?

11.66 How can a confidence interval estimate for the population mean provide conclusions for the corresponding two-tail hypothesis test for the population mean?

11.67 What is the six-step critical value approach to hypothesis testing?

11.68 What is the five-step p-value approach to hypothesis testing?

APPLYING THE CONCEPTS

11.69 An article in *Marketing News* (T. T. Semon, "Consider a Statistical Insignificance Test," *Marketing News*, February 1, 1999) argued that the level of significance used when comparing two products is often too low—that is, sometimes you should be using an α value greater than 0.05. Specifically, the article recounted testing the proportion of potential customers with a preference for product 1 over product 2. The null hypothesis was that the population proportion of potential customers preferring product 1 was 0.50, and the alternative hypothesis was that it was not equal to 0.50. The p-value for the test was 0.22. The article sug-

gested that, in some cases, this should be enough evidence to reject the null hypothesis.
a. State, in statistical terms, the null and alternative hypotheses for this example.
b. Explain the risks associated with Type I and Type II errors in this case.
c. What would be the consequences if you rejected the null hypothesis for a p-value of 0.22?
d. Why do you think the article suggested raising the value of α?
e. What would you do in this situation?
f. What is your answer in (e) if the p-value equals 0.12? What if it equals 0.06?

11.70 La Quinta Motor Inns developed a computer model to help predict the profitability of sites that are being considered as locations for new hotels. If the computer model predicts large profits, La Quinta buys the proposed site and builds a new hotel. If the computer model predicts small or moderate profits, La Quinta chooses not to proceed with that site. (Data extracted from S. E. Kimes and J. A. Fitzsimmons, "Selecting Profitable Hotel Sites at La Quinta Motor Inns," *Interfaces*, Vol. 20, March–April 1990, pp. 12–20.) This decision-making procedure can be expressed in the hypothesis-testing framework. The null hypothesis is that the site is not a profitable location. The alternative hypothesis is that the site is a profitable location.
a. Explain the risks associated with committing a Type I error in this case.
b. Explain the risks associated with committing a Type II error in this case.
c. Which type of error do you think the executives at La Quinta Motor Inns want to avoid? Explain.

d. How do changes in the rejection criterion affect the probabilities of committing Type I and Type II errors?

11.71 Webcredible, a UK-based consulting firm specializing in websites, intranets, mobile devices, and applications, conducted a survey of 1,132 mobile phone users between February and April 2009. The survey found that 52% of mobile phone users are now using the mobile Internet. (Data extracted from "Email and Social Networking Most Popular Mobile Internet Activities," www.webcredible.co.uk, May 13, 2009.) The authors of the article imply that the survey proves that more than half of all mobile phone users are now using the mobile Internet.

a. Use the five-step p-value approach to hypothesis testing and a 0.05 level of significance to try to prove that more than half of all mobile phone users are now using the mobile Internet.

b. Based on your result in (a), is the claim implied by the authors valid?

c. Suppose the survey found that 53% of mobile phone users are now using the mobile Internet. Repeat parts (a) and (b).

d. Compare the results of (b) and (c).

11.72 The owner of a gasoline station wants to study gasoline purchasing habits of motorists at his station. He selects a random sample of 60 motorists during a certain week, with the following results:

- The amount purchased was $\overline{X} = 11.3$ gallons, $S = 3.1$ gallons.
- Eleven motorists purchased premium-grade gasoline.

a. At the 0.05 level of significance, is there evidence that the population mean purchase was different from 10 gallons?

b. Determine the p-value in (a).

c. At the 0.05 level of significance, is there evidence that less than 20% of all the motorists at the station purchased premium-grade gasoline?

d. What is your answer to (a) if the sample mean equals 10.3 gallons?

e. What is your answer to (c) if 7 motorists purchased premium-grade gasoline?

11.73 An auditor for a government agency is assigned the task of evaluating reimbursement for office visits to physicians paid by Medicare. The audit was conducted on a sample of 75 of the reimbursements, with the following results:

- In 12 of the office visits, there was an incorrect amount of reimbursement.
- The amount of reimbursement was $\overline{X} = \$93.70$, $S = \$34.55$.

a. At the 0.05 level of significance, is there evidence that the population mean reimbursement was less than $100?

b. At the 0.05 level of significance, is there evidence that the proportion of incorrect reimbursements in the population was greater than 0.10?

c. Discuss the underlying assumptions of the test used in (a).

d. What is your answer to (a) if the sample mean equals $90?

e. What is your answer to (b) if 15 office visits had incorrect reimbursements?

11.74 A bank branch located in a commercial district of a city had the business objective of improving the process for serving customers during the noon-to-1:00 P.M. lunch period. The waiting time (defined as the time the customer enters the line until he or she reaches the teller window) of a random sample of 15 customers is collected, and the results are organized (and stored in Bank1) as follows:

| 4.21 | 5.55 | 3.02 | 5.13 | 4.77 | 2.34 | 3.54 | 3.20 |
| 4.50 | 6.10 | 0.38 | 5.12 | 6.46 | 6.19 | 3.79 |

a. At the 0.05 level of significance, is there evidence that the population mean waiting time is less than 5 minutes?

b. What assumption about the population distribution is needed in order to conduct the t test in (a)?

c. Construct a boxplot or a normal probability plot to evaluate the assumption made in (b).

d. Do you think that the assumption needed in order to conduct the t test in (a) is valid? Explain.

e. As a customer walks into the branch office during the lunch hour, she asks the branch manager how long she can expect to wait. The branch manager replies, "Almost certainly not longer than 5 minutes." On the basis of the results of (a), evaluate this statement.

11.75 A manufacturing company produces electrical insulators. If the insulators break when in use, a short circuit is likely to occur. To test the strength of the insulators, destructive testing is carried out to determine how much force is required to break the insulators. Force is measured by observing the number of pounds of force applied to the insulator before it breaks. The following data (stored in Force) are from 30 insulators subjected to this testing:

1,870 1,728 1,656 1,610 1,634 1,784 1,522 1,696 1,592 1,662
1,866 1,764 1,734 1,662 1,734 1,774 1,550 1,756 1,762 1,866
1,820 1,744 1,788 1,688 1,810 1,752 1,680 1,810 1,652 1,736

a. At the 0.05 level of significance, is there evidence that the population mean force required to break the insulator is greater than 1,500 pounds?

b. What assumption about the population distribution is needed in order to conduct the t test in (a)?

c. Construct a histogram, boxplot, or normal probability plot to evaluate the assumption made in (b).

d. Do you think that the assumption needed in order to conduct the t test in (a) is valid? Explain.

11.76 An important quality characteristic used by the manufacturer of Boston and Vermont asphalt shingles is the amount of moisture the shingles contain when they are packaged. Customers may feel that they have purchased a product lacking in quality if they find moisture and wet shingles inside the packaging. In some cases, excessive moisture can cause the granules attached to the shingle for texture and coloring purposes to fall off the shingle, resulting in appearance problems. To monitor the amount of moisture present, the company conducts moisture tests. A shingle is weighed and then dried. The shingle is then reweighed, and, based on the amount of moisture taken out of the product, the pounds of moisture per 100 square feet are calculated. The company would like to show that the mean moisture content is less than 0.35 pound per 100 square feet. The file Moisture includes 36 measurements (in pounds per 100 square feet) for Boston shingles and 31 for Vermont shingles.

a. For the Boston shingles, is there evidence at the 0.05 level of significance that the population mean moisture content is less than 0.35 pound per 100 square feet?

b. Interpret the meaning of the p-value in (a).

c. For the Vermont shingles, is there evidence at the 0.05 level of significance that the population mean moisture content is less than 0.35 pound per 100 square feet?

d. Interpret the meaning of the p-value in (c).

e. What assumption about the population distribution is needed in order to conduct the t tests in (a) and (c)?

f. Construct histograms, boxplots, or normal probability plots to evaluate the assumption made in (a) and (c).

g. Do you think that the assumption needed in order to conduct the t tests in (a) and (c) is valid? Explain.

11.77 Studies conducted by the manufacturer of Boston and Vermont asphalt shingles have shown product weight to be a major factor in the customer's perception of quality. Moreover, the weight represents the amount of raw materials being used and is therefore very important to the company from a cost standpoint. The last stage of the assembly line packages the shingles before the packages are placed on wooden pallets. Once a pallet is full (a pallet for most brands holds 16 squares of shingles), it is weighed, and the measurement is recorded. The file Pallet contains the weight (in pounds) from a sample of 368 pallets of Boston shingles and 330 pallets of Vermont shingles.

a. For the Boston shingles, is there evidence that the population mean weight is different from 3,150 pounds?

b. Interpret the meaning of the p-value in (a).

c. For the Vermont shingles, is there evidence that the population mean weight is different from 3,700 pounds?

d. Interpret the meaning of the p-value in (c).

e. In (a) through (d), do you have to worry about the normality assumption? Explain.

11.78 The manufacturer of Boston and Vermont asphalt shingles provides its customers with a 20-year warranty on most of its products. To determine whether a shingle will last through the warranty period, accelerated-life testing is conducted at the manufacturing plant. Accelerated-life testing exposes the shingle to the stresses it would be subject to in a lifetime of normal use in a laboratory setting via an experiment that takes only a few minutes to conduct. In this test, a shingle is repeatedly scraped with a brush for a short period of time, and the shingle granules removed by the brushing are weighed (in grams). Shingles that experience low amounts of granule loss are expected to last longer in normal use than shingles that experience high amounts of granule loss. The file Granule contains a sample of 170 measurements made on the company's Boston shingles and 140 measurements made on Vermont shingles.

a. For the Boston shingles, is there evidence that the population mean granule loss is different from 0.50 grams?

b. Interpret the meaning of the p-value in (a).

c. For the Vermont shingles, is there evidence that the population mean granule loss is different from 0.50 grams?

d. Interpret the meaning of the p-value in (c).

e. In (a) through (d), do you have to worry about the normality assumption? Explain.

REPORT WRITING EXERCISE

11.79 Referring to the results of Problems 11.76 through 11.78 concerning Boston and Vermont shingles, write a report that evaluates the moisture level, weight, and granule loss of the two types of shingles.

MANAGING ASHLAND MULTICOMM SERVICES

Continuing its monitoring of the upload speed first described in the Chapter 7 Managing Ashland Multi-Comm Services case on page 312, the technical operations department wants to ensure that the mean target upload speed for all Internet service subscribers is at least 0.97 on a standard scale in which the target value is 1.0. Each day, upload speed was measured 50 times, with the following results (stored in **AMS9**).

0.854	1.023	1.005	1.030	1.219	0.977	1.044	0.778	1.122	1.114
1.091	1.086	1.141	0.931	0.723	0.934	1.060	1.047	0.800	0.889
1.012	0.695	0.869	0.734	1.131	0.993	0.762	0.814	1.108	0.805
1.223	1.024	0.884	0.799	0.870	0.898	0.621	0.818	1.113	1.286
1.052	0.678	1.162	0.808	1.012	0.859	0.951	1.112	1.003	0.972

Calculate the sample statistics and determine whether there is evidence that the population mean upload speed is less than 0.97. Write a memo to management that summarizes your conclusions.

DIGITAL CASE

Apply your knowledge about hypothesis testing in this Digital Case, which continues the cereal-fill-packaging dispute first discussed in the Digital Case from Chapter 8.

In response to the negative statements made by the Concerned Consumers About Cereal Cheaters (CCACC) in the Chapter 8 Digital Case, Oxford Cereals recently conducted an experiment concerning cereal packaging. The company claims that the results of the experiment refute the CCACC allegations that Oxford Cereals has been cheating consumers by packaging cereals at less than labeled weights.

Open **OxfordCurrentNews.pdf**, a portfolio of current news releases from Oxford Cereals. Review the relevant press releases and supporting documents. Then answer the following questions:

1. Are the results of the experiment valid? Why or why not? If you were conducting the experiment, is there anything you would change?
2. Do the results support the claim that Oxford Cereals is not cheating its customers?
3. Is the claim of the Oxford Cereals CEO that many cereal boxes contain *more* than 368 grams surprising? Is it true?
4. Could there ever be a circumstance in which the results of the Oxford Cereals experiment *and* the CCACC's results are both correct? Explain

REFERENCES

1. Bradley, J. V., *Distribution-Free Statistical Tests* (Upper Saddle River, NJ: Prentice Hall, 1968).
2. Daniel, W., *Applied Nonparametric Statistics*, 2nd ed. (Boston: Houghton Mifflin, 1990).
3. *Microsoft Excel 2010* (Redmond, WA: Microsoft Corp., 2007).
4. *Minitab Release 16* (State College, PA: Minitab Inc., 2010).

EG11.1 Fundamentals of Hypothesis-Testing Methodology

PHStat2 Use **Z Test for the Mean, sigma known** to perform the Z test for the mean when σ is known. For example, to perform the Z test for the Figure 11.5 cereal-filling example on page 438, select **PHStat → One-Sample Tests → Z Test for the Mean, sigma known**. In the procedure's dialog box (shown below):

1. Enter **368** as the **Null Hypothesis**.
2. Enter **0.05** as the **Level of Significance**.
3. Enter **15** as the **Population Standard Deviation**.
4. Click **Sample Statistics Known** and enter **25** as the **Sample Size** and **372.5** as the **Sample Mean**.
5. Click **Two-Tail Test**.
6. Enter a **Title** and click **OK**.

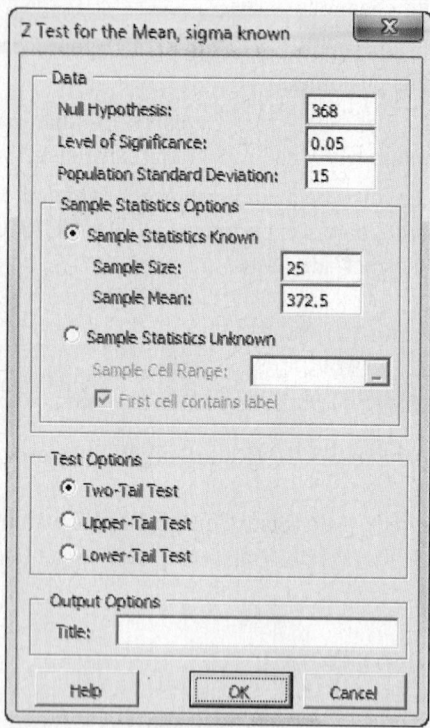

For problems that use unsummarized data, click **Sample Statistics Unknown** in step 4 and enter the cell range of the unsummarized data as the **Sample Cell Range**.

In-Depth Excel Use the **COMPUTE worksheet** of the **Z Mean workbook**, shown in Figure 11.5 on page 438, as a template for performing the two-tail Z test. The worksheet contains the data for the Section 11.1 cereal-filling example. For other problems, change the values in cells B4 through B8 as necessary.

In cells B15 and B16, **NORMSINV(*level of significance / 2*)** and **NORMSINV(1 - *level of significance / 2*)** computes the lower and upper critical values. The expression **2 * (1 − NORMSDIST (*absolute value of the Z test statistic*))** computes the p-value for the two-tail test in cell B17. In cell A18, **IF(*p-value < level of significance*, *display reject message*, *display do not reject message*)** determines which message to display in the cell.

EG11.3 t Test of Hypothesis for the Mean (σ Unknown)

PHStat2 Use **t Test for the Mean, sigma unknown** to perform the t test for the mean when σ is unknown. For example, to perform the t test for the Figure 11.7 sales invoice example on page 450, select **PHStat → One-Sample Tests → t Test for the Mean, sigma unknown**. In the procedure's dialog box (shown on the top of page 481):

1. Enter **120** as the **Null Hypothesis**.
2. Enter **0.05** as the **Level of Significance**.
3. Click **Sample Statistics Known** and enter **12** as the **Sample Size**, **112.85** as the **Sample Mean**, and **20.8** as the **Sample Standard Deviation**.
4. Click **Two-Tail Test**.
5. Enter a **Title** and click **OK**.

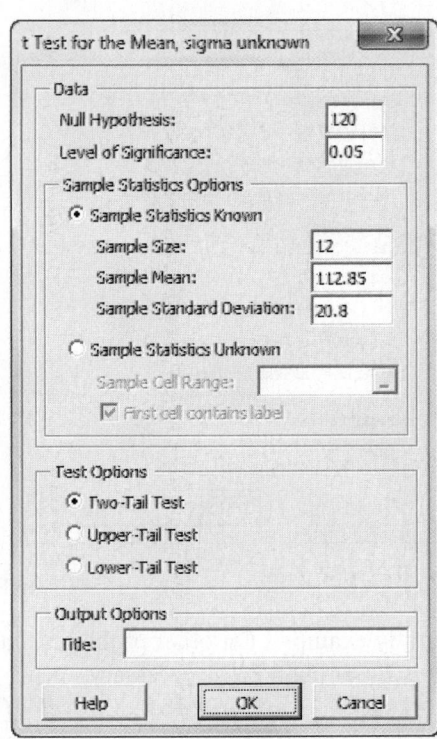

Sample Tests → t Test for the Mean, sigma unknown. In the procedure's dialog box (shown below):

1. Enter **174.22** as the **Null Hypothesis**.

2. Enter **0.05** as the **Level of Significance**.

3. Click **Sample Statistics Known** and enter **25** as the **Sample Size**, **162.96** as the **Sample Mean**, and **20.2** as the **Sample Standard Deviation**.

4. Click **Lower-Tail Test**.

5. Enter a **Title** and click **OK**.

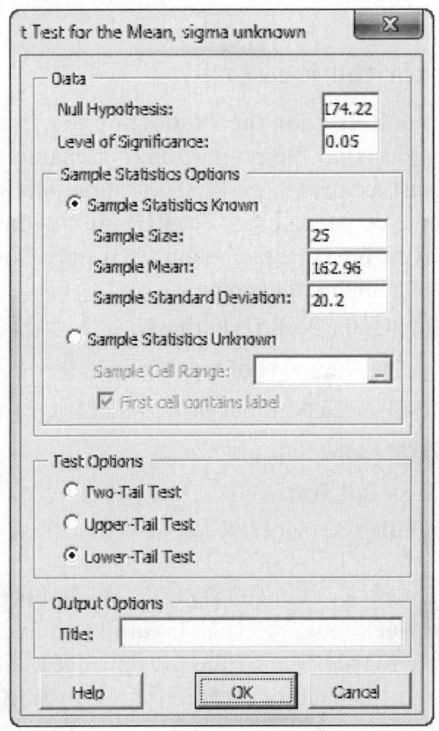

For problems that use unsummarized data, click **Sample Statistics Unknown** in step 3 and enter the cell range of the unsummarized data as the **Sample Cell Range**.

In-Depth Excel Use the **COMPUTE worksheet** of the **T mean workbook**, shown in Figure 11.7 on page 450, as a template for performing the two-tail *t* test. The worksheet contains the data for the Section 11.3 sales invoice example. For other problems, change the values in cells B4 through B8 as necessary.

In cells B16 and B17, the worksheet uses the expressions **-TINV**(*level of significance*, *degrees of freedom*) and **TINV**(*level of significance*, *degrees of freedom*) to compute the lower and upper critical values, respectively. In cell B18, the worksheet uses **TDIST**(*absolute value of the t test statistic*, *degrees of freedom*, **2**) to compute the *p*-value. The worksheet also uses an **IF** function to determine which message to display in cell A19.

EG11.4 One-Tail Tests

PHStat2 Click either **Lower-Tail Test** or **Upper-Tail Test** in the procedure dialog boxes discussed in Sections EG11.1 and EG11.3 to perform a one-tail test. For example, to perform the Figure 11.13 one-tail test for the drive-through time study example on page 461, select **PHStat → One-**

In-Depth Excel Modify the functions discussed in Section EG11.1 and EG11.3 to perform one-tail tests. For the Section EG11.1 *Z* test, enter **NORMSINV**(*level of significance*) or **NORMSINV**(**1** − *level of significance*) to compute the lower-tail or upper-tail critical value. Enter **NORMSDIST**(*Z test statistic*) or **1** − **NORMSDIST**(*absolute value of the Z test statistic*) to compute the lower-tail or upper-tail *p*-value. For the Section EG11.3 *t* test, enter **-TINV**(**2** * *level of significance*, *degrees of freedom*) or **TINV**(**2** * *level of significance*, *degrees of freedom*) to compute the lower-tail or upper-tail critical values.

Computing *p*-values is more complex. If the *t* test statistic is less than zero, the lower-tail *p*-value is equal to **TDIST**(*absolute value of the t test statistic*, *degrees of* *freedom*, **1**), and the upper-tail *p*-value is equal to **1 −** **TDIST**(*absolute value of the t test statistic*, *degrees of freedom*, **1**). If the *t* test statistic is greater than or equal to zero, the values are reversed.

Use the **COMPUTE_LOWER worksheet** or the **COMPUTE_UPPER worksheet** of the **Z Mean workbook** or the **T mean workbook** as a template for performing one-tail *t* tests. Open to the **COMPUTE_ALL_FORMULAS worksheet** of these workbooks to examine all the formulas used their worksheets.

EG11.5 Z Test of Hypothesis for the Proportion

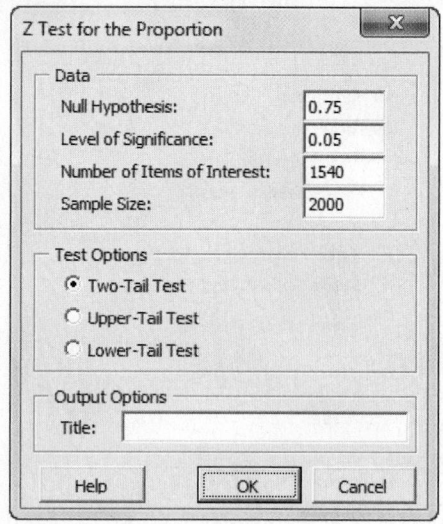

PHStat2 Use **Z Test for the Proportion** to perform the *Z* test of hypothesis for the proportion. For example, to perform the *Z* test for the Figure 11.16 vacation Internet access study example on page 468, select **PHStat → One-Sample Tests → Z Test for the Proportion**. In the procedure's dialog box (shown in the right column):

1. Enter **0.75** as the **Null Hypothesis**.
2. Enter **0.05** as the **Level of Significance**.
3. Enter **1540** as the **Number of Items of Interest**.
4. Enter **2000** as the **Sample Size**.
5. Click **Two-Tail Test**.
6. Enter a **Title** and click **OK**.

In-Depth Excel Use the **COMPUTE worksheet** of the **Z Proportion workbook**, shown in Figure 11.16 on page 468, as a template for performing the two-tail *Z* test. The worksheet contains the data for the Section 11.5 vacation Inter-

net access study example. For other problems, change the values in cells B4 through B7 as necessary.

The worksheet uses **NORMSINV**(*level of significance* / **2**) and **NORMSINV**(**1 -** *level of significance* / **2**) to compute the lower and upper critical values in cells B15 and B16. In cell B17, the worksheet uses the expression **2 * (1 − NORMSDIST**(*absolute value of the Z test statistic*) to compute the *p*-value. The worksheet also uses an **IF** function to determine which message to display in cell A18.

Use the **COMPUTE_LOWER worksheet** or **COMPUTE_UPPER worksheet** as a template for performing one-tail tests. Open to the **COMPUTE_ALL_FORMULAS worksheet** to examine all the formulas used in the one-tail test worksheets.

12 Hypothesis Testing: Two-Sample Tests

Learning Objectives

In this chapter, you learn how to use hypothesis testing for comparing the difference between:

- The means of two independent populations
- The means of two related populations
- The proportions of two independent populations
- The variances of two independent populations
- The means of more than two populations

Michael Bradley / Getty Images

@ BLK Beverages

Does the type of display used in a supermarket affect the sales of products? As the regional sales manager for BLK Beverages, you want to compare the sales volume of BLK Cola when the product is placed in the normal shelf location to the sales volume when the product is featured in a special end-aisle display. To test the effectiveness of the end-aisle displays, you select 20 stores from the Food Pride supermarket chain that all experience similar storewide sales volumes. You then randomly assign 10 of the 20 stores to sample 1 and 10 stores to sample 2. The managers of the 10 stores in sample 1 place the BLK Cola in the normal shelf location, alongside the other cola products. The 10 stores in sample 2 use the special end-aisle promotional display. At the end of one week, the sales of BLK Cola are recorded. How can you determine whether sales of BLK Cola using the end-aisle displays are the same as those when the cola is placed in the normal shelf location? How can you decide if the variability in BLK Cola sales from store to store is the same for the two types of displays? How could you use the answers to these questions to improve sales of BLK Cola?

Travis Manley / Shutterstock.com

H ypothesis testing provides a *confirmatory* approach to data analysis. In Chapter 9, you learned a variety of commonly used hypothesis-testing procedures that relate to a single sample of data selected from a single population. In this chapter, you learn how to extend hypothesis testing to **two-sample tests** that compare statistics from samples of data selected from two populations. One such test for the BLK Beverages scenario would be "Are the mean weekly sales of BLK Cola when using the normal shelf location (one population) equal to the mean weekly sales of BLK Cola when using an end-aisle display (a second population)?"

Flow chart for hypothesis test of two population parameters

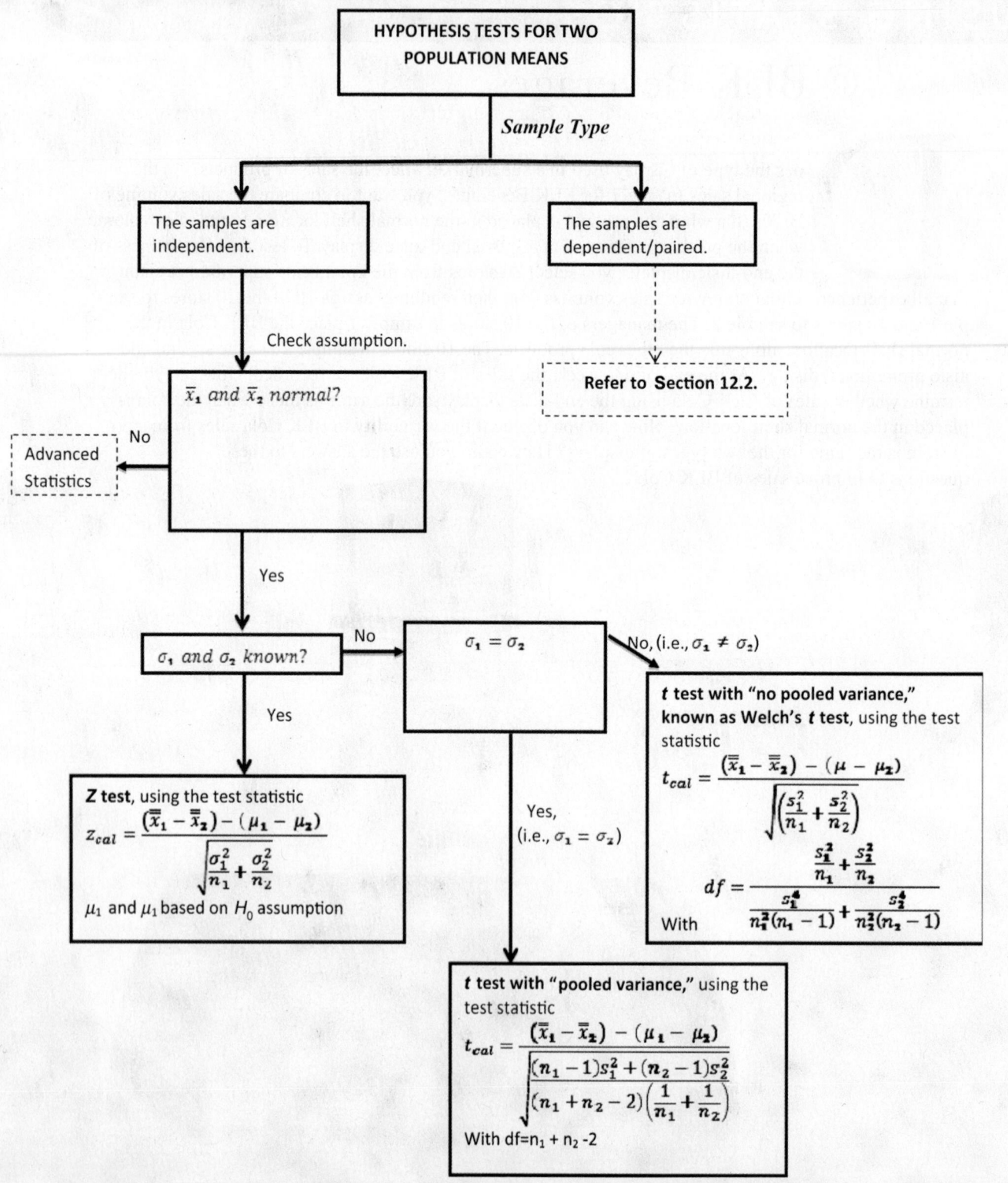

12.1 Comparing the Means of Two Independent Populations

Worksheet data for samples taken from two independent populations can be stored either in stacked or unstacked format, as discussed in Section 2.3. Examples throughout this chapter use unstacked data. By using the techniques discussed in either Excel Section EG2.3 or Minitab Section MG2.3, you can rearrange stacked data as unstacked data.

In Sections 10.1 and 11.1, you learned that in almost all cases, you would not know the population standard deviation of the population under study. Likewise, when you take a random sample from each of two independent populations, you almost always do not know the standard deviations of either population. However, you also need to know whether you can assume that the variances in the two populations are equal because the method you use to compare the means of each population depends on whether you can assume that the variances of the two populations are equal.

Pooled-Variance *t* Test for the Difference Between Two Means

If you assume that the random samples are independently selected from two populations and that the populations are normally distributed and have equal variances, you can use a **pooled-variance *t* test** to determine whether there is a significant difference between the means of the two populations. If the populations are not normally distributed, the pooled-variance *t* test can still be used if the sample sizes are large enough (typically ≥ 30 for each sample[1]).

[1]Review the Section 8.4 discussion about the Central Limit Theorem on page 334 to understand more about "large enough" sample sizes.

Using subscripts to distinguish between the population mean of the first population, μ_1, and the population mean of the second population, μ_2, the null hypothesis of no difference in the means of two independent populations can be stated as

$$H_0: \mu_1 = \mu_2 \quad \text{or} \quad \mu_1 - \mu_2 = 0$$

and the alternative hypothesis, that the means are not the same, can be stated as

$$H_1: \mu_1 \neq \mu_2 \quad \text{or} \quad \mu_1 - \mu_2 \neq 0$$

To test the null hypothesis, use the pooled-variance *t* test statistic t_{STAT} shown in Equation (12.1). The pooled-variance *t* test gets its name from the fact that the test statistic pools, or combines, the two sample variances S_1^2 and S_2^2 to compute S_p^2, the best estimate of the variance common to both populations, under the assumption that the two population variances are equal.[2]

[2]When the two sample sizes are equal (i.e., $n_1 = n_2$), the equation for the pooled variance can be simplified to
$$S_p^2 = \frac{S_1^2 + S_2^2}{2}$$

POOLED-VARIANCE *t* TEST FOR THE DIFFERENCE BETWEEN TWO MEANS

$$t_{STAT} = \frac{(\bar{X}_1 - \bar{X}_2) - (\mu_1 - \mu_2)}{\sqrt{S_p^2\left(\dfrac{1}{n_1} + \dfrac{1}{n_2}\right)}} \qquad \text{(12.1)}$$

where

$$S_p^2 = \frac{(n_1 - 1)S_1^2 + (n_2 - 1)S_2^2}{(n_1 - 1) + (n_2 - 1)}$$

and

S_p^2 = pooled variance

$\bar{X}_1$ = mean of the sample taken from population 1

S_1^2 = variance of the sample taken from population 1

n_1 = size of the sample taken from population 1

$\bar{X}_2$ = mean of the sample taken from population 2

S_2^2 = variance of the sample taken from population 2

n_2 = size of the sample taken from population 2

The t_{STAT} test statistic follows a *t* distribution with $n_1 + n_2 - 2$ degrees of freedom.

For a given level of significance, α, in a two-tail test, you reject the null hypothesis if the computed t_{STAT} test statistic is greater than the upper-tail critical value from the t distribution or if the computed t_{STAT} test statistic is less than the lower-tail critical value from the t distribution. Figure 12.1 displays the regions of rejection.

FIGURE 12.1

Regions of rejection and nonrejection for the pooled-variance t test for the difference between the means (two-tail test)

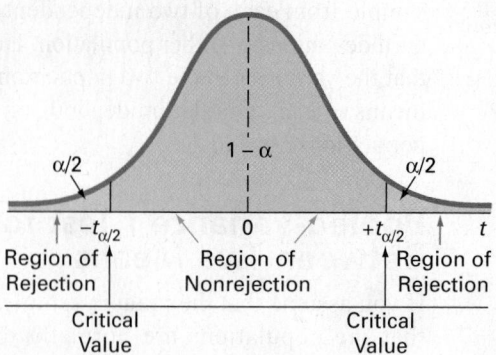

In a one-tail test in which the rejection region is in the lower tail, you reject the null hypothesis if the computed t_{STAT} test statistic is less than the lower-tail critical value from the t distribution. In a one-tail test in which the rejection region is in the upper tail, you reject the null hypothesis if the computed t_{STAT} test statistic is greater than the upper-tail critical value from the t distribution.

To demonstrate the pooled-variance t test, return to the BLK Beverages scenario on page 485. You define the business objective as determining whether the mean weekly sales of BLK Cola are the same when using a normal shelf location and when using an end-aisle display. There are two populations of interest. The first population is the set of all possible weekly sales of BLK Cola if all the Food Pride Supermarkets used the normal shelf location. The second population is the set of all possible weekly sales of BLK Cola if all the Food Pride Supermarkets used the end-aisle displays. You collect the data from a sample of 10 Food Pride Supermarkets that have been assigned a normal shelf location and another sample of 10 Food Pride Supermarkets that have been assigned an end-aisle display. You organize and store the results in Cola. Table 12.1 contains the BLK Cola sales (in number of cases) for the two samples.

TABLE 12.1

Comparing BLK Cola Weekly Sales from Two Different Display Locations (in number of cases)

		Display Location							
		Normal					**End-Aisle**		
22	34	52	62	30	52	71	76	54	67
40	64	84	56	59	83	66	90	77	84

The null and alternative hypotheses are

$$H_0: \mu_1 = \mu_2 \quad \text{or} \quad \mu_1 - \mu_2 = 0$$

$$H_1: \mu_1 \neq \mu_2 \quad \text{or} \quad \mu_1 - \mu_2 \neq 0$$

Assuming that the samples are from normal populations having equal variances, you can use the pooled-variance t test. The t_{STAT} test statistic follows a t distribution with $10 + 10 - 2 = 18$ degrees of freedom. Using an $\alpha = 0.05$ level of significance, you divide the rejection region into the two tails for this two-tail test (i.e., two equal parts of 0.025 each). Table E.3 shows that the critical values for this two-tail test are $+2.1009$ and -2.1009. As shown in Figure 12.2, the decision rule is

$$\text{Reject } H_0 \text{ if } t_{STAT} > +2.1009$$

$$\text{or if } t_{STAT} < -2.1009;$$

$$\text{otherwise do not reject } H_0.$$

FIGURE 12.2

Two-tail test of hypothesis for the difference between the means at the 0.05 level of significance with 18 degrees of freedom

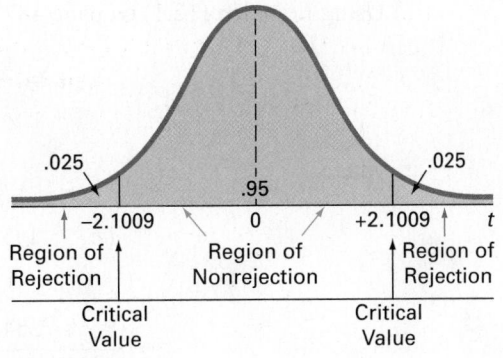

.025 | .95 | .025

−2.1009 | 0 | +2.1009 | t

Region of Rejection | Region of Nonrejection | Region of Rejection

Critical Value | | Critical Value

Find t critical value using calculator:

To find the t critical value, use the Casio Calculator fx-9750GII and follow the following calculator steps:

Note: Fx-9750G Plus does not have this option, therefore you have to use the Table G3 in the Appendix.

From the **Main Menu** select:

STAT F5 (DIST) **F2** (t) **F3**(Invt)   then enter the following items:

Inverse Student-t
Data   : **F2**(Var)   ▼
Area   : **0.025**   **EXE** (Note: divide a by 2 because it is a two-tailed test)
df   : **18**   **EXE** (Note: Equal variance with df=$n_1+n_2-2=10+10-2=18$)
Save Res : None
Execute

Now key **EXE** or **F1**(CALC)

The calculator will now show the results:

Inverse Student-t
x-Inv = 2.10092204

From Figure 12.3, the computed t_{STAT} test statistic for this test is -3.0446 and the p-value is 0.0070.

FIGURE 12.3

SPSS t-test results for the two display locations

Group Statistics

Display		N	Mean	Std. Deviation	Std. Error Mean
Weekly Sales	Normal	10	50.30	18.726	5.922
	End-Aisle	10	72.00	12.543	3.967

Independent Samples Test

		Levene's Test for Equality of Variances		t Test for Equality of Means					95% Confidence Interval of the Difference	
		F	Sig.	t	df	Sig. (2-tailed)	Mean Difference	Std. Error Difference	Lower	Upper
Weekly Sales	Equal variances assumed	1.745	.203	−3.045	18	.007	−21.700	7.127	−36.674	−6.726
	Equal variances not assumed			−3.045	15.723	.008	−21.700	7.127	−36.831	−6.569

Using Equation (12.1) on page 487 and the descriptive statistics provided in Figure 12.3,

$$t_{STAT} = \frac{(\bar{X}_1 - \bar{X}_2) - (\mu_1 - \mu_2)}{\sqrt{S_p^2\left(\frac{1}{n_1} + \frac{1}{n_2}\right)}}$$

where

$$S_p^2 = \frac{(n_1 - 1)S_1^2 + (n_2 - 1)S_2^2}{(n_1 - 1) + (n_2 - 1)}$$

$$= \frac{9(18.7264)^2 + 9(12.5433)^2}{9 + 9} = 254.0056$$

Therefore,

$$t_{STAT} = \frac{(50.3 - 72.0) - 0.0}{\sqrt{254.0056\left(\frac{1}{10} + \frac{1}{10}\right)}} = \frac{-21.7}{\sqrt{50.801}} = -3.0446$$

You reject the null hypothesis because $t_{STAT} = -3.0446 < -2.1009$ and the p-value is 0.0070. In other words, the probability that $t_{STAT} > 3.0446$ or $t_{STAT} < -3.0446$ is equal to 0.0070. This p-value indicates that if the population means are equal, the probability of observing a difference this large or larger in the two sample means is only 0.0070. Because the p-value is less than $\alpha = 0.05$, there is sufficient evidence to reject the null hypothesis. You can conclude that the mean sales are different for the normal shelf location and the end-aisle location. Based on these results, the sales are lower for the normal location (i.e., higher for the end-aisle location).

In testing for the difference between the means, you assume that the populations are normally distributed, with equal variances. For situations in which the two populations have equal variances, the pooled-variance t test is **robust** (i.e., not sensitive) to moderate departures from the assumption of normality, provided that the sample sizes are large. In such situations, you can use the pooled-variance t test without serious effects on its power. However, if you cannot assume that both populations are normally distributed, you have two choices. You can use a nonparametric procedure, such as the Wilcoxon rank sum test (see references 1 and 2), that does not depend on the assumption of normality for the two populations, or you can use a normalizing transformation (see reference 9) on each of the outcomes and then use the pooled-variance t test.

To check the assumption of normality in each of the two populations, construct the boxplot of the sales for the two display locations shown in Figure 12.4. For these two small samples, there appears to be only moderate departure from normality, so the assumption of normality needed for the t test is not seriously violated.

FIGURE 12.4

Excel and Minitab boxplots of the sales for the two display locations

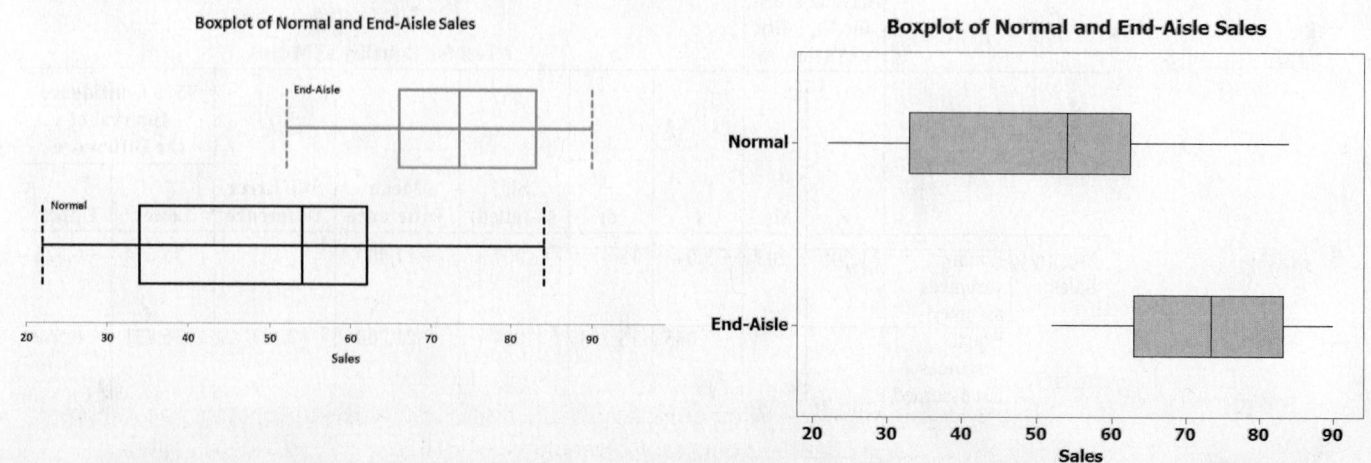

Example 12.1 provides another application of the pooled-variance t test.

EXAMPLE 12.1

Testing for the Difference in the Mean Delivery Times

You and some friends have decided to test the validity of an advertisement by a local pizza restaurant, which says it delivers to the dormitories faster than a local branch of a national chain. Both the local pizza restaurant and national chain are located across the street from your college campus. You define the variable of interest as the delivery time, in minutes, from the time the pizza is ordered to when it is delivered. You collect the data by ordering 10 pizzas from the local pizza restaurant and 10 pizzas from the national chain at different times. You organize and store the data in `PizzaTime`. Table 12.2 shows the delivery times.

TABLE 12.2

Delivery Times (in minutes) for Local Pizza Restaurant and National Pizza Chain

Local		Chain	
16.8	18.1	22.0	19.5
11.7	14.1	15.2	17.0
15.6	21.8	18.7	19.5
16.7	13.9	15.6	16.5
17.5	20.8	20.8	24.0

At the 0.05 level of significance, is there evidence that the mean delivery time for the local pizza restaurant is less than the mean delivery time for the national pizza chain?

SOLUTION Because you want to know whether the mean is *lower* for the local pizza restaurant than for the national pizza chain, you have a one-tail test with the following null and alternative hypotheses:

$H_0: \mu_1 \geq \mu_2$ (The mean delivery time for the local pizza restaurant is equal to or greater than the mean delivery time for the national pizza chain.)

$H_1: \mu_1 < \mu_2$ (The mean delivery time for the local pizza restaurant is less than the mean delivery time for the national pizza chain.)

Figure 12.5 displays the results for the pooled-variance t test for these data.

FIGURE 12.5

SPSS results of the pooled t-test (i.e. Equal variances assumed) for the pizza delivery times data

Group Statistics

Pizza Restaurant		N	Mean	Std. Deviation	Std. Error Mean
Delivery Time	Local Pizza Restaurant	10	16.700	3.0955	.9789
	National Pizza Chain	10	18.880	2.8662	.9064

Independent Samples Test

		Levene's Test for Equality of Variances		t Test for Equality of Means					95% Confidence Interval of the Difference	
		F	Sig.	t	df	Sig. (2-tailed)	Mean Difference	Std. Error Difference	Lower	Upper
Delivery Time	Equal variances assumed	.001	.980	−1.634	18	.120	−2.1800	1.3341	−4.9828	.6228
	Equal variances not assumed			−1.634	17.894	.120	−2.1800	1.3341	−4.9840	.6240

Note: By default, SPSS performs a two-tailed t-test. For a one-tailed t-test, you have to divide the p-value by 2. The p-value would be 0.06 (0.120 ÷ 2) to test the hypothesis.

To illustrate the computations, using Equation (12.1) on page 487,

$$t_{STAT} = \frac{(\bar{X}_1 - \bar{X}_2) - (\mu_1 - \mu_2)}{\sqrt{S_p^2\left(\frac{1}{n_1} + \frac{1}{n_2}\right)}}$$

where

$$S_p^2 = \frac{(n_1 - 1)S_1^2 + (n_2 - 1)S_2^2}{(n_1 - 1) + (n_2 - 1)}$$

$$= \frac{9(3.0955)^2 + 9(2.8662)^2}{9 + 9} = 8.8987$$

Therefore,

$$t_{STAT} = \frac{(16.7 - 18.88) - 0.0}{\sqrt{8.8987\left(\frac{1}{10} + \frac{1}{10}\right)}} = \frac{-2.18}{\sqrt{1.7797}} = -1.6341$$

You do not reject the null hypothesis because $t_{STAT} = -1.6341 > -1.7341$. The p-value (as computed in Figure 12.5) is 0.0598. This p-value indicates that the probability that $t_{STAT} < -1.6341$ is equal to 0.0598. In other words, if the population means are equal, the probability that the sample mean delivery time for the local pizza restaurant is at least 2.18 minutes faster than the national chain is 0.0598. Because the p-value is greater than $\alpha = 0.05$, there is insufficient evidence to reject the null hypothesis. Based on these results, there is insufficient evidence for the local pizza restaurant to make the advertising claim that it has a faster delivery time.

CASIO Calculator Instruction for t-Test

Refer to Example 12.1: At the 0.05 level of significance, is there evidence that the mean delivery time for the local pizza restaurant is less than the mean delivery time for the national pizza chain?

To test the hypothesis, follow these calculator steps:

From the **Main Menu** select **STAT**.

Enter the "Local" data in **List 1** and "Chain" data in **List 2** as shown below:

LIST 1	LIST 2
16.8	22.0
11.7	15.2
15.6	18.7
⋮	⋮
⋮	⋮
20.8	24.0

Now, from the **STAT mode** select the following:

F3(TEST) **F2(t)** **F2(2-S)**. Then enter the following items:

2-Sample tTest

Data	: F1(List)	▼
μ1	: $< \mu$2	(F2)
List (1)	: List 1	▼ [Note: To change the list number, select F1(List).]
List (2)	: List 2	▼ [Note: To change the list number, select F1(List).]
Freq (1)	: 1	EXE
Freq (2)	: 1	EXE
Pooled	: On	(F1) [Note: Equal variance]
Save Res	: None	

Now press EXE or F1(Calc).

The calculator will show the following results:

2-Sample tTest

$\mu 1 < \mu 2$

t   = −1.6341015

p   = 0.05980277

df = 18

x̄1 = 16.7

x̄2 = 18.88

sx1 = 3.09551647

sx2 = 2.86620151

sp = 2.9830633

n1 = 10

n2 = 10

In testing for the difference between the means, you assume that the populations are normally distributed, with equal variances. For situations in which the two populations have equal variances, the pooled-variance t test is **robust** (or not sensitive) to moderate departures from the assumption of normality, provided that the sample sizes are large. In such situations, you can use the pooled-variance t test without serious effects on its power. However, if you cannot assume that both populations are normally distributed, you have two choices. You can use a nonparametric procedure, such as the Wilcoxon rank sum test (see references 1 and 2), that does not depend on the assumption of normality for the two populations, or you can use a normalizing transformation (see reference 9) on each of the outcomes and then use the pooled-variance t test.

To check the assumption of normality in each of the two populations, observe the boxplot of the sales for the two display locations in Figure 12.6. For these two small samples, there appears to be only moderate departure from normality, so the assumption of normality needed for the t test is not seriously violated.

Separate-Variance t Test for the Difference Between Two Means

In testing for the difference between the means of two independent populations when the population variances are assumed to be equal, the sample variances are pooled together into a common estimate S_p^2. However, if you cannot make this assumption, then the pooled-variance t test is inappropriate. In this case, you should use the **separate-variance t test** developed by Satterthwaite. This test procedure includes the two separate sample variances in the computation of the t-test statistic. Although the computations for the separate-variance t test are complicated, you can use SPSS to perform the test.

Figure 12.7 illustrates SPSS results for this separate-variance t test. Note that SPSS rounds the degrees of freedom.

In Figure 12.7, the test statistic $t_{CALC} = -3.045$ and the p-value is $0.008 < 0.05$. Thus, the results for the separate-variance t test are almost exactly the same as those of the pooled-variance t test. The assumption of equality of population variances had no real effect on the results. Sometimes, however, the results from the pooled-variance and separate-variance t tests conflict because the assumption of equal variances is violated. Therefore, it is important that you evaluate the assumptions and use those results as a guide in appropriately selecting a test procedure. In Section 12.4, the F test is used to determine whether there is evidence of a difference in the two population variances. The results of that test can help you determine which of the t tests—pooled-variance or separate-variance—is more appropriate.

FIGURE 12.6

Minitab boxplot for the
sales for two display
locations

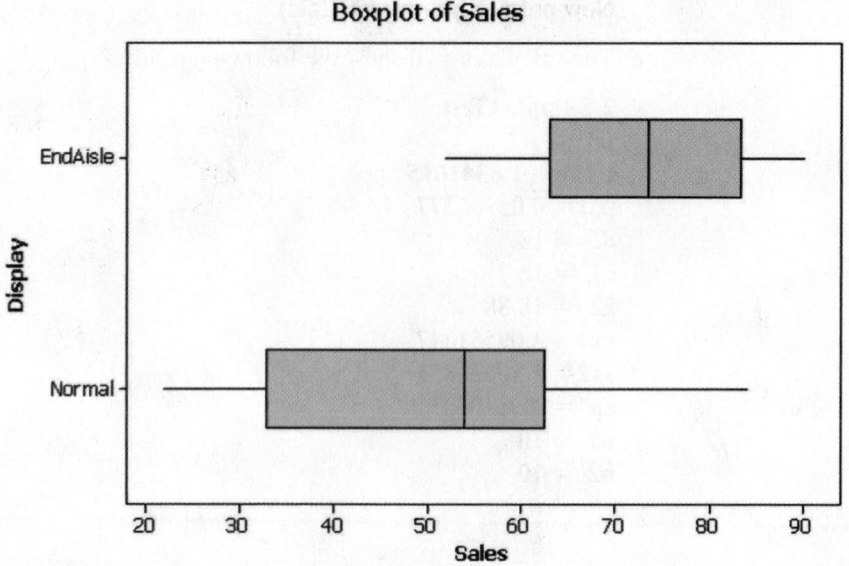

FIGURE 12.7

SPSS results of the
separate-variance t test for
the display location data

Group Statistics

Display		N	Mean	Std. Deviation	Std. Error Mean
Weekly Sales	Normal	10	50.30	18.726	5.922
	End-Aisle	10	72.00	12.543	3.967

Independent Samples Test

		Levene's Test for Equality of Variances		t Test for Equality of Means					95% Confidence Interval of the Difference	
		F	Sig.	t	df	Sig. (2-tailed)	Mean Difference	Std. Error Difference	Lower	Upper
Weekly Sales	Equal variances assumed	1.745	.203	−3.045	18	.007	−21.700	7.127	−36.674	−6.726
	Equal variances not assumed			−3.045	15.723	.008	−21.700	7.127	−36.831	−6.569

CALCULATOR LESSON 12A

CFX-9850GB CALCULATOR

Lesson 12A—Z Test and t Test of Two Means

EXAMPLE 12.2

A company that makes bolts that are used on an automotive component uses two machines to make these bolts. It has been determined by past studies that the standard deviation of the bolt diameters made by machine 1 is 0.025 mm and the standard deviation of the bolt diameters of machine 2 is 0.022 mm. Both machines have a dial to set for the desired diameter. Recently, the company used both machines to fill a large order. The customer found that many of the bolts from a certain package were too large and made a complaint. It was determined that the package in question was made by machine 2. The manufacturer decided to take samples of the bolts from both machines to test to see whether the mean diameter of the bolts from machine 2 was significantly larger than the mean diameter from machine 1 when the dial was set to the same diameter on each machine. The sample of 100 bolts from machine 1 had a mean diameter of 5.02 mm, and the sample of 100 bolts from machine 2 had a mean diameter of 5.09 mm. At the 5% level of significance, what is the conclusion?

Solution: From the **Main Menu** select the following:

STAT F3(test) **F1**(Z) **F2**(2-S). Then enter the following items:

2-Sample ZTest

Data	: **F2**(Var)	▼
$\mu 1$	: **F2**($<\mu 2$)	▼
$\sigma 1$	: **0.025**	**EXE**
$\sigma 2$	: **0.022**	**EXE**
$\bar{x}1$	: **5.02**	**EXE**
n1	: **100**	**EXE**
$\bar{x}2$	: **5.09**	**EXE**
n2	: **100**	**EXE**

Now key **EXE** or **F1**(Calc)

The calculator will now show the results:

2-Sample ZTest

$\mu 1$	$< \mu 2$
z_{CALC}	$= -21.019978$
p	$= 2.1531E\text{-}98$
$\bar{x}1$	$= 5.02$
$\bar{x}2$	$= 5.09$
n1	$= 100$
n2	$= 100$

Since the *p*-value < 0.05, the conclusion is to *reject* the null hypothesis. In other words, the mean diameter of bolts produced by machine 2 is greater than the mean of machine 1.

EXAMPLE 12.3

A work team has developed a new process to assemble a certain component. Its members would like to know if this new process has significantly reduced the time to assemble the component. They have taken samples of 50 components produced by the existing process and 40 components produced by the new process. The mean and standard deviation of the assembly times for the existing process were 73.2 minutes and 3.6 minutes, respectively. The mean time was 71.4 minutes, with a standard deviation of 3.2 minutes for the components assembled by the new process. Assume that the times for both processes are normally distributed, with the same variance. At the 1% level of significance, does this evidence indicate that the new process is quicker than the old process?

Solution: Let sample 1 be the existing process sample and sample 2 the new process. From the **Main Menu** select the following:

STAT F3(test) **F2**(t) **F2**(2-S). Then enter the following items:

2-Sample tTest

Data	: **F2**(Var)	▼
$\mu 1$	: **F3**(>$\mu 2$)	▼
$\bar{x}1$	: **73.2**	**EXE**
x1_n-1	: **3.6**	**EXE**
n1	: **50**	**EXE**
$\bar{x}12$	: **71.4**	**EXE**
x2σn-1	: **3.2**	**EXE**
n2	: **40**	**EXE**
Pooled	: **F1**(On)	**EXE**

(Note: If you select **F1(On)**, you are using the *t* test pooled-variance procedure; if you select **F2(OFF)**, you are using the *t* test separate variance.)

The calculator will now show the results:

2-Sample tTest

$\mu 1$	> $\mu 2$
t	=2.4749
p	=7.6215E-03 (=0.0076215)
df	=88
1	=73.2
2	=71.4
$\bar{x}1\sigma$n-1	=3.6
$\bar{x}2\sigma$n-1	=3.2
xPσn-1	=3.4285
n1	=50
n2	=40

Since the *p*-value < 0.01, the conclusion is to reject the null hypothesis. In other words, the evidence does indicate that the average time to assemble the component by the new process is less than the average time to assemble the component by the existing process, (i.e., the new process is faster).

EXAMPLE 12.4   We wish to determine if there is a difference in the braking distances for two types of tires. Use the 5% level of significance and assume that the braking distances for each type of tire are normally distributed, with the same variance. Based on the data for the samples of tires shown, at the 5% level of significance, should we conclude that there is a difference in the mean braking distance?

Braking distance (metres)

Tire A	Tire B
83	75
79	84
82	76
84	83
80	85
81	78
	83

Solution: Enter the data for Tire A in List 1 and the data for Tire B in List 2. From the **Main Menu** select the following:

STAT F3(test) **F2**(t) **F2**(2-S). Then enter the following items:

2-Sample t Test

Data	: **F1**(List)	▼
µ1	: **F1**($\neq$µ2)	▼
List1	: **F1**(List1)	▼
List2	: **F2**(List2)	▼
Freq	: 1	▼
Freq	: 1	▼
Pooled	: **F1**(On)	**EXE**

The calculator will now show the results:

2-Sample t Test

µ1	$\neq$µ2
t	=0.50699
p	=0.62217
df	=11
$\bar{x}$1	=81.5
$\bar{x}$2	=80.571
x1σn-1	=1.8708
x2σn-1	=4.1173
xPσn-1	=3.292
n1	=6
n2	=7

Since the *p*-value > 0.05, the conclusion is to *not reject* the null hypothesis. In other words, the evidence does not indicate that the average stopping distance is different for the two types of tires.

CALCULATOR LESSON 12B

CASIO FX-9750GII CALCULATOR

Lesson 12B—Z Test and *t* Test of Two Means

EXAMPLE 12.5

A company that makes bolts that are used on an automotive component uses two machines to make these bolts. It has been determined by past studies that the standard deviation of the bolt diameters made by machine 1 is 0.025 mm and the standard deviation of the bolt diameters of machine 2 is 0.022 mm. Both machines have a dial to set for the desired diameter. Recently, the company used both machines to fill a large order. The customer found that many of the bolts from a certain package were too large and made a complaint. It was determined that the package in question was made by machine 2. The manufacturer decided to take samples of the bolts from both machines to test to see whether the mean diameter of the bolts from machine 2 was significantly larger than the mean diameter of the bolts from machine 1 when the dial was set to the same diameter on each machine. The sample of 100 bolts from machine 1 had a mean diameter of 5.02 mm and the sample of 100 bolts from machine 2 had a mean diameter of 5.09 mm when the dial on both machines was set at 5.00 mm. At the 5% level of significance, what is the conclusion?

Solution: From the **Main Menu** select the following:

STAT   F3(test)   **F1**(Z)   **F2**(2-S). Then enter the following items:

2-Sample ZTest

Data	: **F2**(Var)	▼
μ1	: **F2**(<μ2)	▼
σ1	: 0.025	**EXE**
σ2	: 0.022	**EXE**
$\bar{x}$1	: 5.023	**EXE**
n1	: 100	**EXE**
$\bar{x}$2	: 5.031	**EXE**
n2	: 100	**EXE**
Save Res	: NONE	

Now press **EXE**, **F1**(Calc), or **F6**(DRAW).

If you select **F6**(DRAW), you will see a normal distribution.

If you select either **EXE** or **F1**(Calc), the calculator will show the results:

2-Sample ZTest

μ1	<μ2
z_{CALC}	=−21.019978
p	=2.1531E-98
$\bar{x}$1	=5.02
$\bar{x}$2	=5.09
n1	=100
n2	=100

Since the *p*-value < 0.05, the conclusion is to *reject* the null hypothesis. In other words, the mean diameter of the bolts produced by machine 2 is greater than the mean diameter of the bolts produced by machine 1.

EXAMPLE 12.6

A work team has developed a new process to assemble a certain component. Its members would like to know if this new process has significantly reduced the time to assemble the component. They have taken samples of 50 components produced by the existing process and 40 components produced by the new process. The mean and standard deviation of the assembly times for the existing process were 73.2 minutes and 3.6 minutes, respectively. The mean time was 71.4 minutes, with a standard deviation of 3.2 minutes for the components assembled by the new process. Assume that the times for both processes are normally distributed with the same variance. At the 1% level of significance, does this evidence indicate that the new process is quicker than the old process?

Solution: Let sample 1 be the existing process sample and sample 2 the new process. From the **Main Menu** select the following:

STAT   F3(test)   **F2**(t)   **F2**(2-S). Then enter the following items:

2-Sample tTest

Data	: **F2**(Var)	▼
μ1	: **F3**(>μ2)	▼
$\bar{x}$1	: 73.2	**EXE**
sx1	: 3.6	**EXE**
n1	: 50	**EXE**
$\bar{x}$2	: 71.4	**EXE**
sx2	: 3.2	**EXE**
n2	: 40	**EXE**
Pooled	: **F1**(On)	**EXE**
Save Res	: None	

Now press **EXE**, **F1**(Calc), or **F6**(DRAW).

If you select **F6**(DRAW), you will see a normal distribution.

If you select either **EXE** or **F1**(Calc), the calculator will show the results:

2-Sample tTest

$\mu 1$	$>\mu 2$
t	$=2.47493233$
p	$=7.6215\text{E-}03$ $(=0.0076215)$
df	$=88$
$\bar{x}1$	$=73.2$
$\bar{x}2$	$=71.4$
sx1	$=3.6$
sx2	$=3.2$
sp	$=3.42849026$
n1	$=50$
n2	$=40$

Since the *p*-value < 0.01, the conclusion is to *reject* the null hypothesis. In other words, the evidence does indicate that the average time to assemble the component by the new process is less than the average time to assemble the component by the existing process (i.e., the new process is faster).

EXAMPLE 12.7

We wish to determine if there is a difference in the braking distances for two types of tires. Use the 5% level of significance and assume that the braking distances for each type of tire are normally distributed with the same variance. Based on the data for the samples of tires shown, at the 5% level of significance, should we conclude that there is a difference in the mean braking distance?

Braking distance (metres)

Tire A	Tire B
83	75
79	84
82	76
84	83
80	85
81	78
	83

Solution: Enter the data for Tire A in List 1 and the data for Tire B in List 2. From the **Main Menu** select the following:

STAT   F3(test)   **F2**(t)   **F2**(2-S). Then enter the following items:

2-Sample tTest

Data	: **F1**(List)	▼
$\mu 1$	: **F1**($\neq \mu 2$)	▼
List1	: **F1**(List1)	▼
List2	: **F1**(List2)	▼
Freq	: 1	▼
Freq	: 1	▼
Pooled	: **F1**(On)	**EXE**
Save Res	: None	

Now press **EXE**, or **F1**(Calc), or **F6**(DRAW).

If you select **F6**(DRAW), you will see a normal distribution.

If you select either **EXE** or **F1**(Calc), the calculator will show the results:

2-Sample tTest

$\mu 1$	$\neq \mu 2$
t	$=0.50699126$
p	$=0.62216994$
df	$=11$
$\bar{x}1$	$=81.5$
$\bar{x}2$	$=80.5714286$
sx1	$=1.87082869$
sx2	$=4.11732692$
sp	$=3.2920605$
n1	$=6$
n2	$=7$

Since the p-value > 0.05, the conclusion is to *not reject* the null hypothesis. In other words, the evidence does not indicate that the average stopping distance is different for the two types of tires.

SPSS—VERSION 16—Two Independent Samples t Test

We will use the scenario "Delivery Times for Local Pizza Restaurant and National Pizza Chain" (Example 12.1) to demonstrate how to perform two independent samples t test using SPSS.

A local pizza restaurant located close to a college campus advertises that its delivery time to a college dormitory is less than that of a local branch of a national pizza chain. In order to determine whether this advertisement is valid, you and some friends have decided to order 10 pizzas from the local pizza restaurant and 10 pizzas from the national chain, all at different times. The data are shown below:

Local	Chain
16.8	22.0
11.7	15.2
15.6	18.7
16.7	15.6
17.5	20.8
18.1	19.5
14.1	17.0
21.8	19.5
13.9	16.5
20.8	24.0

At the 0.05 level of significance, is there evidence that the mean delivery time is lower for the local pizza restaurant than for the national pizza chain?

Solution:

Performing an Independent-Samples *t* Test on SPSS—Version 16

Step 1: Open the SPSS Data Editor.

Click **"cancel"** to cancel the SPSS opening window.

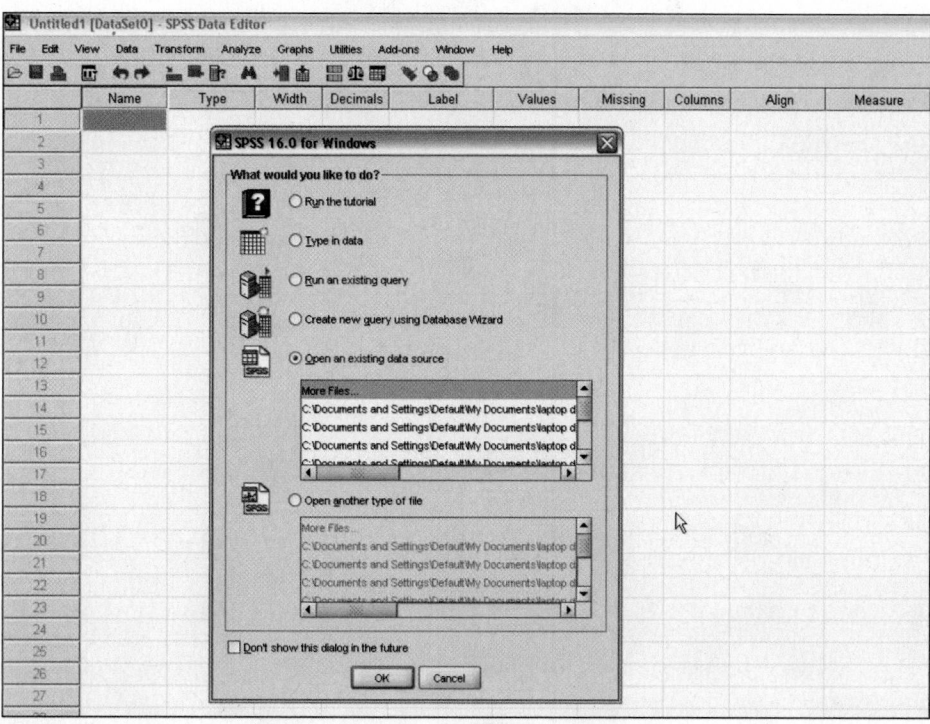

Step 2: Define the variables and give the variables a label.

Click **"Variable View"** (at the bottom of the window) to go to the variable view window to define the variables and fix the data at zero or one decimal places.

- Enter the first variable name, "Restaurant," and then click **Values.** Type "1" in the value box, type "Local Pizza Restaurant" in the Label box, and then click **Add.** Similarly, enter "2" for "National Pizza Chain".

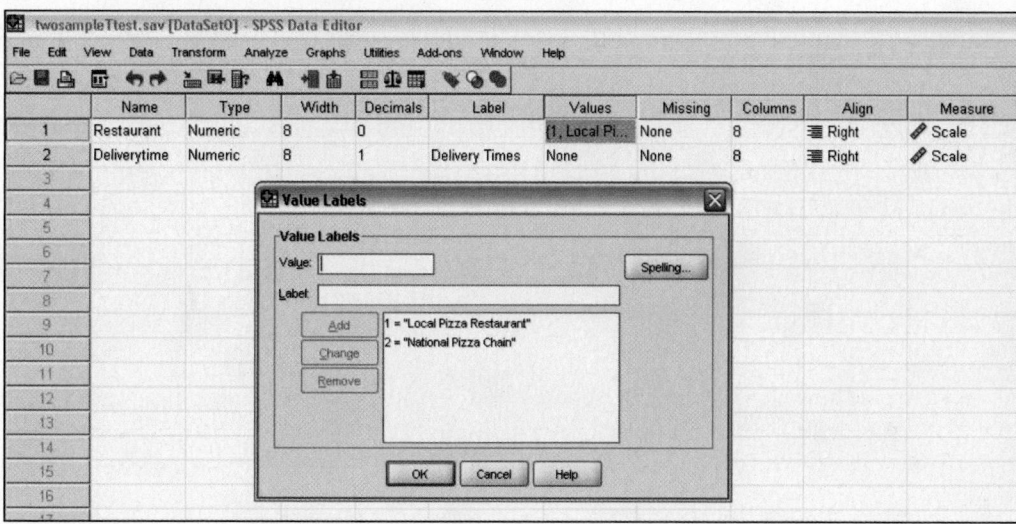

- Enter the second variable name, "Deliverytime," and label it as "Delivery Times".

Step 3: Create a SPSS data file.

Click **Data View** to return to the data view window. Now, enter the raw data on page 493 into the respective column of variables.

	twosampleTtest.sav [DataSet0] - SPSS Data Editor						
File Edit View Data Transform Analyze Graphs Utilities Add-ons Window Help							
29 :							
	Restaurant	Deliverytime	var	var	var	var	
1	1	16.8					
2	1	11.7					
3	1	15.6					
4	1	16.7					
5	1	17.5					
6	1	18.1					
7	1	14.1					
8	1	21.8					
9	1	13.9					
10	1	20.8					
11	2	22.0					
12	2	15.2					
13	2	18.7					
14	2	15.6					
15	2	20.8					
16	2	19.5					
17	2	17.0					
18	2	19.5					
19	2	16.5					
20	2	24.0					
21							

After you have entered all the data, save the file as "twosampleTtest.sav" (or any filename).

Step 3: Perform a two independent samples *t* Test.

Make the following menu selections:

Analyze → Compare Means → Independent-Samples T Test

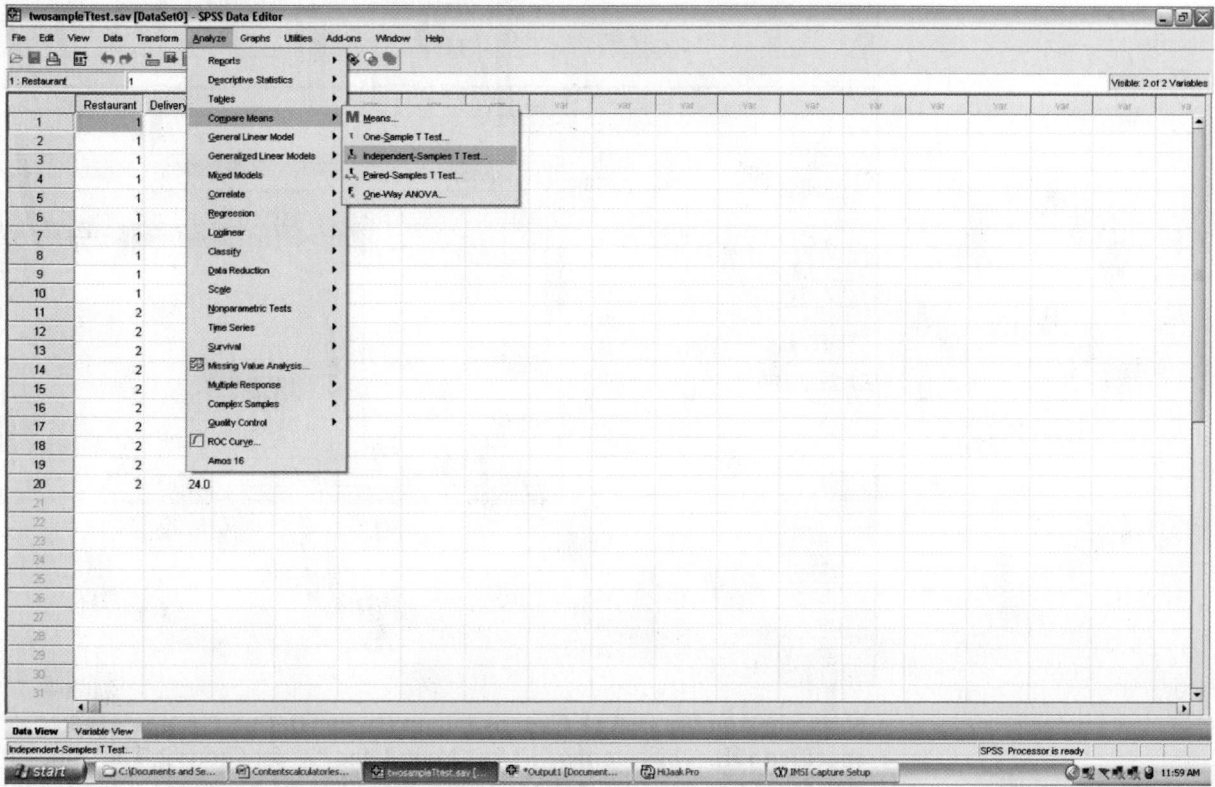

At this point, the **Independent-Samples T Test** dialog box will appear. Make these entries in the **Independent-Samples T Test** dialog box:

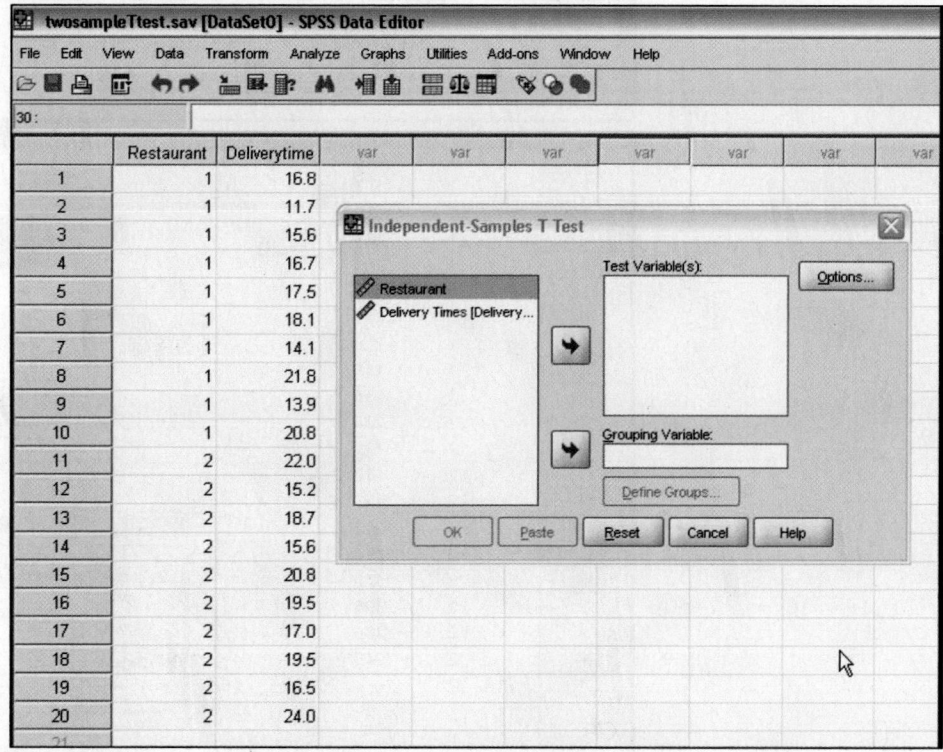

- Highlight the "Delivery Times" variable and click on the arrow key (→). The variable will automatically fall into the **Test Variable(s)** box.

- Highlight the "Restaurant" variable and click on the arrow key (→). The variable will automatically fall into the **Grouping Variable** box.

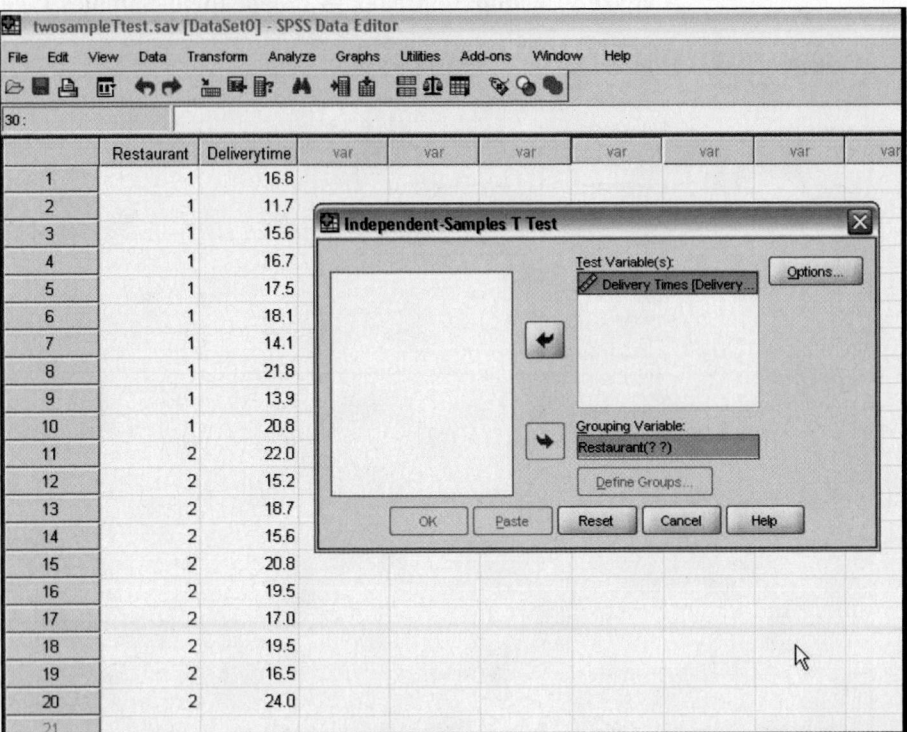

- Next, click on the **Define Groups** button. In the **Define Groups** window, select **Use specified values** by entering "1" for Group 1 and "2" for Group 2. The values of "1" and "2" depend on how you define the two groups at the beginning when you define the variables. Then click on the **Continue** button to return to the "Independent-Samples T Test" window.

- Click on the **OK** button to obtain the SPSS results.

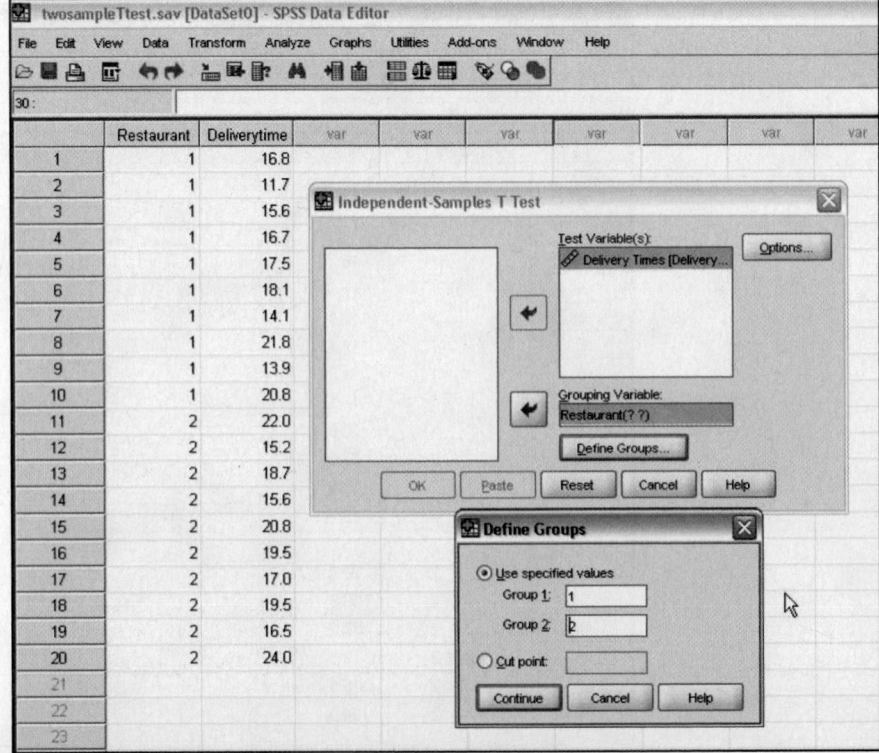

Step 3: Go to **SPSS Viewer** to obtain your SPSS results.

SPSS output: *t* **Test**

Group Statistics

Restaurant		N	Mean	Std. Deviation	Std. Error Mean
Delivery Times	Local Pizza Restaurant	10	16.700	3.0955	.9789
	National Pizza Chain	10	18.880	2.8662	.9064

Independent Samples Test

		Levene's Test for Equality of Variances		*t* Test for Equality of Means						
									95% Confidence Interval of the Difference	
		F	Sig.	t	df	Sig. (2-tailed)	Mean Difference	Std. Error Difference	Lower	Upper
Delivery Times	Equal variances assumed	.001	.980	−1.634	18	.120	−2.1800	1.3341	−4.9828	.6228
	Equal variances not assumed			−1.634	17.894	.120	−2.1800	1.3341	−4.9840	.6240

Problems for Section 12.1

LEARNING THE BASICS

12.1 If you have samples of $n_1 = 12$ and $n_2 = 15$, in performing the pooled-variance t test, how many degrees of freedom do you have?

12.2 Assume that you have a sample of $n_1 = 8$, with the sample mean $\overline{X}_1 = 42$, and a sample standard deviation $S_1 = 4$, and you have an independent sample of $n_2 = 15$ from another population with a sample mean of $\overline{X}_2 = 34$ and a sample standard deviation $S_2 = 5$.
a. What is the value of the pooled-variance t_{STAT} test statistic for testing $H_0: \mu_1 = \mu_2$?
b. In finding the critical value, how many degrees of freedom are there?
c. Using the level of significance $\alpha = 0.01$, what is the critical value for a one-tail test of the hypothesis $H_0: \mu_1 \leq \mu_2$ against the alternative, $H_1: \mu_1 > \mu_2$?
d. What is your statistical decision?

12.3 What assumptions about the two populations are necessary in Problem 12.2?

12.4 Referring to Problem 12.2, construct a 95% confidence interval estimate of the population mean difference between μ_1 and μ_2.

12.5 Referring to Problem 12.2, if $n_1 = 5$ and $n_2 = 4$, how many degrees of freedom do you have?

12.6 Referring to Problem 12.2, if $n_1 = 5$ and $n_2 = 4$, at the 0.01 level of significance, is there evidence that $\mu_1 > \mu_2$?

APPLYING THE CONCEPTS

12.7 When people make estimates, they are influenced by anchors to their estimates. A study was conducted in which students were asked to estimate the number of calories in a cheeseburger. One group was asked to do this after thinking about a calorie-laden cheesecake. A second group was asked to do this after thinking about an organic fruit salad. The mean number of calories estimated in a cheeseburger was 780 for the group that thought about the cheesecake and 1,041 for the group that thought about the organic fruit salad. (Data extracted from "Drilling Down, Sizing Up a Cheeseburger's Caloric Heft," *The New York Times*, October 4, 2010, p. B2.) Suppose that the study was based on a sample of 20 people who thought about the cheesecake first and 20 people who thought about the organic fruit salad first, and the standard deviation of the number of calories in the cheeseburger was 128 for the people who thought about the cheesecake first and 140 for the people who thought about the organic fruit salad first.

a. State the null and alternative hypothesis if you want to determine whether the mean estimated amount of calories in the cheeseburger is lower for the people who thought about the cheesecake first than for the people who thought about the organic fruit salad first.

b. In the context of this study, what is the meaning of the Type I error?

c. In the context of this study, what is the meaning of the Type II error?

d. At the 0.01 level of significance, is there evidence that the mean estimated amount of calories in the cheeseburger is lower for the people who thought about the cheesecake first than for the people who thought about the organic fruit salad first?

12.8 A recent study ("Snack Ads Spur Children to Eat More," *The New York Times*, July 20, 2009, p. B3) found that children who watched a cartoon with food advertising ate, on average, 28.5 grams of Goldfish crackers as compared to an average of 19.7 grams of Goldfish crackers for children who watched a cartoon without food advertising. Although there were 118 children in the study, neither the sample size in each group nor the sample standard deviations were reported. Suppose that there were 59 children in each group, and the sample standard deviation for those children who watched the food ad was 8.6 grams and the sample standard deviation for those children who did not watch the food ad was 7.9 grams.

a. Assuming that the population variances are equal and $\alpha = 0.05$, is there evidence that the mean amount of Goldfish crackers eaten was significantly higher for the children who watched food ads?

b. Assuming that the population variances are equal, construct a 95% confidence interval estimate of the difference between the mean amount of Goldfish crackers eaten by the children who watched and did not watch the food ad.

c. Compare the results of (a) and (b) and discuss.

12.9 A problem with a telephone line that prevents a customer from receiving or making calls is upsetting to both the customer and the telephone company. The file **Phone** contains samples of 20 problems reported to two different offices of a telephone company and the time to clear these problems (in minutes) from the customers' lines:

Central Office I Time to Clear Problems (minutes)

1.48	1.75	0.78	2.85	0.52	1.60	4.15	3.97	1.48	3.10
1.02	0.53	0.93	1.60	0.80	1.05	6.32	3.93	5.45	0.97

Central Office II Time to Clear Problems (minutes)

7.55	3.75	0.10	1.10	0.60	0.52	3.30	2.10	0.58	4.02
3.75	0.65	1.92	0.60	1.53	4.23	0.08	1.48	1.65	0.72

a. Assuming that the population variances from both offices are equal, is there evidence of a difference in the mean waiting time between the two offices? (Use $\alpha = 0.05$.)

b. Find the p-value in (a) and interpret its meaning.

c. What other assumption is necessary in (a)?

d. Assuming that the population variances from both offices are equal, construct and interpret a 95% confidence interval estimate of the difference between the population means in the two offices.

SELF Test **12.10** The Computer Anxiety Rating Scale (CARS) measures an individual's level of computer anxiety, on a scale from 20 (no anxiety) to 100 (highest level of anxiety). Researchers at Miami University administered CARS to 172 business students. One of the objectives of the study was to determine whether there is a difference in the level of computer anxiety experienced by female and male business students. They found the following:

	Males	Females
$\overline{X}$	40.26	36.85
S	13.35	9.42
n	100	72

Source: Data extracted from T. Broome and D. Havelka, "Determinants of Computer Anxiety in Business Students," *The Review of Business Information Systems,* Spring 2002, 6(2), pp. 9–16.

a. At the 0.05 level of significance, is there evidence of a difference in the mean computer anxiety experienced by female and male business students?

b. Determine the p-value and interpret its meaning.

c. What assumptions do you have to make about the two populations in order to justify the use of the t test?

12.11 An important feature of digital cameras is battery life, the number of shots that can be taken before the battery needs to be recharged. The file **DigitalCameras** contains the battery life of 29 subcompact cameras and 16 compact cameras. (Data extracted from "Digital Cameras," *Consumer Reports,* July 2009, pp. 28–29.)

a. Assuming that the population variances from both types of digital cameras are equal, is there evidence of a difference in the mean battery life between the two types of digital cameras ($\alpha = 0.05$)?

b. Determine the p-value in (a) and interpret its meaning.

c. Assuming that the population variances from both types of digital cameras are equal, construct and interpret a 95% confidence interval estimate of the difference between the population mean battery life of the two types of digital cameras.

12.12 A bank with a branch located in a commercial district of a city has the business objective of developing an improved process for serving customers during the noon-to-1 P.M. lunch period. Management decides to first study the waiting time in the current process. The waiting time is defined as the time that elapses from when the customer enters the line until he or she reaches the teller window. Data are collected from a random sample of 15 customers, and the results (in minutes) are as follows (and stored in Bank1):

4.21 5.55 3.02 5.13 4.77 2.34 3.54 3.20
4.50 6.10 0.38 5.12 6.46 6.19 3.79

Suppose that another branch, located in a residential area, is also concerned with improving the process of serving customers in the noon-to-1 P.M. lunch period. Data are collected from a random sample of 15 customers, and the results are as follows (and stored in Bank2):

9.66 5.90 8.02 5.79 8.73 3.82 8.01 8.35
10.49 6.68 5.64 4.08 6.17 9.91 5.47

a. Assuming that the population variances from both banks are equal, is there evidence of a difference in the mean waiting time between the two branches? (Use $\alpha = 0.05$.)
b. Determine the *p*-value in (a) and interpret its meaning.
c. In addition to equal variances, what other assumption is necessary in (a)?
d. Construct and interpret a 95% confidence interval estimate of the difference between the population means in the two branches.

12.13 Repeat Problem 12.12 (a), assuming that the population variances in the two branches are not equal. Compare the results with those of Problem 12.12 (a).

12.14 In intaglio printing, a design or figure is carved beneath the surface of hard metal or stone. The business objective of an intaglio printing company is to determine whether there are differences in the mean surface hardness of steel plates, based on two different surface conditions—untreated and treated by lightly polishing with emery paper. An experiment is designed in which 40 steel plates are randomly assigned—20 plates are untreated and 20 plates are treated. The results of the experiment (stored in Intaglio) are as follows:

Untreated		Treated	
164.368	177.135	158.239	150.226
159.018	163.903	138.216	155.620
153.871	167.802	168.006	151.233
165.096	160.818	149.654	158.653
157.184	167.433	145.456	151.204
154.496	163.538	168.178	150.869
160.920	164.525	154.321	161.657
164.917	171.230	162.763	157.016
169.091	174.964	161.020	156.670
175.276	166.311	167.706	147.920

a. Assuming that the population variances from both conditions are equal, is there evidence of a difference in the mean surface hardness between untreated and treated steel plates? (Use $\alpha = 0.05$.)

b. Determine the *p*-value in (a) and interpret its meaning.
c. In addition to equal variances, what other assumption is necessary in (a)?
d. Construct and interpret a 95% confidence interval estimate of the difference between the population means from treated and untreated steel plates.

12.15 Repeat Problem 12.14 (a), assuming that the population variances from untreated and treated steel plates are not equal. Compare the results with those of Problem 12.14 (a).

12.16 Do young children use cell phones? Apparently so, according to a recent study (A. Ross, "Message to Santa; Kids Want a Phone," *Palm Beach Post*, December 16, 2008, pp. 1A, 4A), which stated that cell phone users under 12 years of age averaged 137 calls per month as compared to 231 calls per month for cell phone users 13 to 17 years of age. No sample sizes were reported. Suppose that the results were based on samples of 50 cell phone users in each group and that the sample standard deviation for cell phone users under 12 years of age was 51.7 calls per month and the sample standard deviation for cell phone users 13 to 17 years of age was 67.6 calls per month.

a. Assuming that the variances in the populations of cell phone users are equal, is there evidence of a difference in the mean cell phone usage between cell phone users under 12 years of age and cell phone users 13 to 17 years of age? (Use a 0.05 level of significance.)
b. In addition to equal variances, what other assumption is necessary in (a)?

12.17 Nondestructive evaluation is a method that is used to describe the properties of components or materials without causing any permanent physical change to the units. It includes the determination of properties of materials and the classification of flaws by size, shape, type, and location. This method is most effective for detecting surface flaws and characterizing surface properties of electrically conductive materials. Data were collected that classified each component as having a flaw or not, based on manual inspection and operator judgment, and the data also reported the size of the crack in the material. Do the components classified as unflawed have a smaller mean crack size than components classified as flawed? The results in terms of crack size (in inches) are stored in Crack . (Data extracted from B. D. Olin and W. Q. Meeker, "Applications of Statistical Methods to Nondestructive Evaluation," *Technometrics*, 38, 1996, p. 101.)

a. Assuming that the population variances are equal, is there evidence that the mean crack size is smaller for the unflawed specimens than for the flawed specimens? (Use $\alpha = 0.05$.)
b. Repeat (a), assuming that the population variances are not equal.
c. Compare the results of (a) and (b).

12.2 *F* Test for the Ratio of Two Variances

Often you need to determine whether two independent populations have the same variability. By testing variances, you can detect differences in the variability in two independent populations. One important reason to test for the difference between the variances of two populations is to determine whether to use the pooled-variance *t* test (which assumes equal variances) or the separate-variance *t* test (which does not assume equal variances) while comparing the means of two independent populations.

The test for the difference between the variances of two independent populations is based on the ratio of the two sample variances. If you assume that each population is normally distributed, then the ratio S_1^2/S_2^2 follows the *F* distribution (see Table E.5). The critical values of the **F distribution** in Table E.5 depend on the degrees of freedom in the two samples. The degrees of freedom in the numerator of the ratio are for the first sample, and the degrees of freedom in the denominator are for the second sample. Equation (12.2) defines the **F test for the ratio of two variances**.

F TEST STATISTIC FOR TESTING THE RATIO OF TWO VARIANCES

The F_{STAT} test statistic is equal to the variance of sample 1 divided by the variance of sample 2.

$$F_{STAT} = \frac{S_1^2}{S_2^2} \qquad (12.2)$$

where

S_1^2 = variance of sample 1

S_2^2 = variance of sample 2

n_1 = sample size selected from population 1

n_2 = sample size selected from population 2

$n_1 - 1$ = degrees of freedom from sample 1 (i.e., the numerator degrees of freedom)

$n_2 - 1$ = degrees of freedom from sample 2 (i.e., the denominator degrees of freedom)

The F_{STAT} test statistic follows an *F* distribution with $n_1 - 1$ and $n_2 - 1$ degrees of freedom.

F Critical Value

1. For a two tail test: The two critical values are F_U (*F* **Upper**) and F_L (*F* **Lower**)

$$F_U = F_{a/2, n_1-1, n_2-1}$$

$$F_L = F_{1-a/2, n_1-1, n_2-1} = \frac{1}{F_{a/2, n_2-1, n_1-1}}$$

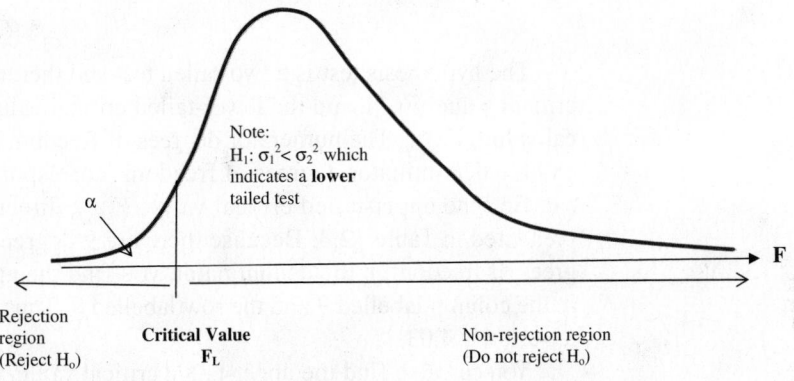

Note:
H_1: $\sigma_1^2 \neq \sigma_2^2$ which
indicates a two
tailed test

$\alpha/2$

$\alpha/2$

F

Rejection
region
(Reject H_o)

Critical Value
F_L

Non-rejection region
(Do not reject H_o)

Critical Value
F_U

Rejection region
(Reject H_o)

2. For a lower-tailed test (left tailed test): The critical value is F_L (*F* **Lower**)

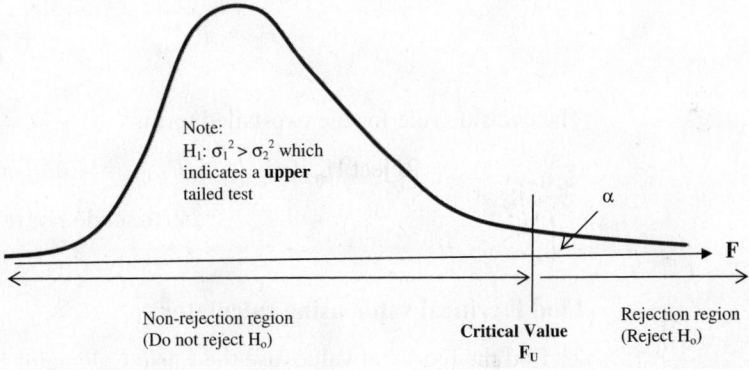

Note:
H_1: $\sigma_1^2 < \sigma_2^2$ which
indicates a **lower**
tailed test

α

F

Rejection
region
(Reject H_o)

Critical Value
F_L

Non-rejection region
(Do not reject H_o)

3. For a upper-tailed test (right tailed test): The critical value is F_U (*F* **Upper**)

Note:
H_1: $\sigma_1^2 > \sigma_2^2$ which
indicates a **upper**
tailed test

α

F

Non-rejection region
(Do not reject H_o)

Critical Value
F_U

Rejection region
(Reject H_o)

For a given level of significance, α, to test the null hypothesis of equality of population variances:

$$H_0: \sigma_1^2 = \sigma_2^2$$

against the alternative hypothesis that the two population variances are not equal:

$$H_1: \sigma_1^2 \neq \sigma_2^2$$

you reject the null hypothesis if the computed F_{STAT} test statistic is greater than the upper-tail critical value, $F_{U\alpha/2}$ or F_{CALC} test statistic is less than the lower-tail critical value, $F_{L,\alpha/2}$ from the F distribution, with $n_1 - 1$ degrees of freedom in the numerator and $n_2 - 1$ degrees of freedom in the denominator. Thus, the decision rule is

$$\text{Reject } H_0 \text{ if } F_{CALC} > F_{U\alpha/2}; \text{ or } F_{CALC} < F_{L,\alpha/2}$$

$$\text{otherwise, do not reject } H_0.$$

To illustrate how to use the F test to determine whether the two variances are equal, return to the BLK Beverages scenario on page 485 concerning the sales of BLK Cola in two different display locations. To determine whether to use the pooled-variance t test or the separate-variance t test in Section 12.1, you can test the equality of the two population variances. The null and alternative hypotheses are

$$H_0: \sigma_1^2 = \sigma_2^2$$
$$H_1: \sigma_1^2 \neq \sigma_2^2$$

The hypothesis test is a two-tailed test and therefore you have to compute the upper-tailed critical value, $F_{U,\alpha/2}$ and the lower-tailed critical value, $F_{L,\alpha/2}$. First find the upper-tailed critical value, $F_{U,\alpha/2}$. The numerator degrees of freedom (corresponds to sample 1) is $10 - 1 = 9$ and the denominator degrees of freedom (corresponds to sample 2) is also $10 - 1 = 9$. You can find the upper-tailed critical value, $F_{U,\alpha/2}$ directly from Table A.5, a portion of which is presented in Table 12.3. Because there are 9 degrees of freedom in the numerator and 9 degrees of freedom in the denominator, you find the upper-tail critical value, $F_{U,\alpha/2}$, by looking in the column labelled 9 and the row labelled 9. Thus, the upper-tail critical value of this F distribution is 4.03.

You can also find the upper-tailed critical value, $F_{U,\alpha/2}$ from the calculator (refer to *Find F critical value using calculator*).

You can find the lower-tailed critical value, $F_{L,\alpha/2}$ using the following formula.

$$F_L = F_{1-\alpha/2, n_1-1, n_2-1} = \frac{1}{F_{\alpha/2, n_2-1, n_1-1}}$$

The decision rule for the two-tailed test is

$$\text{Reject } H_0 \text{ if } F_{CALC} > F_{U,\alpha/2} = 4.03 \quad \text{or} \quad F_{CALC} < F_{L,\alpha/2} = 0.248$$

$$\text{Otherwise, do not reject } H_0.$$

Find F critical value using calculator:

To find the F critical value, use the Casio Calculator fx-9750GII and follow the following calculator steps:

Note: Fx-9750G Plus does not have this option; therefore you have to use the Table A.5 in the Appendix.

From the **Main Menu** select:

STAT F5 (DIST) **F4** (F) **F3**(InvF)   then enter the following items:

Inverse F
Data   : F2(Var)   ▼
Area   : 0.025   EXE   (Note: It is a two tailed test for F distribution, $\alpha \div 2$)
n:df   : 9   EXE   (Note: n:df corresponds to the sample 1 happens to be in the numerator)
d:df   : 9   EXE   (Note: d:df corresponds to the sample 2 happens to be in the denominator)

Save Res : None

Execute

Now key **EXE** or **F1**(CALC)

The calculator will now show the results:

Inverse F

x-Inv = 4.02599416

The critical value defines the rejection and non-rejection regions.

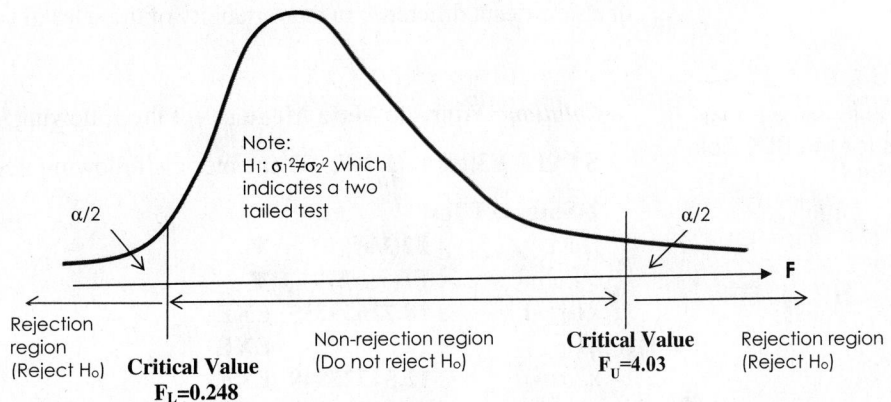

Note:
Apply the formula to compute F_L.

$$F_L = F_{1-\alpha/2,n_1-1,n_2-1} = \frac{1}{F_{\alpha/2,n_2-1,n_1-1}} = \frac{1}{F_{0.025,9,9}} = \frac{1}{4.02599416} = 0.248386$$

TABLE 12.3

Finding the Upper-Tail
Critical Value of *F* with
9 and 9 Degrees of
Freedom for an Upper-
Tail Area of 0.025

		Cumulative Probabilities = 0.975					
		Upper-Tail Area = 0.025					
		Numerator df_1					
Denominator df_2	**1**	**2**	**3**	**...**	**7**	**8**	**9**
1	647.80	799.50	864.20	...	948.20	956.70	963.30
2	38.51	39.00	39.17	...	39.36	39.37	39.39
3	17.44	16.04	15.44	...	14.62	14.54	14.47
.	.	.	.		.	.	.
.	.	.	.		.	.	.
.	.	.	.		.	.	.
7	8.07	6.54	5.89	...	4.99	4.90	4.82
8	7.57	6.06	5.42	...	4.53	4.43	4.36
9	7.21	5.71	5.08	...	4.20	4.10	4.03

Source: Extracted from Table E.5.

Using Equation (12.2) on page 508 and the cola sales data (see Table 12.1 on page 488),

$$S_1^2 = (18.7264)^2 = 350.6778 \quad S_2^2 = (12.5433)^2 = 157.3333$$

so that

$$F_{STAT} = \frac{S_1^2}{S_2^2}$$

$$= \frac{350.6778}{157.3333} = 2.2289$$

Because $F_{STAT} = 2.2289 < 4.03$, you do not reject H_0. Figure 12.8 shows the results for this test, including the p-value, 0.248. Because $0.248 > 0.05$, you conclude that there is no evidence of a significant difference in the variability of the sales of cola for the two display locations.

FIGURE 12.8

Casio calculator F-test results for the BLK Cola sales data

Solution: From the **Main Menu** select the following:

STAT   F3(test)   **F4**(F). Then enter the following items:

2-Sample FTest
Data	: **F2**(Var)	▼
σ1	: **F1**($\neq\sigma$2)	▼
x1σn-1	: **18.72639255**	**EXE**
n1	: **10**	**EXE**
x2σn-1	: **12.54325848**	**EXE**
n2	: **10**	**EXE**

Now press **EXE** or **F1** (Calc).

The calculator will now show the results:

2-Sample FTest
σ1	$\neq\sigma$2
F	=2.2289
p	=0.2482
x1σn-1	=18.726
x2σn-1	=12.543
n1	=10
n2	=10

In testing for a difference between two variances using the F test described in this section, you assume that each of the two populations is normally distributed. The F test is very sensitive to the normality assumption. If boxplots or normal probability plots suggest even a mild departure from normality for either of the two populations, you should not use the F test. If this happens, you should use the Levene test (see Section 12.5) or a nonparametric approach (see references 1 and 2).

In testing for the equality of variances as part of assessing the validity of the pooled-variance t test procedure, the F test is a two-tail test with $\alpha/2$ in the upper tail. However, when you are interested in examining the variability in situations other than the pooled-variance t test, the F test is often a one-tail test. Example 12.4 illustrates a one-tail test.

EXAMPLE 12.8

A One-Tail Test for the Difference Between Two Variances

A professor in the accounting department of a business school would like to determine whether there is more variability in the final exam scores of students taking the introductory accounting course who are not majoring in accounting than for students taking the course who are majoring in accounting. Random samples of 13 non-accounting majors and 10 accounting majors are selected from the professor's class roster in his large lecture, and the following results are computed based on the final exam scores:

Non-accounting: $n_1 = 13$ $S_1^2 = 210.2$

Accounting: $n_2 = 10$ $S_2^2 = 36.5$

At the 0.05 level of significance, is there evidence that there is more variability in the final exam scores of students taking the introductory accounting course who are not majoring in accounting than for students taking the course who are majoring in accounting? Assume that the population final exam scores are normally distributed.

SOLUTION   The null and alternative hypotheses are

$$H_0: \sigma_{NA}^2 \leq \sigma_A^2$$
$$H_1: \sigma_{NA}^2 > \sigma_A^2$$

The F_{STAT} test statistic is given by Equation (12.7) on page 357:

$$F_{STAT} = \frac{S_1^2}{S_2^2}$$

You use Table E.5 to find the upper critical value of the F distribution. With $n_1 - 1 = 13 - 1 = 12$ degrees of freedom in the numerator, $n_2 - 1 = 10 - 1 = 9$ degrees of freedom in the denominator, and $\alpha = 0.05$, the upper-tail critical value, $F_{0.05}$, is 3.07. The decision rule is

$$\text{Reject } H_0 \text{ if } F_{STAT} > 3.07;$$

$$\text{otherwise, do not reject } H_0.$$

From Equation (12.2) on page 508,

$$F_{STAT} = \frac{S_1^2}{S_2^2}$$

$$= \frac{210.2}{36.5} = 5.7589$$

Because $F_{STAT} = 5.7589 > 3.07$, you reject H_0. Using a 0.05 level of significance, you conclude that there is evidence that there is more variability in the final exam scores of students taking the introductory accounting course who are not majoring in accounting than for students taking the course who are majoring in accounting.

CALCULATOR LESSON 13A

**CFX-9850GB
CALCULATOR**

EXAMPLE 12.9

Lesson 13A—*F* Test of Two Variances

Recall the following example from Calculator Lesson 10.

A work team has developed a new process to assemble a certain component. Its members would like to know if this new process has significantly reduced the time to assemble the component. They have taken samples of 50 components produced by the existing process and 40 components produced by the new process. The mean and standard deviation of the assembly times for the existing process were 73.2 minutes and 3.6 minutes, respectively. The mean time was 71.4 minutes, with a standard deviation of 3.2 minutes, for the components assembled by the new process. Assume that the times for both processes are normally distributed, with the same variance.

Suppose that instead of assuming that the variances of the assembly times for the two processes are equal, we do an *F* test to see if there is evidence to support such an assumption. Test at the 5% level of significance.

Solution: Let sample 1 be the existing process sample and sample 2 the new process. From the **Main Menu** select the following:

STAT   F3(test)   **F4**(F). Then enter the following items:

2-Sample FTest

Data	: **F2**(Var)	▼
$\sigma 1$	: **F1**($\neq\sigma 2$)	▼
x1σn-1	: **3.6**	**EXE**
n1	: **50**	**EXE**
x2σn-1	: **3.2**	**EXE**
n2	: **40**	**EXE**

Now press **EXE** or **F1**(Calc).

The calculator will now show the results:

2-Sample FTest

$\sigma 1$	$\neq\sigma 2$
F	=1.2656
p	=0.44965
x1σn-1	=3.6
x2σn-1	=3.2
n1	=50
n2	=40

Since the *p*-value > 0.05, the conclusion is to *not reject* the null hypothesis. In other words, the evidence does not indicate that the variances of the assembly times for the two processes are different (i.e., the variances are approximately the same).

EXAMPLE 12.10   Recall the following example from Lesson 10.

We wish to determine if there is a difference in the braking distances for two types of tires. Use the 5% level of significance and assume that the braking distances for each type of tire are normally distributed, with the same variance. The data are as follows:

Braking distance (metres)

Tire A	Tire B
83	75
79	84
82	76
84	83
80	85
81	78
	83

Suppose we test to see if the assumption about equal variances seems reasonable at the 5% level.

Solution: Enter the data for Tire A in List 1 and the data for Tire B in List 2. From the **Main Menu** select the following:

STAT   F3(test)   **F4**(F). Then enter the following items:

2-Sample FTest

Data	: **F1**(List)	▼
$\sigma 1$	: **F1**($\neq\sigma 2$)	▼
List1	: **F1**(List1)	▼
List2	: **F2**(List2)	▼
Freq	: **1**	▼
Freq	: **1**	**EXE**

The calculator will now show the results:

σ1	$\neq$σ2
F	=0.20646
p	=0.10432
x1σn-1	=1.8708
x2σn-1	=4.1173
$\bar{x}$1	=81.5
$\bar{x}$2	=80.571
n1	=6
n2	=7

Since the *p*-value > 0.05, the conclusion is to *not reject* the null hypothesis. In other words, the evidence does not indicate that the variances of the stopping distances for the two types of tires are different (i.e., the variances are approximately the same).

CALCULATOR LESSON 13B

CASIO FX-9750GII CALCULATOR

Lesson 13B—*F* Test of Two Variances

EXAMPLE 12.11

Recall the following example from Calculator Lesson 11.

A work team has developed a new process to assemble a certain component. Its members would like to know if this new process has significantly reduced the time to assemble the component. They have taken samples of 50 components produced by the existing process and 40 components produced by the new process. The mean and standard deviation of the assembly times for the existing process were 73.2 minutes and 3.6 minutes, respectively. The mean time was 71.4 minutes, with a standard deviation of 3.2 minutes, for the components assembled by the new process. Assume that the times for both processes are normally distributed, with the same variance.

Suppose that instead of assuming that the variances of the assembly times for the two processes are equal, we do an *F* test to see if there is evidence to support such an assumption. Test at the 5% level of significance.

Solution: Let sample 1 be the existing process sample, and sample 2 the new process. From the **Main Menu** select the following:

STAT F3(test) **F4**(F). Then enter the following items:

2-Sample F Test

Data	: **F2**(Var)	▼
σ1	: **F1**($\neq$σ2)	▼
sx1	: **3.6**	**EXE**
n1	: **50**	**EXE**
sx2	: **3.2**	**EXE**
n2	: **40**	**EXE**
Save Res	: None	

Now press **EXE**, **F1**(Calc), or **F6**(DRAW).

If you select **F6**(DRAW), you will see a normal distribution.

If you select either **EXE** or **F1**(Calc), the calculator will show the results:

2-Sample FTest

σ1	≠σ2
F	=1.265625
p	=0.44965583
sx1	=3.6
sx2	=3.2
n1	=50
n2	=40

Since the *p*-value > 0.05, the conclusion is to *not reject* the null hypothesis. In other words, the evidence does not indicate that the variances of the assembly times for the two processes are different (i.e., the variances are approximately the same).

EXAMPLE 12.12   Recall the following example from Lesson 11.

We wish to determine if there is a difference in the braking distances for two types of tires. Use the 5% level of significance and assume that the braking distances for each type of tire are normally distributed with the same variance. Based on the data …

Braking distance (metres)	
Tire A	Tire B
83	75
79	84
82	76
84	83
80	85
81	78
	83

Suppose we test to see if the assumption about equal variances seems reasonable at the 5% level.

Solution: Enter the data for Tire A in List 1 and the data for Tire B in List 2. From the **Main Menu** select the following:

STAT   F3(test)   **F4**(F). Then enter the following items:

2-Sample FTest

Data	: **F1**(List)	▼
σ1	: **F1**(≠σ2)	▼
List1	: **F1**(List1)	▼
List2	: **F2**(List2)	▼
Freq	: 1	▼
Freq	: 1	**EXE**
Save Res	: None	

Now press **EXE**, **F1**(Calc), or **F6**(DRAW).

If you select **F6**(DRAW), you will see a normal distribution.

If you select either **EXE** or **F1**(Calc), the calculator will show the results:

2-Sample FTest

σ1	≠σ2
F	=0.20646067
p	=0.10432125
$\bar{x}$1	=81.5
$\bar{x}$2	=80.5714286
sx1	=1.87082869
sx2	=4.11732692
n1	=6
n2	=7

Since the *p*-value > 0.05, the conclusion is to *not reject* the null hypothesis. In other words, the evidence does not indicate that the variances of the stopping distances for the two types of tires are different (i.e., the variances are approximately the same).

Problems for Section 12.2

LEARNING THE BASICS

12.18 Determine the upper-tail critical values of *F* in each of the following two-tail tests.
a. $\alpha = 0.10, n_1 = 16, n_2 = 21$
b. $\alpha = 0.05, n_1 = 16, n_2 = 21$
c. $\alpha = 0.01, n_1 = 16, n_2 = 21$

12.19 Determine the upper-tail critical value of *F* in each of the following one-tail tests.
a. $\alpha = 0.05, n_1 = 16, n_2 = 21$
b. $\alpha = 0.01, n_1 = 16, n_2 = 21$

12.20 The following information is available for two samples selected from independent normally distributed populations:

$$\text{Population A}: \quad n_1 = 25 \quad S_1^2 = 16$$

$$\text{Population B}: \quad n_2 = 25 \quad S_2^2 = 25$$

a. Which sample variance do you place in the numerator of F_{STAT}?
b. What is the value of F_{STAT}?

12.21 The following information is available for two samples selected from independent normally distributed populations:

$$\text{Population A}: \quad n_1 = 25 \quad S_1^2 = 161.9$$

$$\text{Population B}: \quad n_2 = 25 \quad S_2^2 = 133.7$$

What is the value of F_{STAT} if you are testing the null hypothesis $H_0: \sigma_1^2 = \sigma_2^2$?

12.22 In Problem 12.21, how many degrees of freedom are there in the numerator and denominator of the *F* test?

12.23 In Problems 12.21 and 12.22, what is the upper-tail critical value for *F* if the level of significance, α, is 0.05 and the alternative hypothesis is $H_1: \sigma_1^2 \neq \sigma_2^2$?

12.24 In Problems 12.21 through 12.23, what is your statistical decision?

12.25 The following information is available for two samples selected from independent but very right-skewed populations:

$$\text{Population A}: \quad n_1 = 16 \quad S_1^2 = 47.3$$

$$\text{Population B}: \quad n_2 = 13 \quad S_2^2 = 36.4$$

Should you use the *F* test to test the null hypothesis of equality of variances? Discuss.

12.26 In Problem 12.25, assume that two samples are selected from independent normally distributed populations.
a. At the 0.05 level of significance, is there evidence of a difference between σ_1^2 and σ_2^2?
b. Suppose that you want to perform a one-tail test. At the 0.05 level of significance, what is the upper-tail critical value of *F* to determine whether there is evidence that $\sigma_1^2 > \sigma_2^2$? What is your statistical decision?

APPLYING THE CONCEPTS

12.27 A problem with a telephone line that prevents a customer from receiving or making calls is upsetting to both the customer and the telephone company. The file **Phone** contains samples of 20 problems reported to two different offices of a telephone company and the time to clear these problems (in minutes) from the customers' lines.

a. At the 0.05 level of significance, is there evidence of a difference in the variability of the time to clear problems between the two central offices?
b. Interpret the p-value.
c. What assumption do you need to make in (a) about the two populations in order to justify your use of the F test?
d. Based on the results of (a) and (b), which t test defined in Section 12.1 should you use to compare the mean time to clear problems in the two central offices?

SELF ✓ **Test** **12.28** The Computer Anxiety Rating Scale (CARS) measures an individual's level of computer anxiety, on a scale from 20 (no anxiety) to 100 (highest level of anxiety). Researchers at Miami University administered CARS to 172 business students. One of the objectives of the study was to determine whether there is a difference between the level of computer anxiety experienced by female students and male students. They found the following:

	Males	Females
$\overline{X}$	40.26	36.85
S	13.35	9.42
n	100	72

Source: Data extracted from T. Broome and D. Havelka, "Determinants of Computer Anxiety in Business Students," *The Review of Business Information Systems,* Spring 2002, 6(2), pp. 9–16.

a. At the 0.05 level of significance, is there evidence of a difference in the variability of the computer anxiety experienced by males and females?
b. Interpret the p-value.
c. What assumption do you need to make about the two populations in order to justify the use of the F test?
d. Based on (a) and (b), which t test defined in Section 12.1 should you use to test whether there is a significant difference in mean computer anxiety for female and male students?

12.29 A bank with a branch located in a commercial district of a city has the business objective of improving the process for serving customers during the noon-to-1 P.M. lunch period. To do so, the waiting time (defined as the time elapsed from when the customer enters the line until he or she reaches the teller window) needs to be shortened to increase customer satisfaction. A random sample of 15 customers is selected (and stored in **Bank1**), and the results (in minutes) are as follows:

4.21   5.55   3.02   5.13   4.77   2.34   3.54   3.20
4.50   6.10   0.38   5.12   6.46   6.19   3.79

Suppose that another branch, located in a residential area, is also concerned with the noon-to-1 P.M. lunch period. A random sample of 15 customers is selected (and stored in **Bank2**), and the results (in minutes) are as follows:

9.66   5.90   8.02   5.79   8.73   3.82   8.01   8.35
10.49   6.68   5.64   4.08   6.17   9.91   5.47

a. Is there evidence of a difference in the variability of the waiting time between the two branches? (Use $\alpha = 0.05$.)
b. Determine the p-value in (a) and interpret its meaning.
c. What assumption about the population distribution of each bank is necessary in (a)? Is the assumption valid for these data?
d. Based on the results of (a), is it appropriate to use the pooled-variance t test to compare the means of the two branches?

12.30 An important feature of digital cameras is battery life, the number of shots that can be taken before the battery needs to be recharged. The file **DigitalCameras** contains battery life information for 29 subcompact cameras and 16 compact cameras. (Data extracted from "Digital Cameras," *Consumer Reports*, July 2009, pp. 28–29.)

a. Is there evidence of a difference in the variability of the battery life between the two types of digital cameras? (Use $\alpha = 0.05$.)
b. Determine the p-value in (a) and interpret its meaning.
c. What assumption about the population distribution of the two types of cameras is necessary in (a)? Is the assumption valid for these data?
d. Based on the results of (a), which t test defined in Section 12.1 should you use to compare the mean battery life of the two types of cameras?

12.31 Do young children use cell phones? Apparently so, according to a recent study (A. Ross, "Message to Santa; Kids Want a Phone," *Palm Beach Post*, December 16, 2008, pp. 1A, 4A), which stated that cell phone users under 12 years of age averaged 137 calls per month as compared to 231 calls per month for cell phone users 13 to 17 years of age. No sample sizes were reported. Suppose that the results were based on samples of 50 cell phone users in each group and that the sample standard deviation for cell phone users under 12 years of age was 51.7 calls per month and the sample standard deviation for cell phone users 13 to 17 years of age was 67.6 calls per month.

a. Using a 0.05 level of significance, is there evidence of a difference in the variances of cell phone usage between cell phone users under 12 years of age and cell phone users 13 to 17 years of age?
b. On the basis of the results in (a), which t test defined in Section 12.1 should you use to compare the means of the two groups of cell phone users? Discuss.

12.32 Is there a difference in the variation of the yield of five-year CDs in different cities? The file **FiveYearCDRate** contains the yields for a five-year certificate of deposit (CD) for 9 banks in New York and 9 banks in Los Angeles, as of May 13, 2011. (Data extracted from **www.Bankrate .com**, May 13, 2011.) At the 0.05 level of significance, is there evidence of a difference in the variance of the yield of five-year CDs in the two cities? Assume that the population yields are normally distributed.

12.3 Comparing the Means of Two Related Populations

The hypothesis-testing procedures presented in Section 12.1 enable you to make comparisons and examine differences in the means of two *independent* populations. In this section, you will learn about a procedure for analyzing the difference between the means of two populations when you collect sample data from populations that are related—that is, when results of the first population are *not* independent of the results of the second population.

There are two situations that involve related data between populations. Either you take repeated measurements from the same set of items or individuals or you match items or individuals according to some characteristic. In either situation, you are interested in the *difference between the two related values* rather than the *individual values* themselves.

When you take **repeated measurements** on the same items or individuals, you assume that the same items or individuals will behave alike if treated alike. Your objective is to show that any differences between two measurements of the same items or individuals are due to different treatment conditions. For example, when performing a taste-testing experiment comparing two beverages, you can use each person in the sample as his or her own control so that you can have *repeated measurements* on the same individual.

Another example of repeated measurements involves the pricing of the same goods from two different vendors. For example, have you ever wondered whether new textbook prices at a local college bookstore are different from the prices offered at a major online retailer? You could take two independent samples, that is, select two different sets of textbooks, and then use the hypothesis tests discussed in Section 12.1.

However, by random chance, the first sample may have many large-format hardcover textbooks and the second sample may have many small trade paperback books. This would imply that the first set of textbooks will always be more expensive than the second set of textbooks, regardless of where they are purchased. That observation means that using the Section 12.1 tests would not be a good choice. The better choice would be to use two related samples, that is, to determine the price of the same sample of textbooks at both the local bookstore and the online retailer.

The second situation that involves related data between populations is when you have **matched samples**. Here items or individuals are paired together according to some characteristic of interest. For example, in test marketing a product in two different advertising campaigns, a sample of test markets can be *matched* on the basis of the test market population size and/or demographic variables. By accounting for the differences in test market population size and/or demographic variables, you are better able to measure the effects of the two different advertising campaigns.

Regardless of whether you have matched samples or repeated measurements, the objective is to study the difference between two measurements by reducing the effect of the variability that is due to the items or individuals themselves. Table 12.4 shows the differences in the individual values for two related populations. To read this table, let $X_{11}, X_{12}, \ldots, X_{1n}$ represent the n values from a sample. And let $X_{21}, X_{22}, \ldots, X_{2n}$ represent either the corresponding n matched values from a second sample or the corresponding n repeated measurements from the initial sample. Then, $D_1, D_2, \ldots, D_n$ will represent the corresponding set of n difference *scores* such that

$$D_1 = X_{11} - X_{21}, D_2 = X_{12} - X_{22}, \ldots, \text{and } D_n = X_{1n} - X_{2n}.$$

To test for the mean difference between two related populations, you treat the difference scores, each D_i, as values from a single sample.

TABLE 12.4

Determining the
Difference Between Two
Related Samples

| | Sample | | |
Value	1	2	Difference
1	X_{11}	X_{21}	$D_1 = X_{11} - X_{21}$
2	X_{12}	X_{22}	$D_2 = X_{12} - X_{22}$
.	.	.	.
.	.	.	.
.	.	.	.
i	X_{1i}	X_{2i}	$D_i = X_{1i} - X_{2i}$
.	.	.	.
.	.	.	.
.	.	.	.
n	X_{1n}	X_{2n}	$D_n = X_{1n} - X_{2n}$

Flowchart for hypothesis test of one population parameter

FIGURE 12.9

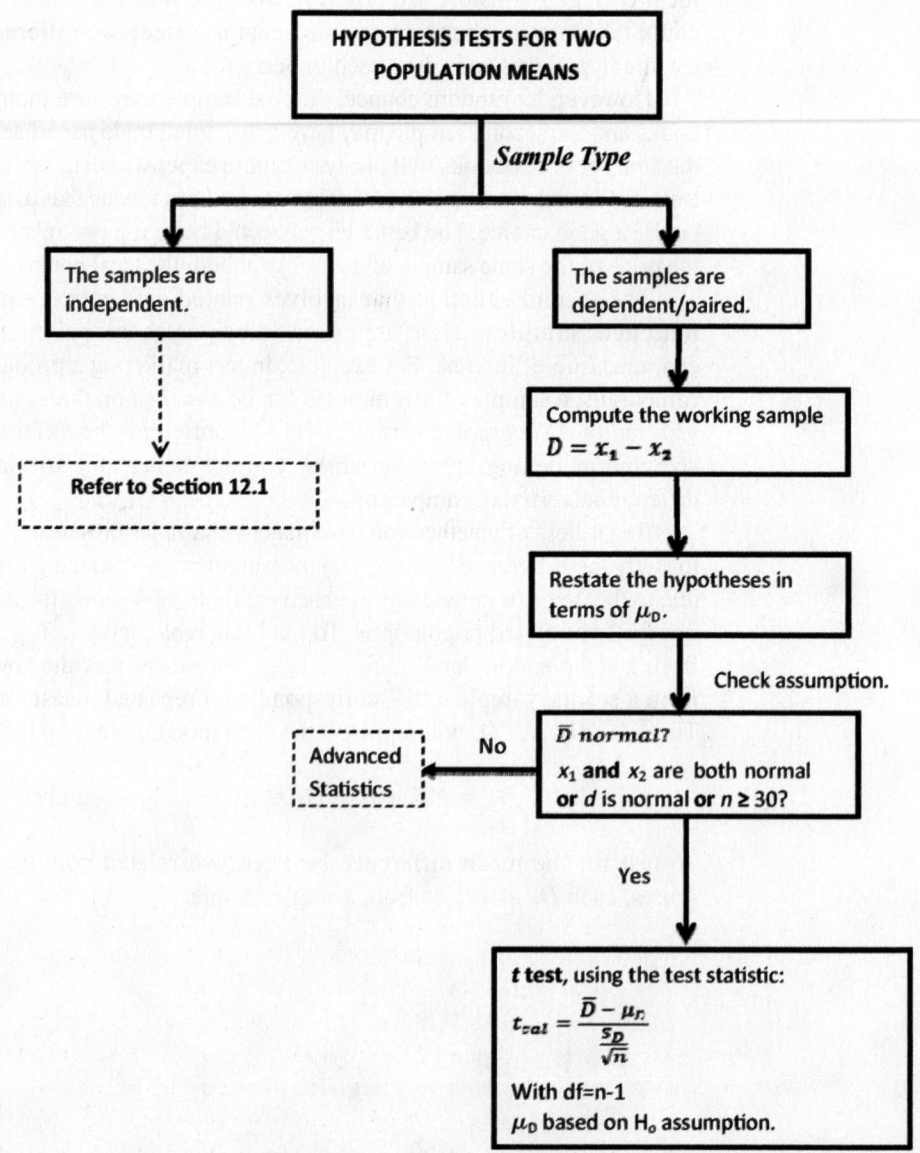

Paired *t* Test

If you assume that the difference scores are randomly and independently selected from a population that is normally distributed, you can use the **paired *t* test for the mean difference** in related populations to determine if there is a significant population mean difference. As with the one-sample *t* test developed in Section 11.2 [see Equation (11.2) on page 448], the paired *t* test statistic follows the *t* distribution with $n - 1$ degrees of freedom. Although the paired *t* test assumes that the population is normally distributed, you can use this test as long as the sample size is not very small and the population is not highly skewed.

To test the null hypothesis that there is no difference in the means of two related populations:

$$H_0: \mu_D = 0 \ (\text{where } \mu_D = \mu_1 - \mu_2)$$

against the alternative that the means are not the same:

$$H_1: \mu_D \neq 0$$

you compute the t_{STAT} test statistic using Equation (12.3).

PAIRED *t* TEST FOR THE MEAN DIFFERENCE

$$t_{STAT} = \frac{\overline{D} - \mu_D}{\dfrac{S_D}{\sqrt{n}}} \tag{12.3}$$

where

μ_D = hypothesized mean difference

$$\overline{D} = \frac{\displaystyle\sum_{i=1}^{n} D_i}{n}$$

$$S_D = \sqrt{\frac{\displaystyle\sum_{i=1}^{n} (D_i - \overline{D})^2}{n - 1}}$$

The t_{STAT} test statistic follows a *t* distribution with $n - 1$ degrees of freedom.

For a two-tail test with a given level of significance, α, you reject the null hypothesis if the computed t_{STAT} test statistic is greater than the upper-tail critical value $t_{\alpha/2}$ from the *t* distribution, or if the computed t_{STAT} test statistic is less than the lower-tail critical value $-t_{\alpha/2}$ from the *t* distribution. The decision rule is

$$\text{Reject } H_0 \text{ if } t_{STAT} > t_{\alpha/2}$$

$$\text{or if } t_{STAT} < -t_{\alpha/2};$$

$$\text{otherwise, do not reject } H_0.$$

You can use the paired *t* test for the mean difference to investigate a question raised earlier in this section: Are new textbook prices at a local college bookstore different from the prices offered at a major online retailer?

In this repeated-measurements experiment, you use one set of textbooks. For each textbook, you determine the price at the local bookstore and the price at the online retailer. By determining the two prices for the same textbooks, you can reduce the variability in the prices compared with what would occur if you used two independent sets of textbooks. This approach focuses on the differences between the prices of the same textbooks offered by the two retailers.

You collect data by conducting an experiment from a sample of $n = 19$ textbooks used primarily in business school courses during the summer 2010 semester at a local college. You determine the college bookstore price and the online price (which includes shipping costs, if any). You organize and store the data in BookPrices. Table 12.5 shows the results.

TABLE 12.5

Prices of Textbooks at the College Bookstore and at an Online Retailer

Author	Title	Bookstore	Online
Pride	Business 10/e	132.75	136.91
Carroll	Business and Society	201.50	178.58
Quinn	Ethics for the Information Age	80.00	65.00
Bade	Foundations of Microeconomics 5/e	153.50	120.43
Case	Principles of Macroeconomics 9/e	153.50	217.99
Brigham	Financial Management 13/e	216.00	197.10
Griffin	Organizational Behavior 9/e	199.75	168.71
George	Understanding and Managing Organizational Behavior 5/e	147.00	178.63
Grewal	Marketing 2/e	132.00	95.89
Barlow	Abnormal Psychology	182.25	145.49
Foner	Give Me Liberty: Seagull Ed. (V2) 2/e	45.50	37.60
Federer	Mathematical Interest Theory 2/e	89.95	91.69
Hoyle	Advanced Accounting 9/e	123.02	148.41
Haviland	Talking About People 4/e	57.50	53.93
Fuller	Information Systems Project Management	88.25	83.69
Pindyck	Macroeconomics 7/e	189.25	133.32
Mankiw	Macroeconomics 7/e	179.25	151.48
Shapiro	Multinational Financial Management 9/e	210.25	147.30
Losco	American Government 2010 Edition	66.75	55.16

Your objective is to determine whether there is any difference in the mean textbook price between the college bookstore and the online retailer. In other words, is there evidence that the mean price is different between the two sellers of textbooks? Thus, the null and alternative hypotheses are

$H_0: \mu_D = 0$ (There is no difference in the mean price between the college bookstore and the online retailer.)

$H_1: \mu_D \neq 0$ (There is a difference in the mean price between the college bookstore and online retailer.)

Choosing the level of significance $\alpha = 0.05$ and assuming that the differences are normally distributed, you use the paired t test [Equation (12.3)]. For a sample of $n = 19$ textbooks, there are $n - 1 = 18$ degrees of freedom. Using Table E.3, the decision rule is

$$\text{Reject } H_0 \text{ if } t_{STAT} > 2.1009$$

$$\text{or if } t_{STAT} < -2.1009;$$

$$\text{otherwise, do not reject } H_0.$$

For the $n = 19$ differences (see Table 12.6), the sample mean difference is

$$\overline{D} = \frac{\sum\limits_{i=1}^{n} D_i}{n} = \frac{240.66}{19} = 12.6663$$

and

$$S_D = \sqrt{\frac{\sum\limits_{i=1}^{n}(D_i - \overline{D})^2}{n-1}} = 30.4488$$

From Equation (12.3) on page 521,

$$t_{STAT} = \frac{\overline{D} - \mu_D}{\dfrac{S_D}{\sqrt{n}}} = \frac{12.6663 - 0}{\dfrac{30.4488}{\sqrt{19}}} = 1.8132$$

Because $-2.1009 < t_{STAT} = 1.8132 < 2.1009$, you do not reject the null hypothesis, H_0 (see Figure 12.10). There is insufficient evidence of a difference in the mean price of textbooks purchased at the college bookstore and the online retailer.

FIGURE 12.10

Two-tail paired t test at the 0.05 level of significance with 18 degrees of freedom

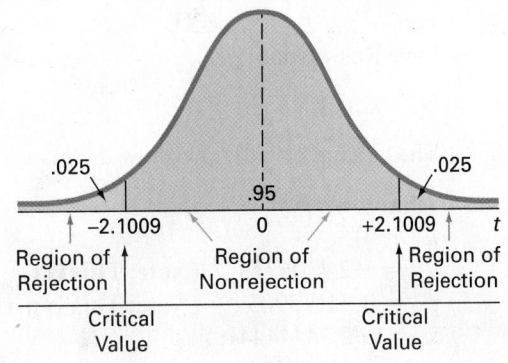

Model	Members	Government	Difference (D_i)
2005 Ford F-150	14.3	16.8	−2.5
2005 Chevrolet Silverado	15.0	17.8	−2.8
2002 Honda Accord LX	27.8	26.2	+1.6
2002 Honda Civic	27.9	33.2	−5.3
2004 Honda Civic Hybrid	48.8	47.6	+1.2
2002 Ford Explorer	16.8	18.3	−1.5
2005 Toyota Camry	23.7	28.5	−4.8
2003 Toyota Corolla	32.8	33.1	−0.3
2005 Toyota Prius	37.3	44.0	−6.7

TABLE 12.6

Repeated Measurements of Gasoline Mileage for Real-Life Driving by AAA Members and Driving Done According to Government Standards

Calculator Solution

Refer to the data in Table 12.6. At the 0.05 level of significance, is there evidence that the mean gasoline mileage is different between driving by members and driving according to government standards?

Null Hypothesis: $H_0 : \mu_D = 0$

Alternative Hypothesis: $H_1 : \mu_D \neq 0$

To test the hypothesis, follow these calculator steps:

From the **Main Menu** select **STAT**

Enter the "Difference between Members and Government" data into **List 1**.

LIST 1
−2.5
−2.8
+1.6
−5.3
+1.2
−1.5
−4.8
−0.3
−6.7

Now, from the **STAT mode** select:

F3(TEST) **F2**(t) **F1**(1-S)   then enter the following items:

1-Sample tTest
Data   : **F1**(List) ▼
μ : ≠ μ0 **(F1)**   (Note: $H_1 : \mu_D \neq 0$)
μ0   : 0
List   : **List 1**   ▼ **(Note: To change the list number, select F1(List)**
Freq   : 1   **EXE**
Save Res : None

Now key **EXE** or **F1**(Calc)

The calculator will now show the results:

1-Sample tTest
$\mu \neq 0$
t   = −2.4306723   **(Note: This is t_{calc} = −2.431)**
p   = 0.04115905   **(Note: This is p-value = 0.041)**
x̄   = −2.3444444
sx = 2.89357526
n   = 9

To evaluate the validity of the assumption of normality, you construct a boxplot of the differences, as shown in Figure 12.11.

FIGURE 12.11
Excel and Minitab boxplots for the textbook price data

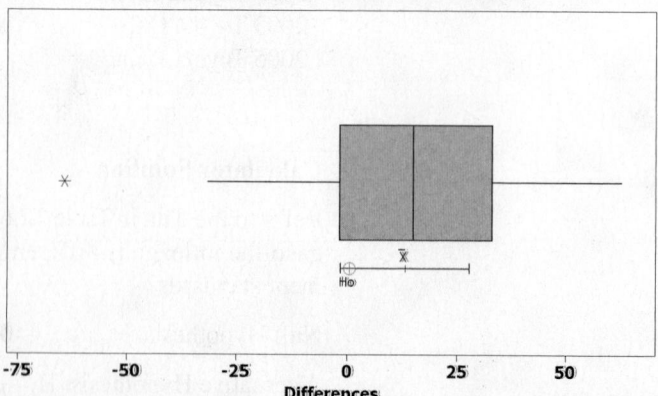

For an Excel boxplot of the differences, use column C of the *PtCalcs worksheet*, discussed in the Section EG12.3 In-Depth Excel instructions.

The Figure 12.11 boxplots show approximate symmetry except for one extreme value. Thus, the data do not greatly contradict the underlying assumption of normality. If a boxplot, histogram, or normal probability plot reveals that the assumption of underlying normality in the population is severely violated, then the *t* test may be inappropriate, especially if the sample size is small. If you believe that the *t* test is inappropriate, you can use either a *nonparametric* procedure that does not make the assumption of underlying normality (see references 1 and 2) or make a data transformation (see reference 9) and then recheck the assumptions to determine whether you should use the *t* test.

EXAMPLE 12.13

Paired *t* Test of Pizza Delivery Times

Recall from Example 12.1 on page 491 that a local pizza restaurant situated across the street from your college campus advertises that it delivers to the dormitories faster than the local branch of a national pizza chain. In order to determine whether this advertisement is valid, you and some friends have decided to order 10 pizzas from the local pizza restaurant and 10 pizzas from the national chain. In fact, each time you ordered a pizza from the local pizza restaurant, at the same time, your friends ordered a pizza from the national pizza chain. Thus, you have matched samples. For each of the 10 times that pizzas were ordered, you have one measurement from the local pizza restaurant and one from the national chain. At the 0.05 level of significance, is the mean delivery time for the local pizza restaurant less than the mean delivery time for the national pizza chain?

SOLUTION Use the paired *t* test to analyze the Table 12.7 data (stored in `PizzaTime`). Figure 12.12 shows the paired *t* test results for the pizza delivery data.

TABLE 12.7

Delivery Times for Local Pizza Restaurant and National Pizza Chain

Time	Local	Chain	Difference
1	16.8	22.0	−5.2
2	11.7	15.2	−3.5
3	15.6	18.7	−3.1
4	16.7	15.6	1.1
5	17.5	20.8	−3.3
6	18.1	19.5	−1.4
7	14.1	17.0	−2.9
8	21.8	19.5	2.3
9	13.9	16.5	−2.6
10	20.8	24.0	−3.2
			−21.8

FIGURE 12.12

SPSS paired t-test results for the pizza delivery data

Paired Samples Statistics

		Mean	N	Std. Deviation	Std. Error Mean
Pair 1	Local	16.700	10	3.0955	.9789
	Chain	18.880	10	2.8662	.9064

Paired Samples Correlations

		N	Correlation	Sig.
Pair 1	Local & Chain	10	.714	.020

Paired Samples Test

		Paired Differences							
					95% Confidence Interval of the Difference				
		Mean	Std. Deviation	Std. Error Mean	Lower	Upper	t	df	Sig. (2-tailed)
Pair 1	Local—Chain	−2.1800	2.2641	.7160	−3.7997	−.5603	−3.045	9	.014

The null and alternative hypotheses are

$H_0: \mu_D \geq 0$ (Mean delivery time for the local pizza restaurant is greater than or equal to the mean delivery time for the national pizza chain.)

$H_1: \mu_D < 0$ (Mean delivery time for the local pizza restaurant is less than the mean delivery time for the national pizza chain.)

Choosing the level of significance $\alpha = 0.05$ and assuming that the differences are normally distributed, you use the paired t test [Equation (12.3) on page 521]. For a sample of $n = 10$ delivery times, there are $n - 1 = 9$ degrees of freedom. Using Table E.3, the decision rule is

$$\text{Reject } H_0 \text{ if } t_{STAT} < -t_{0.05} = -1.8331;$$

$$\text{otherwise, do not reject } H_0.$$

To illustrate the computations, for $n = 10$ differences (see Table 12.7), the sample mean difference is

$$\overline{D} = \frac{\sum\limits_{i=1}^{n} D_i}{n} = \frac{-21.8}{10} = -2.18$$

and the sample standard deviation of the difference is

$$S_D = \sqrt{\frac{\sum\limits_{i=1}^{n}(D_i - \overline{D})^2}{n - 1}} = 2.2641$$

From Equation (12.3) on page 521,

$$t_{STAT} = \frac{\overline{D} - \mu_D}{\dfrac{S_D}{\sqrt{n}}} = \frac{-2.18 - 0}{\dfrac{2.2641}{\sqrt{10}}} = -3.0448$$

Because $t_{STAT} = -3.0448$ is less than -1.8331, you reject the null hypothesis, H_0 (the p-value is $0.0070 < 0.05$). There is evidence that the mean delivery time is lower for the local pizza restaurant than for the national pizza chain.

This conclusion is different from the one you reached in Example 12.1 on page 491 when you used the pooled-variance t test for these data. By pairing the delivery times, you are able to focus on the differences between the two pizza delivery services and not the variability created by ordering pizzas at different times of day. The paired t test is a more powerful statistical procedure that is better able to detect the difference between the two pizza delivery services because you are controlling for the time of day they were ordered.

Casio Calculator Instruction

Refer to Example 12.13: At the 0.05 level of significance, is there evidence that the mean delivery time for the local pizza restaurant is less than the mean delivery time for the national pizza chain?

To test the hypothesis, follow these calculator steps:

From the **Main Menu** select **STAT**.

Enter the "Difference Between Local and Chain" data into **List 1**.

LIST 1

-5.2
-3.5
-3.1
1.1
-3.3
-1.4
-2.9
2.3
-2.6
-3.2

Now, from the **STAT mode**, select the following:

F3(TEST)   **F2**(t)   **F1**(1-S). Then enter the following items:

1-Sample t Test

Data	: **F1**(List)	▼
μ	: $< \mu 0$	**(F2)**
$\mu 0$	: 0	
List	: **List 1**	▼ [Note: To change the list number, select **F1**(List).]
Freq	: 1	**EXE**
Save Res	: None	

Now press **EXE** or **F1**(Calc).

The calculator will now show the results:

1-Sample t Test

μ < 0
t $= -3.044793$
p $= 6.9548E\text{-}03$
$\bar{x}$ $= -2.18$
sx $= 2.26411621$
n $=10$

SPSS—VERSION 16—Paired–Samples *t* Test

We will use the data depicted in Table 1 to demonstrate how to perform a paired–samples *t* test using SPSS. The data consist of the processing time for financial applications projects that use the current market leader and a new software package.

The results are for a sample of 10 financial applications projects as shown below:

FIGURE 12.13

Table 1	PROCESSING TIMES (IN SECONDS)	
Applications Project	**By Current Market Leader**	**By New Software Package**
1	9.98	9.88
2	9.88	9.86
3	9.84	9.75
4	9.99	9.80
5	9.94	9.87
6	9.84	9.84
7	9.86	9.87
8	10.12	9.86
9	9.90	9.83
10	9.91	9.86

At the 0.05 level of significance, is there evidence that the mean processing time is greater when the financial applications projects use the current market leader rather than the new software package?

Solution:

Performing a Paired-Samples *t* Test on SPSS—Version 16

Step 1: Open the SPSS Data Editor.

Click **Cancel** to close the SPSS opening window.

FIGURE 12.14

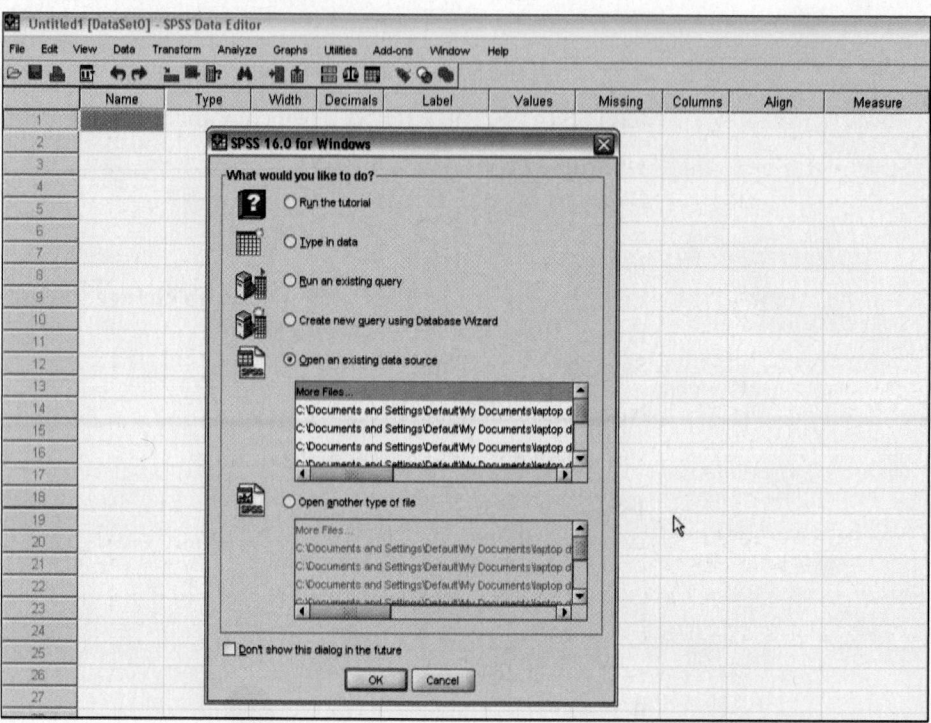

Step 2: Define the variables and give the variables a label.

Click **Variable View** (at the bottom of the window). In the **Variable View** window, define the variables and fix the data at zero or one decimal places.

- Enter the name of the first variable, "Current," and give the variable a label, **"By current market leader."**

- Enter the name of the second variable, "new," and label it as **"By new software package."**

The Variable View window is shown below.

FIGURE 12.15

	Name	Type	Width	Decimals	Label	Values	Missing	Columns	Align	Measure
1	current	Numeric	8	1	By current market leader	None	None	8	Right	Scale
2	new	Numeric	8	1	By new software package	None	None	8	Right	Scale
3										

Step 3: Create a SPSS data file.

Click **Data View** to return to the Data View window. Now, enter the raw data into the respective column of variables.

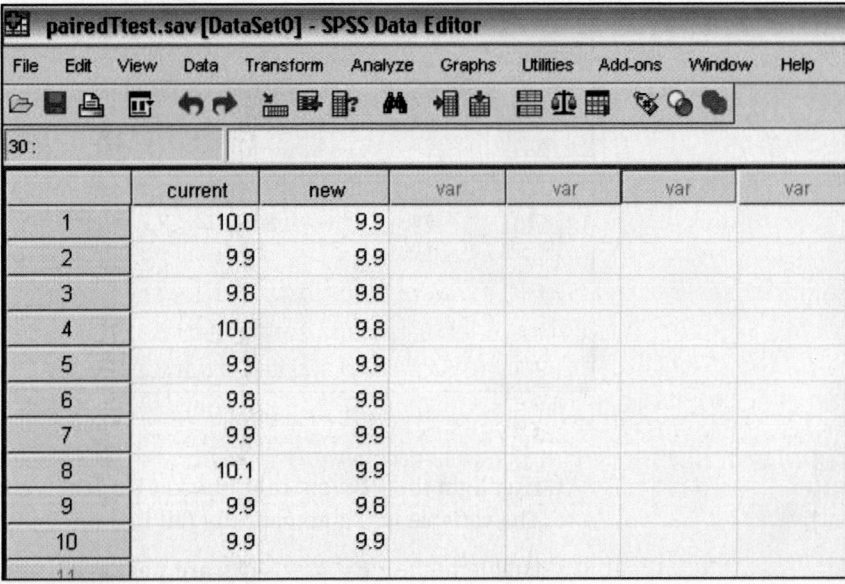

After you have entered all the data, save the file as "pairedTtest.sav" (or any filename).

Step 3: Perform the paired-samples *t* test.

Make the following menu selections:

Analyze → Compare Means → Paired-Samples T Test

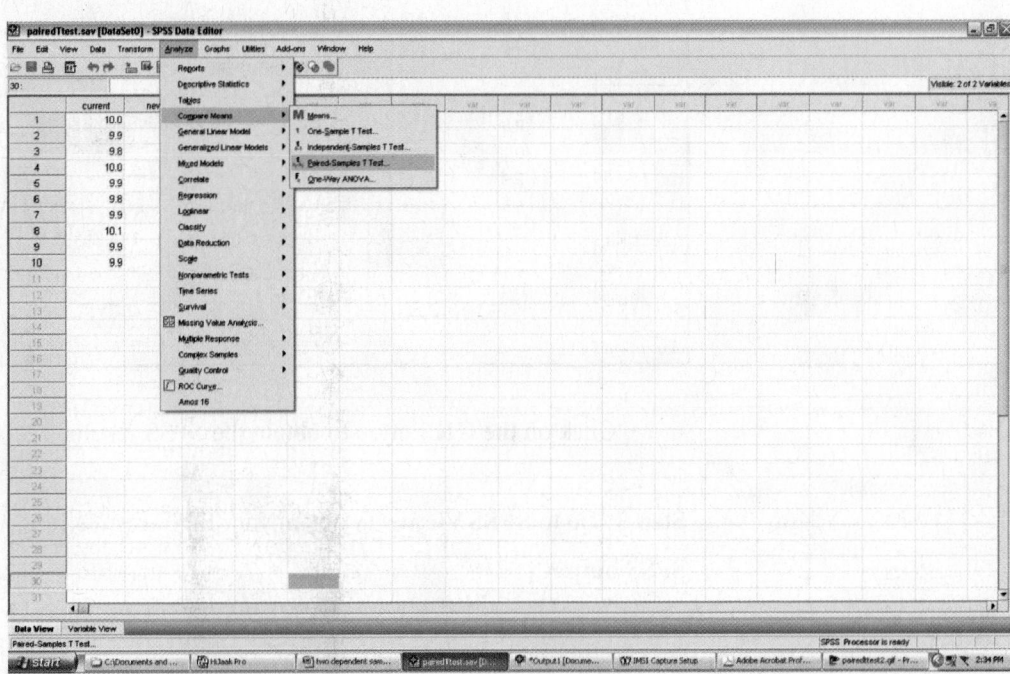

At this point, the **Paired-Samples T Test** dialog box will appear. Make these entries in the **Paired-Samples T Test** dialog box:

FIGURE 12.18

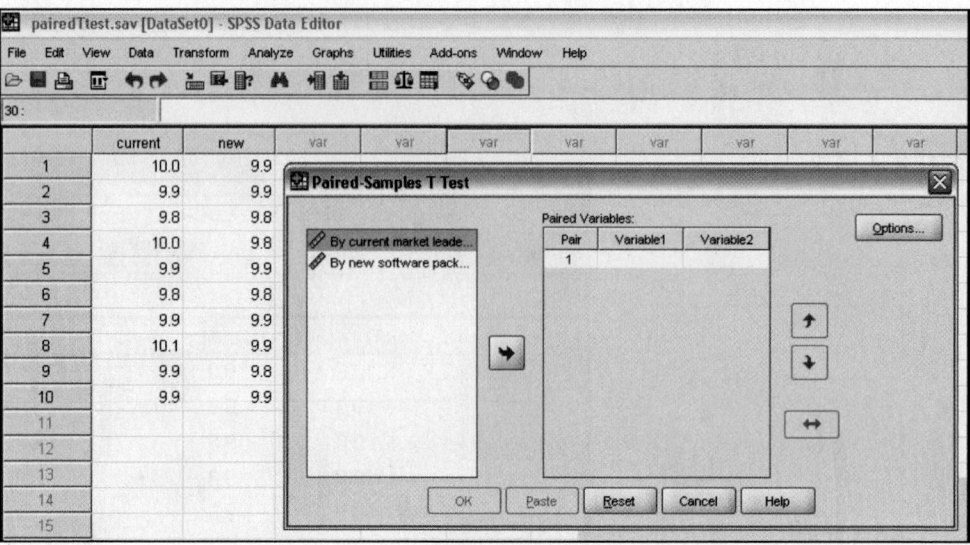

- Highlight the **"By current market leader"** variable and click on the arrow key (→). The variable will automatically fall into the **Pair 1—Variable 1** cell.

- Highlight the **"By new software package"** variable and click on the arrow key (→). The variable will automatically fall into the **Pair 1—Variable 2** cell.

FIGURE 12.19

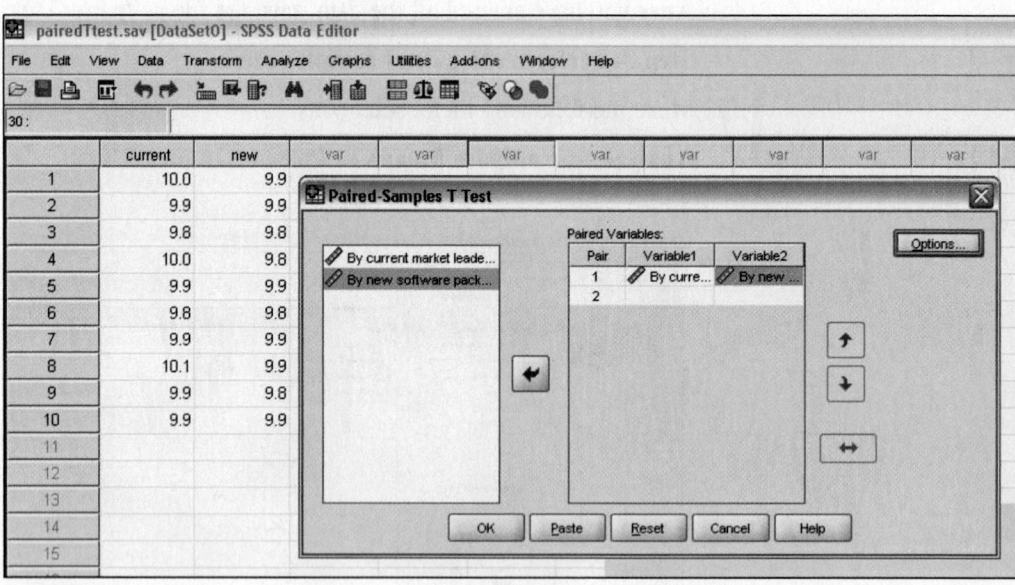

- Click on the **OK** button to obtain the SPSS results.

Step 3: Go to **SPSS Viewer** to obtain your SPSS results.

SPSS output:

t **Test**

FIGURE 12.20

Paired Samples Statistics

		Mean	N	Std. Deviation	Std. Error Mean
Pair 1	By current market leader	9.926	10	.0863	.0273
	By new software package	9.842	10	.0399	.0126

Paired Samples Correlations

		N	Correlation	Sig.
Pair 1	By current market leader & by new software package	10	.280	.434

Paired Samples Test

| | | Paired Differences | | | | | | | |
| | | | | | 95% Confidence Interval of the Difference | | | | |
		Mean	Std. Deviation	Std. Error Mean	Lower	Upper	t	df	Sig. (2-tailed)
Pair 1	By current—market leader—by new software package	.0840	.0844	.0267	.0237	.1443	3.149	9	.012

Confidence Interval Estimate for the Mean Difference

Instead of, or in addition to, testing for the difference between the means of two related populations, you can use Equation (12.4) to construct a confidence interval estimate for the mean difference.

CONFIDENCE INTERVAL ESTIMATE FOR THE MEAN DIFFERENCE

$$\overline{D} \pm t_{\alpha/2} \frac{S_D}{\sqrt{n}}$$

or

$$\overline{D} - t_{\alpha/2} \frac{S_D}{\sqrt{n}} \leq \mu_D \leq \overline{D} + t_{\alpha/2} \frac{S_D}{\sqrt{n}} \qquad (12.4)$$

where $t_{\alpha/2}$ is the critical value of the t distribution, with $n - 1$ degrees of freedom, for an area of $\alpha/2$ in the upper tail.

Recall the example comparing textbook prices on page 522. Using Equation (12.4), $\overline{D} = 12.6663$, $S_D = 30.4488$, $n = 19$, and $t_{\alpha/2} = 2.1009$ (for 95% confidence and $n - 1 = 18$ degrees of freedom),

$$12.6663 \pm (2.1009)\frac{30.4488}{\sqrt{19}}$$

$$12.6663 \pm 14.6757$$

$$-2.0094 \le \mu_D \le 27.342$$

Thus, with 95% confidence, the mean difference in textbook prices between the college bookstore and the online retailer is between –$2.0094 and $27.342. Because the interval estimate contains zero, you can conclude that there is insufficient evidence of a difference in the population means. There is insufficient evidence of a difference in the mean prices of textbooks at the college bookstore and the online retailer.

Problems for Section 12.3

LEARNING THE BASICS

12.33 An experimental design for a paired t test has 20 pairs of identical twins. How many degrees of freedom are there in this t test?

12.34 Fifteen volunteers are recruited to participate in an experiment. A measurement is made (such as blood pressure) before each volunteer is asked to read a particularly upsetting passage from a book and after each volunteer reads the passage from the book. In the analysis of the data collected from this experiment, how many degrees of freedom are there in the test?

APPLYING THE CONCEPTS

✓SELF **12.35** Nine experts rated two brands of Colombian
Test coffee in a taste-testing experiment. A rating on a 7-point scale (1 = extremely unpleasing, 7 = extremely pleasing) is given for each of four characteristics: taste, aroma, richness, and acidity. The following data (stored in **Coffee**) display the ratings accumulated over all four characteristics.

	Brand	
Expert	**A**	**B**
C.C.	24	26
S.E.	27	27
E.G.	19	22
B.L.	24	27
C.M.	22	25
C.N.	26	27
G.N.	27	26
R.M.	25	27
P.V.	22	23

a. At the 0.05 level of significance, is there evidence of a difference in the mean ratings between the two brands?
b. What assumption is necessary about the population distribution in order to perform this test?

c. Determine the p-value in (a) and interpret its meaning.
d. Construct and interpret a 95% confidence interval estimate of the difference in the mean ratings between the two brands.

12.36 In industrial settings, alternative methods often exist for measuring variables of interest. The data in **Measurement** (coded to maintain confidentiality) represent measurements in-line that were collected from an analyzer during the production process and from an analytical lab. (Data extracted from M. Leitnaker, "Comparing Measurement Processes: In-line Versus Analytical Measurements," *Quality Engineering*, 13, 2000–2001, pp. 293–298.)
a. At the 0.05 level of significance, is there evidence of a difference in the mean measurements in-line and from an analytical lab?
b. What assumption is necessary about the population distribution in order to perform this test?
c. Use a graphical method to evaluate the validity of the assumption in (a).
d. Construct and interpret a 95% confidence interval estimate of the difference in the mean measurements in-line and from an analytical lab.

12.37 Is there a difference in the prices at a warehouse club such as Costco and store brands? To investigate this, a random sample of 10 purchases was selected, and the prices were compared. (Data extracted from "Shop Smart and Save Big," *Consumer Reports*, May 2009, p. 17.) The prices for the products are stored in **Shopping1**.
a. At the 0.05 level of significance, is there evidence of a difference between the mean price of Costco purchases and store-brand purchases?
b. What assumption is necessary about the population distribution in order to perform this test?
c. Construct a 95% confidence interval estimate of the mean difference in price between Costco and store brands. Interpret the interval.
d. Compare the results of (a) and (c).

12.38 In tough economic times, the business staff at magazines are challenged to sell advertising space in their publications. Thus, one indicator of a weak economy is the decline in the number of "ad pages" that magazines have sold. The file Ad Pages contains the number of ad pages found in the May 2008 and May 2009 issues of 12 men's magazines. (Data extracted from W. Levith, "Magazine Monitor," *Mediaweek*, April 20, 2009, p. 53.)

a. At the 0.05 level of significance, is there evidence that the mean number of ad pages was higher in May 2008 than in May 2009?
b. What assumption is necessary about the population distribution in order to perform this test?
c. Use a graphical method to evaluate the validity of the assumption in (b).
d. Construct and interpret a 95% confidence interval estimate of the difference in the mean number of ad pages in men's magazines between May 2008 and May 2009.

12.39 Multiple myeloma, or blood plasma cancer, is characterized by increased blood vessel formulation (angiogenesis) in the bone marrow that is a predictive factor in survival. One treatment approach used for multiple myeloma is stem cell transplantation with the patient's own stem cells. The following data (stored in Myeloma) represent the bone marrow microvessel density for patients who had a complete response to the stem cell transplant (as measured by blood and urine tests). The measurements were taken immediately prior to the stem cell transplant and at the time the complete response was determined.

a. At the 0.05 level of significance, is there evidence that the mean bone marrow microvessel density is higher before the stem cell transplant than after the stem cell transplant?
b. Interpret the meaning of the *p*-value in (a).

Patient	Before	After
1	158	284
2	189	214
3	202	101
4	353	227
5	416	290
6	426	176
7	441	290

Source: Data extracted from S. V. Rajkumar, R. Fonseca, T. E. Witzig, M. A. Gertz, and P. R. Greipp, "Bone Marrow Angiogenesis in Patients Achieving Complete Response After Stem Cell Transplantation for Multiple Myeloma," *Leukemia*, 1999, 13, pp. 469–472.

c. Construct and interpret a 95% confidence interval estimate of the mean difference in bone marrow microvessel density before and after the stem cell transplant.
d. What assumption is necessary about the population distribution in order to perform the test in (a)?

12.40 Over the past year, the vice president for human resources at a large medical center has run a series of three-month workshops aimed at increasing worker motivation and performance. To check the effectiveness of the workshops, she selected a random sample of 35 employees from the personnel files. She collected the employee performance ratings recorded before and after workshop attendance and stored the paired ratings, along with descriptive statistics and the results of a paired *t* test in the **Perform Excel workbook (Perform.xls)** and in the **Perform Minitab project (Perform.mpj)**. Review her results and state your findings and conclusions in a report to the vice president for human resources.

Paired Samples Statistics

		Mean	N	Std. Deviation	Std. Error Mean
Pair 1	Before	74.54	35	8.995	1.520
	After	79.80	35	6.096	1.030

Paired Samples Correlations

		N	Correlation	Sig.
Pair 1	Before & After	35	−.134	.442

Paired Samples Test

		Paired Differences							
					95% Confidence Interval of the Difference				
		Mean	Std. Deviation	Std. Error Mean	Lower	Upper	t	df	Sig. (2-tailed)
Pair 1	Before—After	−5.257 5.257	11.523	1.948	−9.216	−1.299	−2.699	34	.011

12.41 The data in `Concrete1` represent the compressive strength, in thousands of pounds per square inch (psi), of 40 samples of concrete taken two and seven days after pouring.

Source: Data extracted from O. Carrillo-Gamboa and R. F. Gunst, "Measurement-Error-Model Collinearities," *Technometrics,* 34, 1992, pp. 454–464.

a. At the 0.01 level of significance, is there evidence that the mean strength is lower at two days than at seven days?
b. What assumption is necessary about the population distribution in order to perform this test?
c. Find the *p*-value in (a) and interpret its meaning.

12.4 Comparing the Proportions of Two Independent Populations

Often, you need to make comparisons and analyze differences between two population proportions. You can perform a test for the difference between two proportions selected from independent populations by using two different methods. This section presents a procedure whose test statistic, Z_{STAT}, is approximated by a standardized normal distribution. In Section 15.1, a procedure whose test statistic, χ^2_{STAT}, is approximated by a chi-square distribution is used. As you will see when you read that section, the results from these two tests are equivalent.

Z Test for the Difference Between Two Proportions

In evaluating differences between two population proportions, you can use a **Z test for the difference between two proportions**. The Z_{STAT} test statistic is based on the difference between two sample proportions $(p_1 - p_2)$. This test statistic, given in Equation (12.5), approximately follows a standardized normal distribution for large enough sample sizes.

Z TEST FOR THE DIFFERENCE BETWEEN TWO PROPORTIONS

$$Z_{STAT} = \frac{(p_1 - p_2) - (\pi_1 - \pi_2)}{\sqrt{\bar{p}(1 - \bar{p})\left(\frac{1}{n_1} + \frac{1}{n_2}\right)}} \tag{12.5}$$

with

$$\bar{p} = \frac{X_1 + X_2}{n_1 + n_2} \qquad p_1 = \frac{X_1}{n_1} \qquad p_2 = \frac{X_2}{n_2}$$

where

p_1 = proportion of items of interest in sample 1
X_1 = number of items of interest in sample 1
n_1 = sample size of sample 1
π_1 = proportion of items of interest in population 1
p_2 = proportion of items of interest in sample 2
X_2 = number of items of interest in sample 2
n_2 = sample size of sample 2
π_2 = proportion of items of interest in population 2
$\bar{p}$ = pooled estimate of the population proportion of items of interest

The Z_{STAT} test statistic approximately follows a standardized normal distribution.

Under the null hypothesis in the Z test for the difference between two proportions, you assume that the two population proportions are equal ($\pi_1 = \pi_2$). Because the pooled estimate for the population proportion is based on the null hypothesis, you combine, or pool, the two sample proportions to compute $\bar{p}$, an overall estimate of the common population proportion. This estimate is equal to the number of items of interest in the two samples combined ($X_1 + X_2$) divided by the total sample size from the two samples combined ($n_1 + n_2$).

As shown in the following table, you can use this Z test for the difference between population proportions to determine whether there is a difference in the proportion of items of interest in the two populations (two-tail test) or whether one population has a higher proportion of items of interest than the other population (one-tail test):

Two-Tail Test	**One-Tail Test**	**One-Tail Test**
$H_0: \pi_1 = \pi_2$	$H_0: \pi_1 \geq \pi_2$	$H_0: \pi_1 \leq \pi_2$
$H_1: \pi_1 \neq \pi_2$	$H_1: \pi_1 < \pi_2$	$H_1: \pi_1 > \pi_2$

where

$$\pi_1 = \text{proportion of items of interest in population 1}$$

$$\pi_2 = \text{proportion of items of interest in population 2}$$

To test the null hypothesis that there is no difference between the proportions of two independent populations:

$$H_0: \pi_1 = \pi_2$$

against the alternative that the two population proportions are not the same:

$$H_1: \pi_1 \neq \pi_2$$

you use the Z_{STAT} test statistic, given by Equation (12.5). For a given level of significance, α, you reject the null hypothesis if the computed Z_{STAT} test statistic is greater than the upper-tail critical value from the standardized normal distribution or if the computed Z_{STAT} test statistic is less than the lower-tail critical value from the standardized normal distribution.

To illustrate the use of the Z test for the equality of two proportions, suppose that you are the manager of T.C. Resort Properties, a collection of five upscale resort hotels located on two tropical islands. On one of the islands, T.C. Resort Properties has two hotels, the Beachcomber and the Windsurfer. You have defined the business objective as improving the return rate of guests at the Beachcomber and the Windsurfer hotels. On the questionnaire completed by hotel guests upon their departure, one question asked is whether the guest is likely to return to the hotel. Responses to this and other questions were collected from 227 guests at the Beachcomber and 262 guests at the Windsurfer. The results for this question indicated that 163 of 227 guests at the Beachcomber responded yes, they were likely to return to the hotel and 154 of 262 guests at the Windsurfer responded yes, they were likely to return to the hotel. At the 0.05 level of significance, is there evidence of a significant difference in guest satisfaction (as measured by the likelihood to return to the hotel) between the two hotels?

The null and alternative hypotheses are

$$H_0: \pi_1 = \pi_2 \quad \text{or} \quad \pi_1 - \pi_2 = 0$$

$$H_1: \pi_1 \neq \pi_2 \quad \text{or} \quad \pi_1 - \pi_2 \neq 0$$

Using the 0.05 level of significance, the critical values are -1.96 and $+1.96$ (see Figure 12.21), and the decision rule is

$$\text{Reject } H_0 \text{ if } Z_{STAT} < -1.96$$

$$\text{or if } Z_{STAT} > +1.96;$$

$$\text{otherwise, do not reject } H_0.$$

FIGURE 12.21

Regions of rejection and nonrejection when testing a hypothesis for the difference between two proportions at the 0.05 level of significance

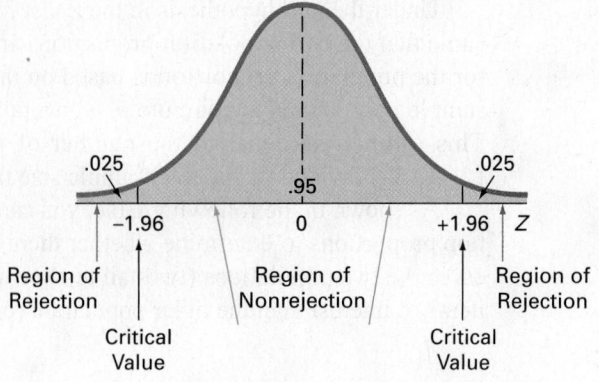

Using Equation (12.5) on page 534,

$$Z_{STAT} = \frac{(p_1 - p_2) - (\pi_1 - \pi_2)}{\sqrt{\bar{p}(1 - \bar{p})\left(\dfrac{1}{n_1} + \dfrac{1}{n_2}\right)}}$$

where

$$p_1 = \frac{X_1}{n_1} = \frac{163}{227} = 0.7181 \quad p_2 = \frac{X_2}{n_2} = \frac{154}{262} = 0.5878$$

and

$$\bar{p} = \frac{X_1 + X_2}{n_1 + n_2} = \frac{163 + 154}{227 + 262} = \frac{317}{489} = 0.6483$$

so that

$$Z_{STAT} = \frac{(0.7181 - 0.5878) - (0)}{\sqrt{0.6483(1 - 0.6483)\left(\dfrac{1}{227} + \dfrac{1}{262}\right)}}$$

$$= \frac{0.1303}{\sqrt{(0.228)(0.0082)}}$$

$$= \frac{0.1303}{\sqrt{0.00187}}$$

$$= \frac{0.1303}{0.0432} = +3.0088$$

Using the 0.05 level of significance, you reject the null hypothesis because $Z_{STAT} = +3.0088 > +1.96$. The p-value is 0.0026 (computed using Table E.2 or from Figure 12.22) and indicates that if the null hypothesis is true, the probability that a Z_{STAT} test statistic is less than -3.0088 is 0.0013, and, similarly, the probability that a Z_{STAT} test statistic is greater than $+3.0088$ is 0.0013. Thus, for this two-tail test, the p-value is $0.0013 + 0.0013 = 0.0026$. Because $0.0026 < \alpha = 0.05$, you reject the null hypothesis. There is evidence to conclude that the two hotels are significantly different with respect to guest satisfaction; a greater proportion of guests are willing to return to the Beachcomber than to the Windsurfer.

FIGURE 12.22

Casio calculator results for the Z test for the difference between two proportions for the hotel guest satisfaction problem

Solution: From the **Main Menu** select the following:

STAT, F3(test), **F1**(Z), and **F4**(2-P). Then enter the following items:

2-Prop ZTest

p1	: F1($\neq$p2) ▼	
x1	: **163**	**EXE**
n1	: **227**	**EXE**
x2	: **154**	**EXE**
n2	: **262**	**EXE**

Now press **EXE** or **F1** (Calc).

The calculator will now show the results:

2-Prop ZTest

p1	$\neq$p2
z	=3.00875353
p	=2.6232E-03 (=0.0026232)
$\hat{p}1$	=0.71806167
$\hat{p}2$	=0.58778626
$\hat{p}3$	=0.64826175
n1	=227
n2	=262

EXAMPLE 12.14

Testing for the Difference Between Two Proportions

A growing concern about privacy on the Internet has led more people to monitor their online identities. (Data extracted from "Drilling Down: Managing Reputations on Social Sites," *The New York Times*, June 14, 2010, p. B2B.) The survey reported that 44% of Internet users ages 18 to 29 have taken steps to restrict the amount of information available about themselves online as compared to 20% of Internet users older than 65 who have done the same thing. The sample size in each group was not reported. Suppose that the survey consisted of 100 individuals in each age group. At the 0.05 level of significance, is the proportion of Internet users ages 18 to 29 who have taken steps to restrict the amount of information available about themselves online greater than the proportion of Internet users older than 65 who have done the same thing?

SOLUTION Because you want to know whether there is evidence that the proportion in the 18-to-29 age group is *greater* than in the over-65 age group, you have a one-tail test. The null and alternative hypotheses are

$H_0: \pi_1 \leq \pi_2$ (The proportion of Internet users ages 18 to 29 who have taken steps to restrict the amount of information available about themselves online is less than or equal to the proportion of Internet users older than 65 who have done the same thing.)

$H_1: \pi_1 > \pi_2$ (The proportion of Internet users ages 18 to 29 who have taken steps to restrict the amount of information available about themselves online is greater than the proportion of Internet users older than 65 who have done the same thing.)

Using the 0.05 level of significance, for the one-tail test in the upper tail, the critical value is +1.645. The decision rule is

$$\text{Reject } H_0 \text{ if } Z_{STAT} > +1.645;$$

$$\text{otherwise, do not reject } H_0.$$

Using Equation (12.5) on page 534,

$$Z_{STAT} = \frac{(p_1 - p_2) - (\pi_1 - \pi_2)}{\sqrt{\bar{p}(1 - \bar{p})\left(\dfrac{1}{n_1} + \dfrac{1}{n_2}\right)}}$$

where

$$p_1 = \frac{X_1}{n_1} = \frac{44}{100} = 0.44 \quad p_2 = \frac{X_2}{n_2} = \frac{20}{100} = 0.20$$

and

$$\bar{p} = \frac{X_1 + X_2}{n_1 + n_2} = \frac{44 + 20}{100 + 100} = \frac{64}{200} = 0.32$$

so that

$$Z_{STAT} = \frac{(0.44 - 0.20) - (0)}{\sqrt{0.32(1 - 0.32)\left(\dfrac{1}{100} + \dfrac{1}{100}\right)}}$$

$$= \frac{0.24}{\sqrt{(0.2176)(0.02)}}$$

$$= \frac{0.24}{\sqrt{0.004352}}$$

$$= \frac{0.24}{0.06597} = +3.638$$

Using the 0.05 level of significance, you reject the null hypothesis because $Z_{STAT} = +3.638 > +1.645$. The p-value is approximately 0.0001. Therefore, if the null hypothesis is true, the probability that a Z_{STAT} test statistic is greater than $+3.638$ is approximately 0.0001 (which is less than $\alpha = 0.05$). You conclude that there is evidence that the proportion of Internet users ages 18 to 29 who have taken steps to restrict the amount of information available about themselves online is greater than the proportion of Internet users older than 65 who have done the same thing.

CALCULATOR LESSON 14A

CFX-9850GB CALCULATOR

Lesson 14A—Z Test of Two Proportions

EXAMPLE 12.15

A political candidate thinks that his level of support is different among male and female voters and would like to address this issue if it is true. Random samples of 200 male voters and 100 female voters in his riding revealed that 85 of the men would vote for the candidate but only 35 of the women would. At the 10% level of significance, what conclusion should the candidate make regarding the level of support?

Solution:

Let π_1 = the proportion of male voters that will vote for the candidate

π_2 = the proportion of female voters that will vote for the candidate

From the **Main Menu** select the following:

STAT,   F3(test),   **F1**(Z), and   **F4**(2-P). Then enter the following items:

2-Prop ZTest

p1	: **F1**($\neq$p2) ▼	
x1	: **85**	**EXE**
n1	: **200**	**EXE**
x2	: **35**	**EXE**
n2	: **100**	**EXE**

Now press **EXE** or **F1**(Calc),

The calculator will now show the results:

2-Prop ZTest

p1	$\neq$p2
z	=1.25
p	=0.21129
$\hat{p}1$	=0.425
$\hat{p}2$	=0.35
$\hat{p}$	=0.4
n1	=200
n2	=100

Since the *p*-value > 0.10, the conclusion is to *not reject* the null hypothesis. In other words, the evidence indicates that the level of support for the candidate is almost the same among both male and female voters.

CALCULATOR LESSON 14B

CASIO FX-9750GII CALCULATOR

Lesson 14B—Z Test of Two Proportions

EXAMPLE 12.16

A political candidate thinks that his level of support is different among male and female voters and would like to address this issue if it is true. Random samples of 200 male voters and 100 female voters in his riding revealed that 85 of the men would vote for the candidate but only 35 of the women would. At the 10% level of significance, what conclusion should the candidate make regarding the level of support?

Solution:

Let π_1 = the proportion of male voters that will vote for the candidate

  π_2 = the proportion of female voters that will vote for the candidate

From the **Main Menu** select the following:

STAT,   F3(test),   **F1**(Z), and   **F4**(2-P). Then enter the following items:

2-Prop ZTest

p1	: **F1**($\neq$p2) ▼	
x1	: **85**	**EXE**
n1	: **200**	**EXE**
x2	: **35**	**EXE**
n2	: **100**	**EXE**
Save Res	: None	

Now press **EXE, F1(Calc), or F6(DRAW)**.

If you select **F6(DRAW)**, you will see a normal distribution.

If you select either **EXE** or **F1(Calc)**, the calculator will show the results:

2-Prop ZTest

p1	$\neq$p2
z	=1.25
p	=0.21129954
$\hat{p}1$	=0.425
$\hat{p}2$	=0.35
$\hat{p}$	=0.4
n1	=200
n2	=100

Since the *p*-value > 0.10, the conclusion is to *not reject* the null hypothesis. In other words, the evidence indicates that the level of support for the candidate is almost the same among both male and female voters.

Problems for Section 12.4

LEARNING THE BASICS

12.42 Let $n_1 = 100, X_1 = 50, n_2 = 100$, and $X_2 = 30$.
a. At the 0.05 level of significance, is there evidence of a significant difference between the two population proportions?
b. Construct a 95% confidence interval estimate for the difference between the two population proportions.

12.43 Let $n_1 = 100, X_1 = 45, n_2 = 50$, and $X_2 = 25$.
a. At the 0.01 level of significance, is there evidence of a significant difference between the two population proportions?
b. Construct a 99% confidence interval estimate for the difference between the two population proportions.

APPLYING THE CONCEPTS

12.44 A survey of 1,085 adults asked, "Do you enjoy shopping for clothing for yourself?" The results (data extracted from "Split Decision on Clothes Shopping," *USA Today*, January 28, 2011, p. 1B) indicated that 51% of the females enjoyed shopping for clothing for themselves as compared to 44% of the males. The sample sizes of males and females was not provided. Suppose that of 542 males, 238 said that they enjoyed shopping for clothing for themselves while of 543 females, 276 said that they enjoyed shopping for clothing for themselves.
a. Is there evidence of a significant difference between males and females in the proportion who enjoy shopping for clothing for themselves at the 0.01 level of significance?
b. Find the *p*-value in (a) and interpret its meaning.

c. Construct and interpret a 99% confidence interval estimate for the difference between the proportion of males and females who enjoy shopping for clothing for themselves.
d. What are your answers to (a) through (c) if 218 males enjoyed shopping for clothing for themselves?

12.45 Does it take more effort to be removed from an email list than it used to? A study of 100 large online retailers revealed the following:

YEAR	NEED THREE OR MORE CLICKS TO BE REMOVED	
	Yes	No
2009	39	61
2008	7	93

Source: Data extracted from "More Clicks to Escape an Email List," *The New York Times*, March 29, 2010, p. B2.

a. Set up the null and alternative hypotheses to try to determine whether it takes more effort to be removed from an email list than it used to.
b. Conduct the hypothesis test defined in (a), using the 0.05 level of significance.
c. Does the result of your test in (b) make it appropriate to claim that it takes more effort to be removed from an email list than it used to?

12.46 Some people enjoy the *anticipation* of an upcoming product or event and prefer to pay in advance and delay the actual consumption/delivery date. In other cases, people do not want a delay. An article in the *Journal of Marketing Research* reported on an experiment in which 50 individuals were told that they had just purchased a ticket to a concert and 50 were told that they had just purchased a personal digital assistant (PDA). The participants were then asked to indicate their preferences for attending the concert or receiving the PDA. Did they prefer tonight or tomorrow, or would they prefer to wait two to four weeks? The individuals were told to ignore their schedule constraints in order to better measure their willingness to delay the consumption/delivery of their purchase. The following table gives partial results of the study:

When to Receive Purchase	Concert	PDA
Tonight or tomorrow	28	47
Two to four weeks	22	3
Total	50	50

Source: Data adapted from O. Amir and D. Ariely, "Decisions by Rules: The Case of Unwillingness to Pay for Beneficial Delays," *Journal of Marketing Research,* February 2007, Vol. XLIV, pp. 142–152.

a. What proportion of the participants would prefer to delay the date of the concert?
b. What proportion of the participants would prefer to delay receipt of a new PDA?
c. Using the 0.05 level of significance, is there evidence of a significant difference in the proportion willing to delay the date of the concert and the proportion willing to delay receipt of a new PDA?

SELF Test **12.47** Do people of different age groups differ in their beliefs about response time to email messages? A survey by the Center for the Digital Future of the University of Southern California reported that 70.7% of users over 70 years of age believe that email messages should be answered quickly as compared to 53.6% of users 12 to 50 years old. (Data extracted from A. Mindlin, "Older E-mail Users Favor Fast Replies," *The New York Times*, July 14, 2008, p. B3.) Suppose that the survey was based on 1,000 users over 70 years of age and 1,000 users 12 to 50 years old.
a. At the 0.01 level of significance, is there evidence of a significant difference between the two age groups in the proportion that believe that email messages should be answered quickly?
b. Find the *p*-value in (a) and interpret its meaning.

12.48 A survey was conducted of 665 consumer magazines on the practices of their websites. Of these, 273 magazines reported that online-only content is copy-edited as rigorously as print content; 379 reported that online-only content is fact-checked as rigorously as print content. (Data extracted from S. Clifford, "Columbia Survey Finds a Slack Editing Process of Magazine Web Sites," *The New York Times*, March 1, 2010, p. B6.) Suppose that a sample of 500 newspapers revealed that 252 reported that online-only content is copy-edited as rigorously as print content and 296 reported that online-only content is fact-checked as rigorously as print content.
a. At the 0.05 level of significance, is there evidence of a difference between consumer magazines and newspapers in the proportion of online-only content that is copy-edited as rigorously as print content ?
b. Find the *p*-value in (a) and interpret its meaning.
c. At the 0.05 level of significance, is there evidence of a difference between consumer magazines and newspapers in the proportion of online-only content that is fact-checked as rigorously as print content?

12.49 How do Americans feel about ads on websites? A survey of 1,000 adult Internet users found that 670 opposed ads on websites. (Data extracted from S. Clifford, "Tacked for Ads? Many Americans Say No Thanks," *The New York Times*, September 30, 2009, p. B3). Suppose that a survey of 1,000 Internet users age 12–17 found that 510 opposed ads on websites.
a. At the 0.05 level of significance, is there evidence of a difference between adult Internet users and Internet users age 12–17 in the proportion who oppose ads?
b. Find the *p*-value in (a) and interpret its meaning.

12.50 Where people turn for news is different for various age groups. (Data extracted from "Cellphone Users Who Access News on Their Phones," *USA Today*, March 1, 2010, p. 1A.) A study was conducted on the use of cell phones for accessing news. The study reported that 47% of users under age 50 and 15% of users age 50 and over accessed news on their cell phones. Suppose that the survey consisted of 1,000 users under age 50, of whom 470 accessed news on their cell phones, and 891 users age 50 and over, of whom 134 accessed news on their cell phones.
a. Is there evidence of a significant difference in the proportion of users under age 50 and users 50 years and older that accessed the news on their cell phones? (Use $\alpha = 0.05$.)
b. Determine the *p*-value in (a) and interpret its meaning.
c. Construct and interpret a 95% confidence interval estimate for the difference between the population proportion of users under 50 years old and those 50 years or older who access the news on their cell phones.

USING STATISTICS   @ BLK Beverages Revisited

Michael Bradley / Getty Images

In the Using Statistics scenario, you were the regional sales manager for BLK Beverages. You compared the sales volume of BLK Cola when the product is placed in the normal shelf location to the sales volume when the product is featured in a special end-aisle display. An experiment was performed in which 10 stores used the normal shelf location and 10 stores used the end-aisle displays. Using a *t* test for the difference between two means, you were able to conclude that the mean sales using end-aisle location are higher than the mean sales for the normal shelf location. A confidence interval allowed you to infer with 95% confidence that the end-aisle location sells, on average, 6.73 to 36.67 cases more than the normal shelf location. You also performed the *F* test for the difference between two variances to see if the store-to-store variability in sales in stores using the end-aisle location differed from the store-to-store variability in sales in stores using the normal shelf location. You concluded that there was no significant difference in the variability of the sales of cola for the two display locations. As regional sales manager, your next step in increasing sales is to convince more stores to use the special end-aisle display.

SUMMARY

In this chapter, you were introduced to a variety of tests for two or more samples. For situations in which the samples are independent, you learned statistical test procedures for analyzing possible differences between means, variances, and proportions. In addition, you learned a test procedure that is frequently used when analyzing differences between the means of two related samples. Remember that you need to select the test that is most appropriate for a given set of conditions and to critically investigate the validity of the assumptions underlying each of the hypothesis-testing procedures.

The roadmap in Figure 12.23 illustrates the steps needed in determining which two-sample test of hypothesis to use. The following are the questions you need to consider:

1. What type of data do you have? If you are dealing with categorical variables, use the *Z* test for the difference between two proportions. (This test assumes independent samples.)

2. If you have a numerical variable, determine whether you have independent samples or related samples. If you have related samples, and you can assume approximate normality, use the paired *t* test.

3. If you have independent samples, is your focus on variability or central tendency? If the focus is on variability, and you can assume approximate normality, use the *F* test.

4. If your focus is central tendency and you can assume approximate normality, determine whether you can assume that the variances of the two populations are equal. (This assumption can be tested using the *F* test.)

5. If you can assume that the two populations have equal variances, use the pooled-variance *t* test. If you cannot assume that the two populations have equal variances, use the separate-variance *t* test.

6. If you have more than two independent samples, you can use the one-way ANOVA.

FIGURE 12.23

Roadmap for selecting a
test of hypothesis for
two or more samples

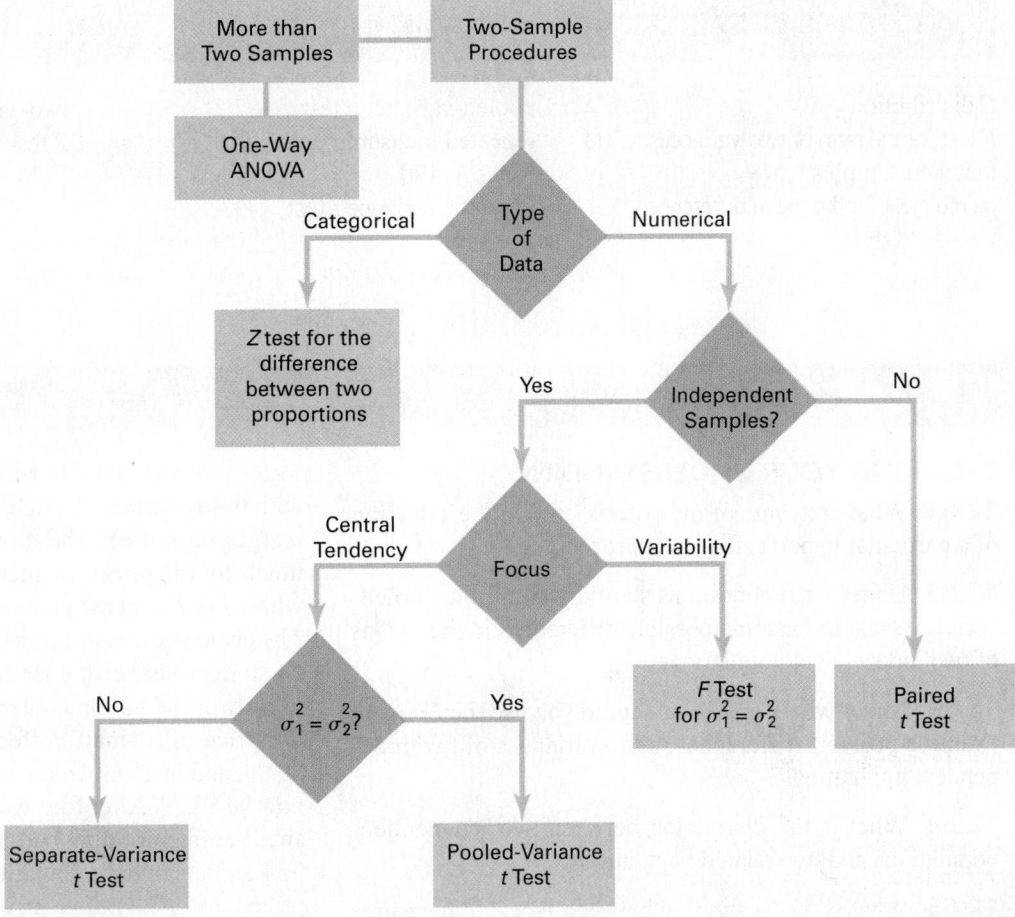

KEY EQUATIONS

Pooled-Variance *t* Test for the Difference Between Two Means

$$t_{STAT} = \frac{(\bar{X}_1 - \bar{X}_2) - (\mu_1 - \mu_2)}{\sqrt{S_p^2\left(\frac{1}{n_1} + \frac{1}{n_2}\right)}}$$

F Test Statistic for Testing the Ratio of Two Variances

$$F_{STAT} = \frac{S_1^2}{S_2^2}$$

Paired *t* Test for the Mean Difference

$$t_{STAT} = \frac{\bar{D} - \mu_D}{\frac{S_D}{\sqrt{n}}}$$

Confidence Interval Estimate for the Mean Difference

$$\bar{D} \pm t_{\alpha/2}\frac{S_D}{\sqrt{n}}$$

or

$$\bar{D} - t_{\alpha/2}\frac{S_D}{\sqrt{n}} \le \mu_D \le \bar{D} + t_{\alpha/2}\frac{S_D}{\sqrt{n}}$$

Z Test for the Difference Between Two Proportions

$$Z_{STAT} = \frac{(p_1 - p_2) - (\pi_1 - \pi_2)}{\sqrt{\bar{p}(1 - \bar{p})\left(\frac{1}{n_1} + \frac{1}{n_2}\right)}}$$

KEY TERMS

F distribution 508
F test for the ratio of two variances 508
matched samples 519
paired t test for the mean difference 521

pooled-variance t test 487
repeated measurements 519
robust 490
separate-variance t test 493

two-sample test 486
Z test for the difference
between two proportions 534

PROBLEMS

CHECKING YOUR UNDERSTANDING

12.51 What are some of the criteria used in the selection of a particular hypothesis-testing procedure?

12.52 Under what conditions should you use the pooled-variance t test to examine possible differences in the means of two independent populations?

12.53 Under what conditions should you use the F test to examine possible differences in the variances of two independent populations?

12.54 What is the distinction between two independent populations and two related populations?

12.55 What is the distinction between repeated measurements and matched items?

12.56 When you have two independent populations, explain the similarities and differences between the test of hypothesis for the difference between the means and the confidence interval estimate for the difference between the means.

12.57 Under what conditions should you use the paired t test for the mean difference between two related populations?

12.58 In a one-way ANOVA, what is the difference between the among-groups variance MSA and the within-groups variance MSW?

12.59 What are the assumptions of ANOVA?

12.60 Under what conditions should you use the one-way ANOVA F test to examine possible differences among the means of c independent populations?

12.61 What is the difference between the one-way ANOVA F test and the Levene test?

APPLYING THE CONCEPTS

12.62 The per-store daily customer count (i.e., the mean number of customers in a store in one day) for a nationwide convenience store chain that operates nearly 10,000 stores has been steady, at 900, for some time. To increase the customer count, the chain is considering cutting prices for coffee beverages. The small size will now be $0.59 instead of

$0.99, and medium size will be $0.69 instead of $1.19. Even with this reduction in price, the chain will have a 40% gross margin on coffee. The question to be determined is how much to cut prices to increase the daily customer count without reducing the gross margin on coffee sales too much. The chain decides to carry out an experiment in a sample of 30 stores where customer counts have been running almost exactly at the national average of 900. In 15 of the stores, the price of a small coffee will now be $0.59 instead of $0.99, and in 15 other stores, the price of a small coffee will now be $0.79. After four weeks, the 15 stores that priced the small coffee at $0.59 had a mean daily customer count of 964 and a standard deviation of 88, and the 15 stores that priced the small coffee at $0.79 had a mean daily customer count of 941 and a standard deviation of 76. Analyze these data (use the 0.05 level of significance) and answer the following questions.
a. Does reducing the price of a small coffee to either $0.59 or $0.79 increase the mean per-store daily customer count?
b. If reducing the price of a small coffee to either $0.59 or $0.79 increases the mean per-store daily customer count, is there any difference in the mean per-store daily customer count between stores in which a small coffee was priced at $0.59 and stores in which a small coffee was priced at $0.79?
c. What price do you recommend that a small coffee should be sold for?

12.63 A study conducted in March 2009 found that about half of U.S. adults trusted the U.S. government more than U.S. business to solve the economic problems of the United States. However, when the population is subdivided by political party affiliation, the results are very different. The study showed that 72% of Democrats trusted the government more, but only 29% of Republicans trusted the government more. Suppose that you are in charge of updating the study. You will take a national sample of Democrats and a national sample of Republicans and then try to use the results to show statistical evidence that the proportion of Democrats trusting the government more than business is greater than the proportion of Republicans trusting the government more than business.

a. What are the null and alternative hypotheses?
b. What is a Type I error in the context of this study?
c. What is a Type II error in the context of this study?

12.64 The American Society for Quality (ASQ) conducted a salary survey of all its members. ASQ members work in all areas of manufacturing and service-related institutions, with a common theme of an interest in quality. Two job titles are master black belt and green belt. (See Section 9.4, for a description of these titles in a Six Sigma quality improvement initiative.) Descriptive statistics concerning salaries for these two job titles are given in the following table:

Job Title	Sample Size	Mean	Standard Deviation
Master Black Belt	86	113,276	26,466
Green belt	15	75,917	29,000

Source: Data extracted from J. Seaman and I. Allen, "Revealing Answers," *Quality Progress,* December 2010, p. 31.

a. Using a 0.05 level of significance, is there a difference in the variability of salaries between master black belts and green belts?
b. Based on the result of (a), which *t* test defined in Section 12.1 is appropriate for comparing mean salaries?
c. Using a 0.05 level of significance, is the mean salary of master black belts greater than the mean salary of green belts?

12.65 Do male and female students study the same amount per week? In 2007, 58 sophomore business students were surveyed at a large university that has more than 1,000 sophomore business students each year. The file **StudyTime** contains the gender and the number of hours spent studying in a typical week for the sampled students.
a. At the 0.05 level of significance, is there a difference in the variance of the study time for male students and female students?
b. Using the results of (a), which *t* test is appropriate for comparing the mean study time for male and female students?
c. At the 0.05 level of significance, conduct the test selected in (b).
d. Write a short summary of your findings.

12.66 Two professors wanted to study how students from their two universities compared in their capabilities of using Excel spreadsheets in undergraduate information systems courses. (Data extracted from H. Howe and M. G. Simkin, "Factors Affecting the Ability to Detect Spreadsheet Errors," *Decision Sciences Journal of Innovative Education*, January 2006, pp. 101–122.) A comparison of the student demographics was also performed. One school is a state university in the western United States, and the other school is a state

university in the eastern United States. The following table contains information regarding the ages of the students:

School	Sample Size	Mean	Standard Deviation
Western	93	23.28	6.29
Eastern	135	21.16	1.32

a. Using a 0.01 level of significance, is there evidence of a difference in the variances of the age of students at the western school and at the eastern school?
b. Discuss the practical implications of the test performed in (a). Address, specifically, the impact equal (or unequal) variances in age has on teaching an undergraduate information systems course.
c. To test for a difference in the mean age of students, is it most appropriate to use the pooled-variance *t* test or the separate-variance *t* test?

The following table contains information regarding the years of spreadsheet usage of the students:

School	Sample Size	Mean	Standard Deviation
Western	93	2.6	2.4
Eastern	135	4.0	2.1

d. Using a 0.01 level of significance, is there evidence of a difference in the variances of the years of spreadsheet usage of students at the western school and at the eastern school?
e. Based on the results of (d), use the most appropriate test to determine, at the 0.01 level of significance, whether there is evidence of a difference in the mean years of spreadsheet usage of students at the western school and at the eastern school.

12.67 The file **Restaurants** contains the ratings for food, décor, service, and the price per person for a sample of 50 restaurants located in a city and 50 restaurants located in a suburb. Completely analyze the differences between city and suburban restaurants for the variables food rating, décor rating, service rating, and cost per person, using $\alpha = 0.05$.
Source: Data extracted from *Zagat Survey 2010: New York City Restaurants* and *Zagat Survey 2009–2010: Long Island Restaurants.*

12.68 A computer information systems professor is interested in studying the amount of time it takes students enrolled in the introduction to computers course to write and run a program in Visual Basic. The professor hires you to analyze the following results (in minutes) from a random sample of nine students (the data are stored in the **VB** file):

$$10 \quad 13 \quad 9 \quad 15 \quad 12 \quad 13 \quad 11 \quad 13 \quad 12$$

a. At the 0.05 level of significance, is there evidence that the population mean amount is greater than 10 minutes? What will you tell the professor?

b. Suppose that the professor, when checking her results, realizes that the fourth student needed 51 minutes rather than the recorded 15 minutes to write and run the Visual Basic program. At the 0.05 level of significance, reanalyze the question posed in (a), using the revised data. What will you tell the professor now?

c. The professor is perplexed by these paradoxical results and requests an explanation from you regarding the justification for the difference in your findings in (a) and (b). Discuss.

d. A few days later, the professor calls to tell you that the dilemma is completely resolved. The original number 15 (the fourth data value) was correct, and therefore your findings in (a) are being used in the article she is writing for a computer journal. Now she wants to hire you to compare the results from that group of introduction to computers students against those from a sample of 11 computer majors in order to determine whether there is evidence that computer majors can write a Visual Basic program in less time than introductory students. For the computer majors, the sample mean is 8.5 minutes, and the sample standard deviation is 2.0 minutes. At the 0.05 level of significance, completely analyze these data. What will you tell the professor?

e. A few days later, the professor calls again to tell you that a reviewer of her article wants her to include the p-value for the "correct" result in (a). In addition, the professor inquires about an unequal-variances problem, which the reviewer wants her to discuss in her article. In your own words, discuss the concept of p-value and also describe the unequal-variances problem. Then, determine the p-value in (a) and discuss whether the unequal-variances problem had any meaning in the professor's study.

12.69 An article (A. Jennings, "What's Good for a Business Can Be Hard on Friends," *The New York Times*, August 4, 2007, pp. C1–C2) reported that according to a poll, the mean number of cell phone calls per month was 290 for 18- to 24-year-olds and 194 for 45- to 54-year-olds, whereas the mean number of text messages per month was 290 for 18- to 24-year-olds and 57 for 45- to 54-year-olds. Suppose that the poll was based on a sample of 100 18- to 24-year-olds and 100 45- to 54-year-olds and that the standard deviation of the number of cell phone calls per month was 100 for 18- to 24-year-olds and 90 for 45- to 54-year-olds, whereas the standard deviation of the number of text messages per month was 90 for 18- to 24-year-olds and 77 for 45- to 54-year-olds. Assume a level of significance of 0.05.

a. Is there evidence of a difference in the variances of the number of cell phone calls per month for 18- to 24-year-olds and for 45- to 54-year-olds?

b. Is there evidence of a difference in the mean number of cell phone calls per month for 18- to 24-year-olds and for 45- to 54-year-olds?

c. Construct and interpret a 95% confidence interval estimate for the difference in the mean number of cell phone calls per month for 18- to 24-year-olds and 45- to 54-year-olds.

d. Is there evidence of a difference in the variances of the number of text messages per month for 18- to 24-year-olds and 45- to 54-year-olds?

e. Is there evidence of a difference in the mean number of text messages per month for 18- to 24-year-olds and 45- to 54-year-olds?

f. Construct and interpret a 95% confidence interval estimate for the difference in the mean number of text messages per month for 18- to 24-year-olds and 45- to 54-year-olds.

g. Based on the results of (a) through (f), what conclusions can you make concerning cell phone and text message usage between 18- to 24-year-olds and 45- to 54-year-olds?

12.70 The lengths of life (in hours) of a sample of 40 100-watt light bulbs produced by manufacturer A and a sample of 40 100-watt light bulbs produced by manufacturer B are stored in `Bulbs`. Completely analyze the differences between the lengths of life of the bulbs produced by the two manufacturers. (Use $\alpha = 0.05$.)

12.71 A hotel manager looks to enhance the initial impressions that hotel guests have when they check in. Contributing to initial impressions is the time it takes to deliver a guest's luggage to the room after check-in. A random sample of 20 deliveries on a particular day were selected in Wing A of the hotel, and a random sample of 20 deliveries were selected in Wing B. The results are stored in `Luggage`. Analyze the data and determine whether there is a difference in the mean delivery time in the two wings of the hotel. (Use $\alpha = 0.05$.)

12.72 According to Census estimates, there are about 20 million children between 8 and 12 years old (referred to as *tweens*) in the United States in 2009. A recent survey of 1,223 8- to 12-year-old children (S. Jayson, "It's Cooler Than Ever to Be a Tween," *USA Today*, February 4, 2009, pp. 1A, 2A) reported the following results. Suppose the survey was based on 600 boys and 623 girls.

What Tweens Did in the Past Week	Boys	Girls
Played a game on a video game system	498	243
Read a book for fun	276	324
Gave product advice to parents	186	181
Shopped at a mall	144	262

For *each type of activity*, determine whether there is a difference between boys and girls at the 0.05 level of significance.

12.73 The manufacturer of Boston and Vermont asphalt shingles knows that product weight is a major factor in the customer's perception of quality. Moreover, the weight represents the amount of raw materials being used and is therefore very important to the company from a cost standpoint. The last stage of the assembly line packages the shingles before they are placed on wooden pallets. Once a pallet is full (a pallet for most brands holds 16 squares of shingles), it is weighed, and the measurement is recorded. The file `Pallet` contains the weight (in pounds) from a sample of 368 pallets of Boston shingles and 330 pallets of Vermont shingles. Completely analyze the differences in the weights of the Boston and Vermont shingles, using $\alpha = 0.05$.

12.74 The manufacturer of Boston and Vermont asphalt shingles provides its customers with a 20-year warranty on most of its products. To determine whether a shingle will last as long as the warranty period, the manufacturer conducts accelerated-life testing. Accelerated-life testing exposes the shingle to the stresses it would be subject to in a lifetime of normal use in a laboratory setting via an experiment that takes only a few minutes to conduct. In this test, a shingle is repeatedly scraped with a brush for a short period of time, and the shingle granules removed by the brushing are weighed (in grams). Shingles that experience low amounts of granule loss are expected to last longer in normal use than shingles that experience high amounts of granule loss. In this situation, a shingle should experience no more than 0.8 grams of granule loss if it is expected to last the length of the warranty period. The file Granule contains a sample of 170 measurements made on the company's Boston shingles and 140 measurements made on Vermont shingles. Completely analyze the differences in the granule loss of the Boston and Vermont shingles, using $\alpha = 0.05$.

12.75 There are a very large number of mutual funds from which an investor can choose. Each mutual fund has its own mix of different types of investments. The data in BestFunds present the 3-year annualized return, 5-year annualized return, 10-year annualized return, and expense ratio (in %) for the 10 best mutual funds according to the *U.S. News & World Report* score for large cap value and large cap growth mutual funds. (Data extracted from K. Shinkle, "The Best Funds for the Long Term, *U.S. News & World Report*, Summer 2010, pp. 52–56.) Analyze the data and determine whether any differences exist between large cap value and large cap growth mutual funds. (Use the 0.05 level of significance.)

12.76 There are a very large number of mutual funds from which an investor can choose. Each mutual fund has its own mix of different types of investments. The data in BestFunds2 represent the 3-year annualized return, 5-year annualized return, 10-year annualized return, and expense ratio (in %) for the 10 mutual funds rated best by the *U.S. News & World Report* for foreign large-cap blend, small-cap blend, mid-cap blend, large-cap blend, and diversified emerging markets categories. (Data extracted from K. Shinkle, "The Best Funds for the Long Term, *U.S. News & World Report*, Summer 2010, pp. 52–56.) Analyze the data and determine whether any differences exist between foreign large-cap blend, small-cap blend, mid-cap blend, large-cap blend, and diversified emerging market mutual funds. (Use the 0.05 level of significance.)

12.77 The data in BestFunds3 represent the 3-year annualized return, 5-year annualized return, 10-year annualized return, and expense ratio (in %) for the 10 mutual funds rated best by the *U.S. News & World Report* for intermediate municipal bond, short-term bond, and intermediate-term bond categories. (Data extracted from K. Shinkle, "The Best Funds for the Long Term, *U.S. News & World Report*, Summer 2010, pp. 52–56.) Analyze the data and determine whether any differences exist between intermediate municipal bond, short-term bond, and intermediate-term bond mutual funds. (Use the 0.05 level of significance.)

REPORT WRITING EXERCISE

12.78 Referring to the results of Problems 12.73 and 12.74 concerning the weight and granule loss of Boston and Vermont shingles, write a report that summarizes your conclusions.

TEAM PROJECT

The file Bond Funds contains information regarding eight variables from a sample of 184 bond mutual funds:

> Type—Type of bonds comprising the bond fund (intermediate government or short-term corporate)
> Assets—In millions of dollars
> Fees—Sales charges (no or yes)
> Expense ratio—Ratio of expenses to net assets, in percentage
> Return 2009—Twelve-month return in 2009
> Three-year return—Annualized return, 2007–2009
> Five-year return—Annualized return, 2005–2009
> Risk—Risk-of-loss factor of the mutual fund (below average, average, or above average)

12.79 Completely analyze the differences between bond mutual funds without fees and bond mutual funds with fees in terms of 2009 return, three-year return, five-year return, and expense ratio. Write a report summarizing your findings.

12.80 Completely analyze the difference between intermediate government bond mutual funds and short-term corporate bond mutual funds in terms of 2009 return, three-year return, five-year return, and expense ratio. Write a report summarizing your findings.

12.81 Completely analyze the difference between below-average-risk, average-risk, and above-average-risk bond mutual funds in terms of 2009 return, three-year return, five-year return, and expense ratio. Write a report summarizing your findings.

STUDENT SURVEY DATABASE

12.82 Problem 1.21 on page 20 describes a survey of 62 undergraduate students (stored in UndergradSurvey).
a. At the 0.05 level of significance, is there evidence of a difference between males and females in grade point average, expected starting salary, number of social networking sites registered for, age, spending on textbooks and supplies, text messages sent in a week, and the wealth needed to feel rich?

b. At the 0.05 level of significance, is there evidence of a difference between students who plan to go to graduate school and those who do not plan to go to graduate school in grade point average, expected starting salary, number of social networking sites registered for, age, spending on textbooks and supplies, text messages sent in a week, and the wealth needed to feel rich?

12.83 Problem 1.21 on page 20 describes a survey of 62 undergraduate students (stored in UndergradSurvey).
a. Select a sample of undergraduate students at your school and conduct a similar survey for them.
b. For the data collected in (a), repeat (a) and (b) of Problem 12.82.
c. Compare the results of (b) to those of Problem 12.82.

12.84 Problem 1.22 on page 21 describes a survey of 44 MBA students (stored in GradSurvey). For these data, at the 0.05 level of significance, is there evidence of a difference between males and females in age, undergraduate grade point average, graduate grade point average, expected salary upon graduation, spending on textbooks and supplies, text messages sent in a week, and the wealth needed to feel rich?

12.85 Problem 1.22 on page 21 describes a survey of 44 MBA students (stored in GradSurvey).
a. Select a sample of graduate students in your MBA program and conduct a similar survey for those students.
b. For the data collected in (a), repeat Problem 12.84.
c. Compare the results of (b) to those of Problem 12.84.

12.86 Problem 1.21 on page 20 describes a survey of 62 undergraduate students (stored in UndergradSurvey). For these data,
a. at the 0.05 level of significance, is there evidence of a difference based on academic major in grade point average, expected starting salary, age, number of social networking sites registered for, spending on textbooks and supplies, number of text messages sent in a typical week, and the wealth needed to feel rich?
b. at the 0.05 level of significance, is there evidence of a difference based on graduate school intention in grade point average, expected starting salary, age, number of social net-

working sites registered for, spending on textbooks and supplies, number of text messages sent in a typical week, and the wealth needed to feel rich?
c. at the 0.05 level of significance, is there evidence of a difference based on employment status in grade point average, expected starting salary, age, number of social networking sites registered for, spending on textbooks and supplies, number of text messages sent in a typical week, and the wealth needed to feel rich?

12.87 Problem 1.21 on page 20 describes a survey of 62 undergraduate students (stored in UndergradSurvey).
a. Select a sample of undergraduate students at your school and conduct a similar survey for those students.
b. For the data collected in (a), repeat (a) through (c) of Problem 12.86.
c. Compare the results of (b) to those of Problem 12.86.

12.88 Problem 1.22 on page 21 describes a survey of 44 MBA students (stored in GradSurvey). For these data, at the 0.05 level of significance,
a. is there evidence of a difference, based on undergraduate major, in age, undergraduate grade point average, graduate grade point average, expected salary upon graduation, number of text messages sent in a typical week, spending on textbooks and supplies, and the wealth needed to feel rich?
b. is there evidence of a difference, based on graduate major, in age, undergraduate grade point average, graduate grade point average, expected salary upon graduation, number of text messages sent in a typical week, spending on textbooks and supplies, and the wealth needed to feel rich?
c. is there evidence of a difference, based on employment status, in age, undergraduate grade point average, graduate grade point average, expected salary upon graduation, number of text messages sent in a typical week, spending on textbooks and supplies, and the wealth needed to feel rich?

12.89 Problem 1.22 on page 21 describes a survey of 44 MBA students (stored in GradSurvey).
a. Select a sample of graduate students in your MBA program and conduct a similar survey for those students.
b. For the data collected in (a), repeat (a) through (c) of Problem 12.88.
c. Compare the results of (b) to those of Problem 12.88.

MANAGING ASHLAND MULTICOMM SERVICES

Phase 1

AMS communicates with customers who subscribe to cable television services through a special secured email system that sends messages about service changes, new features, and billing information to in-home digital set-top boxes for later display. To enhance customer service, the operations department established the business objective of reducing the amount of time to fully update each subscriber's set of messages. The department selected two candidate messaging systems and conducted an experiment in which 30 randomly chosen cable subscribers were assigned one of the two systems (15 assigned to each system). Update times were measured, and the results are organized in Table AMS12.1 (and stored in AMS12-1).

EXERCISES

1. Analyze the data in Table AMS12.1 and write a report to the computer operations department that indicates your findings. Include an appendix in which you discuss the reason you selected a particular statistical test to compare the two independent groups of callers.

2. Suppose that instead of the research design described in the case, there were only 15 subscribers sampled, and the update process for each subscriber e-mail was measured for each of the two messaging systems. Suppose the results were organized in Table AMS12.1— making each row in the table a pair of values for an individual subscriber. Using these suppositions, reanalyze the Table AMS12.1 data and write a report for presentation to the team that indicates your findings.

TABLE AMS12.1

Download Time for Two Different E-mail Interfaces

Email Interface 1	Email Interface 2
4.13	3.71
3.75	3.89
3.93	4.22
3.74	4.57
3.36	4.24
3.85	3.90
3.26	4.09
3.73	4.05
4.06	4.07
3.33	3.80
3.96	4.36
3.57	4.38
3.13	3.49
3.68	3.57
3.63	4.74

Phase 2

The computer operations department had a business objective of reducing the amount of time to fully update each subscriber's set of messages in a special secured e-mail system. An experiment was conducted in which 24 subscribers were selected and three different messaging systems were used. Eight subscribers were assigned to each system, and the update times were measured. The results (stored in AMS12-2) are presented in Table AMS12.2.

Exercise

3. Analyze the data in Table AMS12.2 and write a report to the computer operations department that indicates your findings. Include an appendix in which you discuss the reason you selected a particular statistical test to compare the three e-mail interfaces.

TABLE AMS12.2

Update Times for Three Different Systems

System1	System2	System3
38.8	41.8	32.9
42.1	36.4	36.1
45.2	39.1	39.2
34.8	28.7	29.3
48.3	36.4	41.9
37.8	36.1	31.7
41.1	35.8	35.2
43.6	33.7	38.1

DIGITAL CASE

Apply your knowledge about hypothesis testing in this Digital Case, which continues the cereal-fill packaging dispute Digital Case from Chapters 8 and 11.

Part 1

Even after the recent public experiment about cereal box weights, Consumers Concerned About Cereal Cheaters (CCACC) remains convinced that Oxford Cereals has misled the public. The group has created and circulated **MoreCheating.pdf,** a document in which it claims that cereal boxes produced at Plant Number 2 in Springville weigh less than the claimed mean of 368 grams. Review this document and then answer the following questions:

1. Do the CCACC's results prove that there is a statistically significant difference in the mean weights of cereal boxes produced at Plant Numbers 1 and 2?

2. Perform the appropriate analysis to test the CCACC's hypothesis. What conclusions can you reach based on the data?

Part 2

After reviewing the CCACC's latest document, Oxford Cereals has released **SecondAnalysis.pdf**, a press kit that Oxford Cereals has assembled to refute the claim that it is guilty of using selective data. Review the Oxford Cereals press kit and then answer the following questions:

3. Does Oxford Cereals have a legitimate argument? Why or why not?

4. Assuming that the samples Oxford Cereals has posted were randomly selected, perform the appropriate analysis to resolve the ongoing weight dispute.

5. What conclusions can you reach from your results? If you were called as an expert witness, would you support the claims of the CCACC or the claims of Oxford Cereals? Explain.

REFERENCES

1. Conover, W. J., *Practical Nonparametric Statistics*, 3rd ed. (New York: Wiley, 2000).
2. Daniel, W., *Applied Nonparametric Statistics*, 2nd ed. (Boston: Houghton Mifflin, 1990).
3. Hicks, C. R., and K. V. Turner, *Fundamental Concepts in the Design of Experiments*, 5th ed. (New York: Oxford University Press, 1999).
4. Kutner, M. H, J. Neter, C. Nachtsheim, and W. Li, *Applied Linear Statistical Models*, 5th ed. (New York: McGraw-Hill-Irwin, 2005).
5. Levine, D. M., *Statistics for Six Sigma Green Belts* (Upper Saddle River, NJ: Financial Times/Prentice Hall, 2006).
6. *Microsoft Excel 2010* (Redmond, WA: Microsoft Corp., 2010).
7. *Minitab Release 16* (State College, PA: Minitab, Inc., 2010).
8. Satterthwaite, F. E., "An Approximate Distribution of Estimates of Variance Components," *Biometrics Bulletin*, 2(1946): 110–114.
9. Snedecor, G. W., and W. G. Cochran, *Statistical Methods*, 8th ed. (Ames, IA: Iowa State University Press, 1989).
10. Winer, B. J., D. R. Brown, and K. M. Michels, *Statistical Principles in Experimental Design*, 3rd ed. (New York: McGraw-Hill, 1989).

SPSS—Version 15 Lesson 3

Introduction

OVERVIEW

We will use SPSS 15.0 Student Version for this course. When you open SPSS, either by clicking the shortcut icon, by selecting **programs/SPSS/spsswin** from the Explorer window, or by clicking **start/SPSS**, a "What would you like to do?" menu appears. It allows you to select one of the following:

Run the tutorial
Type in data
Run an existing query
Create new query using Database Wizard
Open an existing data source

As you gain experience with SPSS, you will probably skip this screen by clicking on Cancel or you will select "Don't show this dialog in the future."

The **Tutorial** feature provides a useful introduction to various aspects of SPSS. To view a tutorial, follow these instructions:

From the opening menu, select **Run the tutorial/OK.**

> Or if you have passed this window:

Help/Tutorial

You will now be shown an **Introduction** tutorial on SPSS version 15. Click on the word *Introduction* to view the expanded list of topics and then click *Sample Files.* Use the Next button (right arrow) until you have viewed information on the following topics:

Sample Files
Starting SPSS
Opening a Data File
Running an Analysis*
Viewing Results*
Creating Charts*
Using the Help System
Help Contents Tab
Help Index Tab
Dialog Box Help
Statistics Coach (skip)
Case Studies (skip)
Reading Data
Basic Structure of an SPSS Data File
Reading an SPSS Data File
Reading Data from Spreadsheets

Close the tutorial at this point.

*Do not study these topics in this tutorial. It is useful to quickly look at the demonstration in order to get an idea of what types of things we will be using SPSS for. You can always go through this tutorial at another time, although you may find it more useful choosing a tutorial on the specific topic that you are interested in learning about.

At the end of the *Introduction* tutorial, return to SPSS Data Editor window by clicking the **Untitled1[DataSet0] – SPSS Data Editor** button at the very bottom of the screen.

Now click on **Help/Topics/**if necessary click **Contents** tab / under **Core System**/select **Data Editor.** Read the information regarding the data editor.

Now choose **Entering Data** from the 'Related Topics' list. Read the general information.

Now choose **To Enter Numeric Data** and **To Enter Non-numeric Data from the** 'Related Topics' list.

You may have to come back to this screen at other times during the course to receive guidance on how to enter various data.

The **Help** feature is also useful for finding information on specific topics. This feature works similarly to the Help feature in MS Word or Excel.

Summary

SPSS uses a routine of four basic steps.

1. Input data into the data editor.
2. Select a procedure from the menus.
3. Select variables for analysis.
4. Examine and modify the results.

SPSS utilizes two important file types: data files, and output files.

Data file: Data are input into an Untitled Data Editor worksheet until it is renamed and saved by the researcher. Data files are identified by the extension **.sav** on the filename chosen by the researcher.

Output file: The SPSS output appears in a viewer window titled **Output1**, which may be renamed and saved by the researcher. Output files are identified by the extension **.spo** (SPSS Output). It is possible to edit the viewer window. The output may be rearranged, other output may be inserted, output may be deleted, and tables may be edited using the SPSS word processing capability.

You will switch between windows by using methods similar to those used in other computer packages (i.e., click on the appropriate buttons on the Start button bar at the very bottom of the screen).

Entering, Saving, and Printing Data

The following data were obtained by surveying 25 customers who used a bank machine that has just recently been installed in a downtown restaurant.

The survey took note of the customer's gender, how long the customer waited in line (rounded to the nearest minute), the type of transaction the customer performed, and the amount involved in the transaction. (A simplified scenario is presented in which each customer performed only one transaction.) The results are shown in the table below.

Customer	Gender	Waiting Time (minutes)	Type of Transaction	Amount ($)
1	Male	5	Withdrawal	100
2	Female	6	Bill Payment	83.56
3	Female	12	Withdrawal	60
4	Male	15	Withdrawal	40
5	Male	18	Deposit	512.81
6	Male	4	Bill Payment	56.82
7	Female	5	Withdrawal	200
8	Male	4	Deposit	2,315.23

Customer	Gender	Waiting Time (minutes)	Type of Transaction	Amount ($)
9	Male	14	Withdrawal	120
10	Female	21	Withdrawal	100
11	Female	0	Bill Payment	112.15
12	Male	7	Deposit	648.65
13	Male	8	Withdrawal	80
14	Male	9	Deposit	847.97
15	Female	16	Withdrawal	120
16	Male	6	Withdrawal	100
17	Female	6	Bill Payment	72.49
18	Male	12	Bill Payment	87.63
19	Female	11	Withdrawal	100
20	Male	2	Withdrawal	200
21	Male	1	Deposit	638.92
22	Female	3	Withdrawal	40
23	Female	9	Withdrawal	100
24	Male	14	Bill Payment	38.47
25	Male	3	Withdrawal	100

Example 1a:

Open SPSS and select **Type in data/OK** from the opening menu. Now click on the Variable View tab. A variable definition summary screen now appears. In the first column, enter the four variable names: gender, waittime, transtyp, and amount. Now skip to the decimals column and adjust the first three variables to have '0' decimals. The fourth variable will have the default of '2' decimals.

In the Label column, enter the following labels:

Gender
Waiting Time (minutes)
Type of Transaction
Amount of the Transaction

Now you will perform two labelling procedures. Click on the Values button for the 'gender' variable. Use the value '0' to represent females and the value '1' to represent males. To do this, type '0' in the **Value** Box, type 'Female' in the **Value Label** box, and then click the the **Add** button. Repeat the same process for the 'Male' label. When finished with the label values, click the **OK** button.

Now click on the Values button for the 'transtyp' variable. Use the following values:

1 = Withdrawal
2 = Deposit
3 = Bill Payment

Move the cursor to the **Align** column and click on the ▼ to activate the pop-up menu. Select **Center** for the first three variables.

Move the cursor to the **Type** column for the 'amount' variable. Click on the numeric button. Choose **Dollar/$#,###.##/OK.**

Now click on the Data View tab and enter the data as follows:

1	5	1	100
0	6	3	83.56
0	12	1	60
.	.	.	.
.	.	.	.
.	.	.	.

The input data will now appear exactly as shown below.

	gender	waittime	transtyp	amount	var
1	1	5	1	$100.00	
2	0	6	3	$83.56	
3	0	12	1	$60.00	
4	1	15	1	$40.00	
5	1	18	2	$512.81	
6	1	4	3	$56.82	
7	0	5	1	$200.00	
8	1	4	2	$2315.23	
9	1	14	1	$120.00	
10	0	21	1	$100.00	
11	0	0	3	$112.15	
12	1	7	2	$648.65	
13	1	8	1	$80.00	
14	1	9	2	$847.97	
15	0	16	1	$120.00	
16	1	6	1	$100.00	
17	0	6	3	$72.49	
18	1	12	3	$87.63	
19	0	11	1	$100.00	
20	1	2	1	$200.00	
21	1	1	2	$638.92	
22	0	3	1	$40.00	
23	0	9	1	$100.00	
24	1	14	3	$38.47	
25	1	3	1	$100.00	
26					

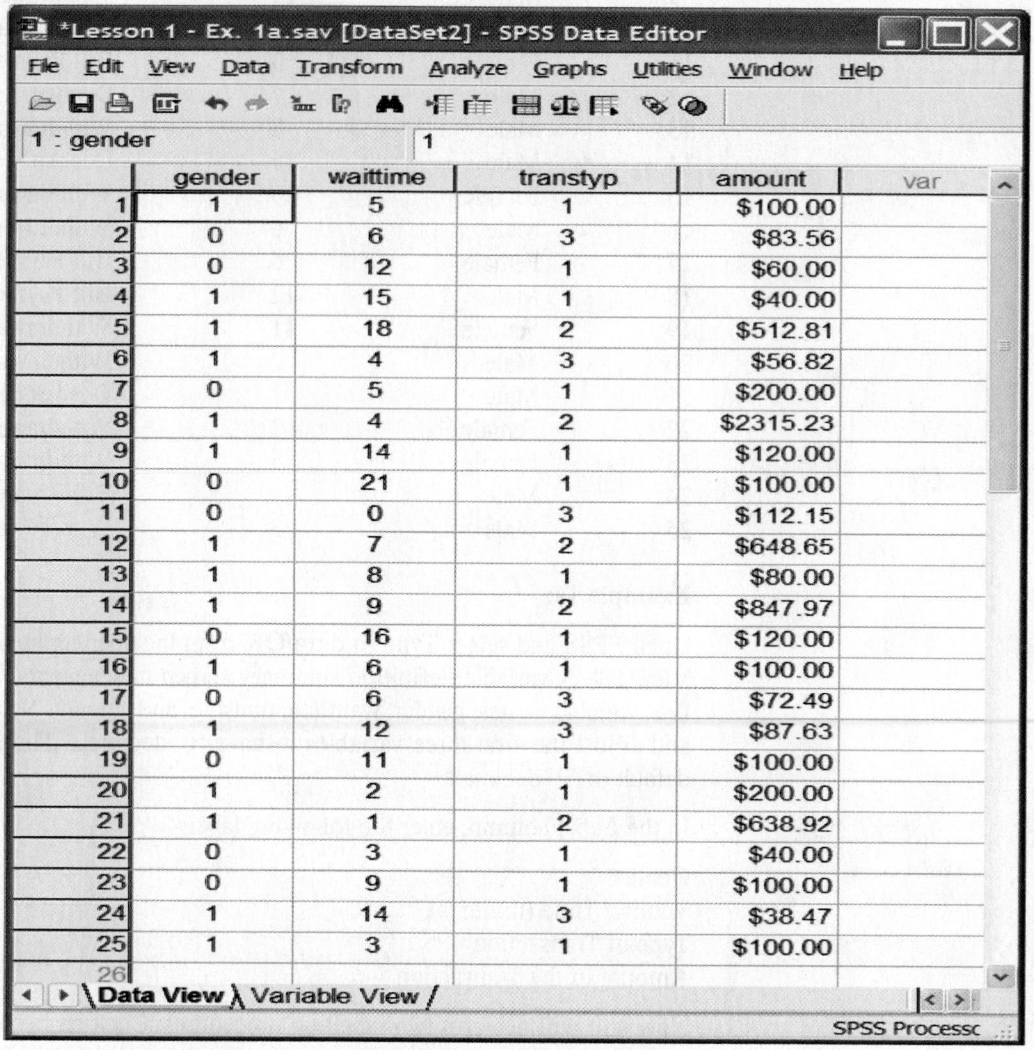

To save these data, select the following from the main toolbar:

File / Save as (select the appropriate drive and folder) key in the filename Lesson1 – Ex. 1a (in the File name box) and verify that the 'Save as type' box contains SPSS (*.sav). Click Save.

To print this file, select the following from the main toolbar:

File / Print / All / OK

You should obtain the printout as shown on the following page. Note that the 'case number' column is included.

	gender	waitingtime	transtype	amount
1	Male	5	Withdrawal	100
2	Female	6	Bill Payment	83.56
3	Female	12	Withdrawal	60
4	Male	15	Withdrawal	40
5	Male	18	Deposit	512.81
6	Male	4	Bill Payment	56.82
7	Female	5	Withdrawal	200
8	Male	4	Deposit	2,315.23
9	Male	14	Withdrawal	120
10	Female	21	Withdrawal	100
11	Female	0	Bill Payment	112.15

	gender	waitingtime	transtype	amount
12	Male	7	Deposit	648.65
13	Male	8	Withdrawal	80
14	Male	9	Deposit	847.97
15	Female	16	Withdrawal	120
16	Male	6	Withdrawal	100
17	Female	6	Bill Payment	72.49
18	Male	12	Bill Payment	87.63
19	Female	11	Withdrawal	100
20	Male	2	Withdrawal	200
21	Male	1	Deposit	638.92
22	Female	3	Withdrawal	40
23	Female	9	Withdrawal	100
24	Male	14	Bill Payment	38.47
25	Male	3	Withdrawal	100

If you want someone else to be able to understand your input data, then you should print a copy showing the labels associated with the variable values. From the main toolbar, select **View / Value Labels.**

In order to read the labels better, you may want to widen the transtyp column by clicking on the **Variable View** tab and placing the cursor in the third variable cell in the **Columns** column and increasing the value from 8 to 11.

The data will now appear as follows:

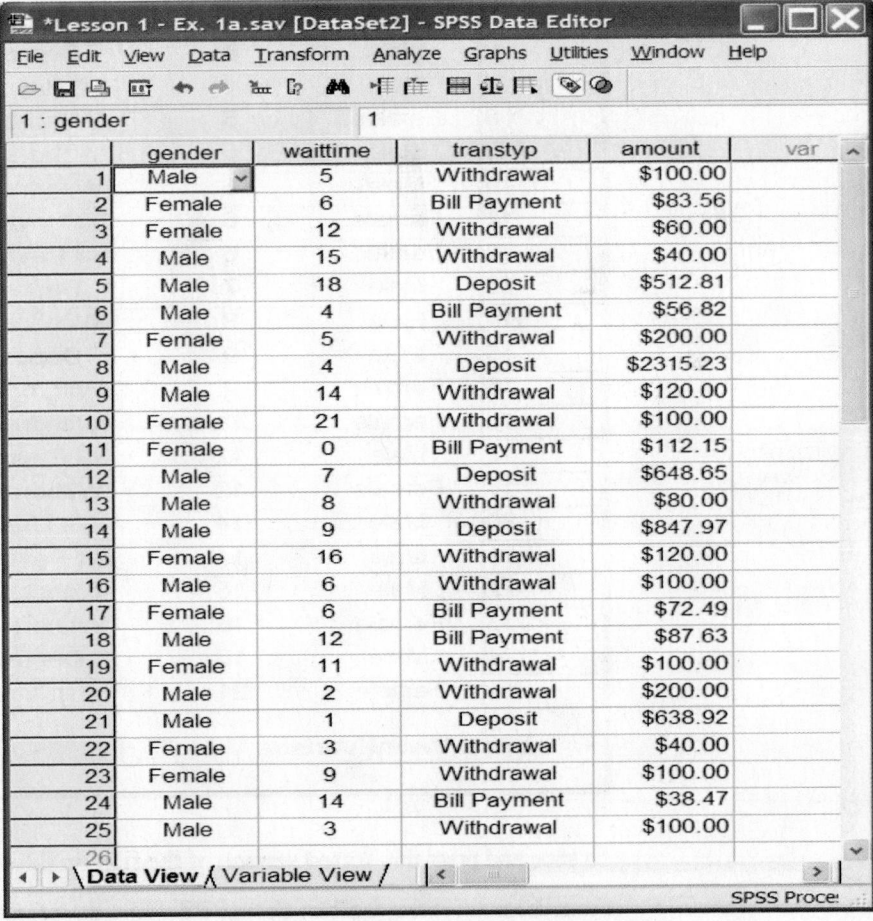

Note that if you print the data now, they will appear as they do on the screen.

Sorting Data

At this stage you should read the following SPSS help feature. Make summary notes as you go along.

Help / Topics / Index / type 'sort' and then click the Display button.

Read the Help information.

Example 1b:

Suppose we want to sort the cases in ascending order based on the waiting time and if waiting times are equal then in descending order of the amount of the transaction.

Make sure you are in Data View. Select the following from the main toolbar:

Data / Sort Cases / then highlight **Waiting Time (Minutes) [waittime]** ▶ **Ascending** / then highlight **Amount of Transaction [amount]** ▶ **Descending** / OK.

You should now have the data as shown below.

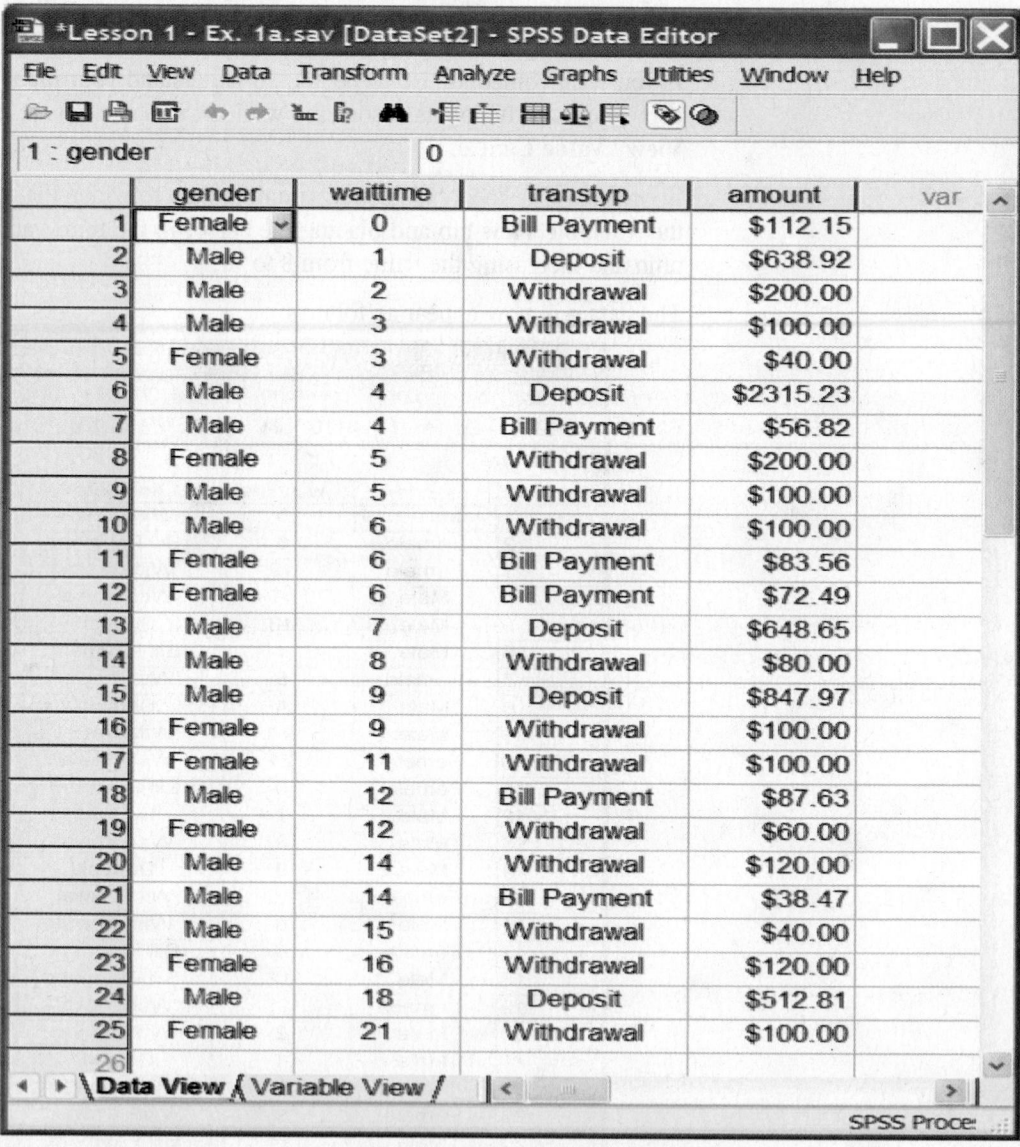

To save and print this sorted version of the file, do the following:

From the main menu toolbar, choose **File/Save as**. Select the appropriate drive, enter the file-name **Lesson 1 – Ex. 1b**, and check that the Save as type box contains SPSS(*sav). **Save**.

If you want to print these data, select **File / Print / All / OK**.

Then, to leave SPSS, select **File / Exit**.

CHAPTER 12 EXCEL GUIDE

EG12.1 Comparing the Means of Two Independent Populations

Pooled-Variance *t* Test for the Difference Between Two Means

PHStat2 Use **Pooled-Variance t Test** to perform the pooled-variance *t* test. For example, to perform the Figure 12.3 pooled-variance *t* test for the BLK Cola data shown on page 489, open to the **DATA worksheet** of the **COLA workbook**. Select **PHStat → Two-Sample Tests (Unsummarized Data) → Pooled-Variance t Test**. In the procedure's dialog box (shown below):

1. Enter **0** as the **Hypothesized Difference**.
2. Enter **0.05** as the **Level of Significance**.
3. Enter **A1:A11** as the **Population 1 Sample Cell Range**.
4. Enter **B1:B11** as the **Population 2 Sample Cell Range**.
5. Check **First cells in both ranges contain label**.
6. Click **Two-Tail Test**.
7. Enter a **Title** and click **OK**.

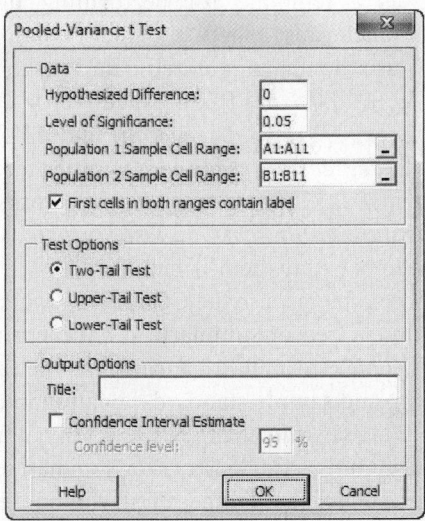

For problems that use summarized data, select **PHStat → Two-Sample Tests (Summarized Data) → Pooled-Variance t Test**. In that procedure's dialog box, enter the hypothesized difference and level of significance, as well as the sample size, sample mean, and sample standard deviation for each sample.

In-Depth Excel Use the **COMPUTE worksheet** of the **Pooled-Variance T workbook**, shown in Figure 12.3 on page 489, as a template for performing the two-tail pooled-variance *t* test. The worksheet contains data and formulas to use the unsummarized data for the BLK Cola example. In cell B25 and B26, respectively, the worksheet uses the

expressions **-TINV(*level of significance, degrees of freedom*)** and **TINV(*level of significance, degrees of freedom*)** to compute the lower and upper critical values. In cell B26, **TDIST(*absolute value of the t test statistic, degrees of freedom,* 2)** computes the *p*-value.

For other problems, use the COMPUTE worksheet with either unsummarized or summarized data. For unsummarized data, keep the formulas that calculate the sample size, sample mean, and sample standard deviation in cell ranges B7:B9 and B11:B13 and change the data in columns A and B in the **DATACOPY worksheet**. For summarized data, replace the formulas in cell ranges B7:B9 and B11:B13 with the sample statistics and ignore the DATACOPY worksheet.

Use the similar **COMPUTE_LOWER** or **COMPUTE_UPPER worksheets** in the same workbook as templates for performing one-tail pooled-variance *t* tests. These worksheets can also use either unsummarized or summarized data.

Analysis ToolPak Use **t-Test: Two-Sample Assuming Equal Variances** to perform the pooled-variance *t* test for unsummarized data. For example, to create results equivalent to those in the Figure 12.3 pooled-variance *t* test for the BLK Cola example on page 489, open to the **DATA worksheet** of the **COLA workbook** and:

1. Select **Data → Data Analysis**.
2. In the Data Analysis dialog box, select **t-Test: Two-Sample Assuming Equal Variances** from the **Analysis Tools** list and then click **OK**.

In the procedure's dialog box (shown below):

3. Enter **A1:A11** as the **Variable 1 Range** and enter **B1:B11** as the **Variable 2 Range**.
4. Enter **0** as the **Hypothesized Mean Difference**.
5. Check **Labels** and enter **0.05** as **Alpha**.
6. Click **New Worksheet Ply**.
7. Click **OK**.

Results (shown below) appear in a new worksheet that contains both two-tail and one-tail test critical values and *p*-values. Unlike Figure 12.3, only the positive (upper) critical value is listed for the two-tail test.

	A	B	C
1	t-Test: Two-Sample Assuming Equal Variances		
2			
3		*Normal*	*EndAisle*
4	Mean	50.3	72
5	Variance	350.6778	157.3333
6	Observations	10	10
7	Pooled Variance	254.0056	
8	Hypothesized Mean Difference	0	
9	df	18	
10	t Stat	-3.04455	
11	P(T<=t) one-tail	0.003487	
12	t Critical one-tail	1.734064	
13	P(T<=t) two-tail	0.006975	
14	t Critical two-tail	2.100922	

Confidence Interval Estimate for the Difference Between Two Means

PHStat2 Use the *PHStat2* instructions for the pooled-variance *t* test. In step 7, also check **Confidence Interval Estimate** and enter a **Confidence Level** in its box, in addition to entering a **Title** and clicking **OK**.

In-Depth Excel Use the *In-Depth Excel* instructions for the pooled-variance *t* test. The worksheets in the **Pooled-Variance T workbook** include a confidence interval estimate for the difference between two means in the cell range D3:E16.

t Test for the Difference Between Two Means Assuming Unequal Variances

PHStat2 Use **Separate-Variance t Test** to perform this *t* test. For example, to perform the Figure 12.6 separate-variance *t* test for the BLK Cola data on page 494, open to the **DATA worksheet** of the **COLA workbook**. Select **PHStat → Two-Sample Tests (Unsummarized Data) → Separate-Variance t Test**. In the procedure's dialog box (shown at the top of the right column):

1. Enter **0** as the **Hypothesized Difference**.
2. Enter **0.05** as the **Level of Significance**.
3. Enter **A1:A11** as the **Population 1 Sample Cell Range**.
4. Enter **B1:B11** as the **Population 2 Sample Cell Range**.
5. Check **First cells in both ranges contain label**.
6. Click **Two-Tail Test**.
7. Enter a **Title** and click **OK**.

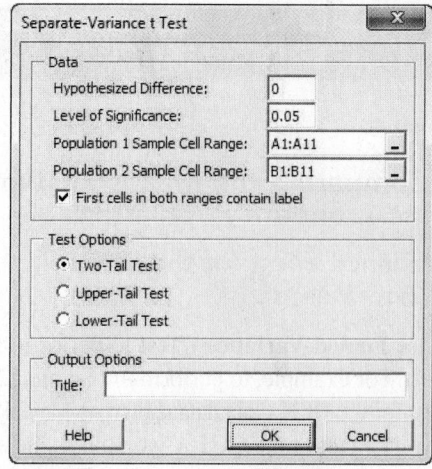

For problems that use summarized data, select **PHStat → Two-Sample Tests (Summarized Data) → Separate-Variance t Test**. In that procedure's dialog box, enter the hypothesized difference and the level of significance, as well as the sample size, sample mean, and sample standard deviation for each group.

In-Depth Excel Use the **COMPUTE worksheet** of the **Separate-Variance T workbook**, shown in Figure 12.6 on page 494, as a template for performing the two-tail separate-variance *t* test. The worksheet contains data and formulas to use the unsummarized data for the BLK Cola example. In cells B25 and B26, respectively, **-TINV(*level of significance, degrees of freedom*)** and **TINV(*level of significance, degrees of freedom*)** computes the lower and upper critical values. In cell B27, the worksheet uses **TDIST(*absolute value of the t test statistic, degrees of freedom*, 2)** to compute the *p*-value.

For other problems, use the COMPUTE worksheet with either unsummarized or summarized data. For unsummarized data, keep the formulas that calculate the sample size, sample mean, and sample standard deviation in cell ranges B7:B9 and B11:B13 and change the data in columns A and B in the **DATACOPY worksheet**. For summarized data, replace the formulas in cell ranges B7:B9 and B11:B13 with the sample statistics and ignore the DATACOPY worksheet. Use the similar **COMPUTE_LOWER** and **COMPUTE_UPPER worksheets** in the same workbook as templates for performing one-tail *t* tests.

Analysis ToolPak Use **t-Test: Two-Sample Assuming Unequal Variances** to perform the separate-variance *t* test for unsummarized data. For example, to create results equivalent to those in the Figure 12.6 separate-variance *t* test for the BLK Cola data on page 494, open to the **DATA worksheet** of the **COLA workbook** and:

1. Select **Data → Data Analysis**.
2. In the Data Analysis dialog box, select **t-Test: Two-Sample Assuming Unequal Variances** from the **Analysis Tools** list and then click **OK**.

In the procedure's dialog box (shown below):

3. Enter **A1:A11** as the **Variable 1 Range** and enter **B1:B11** as the **Variable 2 Range**.

4. Enter **0** as the **Hypothesized Mean Difference**.

5. Check **Labels** and enter **0.05** as **Alpha**.

6. Click **New Worksheet Ply**.

7. Click **OK**.

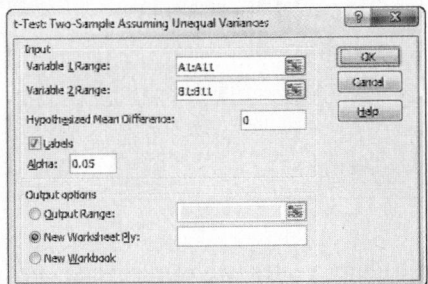

Results (shown below) appear in a new worksheet that contains both two-tail and one-tail test critical values and *p*-values. Unlike Figure 12.6, only the positive (upper) critical value is listed for the two-tail test. Because the Analysis ToolPak uses table lookups to approximate the critical values and the *p*-value, the results will differ slightly from the values shown in Figure 12.6.

▲	A	B	C
1	t-Test: Two-Sample Assuming Unequal Variances		
2			
3		Normal	EndAisle
4	Mean	50.3	72
5	Variance	350.6778	157.3333
6	Observations	10	10
7	Hypothesized Mean Difference	0	
8	df	16	
9	t Stat	-3.04455	
10	P(T<=t) one-tail	0.003863	
11	t Critical one-tail	1.745884	
12	P(T<=t) two-tail	0.007726	
13	t Critical two-tail	2.119905	

EG12.2 *F* Test for the Ratio of Two Variances

PHStat2 Use **F Test for Differences in Two Variances** to perform this *F* test. For example, to perform the Figure 12.13 *F* test for the BLK Cola sales data on page 527, open to the **DATA worksheet** of the **COLA workbook**. Select **PHStat → Two-Sample Tests (Unsummarized Data) → F Test for Differences in Two Variances**. In the procedure's dialog box (shown below):

1. Enter **0.05** as the **Level of Significance**.

2. Enter **A1:A11** as the **Population 1 Sample Cell Range**.

3. Enter **B1:B11** as the **Population 2 Sample Cell Range**.

4. Check **First cells in both ranges contain label**.

5. Click **Two-Tail Test**.

6. Enter a **Title** and click **OK**.

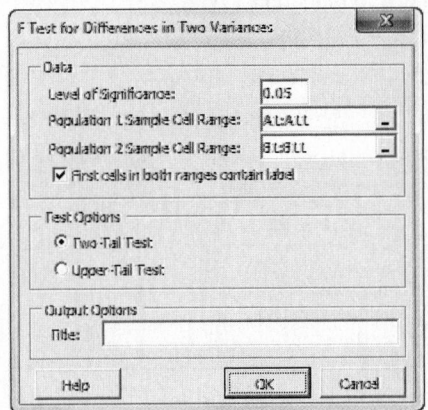

For problems that use summarized data, select **PHStat → Two-Sample Tests (Summarized Data) → F Test for Differences in Two Variances**. In that procedure's dialog box, enter the level of significance and the sample size and sample variance for each sample.

In-Depth Excel Use the **COMPUTE worksheet** of the **F Two Variances workbook**, shown in Figure 12.13 on page 527, as a template for performing the two-tail *F* test for the ratio of two variances. The worksheet contains data and formulas for using the unsummarized data for the BLK Cola example. In cell B18, the worksheet uses **FINV(*level of significance / 2, population 1 sample degrees of freedom, population 2 sample degrees of freedom*)** to compute the upper critical value and in cell B19 uses the equivalent of the expression **2 * FDIST(*F test statistic, population 1 sample degrees of freedom, population 2 sample degrees of freedom*)** to compute the *p*-value.

For other problems using unsummarized data, paste the unsummarized data into columns A and B of the **DATACOPY worksheet**. For summarized data, replace the COMPUTE worksheet formulas in cell ranges B6:B7 and B9:B10 with the sample statistics and ignore the DATACOPY worksheet. Use the similar **COMPUTE_UPPER worksheet** in the same workbook as a template for performing the upper-tail test.

Analysis ToolPak Use the **F-Test Two-Sample for Variances** procedure to perform the *F* test for the difference between two variances for unsummarized data. For example, to create results equivalent to those in the Figure 12.13 *F* test for the BLK Cola sales data on page 527, open to the **DATA worksheet** of the **COLA workbook** and:

1. Select **Data → Data Analysis**.

2. In the Data Analysis dialog box, select **F-Test Two-Sample for Variances** from the **Analysis Tools** list and then click **OK**.

In the procedure's dialog box (shown below):

3. Enter **A1:A11** as the **Variable 1 Range** and enter **B1:B11** as the **Variable 2 Range**.

4. Check **Labels** and enter **0.05** as **Alpha**.

5. Click **New Worksheet Ply**.

6. Click **OK**.

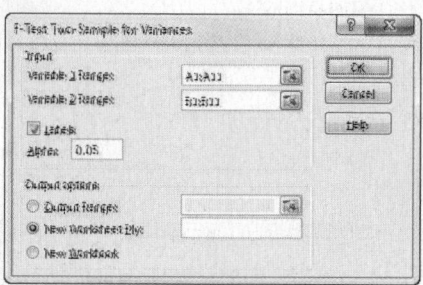

Results (shown below) appear in a new worksheet and include only the one-tail test *p*-value (0.124104), which must be doubled for the two-tail test shown in Figure 12.13 on page 527.

	A	B	C
1	F-Test Two-Sample for Variances		
2			
3		Normal	End-Aisle
4	Mean	50.3	72
5	Variance	350.6778	157.3333
6	Observations	10	10
7	df	9	9
8	F	2.228884	
9	P(F<=f) one-tail	0.124104	
10	F Critical one-tail	3.178893	

EG12.3 Comparing the Means of Two Related Populations

Paired t Test

PHStat2 Use **Paired t Test** to perform the paired *t* test. For example, to perform the Figure 12.8 paired *t* test for the textbook price data on page 512, open to the **DATA worksheet** of the **BookPrices workbook**. Select **PHStat → Two-Sample Tests (Unsummarized Data) → Paired t Test**. In the procedure's dialog box (shown in the right column):

1. Enter **0** as the **Hypothesized Mean Difference**.

2. Enter **0.05** as the **Level of Significance**.

3. Enter **C1:C20** as the **Population 1 Sample Cell Range**.

4. Enter **D1:D20** as the **Population 2 Sample Cell Range**.

5. Check **First cells in both ranges contain label**.

6. Click **Two-Tail Test**.

7. Enter a **Title** and click **OK**.

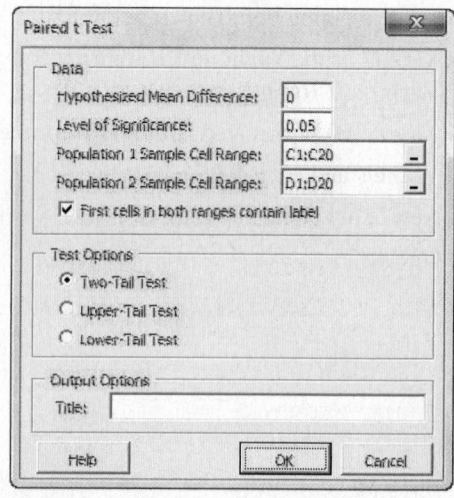

The procedure creates two worksheets, one of which is similar to the PtCalcs worksheet discussed in the following *In-Depth Excel* section. For problems that use summarized data, select **PHStat → Two-Sample Tests (Summarized Data) → Paired t Test**. In that procedure's dialog box, enter the hypothesized mean difference and the level of significance, as well as the sample size, sample mean, and sample standard deviation for each sample.

In-Depth Excel Use the **COMPUTE** and **PtCalcs** worksheets of the **Paired T workbook**, as a template for performing the two-tail paired *t* test. The PtCalcs worksheet contains the differences and other intermediate calculations that allow the COMPUTE worksheet, shown in Figure 12.8 on page 512, to compute the sample size, $\overline{D}$, and S_D.

The COMPUTE and PtCalcs worksheets contain the data and formulas for the unsummarized data for the textbook prices example. In cells B16 and B17, respectively, the COMPUTE worksheet uses -**TINV**(*level of significance*, *degrees of freedom*) and **TINV**(*level of significance*, *degrees of freedom*) to compute the lower and upper critical values. In cell B18, the worksheet uses **TDIST**(*absolute value of the t test statistic*, *degrees of freedom*, *2*) to compute the *p*-value.

For other problems, paste the unsummarized data into columns A and B of the PtCalcs worksheet. For sample sizes greater than 19, select the cell range C20:D20 and copy the formulas in those cells down through the last data row. For sample sizes less than 19, delete the column C and D formulas for which there are no column A and B values. If you know the sample size, $\overline{D}$, and S_D values, you can ignore the PtCalcs worksheet and enter the values in cells B8, B9, and B11 of the COMPUTE worksheet, overwriting the formulas that those cells contain. Use the similar **COMPUTE_LOWER** and **COMPUTE_UPPER worksheets** in the same workbook as templates for performing one-tail tests.

Analysis ToolPak Use **t-Test: Paired Two Sample for Means** to perform the paired *t* test for unsummarized data. For example, to create results equivalent to those in the Figure 12.8 paired *t* test for the textbook price data on page 512, open to the **DATA worksheet** of the **BookPrices workbook** and:

1. Select **Data → Data Analysis**.

2. In the Data Analysis dialog box, select **t-Test: Paired Two Sample for Means** from the **Analysis Tools** list and then click **OK**.

In the procedure's dialog box (shown below):

3. Enter **C1:C20** as the **Variable 1 Range** and enter **D1:D20** as the **Variable 2 Range**.

4. Enter **0** as the **Hypothesized Mean Difference**.

5. Check **Labels** and enter **0.05** as **Alpha**.

6. Click **New Worksheet Ply**.

7. Click **OK**.

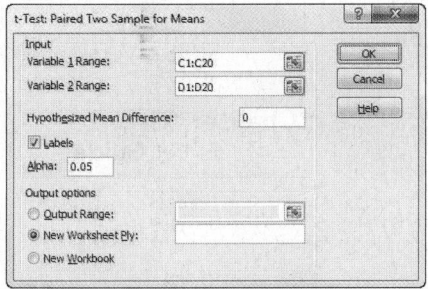

Results (shown below) appear in a new worksheet that contains both two-tail and one-tail test critical values and *p*-values. Unlike Figure 12.8, only the positive (upper) critical value is listed for the two-tail test.

	A	B	C
1	t-Test: Paired Two Sample for Means		
2			
3		Bookstore	Online
4	Mean	139.3668	126.7005
5	Variance	3028.359	2704.292
6	Observations	19	19
7	Pearson Correlation	0.839615	
8	Hypothesized Mean Difference	0	
9	df	18	
10	t Stat	1.813248	
11	P(T<=t) one-tail	0.043252	
12	t Critical one-tail	1.734064	
13	P(T<=t) two-tail	0.086504	
14	t Critical two-tail	2.100922	

EG12.4 Comparing the Proportions of Two Independent Populations

Z Test for the Difference Between Two Proportions

PHStat2 Use **Z Test for Differences in Two Proportions** to perform this Z test. For example, to perform the Figure 12.12 Z test for the hotel guest satisfaction survey on page 525, select **PHStat → Two-Sample Tests (Summarized Data) → Z Test for Differences in Two Proportions**. In the procedure's dialog box (shown below):

1. Enter **0** as the **Hypothesized Difference**.

2. Enter **0.05** as the **Level of Significance**.

3. For the Population 1 Sample, enter **163** as the **Number of Items of Interest** and **227** as the **Sample Size**.

4. For the Population 2 Sample, enter **154** as the **Number of Items of Interest** and **262** as the **Sample Size**.

5. Click **Two-Tail Test**.

6. Enter a **Title** and click **OK**.

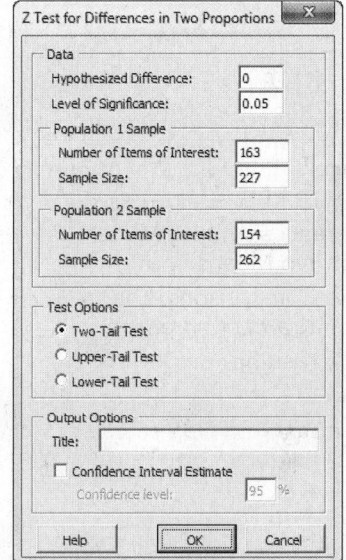

In-Depth Excel Use the **COMPUTE worksheet** of the **Z Two Proportions workbook**, shown in Figure 12.12 on page 525, as a template for performing the two-tail Z test for the difference between two proportions. The worksheet contains data for the hotel guest satisfaction survey. In cells B21 and B22 respectively, the worksheet uses **NORMSINV** (*level of significance*/**2**) and **NORMSINV(1 -** *level of significance*/**2**) to compute the lower and upper critical values. In cell B23, the worksheet uses the expression **2 * (1 - NORMSDIST(***absolute value of the Z test statistic***))** to compute the *p*-value.

For other problems, change the values in cells B4, B5, B7, B8, B10, and B11 as necessary. Use the similar **COMPUTE_LOWER** and **COMPUTE_UPPER worksheets** in the same workbook as templates for performing one-tail separate-variance *t* tests.

Confidence Interval Estimate for the Difference Between Two Proportions

PHStat2 Use the *PHStat2* instructions for the Z test for the difference between two proportions. In step 6, also check **Confidence Interval Estimate** and enter a **Confidence Level** in its box, in addition to entering a **Title** and clicking **OK**.

In-Depth Excel Use the *In-Depth Excel* instructions for the Z test for the difference between two proportions. The worksheets in the **Z Two Proportions workbook** include a confidence interval estimate for the difference between two means in the cell range D3:E16.

13 One-Way ANOVA

Learning Objectives

In this chapter, you learn how to use hypothesis testing for comparing:

• The means of more than two populations using ANOVA technique

13.1 One-Way Analysis of Variance

In Sections 12.1 through 12.4, you used hypothesis testing to reach conclusions about possible differences between two populations. In many situations, you need to examine differences among more than two **groups**. The groups involved are classified according to **levels** of a **factor** of interest. For example, a factor such as the price for which a product is sold may have several groups defined by *numerical levels* such as $0.59, $0.79, and $0.99, and a factor such as preferred supplier for a parachute manufacturer may have several groups defined by *categorical levels* such as Supplier 1, Supplier 2, Supplier 3, and Supplier 4. When there is only one factor, the experimental design is called a **completely randomized design**.

Organize multiple-sample data as unstacked data, one column per group, in order to make best use of the Excel and Minitab procedures that support the methods discussed in this section.

One-Way ANOVA *F* Test for Differences Among More Than Two Means

When you are analyzing a numerical variable and certain assumptions are met, you use the **analysis of variance (ANOVA)** to compare the means of the groups. The ANOVA procedure used for the completely randomized design is referred to as the **one-way ANOVA**, and it is an extension of the pooled variance *t* test for the difference between two means discussed in Section 12.1. Although ANOVA is an acronym for *analysis of variance*, the term is misleading because the objective in ANOVA is to analyze differences among the group means, *not* the variances. However, by analyzing the variation among and within the groups, you can reach conclusions about possible differences in group means. In ANOVA, the total variation is subdivided into variation that is due to differences *among* the groups and variation that is due to differences *within* the groups (see Figure 13.1). **Within-group variation** measures random variation. **Among-group variation** is due to differences from group to group. The symbol c is used to indicate the number of groups.

FIGURE 13.1

Partitioning the total variation in a completely randomized design

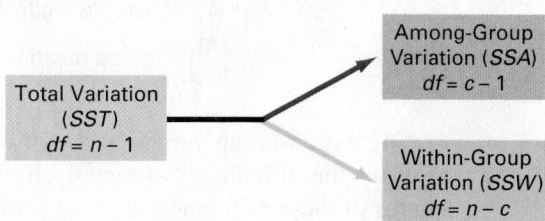

Partitioning the Total Variation
$SST = SSA + SSW$

Total Variation
(SST)
$df = n - 1$

Among-Group Variation (SSA)
$df = c - 1$

Within-Group Variation (SSW)
$df = n - c$

Assuming that the c groups represent populations whose values are randomly and independently selected, follow a normal distribution, and have equal variances, the null hypothesis of no differences in the population means:

$$H_0: \mu_1 = \mu_2 = \cdots = \mu_c$$

is tested against the alternative that not all the c population means are equal:

$$H_1: \text{Not all } \mu_j \text{ are equal (where } j = 1, 2, \ldots, c).$$

To perform an ANOVA test of equality of population means, you subdivide the total variation in the values into two parts—that which is due to variation among the groups and that which is due to variation within the groups. The **total variation** is represented by the **sum of squares total (SST)**. Because the population means of the c groups are assumed to be equal under the null hypothesis, you compute the total variation among all the values by summing the squared differences between each individual value and the **grand mean**, $\bar{\bar{X}}$. The grand mean is the mean of all the values in all the groups combined. Equation (13.1) shows the computation of the total variation.

TOTAL VARIATION IN ONE-WAY ANOVA

$$SST = \sum_{j=1}^{c} \sum_{i=1}^{n_j} (X_{ij} - \bar{\bar{X}})^2 \qquad (13.1)$$

where

$$\bar{\bar{X}} = \frac{\sum_{j=1}^{c} \sum_{i=1}^{n_j} X_{ij}}{n} = \text{Grand mean}$$

$X_{ij} = i$th value in group j

$n_j = $ number of values in group j

$n = $ total number of values in all groups combined

(that is, $n = n_1 + n_2 + \cdots + n_c$)

$c = $ number of groups

You compute the among-group variation, usually called the **sum of squares among groups (SSA)**, by summing the squared differences between the sample mean of each group, $\bar{X}_j$, and the grand mean, $\bar{\bar{X}}$, weighted by the sample size, n_j, in each group. Equation (13.2) shows the computation of the among-group variation.

AMONG-GROUP VARIATION IN ONE-WAY ANOVA

$$SSA = \sum_{j=1}^{c} n_j (\bar{X}_j - \bar{\bar{X}})^2 \qquad (13.2)$$

where

$c = $ number of groups

$n_j = $ number of values in group j

$\bar{X}_j = $ sample mean of group j

$\bar{\bar{X}} = $ grand mean

The within-group variation, usually called the **sum of squares within groups (SSW)**, measures the difference between each value and the mean of its own group and sums the squares of these differences over all groups. Equation (13.3) shows the computation of the within-group variation.

WITHIN-GROUP VARIATION IN ONE-WAY ANOVA

$$SSW = \sum_{j=1}^{c} \sum_{i=1}^{n_j} (X_{ij} - \bar{X}_j)^2 \qquad (13.3)$$

where

$$X_{ij} = i\text{th value in group } j$$

$$\bar{X}_j = \text{sample mean of group } j$$

Because you are comparing c groups, there are $c - 1$ degrees of freedom associated with the sum of squares among groups. Because each of the c groups contributes $n_j - 1$ degrees of freedom, there are $n - c$ degrees of freedom associated with the sum of squares within groups. In addition, there are $n - 1$ degrees of freedom associated with the sum of squares total because you are comparing each value, X_{ij}, to the grand mean, $\bar{\bar{X}}$, based on all n values.

If you divide each of these sums of squares by its respective degrees of freedom, you have three variances, which in ANOVA are called **mean square** terms: MSA (mean square among), MSW (mean square within), and MST (mean square total).

MEAN SQUARES IN ONE-WAY ANOVA

$$MSA = \frac{SSA}{c - 1} \tag{13.4a}$$

$$MSW = \frac{SSW}{n - c} \tag{13.4b}$$

$$MST = \frac{SST}{n - 1} \tag{13.4c}$$

Although you want to compare the means of the c groups to determine whether a difference exists among them, the name ANOVA comes from the fact that you are comparing variances. If the null hypothesis is true and there are no differences in the c group means, all three mean squares (or *variances*)—MSA, MSW, and MST—provide estimates of the overall variance in the data. Thus, to test the null hypothesis:

$$H_0\colon \mu_1 = \mu_2 = \cdots = \mu_c$$

against the alternative:

$$H_1\colon \text{Not all } \mu_j \text{ are equal (where } j = 1, 2, \ldots, c)$$

you compute the one-way ANOVA F_{STAT} test statistic as the ratio of MSA to MSW, as in Equation (13.5).

ONE-WAY ANOVA F_{STAT} TEST STATISTIC

$$F_{STAT} = \frac{MSA}{MSW} \tag{13.5}$$

The F_{STAT} test statistic follows an F distribution, with $c - 1$ degrees of freedom in the numerator and $n - c$ degrees of freedom in the denominator. For a given level of significance, α, you reject the null hypothesis if the F_{STAT} test statistic computed in Equation (13.5) is greater than the upper-tail critical value, F_α, from the F distribution with $c - 1$ degrees of freedom in the numerator and $n - c$ in the denominator (see Table E.5). Thus, as shown in Figure 13.2, the decision rule is

$$\text{Reject } H_0 \text{ if } F_{STAT} > F_\alpha;$$

$$\text{otherwise, do not reject } H_0.$$

FIGURE 13.2

Regions of rejection and nonrejection when using ANOVA

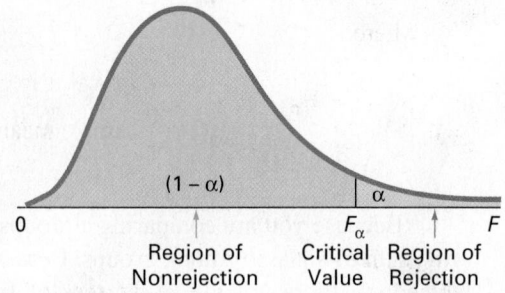

(1 – α)

α

0

F_α

F

Region of Nonrejection

Critical Value

Region of Rejection

If the null hypothesis is true, the computed F_{STAT} test statistic is expected to be approximately equal to 1 because both the numerator and denominator mean square terms are estimating the overall variance in the data. If H_0 is false (and there are differences in the group means), the computed F_{STAT} test statistic is expected to be larger than 1 because the numerator, MSA, is estimating the differences among groups in addition to the overall variability in the values, while the denominator, MSW, is measuring only the overall variability in the values. Thus, when you use the ANOVA procedure, you reject the null hypothesis at a selected level of significance, α, only if the computed F_{STAT} test statistic is greater than F_α, the upper-tail critical value of the F distribution having $c - 1$ and $n - c$ degrees of freedom, as illustrated in Figure 13.2.

The results of an analysis of variance are usually displayed in an **ANOVA summary table**, as shown in Table 13.1. The entries in this table include the sources of variation (i.e., among-groups, within-groups, and total), the degrees of freedom, the sum of squares, the mean squares (i.e., the variances), and the computed F_{STAT} test statistic. The p-value, the probability of having an F_{STAT} value as large as or larger than the one computed, given that the null hypothesis is true, usually appears also. The p-value allows you to reach conclusions about the null hypothesis without needing to refer to a table of critical values of the F distribution. If the p-value is less than the chosen level of significance, α, you reject the null hypothesis.

TABLE 13.1

Analysis-of-Variance Summary Table

Source	Degrees of Freedom	Sum of Squares	Mean Square (Variance)	F
Among groups	$c - 1$	SSA	$MSA = \dfrac{SSA}{c - 1}$	$F_{STAT} = \dfrac{MSA}{MSW}$
Within groups	$n - c$	SSW	$MSW = \dfrac{SSW}{n - c}$	
Total	$n - 1$	SST		

To illustrate the one-way ANOVA F test, you can consider a company that weaves parachutes using synthetic fibers purchased from one of four different suppliers. You define the business problem as whether significant differences exist in the strength of parachutes woven using synthetic fiber purchased from each of the four suppliers. The strength of the parachutes is measured by placing them in a testing device that pulls on both ends of a parachute until it tears apart. The amount of force required to tear the parachute is measured on a tensile-strength scale, where the larger the value, the stronger the parachute.

Five parachutes are woven using the fiber supplied by each group—Supplier 1, Supplier 2, Supplier 3, and Supplier 4. You perform the experiment of testing the strength of each of the 20 parachutes by collecting the tensile strength measurement of each parachute. Results are organized by group and stored in Parachute . Those results, along with the sample mean and the sample standard deviation of each group are shown in Figure 13.3a.

FIGURE 13.3a

SPSS report of tensile strength for parachutes woven with synthetic fibers from four different suppliers along with the sample mean, sample standard deviation, minimum value and maximum value

Report

Tensile-Strength Scale

Suppliers	Mean	N	Std. Deviation	Minimum	Maximum
Supplier 1	19.5200	5	2.69017	17.20	24.00
Supplier 2	24.2600	5	1.91911	21.20	26.30
Supplier 3	22.8400	5	2.13378	20.60	25.20
Supplier 4	21.1600	5	2.98379	17.50	25.40
Total	21.9450	20	2.90906	17.20	26.30

In Figure 13.3b, observe that there are differences in the sample means for the four suppliers. For Supplier 1, the mean tensile strength is 19.52. For Supplier 2, the mean tensile strength is 24.26. For Supplier 3, the mean tensile strength is 22.84, and for Supplier 4, the mean tensile strength is 21.16. What you need to determine is whether these sample results are sufficiently different to conclude that the *population* means are not all equal.

In the scatter plot shown in Figure 13.4, you can visually inspect the data and see how the measurements of tensile strength distribute. You can also observe differences among the groups as well as within groups. If the sample sizes in each group were larger, you could develop stem-and-leaf displays, boxplots (see Figure 13.4b), and normal probability plots (see Figure 13.4c) to evaluate the assumption of normality in each group.

FIGURE 13.3b

Mean Plots of tensile strength for parachutes woven with synthetic fibers from four different suppliers.

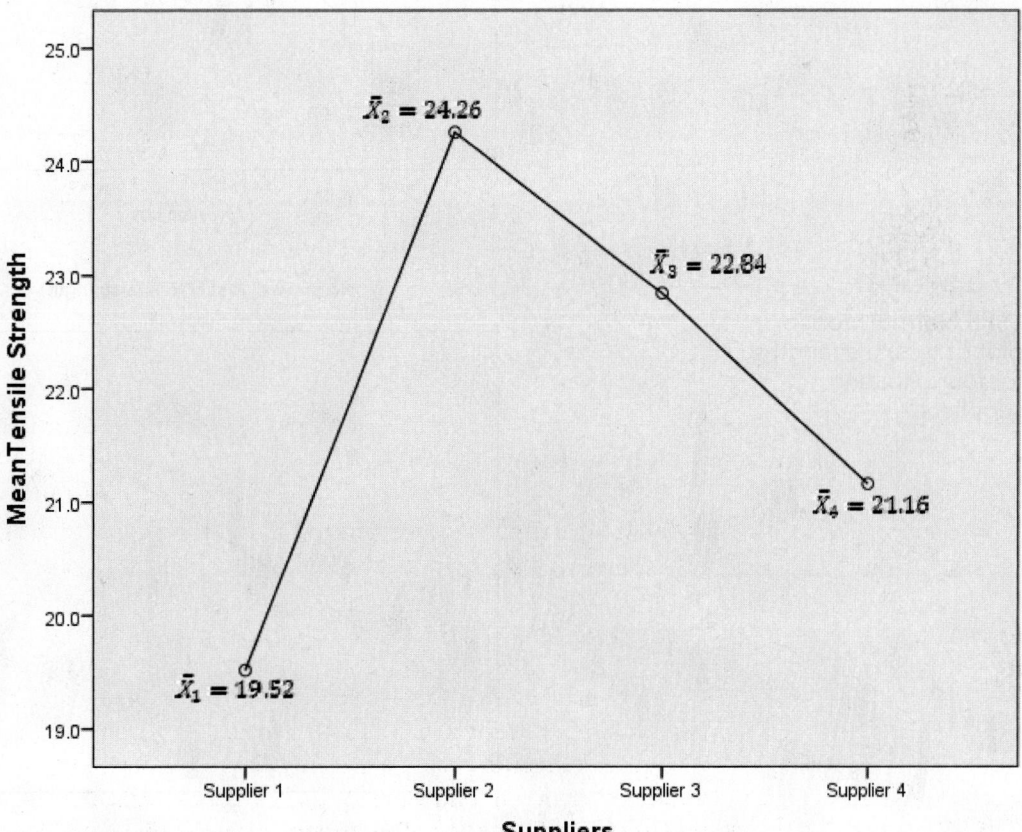

FIGURE 13.4
SSPS scatter plot of
tensile strengths for four
different suppliers

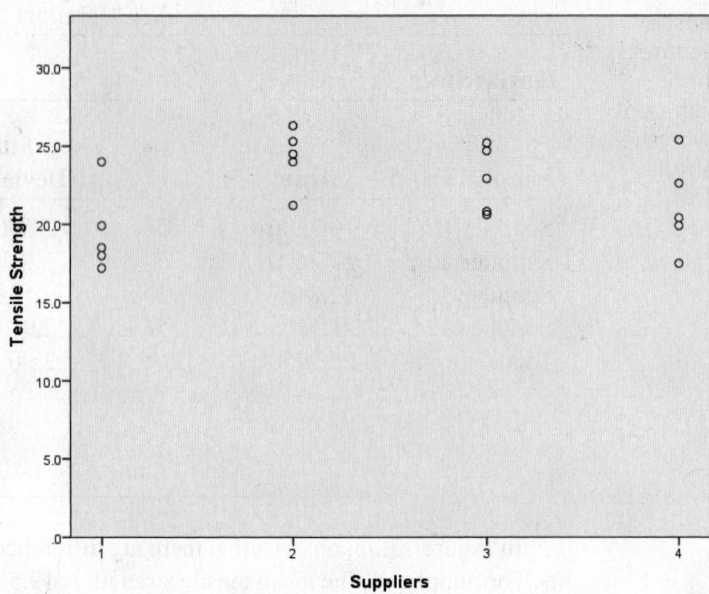

FIGURE 13.4b
SSPS box plot of tensile
strengths for four
different suppliers

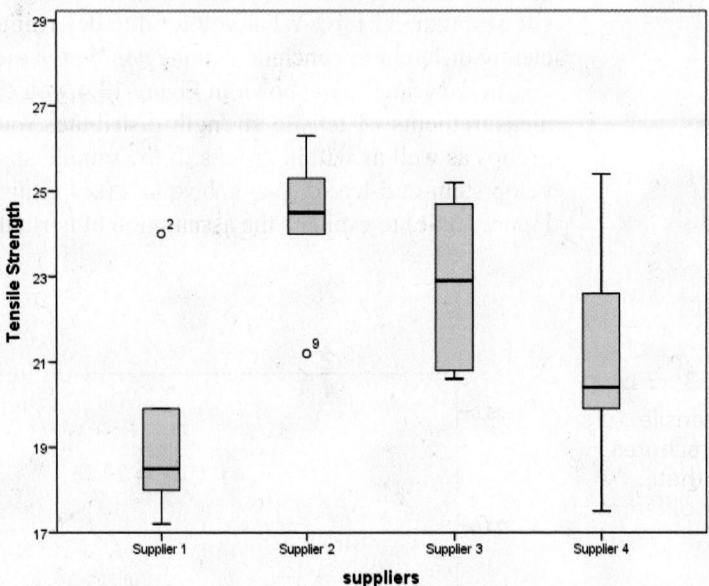

FIGURE 13.4c
SSPS Normal probability
plot of tensile strengths
for four different
suppliers

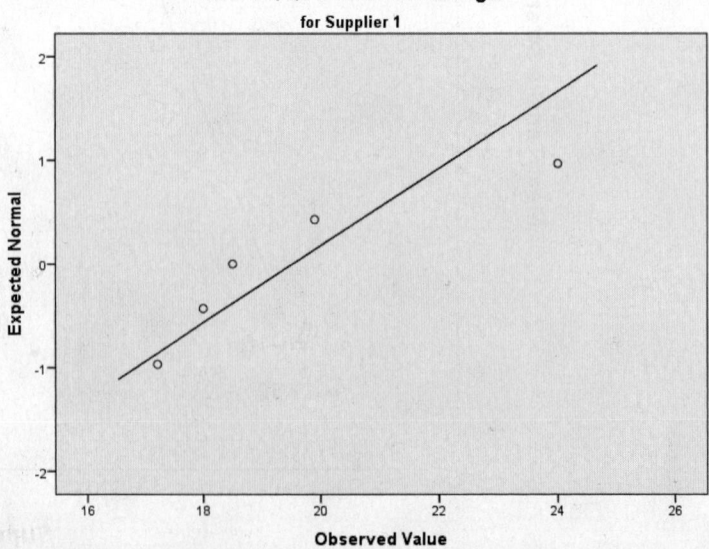

FIGURE 13.4c
continued

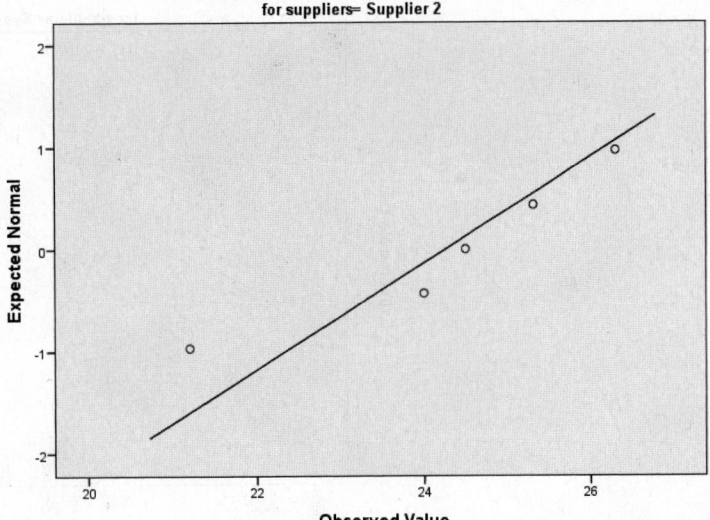

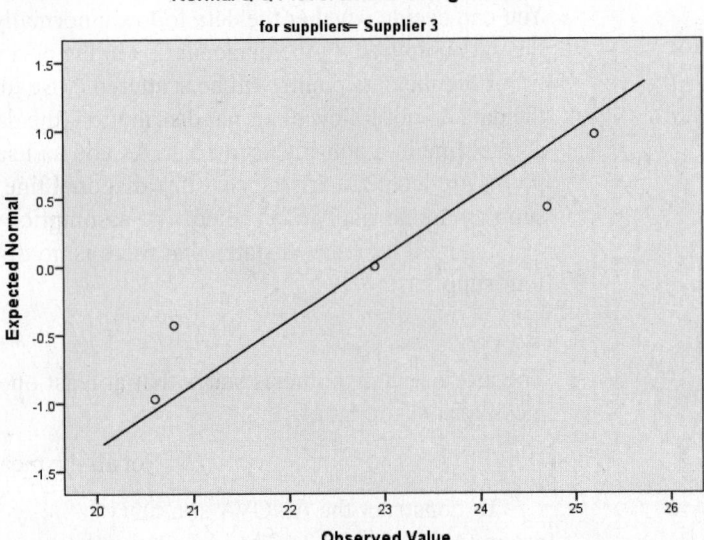

FIGURE 13.4c
continued

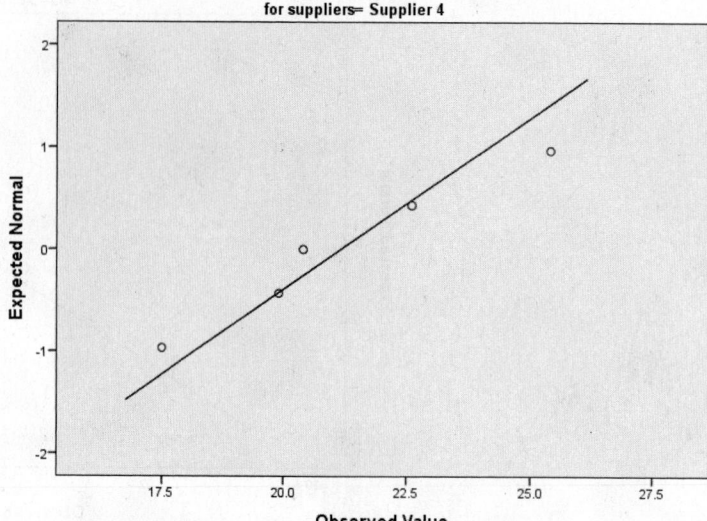

It is not easy to evaluate the normality of the data from the boxplots (Figure 13.4b). You create the normal Q-Q plots (Figure 13.4c) to verify the normality assumption graphically. You can decide whether the data follow a normally distribution by looking at the dispersion of the data points along the diagonal line in the normal Q-Q plot. If the data follow a normal distribution, the data points will be scattered close to the diagonal line in the normal Q-Q plot. If the data do not follow a normal distribution, the data points would be scattered far from the diagonal line in a non-linear manner. As you can see from the four normal Q-Q plots, the data points are located fairly close to the diagonal line and you can conclude that the data for each supplier are normally distributed. The assumption of normality is satisfied.

The null hypothesis states that there is no difference in mean tensile strength among the four suppliers:

$$H_0: \mu_1 = \mu_2 = \mu_3 = \mu_4$$

The alternative hypothesis states that at least one of the suppliers differs with respect to the mean tensile strength:

$$H_1: \text{Not all the means are equal.}$$

To construct the ANOVA summary table, you first compute the sample means in each group (see Figure 13.3). Then you compute the grand mean by summing all 20 values and dividing by the total number of values:

$$\bar{\bar{X}} = \frac{\displaystyle\sum_{j=1}^{c}\sum_{i=1}^{n_j} X_{ij}}{n} = \frac{438.9}{20} = 21.945$$

Then, using Equations (13.1) through (13.3) on page 564, you compute the sum of squares:

$$SSA = \sum_{j=1}^{c} n_j (\bar{X}_j - \bar{\bar{X}})^2 = (5)(19.52 - 21.945)^2 + (5)(24.26 - 21.945)^2$$

$$+ (5)(22.84 - 21.945)^2 + (5)(21.16 - 21.945)^2$$

$$= 63.2855$$

$$SSW = \sum_{j=1}^{c}\sum_{i=1}^{n_j}(X_{ij}-\bar{X}_j)^2$$

$$= (18.5-19.52)^2 + \cdots + (18-19.52)^2 + (26.3-24.26)^2 + \cdots + (24.5-24.26)^2$$

$$+ (20.6-22.84)^2 + \cdots + (22.9-22.84)^2 + (25.4-21.16)^2 + \cdots + (20.4-21.16)^2$$

$$= 97.5040$$

$$SST = \sum_{j=1}^{c}\sum_{i=1}^{n_j}(X_{ij}-\bar{\bar{X}})^2$$

$$= (18.5-21.945)^2 + (24-21.945)^2 + \cdots + (20.4-21.945)^2$$

$$= 160.7895$$

You compute the mean squares by dividing the sum of squares by the corresponding degrees of freedom [see Equation (13.4) on page 565]. Because $c = 4$ and $n = 20$,

$$MSA = \frac{SSA}{c-1} = \frac{63.2855}{4-1} = 21.0952$$

$$MSW = \frac{SSW}{n-c} = \frac{97.5040}{20-4} = 6.0940$$

so that using Equation (13.5) on page 565,

$$F_{STAT} = \frac{MSA}{MSW} = \frac{21.0952}{6.0940} = 3.4616$$

For a selected level of significance, α, you find the upper-tail critical value, F_α, from the F distribution using Table E.5. A portion of Table E.5 is presented in Table 13.2. In the parachute supplier example, there are 3 degrees of freedom in the numerator and 16 degrees of freedom in the denominator. F_α, the upper-tail critical value at the 0.05 level of significance, is 3.24.

TABLE 13.2

Finding the Critical Value of F with 3 and 16 Degrees of Freedom at the 0.05 Level of Significance

Cumulative Probabilities = 0.95
Upper-Tail Area = 0.05

Denominator df_2	1	2	3	4	5	6	7	8	9
11	4.84	3.98	3.59	3.36	3.20	3.09	3.01	2.95	2.90
12	4.75	3.89	3.49	3.26	3.11	3.00	2.91	2.85	2.80
13	4.67	3.81	3.41	3.18	3.03	2.92	2.83	2.77	2.71
14	4.60	3.74	3.34	3.11	2.96	2.85	2.76	2.70	2.65
15	4.54	3.68	3.29	3.06	2.90	2.79	2.71	2.64	2.59
16	4.49	3.63	3.24	3.01	2.85	2.74	2.66	2.59	2.54

Numerator df_1

Source: Extracted from Table E.5.

Because $F_{STAT} = 3.4616$ is greater than $F_\alpha = 3.24$, you reject the null hypothesis (see Figure 13.5). You conclude that there is a significant difference in the mean tensile strength among the four suppliers.

FIGURE 13.5

Regions of rejection and nonrejection for the one-way ANOVA at the 0.05 level of significance, with 3 and 16 degrees of freedom

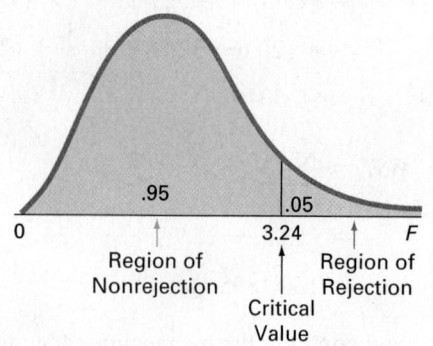

Find F critical value using calculator:

To find the F critical value, use the Casio Calculator fx-9750GII and follow the following calculator steps:

Note: Fx-9750G Plus does not have this option; therefore you have to use the Table G3 in the Appendix.

From the **Main Menu** select:

STAT F5 (DIST) **F4** (F) **F3**(InvF)   then enter the following items:

Inverse F
Data   : F2(Var) ▼
Area   : 0.05   **EXE**   **(Note: It is an upper tailed test for F distribution.)**
n:df   : 3   **EXE**   **(Note: n:df corresponds to the "Between Groups" shown in the ANOVA summary table)**
d:df   : 16   **EXE**   **(Note: d:df corresponds to the "Within Groups" shown in the ANOVA summary table)**
Save Res : None
Execute

Now key **EXE** or **F1**(CALC)

The calculator will now show the results:

Inverse F

x-Inv = 3.23887152

The critical value defines the rejection and non-rejection regions.

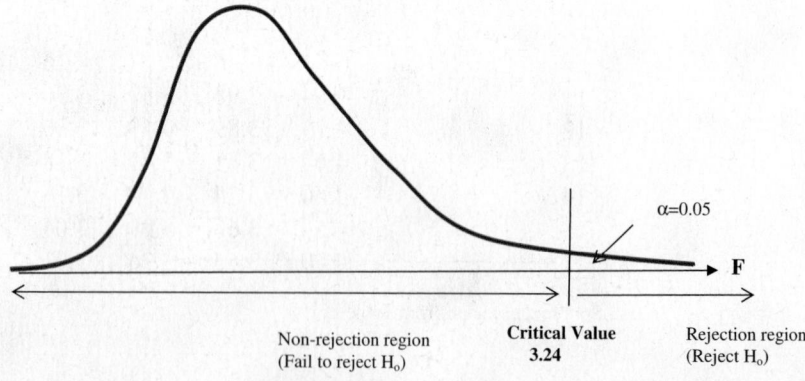

Figure 13.6 shows the ANOVA results for the parachute experiment, including the *p*-value. In Figure 13.6, what Table 13.1 (see page 566) labels Among Groups is labeled Between Groups in the Excel results and Factor in the Minitab results. What Table 13.2 labels Within Groups is labeled Error in the Minitab results.

FIGURE 13.6
SPSS ANOVA results for
the parachute example

ANOVA

tensile-strength scale

	Sum of Squares	df	Mean Square	F	Sig.
Between Groups	63.285	3	21.095	3.462	.041
Within Groups	97.504	16	6.094		
Total	160.789	19			

The *p*-value, or probability of getting a computed F_{STAT} statistic of 3.4616 or larger when the null hypothesis is true, is 0.0414. Because this *p*-value is less than the specified α of 0.05, you reject the null hypothesis. The *p*-value 0.0414 indicates that there is a 4.14% chance of observing differences this large or larger if the population means for the four suppliers are all equal. After performing the one-way ANOVA and finding a significant difference among the suppliers, you still do not know *which* suppliers differ. All you know is that there is sufficient evidence to state that the population means are not all the same. In other words, one or more population means are significantly different. To determine which suppliers differ, you can use a multiple comparisons procedure such as the Tukey-Kramer procedure.

Multiple Comparisons: The Tukey-Kramer Procedure

In the parachute company example, you used the one-way ANOVA *F* test to determine that there was a difference among the suppliers. The next step is to construct **multiple comparisons** to determine which suppliers are different.

FIGURE 13.7
SPSS Tukey-Kramer
procedure worksheet for
the parachute example

Post Hoc Tests

Multiple Comparisons

tensile-strength scale
Tukey HSD

(I) Suppliers	(J) Suppliers	Mean Difference (I-J)	Std. Error	Sig.	95% Confidence Interval Lower Bound	Upper Bound
Supplier 1	Supplier 2	−4.74000*	1.56128	.036	−9.2069	−.2731
	Supplier 3	−3.32000	1.56128	.187	−7.7869	1.1469
	Supplier 4	−1.64000	1.56128	.723	−6.1069	2.8269
Supplier 2	Supplier 1	4.74000*	1.56128	.036	.2731	9.2069
	Supplier 3	1.42000	1.56128	.800	−3.0469	5.8869
	Supplier 4	3.10000	1.56128	.234	−1.3669	7.5669
Supplier 3	Supplier 1	3.32000	1.56128	.187	−1.1469	7.7869
	Supplier 2	−1.42000	1.56128	.800	−5.8869	3.0469
	Supplier 4	1.68000	1.56128	.708	−2.7869	6.1469
Supplier 4	Supplier 1	1.64000	1.56128	.723	−2.8269	6.1069
	Supplier 2	−3.10000	1.56128	.234	−7.5669	1.3669
	Supplier 3	−1.68000	1.56128	.708	−6.1469	2.7869

The mean difference is significant at the 0.05 level.

Results:

1. Since the p-value $= 0.036 < 0.05$, reject the null hypothesis; there is evidence to indicate that the means for suppliers 1 and 2 are different.
2. Since the p-value $= 0.187 > 0.05$, do not reject the null hypothesis; there is **no** evidence to indicate that the means for suppliers 1 and 3 are different.
3. Since the p-value $= 0.723 > 0.05$, do not reject the null hypothesis; there is **no** evidence to indicate that the means for suppliers 1 and 4 are different.
4. Since the p-value $= 0.800 > 0.05$, do not reject the null hypothesis; there is **no** evidence to indicate that the means for suppliers 2 and 3 are different.
5. Since the p-value $= 0.234 > 0.05$, do not reject the null hypothesis; there is **no** evidence to indicate that the means for suppliers 2 and 4 are different.
6. Since the p-value $= 0.708 > 0.05$, do not reject the null hypothesis; there is **no** evidence to indicate that the means for suppliers 3 and 4 are different.

ANOVA Assumptions

In Chapter 11 and Sections 12.1–12.4, you learned about the assumptions required in order to use each hypothesis-testing procedure and the consequences of departures from these assumptions. To use the one-way ANOVA F test, you must make the following assumptions about the populations:

- Randomness and independence
- Normality
- Homogeneity of variance

The first assumption, **randomness and independence**, is critically important. The validity of any experiment depends on random sampling and/or the randomization process. To avoid biases in the outcomes, you need to select random samples from the c groups or use the randomization process to randomly assign the items to the c levels of the factor. Selecting a random sample, or randomly assigning the levels, ensures that a value from one group is independent of any other value in the experiment. Departures from this assumption can seriously affect inferences from the ANOVA. These problems are discussed more thoroughly in References 3 and 4.

The second assumption, **normality**, states that the sample values in each group are from a normally distributed population. Just as in the case of the t test, the one-way ANOVA F test is fairly robust against departures from the normal distribution. As long as the distributions are not extremely different from a normal distribution, the level of significance of the ANOVA F test is usually not greatly affected, particularly for large samples. You can assess the normality of each of the c samples by constructing a normal probability plot or a boxplot.

The third assumption, **homogeneity of variance**, states that the variances of the c groups are equal (i.e., $\sigma_1^2 = \sigma_2^2 = \cdots = \sigma_c^2$). If you have equal sample sizes in each group, inferences based on the F distribution are not seriously affected by unequal variances. However, if you have unequal sample sizes, unequal variances can have a serious effect on inferences from the ANOVA procedure. Thus, when possible, you should have equal sample sizes in all groups. You can use the Levene test for homogeneity of variance presented next to test whether the variances of the c groups are equal.

When only the normality assumption is violated, you can use the Kruskal-Wallis rank test, a nonparametric procedure (see References 1 and 2). When only the homogeneity-of-variance assumption is violated, you can use procedures similar to those used in the separate-variance t test of Section 12.1 (see references 1 and 2). When both the normality and homogeneity-of-variance assumptions have been violated, you need to use an appropriate data transformation that both normalizes the data and reduces the differences in variances (see reference 4) or use a more general nonparametric procedure (see references 1 and 2).

Check the Homogeneity of Variance Assumption (Using SPSS)

Although the one-way ANOVA F test is relatively robust with respect to the assumption of equal group variances, large differences in the group variances can seriously affect the level of significance and the power of the F test. One powerful yet simple procedure for testing the equality of the variances is the modified **Levene test** (see references 1 and 4). To test for the homogeneity of variance, you use the following null hypothesis:

$$H_0: \sigma_1^2 = \sigma_2^2 = \cdots = \sigma_c^2$$

against the alternative hypothesis:

$$H_1: \text{Not all } \sigma_j^2 \text{ are equal } (j = 1, 2, 3, \ldots, c)$$

To test the null hypothesis of equal variances, you first compute the absolute value of the difference between each value and the median of the group. Then you perform a one-way ANOVA on these *absolute differences*. Most statisticians suggest using a level of significance of $\alpha = 0.05$ when performing the ANOVA. To illustrate the modified Levene test, return to the parachute supplier example concerning the tensile strength of parachutes listed in Figure 13.3 on page 567. Table 13.3 summarizes the absolute differences from the median of each supplier.

TABLE 13.3

Absolute Differences from the Median Tensile Strength for Four Suppliers

Supplier 1 (Median = 18.5)	Supplier 2 (Median = 24.5)	Supplier 3 (Median = 22.9)	Supplier 4 (Median = 20.4)
$\lvert 18.5 - 18.5 \rvert = 0.0$	$\lvert 26.3 - 24.5 \rvert = 1.8$	$\lvert 20.6 - 22.9 \rvert = 2.3$	$\lvert 25.4 - 20.4 \rvert = 5.0$
$\lvert 24.0 - 18.5 \rvert = 5.5$	$\lvert 25.3 - 24.5 \rvert = 0.8$	$\lvert 25.2 - 22.9 \rvert = 2.3$	$\lvert 19.9 - 20.4 \rvert = 0.5$
$\lvert 17.2 - 18.5 \rvert = 1.3$	$\lvert 24.0 - 24.5 \rvert = 0.5$	$\lvert 20.8 - 22.9 \rvert = 2.1$	$\lvert 22.6 - 20.4 \rvert = 2.2$
$\lvert 19.9 - 18.5 \rvert = 1.4$	$\lvert 21.2 - 24.5 \rvert = 3.3$	$\lvert 24.7 - 22.9 \rvert = 1.8$	$\lvert 17.5 - 20.4 \rvert = 2.9$
$\lvert 18.0 - 18.5 \rvert = 0.5$	$\lvert 24.5 - 24.5 \rvert = 0.0$	$\lvert 22.9 - 22.9 \rvert = 0.0$	$\lvert 20.4 - 20.4 \rvert = 0.0$

Using the absolute differences given in Table 13.3, you perform a one-way ANOVA (see Figure 13.8).

SPSS Instruction to Obtain Levene Test of Equal Variance

Make the following menu selections: **Analyze – Compare Means – One-Way ANOVA**

Click "**Option**" button and under "**Statistics**", check "**Homogeneity of variance test**". Then click **Continue** and then **OK** to run the one-way ANOVA test. You will obtain the result table of test of homogeneity of variances as shown in Figure 13.8.

FIGURE 13.8

SPSS ANOVA Levene test and ANOVA results

See Figure 13.18 to create the table of Test of Homogeneity of Variances.

Test of Homogeneity of Variances

tensile-strength scale

Levene Statistic	df1	df2	Sig.
.430	3	16	.734

"**Sig**" is *p*-value
Since *p*-value is greater than α (i.e. 0.734 > 0.05, you reject the null hypothesis and assume equal variance. The homogeneity of variance assumption is satisfied.

ANOVA

tensile-strength scale

	Sum of Squares	df	Mean Square	F	Sig.
Between Groups	63.285	3	21.095	3.462	.041
Within Groups	97.504	16	6.094		
Total	160.789	19			

Since *p*-value is less than α (i.e. 0.041 > 0.05, you reject the null hypothesis and conclude that there is a significant difference in the mean tensile strength among the four suppliers. Which means differ? You have to perform the multiple comparison procedure.

From the Figure 13.8 Excel results, observe that $F_{STAT} = 0.2068$. (Excel labels this value F. Minitab labels the value Test statistic and reports a value of 0.21.) Because $F_{STAT} = 0.2068 < 3.2389$ (or the p-value $= 0.8902 > 0.05$), you do not reject H_0. There is no evidence of a significant difference among the four variances. In other words, it is reasonable to assume that the materials from the four suppliers produce parachutes with an equal amount of variability. Therefore, the homogeneity-of-variance assumption for the ANOVA procedure is justified.

Example 13.1 illustrates another example of the one way ANOVA.

EXAMPLE 13.1

ANOVA of the Speed of Drive-Through Service at Fast-Food Chains

For fast-food restaurants, the drive-through window is an increasing source of revenue. The chain that offers the fastest service is likely to attract additional customers. Each month *QSR Magazine*, **www.qsrmagazine.com**, publishes its results of drive-through service times (from menu board to departure) at fast-food chains. In a recent month, the mean time was 134.09 seconds for Wendy's, 163.17 seconds for Taco Bell, 166.65 seconds for Burger King, 174.22 seconds for McDonald's, and 194.58 seconds for KFC. Suppose the study was based on 20 customers for each fast-food chain. Table 13.4 contains the ANOVA table for this problem.

TABLE 13.4

ANOVA Summary Table of Drive-Through Service Times at Fast-Food Chains

Source	Degrees of Freedom	Sum of Squares	Mean Squares	F	p-value
Among chains	4	38,191.9096	9,547.9774	73.1086	0.0000
Within chains	95	12,407.00	130.60		

At the 0.05 level of significance, is there evidence of a difference in the mean drive-through service times of the five chains?

SOLUTION

$H_0: \mu_1 = \mu_2 = \mu_3 = \mu_4 = \mu_5$ where 1 = Wendy's, 2 = Taco Bell, 3 = Burger King, 4 = McDonalds, 5 = KFC

H_1: Not all μ_j are equal   where $j = 1, 2, 3, 4, 5$

Decision rule: If p-value < 0.05, reject H_0. Because the p-value is virtually 0, which is less than $\alpha = 0.05$, reject H_0.

You have sufficient evidence to conclude that the mean drive-through times of the five chains are not all equal.

To determine which of the means are significantly different from one another, use the Tukey-Kramer procedure to establish the critical range:

Critical value of Q with 5 and 95 degrees of freedom ≈ 3.92

$$\text{Critical range} = Q_\alpha \sqrt{\left(\frac{MSW}{2}\right)\left(\frac{1}{n_j} + \frac{1}{n_{j'}}\right)} = (3.92)\sqrt{\left(\frac{130.6}{2}\right)\left(\frac{1}{20} + \frac{1}{20}\right)}$$

$$= 10.02$$

Any observed difference greater than 10.02 is considered significant. The mean drive-through service times are different between Wendy's (mean of 134.09 seconds) and each of the other four chains and between KFC (mean of 194.58 seconds) and the other four chains. In addition, the mean drive-through service time is different between McDonald's and Taco Bell. Thus, with 95% confidence, you can conclude that the mean drive-through service time for Wendy's is faster than those of Burger King, Taco Bell, McDonald's, and KFC. The mean drive-through service time for KFC is slower than those of Wendy's, Burger King, Taco Bell, McDonald's. In addition, the mean drive-through service time for McDonald's is slower than for Taco Bell.

CALCULATOR LESSON 15A

CFX-9850GB CALCULATOR

EXAMPLE: The Perfect Parachute Company

Lesson 15A—One-Way ANOVA

We will use the scenario "The Perfect Parachute Company" to demonstrate how to perform one-way ANOVA on the calculator.

A research was conducted to determine if any significant differences exist in the strength of parachutes woven from synthetic fibers from the four suppliers. Five parachutes were woven for each group—Supplier 1, Supplier 2, Supplier 3, and Supplier 4. The amount of force required to tear the parachute is measured on a tensile-strength scale on which the larger the value, the stronger the parachute. The data are shown below:

TABLE 13.5

Summary of the Results of the Four Suppliers

Supplier 1	Supplier 2	Supplier 3	Supplier 4
18.5	26.3	20.6	25.4
24.0	25.3	25.2	19.9
17.2	24.0	20.8	22.6
19.9	21.2	24.7	17.5
18.0	24.5	22.9	20.4

Solution: First enter data into **List 1** (corresponding to Supplier 1), **List 2** (corresponding to Supplier 2), **List 3** (corresponding to Supplier 3) and **List 4** (corresponding to Supplier 4).

Now, from the **Main Menu** select the following:

STAT TEST (F3) ANOV (F5). Then enter the following items:

ANOVA
How many   : 4 (press **F3**)
List 1   : List 1 (F1)
List 2   : List 2 (F2)
List 3   : List 3 (F3)
List 4   : List 4 (F4)
Execute

Now press **EXE** or **F1** (Calc).

The calculator will show the results:

ANOVA
F	=3.4616
p	=0.041365
xpσn-1	=2.4686
Fdf	=3
SS	=63.285
MS	=21.095
Edf	=16
SSe	=97.504
MSe	=6.094

Since the p-value < 0.05, the conclusion is to reject the null hypothesis. In other words, there is a significant difference in the mean tensile strength among the products from the four suppliers. However, we do not know which suppliers differ. To answer this question, we perform the Tukey procedure using SPSS (see Figure 13.7).

CALCULATOR LESSON 15B

FX-9850GII CALCULATOR

EXAMPLE: The Perfect Parachute Company

Lesson 15B—One-Way ANOVA

We will use the scenario "The Perfect Parachute Company" to demonstrate how to perform one-way ANOVA on the calculator.

A research was conducted to determine if any significant differences exist in the strength of parachutes woven from synthetic fibers from the four suppliers. Five parachutes were woven for each group—Supplier 1, Supplier 2, Supplier 3, and Supplier 4. The amount of force required to tear the parachute is measured on a tensile-strength scale on which the larger the value, the stronger the parachute. The data are shown below:

TABLE 13.6
Summary of the Results of the Four Suppliers

Supplier 1	Supplier 2	Supplier 3	Supplier 4
18.5	26.3	20.6	25.4
24.0	25.3	25.2	19.9
17.2	24.0	20.8	22.6
19.9	21.2	24.7	17.5
18.0	24.5	22.9	20.4

Solution:

A. First enter data in **List 1** and **List 2** as follows:

Factor A	Dependent
List 1	List 2
1	18.5
1	24.0
1	17.2
1	19.9
1	18.0
2	26.3
2	25.3
2	24.0
2	21.2
2	24.5
3	20.6
3	25.2
3	20.8
3	24.7
3	22.9
4	25.4
4	19.9
4	22.6
4	17.5
4	20.4

B. Perform the ANOVA procedure

From the **Main Menu** select the following:

STAT   TEST(F3) ANOV(F5).   Then enter the following items:

ANOVA
How many   : 1 (press **F1**)
Factor A   : List 1 (F1)
Dependnt   : List 2 (F1)
Save Res   : None
Execute

Now press **EXE** or **F1**(Calc).
The calculator will show the results:

ANOVA

	df	SS	mS	F	p
A	3	63.285	21.095	3.4616	0.0413
ERR	16	97.504	6.094		

Since the p-value < 0.05, the conclusion is to reject the null hypothesis. In other words, there is a significant difference in the mean tensile strength among the products from the four suppliers. However, we do not know which suppliers differ. To answer this question, we perform the Tukey procedure using SPSS.

SPSS—VERSION 16—ANOVA

We will use the scenario "The Perfect Parachute Company" to demonstrate how to perform one-way ANOVA using SPSS.

A research was conducted to determine if any significant differences exist in the strength of parachutes woven from synthetic fibers from the four suppliers. Five parachutes were woven for each group—Supplier 1, Supplier 2, Supplier 3 and, Supplier 4. The amount of force required to tear the parachute is measured on a tensile-strength scale on which the larger the value, the stronger the parachute. The data are shown below:

FIGURE 13.9

Supplier 1	Supplier 2	Supplier 3	Supplier 4
18.5	26.3	20.6	25.4
24.0	25.3	25.2	19.9
17.2	24.0	20.8	22.6
19.9	21.2	24.7	17.5
18.0	24.5	22.9	20.4

Solution:

Performing a one-way ANOVA on SPSS—Version 16

Step 1: Open the SPSS Data Editor.

Click **Cancel** to cancel the SPSS opening window.

FIGURE 13.10

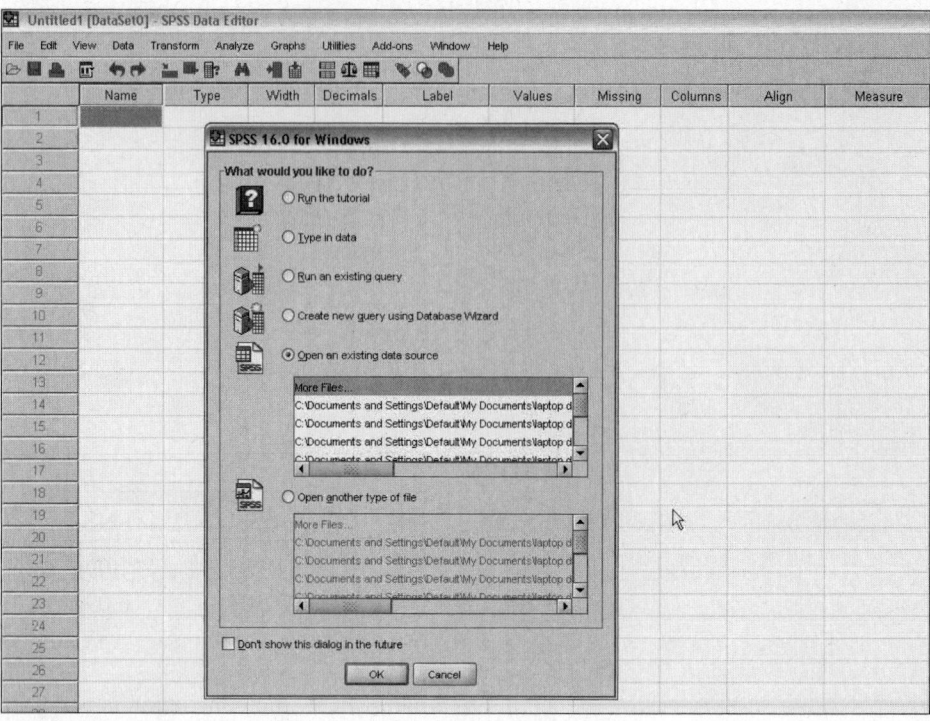

Step 2: Define the variables and give the variables a label.

Click **"Variable View"** (at the bottom of the window) to go to the variable view window to define the variables and fix the data at zero or one decimal places.

- Enter the first variable name, "suppliers," and then click **Values.** Enter "1" in the value box, enter **"Supplier 1"** in the Label box, and then click **Add.** Similarly, enter the data for the other three suppliers.

FIGURE 13.11

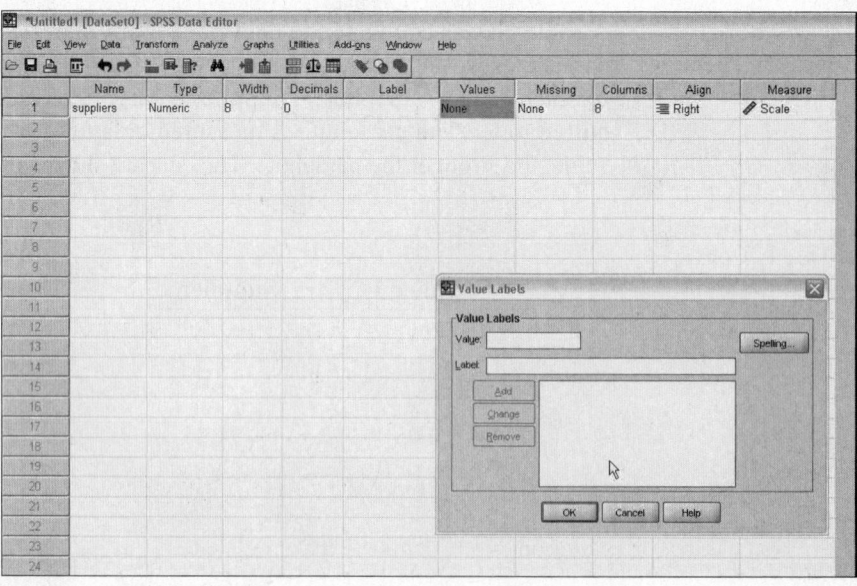

- Enter the second variable name, "Strength" and label it as "tensile-strength scale."

FIGURE 13.12

	Name	Type	Width	Decimals	Label	Values	Missing	Columns	Align	Measure
1	suppliers	Numeric	8	0		{1, Supplier...	None	8	Right	Scale
2	Strength	Numeric	8	2	tensile-strength...	None	None	8	Right	Scale

Step 3: Create a SPSS data file.

Click **"Data View"** to return to the Data View window. Now, enter the raw data into the respective column of variables.

FIGURE 13.13

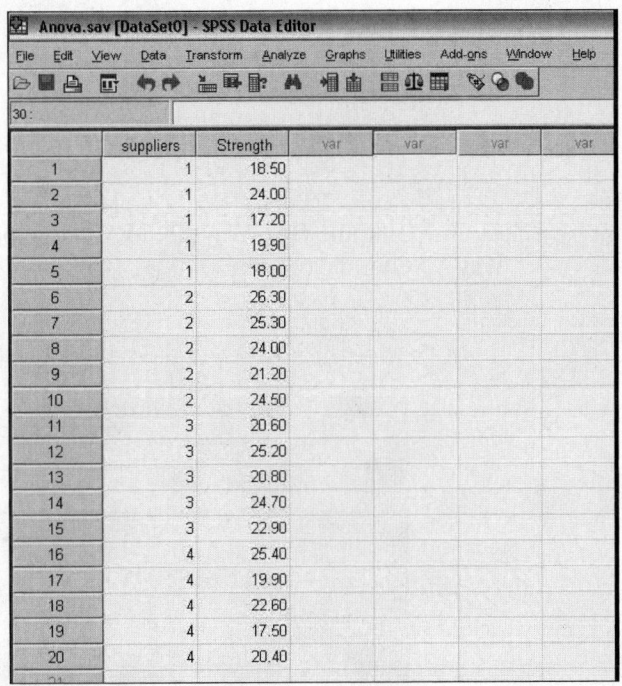

	suppliers	Strength	var	var	var	var
1	1	18.50				
2	1	24.00				
3	1	17.20				
4	1	19.90				
5	1	18.00				
6	2	26.30				
7	2	25.30				
8	2	24.00				
9	2	21.20				
10	2	24.50				
11	3	20.60				
12	3	25.20				
13	3	20.80				
14	3	24.70				
15	3	22.90				
16	4	25.40				
17	4	19.90				
18	4	22.60				
19	4	17.50				
20	4	20.40				

After you have entered all the data, save the file as "Anova.sav" (or any filename).

Step 4: Perform ANOVA.

Make the following menu selections:

Analyze   Compare Means   One-Way ANOVA

FIGURE 13.14

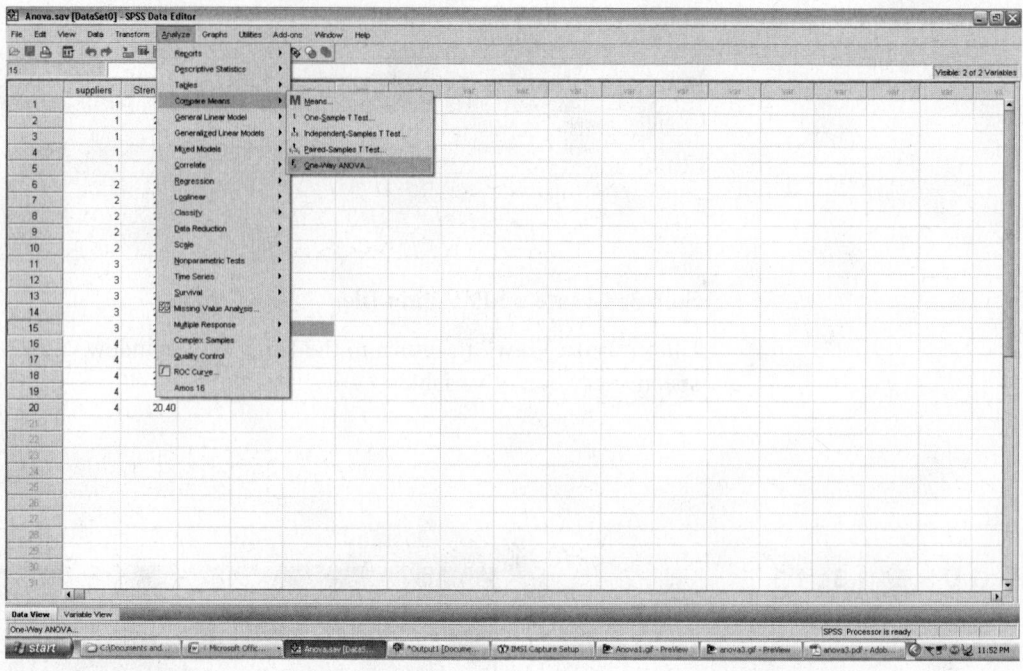

At this point, the **One-Way ANOVA** dialog box will appear. Make these entries in the **One-Way ANOVA** dialog box:

FIGURE 13.15

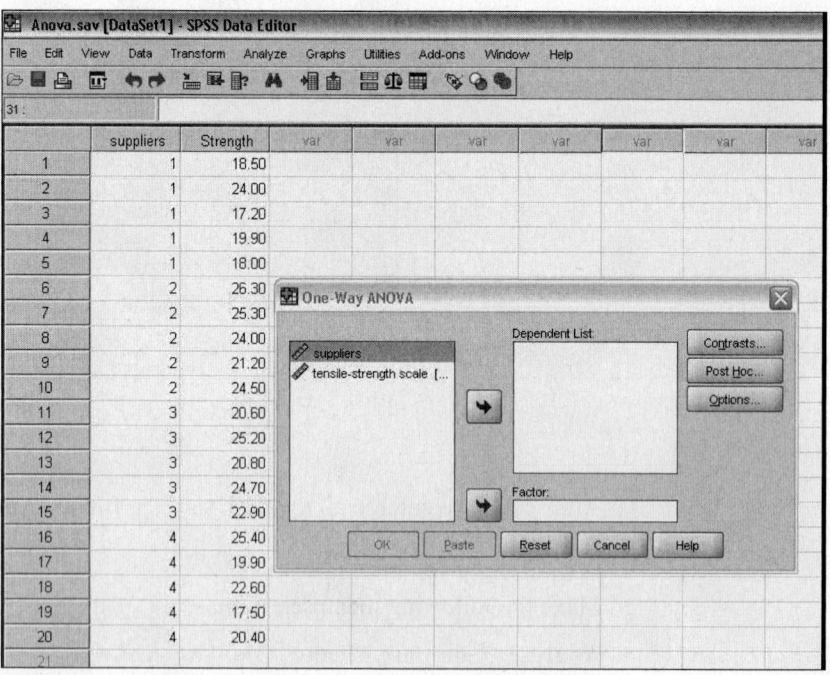

- Highlight on the **"tensile-strength scale"** variable and click on the top arrow key (♦). The variable will automatically fall into the **Dependent List** box.

- Highlight on the **"Suppliers"** variable and click on the bottom arrow key (♦). The variable will automatically fall into the **Factor** box.

FIGURE 13.16

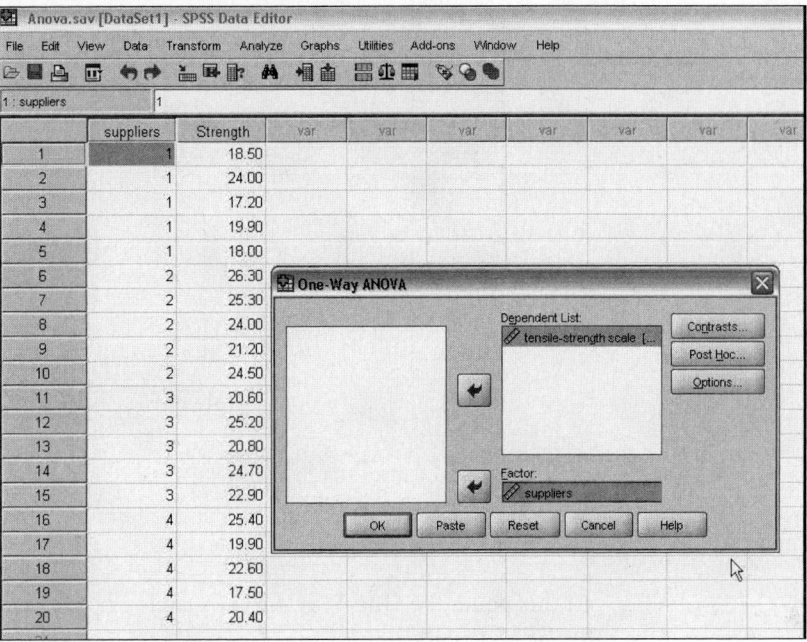

To Perform the Post-Hoc Comparison Procedure

- Click on the **Post-Hoc** button. In the "One-Way ANOVA: Post Hoc Multiple Comparisons" window, select **Tukey** as the comparison method. Then click on the **Continue** button to return to the "One-Way ANOVA" window.

FIGURE 13.17

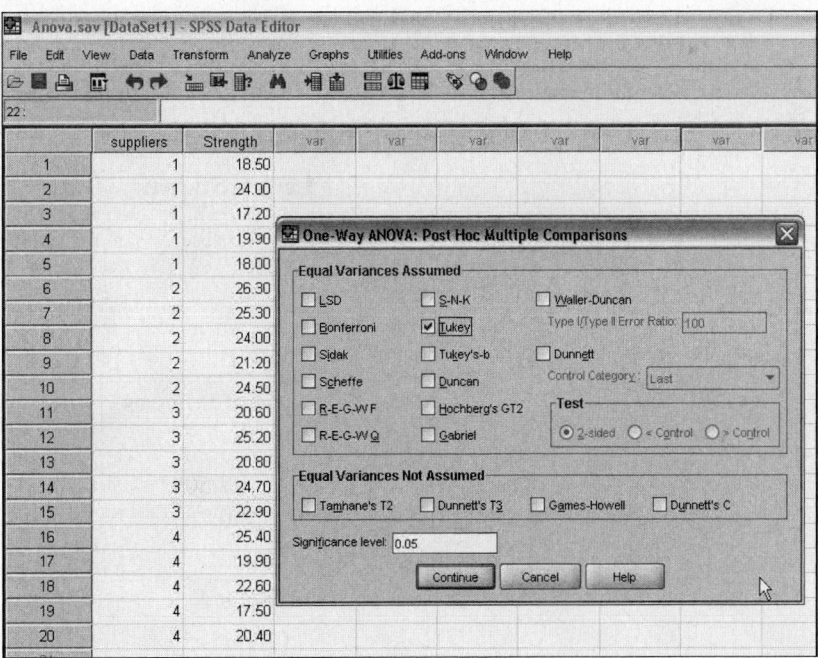

Test for Homogeneity of Variance

- Click on the **Options** button. In the "One-Way ANOVA: Options" window, select **Homogeneity of variance test** to test for the equality of variances. Then click on the **Continue** button to return to the "One-Way ANOVA" window.

FIGURE 13.18

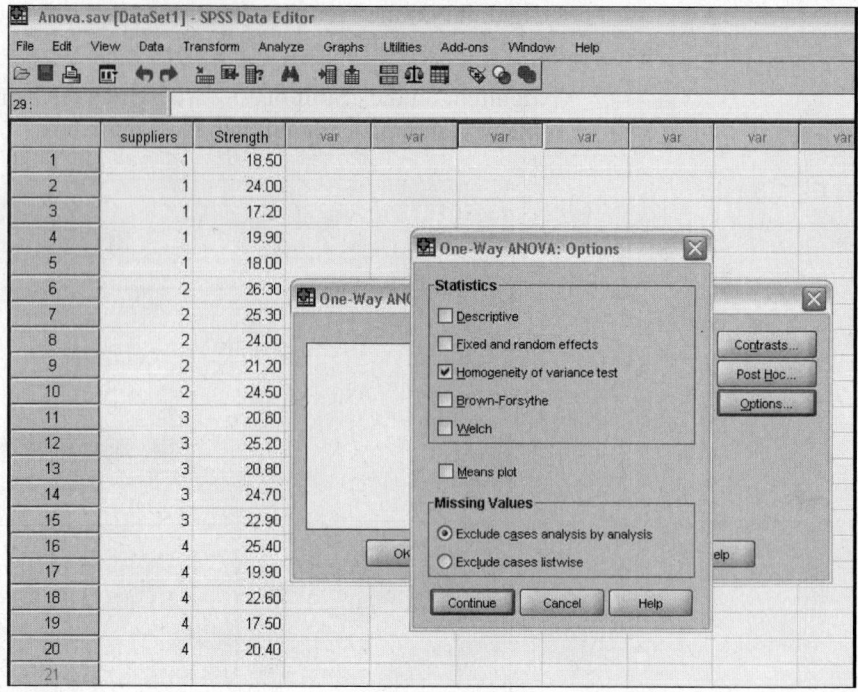

At this point, the **One-Way ANOVA** dialog box will appear. Click on the **OK** button to obtain the SPSS results.

Step 3: Go to **SPSS Viewer** to obtain your SPSS results.

SPSS output:

FIGURE 13.19

Oneway

Test of Homogeneity of Variances

tensile-strength scale

Levene Statistic	df1	df2	Sig.
.430	3	16	.734

ANOVA

tensile-strength scale

	Sum of Squares	df	Mean Square	F	Sig.
Between Groups	63.285	3	21.095	3.462	.041
Within Groups	97.504	16	6.094		
Total	160.789	19			

FIGURE 13.20

Post Hoc Tests

Multiple Comparisons

tensile-strength scale
Tukey HSD

(I) Suppliers	(J) Suppliers	Mean Difference (I-J)	Std. Error	Sig.	95% Confidence Interval Lower Bound	Upper Bound
Supplier 1	Supplier 2	−4.74000*	1.56128	.036	−9.2069	−.2731
	Supplier 3	−3.32000	1.56128	.187	−7.7869	1.1469
	Supplier 4	−1.64000	1.56128	.723	−6.1069	2.8269
Supplier 2	Supplier 1	4.74000*	1.56128	.036	.2731	9.2069
	Supplier 3	1.42000	1.56128	.800	−3.0469	5.8869
	Supplier 4	3.10000	1.56128	.234	−1.3669	7.5669
Supplier 3	Supplier 1	3.32000	1.56128	.187	−1.1469	7.7869
	Supplier 2	−1.42000	1.56128	.800	−5.8869	3.0469
	Supplier 4	1.68000	1.56128	.708	−2.7869	6.1469
Supplier 4	Supplier 1	1.64000	1.56128	.723	−2.8269	6.1069
	Supplier 2	−3.10000	1.56128	.234	−7.5669	1.3669
	Supplier 3	−1.68000	1.56128	.708	−6.1469	2.7869

* The mean difference is significant at the 0.05 level.

Homogeneous Subsets

tensile-strength scale

Tukey HSD

Suppliers	N	Subset for alpha = 0.05 1	2
Supplier 1	5	19.5200	
Supplier 4	5	21.1600	21.1600
Supplier 3	5	22.8400	22.8400
Supplier 2	5		24.2600
Sig.		.187	.234

Means for groups in homogeneous subsets are displayed.

Problems for Section 13.1

LEARNING THE BASICS

13.1 An experiment has a single factor with five groups and seven values in each group.
a. How many degrees of freedom are there in determining the among-group variation?
b. How many degrees of freedom are there in determining the within-group variation?
c. How many degrees of freedom are there in determining the total variation?

13.2 You are working with the same experiment as in Problem 13.1.
a. If $SSA = 60$ and $SST = 210$, what is SSW?
b. What is MSA?
c. What is MSW?
d. What is the value of F_{STAT}?

13.3 You are working with the same experiment as in Problems 13.1 and 13.2.
a. Construct the ANOVA summary table and fill in all values in the table.
b. At the 0.05 level of significance, what is the upper-tail critical value from the F distribution?
c. State the decision rule for testing the null hypothesis that all five groups have equal population means.
d. What is your statistical decision?

13.4 Consider an experiment with three groups, with seven values in each.
a. How many degrees of freedom are there in determining the among-group variation?
b. How many degrees of freedom are there in determining the within-group variation?
c. How many degrees of freedom are there in determining the total variation?

13.5 Consider an experiment with four groups, with eight values in each. For the ANOVA summary table below, fill in all the missing results:

Source	Degrees of Freedom	Sum of Squares	Mean Square (Variance)	F
Among groups	$c - 1 = ?$	$SSA = ?$	$MSA = 80$	$F_{STAT} = ?$
Within groups	$n - c = ?$	$SSW = 560$	$MSW = ?$	
Total	$n - 1 = ?$	$SST = ?$		

13.6 You are working with the same experiment as in Problem 13.5.

a. At the 0.05 level of significance, state the decision rule for testing the null hypothesis that all four groups have equal population means.
b. What is your statistical decision?
c. At the 0.05 level of significance, what is the upper-tail critical value from the Studentized range distribution?
d. To perform the Tukey-Kramer procedure, what is the critical range?

APPLYING THE CONCEPTS

13.7 The Computer Anxiety Rating Scale (CARS) measures an individual's level of computer anxiety, on a scale from 20 (no anxiety) to 100 (highest level of anxiety). Researchers at Miami University administered CARS to 172 business students. One of the objectives of the study was to determine whether there are differences in the amount of computer anxiety experienced by students with different majors. They found the following:

Source	Degrees of Freedom	Sum of Squares	Mean Squares	F
Among majors	5	3,172		
Within majors	166	21,246		
Total	171	24,418		

Major	n	Mean
Marketing	19	44.37
Management	11	43.18
Other	14	42.21
Finance	45	41.80
Accountancy	36	37.56
MIS	47	32.21

Source: Data Extracted from T. Broome and D. Havelka, "Determinants of Computer Anxiety in Business Students," *The Review of Business Information Systems*, Spring 2002, 6(2), pp. 9–16.

a. Complete the ANOVA summary table.
b. At the 0.05 level of significance, is there evidence of a difference in the mean computer anxiety experienced by different majors?
c. If the results in (b) indicate that it is appropriate, use the Tukey-Kramer procedure to determine which majors differ in mean computer anxiety. Discuss your findings.

✓SELF Test **13.8** Students in a business statistics course performed a completely randomized design to test the strength of four brands of trash bags. One-pound weights were placed into a bag, one at a time, until the bag broke. A total of

40 bags, 10 for each brand, were used. The data in `Trashbags` give the weight (in pounds) required to break the trash bags.

a. At the 0.05 level of significance, is there evidence of a difference in the mean strength of the four brands of trash bags?

b. If appropriate, determine which brands differ in mean strength.

c. At the 0.05 level of significance, is there evidence of a difference in the variation in strength among the four brands of trash bags?

d. Which brand(s) should you buy, and which brand(s) should you avoid? Explain.

13.9 A hospital conducted a study of the waiting time in its emergency room. The hospital has a main campus and three satellite locations. Management had a business objective of reducing waiting time for emergency room cases that did not require immediate attention. To study this, a random sample of 15 emergency room cases that did not require immediate attention at each location were selected on a particular day, and the waiting time (measured from check-in to when the patient was called into the clinic area) was measured. The results are stored in `ERWaiting`.

a. At the 0.05 level of significance, is there evidence of a difference in the mean waiting times in the four locations?

b. If appropriate, determine which locations differ in mean waiting time.

c. At the 0.05 level of significance, is there evidence of a difference in the variation in waiting time among the four locations?

13.10 A manufacturer of pens has hired an advertising agency to develop an advertising campaign for the upcoming holiday season. To prepare for this project, the research director decides to initiate a study of the effect of advertising on product perception. An experiment is designed to compare five different advertisements. Advertisement A greatly undersells the pen's characteristics. Advertisement B slightly undersells the pen's characteristics. Advertisement C slightly oversells the pen's characteristics. Advertisement D greatly oversells the pen's characteristics. Advertisement E attempts to correctly state the pen's characteristics. A sample of 30 adult respondents, taken from a larger focus group, is randomly assigned to the five advertisements (so that there are 6 respondents to each). After reading the advertisement and developing a sense of "product expectation," all respondents unknowingly receive the same pen to evaluate. The respondents are permitted to test the pen and the plausibility of the advertising copy. The respondents are then asked to rate the pen from 1 to 7 (lowest to highest) on the product characteristic scales of appearance, durability, and writing performance. The *combined* scores of three ratings (appearance, durability, and writing performance) for the 30 respondents (stored in `Pen`) are as follows:

A	B	C	D	E
15	16	8	5	12
18	17	7	6	19
17	21	10	13	18
19	16	15	11	12
19	19	14	9	17
20	17	14	10	14

a. At the 0.05 level of significance, is there evidence of a difference in the mean rating of the pens following exposure to five advertisements?

b. If appropriate, determine which advertisements differ in mean ratings.

c. At the 0.05 level of significance, is there evidence of a difference in the variation in ratings among the five advertisements?

d. Which advertisement(s) should you use, and which advertisement(s) should you avoid? Explain.

13.11 The per-store daily customer count (i.e., the mean number of customers in a store in one day) for a nationwide convenience store chain that operates nearly 10,000 stores has been steady, at 900, for some time. To increase the customer count, the chain is considering cutting prices for coffee beverages. The question to be determined is how much to cut prices to increase the daily customer count without reducing the gross margin on coffee sales too much. You decide to carry out an experiment in a sample of 24 stores where customer counts have been running almost exactly at the national average of 900. In 6 of the stores, the price of a small coffee will now be $0.59, in 6 stores the price of a small coffee will now be $0.69, in 6 stores, the price of a small coffee will now be $0.79, and in 6 stores, the price of a small coffee will now be $0.89. After four weeks of selling the coffee at the new price, the daily customer count in the stores was recorded and stored in `CoffeeSales`.

a. At the 0.05 level of significance, is there evidence of a difference in the daily customer count based on the price of a small coffee?

b. If appropriate, determine which prices differ in daily customer counts.

c. At the 0.05 level of significance, is there evidence of a difference in the variation in daily customer count among the different prices?

d. What effect does your result in (c) have on the validity of the results in (a) and (b)?

13.12 Integrated circuits are manufactured on silicon wafers through a process that involves a series of steps. An experiment was carried out to study the effect on the yield of using three methods in the cleansing step (coded to maintain confidentiality). The results (stored in `Yield-OneWay`) are as follows:

New1	New2	Standard
38	29	31
34	35	23
38	34	38
34	20	29
19	35	32
28	37	30

Source: Data Extracted from J. Ramirez and W. Taam, "An Autologistic Model for Integrated Circuit Manufacturing," *Journal of Quality Technology*, 2000, 32, pp. 254–262.

a. At the 0.05 level of significance, is there evidence of a difference in the mean yield among the methods used in the cleansing steps?
b. If appropriate, determine which methods differ in mean yields.
c. At the 0.05 level of significance, is there evidence of a difference in the variation in yields among the different methods?
d. What effect does your result in (c) have on the validity of the results in (a) and (b)?

13.13 A pet food company has a business objective of expanding its product line beyond its current kidney- and shrimp-based cat foods. The company developed two new products, one based on chicken livers and the other based on salmon. The company conducted an experiment to compare the two new products with its two existing ones, as well as a generic beef-based product sold in a supermarket chain.

For the experiment, a sample of 50 cats from the population at a local animal shelter was selected. Ten cats were randomly assigned to each of the five products being tested. Each of the cats was then presented with 3 ounces of the selected food in a dish at feeding time. The researchers defined the variable to be measured as the number of ounces of food that the cat consumed within a 10-minute time interval that began when the filled dish was presented. The results for this experiment are summarized in the following table and stored in `CatFood`.

Kidney	Shrimp	Chicken Liver	Salmon	Beef
2.37	2.26	2.29	1.79	2.09
2.62	2.69	2.23	2.33	1.87
2.31	2.25	2.41	1.96	1.67
2.47	2.45	2.68	2.05	1.64
2.59	2.34	2.25	2.26	2.16
2.62	2.37	2.17	2.24	1.75
2.34	2.22	2.37	1.96	1.18
2.47	2.56	2.26	1.58	1.92
2.45	2.36	2.45	2.18	1.32
2.32	2.59	2.57	1.93	1.94

a. At the 0.05 level of significance, is there evidence of a difference in the mean amount of food eaten among the various products?
b. If appropriate, determine which products differ in the mean amount of food eaten?
c. At the 0.05 level of significance, is there evidence of a significant difference in the variation in the amount of food eaten among the various products?
d. What should the pet food company conclude? Fully describe the pet food company's options with respect to the products.

13.14 A sporting goods manufacturing company wanted to compare the distance traveled by golf balls produced using four different designs. Ten balls were manufactured with each design and were brought to the local golf course for the club professional to test. The order in which the balls were hit with the same club from the first tee was randomized so that the pro did not know which type of ball was being hit. All 40 balls were hit in a short period of time, during which the environmental conditions were essentially the same. The results (distance traveled in yards) for the four designs are stored in `Golfball` and shown in the following table.

	Design		
1	**2**	**3**	**4**
206.32	217.08	226.77	230.55
207.94	221.43	224.79	227.95
206.19	218.04	229.75	231.84
204.45	224.13	228.51	224.87
209.65	211.82	221.44	229.49
203.81	213.90	223.85	231.10
206.75	221.28	223.97	221.53
205.68	229.43	234.30	235.45
204.49	213.54	219.50	228.35
210.86	214.51	233.00	225.09

a. At the 0.05 level of significance, is there evidence of a difference in the mean distances traveled by the golf balls with different designs?
b. If the results in (a) indicate that it is appropriate, use the Tukey-Kramer procedure to determine which designs differ in mean distances.
c. What assumptions are necessary in (a)?
d. At the 0.05 level of significance, is there evidence of a difference in the variation of the distances traveled by the golf balls with different designs?
e. What golf ball design should the manufacturing manager choose? Explain.

SUMMARY

In this chapter, you were introduced to a variety of tests for two or more samples. For situations in which the samples are independent, you learned statistical test procedures for analyzing possible differences between means, variances, and proportions. In addition, you learned a test procedure that is frequently used when analyzing differences between the means of two related samples. Remember that you need to select the test that is most appropriate for a given set of conditions and to critically investigate the validity of the assumptions underlying each of the hypothesis-testing procedures.

1. If you have more than two independent samples, you can use the one-way ANOVA.

Table 13.7 provides a list of topics covered in this chapter.

TABLE 13.7

Summary of Topics in Chapters 12 and 13

Type of Analysis	Numerical	Categorical
	Types of Data	
Comparing two populations	t tests for the difference in the means of two independent populations (Section 12.1)	Z test for the difference between two proportions (Section 12.4)
	Paired t test (Section 12.3)	
	F test for the difference between two variances (Section 12.2)	
Comparing more than two populations	One-way ANOVA (Section 13.1)	

KEY EQUATIONS

Total Variation in One-Way ANOVA

$$SST = \sum_{j=1}^{c} \sum_{i=1}^{n_j} (X_{ij} - \bar{\bar{X}})^2$$

Among-Group Variation in One-Way ANOVA

$$SSA = \sum_{j=1}^{c} n_j (\bar{X}_j - \bar{\bar{X}})^2$$

Within-Group Variation in One-Way ANOVA

$$SSW = \sum_{j=1}^{c} \sum_{i=1}^{n_j} (X_{ij} - \bar{X}_j)^2$$

Mean Squares in One-Way ANOVA

$$MSA = \frac{SSA}{c-1}$$

$$MSW = \frac{SSW}{n-c}$$

$$MST = \frac{SST}{n-1}$$

One-Way ANOVA F_{STAT} Test Statistic

$$F_{STAT} = \frac{MSA}{MSW}$$

KEY TERMS

among-group variation   563
analysis of variance (ANOVA)   563
ANOVA summary table   566
completely randomized design   563
factor   563
grand mean, $\bar{\bar{X}}$ 564
group   563
homogeneity of variance   574
level   563
Levene test   575

mean square   565
multiple comparisons   573
normality   574
one-way ANOVA   563
randomness and independence   574
sum of squares among
 groups (SSA)   564
sum of squares total (SST)   564

sum of squares within
 groups (SSW)   564
total variation   564
within-group
 variation   563

PROBLEMS

LEARNING THE BASICS

13.15 What are some of the criteria used in the selection of a particular hypothesis-testing procedure?

13.16 Under what conditions should you use the pooled-variance t test to examine possible differences in the means of two independent populations?

13.17 Under what conditions should you use the F test to examine possible differences in the variances of two independent populations?

13.18 What is the distinction between two independent populations and two related populations?

13.19 What is the distinction between repeated measurements and matched items?

13.20 When you have two independent populations, explain the similarities and differences between the test of hypothesis for the difference between the means and the confidence interval estimate of the difference between the means.

13.21 What are the assumptions of ANOVA?

13.22 Under what conditions should you select the one-way ANOVA F test to examine possible differences among the means of c independent populations?

13.23 When and how should you use multiple comparison procedures for evaluating pairwise combinations of the group means?

APPLYING THE CONCEPTS

13.24 A study compared music compact disc prices for Internet-based retailers and traditional brick-and-mortar retailers [extracted from L. Zoonky and S. Gosain, "A Longitudinal Price Comparison for Music CDs in Electronic and Brick-and-Mortar Markets: Pricing Strategies in Emergent Electronic Commerce," *Journal of Business*

Strategies, Spring 2002, 19(1), pp. 55–72]. Before collecting the data, the researchers carefully defined several research hypotheses, including the following:

1. The price dispersion on the Internet is lower than the price dispersion in the brick-and-mortar market.
2. Prices in electronic markets are lower than prices in physical markets.
   a. Consider research hypothesis 1. Write the null and alternative hypotheses in terms of population parameters. Carefully define the population parameters used.
   b. Define a Type I and Type II error for the hypotheses in (a).
   c. What type of statistical test should you use?
   d. What assumptions are needed to perform the test you selected?
   e. Repeat (a) through (d) for research hypothesis 2.

13.25 The pet-drug market is growing very rapidly. Before new pet drugs can be introduced into the marketplace, they must be approved by the U.S. Food and Drug Administration (FDA). In 1999, the Novartis company was trying to get Anafranil, a drug to reduce dog anxiety, approved. According to an article (E. Tanouye, "The Ow in Bowwow: With Growing Market in Pet Drugs, Makers Revamp Clinical Trials," *The Wall Street Journal*, April 13, 1999), Novartis had to find a way to translate a dog's anxiety symptoms into numbers that could be used to prove to the FDA that the drug had a statistically significant effect on the condition.
   a. What is meant by the phrase *statistically significant effect*?
   b. Consider an experiment in which dogs suffering from anxiety are divided into two groups. One group will be given Anafranil, and the other will be given a placebo (i.e., a drug without active ingredients). How can you translate a dog's anxiety symptoms into numbers? In other words, define a continuous variable, X_1, that mea-

sures the effectiveness of the drug Anafranil, and X_2, that measures the effectiveness of the placebo.

c. Building on your answer to part (b), define the null and alternative hypotheses for this study.

13.26 In response to lawsuits filed against the tobacco industry, many companies, such as Philip Morris, are running television advertisements that are supposed to educate teenagers about the dangers of smoking. Are these tobacco industry antismoking campaigns successful? Are state-sponsored antismoking commercials more effective? An article (G. Fairclough, "Philip Morris's Antismoking Campaign Draws Fire," *The Wall Street Journal*, April 6, 1999, p. B1) discussed a study in California that compared commercials made by the state of California and commercials produced by Philip Morris. Researchers showed the state ads and the Philip Morris ads to a group of California teenagers and measured the effectiveness of both. The researchers concluded that the state ads were more effective in relaying the dangers of smoking than the Philip Morris ads. The article suggests, however, that the study is not *statistically reliable* because the sample size was too small and because the study specifically selected participants who are considered more likely to start smoking than others.

a. How do you think the researchers measured effectiveness?
b. Define the null and alternative hypotheses for this study.
c. Explain the risks associated with Type I and Type II errors in this study.
d. What type of test is most appropriate in this situation?
e. What do you think is meant by the phrase *statistically reliable*?

13.27 Do male and female students study the same amount per week? In 2007, 58 sophomore business students were surveyed at a large university, which has over 1,000 sophomore business students each year. The file **Studytime** contains the gender and the number of hours spent studying in a typical week for the sampled students.

a. At the 0.05 level of significance, is there a difference in the variance of the study time for male students and female students?
b. Using the results of (a), which *t* test is appropriate to compare the mean study time for male and female students?
c. At the 0.05 level of significance, conduct the test selected in (b).
d. Write a short summary of your findings.

13.28 Two professors wanted to study how students from their two universities compared in their capabilities of using Excel spreadsheets in undergraduate information systems courses (data extracted from H. Howe and M. G. Simkin, "Factors Affecting the Ability to Detect Spreadsheet Errors," *Decision Sciences Journal of Innovative Education*, January 2006, pp. 101–122). A comparison of the student demographics was also performed. One school is a

state university in the Western United States, and the other school is a state university in the Eastern United States. The following table contains information regarding the ages of the students:

School	Sample Size	Mean Age	Standard Deviation
Western	93	23.28	6.29
Eastern	135	21.16	1.32

a. Using a 0.01 level of significance, is there evidence of a difference between the variances in age of students at the Western school and at the Eastern school?
b. Discuss the practical implications of the test performed in (a). Address, specifically, the impact equal (or unequal) variances in age has on teaching an undergraduate information systems course.
c. To test for a difference in the mean age of students, is it most appropriate to use the pooled-variance *t* test or the separate-variance *t* test?

The following table contains information regarding the years of spreadsheet usage of the students:

School	Sample Size	Mean Years	Standard Deviation
Western	93	2.6	2.4
Eastern	135	4.0	2.1

d. Using a 0.01 level of significance, is there evidence of a difference between the variances in years of spreadsheet usage of students at the Western school and those of students at the Eastern school?
e. Based on the results of (d), use the most appropriate test to determine, at the 0.01 level of significance, whether there is evidence of a difference in the mean years of spreadsheet usage of students at the Western school and at the Eastern school.

13.29 The data file **Restaurants** contains the ratings for food, decor, service, and the price per person for a sample of 50 restaurants located in an urban area and 50 restaurants located in a suburban area. Completely analyze the differences between urban and suburban restaurants for the variables food rating, decor rating, service rating, and price per person, using $\alpha = 0.05$.

Source: *Data extracted from* Zagat Survey 2006: New York City Restaurants *and* Zagat Survey 2005–2006: Long Island Restaurants.

13.30 A computer information systems professor is interested in studying the amount of time it takes students enrolled in the introduction to computers course to write and run a program in Visual Basic. The professor hires you to analyze the following results (in minutes) from a random sample of nine students (the data are stored in the **VB** file):

$$10 \quad 13 \quad 9 \quad 15 \quad 12 \quad 13 \quad 11 \quad 13 \quad 12$$

a. At the 0.05 level of significance, is there evidence that the population mean amount is greater than 10 minutes? What will you tell the professor?

b. Suppose the professor, when checking her results, realizes that the fourth student needed 51 minutes rather than the recorded 15 minutes to write and run the Visual Basic program. At the 0.05 level of significance, reanalyze the question posed in (a), using the revised data. What will you tell the professor now?

c. The professor is perplexed by these paradoxical results and requests an explanation from you regarding the justification for the difference in your findings in (a) and (b). Discuss.

d. A few days later, the professor calls to tell you that the dilemma is completely resolved. The original number 15 (the fourth data value) was correct, and therefore your findings in (a) are being used in the article she is writing for a computer journal. Now she wants to hire you to compare the results from that group of introduction to computers students against those from a sample of 11 computer majors in order to determine whether there is evidence that computer majors can write a Visual Basic program in less time than introductory students. For the computer majors, the sample mean is 8.5 minutes, and the sample standard deviation is 2.0 minutes. At the 0.05 level of significance, completely analyze these data. What will you tell the professor?

e. A few days later, the professor calls again to tell you that a reviewer of her article wants her to include the p-value for the "correct" result in (a). In addition, the professor inquires about an unequal-variances problem, which the reviewer wants her to discuss in her article. In your own words, discuss the concept of p-value and also describe the unequal-variances problem. Then, determine the p-value in (a) and discuss whether the unequal-variances problem had any meaning in the professor's study.

13.31 An article in *The New York Times* (A. Jennings, "What's Good for a Business Can be Hard on Friends," *The New York Times*, August 4, 2007, pp. C1–C2) reported that according to a poll, the mean number of cellphone calls per month was 290 for 18- to 24-year-olds and 194 for 45- to 54-year-olds, whereas the mean number of text messages per month was 290 for 18- to 24-year-olds and 57 for 45- to 54-year-olds. Suppose that the poll was based on a sample of 100 18- to 24-year-olds and 100 45- to 54-year-olds, and that the standard deviation of the number of cellphone calls per month was 100 for 18- to 24-year-olds and 90 for 45- to

54-year-olds, whereas the standard deviation of the number of text messages per month was 90 for 18- to 24-year-olds and 77 for 45- to 54-year-olds.

Use a level of significance of 0.05.

a. Is there evidence of a difference in the variances of the number of cellphone calls per month for 18- to 24-year-olds and 45- to 54-year-olds?

b. Is there evidence of a difference in the mean number of cellphone calls per month for 18- to 24-year-olds and 45- to 54-year-olds?

c. Construct and interpret a 95% confidence interval estimate of the difference in the mean number of cellphone calls per month for 18- to 24-year-olds and 45- to 54-year-olds.

d. Is there evidence of a difference in the variances of the number of text messages per month for 18- to 24-year-olds and 45- to 54-year-olds?

e. Is there evidence of a difference in the mean number of text messages per month for 18- to 24-year-olds and 45- to 54-year-olds?

f. Construct and interpret a 95% confidence interval estimate of the difference in the mean number of text messages per month for 18- to 24-year-olds and 45- to 54-year-olds.

g. Based on the results of (a) through (f), what conclusions can you make concerning cellphone and text message usage between 18- to 24-year-olds and 45- to 54-year-olds?

13.32 The lengths of life (in hours) of a sample of forty 100-watt lightbulbs produced by manufacturer A and a sample of forty 100-watt lightbulbs produced by manufacturer B are in the file **Bulbs**. Completely analyze the differences between the lengths of life of the bulbs produced by the two manufacturers (use $\alpha = 0.05$).

13.33 A hotel manager is concerned with increasing the return rate for hotel guests. One aspect of first impressions by guests relates to the time it takes to deliver the guest's luggage to the room after check-in to the hotel. A random sample of 20 deliveries on a particular day were selected in Wing A of the hotel, and a random sample of 20 deliveries were selected in Wing B. The results are stored in the file **Luggage**. Analyze the data and determine whether there is a difference in the mean delivery time in the two wings of the hotel. (Use $\alpha = 0.05$.)

13.34 Many companies are finding that customers are using various types of online content before purchasing products (data extracted from K. Spors, "How Are We Doing?" *Wall Street Journal*, November 13, 2006, p. R9). The following results are the percentages of adults and youths who use various sources of online content. Suppose the survey was based on 100 adults and 100 youths.

TYPE OF ONLINE CONTENT	USE ONLINE CONTENT	
	Adult	Youth
Customer product ratings/reviews	71	81
For-sale listings with seller ratings	69	77
For-sale listings without seller ratings	58	65
Online classified ads	57	66
Message-board posts	57	71
Web blogs	55	67
Dating site profiles/personals	49	59
Peer-generated and peer-reference information	49	68
Peer-posted event listings	46	71

For *each type of online content*, determine whether there is a difference between adults and youths in the proportion that uses the type of online content at the 0.05 level of significance.

13.35 The manufacturer of Boston and Vermont asphalt shingles knows that product weight is a major factor in the customer's perception of quality. Moreover, the weight represents the amount of raw materials being used and is therefore very important to the company from a cost standpoint. The last stage of the assembly line packages the shingles before they are placed on wooden pallets. Once a pallet is full (a pallet for most brands holds 16 squares of shingles), it is weighed, and the measurement is recorded. The data file **Pallet** contains the weight (in pounds) from a sample of 368 pallets of Boston shingles and 330 pallets of Vermont shingles. Completely analyze the differences in the weights of the Boston and Vermont shingles, using $\alpha = 0.05$.

13.36 The manufacturer of Boston and Vermont asphalt shingles provides its customers with a 20-year warranty on most of its products. To determine whether a shingle will last as long as the warranty period, accelerated-life testing is conducted at the manufacturing plant. Accelerated-life testing exposes the shingle to the stresses it would be subject to in a lifetime of normal use in a laboratory setting via an experiment that takes only a few minutes to conduct. In this test, a shingle is repeatedly scraped with a brush for a short period of time, and the shingle granules removed by the brushing are weighed (in grams). Shingles that experience low amounts of granule loss are expected to last longer in normal use than shingles that experience high amounts of granule loss. In this situation, a shingle should experience no more than 0.8 grams of granule loss if it is expected to last the length of the warranty period. The data file **Granule** contains a sample of 170 measurements made on the com-

pany's Boston shingles and 140 measurements made on Vermont shingles. Completely analyze the differences in the granule loss of the Boston and Vermont shingles, using $\alpha = 0.05$.

13.37 The quality control director for a clothing manufacturer wants to study the effect of machines on the breaking strength (in pounds) of wool serge material. A batch of the material is cut into square-yard pieces, and these are randomly assigned, 12 each, to the three machines chosen specifically for the experiment. The results (stored in the file **Breakstw**) are shown below:

MACHINE		
I	II	III
115	111	109
115	108	110
119	114	107
117	105	110
114	102	113
114	106	114
109	100	103
110	103	102
106	101	105
112	105	108
115	107	111
111	107	110

a. At the 0.05 level of significance, is there an effect due to machine?
b. Plot the mean breaking strength for each machine.
c. If appropriate, use the Tukey-Kramer procedure to examine differences among machines, using alpha $= 0.05$.
d. What can you conclude about the effects of machines on breaking strength? Explain.

13.38 An operations manager wants to examine the effect of air-jet pressure (in psi) on the breaking strength of yarn. Three different levels of air-jet pressure are to be considered: 30 psi, 40 psi, and 50 psi. A random sample of 18 homogeneous filling yarns are selected from the same batch, and the yarns are randomly assigned, six each, to the three levels of air-jet pressure. The breaking strength scores are in the file **Yarn**.
a. Is there evidence of a significant difference in the variances of the breaking strengths for the three air-jet pressures? (Use $\alpha = 0.05$.)
b. At the 0.05 level of significance, is there evidence of a difference among mean breaking strengths for the three air-jet pressures?

c. If appropriate, use the Tukey-Kramer procedure to determine which air-jet pressures significantly differ with respect to mean breaking strength. (Use $\alpha = 0.05$.)

d. What should the operations manager conclude?

REPORT WRITING EXERCISE

13.39 Referring to the results of Problems 13.35 and 13.36 concerning the weight and granule loss of Boston and Vermont shingles, write a report that summarizes your conclusions.

TEAM PROJECT

The data file **Mutual Funds** contains information regarding nine variables from a sample of 868 mutual funds. The variables are

Category—Type of stocks comprising the mutual fund (small cap, mid cap, or large cap)

Objective—Objective of stocks comprising the mutual fund (growth or value)

Assets—In millions of dollars

Fees—Sales charges (no or yes)

Expense ratio—Ratio of expenses to net assets, in percentage

Return 2006—Twelve-month return in 2006

Three-year return—Annualized return, 2004–2006

Five-year return—Annualized return, 2002–2006

Risk—Risk-of-loss factor of the mutual fund (low, average, or high)

13.40 Completely analyze the difference between mutual funds without fees and mutual funds with fees in terms of 2006 return, three-year return, five-year return, and expense ratio. Write a report summarizing your findings.

13.41 Completely analyze the difference between mutual funds that have a growth objective and mutual funds that have a value objective in terms of 2006 return, three-year return, five-year return, and expense ratio. Write a report summarizing your findings.

13.42 Completely analyze the difference between small cap, mid cap, and large cap mutual funds in terms of 2006 return, three-year return, five-year return, and expense ratio. Write a report summarizing your findings.

13.43 Completely analyze the difference between low-risk, average-risk, and high-risk mutual funds in terms of 2006 return, three-year return, five-year return, and expense ratio. Write a report summarizing your findings.

STUDENT SURVEY DATA BASE

13.44 Problem 1.19 describes a survey of 50 undergraduate students (see the file **Undergradsurvey**). For these data,

a. at the 0.05 level of significance, is there evidence of a difference between males and females in grade point average, expected starting salary, salary expected in five years, age, and spending on textbooks and supplies?

b. at the 0.05 level of significance, is there evidence of a difference between those students who plan to go to graduate school and those who do not plan to go to graduate school in grade point average, expected starting salary, salary expected in five years, age, and spending on textbooks and supplies?

13.45 Problem 1.19 describes a survey of 50 undergraduate students (see the file **Undergradsurvey**).

a. Select a sample of 50 undergraduate students at your school and conduct a similar survey for them.

b. For the data collected in (a), repeat (a) and (b) of Problem 13.42.

c. Compare the results of (b) to those of Problem 13.42.

13.46 Problem 1.20 describes a survey of 40 MBA students (see the file **Gradsurvey**). For these data, at the 0.05 level of significance, is there evidence of a difference between males and females in age, undergraduate grade point average, graduate grade point average, GMAT score, expected salary upon graduation, salary expected in five years, and spending on textbooks and supplies?

13.47 Problem 1.20 describes a survey of 40 MBA students (see the file **Gradsurvey**).

a. Select a sample of 40 graduate students in your MBA program and conduct a similar survey for those students.

b. For the data collected in (a), repeat Problem 13.44.

c. Compare the results of (b) to those of Problem 13.44.

13.48 Problem 1.19 describes a survey of 50 undergraduate students (see the file). For these data at the 0.05 level of significance,

a. is there evidence of a difference, based on academic major, in grade point average, expected starting salary, salary expected in five years, age, and spending on textbooks and supplies?

b. is there evidence of a difference, based on graduate school intention, in grade point average, expected starting salary, salary expected in five years, age, and spending on textbooks and supplies?

c. is there evidence of a difference, based on employment status, in grade point average, expected starting salary, salary expected in five years, age, and spending on textbooks and supplies?

13.49 Problem 1.19 describes a survey of 50 undergraduate students (see the file **Undergradsurvey**).

a. Select a sample of 50 undergraduate students at your school and conduct a similar survey for those students.

b. For the data collected in (a), repeat (a) through (c) of Problem 13.48.

c. Compare the results of (b) to those of Problem 13.46.

13.50 Problem 1.20 describes a survey of 40 MBA students (see the file Gradsurvey). For these data, at the 0.05 level of significance,

a. is there evidence of a difference, based on undergraduate major, in age, undergraduate grade point average, graduate grade point average, GMAT score, expected salary upon graduation, salary expected in five years, and spending on textbooks and supplies?

b. is there evidence of a difference, based on graduate major, in age, undergraduate grade point average, graduate grade point average, GMAT score, expected salary upon graduation, salary expected in five years, and spending on textbooks and supplies?

c. is there evidence of a difference, based on employment status, in age, undergraduate grade point average, graduate grade point average, GMAT score, expected salary upon graduation, salary expected in five years, and spending on textbooks and supplies?

13.51 Problem 1.20 describes a survey of 40 MBA students (see the file Gradsurvey).

a. Select a sample of 40 graduate students in your MBA program and conduct a similar survey for those students.

b. For the data collected in (a), repeat (a) through (c) of Problem 13.50.

c. Compare the results of (b) to those of Problem 13.50.

REFERENCES

1. Conover, W. J., *Practical Nonparametric Statistics*, 3rd ed. (New York: Wiley, 2000).
2. Daniel, W., *Applied Nonparametric Statistics*, 2nd ed. (Boston: Houghton Mifflin, 1990).
3. Hicks, C. R., and K. V. Turner, *Fundamental Concepts in the Design of Experiments*, 5th ed. (New York: Oxford University Press, 1999).
4. *Microsoft Excel 2007* (Redmond, WA: Microsoft Corp., 2007).
5. *Minitab for Windows Version 15* (State College, PA: Minitab, Inc., 2006).
6. Montgomery, D. M., *Design and Analysis of Experiments*, 6th ed. (New York: Wiley, 2005).
7. Neter, J., M. H. Kutner, C. Nachtsheim, and W. Wasserman, *Applied Linear Statistical Models*, 5th ed. (New York: McGraw-Hill-Irwin, 2005).
8. Satterthwaite, F. E., "An Approximate Distribution of Estimates of Variance Components," *Biometrics Bulletin*, 2(1946): 110–114.
9. Snedecor, G. W., and W. G. Cochran, *Statistical Methods*, 8th ed. (Ames, IA: Iowa State University Press, 1989).
10. Winer, B. J., D. R. Brown, and K. M. Michels, *Statistical Principles in Experimental Design*, 3rd ed. (New York: McGraw-Hill, 1989).

CHAPTER 13 EXCEL GUIDE

EG13.1 One-Way Analysis of Variance

One-Way ANOVA *F* Test for Differences Among More Than Two Means

PHStat2 Use **One-Way ANOVA** to perform the one-way ANOVA *F* test. For example, to perform the Figure 13.6 one-way ANOVA for the parachute experiment on page 573, open to the **DATA worksheet** of the **Parachute workbook**. Select **PHStat → Multiple-Sample Tests → One-Way ANOVA**. In the procedure's dialog box (shown below):

1. Enter **0.05** as the **Level of Significance**.
2. Enter **A1:D6** as the **Group Data Cell Range**.
3. Check **First cells contain label**.
4. Enter a **Title**, clear the **Tukey-Kramer Procedure** check box, and click **OK**.

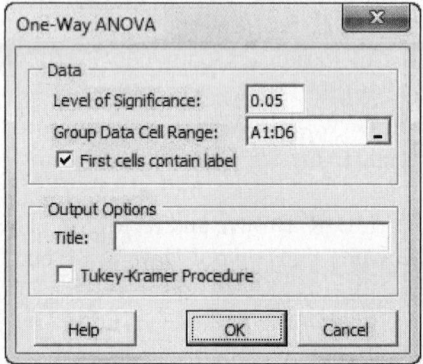

In addition to the worksheet shown in Figure 13.6, this procedure creates an **ASFData worksheet** to hold the data used for the test. See the following *In-Depth Excel* section for a complete description of this worksheet.

In-Depth Excel Use the **COMPUTE worksheet** of the **One-Way ANOVA workbook**, shown in Figure 13.6 on page 573, as a template for performing the one-way ANOVA *F* test. The worksheet performs the test for the Section 13.1 parachute experiment, using the data in the **ASFData worksheet**. The *SSA* in cell B13 is labeled **Between Groups** (not Among Groups) for consistency with the Analysis ToolPak results.

In cell B16, the worksheet uses **DEVSQ(*cell range of data of all groups*)** to compute *SST*, the total variation, and uses an expression in the form *SST* − **DEVSQ(*group 1 data cell range*)** − **DEVSQ(*group 2 data cell range*)** ... − **DEVSQ(*group n data cell range*)** to compute *SSA*, the sum of squares among groups in cell B13. The worksheet also uses the FINV and FDIST worksheet functions to compute

the *F* critical value and the *p*-value in cells F13 and G13, respectively.

Modifying the One-Way ANOVA workbook for use with other problems is a bit more difficult than modifications discussed in the Excel Guide in this and previous chapters, but it can be done using these steps:

1. Paste the data for the problem into the **ASFData worksheet**, overwriting the parachute experiment data.

In the COMPUTE worksheet (see Figure 13.6):

2. Edit the *SST* formula **=DEVSQ(ASFData!A1:D6)** in cell B16 to use the cell range of the new data just pasted into the ASFData worksheet.
3. Edit the cell B13 *SSA* formula so there are as many **DEVSQ(*group n data cell range*)** terms as there are groups.
4. Change the level of significance in cell G17, if necessary.
5. If the problem contains three groups, select **row 8**, right-click, and select **Delete** from the shortcut menu.
6. If the problem contains more than four groups, select **row 8**, right-click, and click **Insert** from the shortcut menu. Repeat this step as many times as necessary.
7. If the problem contains more than four groups, cut and paste the formulas in columns B through E of the new last row of the summary table to the cell range **B8:E8**. (These formulas were in row 8 before you inserted new rows.) For each new row inserted, enter formulas in columns B through E that refer to the next subsequent column in the ASFData worksheet.
8. Adjust table formatting as necessary.

Open to the **COMPUTE_FORMULAS worksheet** of the **One-Way ANOVA workbook** to examine the details of other formulas used in the COMPUTE worksheet. Of note is the expression **COUNTA(ASFData!1:1)**, a novel way to determine the number of groups by counting the number of column heading entries found in row 1 of the ASFData worksheet.

Analysis ToolPak Use **Anova: Single Factor** to perform the one-way ANOVA *F* test. For example, to perform the Figure 13.6 one-way ANOVA for the parachute experiment on page 573, open to the **DATA worksheet** of the **Parachute workbook** and:

1. Select **Data → Data Analysis**.
2. In the Data Analysis dialog box, select **Anova: Single Factor** from the **Analysis Tools** list and then click **OK**.

In the procedure's dialog box (shown below):

3. Enter **A1:D6** as the **Input Range**.

4. Click **Columns**, check **Labels in First Row**, and enter **0.05** as **Alpha**.

5. Click **New Worksheet Ply**.

6. Click **OK**.

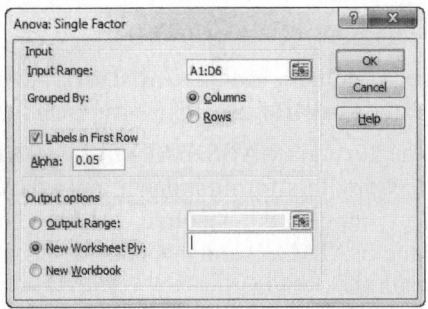

The Analysis ToolPak creates a worksheet that is visually similar to Figure 13.6 but a worksheet that does not include any cell formulas. The ToolPak worksheet also does not contain the level of significance in row 17.

Multiple Comparisons: The Tukey-Kramer Procedure

PHStat2 Use the *PHStat2* instructions for the one-way ANOVA *F* test to perform the Tukey-Kramer procedure, but in step 4, check **Tukey-Kramer Procedure** instead of clearing this check box. The procedure creates a worksheet discussed in the following *In-Depth Excel* section. To complete the worksheet, enter the **Studentized Range *Q* statistic** (look up the value using Table E.6) for the level of significance and the numerator and denominator degrees of freedom that are given in the worksheet.

In-Depth Excel To perform the Tukey-Kramer procedure, first use the *In-Depth Excel* instructions for the one-way ANOVA *F* test. Then open to the appropriate "TK" worksheet in the **One-Way ANOVA workbook** and enter the **Studentized Range *Q* statistic** (look up the value using Table E.6) for the level of significance and the numerator and denominator degrees of freedom that are given in the worksheet.

For example, to create the Tukey-Kramer worksheet for the parachute experiment, use the one-way ANOVA instructions and then open to the **TK4 worksheet**. Enter the **Studentized Range *Q* statistic** (look up the value using Table E.6) in cell B15 for the level of significance and the numerator and denominator degrees of freedom that are given in cells B11 through B13.

Other TK worksheets can be used for problems using three (**TK3**), four (**TK4**), five (**TK5**), six (**TK6**), or seven (**TK7**) groups. When you use either the **TK5**, **TK6**, and

TK7 worksheets, you must also enter the name, sample mean, and sample size for the fifth and, if applicable, sixth and seventh groups. Open to the **TK4_FORMULAS worksheet** of the **One-Way ANOVA workbook** to examine the details of all the formulas found in a TK worksheet.

Analysis ToolPak Adapt the previous *In-Depth Excel* instructions to perform the Tukey-Kramer procedure in conjunction with using the **Anova: Single Factor** procedure. Transfer selected values from the ToolPak results worksheet to one of the TK worksheets in the **One-Way ANOVA workbook**. For example, to perform the Tukey-Kramer procedure for the parachute experiment:

1. Use the **Anova: Single Factor** procedure, as described earlier in this section to create a worksheet that contains ANOVA results for the parachute experiment.

2. Record the name, **sample size** (in the **Count** column), and **sample mean** (in the **Average** column) of each group. Also record the *MSW* value, found in the cell that is the intersection of the **MS** column and **Within Groups** row, and the **denominator degrees of freedom**, found in the cell that is the intersection of the **df** column and **Within Groups** row.

3. Open to the **TK4 worksheet** of the **One-Way ANOVA workbook**.

In the TK4 worksheet:

4. Overwrite the formulas in cell range A5:C8 by entering the name, sample mean, and sample size of each group into that range.

5. Enter **0.05** in cell B11 (the level of significance used in the Anova: Single Factor procedure).

6. Enter **4** in cell B12 as the **Numerator d.f.** (equal to the number of groups).

7. Enter **16** in cell B13 as the **Denominator d.f.**

8. Enter **6.094** in cell B14 as the **MSW**.

9. Enter **4.05** in cell B15 as the **Q Statistic**. (Look up the **Studentized Range *Q* statistic** using Table E.6.)

Levene Test for Homogeneity of Variance

PHStat2 Use **Levene Test** to perform this test. For example, to perform the Figure 13.7 Levene test for the parachute experiment on page 573, open to the **DATA worksheet** of the **Parachute workbook**. Select **PHStat → Multiple-Sample Tests → Levene Test**. In the procedure's dialog box (shown below):

1. Enter **0.05** as the **Level of Significance**.

2. Enter **A1:D6** as the **Sample Data Cell Range**.

3. Check **First cells contain label**.

4. Enter a **Title** and click **OK**.

This procedure works only with data in which the sample sizes of each group are equal. The procedure creates a worksheet that performs the Table 13.3 absolute differences computations (see page 575) as well as the worksheet shown in Figure 13.7 (see page 573). (See the following *In-Depth Excel* section for a description of these worksheets.)

In-Depth Excel Use the **COMPUTE worksheet** of the **Levene workbook**, shown in Figure 13.7 on page 573, as a template for performing the Levene test. The worksheet performs the test using the data in the **AbsDiffs worksheet**, which computes absolute differences based on values in the **DATA worksheet.** These worksheets have been designed for data in which the sample sizes of each group are equal.

The COMPUTE worksheet shares its design with the COMPUTE worksheet of the **One-Way ANOVA workbook.** For other problems in which the absolute differences are already known, paste the absolute differences into the AbsDiffs worksheet. Otherwise, paste the problem data into the DATA worksheet, add formulas to compute the median for each group, and adjust the AbsDiffs worksheet as necessary. For example, for the parachute experiment data, the following steps 1 through 7 were done with the workbook open to the DATA worksheet.

1. Enter the label **Medians** in cell **A7**, the first empty cell in column A.
2. Enter the formula =**MEDIAN(A2:A6)** in cell **A8**. (Cell range A2:A6 contains the data for the first group, Supplier 1.)
3. Copy the cell A8 formula across through column **D**.
4. Open to the **AbsDiffs** worksheet.

In the AbsDiffs worksheet:

5. Enter row 1 column headings **AbsDiff1, AbsDiff2, AbsDiff3**, and **AbsDiff4** in columns A through D.
6. Enter the formula =**ABS(DATA!A2 – DATA!A8)** in cell A2. Copy this formula down through row 6. This formula computes the absolute difference of the first data value (DATA!A2) and the median of the Supplier 1 group data (DATA!A8).
7. Copy the formulas now in cell range A2:A6 across through column D. Absolute differences now appear in the cell range A2:D6.

Analysis ToolPak Use **Anova: Single Factor** with absolute difference data to perform the Levene test. If the absolute differences have not already been computed, use steps 1 through 7 of the preceding *In-Depth Excel* instructions to compute them.

14

Chi-Square Tests

Learning Objectives

In this chapter, you learn:

• How and when to use the chi-square test for contingency tables

Zastol'skiy' victor Leonidovich/Shutterstock.com

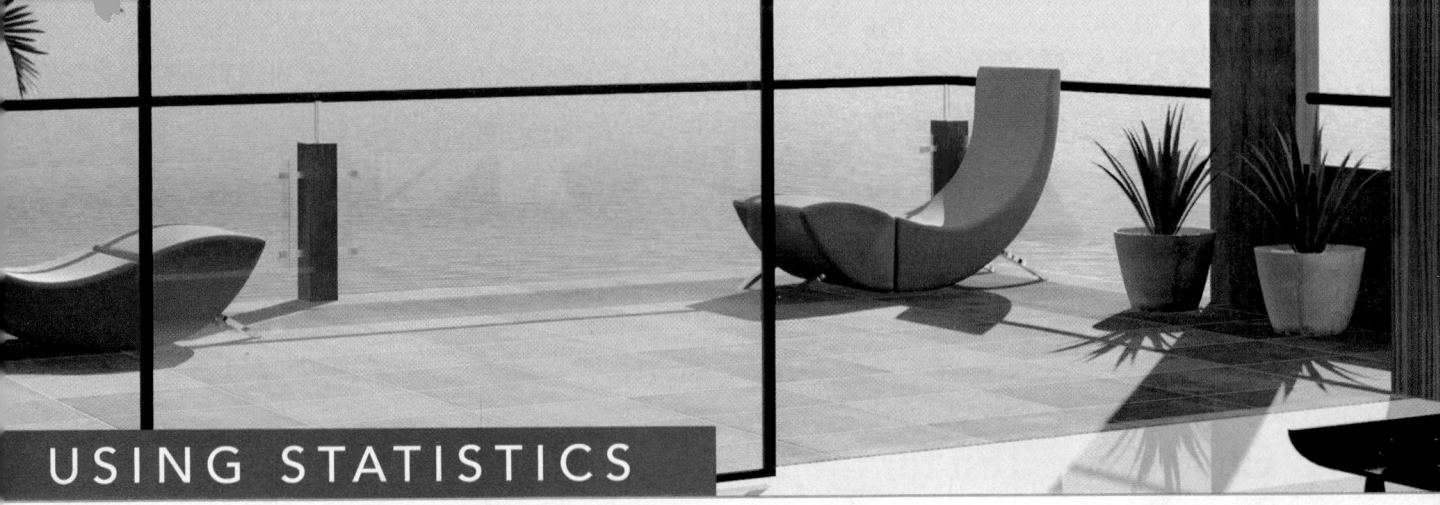

USING STATISTICS

@ T.C. Resort Properties

You are the manager of T.C. Resort Properties, a collection of five upscale hotels located on two tropical islands. Guests who are satisfied with the quality of services during their stay are more likely to return on a future vacation and to recommend the hotel to friends and relatives. You have defined the business objective as improving the return rate at the hotels. To assess the quality of services being provided by your hotels, guests are encouraged to complete a satisfaction survey when they check out. You need to analyze the data from these surveys to determine the overall satisfaction with the services provided, the likelihood that the guests will return to the hotel, and the reasons some guests indicate that they will not return. For example, on one island, T.C. Resort Properties operates the Beachcomber and Windsurfer hotels. Is the perceived quality at the Beachcomber Hotel the same as at the Windsurfer Hotel? If there is a difference, how can you use this information to improve the overall quality of service at T.C. Resort Properties? Furthermore, if guests indicate that they are not planning to return, what are the most common reasons given for this decision? Are the reasons given unique to a certain hotel or common to all hotels operated by T.C. Resort Properties?

KzlKurt/Shutterstock.com

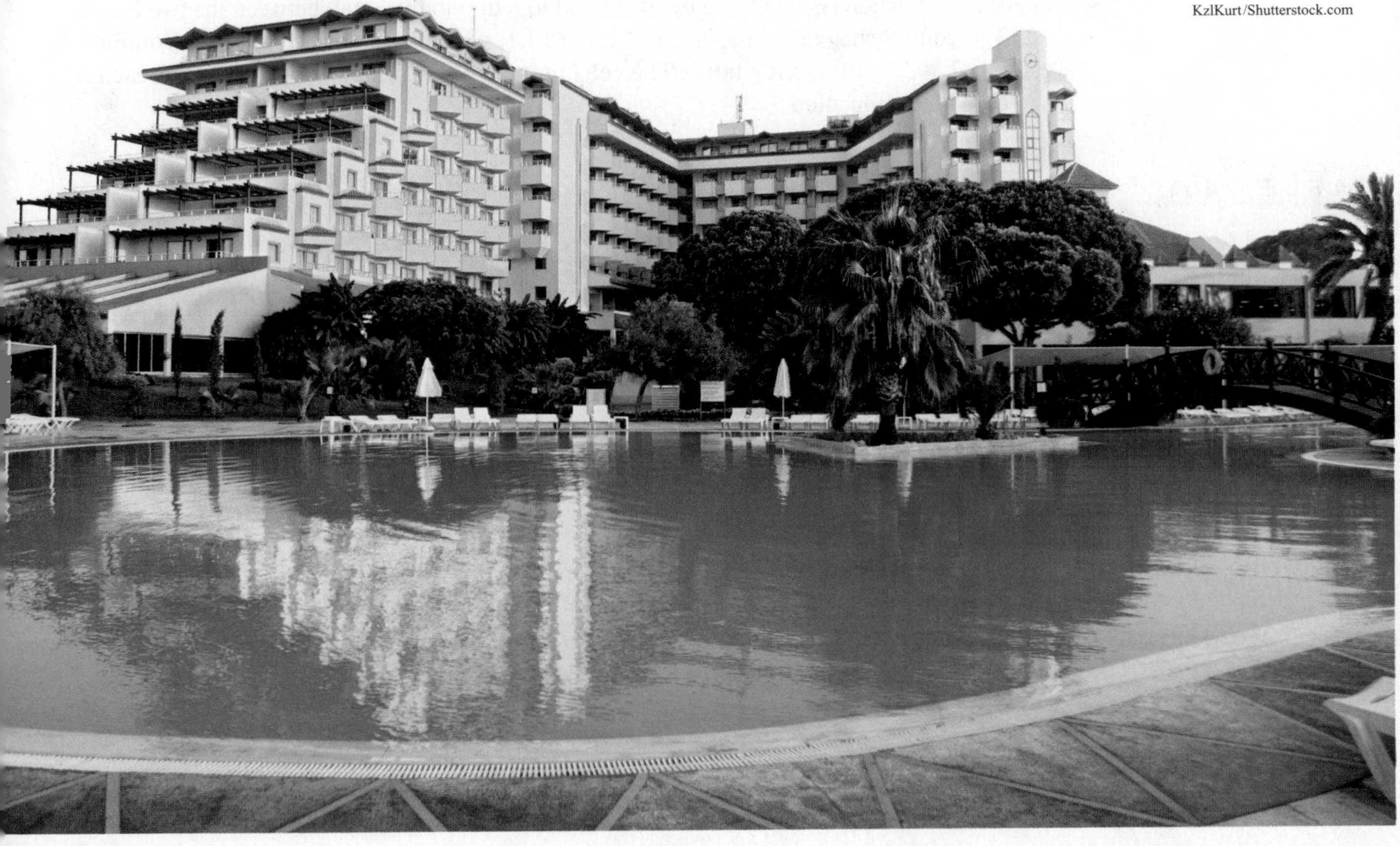

I n the preceding three chapters, you used hypothesis-testing procedures to analyze both numerical and categorical data. Chapter 11 presented some one-sample tests, and Chapters 12 and 13 developed several two-sample tests and discussed the one-way analysis of variance (ANOVA). This chapter extends hypothesis testing to analyze differences between population proportions based on two or more samples, and to test the hypothesis of *independence* in the joint responses to two categorical variables.

14.1 Chi-Square Test for the Difference Between Two Proportions

In Section 12.4, you studied the Z test for the difference between two proportions. In this section, the data are examined from a different perspective. The hypothesis-testing procedure uses a test statistic that is approximated by a chi-square (χ^2) distribution. The results of this χ^2 test are equivalent to those of the Z test described in Section 12.4.

If you are interested in comparing the counts of categorical responses between two independent groups, you can develop a two-way **contingency table** (see Section 3.9) to display the frequency of occurrence of items of interest and items not of interest for each group. In Chapter 5, contingency tables were used to define and study probability.

To illustrate the contingency table, return to the Using Statistics scenario concerning T.C. Resort Properties. On one of the islands, T.C. Resort Properties has two hotels (the Beachcomber and the Windsurfer). You define the business objective as improving the quality of service at T.C. Resort Properties. You collect data from customer satisfaction surveys and focus on the responses to the single question "Are you likely to choose this hotel again?" You organize the results of the survey and determine that 163 of 227 guests at the Beachcomber responded yes to "Are you likely to choose this hotel again?" and 154 of 262 guests at the Windsurfer responded yes to "Are you likely to choose this hotel again?" You want to analyze the results to determine whether, at the 0.05 level of significance, there is evidence of a significant difference in guest satisfaction (as measured by likelihood to return to the hotel) between the two hotels.

The contingency table displayed in Table 14.1, which has two rows and two columns, is called a **2 × 2 contingency table**. The cells in the table indicate the frequency for each row and column combination.

TABLE 14.1

Layout of a 2 × 2 Contingency Table

ROW VARIABLE	COLUMN VARIABLE (GROUP)		
	1	2	Totals
Items of interest	X_1	X_2	X
Items not of interest	$n_1 - X_1$	$n_2 - X_2$	$n - X$
Totals	n_1	n_2	n

where

X_1 = number of items of interest in group 1

X_2 = number of items of interest in group 2

$n_1 - X_1$ = number of items that are not of interest in group 1

$n_2 - X_2$ = number of items that are not of interest in group 2

$X = X_1 + X_2$, the total number of items of interest

$n - X = (n_1 - X_1) + (n_2 - X_2)$, the total number of items that are not of interest

n_1 = sample size in group 1

n_2 = sample size in group 2

$n = n_1 + n_2$ = total sample size

Table 14.2 contains the contingency table for the hotel guest satisfaction study. The contingency table has two rows, indicating whether the guests would return to the hotel or would not return to the hotel, and two columns, one for each hotel. The cells in the table indicate the frequency of each row and column combination. The row totals indicate the number of guests who would return to the hotel and those who would not return to the hotel. The column totals are the sample sizes for each hotel location.

TABLE 14.2

2 × 2 Contingency Table for the Hotel Guest Satisfaction Survey

CHOOSE HOTEL AGAIN?	HOTEL		Total
	Beachcomber	Windsurfer	
Yes	163	154	317
No	64	108	172
Total	227	262	489

To test whether the population proportion of guests who would return to the Beachcomber, π_1, is equal to the population proportion of guests who would return to the Windsurfer, π_2, you can use the χ^2 **test for the difference between two proportions**. To test the null hypothesis that there is no difference between the two population proportions:

$$H_0: \pi_1 = \pi_2$$

against the alternative that the two population proportions are not the same:

$$H_1: \pi_1 \neq \pi_2$$

you use the χ^2_{STAT} test statistic, shown in Equation (14.1).

χ^2 TEST FOR THE DIFFERENCE BETWEEN TWO PROPORTIONS

The χ^2_{STAT} test statistic is equal to the squared difference between the observed and expected frequencies, divided by the expected frequency in each cell of the table, summed over all cells of the table.

$$\chi^2_{STAT} = \sum_{all \text{ cells}} \frac{(f_o - f_e)^2}{f_e} \qquad (14.1)$$

where

f_o = **observed frequency** in a particular cell of a contingency table

f_e = **expected frequency** in a particular cell if the null hypothesis is true

The χ^2_{STAT} test statistic approximately follows a chi-square distribution with 1 degree of freedom.[1]

---

[1]In general, the degrees of freedom in a contingency table are equal to (number of rows − 1) multiplied by (number of columns − 1).

To compute the expected frequency, f_e, in any cell, you need to understand that if the null hypothesis is true, the proportion of items of interest in the two populations will be equal. Then the sample proportions you compute from each of the two groups would differ from each other only by chance. Each would provide an estimate of the common population parameter, π. A statistic that combines these two separate estimates together into one overall estimate of the population parameter provides more information than either of the two separate estimates could provide by itself. This statistic, given by the symbol $\bar{p}$, represents the estimated overall proportion of items of interest for the two groups combined (i.e., the total number of items of interest divided by the total sample size). The complement of $\bar{p}$, $1 - \bar{p}$, represents the estimated overall proportion of items that are not of interest in the two groups. Using the notation presented in Table 14.1 on page 602, Equation (14.2) defines $\bar{p}$.

COMPUTING THE ESTIMATED OVERALL PROPORTION FOR TWO GROUPS

$$\bar{p} = \frac{X_1 + X_2}{n_1 + n_2} = \frac{X}{n} \qquad (14.2)$$

To compute the expected frequency, f_e, for cells that involve items of interest (i.e., the cells in the first row in the contingency table), you multiply the sample size (or column total) for a group by $\bar{p}$. To compute the expected frequency, f_e, for cells that involve items that are not of interest (i.e., the cells in the second row in the contingency table), you multiply the sample size (or column total) for a group by $1 - \bar{p}$.

The χ^2_{STAT} test statistic shown in Equation (14.1) on page 603 approximately follows a **chi-square (χ^2) distribution** (see Table E.4) with 1 degree of freedom. Using a level of significance α, you reject the null hypothesis if the computed χ^2_{STAT} test statistic is greater than χ^2_α, the upper-tail critical value from the χ^2 distribution with 1 degree of freedom. Thus, the decision rule is

Reject H_0 if $\chi^2_{STAT} > \chi^2_\alpha$;

otherwise, do not reject H_0.

Figure 14.1 illustrates the decision rule.

FIGURE 14.1

Regions of rejection and nonrejection when using the chi-square test for the difference between two proportions, with level of significance α

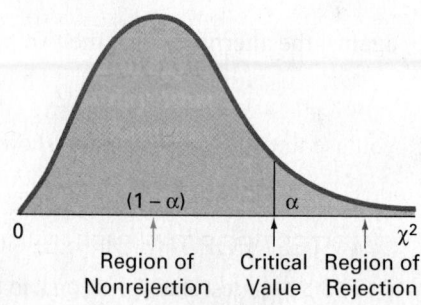

If the null hypothesis is true, the computed χ^2_{STAT} test statistic should be close to zero because the squared difference between what is actually observed in each cell, f_o, and what is theoretically expected, f_e, should be very small. If H_0 is false, then there are differences in the population proportions, and the computed χ^2_{STAT} test statistic is expected to be large. However, what is a large difference in a cell is relative. The same actual difference between f_o and f_e from a cell with a small number of expected frequencies contributes more to the χ^2_{STAT} test statistic than a cell with a large number of expected frequencies.

To illustrate the use of the chi-square test for the difference between two proportions, return to the Using Statistics scenario concerning T.C. Resort Properties on page 601 and the corresponding contingency table displayed in Table 14.2 on page 603. The null hypothesis ($H_0: \pi_1 = \pi_2$) states that there is no difference between the proportion of guests who are likely to choose either of these hotels again. To begin,

$$\bar{p} = \frac{X_1 + X_2}{n_1 + n_2} = \frac{163 + 154}{227 + 262} = \frac{317}{489} = 0.6483$$

$\bar{p}$ is the estimate of the common parameter π, the population proportion of guests who are likely to choose either of these hotels again if the null hypothesis is true. The estimated proportion of guests who are *not* likely to choose these hotels again is the complement of $\bar{p}$, $1 - 0.6483 = 0.3517$. Multiplying these two proportions by the sample size for the Beachcomber Hotel gives the number of guests expected to choose the Beachcomber again and the number not expected to choose this hotel again. In a similar manner, multiplying the two proportions by the Windsurfer Hotel's sample size yields the corresponding expected frequencies for that group.

EXAMPLE 14.1

Computing the Expected Frequencies

Compute the expected frequencies for each of the four cells of Table 14.2 on page 603.

SOLUTION

Yes—Beachcomber: $\bar{p} = 0.6483$ and $n_1 = 227$, so $f_e = 147.16$

Yes—Windsurfer: $\bar{p} = 0.6483$ and $n_2 = 262$, so $f_e = 169.84$

No—Beachcomber: $1 - \bar{p} = 0.3517$ and $n_1 = 227$, so $f_e = 79.84$

No—Windsurfer: $1 - \bar{p} = 0.3517$ and $n_2 = 262$, so $f_e = 92.16$

Table 14.3 presents these expected frequencies next to the corresponding observed frequencies.

TABLE 14.3

Comparing the Observed (f_o) and Expected (f_e) Frequencies

| | HOTEL | | | | |
| | BEACHCOMBER | | WINDSURFER | | |
CHOOSE HOTEL AGAIN?	Observed	Expected	Observed	Expected	Total
Yes	163	147.16	154	169.84	317
No	64	79.84	108	92.16	172
Total	227	227.00	262	262.00	489

To test the null hypothesis that the population proportions are equal:

$$H_0: \pi_1 = \pi_2$$

against the alternative that the population proportions are not equal:

$$H_1: \pi_1 \neq \pi_2$$

you use the observed and expected frequencies from Table 14.3 to compute the χ^2_{STAT} test statistic given by Equation (14.1) on page 603. Table 14.4 presents the calculations.

TABLE 14.4

Computing the χ^2_{STAT} Test Statistic for the Hotel Guest Satisfaction Survey

f_o	f_e	$(f_o - f_e)$	$(f_o - f_e)^2$	$(f_o - f_e)^2/f_e$
163	147.16	15.84	250.91	1.71
154	169.84	−15.84	250.91	1.48
64	79.84	−15.84	250.91	3.14
108	92.16	15.84	250.91	2.72
				9.05

The chi-square (χ^2) distribution is a right-skewed distribution whose shape depends solely on the number of degrees of freedom. You find the critical value for the χ^2 test from Table E.4, a portion of which is presented in Table 14.5.

TABLE 14.5

Finding the Critical Value from the Chi-Square Distribution with 1 Degree of Freedom, Using the 0.05 Level of Significance

	Cumulative Probabilities						
	.005	.01	...	.95	.975	.99	.995
	Upper-Tail Area						
Degrees of Freedom	.995	.99	...	.05	.025	.01	.005
1			...	3.841	5.024	6.635	7.879
2	0.010	0.020	...	5.991	7.378	9.210	10.597
3	0.072	0.115	...	7.815	9.348	11.345	12.838
4	0.207	0.297	...	9.488	11.143	13.277	14.860
5	0.412	0.554	...	11.071	12.833	15.086	16.750

The values in Table 14.5 refer to selected upper-tail areas of the χ^2 distribution. A 2×2 contingency table has $(2 - 1)(2 - 1) = 1$ degree of freedom. Using $\alpha = 0.05$, with 1 degree of freedom, the critical value of χ^2 from Table 14.5 is 3.841. You reject H_0 if the computed χ^2_{STAT} test statistic is greater than 3.841 (see Figure 14.2). Because $\chi^2_{STAT} = 9.05 > 3.841$, you reject H_0. You conclude that the proportion of guests who would return to the Beachcomber is different from the proportion of guests who would return to the Windsurfer.

FIGURE 14.2

Regions of rejection and nonrejection when finding the χ^2 critical value with 1 degree of freedom, at the 0.05 level of significance

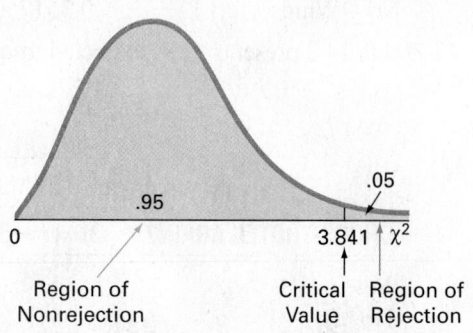

Figure 14.3 shows the results for the Table 14.2 guest satisfaction contingency table on page 603.

FIGURE 14.3

Excel and Minitab chi-square test results for the two-hotel guest satisfaction data

	A	B	C	D	E	F	G
1	Chi-Square Test						
2							
3		Observed Frequencies					
4		Hotel				Calculations	
5	Choose Again?	Beachcomber	Windsurfer	Total		fo-fe	
6	Yes	163	154	317		15.8446	-15.8446
7	No	64	108	172		-15.8446	15.8446
8	Total	227	262	489			
9							
10		Expected Frequencies					
11		Hotel					
12	Choose Again?	Beachcomber	Windsurfer	Total		(fo-fe)^2/fe	
13	Yes	147.1554	169.8446	317		1.7060	1.4781
14	No	79.8446	92.1554	172		3.1442	2.7242
15	Total	227	262	489			
16							
17		Data					
18	Level of Significance	0.05					
19	Number of Rows	2					
20	Number of Columns	2					
21	Degrees of Freedom	1	=(B19 - 1) * (B20 -1)				
22							
23		Results					
24	Critical Value	3.8415	=CHIINV(B18, B21)				
25	Chi-Square Test Statistic	9.0526	=SUM(F13:G14)				
26	p-Value	0.0026	=CHIDIST(B25, B21)				
27	Reject the null hypothesis		=IF(B26 < B18, "Reject the null hypothesis",				
28			"Do not reject the null hypothesis")				
29	Expected frequency assumption						
30	is met.		=IF(OR(B13 < 5, C13 < 5, B14 < 5, C14 < 5),				
			" is violated.", " is met.")				

Chi-Square Test: Beachcomber, Windsurfer

Expected counts are printed below observed counts
Chi-Square contributions are printed below expected counts

	Beachcomber	Windsurfer	Total
1	163	154	317
	147.16	169.84	
	1.706	1.478	
2	64	108	172
	79.84	92.16	
	3.144	2.724	
Total	227	262	489

Chi-Sq = 9.053, DF = 1, P-Value = 0.003

These results include the expected frequencies, χ^2_{STAT}, degrees of freedom, and p-value. The computed χ^2_{STAT} test statistic is 9.0526, which is greater than the critical value of 3.8415 (or the p-value $= 0.0026 < 0.05$), so you reject the null hypothesis that there is no difference in guest satisfaction between the two hotels. The p-value, equal to 0.0026, is the probability of observing sample proportions as different as or more different from the actual difference between the Beachcomber and Windsurfer $(0.718 - 0.588 = 0.13)$ observed in the sample data, if the population proportions for the Beachcomber and Windsurfer hotels are equal. Thus, there is strong evidence to conclude that the two hotels are significantly different with respect to guest satisfaction, as measured by whether a guest is likely to return to the hotel again. From Table 14.3 on page 615 you can see that a greater proportion of guests are likely to return to the Beachcomber than to the Windsurfer.

For the χ^2 test to give accurate results for a 2×2 table, you must assume that each expected frequency is at least 5. If this assumption is not satisfied, you can use alternative procedures, such as Fisher's exact test (see references 1, 2, and 4).

In the hotel guest satisfaction survey, both the Z test based on the standardized normal distribution (see Section 12.4) and the χ^2 test based on the chi-square distribution lead to the same conclusion. You can explain this result by the interrelationship between the standardized normal distribution and a chi-square distribution with 1 degree of freedom. For such situations, the χ^2_{STAT} test statistic is the square of the Z_{STAT} test statistic. For instance, in the guest satisfaction study, the computed Z_{STAT} test statistic is $+3.0088$ and the computed χ^2_{STAT} test statistic is 9.0526. Except for rounding differences, this 9.0526 value is the square of $+3.0088$ [i.e., $(+3.0088)^2 \cong 9.0526$]. Also, if you compare the critical values of the test statistics from the two distributions, at the 0.05 level of significance, the χ^2 value of 3.841 with 1 degree of freedom is the square of the Z value of ±1.96. Furthermore, the p-values for both tests are equal. Therefore, when testing the null hypothesis of equality of proportions:

$$H_0: \pi_1 = \pi_2$$

against the alternative that the population proportions are not equal:

$$H_1: \pi_1 \neq \pi_2$$

the Z test and the χ^2 test are equivalent.

If you are interested in determining whether there is evidence of a *directional* difference, such as $\pi_1 > \pi_2$, you must use the Z test, with the entire rejection region located in one tail of the standardized normal distribution.

In Section 14.2, the χ^2 test is extended to make comparisons and evaluate differences between the proportions among more than two groups. However, you cannot use the Z test if there are more than two groups.

FIGURE 14.4

Casio calculator FX-9750GII result for the hotel guest satisfaction data

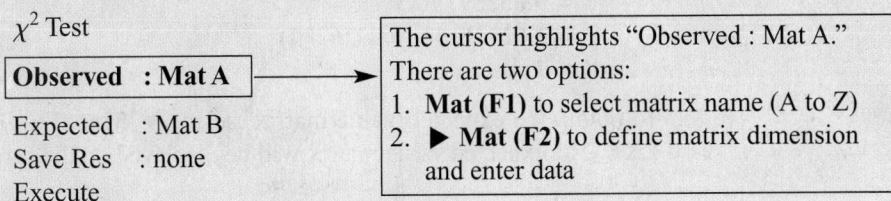

Solution: Use the Casio calculator FX-9750GII.

Press **MENU** and select **STAT**, **TEST** (F3), and **CHI** (F3).
Under option **CHI**, select **2WAY** (F2).

You will see the following on the screen:

χ^2 Test

Observed	: Mat A

Expected : Mat B
Save Res : none
Execute

The cursor highlights "Observed : Mat A."
There are two options:
1. **Mat (F1)** to select matrix name (A to Z)
2. ▶ **Mat (F2)** to define matrix dimension and enter data

To define dimension and enter data, select ▶ Mat (F2). You will see the following on the screen:

Matrx
Mat A   : 2 × 2   **Press DIM(F3) to define or**
Mat B   : None   **change dimension.**
Mat C   : None
Mat D   : None
Mar E   : None
Mat F   : None

Dimension : m × n
m: 2   EXE
n: 2   EXE

After you have entered the dimension for **Mat A**, you will see the **2 × 2 matrix A** appear on the screen. Use this screen to input your data.

A	1	2
1	163 EXE	154 EXE
2	64 EXE	108 EXE

After you enter your data in Matrix A, press **EXIT** two times until you see the following on the screen:

χ^2 Test

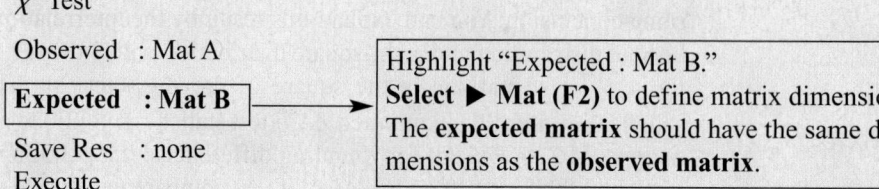

Observed : Mat A

| **Expected   : Mat B** |

Highlight "Expected : Mat B."
Select ▶ Mat (F2) to define matrix dimension. The **expected matrix** should have the same dimensions as the **observed matrix**.

Save Res   : none
Execute

To define dimension, select ▶ Mat (F2). You will see the following on the screen:

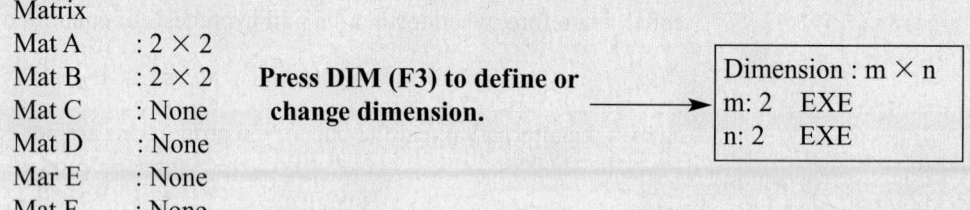

Matrix
Mat A   : 2 × 2
Mat B   : 2 × 2   **Press DIM (F3) to define or**
Mat C   : None   **change dimension.**
Mat D   : None
Mar E   : None
Mat F   : None

Dimension : m × n
m: 2   EXE
n: 2   EXE

You will see **2 × 2 Matrix B**. You are not required to enter any values; the calculator will give you the expected values.

Now press **EXIT** two times until you see the following on the screen:

χ^2 Test
Observed : Mat A
Expected : Mat B
Save Res   : None
Execute

At this point, press either **EXE** or **F1** (Calc).
The calculator will now show the results:

χ^2 **Test**

$\chi^2 = 9.0525978$
$p = 2.6232\text{E-}03\ (0.0026232)$
$df = 1$

To obtain the expected value matrix, select ▶ **Mat** (F6), highlight **MAT B**, and press **EXE**. The expected value matrix will be displayed on the screen as follows:

Ans	1	2
1	14715.54	16984.45
2	798.446	921.554

Problems for Section 14.1

LEARNING THE BASICS

14.1 Determine the critical value of χ^2 with 1 degree of freedom in each of the following circumstances:
a. $\alpha = 0.01$
b. $\alpha = 0.005$
c. $\alpha = 0.10$

14.2 Determine the critical value of χ^2 with 1 degree of freedom in each of the following circumstances:
a. $\alpha = 0.05$
b. $\alpha = 0.025$
c. $\alpha = 0.01$

14.3 Use the following contingency table:

	A	B	Total
1	20	30	50
2	30	45	75
Total	50	75	125

a. Compute the expected frequency for each cell.
b. Compare the observed and expected frequencies for each cell.
c. Compute χ^2_{STAT}. Is it significant at $\alpha = 0.05$?

14.4 Use the following contingency table:

	A	B	Total
1	20	30	50
2	30	20	50
Total	50	50	100

a. Compute the expected frequency for each cell.
b. Compute χ^2_{STAT}. Is it significant at $\alpha = 0.05$?

APPLYING THE CONCEPTS

14.5 A survey of 1,085 adults asked, "Do you enjoy shopping for clothing for yourself?" The results (data extracted from "Split Decision on Clothes Shopping," *USA Today*, January 28, 2011, p. 1B) indicated that 51% of the females enjoyed shopping for clothing for themselves as compared to 44% of the males. The sample sizes of males and females was not provided. Suppose that the results were as shown in the following table:

ENJOY SHOPPING FOR CLOTHING	GENDER		
	Male	Female	Total
Yes	238	276	514
No	304	267	571
Total	542	543	1,085

a. Is there evidence of a significant difference between the proportion of males and females who enjoy shopping for clothing for themselves at the 0.01 level of significance?
b. Determine the *p*-value in (a) and interpret its meaning.
c. What are your answers to (a) and (b) if 218 males enjoyed shopping for clothing and 324 did not?
d. Compare the results of (a) through (c) to those of Problem 10.29 (a), (b), and (d) on page 405.

14.6 Has the ease of removing your name from an e-mail list changed? A study of 100 large online retailers revealed the following:

YEAR	NEED THREE OR MORE CLICKS TO BE REMOVED	
	Yes	No
2009	39	61
2008	7	93

Source: Data extracted from "More Clicks to Escape an E-mail List," *The New York Times*, March 29, 2010, p. B2.

a. Set up the null and alternative hypotheses to try to determine whether the effort it takes to be removed from an e-mail list has changed.
b. Conduct the hypothesis test defined in (a), using the 0.05 level of significance.
c. Why shouldn't you compare the results in (a) to those of Problem 10.30 (b) on page 406?

14.7 A survey was conducted of 665 consumer magazines on the practices of their websites. Of these, 273 magazines reported that online-only content is copy-edited as rigorously as print content; 379 reported that online-only content is fact-checked as rigorously as print content. (Data extracted from S. Clifford, "Columbia Survey Finds a Slack Editing Process of Magazine Web Sites," *The New York Times*, March 1, 2010, p. B6.) Suppose that a sample of 500 newspapers revealed that 252 reported that online-only content is copy-edited as rigorously as print content and 296 reported that online-only content is fact-checked as rigorously as print content.

a. At the 0.05 level of significance, is there evidence of a difference between consumer magazines and newspapers in the proportion of online-only content that is copy-edited as rigorously as print content?
b. Determine the *p*-value in (a) and interpret its meaning.
c. At the 0.05 level of significance, is there evidence of a difference between consumer magazines and newspapers in the proportion of online-only content that is fact-checked as rigorously as print content?
d. Determine the *p*-value in (c) and interpret its meaning.

✓ SELF Test **14.8** Do people of different age groups differ in their response to e-mail messages? A survey by the Center for the Digital Future of the University of Southern California reported that 70.7% of users over age 70 believe that e-mail messages should be answered quickly, as compared to 53.6% of users 12 to 50 years old. (Data extracted from A. Mindlin, "Older E-mail Users Favor Fast Replies," *The New York Times*, July 14, 2008, p. B3.) Suppose that the survey was based on 1,000 users over age 70 and 1,000 users 12 to 50 years old.

a. At the 0.01 level of significance, is there evidence of a significant difference between the two age groups in their belief that e-mail messages should be answered quickly?
b. Determine the *p*-value in (a) and interpret its meaning.
c. Compare the results of (a) and (b) to those of Problem 10.32 on page 406.

14.9 Different age groups use different media sources for news. A study on this issue explored the use of cell phones for accessing news. The study reported that 47% of users under age 50 and 15% of users age 50 and over accessed news on their cell phones. (Data extracted from "Cellphone Users Who Access News on Their Phones," *USA Today*,

March 1, 2010, p. 1A.) Suppose that the survey consisted of 1,000 users under age 50, of whom 470 accessed news on their cell phones, and 891 users age 50 and over, of whom 134 accessed news on their cell phones.

a. Construct a 2 × 2 contingency table.
b. Is there evidence of a significant difference in the proportion that accessed the news on their cell phones between users under age 50 and users 50 years and older? (Use $\alpha = 0.05$.)
c. Determine the *p*-value in (b) and interpret its meaning.
d. Compare the results of (b) and (c) to those of Problem 10.35 (a) and (b) on page 411.

14.10 How do Americans feel about ads on websites? A survey of 1,000 adult Internet users found that 670 opposed ads on websites. (Data extracted from S. Clifford, "Tracked for Ads? Many Americans Say No Thanks," *The New York Times*, September 30, 2009, p. B3.) Suppose that a survey of 1,000 Internet users age 12–17 found that 510 opposed ads on websites.

a. At the 0.05 level of significance, is there evidence of a difference between adult Internet users and Internet users age 12–17 in the proportion who oppose ads?
b. Determine the *p*-value in (a) and interpret its meaning.

14.2 Chi-Square Test for Differences Among More Than Two Proportions

In this section, the χ^2 test is extended to compare more than two independent populations. The letter c is used to represent the number of independent populations under consideration. Thus, the contingency table now has two rows and c columns. To test the null hypothesis that there are no differences among the c population proportions:

$$H_0: \pi_1 = \pi_2 = \cdots = \pi_c$$

against the alternative that not all the c population proportions are equal:

$$H_1: \text{Not all } \pi_j \text{ are equal (where } j = 1, 2, \ldots, c)$$

you use Equation (14.1) on page 603:

$$\chi^2_{STAT} = \sum_{all\ cells} \frac{(f_o - f_e)^2}{f_e}$$

where

f_o = observed frequency in a particular cell of a 2 × c contingency table
f_e = expected frequency in a particular cell if the null hypothesis is true

If the null hypothesis is true and the proportions are equal across all c populations, the c sample proportions should differ only by chance. In such a situation, a statistic that combines these c separate estimates into one overall estimate of the population proportion, π, provides more information than any one of the c separate estimates alone. To expand on Equation (14.2) on page 604, the statistic $\bar{p}$ in Equation (14.3) represents the estimated overall proportion for all c groups combined.

COMPUTING THE ESTIMATED OVERALL PROPORTION FOR c GROUPS

$$\bar{p} = \frac{X_1 + X_2 + \cdots + X_c}{n_1 + n_2 + \cdots + n_c} = \frac{X}{n} \tag{14.3}$$

To compute the expected frequency, f_e, for each cell in the first row in the contingency table, multiply each sample size (or column total) by $\bar{p}$. To compute the expected frequency, f_e, for each cell in the second row in the contingency table, multiply each sample size (or column total) by $(1 - \bar{p})$. The test statistic shown in Equation (14.1) on page 603 approximately follows a chi-square distribution, with degrees of freedom equal to the number of rows in the contingency table minus 1, multiplied by the number of columns in the table minus 1. For a **2 × c contingency table**, there are $c - 1$ degrees of freedom:

$$\text{Degrees of freedom} = (2 - 1)(c - 1) = c - 1$$

Using the level of significance α, you reject the null hypothesis if the computed χ^2_{STAT} test statistic is greater than χ^2_α, the upper-tail critical value from a chi-square distribution with $c - 1$ degrees of freedom. Therefore, the decision rule is

$$\text{Reject } H_0 \text{ if } \chi^2_{STAT} > \chi^2_\alpha;$$

otherwise, do not reject H_0.

Figure 14.5 illustrates this decision rule.

FIGURE 14.5

Regions of rejection and nonrejection when testing for differences among c proportions using the χ^2 test

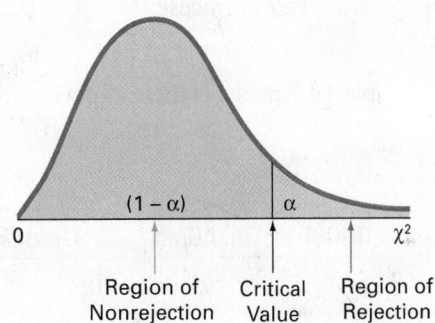

To illustrate the χ^2 test for equality of proportions when there are more than two groups, return to the Using Statistics scenario on page 601 concerning T.C. Resort Properties. Once again, you define the business objective as improving the quality of service, but this time, three hotels located on a different island are to be surveyed. Data are collected from customer satisfaction surveys at these three hotels. You organize the responses into the contingency table shown in Table 14.6.

TABLE 14.6

2 × 3 Contingency Table for Guest Satisfaction Survey

	HOTEL			
CHOOSE HOTEL AGAIN?	**Golden Palm**	**Palm Royale**	**Palm Princess**	**Total**
Yes	128	199	186	513
No	88	33	66	187
Total	216	232	252	700

Because the null hypothesis states that there are no differences among the three hotels in the proportion of guests who would likely return again, you use Equation (14.3) to calculate an estimate of π, the population proportion of guests who would likely return again:

$$\bar{p} = \frac{X_1 + X_2 + \cdots + X_c}{n_1 + n_2 + \cdots + n_c} = \frac{X}{n}$$

$$= \frac{(128 + 199 + 186)}{(216 + 232 + 252)} = \frac{513}{700}$$

$$= 0.733$$

The estimated overall proportion of guests who would *not* be likely to return again is the complement, $(1 - \bar{p})$, or 0.267. Multiplying these two proportions by the sample size for each hotel yields the expected number of guests who would and would not likely return.

EXAMPLE 14.2

Computing the Expected Frequencies

Compute the expected frequencies for each of the six cells in Table 14.6.

SOLUTION

Yes—Golden Palm: $\bar{p} = 0.733$ and $n_1 = 216$, so $f_e = 158.30$

Yes—Palm Royale: $\bar{p} = 0.733$ and $n_2 = 232$, so $f_e = 170.02$

Yes—Palm Princess: $\bar{p} = 0.733$ and $n_3 = 252$, so $f_e = 184.68$

No—Golden Palm: $1 - \bar{p} = 0.267$ and $n_1 = 216$, so $f_e = 57.70$

No—Palm Royale: $1 - \bar{p} = 0.267$ and $n_2 = 232$, so $f_e = 61.98$

No—Palm Princess: $1 - \bar{p} = 0.267$ and $n_3 = 252$, so $f_e = 67.32$

Table 14.7 presents these expected frequencies.

TABLE 14.7

Contingency Table of Expected Frequencies from a Guest Satisfaction Survey of Three Hotels

	HOTEL			
CHOOSE HOTEL AGAIN?	**Golden Palm**	**Palm Royale**	**Palm Princess**	**Total**
Yes	158.30	170.02	184.68	513
No	57.70	61.98	67.32	187
Total	216.00	232.00	252.00	700

To test the null hypothesis that the proportions are equal:

$$H_0: \pi_1 = \pi_2 = \pi_3$$

against the alternative that not all three proportions are equal:

$$H_1: \text{Not all } \pi_j \text{ are equal (where } j = 1, 2, 3)$$

you use the observed frequencies from Table 14.6 and the expected frequencies from Table 14.7 to compute the χ^2_{STAT} test statistic [given by Equation (14.1) on page 603]. Table 14.8 presents the calculations.

TABLE 14.8

Computing the χ^2_{STAT} Test Statistic for the Guest Satisfaction Survey of Three Hotels

f_o	f_e	$(f_o - f_e)$	$(f_o - f_e)^2$	$(f_o - f_e)^2/f_e$
128	158.30	−30.30	918.09	5.80
199	170.02	28.98	839.84	4.94
186	184.68	1.32	1.74	0.01
88	57.70	30.30	918.09	15.91
33	61.98	−28.98	839.84	13.55
66	67.32	−1.32	1.74	0.02
				40.23

You use Table E.4 to find the critical value of the χ^2 test statistic. In the guest satisfaction survey, because there are three hotels, there are $(2 - 1)(3 - 1) = 2$ degrees of freedom. Using $\alpha = 0.05$, the χ^2 critical value with 2 degrees of freedom is 5.991 (see Figure 14.6). Because the computed χ^2_{STAT} test statistic is 40.23, which is greater than this critical value, you reject the null hypothesis.

FIGURE 14.6

Regions of rejection and nonrejection when testing for differences in three proportions at the 0.05 level of significance, with 2 degrees of freedom

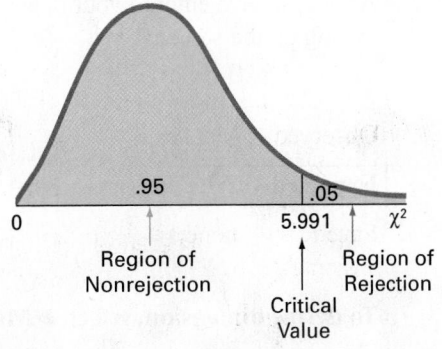

Figure 14.7 shows the results for this problem. The results also report the p-value. Because the p-value is (approximately) 0.0000, less than $\alpha = 0.05$, you reject the null hypothesis. Further, this p-value indicates that there is virtually no chance that there will be differences this large or larger among the three sample proportions, if the population proportions for the three hotels are equal. Thus, there is sufficient evidence to conclude that the hotel properties are different with respect to the proportion of guests who are likely to return.

FIGURE 14.7

Casio calculator result for the guest satisfaction data of Table 14.6

Solution: Use the Casio calculator FX-9750GII.

Press **MENU** and select **STAT**, **TEST** (F3), and **CHI** (F3). Under option **CHI**, select **2WAY** (F2).

You will see the following on the screen:

χ^2 Test

Observed   : Mat A

Expected   : Mat B
Save Res   : none
Execute

The cursor highlights "Observed : Mat A." There are two options:
1. **Mat (F1)** to select matrix name (A to Z)
2. ▶ **Mat (F2)** to define matrix dimension and enter data

To define dimension and enter data, select ▶ Mat (F2). You will see the following on the screen:

Matrx

Mat A : 2 × 3   **Press DIM(F3) to define or**

Mat B : None   **change dimension.**

Mat C : None

Mat D : None

Mar E : None

Mat F : None

| Dimension : m × n |
| m: 2   EXE |
| n: 3   EXE |

After you have entered the dimension for **Mat A**, you will see the **2 × 2 matrix A** appear on the screen. Use this screen to input your data.

A	1	2	3
1	128 EXE	199 EXE	186 EXE
2	88 EXE	33 EXE	66 EXE

After you have entered your data in Matrix A, press **EXIT** two times until you see the following on the screen:

χ^2 Test

Observed : Mat A

Expected : Mat B ⟶

Save Res : none

Execute

> Highlight "Expected : Mat B."
> **Select ▶ Mat (F2) to define matrix dimension.**
> The **expected matrix** should have the same dimensions as the **observed matrix**.

To define dimension, select ▶Mat (F2). You will see the following on the screen:

Matrix

Mat A : 2 × 3

Mat B : 2 × 3   **Press DIM (F3) to define or**

Mat C : None   **change dimension.**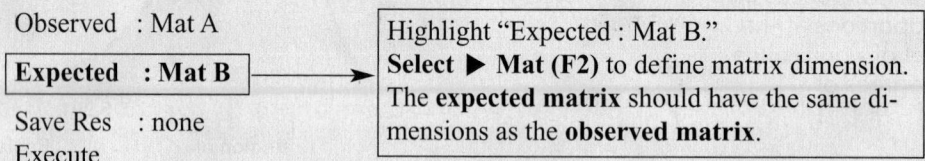

Mat D : None

Mar E : None

Mat F : None

| Dimension : m × n |
| m: 2   EXE |
| n: 3   EXE |

You will see **2 × 3 Matrix B**. You are not required to enter any values; the calculator will give you the expected values.

Now press **EXIT** two times until you see the following on the screen:

χ^2 Test

Observed : Mat A

Expected : Mat B

Save Res : none

Execute

At this point, press either **EXE** or **F1** (Calc).

The calculator will now show the results:

χ^2 **Test**

$\chi^2 = 40.2283986$

$p = 1.8387E\text{-}09 \ (0.0000000018387)$

$df = 2$

To obtain the expected value matrix, select ▶Mat (F6), highlight **MAT B**, and press **EXE**. The calculator will display the expected value matrix displayed on the screen as follows:

Ans	1	2	3
1	15829.71	17002.29	184.68
2	577.029	619.771	67.32

To find the critical value of χ^2, do the following:

To find the critical value of χ^2, use the Casio Calculator FX-9750GII and follow these calculator steps:

Note: The FX-9750G Plus does not have this option; therefore, you have to use the Table A4 in the Appendix.

From the **Main Menu**, select the following:

STAT, **F5** (DIST), **F3** (CHI), and **F3**(InvC). The enter the following items:

Inverse χ^2
Data	: **F2**(Var) ▼	
Area	: **0.05**	
df	: **2 EXE**	[Note: df=(2-1)(3-1)=2]
Save Res	: None	
Execute		

Now press **EXE** or **F1**(CALC).

The calculator will now show the results:

Inverse χ^2
x-Inv = 5.99146455

The critical value is used to define the rejection and nonrejection regions, as shown in the diagram below.

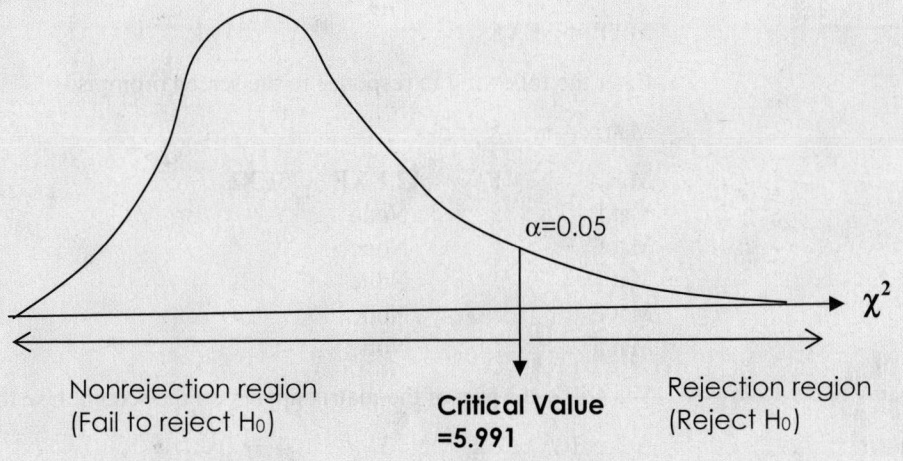

For the χ^2 test to give accurate results when dealing with $2 \times c$ contingency tables, all expected frequencies must be large. The definition of "large" has led to research among statisticians. Some statisticians (see reference 5) have found that the test gives accurate results as long as all expected frequencies are at least 0.5. Other statisticians, more conservative in their approach, believe that no more than 20% of the cells should contain expected frequencies less than 5, and no cells should have expected frequencies less than 1 (see reference 3). As a reasonable compromise between these points of view, to assure the validity of the test, you should make sure that each expected frequency is at least 5. To do this, you may need to collapse two or more low-expected-frequency categories into one category in the contingency table before performing the test. If combining categories is undesirable, you can use one of the available alternative procedures (see references 1, 2, and 6).

CALCULATOR LESSON 16A

CFX-9850GB CALCULATOR

Lesson 16A—Chi-Square Test for Differences Among More Than Two Proportions

EXAMPLE 14.3

(A) Lesson 16A—Chi-Square Test for Differences among more than two proportions

Example

Five printers of different brands are tested using the same paper and graphic output. The results are judged as conforming or nonconforming. At a 5% level of significance, test for a difference in proportion of nonconforming pages. The results are as follows.

TABLE 14.9

	Number of Pages Printed				
	Brand of the Printer				
Classification	A	B	C	D	E
Nonconforming	13	10	16	9	12
Conforming	187	190	184	191	188

Solution: From the **Main Menu**, select the folllowing:

MAT and **EXE**

Enter the following in response to the screen prompts.

Matrix

Mat A	:	**2 EXE**	**5EXE**
Mat B	:	None	
Mat C	:	None	
Mat D	:	None	
Mat E	:	None	
Mat F	:	None	

You will see a part of the matrix appear on the screen. Use this screen to input your data.

A	1	2	3	4 →
1	0	0	0	0
2	0	0	0	0

Enter the data values into the appropriate cells. To begin entering your data, use the arrow key to highlight the cell 1,1 (top left corner of the cell). Type 13 and press **EXE.** The cursor will automatically scroll to the next cell.

A	1	2	3	4	5
1	13 EXE	10 EXE	16 EXE	9 EXE	12 EXE
2	187 EXE	190 EXE	184 EXE	191 EXE	188 EXE

After you enter your data in Matrix A, press **MENU** and select the following:

STAT, EXE, TEST (F3), and **CHI** (F3). Then enter the following items:

χ^2 Test
Observed: Mat A (F1)
Execute
Now press **EXE**.

The calculator will now show the results:

χ^2 Test
$\qquad \chi^2 = 2.6595$
$\qquad p = 0.6163$
$\qquad df = 2$
Expected = Mat Ans

We may obtain the expected value matrix by making the following selection:

MENU, MAT, and **EXE**

Use the cursor ▼ arrow to scroll down to the bottom of the matrix list until the cursor is on;

Mat Ans   : 2 x 5
EXE

The expected value matrix will be displayed on the screen as follows:

Ans	1	2	3	4	5
1	12	12	12	12	12
2	188	188	188	188	188

Conclusion:

Since p-value $= 0.6163$ is greater than α, we do not reject H_0.

The statistical evidence does not indicate that we may conclude that there is a difference in the proportion of nonconforming pages produced by the printers.

CALCULATOR LESSON 16B

**FX-9850GII
CALCULATOR**

Lesson 16B—Chi-Square Test for Differences Among More Than Two Proportions

EXAMPLE 14.4

(A) Lesson 16B—Chi-Square Test for Differences among more than two Proportions

Example.

Five printers of different brands are tested using the same paper and graphic output. The results are judged as conforming or nonconforming. At a 5% level of significance, test for a difference in proportion of nonconforming pages. The results are as followed.

TABLE 14.10

	Number of Pages Printed				
	Brand of the Printer				
Classification	**A**	**B**	**C**	**D**	**E**
Nonconforming	13	10	16	9	12
Conforming	187	190	184	191	188

Solution:

Press **MENU** and select **STAT**, **TEST** (F3), and **CHI** (F3).
Under option **CHI**, select **2WAY** (F2).

You will see the following on the screen:

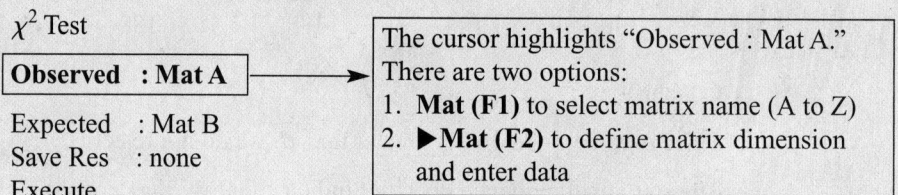

χ^2 Test

Observed : Mat A

Expected : Mat B
Save Res : none
Execute

The cursor highlights "Observed : Mat A."
There are two options:
1. **Mat (F1)** to select matrix name (A to Z)
2. **▶Mat (F2)** to define matrix dimension and enter data

To define dimension and enter data, select ▶Mat (F2). You will see the following on the screen:

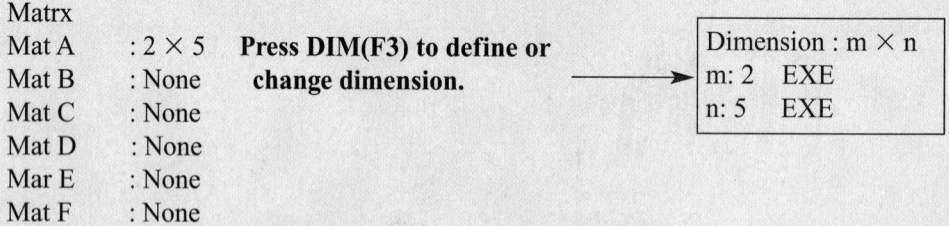

Matrx
Mat A   : 2 × 5   **Press DIM(F3) to define or**
Mat B   : None   **change dimension.**
Mat C   : None
Mat D   : None
Mar E   : None
Mat F   : None

Dimension : m × n
m: 2   EXE
n: 5   EXE

After you have entered the dimension for **Mat A**, you will see the **2 × 5 matrix A** appears on the screen. Use this screen to input your data. Enter the data values into the appropriate cells. To begin entering your data, use the arrow key to highlight the cell 1,1 (top left corner of the cell). Type 13 and press **EXE**. The cursor will automatically scroll to the next cell.

A	1	2	3	4→	5
1	13 EXE	10 EXE	16 EXE	9 EXE	12 EXE
2	187 EXE	190 EXE	184 EXE	191 EXE	188 EXE

After you enter your data in Matrix A, press **EXIT** two times until you see the following on the screen:

χ^2 Test

Observed   : Mat A

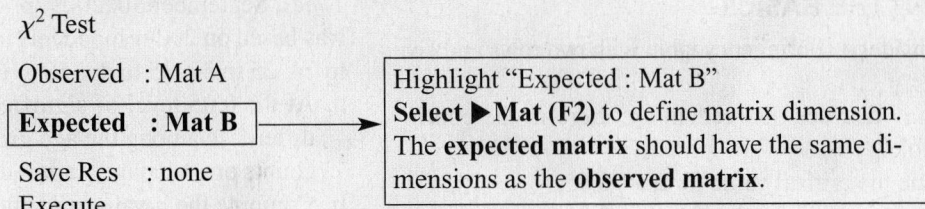

Expected   : Mat B

Save Res   : none
Execute

Highlight "Expected : Mat B"
Select ▶Mat (F2) to define matrix dimension.
The **expected matrix** should have the same dimensions as the **observed matrix**.

To define dimension, select ▶Mat (F2). You will see the following on the screen:

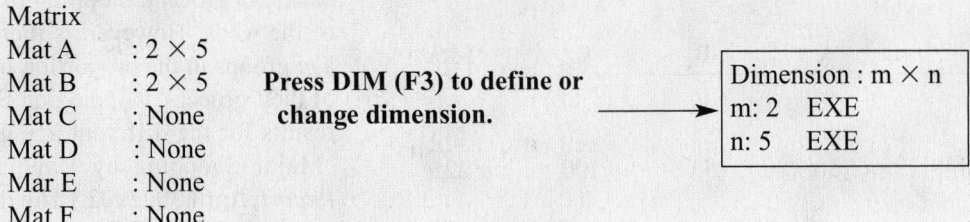

Matrix
Mat A   : 2 × 5
Mat B   : 2 × 5
Mat C   : None
Mat D   : None
Mar E   : None
Mat F   : None

Press DIM (F3) to define or change dimension.

Dimension : m × n
m: 2   EXE
n: 5   EXE

You will see **2 × 5 Matrix B**. You are not required to enter any values; the calculator will give you the expected values.

Now press **EXIT** two times until you see the following on the screen:

χ^2 Test
Observed   : Mat A
Expected   : Mat B
Save Res   : none
Execute

At this point, press either **EXE** or **F1** (Calc).
The calculator will now show the results:

χ^2 Test

$\chi^2 = 2.65957447$
$p = 0.61630686$
$df = 4$

To obtain the expected value matrix, select ▶Mat (F6), highlight **MAT B**, and press **EXE**.
The expected value matrix will be displayed on the screen as follows:

Ans	1	2	3	4	5
1	12	12	12	12	12
2	188	188	188	188	188

Conclusion:
Since p-value $= 0.6163$ is greater than α, we do not reject H_0.
The statistical evidence does not indicate that we may conclude that there is a difference in the proportion of nonconforming pages produced by the printers.

Problems for Section 14.2

LEARNING THE BASICS

14.11 Consider a contingency table with two rows and five columns.
a. How many degrees of freedom are there in the contingency table?
b. Determine the critical value for $\alpha = 0.05$.
c. Determine the critical value for $\alpha = 0.01$.

14.12 Use the following contingency table:

	A	B	C	Total
1	10	30	50	90
2	40	45	50	135
Total	50	75	100	225

a. Compute the expected frequencies for each cell.
b. Compute χ^2_{STAT}. Is it significant at $\alpha = 0.05$?

14.13 Use the following contingency table:

	A	B	C	Total
1	20	30	25	75
2	30	20	25	75
Total	50	50	50	150

a. Compute the expected frequencies for each cell.
b. Compute χ^2_{STAT}. Is it significant at $\alpha = 0.05$?

APPLYING THE CONCEPTS

14.14 How do Americans feel about online ads tailored to their individual interests? A survey of 1,000 adult Internet users found that 55% of the 18 to 24 year olds, 59% of 25 to 34 year olds, 66% of 35 to 49 year olds, 77% of 50 to 64 year olds, and 82% of 65 to 89 year olds opposed such ads. (Data extracted from S. Clifford, "Tracked for Ads? Many Americans Say No Thanks," *The New York Times*, September 30, 2009, p. B3.) Suppose that the survey was based on 200 respondents in each of five age groups: 18 to 24, 25 to 34, 35 to 49, 50 to 64, and 65 to 89.
a. At the 0.05 level of significance, is there evidence of a difference among the age groups in the opposition to ads on web pages tailored to their interests?
b. Determine the *p*-value in (a) and interpret its meaning.

14.15 How do Americans feel about online discounts tailored to their individual interests? A survey of 1,000 adult Internet users found that 37% of the 18 to 24 year olds, 44% of 25 to 34 year olds, 50% of 35 to 49 year olds, 58% of 50 to 64 year olds, and 70% of 65 to 89 year olds opposed such discounts. (Data extracted from S. Clifford, "Tracked for Ads? Many Americans Say No Thanks," *The New York*

Times, September 30, 2009, p. B3.) Suppose that the survey was based on 200 respondents in each of five age groups: 18 to 24, 25 to 34, 35 to 49, 50 to 64, and 65 to 89.
a. At the 0.05 level of significance, is there evidence of a difference among the age groups in the opposition to discounts on web pages tailored to their interests?
b. Compute the *p*-value and interpret its meaning.

SELF Test **14.16** More shoppers do the majority of their grocery shopping on Saturday than any other day of the week. However, is there a difference in the various age groups in the proportion of people who do the majority of their grocery shopping on Saturday? A study showed the results for the different age groups. (Data extracted from "Major Shopping by Day," *Progressive Grocer Annual Report*, April 30, 2002.) The data were reported as percentages, and no sample sizes were given:

	AGE		
MAJOR SHOPPING DAY	Under 35	35–54	Over 54
Saturday	24%	28%	12%
A day other than Saturday	76%	72%	88%

Assume that 200 shoppers for each age group were surveyed.
a. Is there evidence of a significant difference among the age groups with respect to major grocery shopping day? (Use $\alpha = 0.05$.)
b. Determine the *p*-value in (a) and interpret its meaning.
c. Discuss the managerial implications of (a) and (b). How can grocery stores use this information to improve marketing and sales? Be specific.

14.17 Repeat (a) and (b) of Problem 14.16, assuming that only 50 shoppers for each age group were surveyed. Discuss the implications of sample size on the χ^2 test for differences among more than two populations.

14.18 Is there a generation gap in music? A study reported that 45% of 16 to 29 year olds, 42% of 30 to 49 year olds, and 33% of 50 to 64 year olds often listened to rock music. (Data extracted from A. Tugend, "Bridging the Workplace Generation Gap: It Starts with a Text," *The New York Times*, November 7, 2009, p. B5.) Suppose that the study was based on a sample of 200 respondents in each group.
a. Is there evidence of a significant difference among the age groups with respect to the proportion who often listened to rock music? (Use $\alpha = 0.05$.)
b. Determine the *p*-value in (a) and interpret its meaning.

14.19 Is there a generation gap in music? A study reported that 25% of 16 to 29 year olds, 21% of 30 to 49 year olds, and 31% of 50 to 64 year olds often listened to country music. (Data extracted from A. Tugend, "Bridging the Workplace Generation Gap: It Starts with a Text," *The New York Times*, November 7, 2009, p. B5.) Suppose that the study was based on a sample of 200 respondents in each group.

a. Is there evidence of a significant difference among the age groups with respect to the proportion who often listened to country music? (Use $\alpha = 0.05$.)

b. Determine the *p*-value in (a) and interpret its meaning.

14.3 Chi-Square Test of Independence

In Sections 14.1 and 14.2, you used the χ^2 test to evaluate potential differences among population proportions. For a contingency table that has *r* rows and *c* columns, you can generalize the χ^2 test as a *test of independence* for two categorical variables.

For a test of independence, the null and alternative hypotheses follow:

H_0: The two categorical variables are independent (i.e., there is no relationship between them).

H_1: The two categorical variables are dependent (i.e., there is a relationship between them).

Once again, you use Equation (14.1) on page 603 to compute the test statistic:

$$\chi^2_{STAT} = \sum_{all\ cells} \frac{(f_o - f_e)^2}{f_e}$$

FIGURE 14.8

Regions of rejection and nonrejection when testing for independence in an $r \times c$ contingency table, using the χ^2 test

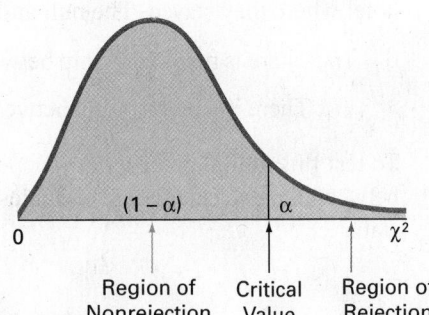

You reject the null hypothesis at the α level of significance if the computed value of the χ^2_{STAT} test statistic is greater than χ^2_α, the upper-tail critical value from a chi-square distribution with $(r - 1)(c - 1)$ degrees of freedom (see Figure 14.8). Thus, the decision rule is

Reject H_0 if $\chi^2_{STAT} > \chi^2_\alpha$;

otherwise, do not reject H_0.

The χ^2 **test of independence** is similar to the χ^2 test for equality of proportions. The test statistics and the decision rules are the same, but the null and alternative hypotheses and conclusions are different. For example, in the guest satisfaction survey of Sections 14.1 and 14.2, there is evidence of a significant difference between the hotels with respect to the proportion of guests who would return. From a different viewpoint, you could conclude that there is a significant relationship between the hotels and the likelihood that a guest would return. However, the two types of tests differ in how the samples are selected.

In a test for equality of proportions, there is one factor of interest, with two or more levels. These levels represent samples drawn from independent populations. The categorical responses in each group or level are classified into two categories, such as *item of interest* and *not an item of interest*. The objective is to make comparisons and evaluate differences between the proportions of the *items of interest* among the various levels. However, in a test for independence, there are two factors of interest, each of which has two or more levels. You select one sample and tally the joint responses to the two categorical variables into the cells of a contingency table.

To illustrate the χ^2 test for independence, suppose that, in the survey on hotel guest satisfaction, respondents who stated that they were not likely to return were asked what was the primary reason for their unwillingness to return to the hotel. Table 14.11 presents the resulting 4×3 contingency table.

TABLE 14.11

Contingency Table of Primary Reason for Not Returning and Hotel

PRIMARY REASON FOR NOT RETURNING	HOTEL			
	Golden Palm	Palm Royale	Palm Princess	Total
Price	23	7	37	67
Location	39	13	8	60
Room accommodation	13	5	13	31
Other	13	8	8	29
Total	88	33	66	187

In Table 14.11, observe that of the primary reasons for not planning to return to the hotel, 67 were due to price, 60 were due to location, 31 were due to room accommodation, and 29 were due to other reasons. As in Table 14.6 on page 611, there were 88 guests at the Golden Palm, 33 guests at the Palm Royale, and 66 guests at the Palm Princess who were not planning to return. The observed frequencies in the cells of the 4×3 contingency table represent the joint tallies of the sampled guests with respect to primary reason for not returning and the hotel where they stayed. The null and alternative hypotheses are

H_0: There is no relationship between the primary reason for not returning and the hotel.

H_1: There is a relationship between the primary reason for not returning and the hotel.

To test this null hypothesis of independence against the alternative that there is a relationship between the two categorical variables, you use Equation (14.1) on page 603 to compute the test statistic:

$$\chi^2_{STAT} = \sum_{all\ cells} \frac{(f_o - f_e)^2}{f_e}$$

where

f_o = observed frequency in a particular cell of the $r \times c$ contingency table

f_e = expected frequency in a particular cell if the null hypothesis of independence is true

To compute the expected frequency, f_e, in any cell, you use the multiplication rule for independent events discussed on page 216 [see Equation (5.7)]. For example, under the null hypothesis of independence, the probability of responses expected in the upper-left-corner cell representing primary reason of price for the Golden Palm is the product of the two separate probabilities $P(\text{Price})$ and $P(\text{Golden Palm})$. Here, the proportion of reasons that are due to price, $P(\text{Price})$, is $67/187 = 0.3583$, and the proportion of all responses from the Golden Palm, $P(\text{Golden Palm})$, is $88/187 = 0.4706$. If the null hypothesis is true, then the primary reason for not returning and the hotel are independent:

$$P(\text{Price and Golden Palm}) = P(\text{Price}) \times P(\text{Golden Palm})$$
$$= (0.3583) \times (0.4706)$$
$$= 0.1686$$

The expected frequency is the product of the overall sample size, n, and this probability, $187 \times 0.1686 = 31.53$. The f_e values for the remaining cells are calculated in a similar manner (see Table 14.12).

Equation (14.4) presents a simpler way to compute the expected frequency.

COMPUTING THE EXPECTED FREQUENCY

The expected frequency in a cell is the product of its row total and column total, divided by the overall sample size.

$$f_e = \frac{\text{Row total} \times \text{Column total}}{n} \qquad (14.4)$$

where

$$\text{Row total} = \text{sum of the frequencies in the row}$$
$$\text{Column total} = \text{sum of the frequencies in the column}$$
$$n = \text{overall sample size}$$

For example, using Equation (14.4) for the upper-left-corner cell (price for the Golden Palm),

$$f_e = \frac{\text{Row total} \times \text{Column total}}{n} = \frac{(67)(88)}{187} = 31.53$$

and for the lower-right-corner cell (other reason for the Palm Princess),

$$f_e = \frac{\text{Row total} \times \text{Column total}}{n} = \frac{(29)(66)}{187} = 10.24$$

Table 14.12 lists the entire set of f_e values.

TABLE 14.12

Contingency Table of Expected Frequencies of Primary Reason for Not Returning with Hotel

PRIMARY REASON FOR NOT RETURNING	HOTEL			Total
	Golden Palm	Palm Royale	Palm Princess	
Price	31.53	11.82	23.65	67
Location	28.24	10.59	21.18	60
Room accommodation	14.59	5.47	10.94	31
Other	13.65	5.12	10.24	29
Total	88.00	33.00	66.00	187

To perform the test of independence, you use the χ^2_{STAT} test statistic shown in Equation (14.1) on page 603. The χ^2_{STAT} test statistic approximately follows a chi-square distribution, with degrees of freedom equal to the number of rows in the contingency table minus 1, multiplied by the number of columns in the table minus 1:

$$\text{Degrees of freedom} = (r - 1)(c - 1)$$
$$= (4 - 1)(3 - 1) = 6$$

Table 14.13 presents the computations for the χ^2_{STAT} test statistic.

TABLE 14.13

Computing the χ^2_{STAT} Test Statistic for the Test of Independence

Cell	f_o	f_e	$(f_o - f_e)$	$(f_o - f_e)^2$	$(f_o - f_e)^2/f_e$
Price/Golden Palm	23	31.53	−8.53	72.76	2.31
Price/Palm Royale	7	11.82	−4.82	23.23	1.97
Price/Palm Princess	37	23.65	13.35	178.22	7.54
Location/Golden Palm	39	28.24	10.76	115.78	4.10
Location/Palm Royale	13	10.59	2.41	5.81	0.55
Location/Palm Princess	8	21.18	−13.18	173.71	8.20
Room/Golden Palm	13	14.59	−1.59	2.53	0.17
Room/Palm Royale	5	5.47	−0.47	0.22	0.04
Room/Palm Princess	13	10.94	2.06	4.24	0.39
Other/Golden Palm	13	13.65	−0.65	0.42	0.03
Other/Palm Royale	8	5.12	2.88	8.29	1.62
Other/Palm Princess	8	10.24	−2.24	5.02	0.49
					27.41

Using the $\alpha = 0.05$ level of significance, the upper-tail critical value from the chi-square distribution with 6 degrees of freedom is 12.592 (see Table E.4). Because $\chi^2_{STAT} = 27.41 > 12.592$, you reject the null hypothesis of independence (see Figure 14.9).

FIGURE 14.9

Regions of rejection and nonrejection when testing for independence in the hotel guest satisfaction survey example at the 0.05 level of significance, with 6 degrees of freedom

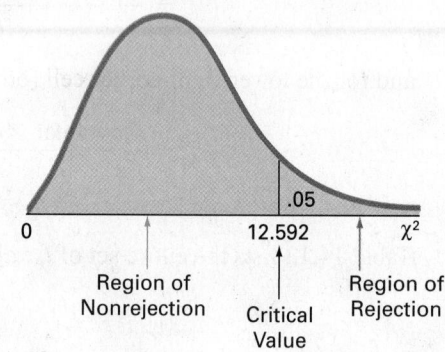

Find χ^2 critical value using calculator:

To find the χ^2 critical value, use the Casio Calculator fx-9750GII and follow the following calculator steps:

> **Note: Fx-9750G Plus does not have this option, therefore you have to use the Table G3 in the Appendix.**

From the **Main Menu** select:

STAT F5 (DIST) **F3** (CHI) **F3**(Invc)   then enter the following items:

Inverse χ^2
Data   : **F2**(Var)   ▼
Area   : **0.05**   **EXE**   (Note: It is an upper tailed test for χ^2 distribution.)
df   : **6**   **EXE**   (Note: df=(c−1)(r−1) =(3−1)(4−1)=6)
Save Res : None
Execute

Now key **EXE** or **F1**(CALC)

The calculator will now show the results:

Inverse χ^2

  x-Inv = 12.5915872

The critical value defines the rejection and non-rejection regions.

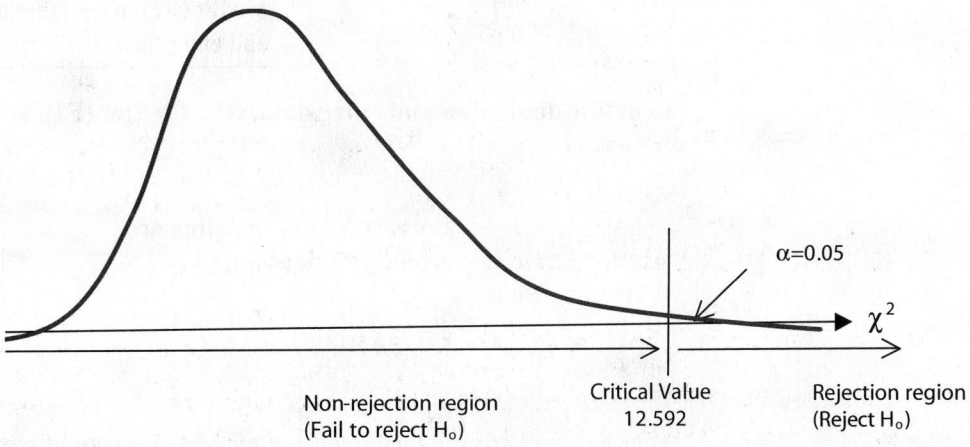

You can use the Casio calculator as indicated in Figure 14.10 to conduct the test of independence using the p-value approach. Because the p-value $= 0.0001 < 0.05$, you reject the null hypothesis of independence. The p-value indicates that there is virtually no chance of having a relationship this strong or stronger between hotels and primary reasons for not returning in a sample, if the primary reasons for not returning are independent of the specific hotels in the entire population. Thus, there is strong evidence of a relationship between primary reason for not returning and the hotel.

Examination of the observed and expected frequencies (see Table 14.13 on page 624) reveals that price is underrepresented as a reason for not returning to the Golden Palm (i.e., $f_o = 23$ and $f_e = 31.53$) but is overrepresented at the Palm Princess. Guests are more satisfied with the price at the Golden Palm than at the Palm Princess. Location is overrepresented as a reason for not returning to the Golden Palm but greatly underrepresented at the Palm Princess. Thus, guests are much more satisfied with the location of the Palm Princess than with that of the Golden Palm.

To ensure accurate results, all expected frequencies need to be large in order to use the χ^2 test when dealing with $r \times c$ contingency tables. As in the case of $2 \times c$ contingency tables in Section 14.2, all expected frequencies should be at least 1. For contingency tables in which one or more expected frequencies are less than 1, you can use the chi-square test after collapsing two or more low-frequency rows into one row (or collapsing two or more low-frequency columns into one column). Merging rows or columns usually results in expected frequencies sufficiently large to assure the accuracy of the χ^2 test.

Solution: Use the Casio calculator FX-9750GII.

Press **MENU** and select **STAT**, **TEST** (F3), and **CHI** (F3).
Under option **CHI**, select **2WAY** (F2).

You will see the following on the screen:

χ^2 Test

Observed   : Mat A

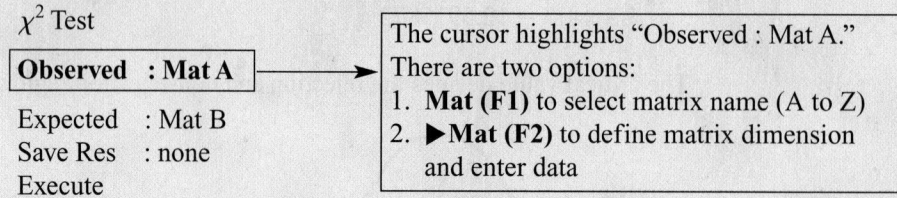

The cursor highlights "Observed : Mat A."
There are two options:
1. **Mat (F1)** to select matrix name (A to Z)
2. **▶Mat (F2)** to define matrix dimension and enter data

Expected   : Mat B
Save Res   : none
Execute

To define dimension and enter data, select ▶Mat (F2). You will see the following on the screen:

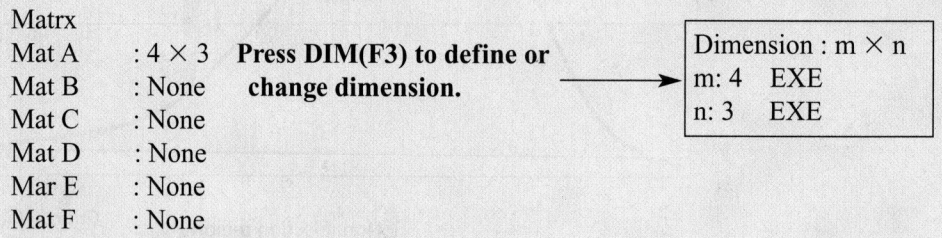

Matrx
Mat A   : 4 × 3   **Press DIM(F3) to define or**
Mat B   : None   **change dimension.**
Mat C   : None
Mat D   : None
Mar E   : None
Mat F   : None

Dimension : m × n
m: 4   EXE
n: 3   EXE

After you have entered the dimension for **Mat A**, you will see the **4 × 3 matrix A** appear on the screen. Use this screen to input your data.

A	1	2	3
1	23	7	37
2	39	13	8
3	13	5	13
4	13	8	8

After you enter your data in Matrix A, press **EXIT** two times until you see the following on the screen:

χ^2 Test

Observed   : Mat A

Expected   : Mat B

Save Res   : none
Execute

To define dimension, select ▶Mat (F2). You will see the following on the screen:

Matrix
Mat A   : 4 × 3
Mat B   : 4 × 3   **Press DIM (F3) to define or**
Mat C   : None   **change dimension.**
Mat D   : None
Mar E   : None
Mat F   : None

You will see **4 × 3 Matrix B**. You are not required to enter any values; the calculator will give you the expected values.

Now press **EXIT** two times until you see the following on the screen:

χ^2 Test
Observed : Mat A
Expected : Mat B
Save Res : none
Execute

At this point, press either **EXE** or **F1** (Calc).
The calculator will now show the results:

χ^2 Test

$$\chi^2 = 27.4104297$$
$$p = 1.2129_{E}\text{-}04$$
$$df = 6$$

To obtain the expected value matrix, select ▶**Mat** (F6), highlight **MAT B**, and press **EXE**.
The expected value matrix will be displayed on the screen as follows:

Ans	1	2	3
1	31.529	11.823	23.647
2	28.235	10.588	21.176
3	14.588	5.4705	10.941
4	13.647	5.1176	10.235

CALCULATOR LESSON 17A

CFX-9850GB CALCULATOR

EXAMPLE 14.5

Lesson 17A—Chi-Square Test for Independence

Lesson 17A—Chi-Square Test for Independence

Example

A copier service has two laser printers used to produce colour transparencies. The thickness of a transparency can create printing problems. Four common problems are smearing, streaking, skipping, and fogging. A random sample reveals the following information. We wish to test whether the problems depend on the printer used. We will use a significance level of 0.05.

TABLE 14.14

	Problems			
Printer	Smearing	Streaking	Skipping	Fogging
A	20	32	44	10
B	10	48	21	15

Solution: From the **Main Menu**, select the following:

MAT and **EXE**

Enter the following in response to the screen prompts.

Matrix

Mat A	:	**2 EXE**	**4EXE**
Mat B	:	None	
Mat C	:	None	
Mat D	:	None	
Mat E	:	None	
Mat F	:	None	

You will see the part of the matrix appears on the screen. Use this screen to input your data.

A	1	2	3	4 →
1	0	0	0	0
2	0	0	0	0

Enter the data values into the appropriate cells. To begin entering your data, use the arrow key to highlight the cell 1,1 (top left corner of the cell). Type 20 and press **EXE.** The cursor will automatically scroll to the next cell.

A	1	2	3	4 →
1	20 EXE	32 EXE	44 EXE	10 EXE
2	10 EXE	48 EXE	21 EXE	15 EXE

After you enter your data in Matrix A, press **MENU** and select the following:

STAT, EXE, TEST (F3), and **CHI** (F3). Then enter the following items:

χ^2 Test
Observed: Mat A (F1)
Execute
Now Press **EXE.**

The calculator will now show the results:

χ^2 Test
$$\chi^2 = 15.005$$
$$p = 1.8116E\text{-}03 \quad (= 0.0018116)$$
$$df = 3$$
Expected = Mat Ans

You may obtain the expected value matrix by making the following selection:

MENU, MAT, and **EXE**

Use the cursor ▼ arrow to scroll down to the bottom of the matrix list until the cursor is on

Mat Ans   : 2 x 4
EXE

You will see the expected value matrix displayed on the screen as follows:

Ans	1	2	3	4 →
1	15.9	42.4	34.45	13.25
2	14.1	37.6	30.55	11.75

Conclusion:

Since p-value = 0.0018 is smaller than α, we reject H_0.

The statistical evidence indicates that we may conclude that there is a difference in the proportion of nonconforming pages produced by the printers.

CALCULATOR LESSON 17B

FX-9850GII CALCULATOR

EXAMPLE 14.6

Lesson 17B—Chi-Square Test for Independence

Lesson 17B—Chi-Square Test for Independence

Example

A copier service has two laser printers used to produce colour transparencies. The thickness of a transparency can create printing problems. Four common problems are smearing, streaking, skipping, and fogging. A random sample reveals the following information. We wish to test whether the problems depend on the printer used. We will use a significance level of 0.05.

TABLE 14.15

Printer	Problems			
	Smearing	Streaking	Skipping	Fogging
A	20	32	44	10
B	10	48	21	15

Solution:

Press **MENU** and select **STAT**, **TEST** (F3), and **CHI** (F3).
Under option **CHI**, select **2WAY** (F2).

You will see the following on the screen:

χ^2 Test

| **Observed** | **: Mat A** |

Expected   : Mat B
Save Res   : none
Execute

The cursor highlights "Observed : Mat A."
There are two options:
1. **Mat (F1)** to select matrix name (A to Z)
2. ▶**Mat (F2)** to define matrix dimension and enter data

To define dimension and enter data, select ▶Mat (F2). You will see the following on the screen:

Matrx
Mat A   : 2 × 4   **Press DIM(F3) to define or**
Mat B   : None   **change dimension.**
Mat C   : None
Mat D   : None
Mar E   : None
Mat F   : None

Dimension : m × n
m: 2   EXE
n: 4   EXE

After you have entered the dimension for **Mat A**, you will see the **2 × 4 matrix A** appear on the screen. Use this screen to input your data.

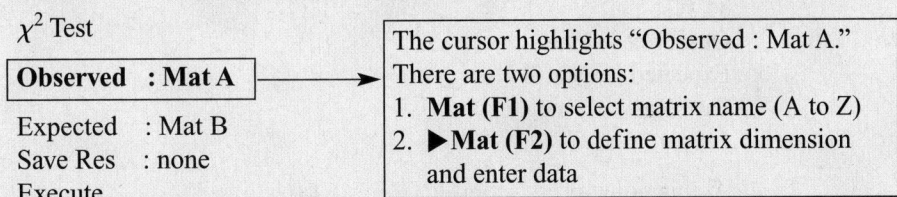

Enter the data values into the appropriate cells. To begin entering your data, use the arrow key to highlight the cell 1,1 (top left corner of the cell). Type 20 and press **EXE**. The cursor will automatically scroll to the next cell.

A	1	2	3	4
1	20 EXE	32 EXE	44 EXE	10 EXE
2	10 EXE	48 EXE	21 EXE	15 EXE

After you enter your data in Matrix A, press **EXIT** two times until you see the following on the screen:

χ^2 Test

Observed : Mat A

Expected   : Mat B ⟶ Highlight "Expected : Mat B."
Select ▶Mat (F2) to define matrix dimension. The **expected matrix** should have the same dimensions as the **observed matrix**.

Save Res   : none
Execute

To define dimension, select ▶Mat (F2). You will see the following on the screen:

Matrix
Mat A   : 2 × 4
Mat B   : 2 × 4   **Press DIM (F3) to define or**   Dimension : m × n
Mat C   : None   **change dimension.** ⟶   m: 2   EXE
Mat D   : None   n: 4   EXE
Mar E   : None
Mat F   : None

You will see **2 × 4 Matrix B**. You are not required to enter any values; the calculator will give you the expected values.

Now press **EXIT** two times until you see the following on the screen:

χ^2 Test
Observed   : Mat A
Expected   : Mat B
Save Res   : none
Execute

At this point, press either **EXE** or **F1** (Calc).
The calculator will now show the results:

χ^2 Test

$$\chi^2 = 15.0058158$$
$$p = 1.8117_E\text{-}03 \ (0.0018117)$$
$$df = 3$$

To obtain the expected value matrix, select **▶Mat (F6)**, highlight **MAT B**, and press **EXE**.
The expected value matrix will be displayed on the screen as follows:

Ans	1	2	3	4 ⟶
1	15.9	42.4	34.45	13.25
2	14.1	37.6	30.55	11.75

Conclusion:
Since p-value = 0.0018 is less than α, we do not reject H_0.
The statistical evidence does not indicate that we may conclude that there is a difference in the proportion of nonconforming pages produced by the printers.

Problems for Section 14.3

LEARNING THE BASICS

14.20 If a contingency table has three rows and four columns, how many degrees of freedom are there for the χ^2 test of independence?

14.21 When performing a χ^2 test of independence in a contingency table with r rows and c columns, determine the upper-tail critical value of the test statistic in each of the following circumstances:
a. $\alpha = 0.05, r = 4$ rows, $c = 5$ columns
b. $\alpha = 0.01, r = 4$ rows, $c = 5$ columns
c. $\alpha = 0.01, r = 4$ rows, $c = 6$ columns
d. $\alpha = 0.01, r = 3$ rows, $c = 6$ columns
e. $\alpha = 0.01, r = 6$ rows, $c = 3$ columns

APPLYING THE CONCEPTS

14.22 The owner of a restaurant serving Continental-style entrées has the business objective of learning more about the patterns of patron demand during the Friday-to-Sunday weekend time period. Data were collected from 630 customers on the type of entrée ordered and the type of dessert ordered and organized into the following table:

TYPE OF DESSERT	TYPE OF ENTRÉE				
	Beef	Poultry	Fish	Pasta	Total
Ice cream	13	8	12	14	47
Cake	98	12	29	6	145
Fruit	8	10	6	2	26
None	124	98	149	41	412
Total	243	128	196	63	630

At the 0.05 level of significance, is there evidence of a relationship between type of dessert and type of entrée?

14.23 Is there a generation gap in the type of music that people listen to? The following table represents the type of favorite music for a sample of 1,000 respondents classified according to their age group:

FAVORITE TYPE	AGE				
	16–29	30–49	50–64	65 and over	Total
Rock	71	62	51	27	211
Rap or hip-hop	40	21	7	3	71
Rhythm and blues	48	46	46	40	180
Country	43	53	59	79	234
Classical	22	28	33	46	129
Jazz	18	26	36	43	123
Salsa	8	14	18	12	52
Total	250	250	250	250	1000

At the 0.05 level of significance, is there evidence of a relationship between favorite type of music and age group?

14.24 A large corporation is interested in determining whether a relationship exists between the commuting time of its employees and the level of stress-related problems observed on the job. A study of 116 workers reveals the following:

COMMUTING TIME	STRESS LEVEL			
	High	Moderate	Low	Total
Under 15 min.	9	5	18	32
15–45 min.	17	8	28	53
Over 45 min.	18	6	7	31
Total	44	19	53	116

a. At the 0.01 level of significance, is there evidence of a significant relationship between commuting time and stress level?
b. What is your answer to (a) if you use the 0.05 level of significance?

14.25 Where people turn for news is different for various age groups. A study indicated where different age groups primarily get their news:

MEDIA	AGE GROUP		
	Under 36	36–50	50 +
Local TV	107	119	133
National TV	73	102	127
Radio	75	97	109
Local newspaper	52	79	107
Internet	95	83	76

At the 0.05 level of significance, is there evidence of a significant relationship between the age group and where people primarily get their news? If so, explain the relationship.

14.26 *USA Today* reported on when the decision of what to have for dinner is made. Suppose the results were based on a survey of 1,000 respondents and considered whether the household included any children under 18 years old. The results are cross-classified in the following table:

	TYPE OF HOUSEHOLD		
WHEN DECISION MADE	**One Adult/No Children**	**Two or More Adults/ Children**	**Two or More Adults/No Children**
Just before eating	162	54	154
In the afternoon	73	38	69
In the morning	59	58	53
A few days before	21	64	45
The night before	15	50	45
Always eat the same thing on this night	2	16	2
Not sure	7	6	7

Source: Data extracted from "What's for Dinner," **www.usatoday.com**, January 10, 2000.

At the 0.05 level of significance, is there evidence of a significant relationship between when the decision is made of what to have for dinner and the type of household?

USING STATISTICS @ T.C. Resort Properties Revisited

I n the Using Statistics scenario, you were the manager of T.C. Resort Properties, a collection of five upscale hotels located on two tropical islands. To assess the quality of services being provided by your hotels, guests are encouraged to complete a satisfaction survey when they check out. You analyzed the data from these surveys to determine the overall satisfaction with the services provided, the likelihood that the guests will return to the hotel, and the reasons given by some guests for not wanting to return.

Zastol'skiy' victor Leonidovich/Shutterstock.com

On one island, T.C. Resort Properties operates the Beachcomber and Windsurfer hotels. You performed a chi-square test for the difference in two proportions and concluded that a greater proportion of guests are willing to return to the Beachcomber Hotel than to the Windsurfer. On the other island, T.C. Resort Properties operates the Golden Palm, Palm Royale, and Palm Princess hotels. To see if guest satisfaction was the same among the three hotels, you performed a chi-square test for the differences among more than two proportions. The test confirmed that the three proportions are not equal, and guests seem to be most likely to return to the Palm Royale and least likely to return to the Golden Palm.

In addition, you investigated whether the reasons given for not returning to the Golden Palm, Palm Royale, and Palm Princess were unique to a certain hotel or common to all three hotels. By performing a chi-square test of independence, you determined that the reasons given for wanting to return or not depended on the hotel where the guests had been staying. By examining the observed and expected frequencies, you concluded that guests were more satisfied with the price at the Golden Palm and were much more satisfied with the location of the Palm Princess. Guest satisfaction with room accommodations was not significantly different among the three hotels.

SUMMARY

Figure 14.11 presents a roadmap for this chapter. First, you used hypothesis testing for analyzing categorical response data from two independent samples and from more than two independent samples. In addition, the rules of probability from Section 5.2 were extended to the hypothesis of independence in the joint responses to two categorical variables.

FIGURE 14.11
Roadmap of Chapter 14

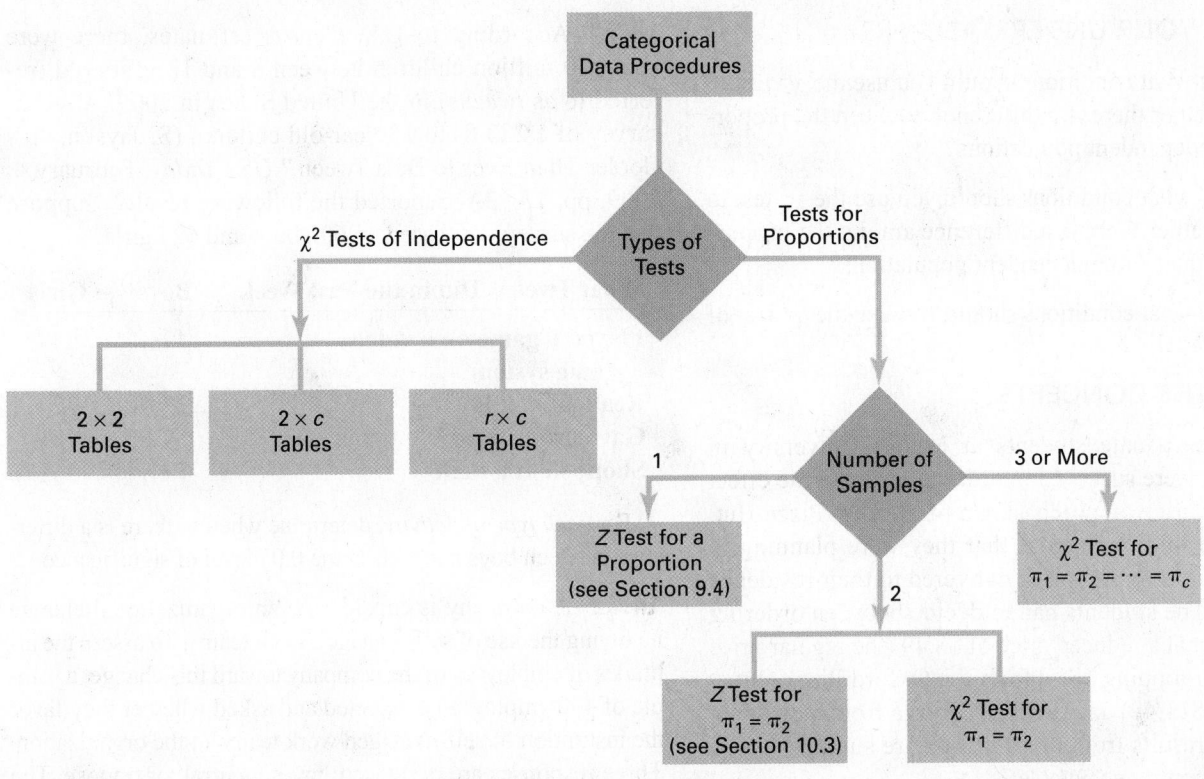

FIGURE 14.11
Roadmap of Chapter 14

KEY EQUATIONS

χ^2 Test for the Difference Between Two Proportions

$$\chi^2_{STAT} = \sum_{all \, cells} \frac{(f_o - f_e)^2}{f_e}$$

Computing the Estimated Overall Proportion for Two Groups

$$\bar{p} = \frac{X_1 + X_2}{n_1 + n_2} = \frac{X}{n}$$

Computing the Estimated Overall Proportion for c Groups

$$\bar{p} = \frac{X_1 + X_2 + \cdots + X_c}{n_1 + n_2 + \cdots + n_c} = \frac{X}{n}$$

Computing the Expected Frequency

$$f_e = \frac{\text{Row total} \times \text{Column total}}{n}$$

KEY TERMS

chi-square (χ^2) distribution 604

chi-square (χ^2) test for the difference between two proportions 603

chi-square (χ^2) test of independence 621

contingency table 602

expected frequency (f_e) 603

observed frequency (f_o) 603

$2 \times c$ contingency table 611

2×2 contingency table 602

PROBLEMS

CHECKING YOUR UNDERSTANDING

14.27 Under what conditions should you use the χ^2 test to determine whether there is a difference between the proportions of two independent populations?

14.28 Under what conditions should you use the χ^2 test to determine whether there is a difference among the proportions of more than two independent populations?

14.29 Under what conditions should you use the χ^2 test of independence?

APPLYING THE CONCEPTS

14.30 Undergraduate students at Miami University in Oxford, Ohio, were surveyed in order to evaluate the effect of gender and price on purchasing a pizza from Pizza Hut. Students were told to suppose that they were planning to have a large two-topping pizza delivered to their residence that evening. The students had to decide between ordering from Pizza Hut at a reduced price of $8.49 (the regular price for a large two-topping pizza from the Oxford Pizza Hut at this time was $11.49) and ordering a pizza from a different pizzeria. The results from this question are summarized in the following contingency table:

GENDER	PIZZERIA		Total
	Pizza Hut	Other	
Female	4	13	17
Male	6	12	18
Total	10	25	35

a. Using a 0.05 level of significance, is there evidence of a significant difference between males and females in their pizzeria selection?
b. What is your answer to (a) if nine of the male students selected Pizza Hut and nine selected another pizzeria?

A subsequent survey evaluated purchase decisions at other prices. These results are summarized in the following contingency table:

PIZZERIA	PRICE			Total
	$8.49	$11.49	$14.49	
Pizza Hut	10	5	2	17
Other	25	23	27	75
Total	35	28	29	92

c. Using a 0.05 level of significance and using the data in the second contingency table, is there evidence of a difference in pizzeria selection based on price?
d. Determine the p-value in (c) and interpret its meaning.

14.31 According to U.S. Census estimates, there were about 20 million children between 8 and 12 years old (referred to as *tweens*) in the United States in 2009. A recent survey of 1,223 8- to 12-year-old children (S. Jayson, "It's Cooler Than Ever to Be a Tween," *USA Today*, February 4, 2009, pp. 1A, 2A) reported the following results. Suppose that the survey was based on 600 boys and 623 girls.

What Tweens Did in the Past Week	Boys	Girls
Played a game on a video game system	498	243
Read a book for fun	276	324
Gave product advice to parents	186	181
Shopped at a mall	144	262

For *each type of activity*, determine whether there is a difference between boys and girls at the 0.05 level of significance.

14.32 A company is considering an organizational change involving the use of self-managed work teams. To assess the attitudes of employees of the company toward this change, a sample of 400 employees is selected and asked whether they favor the institution of self-managed work teams in the organization. Three responses are permitted: favor, neutral, or oppose. The results of the survey, cross-classified by type of job and attitude toward self-managed work teams, are summarized as follows:

TYPE OF JOB	SELF-MANAGED WORK TEAMS			
	Favor	Neutral	Oppose	Total
Hourly worker	108	46	71	225
Supervisor	18	12	30	60
Middle management	35	14	26	75
Upper management	24	7	9	40
Total	185	79	136	400

a. At the 0.05 level of significance, is there evidence of a relationship between attitude toward self-managed work teams and type of job?

The survey also asked respondents about their attitudes toward instituting a policy whereby an employee could take one additional vacation day per month without pay. The results, cross-classified by type of job, are as follows:

TYPE OF JOB	VACATION TIME WITHOUT PAY			
	Favor	Neutral	Oppose	Total
Hourly worker	135	23	67	225
Supervisor	39	7	14	60
Middle management	47	6	22	75
Upper management	26	6	8	40
Total	247	42	111	400

b. At the 0.05 level of significance, is there evidence of a relationship between attitude toward vacation time without pay and type of job?

14.33 A company that produces and markets continuing education programs on DVDs for the educational testing industry has traditionally mailed advertising to prospective customers. A market research study was undertaken to compare two approaches: mailing a sample DVD upon request that contained highlights of the full DVD and sending an e-mail containing a link to a website from which sample material could be downloaded. Of those who responded to either the mailing or the e-mail, the results were as follows in terms of purchase of the complete DVD:

	TYPE OF MEDIA USED		
PURCHASED	**Mailing**	**E-mail**	**Total**
Yes	26	11	37
No	227	247	474
Total	253	258	511

a. At the 0.05 level of significance, is there evidence of a difference in the proportion of DVDs purchased on the basis of the type of media used?
b. On the basis of the results of (a), which type of media should the company use in the future? Explain the rationale for your decision.

The company also wanted to determine which of three sales approaches should be used to generate sales among those who either requested the sample DVD by mail or downloaded the sample DVD but did not purchase the full DVD: (1) targeted e-mail, (2) a DVD that contained additional features, or (3) a telephone call to prospective customers. The 474 respondents who did not initially purchase the full DVD were randomly assigned to one of the three sales approaches. The results, in terms of purchases of the full-program DVD, are as follows:

	SALES APPROACH			
ACTION	**Targeted E-mail**	**More Complete DVD**	**Telephone Call**	**Total**
Purchase	5	17	18	40
Don't purchase	153	141	140	434
Total	158	158	158	474

c. At the 0.05 level of significance, is there evidence of a difference in the proportion of DVDs purchased on the basis of the sales strategy used?

d. On the basis of the results of (c), which sales approach do you think the company should use in the future? Explain the rationale for your decision.

TEAM PROJECT

The file **Bond Funds** contains information regarding eight variables from a sample of 184 bond mutual funds:

Type—Type of bonds comprising the bond mutual fund (intermediate government or short-term corporate)
Assets—In millions of dollars
Fees—Sales charges (no or yes)
Expense ratio—Ratio of expenses to net assets in percentage
Return 2009—Twelve-month return in 2009
Three-year return—Annualized return, 2007–2009
Five-year return—Annualized return, 2005–2009
Risk—Risk-of-loss factor of the bond mutual fund (below average, average, or above average)

14.34 a. Construct a 2 × 2 contingency table, using fees as the row variable and type as the column variable.
b. At the 0.05 level of significance, is there evidence of a difference between intermediate government and short-term corporate bond mutual funds on whether there is a fee?

14.35 a. Construct a 2 × 3 contingency table, using fees as the row variable and risk as the column variable.
b. At the 0.05 level of significance, is there evidence of a difference between below average, average, and above average risk bond mutual funds on whether there is a fee?

14.36 a. Construct a 3 × 2 contingency table, using risk as the row variable and type as the column variable.
b. At the 0.05 level of significance, is there evidence of a relationship between the type of bond mutual fund and its perceived risk?

STUDENT SURVEY DATABASE

14.37 Problem 1.21 on page 20 describes a survey of 62 undergraduate students (stored in **UndergradSurvey**). For these data, construct contingency tables using gender, major, plans to go to graduate school, and employment status. (You need to construct six tables, taking two variables at a time.) Analyze the data at the 0.05 level of significance to determine whether any significant relationships exist among these variables.

14.38 Problem 1.21 on page 20 describes a survey of 62 undergraduate students (stored in **UndergradSurvey**).
a. Select a sample of undergraduate students at your school and conduct a similar survey for those students.
b. For the data collected in (a), repeat Problem 14.37.
c. Compare the results of (b) to those of Problem 14.37.

14.39 Problem 1.22 on page 21 describes a survey of 44 MBA students (see the file [GradSurvey]). For these data, construct contingency tables using gender, undergraduate major, graduate major, and employment status. (You need to construct six tables, taking two variables at a time.) Analyze the data at the 0.05 level of significance to determine whether any significant relationships exist among these variables.

14.40 Problem 1.22 on page 21 describes a survey of 44 MBA students (stored in [GradSurvey]).
a. Select a sample of graduate students in your MBA program and conduct a similar survey for those students.
b. For the data collected in (a), repeat Problem 14.39.
c. Compare the results of (b) to those of Problem 14.39.

MANAGING ASHLAND MULTICOMM SERVICES

Phase 1

Reviewing the results of its research, the marketing department team concluded that a segment of Ashland households might be interested in a discounted trial subscription to the AMS *3-For-All* cable/phone/Internet service. The team decided to test various discounts before determining the type of discount to offer during the trial period. It decided to conduct an experiment using three types of discounts plus a plan that offered no discount during the trial period:

1. No discount for the *3-For-All* cable/phone/Internet service. Subscribers would pay $24.99 per week for the *3-For-All* cable/phone/Internet service during the 90-day trial period.

2. Moderate discount for the *3-For-All* cable/phone/Internet service. Subscribers would pay $19.99 per week for the *3-For-All* cable/phone/Internet service during the 90-day trial period.

3. Substantial discount for the *3-For-All* cable/phone/Internet service. Subscribers would pay $14.99 per week for the *3-For-All* cable/phone/Internet service during the 90-day trial period.

4. Discount restaurant card. Subscribers would be given a Gold card providing a discount of 15% at selected restaurants in Ashland during the trial period.

Each participant in the experiment was randomly assigned to a discount plan. A random sample of 100 subscribers to each plan during the trial period was tracked to determine how many would continue to subscribe to the *3-For-All* service after the trial period. Table AMS14.1 summarizes the results.

TABLE AMS14.1

Number of Subscribers Who Continue Subscriptions After Trial Period with Four Discount Plans

CONTINUE SUBSCRIPTIONS AFTER TRIAL PERIOD	DISCOUNT PLANS				
	No Discount	Moderate Discount	Substantial Discount	Restaurant Card	Total
Yes	24	30	38	51	143
No	76	70	62	49	257
Total	100	100	100	100	400

Exercise

1. Analyze the results of the experiment. Write a report to the team that includes your recommendation for which discount plan to use. Be prepared to discuss the limitations and assumptions of the experiment.

Phase 2

The marketing department team discussed the results of the survey presented in Chapter 10, on pages 418–419. The team realized that the evaluation of individual questions was providing only limited information. In order to further understand the market for the *3-For-All* cable/phone/Internet service, the data were organized in the following contingency tables:

HAS AMS TELE-PHONE SERVICE	HAS AMS INTERNET SERVICE		
	Yes	No	Total
Yes	55	28	83
No	207	128	335
Total	262	156	418

TYPE OF SERVICE	DISCOUNT TRIAL		
	Yes	No	Total
Basic	8	156	164
Enhanced	32	222	254
Total	40	378	418

TYPE OF SERVICE	WATCHES PREMIUM OR ON-DEMAND SERVICES				
	Almost Every Day	Several Times a Week	Almost Never	Never	Total
Basic	2	5	127	30	164
Enhanced	12	30	186	26	254
Total	14	35	313	56	418

WATCHES PREMIUM OR ON-DEMAND SERVICES

DISCOUNT	Almost Every Day	Several Times a Week	Almost Never	Never	Total
Yes	4	5	27	4	40
No	10	30	286	52	378
Total	14	35	313	56	418

METHOD FOR CURRENT SUBSCRIPTION

GOLD CARD	Toll-Free Phone	AMS Website	Direct Mail Reply Card	Good Tunes & More	Other	Total
Yes	10	20	5	1	2	38
No	220	86	41	9	24	380
Total	230	106	46	10	26	418

METHOD FOR CURRENT SUBSCRIPTION

DIS-COUNT	Toll-Free Phone	AMS Website	Direct Mail Reply Card	Good Tunes & More	Other	Total
Yes	11	21	5	1	2	40
No	219	85	41	9	24	378
Total	230	106	46	10	26	418

Exercise

2. Analyze the results of the contingency tables. Write a report for the marketing department team and discuss the marketing implications of the results for Ashland Multi-Comm Services.

DIGITAL CASE

Apply your knowledge of testing for the difference between two proportions in this Digital Case, which extends the T.C. Resort Properties Using Statistics scenario of this chapter.

As T.C. Resort Properties seeks to improve its customer service, the company faces new competition from SunLow Resorts. SunLow has recently opened resort hotels on the islands where T.C. Resort Properties has its five hotels. SunLow is currently advertising that a random survey of 300 customers revealed that about 60% of the customers preferred its "Concierge Class" travel reward program over the T.C. Resorts "TCRewards Plus" program.

Open and review **ConciergeClass.pdf**, an electronic brochure that describes the Concierge Class program and compares it to the T.C. Resorts program. Then answer the following questions:

1. Are the claims made by SunLow valid?

2. What analyses of the survey data would lead to a more favorable impression about T.C. Resort Properties?

3. Perform one of the analyses identified in your answer to step 2.

4. Review the data about the T.C. Resorts properties customers presented in this chapter. Are there any other questions that you might include in a future survey of travel reward programs? Explain.

REFERENCES

1. Conover, W. J., *Practical Nonparametric Statistics*, 3rd ed. (New York: Wiley, 2000).
2. Daniel, W. W., *Applied Nonparametric Statistics*, 2nd ed. (Boston: PWS Kent, 1990).
3. Dixon, W. J., and F. J. Massey, Jr., *Introduction to Statistical Analysis*, 4th ed. (New York: McGraw-Hill, 1983).
4. Hollander, M., and D. A. Wolfe, *Nonparametric Statistical Methods*, 2nd ed. (New York: Wiley, 1999).
5. Lewontin, R. C., and J. Felsenstein, "Robustness of Homogeneity Tests in $2 \times n$ Tables," *Biometrics* 21 (March 1965): 19–33.
6. Marascuilo, L. A., and M. McSweeney, *Nonparametric and Distribution-Free Methods for the Social Sciences* (Monterey, CA: Brooks/Cole, 1977).
7. *Microsoft Excel 2010* (Redmond, WA: Microsoft Corp., 2010).
8. *Minitab Release 16* (State College, PA: Minitab, Inc., 2010).

EG14.1 Chi-Square Test for the Difference Between Two Proportions

PHStat2 Use **Chi-Square Test for Differences in Two Proportions** to perform this chi-square test. For example, to perform the Figure 14.3 test for the two-hotel guest satisfaction data on page 606, select **PHStat → Two-Sample Tests (Summarized Data) → Chi-Square Test for Differences in Two Proportions**. In the procedure's dialog box, enter **0.05** as the **Level of Significance**, enter a **Title**, and click **OK**. In the new worksheet:

1. Read the yellow note about entering values and then press the **Delete** key to delete the note.

2. Enter **Hotel** in cell **B4** and **Choose Again?** in cell **A5**.

3. Enter **Beachcomber** in cell **B5** and **Windsurfer** in cell **C5**.

4. Enter **Yes** in cell **A6** and **No** in cell **A7**.

5. Enter **163**, **64**, **154**, and **108** in cells **B6**, **B7**, **C6**, and **C7**, respectively.

In-Depth Excel Use the **COMPUTE worksheet** of the **Chi-Square workbook**, shown in Figure 14.3 on page 606, as a template for performing this test. The worksheet contains the Table 14.3 two-hotel guest satisfaction data. Use the **CHIINV** and **CHIDIST** functions to help perform the chi-square test for the difference between two proportions. In cell B24, the worksheet uses **CHIINV(*level of significance, degrees of freedom*)** to compute the critical value for the test and in cell B26 uses **CHIDIST(*chi-square test statistic, degrees of freedom*)** to compute the *p*-value. Open to the **COMPUTE_FORMULAS worksheet** to examine the other formulas used in the worksheet.

For other problems, change the **Observed Frequencies** cell counts and row and column labels in rows 4 through 7.

EG14.2 Chi-Square Test for Differences Among More Than Two Proportions

PHStat2 Use **Chi-Square Test** to perform the test for differences among more than two proportions. For example, to perform the Figure 14.7 test for the three-hotel guest satisfaction data on page 613, select **PHStat → Multiple-Sample Tests → Chi-Square Test**. In the procedure's dialog box (shown in the right column):

1. Enter **0.05** as the **Level of Significance**.
2. Enter **2** as the **Number of Rows**.
3. Enter **3** as the **Number of Columns**.
4. Enter a **Title** and click **OK**.

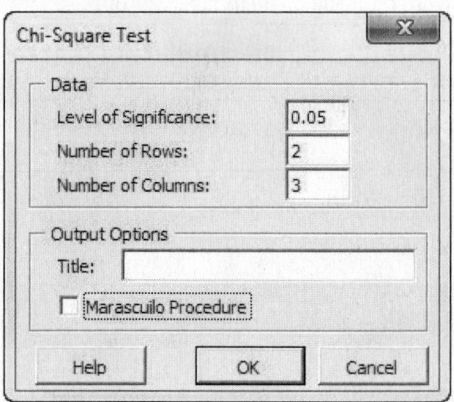

In the new worksheet:

5. Read the yellow note about entering values and then press the **Delete** key to delete the note.

6. Enter the Table 14.6 data on page 611, including row and column labels, in rows 4 through 7.

In-Depth Excel Use the **ChiSquare2x3 worksheet** of the **Chi-Square Worksheets workbook**, shown in Figure 14.7 on page 613, as a model for this chi-square test. The worksheet contains the data for Table 14.6 guest satisfaction data (see page 611). The worksheet uses formulas to compute the expected frequencies and the intermediate results for the chi-square test statistic in much the same way as the COMPUTE worksheet of the Chi-Square workbook discussed in the Section EG14.1 *In-Depth Excel* instructions and shown in Figure 14.3 on page 606. (Open to the **ChiSquare2x3 _FORMULAS worksheet** to examine all the formulas used in the worksheet.)

For other 2 × 3 problems, change the **Observed Frequencies** cell counts and row and column labels in rows 4 through 7. For 2 × 4 problems, use the **ChiSquare2x4 worksheet**. For 2 × 5 problems, use the **ChiSquare2x5 worksheet**. In either case, enter the contingency table data for the problem in the rows 4 through 7 Observed Frequencies area.

EG14.3 Chi-Square Test of Independence

PHStat2 Use **Chi-Square Test** to perform the chi-square test of independence. For example, to perform the Figure 14.9 test for the survey data concerning three hotels on page 624, select **PHStat → Multiple-Sample Tests → Chi-Square Test**. In the procedure's dialog box (shown below):

1. Enter **0.05** as the **Level of Significance**.
2. Enter **4** as the **Number of Rows**.
3. Enter **3** as the **Number of Columns**.
4. Enter a **Title** and click **OK**.

In the new worksheet:

5. Read the yellow note about entering values and then press the **Delete** key to delete the note.
6. Enter the Table 14.11 data on page 622, including row and column labels, in rows 4 through 9.

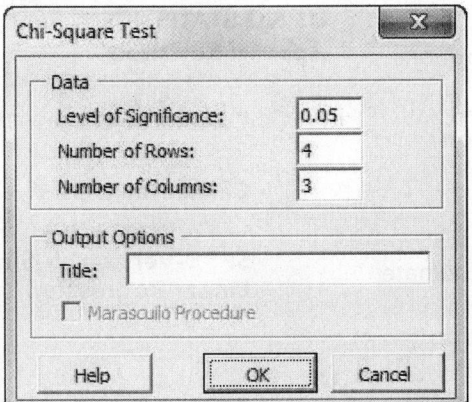

In-Depth Excel Use one of the $r \times c$ worksheets in the **Chi-Square worksheets workbook** to perform the chi-square test of independence. For example, Figure 14.9 on page 624 shows the **ChiSquare4x3 worksheet** that contains the data for Table 14.11 not-returning survey (see page 622). The worksheet computes the expected frequencies and the intermediate results for the chi-square test statistic in much the same way as the COMPUTE worksheet of the Chi-Square workbook discussed in the Section EG14.1 *In-Depth Excel* instructions.

For other 4×3 problems, change the **Observed Frequencies** cell counts and row and column labels in rows 4 through 9. For 3×4 problems, use the **ChiSquare3x4 worksheet**. For 4×3 problems, use the **ChiSquare4x3 worksheet**. For 7×3 problems, use the **ChiSquare7x3 worksheet**. For 8×3 problems, use the **ChiSquare8x3 worksheet**. In each case, enter the contingency table data for the problem in the Observed Frequencies area.

15 Simple Linear Regression

Learning Objectives
In this chapter, you learn:

- How to use regression analysis to predict the value of a dependent variable based on an independent variable
- The meaning of the regression coefficients b_0 and b_1
- How to evaluate the assumptions of regression analysis and know what to do if the assumptions are violated
- How to make inferences about the slope and correlation coefficient
- How to estimate mean values and predict individual values

Dmitriy Shironosov/Shutterstock.com

@ Sunflowers Apparel

The sales for Sunflowers Apparel, a chain of upscale clothing stores for women, have increased during the past 12 years as the chain has expanded the number of stores. Until now, Sunflowers managers selected sites based on subjective factors, such as the availability of a good lease or the perception that a location seemed ideal for an apparel store. As the new director of planning, you need to develop a systematic approach that will lead to making better decisions during the site-selection process. As a starting point, you believe that the size of the store significantly contributes to store sales, and you want to use this relationship in the decision-making process. How can you use statistics so that you can forecast the annual sales of a proposed store based on the size of that store?

crystalfoto/Shutterstock

I n this chapter and the next chapter, you learn how **regression analysis** enables you to develop a model to predict the values of a numerical variable, based on the value of other variables.

In regression analysis, the variable you wish to predict is called the **dependent variable**. The variables used to make the prediction are called **independent variables**. In addition to predicting values of the dependent variable, regression analysis also allows you to identify the type of mathematical relationship that exists between a dependent variable and an independent variable, to quantify the effect that changes in the independent variable have on the dependent variable, and to identify unusual observations. For example, as the director of planning, you might want to predict sales for a Sunflowers store based on the size of the store. Other examples include predicting the monthly rent of an apartment based on its size and predicting the monthly sales of a product in a supermarket based on the amount of shelf space devoted to the product.

This chapter discusses **simple linear regression**, in which a *single* numerical independent variable, X, is used to predict the numerical dependent variable Y, such as using the size of a store to predict the annual sales of the store. Chapter 16 discusses *multiple regression models*, which use *several* independent variables to predict a numerical dependent variable, Y. For example, you could use the amount of advertising expenditures, price, and the amount of shelf space devoted to a product to predict its monthly sales.

15.1 Types of Regression Models

In Section 3.10, you used a **scatter plot** (also known as a **scatter diagram**) to examine the relationship between an X variable on the horizontal axis and a Y variable on the vertical axis. The nature of the relationship between two variables can take many forms, ranging from simple to extremely complicated mathematical functions. The simplest relationship consists of a straight-line relationship, or **linear relationship**. Figure 15.1 illustrates a straight-line relationship.

FIGURE 15.1

A straight-line relationship

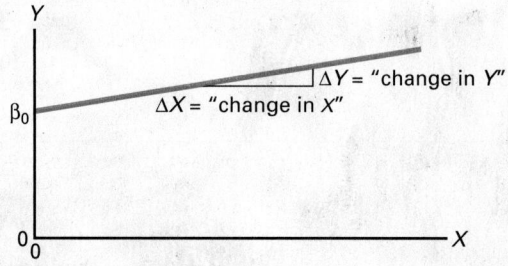

Equation (15.1) represents the straight-line (linear) model.

SIMPLE LINEAR REGRESSION MODEL

$$Y_i = \beta_0 + \beta_1 X_i + \varepsilon_i \qquad\qquad \textbf{(15.1)}$$

where

$\beta_0 = Y$ intercept for the population

$\beta_1 = $ slope for the population

$\varepsilon_i = $ random error in Y for observation i

$Y_i = $ dependent variable (sometimes referred to as the **response variable**) for observation i

$X_i = $ independent variable (sometimes referred to as the predictor, or **explanatory variable**) for observation i

The $Y_i = \beta_0 + \beta_1 X_i$ portion of the simple linear regression model expressed in Equation (15.1) is a straight line. The **slope** of the line, β_1, represents the expected change in Y per unit change in X. It represents the mean amount that Y changes (either positively or negatively) for a one-unit change in X. The **Y intercept**, β_0, represents the mean value of Y when X equals 0. The last component of the model, ε_i, represents the random error in Y for each observation, i. In other words, ε_i is the vertical distance of the actual value of Y_i above or below the expected value of Y_i on the line.

The selection of the proper mathematical model depends on the distribution of the X and Y values on the scatter plot. Figure 15.2 illustrates six different types of relationships.

FIGURE 15.2

Six types of relationships found in scatter plots

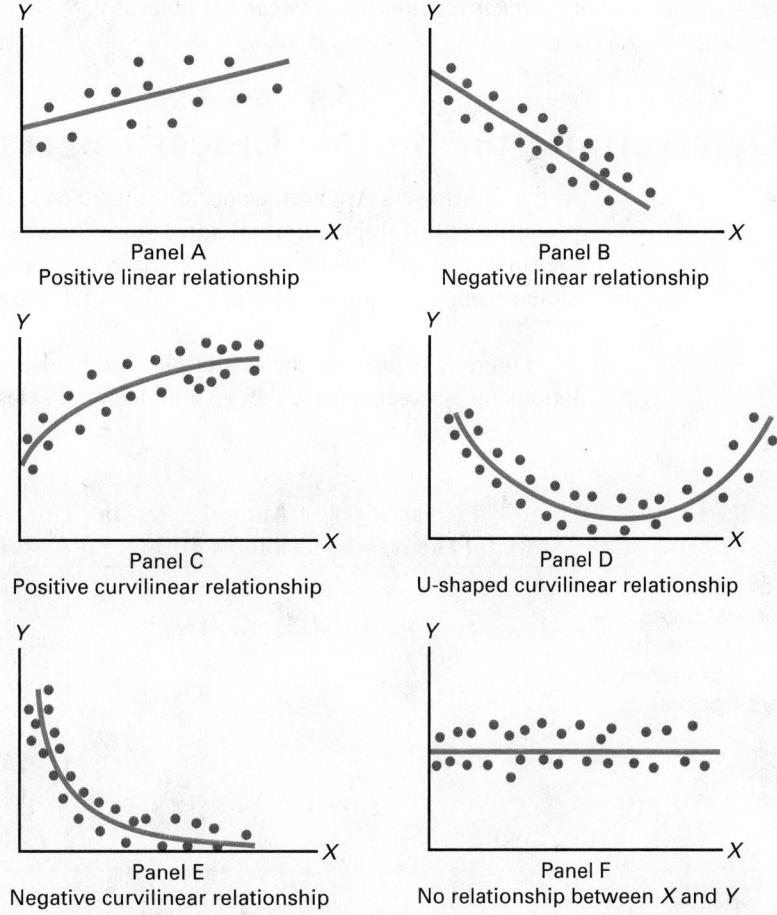

In Panel A, the values of Y are generally increasing linearly as X increases. This panel is similar to Figure 15.3 on page 644, which illustrates the positive relationship between the square footage of the store and the annual sales at branches of the Sunflowers Apparel women's clothing store chain.

Panel B is an example of a negative linear relationship. As X increases, the values of Y are generally decreasing. An example of this type of relationship might be the price of a particular product and the amount of sales.

Panel C shows a positive curvilinear relationship between X and Y. The values of Y increase as X increases, but this increase tapers off beyond certain values of X. An example of a positive curvilinear relationship might be the age and maintenance cost of a machine. As a machine gets older, the maintenance cost may rise rapidly at first but then level off beyond a certain number of years.

Panel D shows a U-shaped relationship between X and Y. As X increases, at first Y generally decreases; but as X continues to increase, Y not only stops decreasing but actually increases above its minimum value. An example of this type of relationship might be the number of errors per hour at a task and the number of hours worked. The number of errors per hour decreases as the individual becomes more proficient at the task, but then it increases beyond a certain point because of factors such as fatigue and boredom.

Panel E illustrates an exponential relationship between X and Y. In this case, Y decreases very rapidly as X first increases, but then it decreases much less rapidly as X increases further. An example of an exponential relationship could be the value of an automobile and its age. The value drops drastically from its original price in the first year, but it decreases much less rapidly in subsequent years.

Finally, Panel F shows a set of data in which there is very little or no relationship between X and Y. High and low values of Y appear at each value of X.

Although scatter plots are useful in visually displaying the mathematical form of a relationship, more sophisticated statistical procedures are available to determine the most appropriate model for a set of variables. The rest of this chapter discusses the model used when there is a *linear* relationship between variables.

15.2 Determining the Simple Linear Regression Equation

In the Sunflowers Apparel scenario on page 641, the business objective of the director of planning is to forecast annual sales for all new stores, based on store size. To examine the relationship between the store size in square feet and its annual sales, data were collected from a sample of 14 stores. Table 15.1 shows the organized data, which are stored in Site .

Figure 15.3 displays the scatter plot for the data in Table 15.1. Observe the increasing relationship between square feet (X) and annual sales (Y). As the size of the store increases,

TABLE 15.1

Square Footage (in Thousands of Square Feet) and Annual Sales (in Millions of Dollars) for a Sample of 14 Branches of Sunflowers Apparel

Store	Square Feet (Thousands)	Annual Sales (in Millions of Dollars)	Store	Square Feet (Thousands)	Annual Sales (in Millions of Dollars)
1	1.7	3.7	8	1.1	2.7
2	1.6	3.9	9	3.2	5.5
3	2.8	6.7	10	1.5	2.9
4	5.6	9.5	11	5.2	10.7
5	1.3	3.4	12	4.6	7.6
6	2.2	5.6	13	5.8	11.8
7	1.3	3.7	14	3.0	4.1

FIGURE 15.3

Scatter plot for the Sunflowers Apparel data

Scatter Diagram for Site Selection

annual sales increase approximately as a straight line. Thus, you can assume that a straight line provides a useful mathematical model of this relationship. Now you need to determine the specific straight line that is the *best* fit to these data.

How to create a scatter plot using Casio calculator fx-9750GII?

Use your Casio calculator and follow the instructions below to create a scatterplot.

First enter the data (Table 15.1) in **List 1** and **List 2** as shown below.

Square feet (thousands): X	Annual sales (in millions of dollars): Y
1.7	3.7
1.6	3.9
2.8	6.7
5.6	9.5
1.3	3.4
2.2	5.6
1.3	3.7
1.1	2.7
3.2	5.5
1.5	2.9
5.2	10.7
4.6	7.6
5.8	11.8
3.0	4.1

Input these values in **List 1** (in your calculator)   Input these values in **List 2** (in your calculator)

From the **Main Menu** select the following:

STAT   F1(GRPH)   **F6**(SET)   and you will see the following screen.

StatGraph1
Graph Type   : Scatter (F1)
Xlist   : List1
Ylist   : List2
Frequency   : 1
Mark Type   :   (F1)

Press **EXE** and then press **F1**(GPH1) to obtain the scatterplot.

The Least-Squares Method

In the preceding section, a statistical model is hypothesized to represent the relationship between two variables, square footage and sales, in the entire population of Sunflowers Apparel stores. However, as shown in Table 15.1, the data are collected from a random sample of stores. If certain assumptions are valid (see Section 15.4), you can use the sample Y intercept, b_0, and the sample slope, b_1, as estimates of the respective population parameters, β_0 and β_1. Equation (15.2) uses these estimates to form the **simple linear regression equation**. This straight line is often referred to as the **prediction line**.

SIMPLE LINEAR REGRESSION EQUATION: THE PREDICTION LINE

The predicted value of Y equals the Y intercept plus the slope multiplied by the value of X.

$$\hat{Y}_i = b_0 + b_1 X_i \tag{15.2}$$

where

$\hat{Y}_i$ = predicted value of Y for observation i

X_i = value of X for observation i

b_0 = sample Y intercept

b_1 = sample slope

Equation (15.2) requires you to determine two **regression coefficients**—b_0 (the sample Y intercept) and b_1 (the sample slope). The most common approach to finding b_0 and b_1 is using the least-squares method. This method minimizes the sum of the squared differences between the actual values (Y_i) and the predicted values ($\hat{Y}_i$) using the simple linear regression equation [i.e., the prediction line; see Equation (15.2)]. This sum of squared differences is equal to

$$\sum_{i=1}^{n} (Y_i - \hat{Y}_i)^2$$

Because $\hat{Y}_i = b_0 + b_1 X_i$,

$$\sum_{i=1}^{n} (Y_i - \hat{Y}_i)^2 = \sum_{i=1}^{n} [Y_i - (b_0 + b_1 X_i)]^2$$

[1] The equations used to compute these results are shown in Examples 15.3 and 15.4 on pages 650–652 and 658–659. You should use software to do these computations for large data sets, given the complex nature of the computations.

Because this equation has two unknowns, b_0 and b_1, the sum of squared differences depends on the sample Y intercept, b_0, and the sample slope, b_1. The **least-squares method** determines the values of b_0 and b_1 that minimize the sum of squared differences around the prediction line. Any values for b_0 and b_1 other than those determined by the least-squares method result in a greater sum of squared differences between the actual values (Y_i) and the predicted values ($\hat{Y}_i$). Figure 15.4 presents the simple linear regression model results for the Table 15.1 Sunflowers Apparel data.[1]

In Figure 15.4, observe that $b_0 = 0.9645$ and $b_1 = 1.6699$. Using Equation (15.2), the prediction line for these data is

$$\hat{Y}_i = 0.9645 + 1.6699 X_i$$

The slope, b_1, is $+1.6699$. This means that for each increase of 1 unit in X, the predicted value of Y is estimated to increase by 1.6699 units. In other words, for each increase of 1.0 thousand square feet in the size of the store, the predicted annual sales are estimated to increase by 1.6699 millions of dollars. Thus, the slope represents the portion of the annual sales that are estimated to vary according to the size of the store.

The Y intercept, b_0, is $+0.9645$. The Y intercept represents the predicted value of Y when X equals 0. Because the square footage of the store cannot be 0, this Y intercept has little or no practical interpretation. Also, the Y intercept for this example is outside the range of the observed values of the X variable, and therefore interpretations of the value of b_0 should be made cautiously. Figure 15.5 displays the actual values and the prediction line. To illustrate a situation in which there is a direct interpretation for the Y intercept, b_0, see Example 15.1.

Model Summary

Model	R	R Square	Adjusted R Square	Std. Error of the Estimate
1	.951[a]	.904	.896	.9664

a. *Predictors: (constant), square feet (thousands)*

ANOVA[b]

Model	Sum of Squares	df	Mean Square	F	Sig.
1 Regression	105.748	1	105.748	113.234	.000[a]
Residual	11.207	12	.934		
Total	116.954	13			

a. *Predictors: (constant), square feet (thousands)*
b. *Dependent Variable: Annual Sales (in millions of dollars)*

Coefficients[a]

Model	Unstandardized Coefficients		Standardized Coefficients	t	Sig.
	B	Std. Error	Beta		
1 (Constant)	.964	.526		1.833	.092
square feet (thousands)	1.670	.157	.951	10.641	.000

a. *Dependent Variable: Annual Sales (in millions of dollars)*

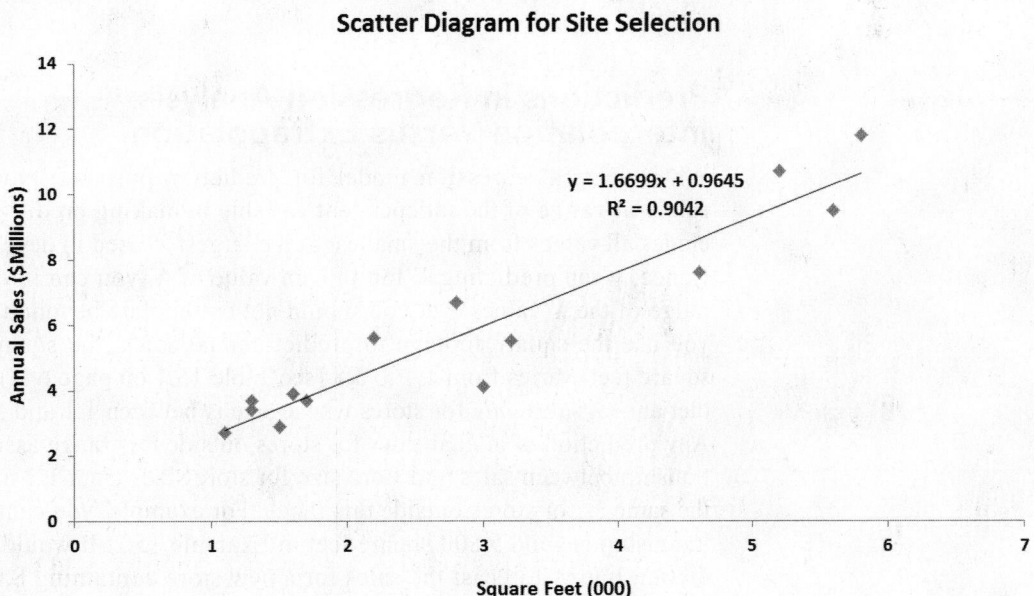

Scatter Diagram for Site Selection

$y = 1.6699x + 0.9645$
$R^2 = 0.9042$

EXAMPLE 15.1

Interpreting the Y Intercept, b_0, and the Slope, b_1

A statistics professor wants to use the number of hours a student studies for a statistics final exam (X) to predict the final exam score (Y). A regression model was fit based on data collected from a class during the previous semester, with the following results:

$$\hat{Y}_i = 35.0 + 3X_i$$

What is the interpretation of the Y intercept, b_0, and the slope, b_1?

SOLUTION The Y intercept $b_0 = 35.0$ indicates that when the student does not study for the final exam, the predicted final exam score is 35.0. The slope $b_1 = 3$ indicates that for each increase of one hour in studying time, the predicted change in the final exam score is +3.0. In other words, the final exam score is predicted to increase by a mean of 3 points for each one-hour increase in studying time.

Return to the Sunflowers Apparel scenario on page 641. Example 15.2 illustrates how you use the prediction line to predict the annual sales.

EXAMPLE 15.2

Predicting Annual Sales Based on Square Footage

Use the prediction line to predict the annual sales for a store with 4,000 square feet.

SOLUTION You can determine the predicted value by substituting $X = 4$ (thousands of square feet) into the simple linear regression equation:

$$\hat{Y}_i = 0.9645 + 1.6699X_i$$
$$\hat{Y}_i = 0.9645 + 1.6699(4) = 7.644 \text{ or } \$7,644,000$$

Thus, a store with 4,000 square feet has predicted annual sales of $7,644,000.

Predictions in Regression Analysis: Interpolation Versus Extrapolation

When using a regression model for prediction purposes, you should consider only the **relevant range** of the independent variable in making predictions. This relevant range includes all values from the smallest to the largest X used in developing the regression model. Hence, when predicting Y for a given value of X, you can interpolate within this relevant range of the X values, but you should not extrapolate beyond the range of X values. When you use the square footage to predict annual sales, the square footage (in thousands of square feet) varies from 1.1 to 5.8 (see Table 15.1 on page 644). Therefore, you should predict annual sales *only* for stores whose size is between 1.1 and 5.8 thousands of square feet. Any prediction of annual sales for stores outside this range assumes that the observed relationship between sales and store size for store sizes from 1.1 to 5.8 thousand square feet is the same as for stores outside this range. For example, you cannot extrapolate the linear relationship beyond 5,800 square feet in Example 15.2. It would be improper to use the prediction line to forecast the sales for a new store containing 8,000 square feet because the relationship between sales and store size may have a point of diminishing returns. If that is true, as square footage increases beyond 5,800 square feet, the effect on sales may become smaller and smaller.

Find prediction value using calculator

Use your Casio calculator and follow the instructions below to find the prediction value of annual sales for a store with 4,000 square feet (X=4).

You have to make sure that the data (Table 15.1) is recorded in the calculator and the simple linear regression is performed prior to computing the prediction value.

To perform the simple linear regression, first enter the data (Table 15.1) in **List 1** and **List 2** as shown below.

Square feet (thousands): X	Annual sales (in millions of dollars): Y
1.7	3.7
1.6	3.9
2.8	6.7
5.6	9.5
1.3	3.4
2.2	5.6
1.3	3.7
1.1	2.7
3.2	5.5
1.5	2.9
5.2	10.7
4.6	7.6
5.8	11.8
3.0	4.1

Input these values in **List 1** (in your calculator)   Input these values in **List 2** (in your calculator)

From the **Main Menu** select the following option:

STAT   F2(Calc)   **F6**(SET)   and you will see the following screen.

1 Var XList   : List 1
1 Var Freq   : List 2
2 Var XList   : List 1
2 Var YList   : List 2
2 Var Freq   : 1

Press **Exe**

For the regression result select **F3**(REG)   **F1**(X)   **F1**(aX+b)

To obtain predicted value for X=4, go to the main menu and select:

MENU RUN-MAT   EXE then enter **4 OPTN** (a black key just under function key F2)

Use the following options at the bottom of the display.
Select   **STAT (F5)** $\bar{y}$ **(F2)**   **EXE**

The calculator will now show the result:
7.643923

We interpret the value as follows:

$\hat{y}$ =0.96447365 + 1.66986231 (4) = 7.643923
We predict that the annual sales will be $7.644 (in millions of dollars) if the size of the store is 4(000) square feet.

Computing the Y Intercept, b_0, and the Slope, b_1

For small data sets, you can use a hand calculator to compute the least-squares regression coefficients. Equations (15.3) and (15.4) give the values of b_0 and b_1, which minimize

$$\sum_{i=1}^{n}(Y_i - \hat{Y}_i)^2 = \sum_{i=1}^{n}[Y_i - (b_0 + b_1 X_i)]^2$$

COMPUTATIONAL FORMULA FOR THE SLOPE, b_1

$$b_1 = \frac{SSXY}{SSX} \qquad (15.3)$$

where

$$SSXY = \sum_{i=1}^{n}(X_i - \overline{X})(Y_i - \overline{Y}) = \sum_{i=1}^{n}X_i Y_i - \frac{\left(\sum_{i=1}^{n}X_i\right)\left(\sum_{i=1}^{n}Y_i\right)}{n}$$

$$SSX = \sum_{i=1}^{n}(X_i - \overline{X})^2 = \sum_{i=1}^{n}X_i^2 - \frac{\left(\sum_{i=1}^{n}X_i\right)^2}{n}$$

COMPUTATIONAL FORMULA FOR THE Y INTERCEPT, b_0

$$b_0 = \overline{Y} - b_1 \overline{X} \qquad (15.4)$$

where

$$\overline{Y} = \frac{\sum_{i=1}^{n}Y_i}{n}$$

$$\overline{X} = \frac{\sum_{i=1}^{n}X_i}{n}$$

EXAMPLE 15.3

Computing the Y Intercept, b_0, and the Slope, b_1

Compute the Y intercept, b_0, and the slope, b_1, for the Sunflowers Apparel data.

SOLUTION In Equations (15.3) and (15.4), five quantities need to be computed to determine b_1 and b_0. These are n, the sample size; $\sum_{i=1}^{n}X_i$, the sum of the X values; $\sum_{i=1}^{n}Y_i$, the sum of the Y values; $\sum_{i=1}^{n}X_i^2$, the sum of the squared X values; and $\sum_{i=1}^{n}X_i Y_i$, the sum of the product of X and Y. For the Sunflowers Apparel data, the number of square feet (X) is used to predict the annual sales (Y) in a store. Table 15.2 presents the computations of the sums needed for the site selection problem. The table also includes $\sum_{i=1}^{n}Y_i^2$, the sum of the squared Y values that will be used to compute SST in Section 15.3.

TABLE 15.2

Computations for the Sunflowers Apparel Data

Store	Square Feet (X)	Annual Sales (Y)	X^2	Y^2	XY
1	1.7	3.7	2.89	13.69	6.29
2	1.6	3.9	2.56	15.21	6.24
3	2.8	6.7	7.84	44.89	18.76
4	5.6	9.5	31.36	90.25	53.20
5	1.3	3.4	1.69	11.56	4.42
6	2.2	5.6	4.84	31.36	12.32
7	1.3	3.7	1.69	13.69	4.81
8	1.1	2.7	1.21	7.29	2.97
9	3.2	5.5	10.24	30.25	17.60
10	1.5	2.9	2.25	8.41	4.35
11	5.2	10.7	27.04	114.49	55.64
12	4.6	7.6	21.16	57.76	34.96
13	5.8	11.8	33.64	139.24	68.44
14	3.0	4.1	9.00	16.81	12.30
Totals	40.9	81.8	157.41	594.90	302.30

Using Equations (15.3) and (15.4), you can compute b_0 and b_1:

$$SSXY = \sum_{i=1}^{n}(X_i - \bar{X})(Y_i - \bar{Y}) = \sum_{i=1}^{n}X_iY_i - \frac{\left(\sum_{i=1}^{n}X_i\right)\left(\sum_{i=1}^{n}Y_i\right)}{n}$$

$$SSXY = 302.3 - \frac{(40.9)(81.8)}{14}$$

$$= 302.3 - 238.97285$$

$$= 63.32715$$

$$SSX = \sum_{i=1}^{n}(X_i - \bar{X})^2 = \sum_{i=1}^{n}X_i^2 - \frac{\left(\sum_{i=1}^{n}X_i\right)^2}{n}$$

$$= 157.41 - \frac{(40.9)^2}{14}$$

$$= 157.41 - 119.48642$$

$$= 37.92358$$

Therefore,

$$b_1 = \frac{SSXY}{SSX}$$

$$= \frac{63.32715}{37.92358}$$

$$= 1.6699$$

And,

$$\bar{Y} = \frac{\sum_{i=1}^{n}Y_i}{n} = \frac{81.8}{14} = 5.842857$$

$$\bar{X} = \frac{\sum_{i=1}^{n}X_i}{n} = \frac{40.9}{14} = 2.92143$$

Therefore,

$$b_0 = \overline{Y} - b_1\overline{X}$$
$$= 5.842857 - (1.6699)(2.92143)$$
$$= 0.9645$$

CASIO Calculator Instruction

Refer to Example 15.3. Compute the Y intercept, b_0, and the slope, b_1, for the Sunflowers Apparel data.

The *Casio Calculator fx-9750GII* can perform a simple linear regression. Follow the following calculator steps to run a simple linear regression.

First, enter the data in **List 1** and **List 2**.

List 1 Square Feet (X)	List 2 Annual Sales (Y)
1.7	3.7
1.6	3.9
2.8	6.7
5.6	9.5
1.3	3.4
2.2	5.6
1.3	3.7
1.1	2.7
3.2	5.5
1.5	2.9
5.2	10.7
4.6	7.6
5.8	11.8
3.0	4.1

From the **Main Menu** select

STAT   F2(CALC)   **F6**(SET), and then set the following items:

1Var XList   :⎫
1Var Freq   :⎬ Do not need to set for **1Var**
2Var XList   : **List1**
2Var YList   : **List2**
2Var Freq   : **1**

Press **EXIT** or **EXE**, and then select **F3 (REG), F1 (X)**.

Either press F1(aX + b) or F2(a + bX) to determine the simple linear regression equation.

If you press F1 (aX + b), you will see the following solution:

LinearReg(ax + b)
    a   = 1.66986231
    b   = 0.96447365
    r   = 0.95088327
    r^2 = 0.904179
    MSe = 0.93388968
    y   = ax + b

From the results given by the calculator, the simple linear regression equation (line) will be Y = 1.66986X + 0.96447.

If you press F2 (a + bX), you will see the following solution:

LinearReg(a + bx)

a	=	0.96447365
b	=	1.66986231
r	=	0.95088327
r^2	=	0.904179
MSe	=	0.93388968
y	=	a + bx

From the results given by the calculator, the simple linear regression equation (line) will be $Y = 0.96447 + 1.66986X$.

Note: Both forms give you the same simple linear regression equation (line).

VISUAL EXPLORATIONS | Exploring Simple Linear Regression Coefficients

Use the Visual Explorations Simple Linear Regression procedure to create a prediction line that is as close as possible to the prediction line defined by the least-squares solution. Open the **Visual Explorations** add-in workbook (see Appendix Section D.4) and select **Add-ins → VisualExplorations → Simple Linear Regression**.

In the Simple Linear Regression dialog box (shown below):

1. Click for the spinner buttons for **b1 slope** (the slope of the prediction line), and **b0 intercept** (the Y intercept of the prediction line) to change the prediction line.
2. Using the visual feedback of the chart, try to create a prediction line that is as close as possible to the prediction line defined by the least-squares estimates. In other words, try to make the **Difference from Target SSE** value as small as possible. (See page 657 for an explanation of SSE.)

At any time, click **Reset** to reset the b_1 and b_0 values or **Solution** to reveal the prediction line defined by the least-squares method. Click **Finish** when you are finished with this exercise.

Using Your Own Regression Data

Select **Simple Linear Regression with your worksheet data** from the **VisualExplorations** menu to explore the simple linear regression coefficients using data you supply from a worksheet. In the procedure's dialog box, enter the cell range of your Y variable as the **Y Variable Cell Range** and the cell range of your X variable as the **X Variable Cell Range**. Click **First cells in both ranges contain a label**, enter a **Title**, and click **OK**. After the scatter plot appears onscreen, continue with the step 1 and step 2 instructions.

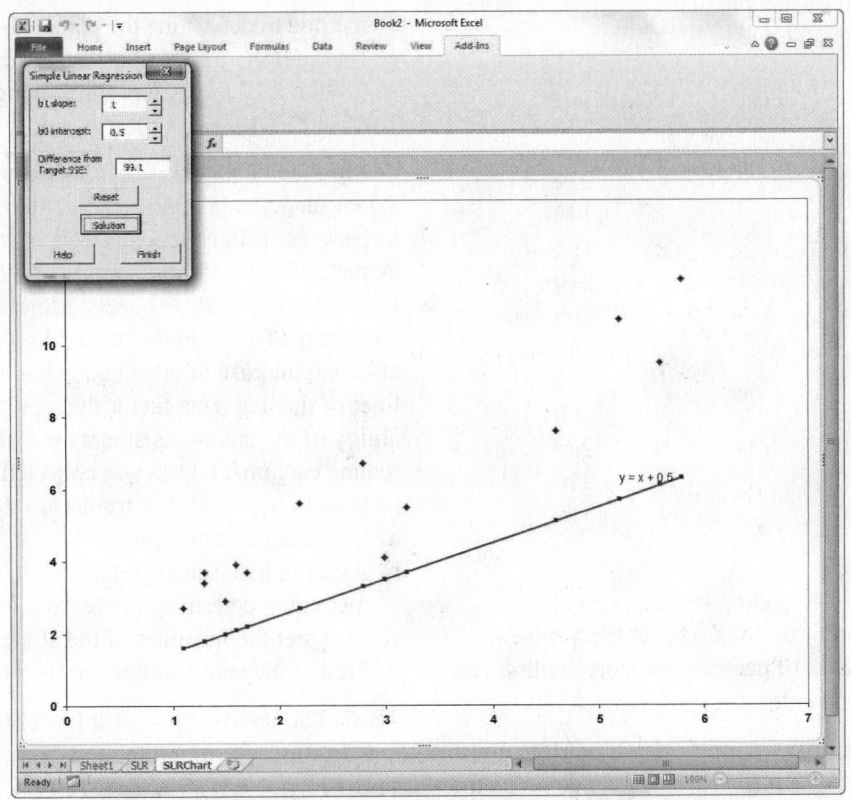

Problems for Section 15.2

LEARNING THE BASICS

15.1 Fitting a straight line to a set of data yields the following prediction line:

$$\hat{Y}_i = 2 + 5X_i$$

a. Interpret the meaning of the Y intercept, b_0.
b. Interpret the meaning of the slope, b_1.
c. Predict the value of Y for $X = 3$.

15.2 If the values of X in Problem 15.1 range from 2 to 25, should you use this model to predict the mean value of Y when X equals

a. 3?
b. −3?
c. 0?
d. 24?

15.3 Fitting a straight line to a set of data yields the following prediction line:

$$\hat{Y}_i = 16 - 0.5X_i$$

a. Interpret the meaning of the Y intercept, b_0.
b. Interpret the meaning of the slope, b_1.
c. Predict the value of Y for $X = 6$.

APPLYING THE CONCEPTS

✓SELF Test **15.4** The marketing manager of a large supermarket chain has the business objective of using shelf space most efficiently. Toward that goal, she would like to use shelf space to predict the sales of pet food. Data is collected from a random sample of 12 equal-sized stores, with the following results (stored in **Petfood**):

Store	Shelf Space (X) (Feet)	Weekly Sales (Y) ($)
1	5	160
2	5	220
3	5	140
4	10	190
5	10	240
6	10	260
7	15	230
8	15	270
9	15	280
10	20	260
11	20	290
12	20	310

a. Construct a scatter plot.
 For these data, $b_0 = 145$ and $b_1 = 7.4$.
b. Interpret the meaning of the slope, b_1, in this problem.
c. Predict the weekly sales of pet food for stores with 8 feet of shelf space for pet food.

15.5 Zagat's publishes restaurant ratings for various locations in the United States. The file **Restaurants** contains the Zagat rating for food, décor, service, and the cost per person for a sample of 100 restaurants located in New York City and in a suburb of New York City. Develop a regression model to predict the price per person, based on a variable that represents the sum of the ratings for food, décor, and service.

Sources: Extracted from *Zagat Survey 2010, New York City Restaurants;* and *Zagat Survey 2009–2010, Long Island Restaurants.*

a. Construct a scatter plot.
 For these data, $b_0 = -28.1975$ and $b_1 = 1.2409$.
b. Assuming a linear cost relationship, use the least-squares method to compute the regression coefficients b_0 and b_1.
c. Interpret the meaning of the Y intercept, b_0, and the slope, b_1, in this problem.
d. Predict the cost per person for a restaurant with a summated rating of 50.

15.6 The owner of a moving company typically has his most experienced manager predict the total number of labor hours that will be required to complete an upcoming move. This approach has proved useful in the past, but the owner has the business objective of developing a more accurate method of predicting labor hours. In a preliminary effort to provide a more accurate method, the owner has decided to use the number of cubic feet moved as the independent variable and has collected data for 36 moves in which the origin and destination were within the borough of Manhattan in New York City and in which the travel time was an insignificant portion of the hours worked. The data are stored in **Moving** .
a. Construct a scatter plot.
b. Assuming a linear relationship, use the least-squares method to determine the regression coefficients b_0 and b_1.
c. Interpret the meaning of the slope, b_1, in this problem.
d. Predict the labor hours for moving 500 cubic feet.

15.7 Starbucks Coffee Co. uses a data-based approach to improving the quality and customer satisfaction of its products. When survey data indicated that Starbucks needed to improve its package sealing process, an experiment was conducted (data extracted from L. Johnson and S. Burrows, "For Starbucks, It's In the Bag," *Quality Progress*, March 2011, pp. 17–23) to determine the factors in the bag-sealing equipment that might be affecting the ease of opening the bag without tearing the inner liner of the bag. One factor that could affect the rating of the ability of the bag to resist tears was the plate gap on the bag-sealing equipment. Data was collected on 19 bags in which the plate gap was varied. The results are stored in **Starbucks** .
a. Construct a scatter plot.
b. Assuming a linear relationship, use the least-squares method to determine the regression coefficients b_0 and b_1.
c. Interpret the meaning of the slope, b_1, in this problem.
d. Predict the tear rating when the plate gap is equal to 0.

15.8 The value of a sports franchise is directly related to the amount of revenue that a franchise can generate. The file **BBRevenue2011** represents the value in 2011 (in millions of dollars) and the annual revenue (in millions of dollars) for the 30 major league baseball franchises. (Data extracted from **www.forbes.com/lists/2011/33//baseball-valuations-11_rank.html**.) Suppose you want to develop a simple linear regression model to predict franchise value based on annual revenue generated.

a. Construct a scatter plot.
b. Use the least-squares method to determine the regression coefficients b_0 and b_1.
c. Interpret the meaning of b_0 and b_1 in this problem.
d. Predict the value of a baseball franchise that generates $150 million of annual revenue.

15.9 An agent for a residential real estate company has the business objective of developing more accurate estimates of the monthly rental cost for apartments. Toward that goal, the agent would like to use the size of an apartment, as defined by square footage to predict the monthly rental cost. The agent selects a sample of 25 apartments in a particular residential neighborhood and collects the following data (stored in Rent).

Rent ($)	Size (Square Feet)
950	850
1,600	1,450
1,200	1,085
1,500	1,232
950	718
1,700	1,485
1,650	1,136
935	726
875	700
1,150	956
1,400	1,100
1,650	1,285
2,300	1,985
1,800	1,369
1,400	1,175
1,450	1,225
1,100	1,245
1,700	1,259
1,200	1,150
1,150	896
1,600	1,361
1,650	1,040
1,200	755
800	1,000
1,750	1,200

a. Construct a scatter plot.
b. Use the least-squares method to determine the regression coefficients b_0 and b_1.
c. Interpret the meaning of b_0 and b_1 in this problem.
d. Predict the monthly rent for an apartment that has 1,000 square feet.

e. Why would it not be appropriate to use the model to predict the monthly rent for apartments that have 500 square feet?
f. Your friends Jim and Jennifer are considering signing a lease for an apartment in this residential neighborhood. They are trying to decide between two apartments, one with 1,000 square feet for a monthly rent of $1,275 and the other with 1,200 square feet for a monthly rent of $1,425. Based on (a) through (d), which apartment do you think is a better deal?

15.10 A company that holds the DVD distribution rights to movies previously released only in theaters has the business objective of developing estimates of the sales revenue of DVDs. Toward this goal, a company analyst plans to use box office gross to predict DVD sales revenue. For 22 movies, the analyst collects the box office gross (in $millions) in the year that they were released and the DVD revenue (in $millions) in the following year. The data are shown below and stored in Movie .

Title	Gross	DVD Revenue
Bolt	109.92	81.60
Madagascar: Escape 2 Africa	177.02	107.54
Quantum of Solace	166.82	44.41
Beverly Hills Chihuahua	93.78	60.21
Marley and Me	106.66	62.82
High School Musical 3 Senior Year	90.22	58.81
Bedtime Stories	85.54	48.79
Role Models	66.70	38.78
Pineapple Express	87.34	44.67
Eagle Eye	101.40	34.88
Fireproof	33.26	31.05
Momma Mia!	144.13	33.14
Seven Pounds	60.15	27.12
Australia	46.69	28.16
Valkyrie	60.73	26.43
Saw V	56.75	26.10
The Curious Case of Benjamin Button	79.30	42.04
Max Payne	40.68	25.03
Body of Lies	39.32	21.45
Nights in Rodanthe	41.80	17.51
Lakeview Terrace	39.26	21.08
The Spirit	17.74	18.78

Sources: Data extracted from **www.the-numbers.com/market/movies2008.php**; and **www.the-numbers.com/dvd/charts/annual/2009.php**.

For these data,
a. construct a scatter plot.
b. assuming a linear relationship, use the least-squares method to determine the regression coefficients b_0 and b_1.
c. interpret the meaning of the slope, b_1, in this problem.
d. predict the sales revenue for a movie DVD that had a box office gross of $75 million.

15.3 Measures of Variation

When using the least-squares method to determine the regression coefficients for a set of data, you need to compute three measures of variation. The first measure, the **total sum of squares** (*SST*), is a measure of variation of the Y_i values around their mean, $\overline{Y}$. The **total variation**, or total sum of squares, is subdivided into **explained variation** and **unexplained variation**. The explained variation, or **regression sum of squares (SSR)**, represents variation that is explained by the relationship between X and Y, and the unexplained variation, or **error sum of squares (SSE)**, represents variation due to factors other than the relationship between X and Y. Figure 15.6 shows these different measures of variation.

FIGURE 15.6

Measures of variation

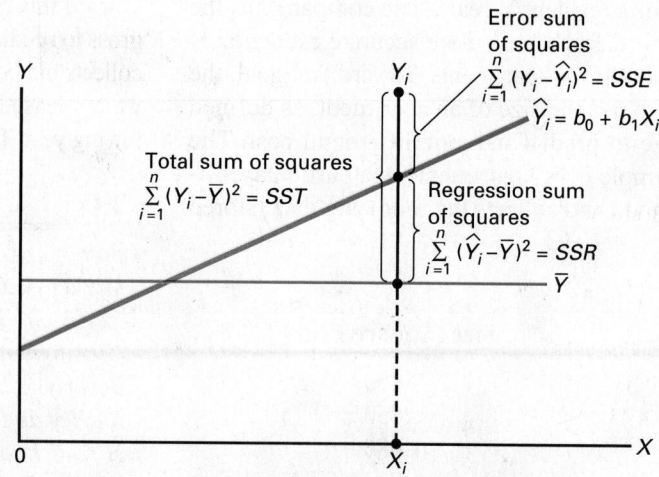

Computing the Sum of Squares

The regression sum of squares (*SSR*) is based on the difference between $\hat{Y}_i$ (the predicted value of Y from the prediction line) and $\overline{Y}$ (the mean value of Y). The error sum of squares (*SSE*) represents the part of the variation in Y that is not explained by the regression. It is based on the difference between Y_i and $\hat{Y}_i$. Equations (15.5), (15.6), (15.7), and (15.8) define these measures of variation and the total sum of squares (*SST*).

MEASURES OF VARIATION IN REGRESSION

The total sum of squares is equal to the regression sum of squares (*SSR*) plus the error sum of squares (*SSE*).

$$SST = SSR + SSE \tag{15.5}$$

TOTAL SUM OF SQUARES (*SST*)

The total sum of squares (*SST*) is equal to the sum of the squared differences between each observed value of Y and the mean value of Y.

$$SST = \text{Total sum of squares}$$

$$= \sum_{i=1}^{n}(Y_i - \overline{Y})^2 \tag{15.6}$$

REGRESSION SUM OF SQUARES (SSR)

The regression sum of squares (SSR) is equal to the sum of the squared differences between each predicted value of Y and the mean value of Y.

$$SSR = \text{Explained variation or regression sum of squares}$$

$$= \sum_{i=1}^{n}(\hat{Y}_i - \bar{Y})^2 \tag{15.7}$$

ERROR SUM OF SQUARES (SSE)

The error sum of squares (SSE) is equal to the sum of the squared differences between each observed value of Y and the predicted value of Y.

$$SSE = \text{Unexplained variation or error sum of squares}$$

$$= \sum_{i=1}^{n}(Y_i - \hat{Y}_i)^2 \tag{15.8}$$

Figure 15.7 shows the sum of squares portion of the Figure 15.4 results for the Sunflowers Apparel data. The total variation, SST, is equal to 116.9543. This amount is subdivided into the sum of squares explained by the regression (SSR), equal to 105.7476, and the sum of squares unexplained by the regression (SSE), equal to 11.2067. From Equation (15.5) on page 656:

$$SST = SSR + SSE$$
$$116.9543 = 105.7476 + 11.2067$$

FIGURE 15.7

SPSS sum of squares for the Sunflowers Apparel data

ANOVA[b]

Model	Sum of Squares	df	Mean Square	F	Sig.
1 Regression	105.748	1	105.748	113.234	.000[a]
Residual	11.207	12	.934		
Total	116.954	13			

a. *Predictors: (constant), square feet (thousands)*
b. *Dependent Variable: Annual Sales (in millions of dollars)*

Coefficients[a]

Model	Unstandardized Coefficients B	Unstandardized Coefficients Std. Error	Standardized Coefficients Beta	t	Sig.
1 (Constant)	.964	.526		1.833	.092
square feet (thousands)	1.670	.157	.951	10.641	.000

a. *Dependent Variable: Annual Sales (in millions of dollars)*

The Coefficient of Determination

By themselves, SSR, SSE, and SST provide little information. However, the ratio of the regression sum of squares (SSR) to the total sum of squares (SST) measures the proportion of variation in Y that is explained by the independent variable X in the regression model. This ratio, called the coefficient of determination, r^2, is defined in Equation (15.9).

COEFFICIENT OF DETERMINATION

The coefficient of determination is equal to the regression sum of squares (i.e., explained variation) divided by the total sum of squares (i.e., total variation).

$$r^2 = \frac{\text{Regression sum of squares}}{\text{Total sum of squares}} = \frac{SSR}{SST} \tag{15.9}$$

The **coefficient of determination** measures the proportion of variation in Y that is explained by the variation in the independent variable X in the regression model.

For the Sunflowers Apparel data, with $SSR = 105.7476$, $SSE = 11.2067$, and $SST = 116.9543$,

$$r^2 = \frac{105.7476}{116.9543} = 0.9042$$

Therefore, 90.42% of the variation in annual sales is explained by the variability in the size of the store as measured by the square footage. This large r^2 indicates a strong linear relationship between these two variables because the regression model has explained 90.42% of the variability in predicting annual sales. Only 9.58% of the sample variability in annual sales is due to factors other than what is accounted for by the linear regression model that uses square footage.

Figure 15.8 presents the regression statistics table portion of the Figure 15.4 results for the Sunflowers Apparel data. This table contains the coefficient of determination (labeled R Square in Excel and R-Sq in Minitab).

FIGURE 15.8 Excel and Minitab regression statistics for the Sunflowers Apparel data

	A	B
3	**Regression Statistics**	
4	Multiple R	0.9509
5	R Square	0.9042
6	Adjusted R Square	0.8962
7	Standard Error	0.9664
8	Observations	14

```
Predictor      Coef    SE Coef      T       P
Constant     0.9645    0.5262    1.83   0.092
Square Feet  1.6699    0.1569   10.64   0.000

S = 0.966380    R-Sq = 90.4%    R-Sq(adj) = 89.6%
```

EXAMPLE 15.4

Computing the Coefficient of Determination

Compute the coefficient of determination, r^2, for the Sunflowers Apparel data.

SOLUTION You can compute SST, SSR, and SSE, which are defined in Equations (15.6), (15.7), and (15.8) on pages 656 and 657, by using Equations (15.10), (15.11), and (15.12).

COMPUTATIONAL FORMULA FOR SST

$$SST = \sum_{i=1}^{n}(Y_i - \bar{Y})^2 = \sum_{i=1}^{n}Y_i^2 - \frac{\left(\sum_{i=1}^{n}Y_i\right)^2}{n} \tag{15.10}$$

COMPUTATIONAL FORMULA FOR *SSR*

$$SSR = \sum_{i=1}^{n}(\hat{Y}_i - \bar{Y})^2$$

$$= b_0\sum_{i=1}^{n}Y_i + b_1\sum_{i=1}^{n}X_iY_i - \frac{\left(\sum_{i=1}^{n}Y_i\right)^2}{n} \quad \textbf{(15.11)}$$

COMPUTATIONAL FORMULA FOR *SSE*

$$SSE = \sum_{i=1}^{n}(Y_i - \hat{Y}_i)^2 = \sum_{i=1}^{n}Y_i^2 - b_0\sum_{i=1}^{n}Y_i - b_1\sum_{i=1}^{n}X_iY_i \quad \textbf{(15.12)}$$

Using the summary results from Table 12.2 on page 491,

$$SST = \sum_{i=1}^{n}(Y_i - \bar{Y})^2 = \sum_{i=1}^{n}Y_i^2 - \frac{\left(\sum_{i=1}^{n}Y_i\right)^2}{n}$$

$$= 594.9 - \frac{(81.8)^2}{14}$$

$$= 594.9 - 477.94571$$

$$= 116.95429$$

$$SSR = \sum_{i=1}^{n}(\hat{Y}_i - \bar{Y})^2$$

$$= b_0\sum_{i=1}^{n}Y_i + b_1\sum_{i=1}^{n}X_iY_i - \frac{\left(\sum_{i=1}^{n}Y_i\right)^2}{n}$$

$$= (0.9645)(81.8) + (1.6699)(302.3) - \frac{(81.8)^2}{14}$$

$$= 105.74726$$

$$SSE = \sum_{i=1}^{n}(Y_i - \hat{Y}_i)^2$$

$$= \sum_{i=1}^{n}Y_i^2 - b_0\sum_{i=1}^{n}Y_i - b_1\sum_{i=1}^{n}X_iY_i$$

$$= 594.9 - (0.9645)(81.8) - (1.6699)(302.3)$$

$$= 11.2067$$

Therefore,

$$r^2 = \frac{105.74726}{116.95429} = 0.9042$$

Standard Error of the Estimate

Although the least-squares method produces the line that fits the data with the minimum amount of prediction error, unless all the observed data points fall on a straight line, the prediction line is not a perfect predictor. Just as all data values cannot be expected to be exactly equal to their mean, neither can all the values in a regression analysis be expected to fall exactly on the prediction line. Figure 15.5 on page 647 illustrates the variability around the prediction line for the Sunflowers Apparel data. Notice that many of the observed values of Y fall near the prediction line, but none of the values are exactly on the line.

The **standard error of the estimate** measures the variability of the observed Y values from the predicted Y values in the same way that the standard deviation in Chapter 3 measures the variability of each value around the sample mean. In other words, the standard error of the estimate is the standard deviation *around* the prediction line, whereas the standard deviation in Chapter 3 is the standard deviation *around* the sample mean. Equation (15.13) defines the standard error of the estimate, represented by the symbol S_{YX}.

STANDARD ERROR OF THE ESTIMATE

$$S_{YX} = \sqrt{\frac{SSE}{n-2}} = \sqrt{\frac{\sum_{i=1}^{n}(Y_i - \hat{Y}_i)^2}{n-2}} \qquad (15.13)$$

where

Y_i = actual value of Y for a given X_i
$\hat{Y}_i$ = predicted value of Y for a given X_i

SSE = error sum of squares

From Equation (15.8) and Figure 15.4 or Figure 15.7 on pages 647 or 657, $SSE = 11.2067$. Thus,

$$S_{YX} = \sqrt{\frac{11.2067}{14-2}} = 0.9664$$

This standard error of the estimate, equal to 0.9664 millions of dollars (i.e., $966,400), is labeled Standard Error in the Figure 15.8 Excel results and S in the Minitab results. The standard error of the estimate represents a measure of the variation around the prediction line. It is measured in the same units as the dependent variable Y. The interpretation of the standard error of the estimate is similar to that of the standard deviation. Just as the standard deviation measures variability around the mean, the standard error of the estimate measures variability around the prediction line. For Sunflowers Apparel, the typical difference between actual annual sales at a store and the predicted annual sales using the regression equation is approximately $966,400.

Problems for Section 15.3

LEARNING THE BASICS

15.11 How do you interpret a coefficient of determination, r^2, equal to 0.80?

15.12 If $SSR = 36$ and $SSE = 4$, determine SST, then compute the coefficient of determination, r^2, and interpret its meaning.

15.13 If $SSR = 66$ and $SST = 88$, compute the coefficient of determination, r^2, and interpret its meaning.

15.14 If $SSE = 10$ and $SSR = 30$, compute the coefficient of determination, r^2, and interpret its meaning.

15.15 If $SSR = 120$, why is it impossible for SST to equal 110?

APPLYING THE CONCEPTS

✓ **SELF** **15.16** In Problem 15.4 on page 654, the marketing
Test manager used shelf space for pet food to predict
weekly sales (stored in Petfood). For those data,
$SSR = 20,535$ and $SST = 30,025$.
a. Determine the coefficient of determination, r^2, and interpret its meaning.
b. Determine the standard error of the estimate.
c. How useful do you think this regression model is for predicting sales?

15.17 In Problem 15.5 on page 654, you used the summated rating to predict the cost of a restaurant meal (stored
in Restaurants). For those data, $SSR = 6,951.3963$ and
$SST = 15,890.11$
a. Determine the coefficient of determination, r^2, and interpret its meaning.
b. Determine the standard error of the estimate.
c. How useful do you think this regression model is for predicting audited sales?

15.18 In Problem 15.6 on page 654, an owner of a moving company wanted to predict labor hours, based on the
cubic feet moved (stored in Moving). Using the results of
that problem,
a. determine the coefficient of determination, r^2, and interpret its meaning.
b. determine the standard error of the estimate.
c. How useful do you think this regression model is for predicting labor hours?

15.19 In Problem 15.7 on page 654, you used the plate gap
on the bag-sealing equipment to predict the tear rating of a
bag of coffee (stored in Starbucks). Using the results of that
problem,
a. determine the coefficient of determination, r^2, and interpret its meaning.

b. determine the standard error of the estimate.
c. How useful do you think this regression model is for
predicting the tear rating based on the plate gap in the
bag-sealing equipment?

15.20 In Problem 15.8 on pages 654–655, you used annual
revenues to predict the value of a baseball franchise (stored
in BBRevenue2011). Using the results of that problem,
a. determine the coefficient of determination, r^2, and interpret its meaning.
b. determine the standard error of the estimate.
c. How useful do you think this regression model is for predicting the value of a baseball franchise?

15.21 In Problem 15.9 on page 655, an agent for a real
estate company wanted to predict the monthly rent for apartments, based on the size of the apartment (stored in Rent).
Using the results of that problem,
a. determine the coefficient of determination, r^2, and interpret its meaning.
b. determine the standard error of the estimate.
c. How useful do you think this regression model is for predicting the monthly rent?
d. Can you think of other variables that might explain the
variation in monthly rent?

15.22 In Problem 15.10 on page 655, you used box office
gross to predict DVD revenue (stored in Movie). Using the
results of that problem,
a. determine the coefficient of determination, r^2, and interpret its meaning.
b. determine the standard error of the estimate.
c. How useful do you think this regression model is for predicting DVD revenue?
d. Can you think of other variables that might explain the
variation in DVD revenue?

15.4 Assumptions

When hypothesis testing and the analysis of variance were discussed in Chapters 11 through
14, the importance of the assumptions to the validity of any conclusions reached was empha-
sized. The assumptions necessary for regression are similar to those of the analysis of variance
because both are part of the general category of *linear models* (reference 4).

The four **assumptions of regression** (known by the acronym LINE) are as follows:

- **L**inearity
- **I**ndependence of errors
- **N**ormality of error
- **E**qual variance

The first assumption, **linearity**, states that the relationship between variables is linear.
Relationships between variables that are not linear are discussed in Reference 4.

The second assumption, **independence of errors**, requires that the errors (ε_i) are independent of one another. This assumption is particularly important when data are collected over
a period of time. In such situations, the errors in a specific time period are sometimes correlated with those of the previous time period.

The third assumption, **normality**, requires that the errors (ε_i) are normally distributed at each value of X. Like the t test and the ANOVA F test, regression analysis is fairly robust against departures from the normality assumption. As long as the distribution of the errors at each level of X is not extremely different from a normal distribution, inferences about β_0 and β_1 are not seriously affected.

The fourth assumption, **equal variance**, or **homoscedasticity**, requires that the variance of the errors (ε_i) be constant for all values of X. In other words, the variability of Y values is the same when X is a low value as when X is a high value. The equal-variance assumption is important when making inferences about β_0 and β_1. If there are serious departures from this assumption, you can use either data transformations or weighted least-squares methods (see reference 4).

15.5 Residual Analysis

Sections 15.2 and 15.3 developed a regression model using the least-squares method for the Sunflowers Apparel data. Is this the correct model for these data? Are the assumptions presented in Section 15.4 valid? **Residual analysis** visually evaluates these assumptions and helps you determine whether the regression model that has been selected is appropriate.

The **residual**, or estimated error value, e_i, is the difference between the observed (Y_i) and predicted ($\hat{Y}_i$) values of the dependent variable for a given value of X_i. A residual appears on a scatter plot as the vertical distance between an observed value of Y and the prediction line. Equation (15.14) defines the residual.

> RESIDUAL
>
> The residual is equal to the difference between the observed value of Y and the predicted value of Y.
>
> $$e_i = Y_i - \hat{Y}_i \qquad (15.14)$$

Evaluating the Assumptions

Recall from Section 15.4 that the four assumptions of regression (known by the acronym LINE) are linearity, independence, normality, and equal variance.

Linearity To evaluate linearity, you plot the residuals on the vertical axis against the corresponding X_i values of the independent variable on the horizontal axis. If the linear model is appropriate for the data, you will not see any apparent pattern in the plot. However, if the linear model is not appropriate, in the residual plot, there will be a relationship between the X_i values and the residuals, e_i.

You can see such a pattern in Figure 15.9. Panel A shows a situation in which, although there is an increasing trend in Y as X increases, the relationship seems curvilinear because the upward trend decreases for increasing values of X. This quadratic effect is highlighted in Panel B, where there is a clear relationship between X_i and e_i. By plotting the residuals, the linear trend of X with Y has been removed, thereby exposing the lack of fit in the simple linear model. Thus, a quadratic model is a better fit and should be used instead of the simple linear model.

FIGURE 15.9
Studying the appropriateness of the simple linear regression model

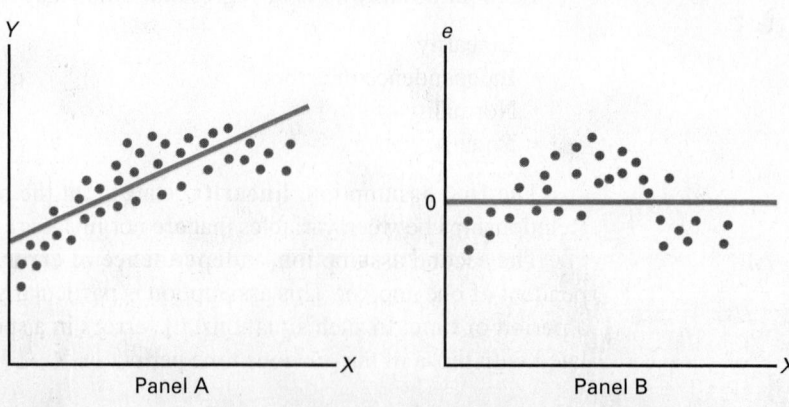

Panel A   Panel B

To determine whether the simple linear regression model is appropriate, return to the evaluation of the Sunflowers Apparel data. Figure 15.10 displays the predicted annual sales values and residuals.

FIGURE 15.10

Table of residuals for the Sunflowers Apparel data

	A	B	C	D	E
1	Observation	Square Feet	Predicted Annual Sales	Annual Sales	Residuals
2	1	1.7	3.803239598	3.7	0.103239598
3	2	1.6	3.636253367	3.9	-0.263746633
4	3	2.8	5.640088147	6.7	-1.059911853
5	4	5.6	10.31570263	9.5	0.815702635
6	5	1.3	3.135294672	3.4	-0.264705328
7	6	2.2	4.638170757	5.6	-0.961829243
8	7	1.3	3.135294672	3.7	-0.564705328
9	8	1.1	2.801322208	2.7	0.101322208
10	9	3.2	6.308033074	5.5	0.808033074
11	10	1.5	3.469267135	2.9	0.569267135
12	11	5.2	9.647757708	10.7	-1.052242292
13	12	4.6	8.645840318	7.6	1.045840318
14	13	5.8	10.6496751	11.8	-1.150324902
15	14	3.0	5.974060611	4.1	1.874060611

To assess linearity, the residuals are plotted against the independent variable (store size, in thousands of square feet) in Figure 15.11. Although there is widespread scatter in the residual plot, there is no clear pattern or relationship between the residuals and X_i. The residuals appear to be evenly spread above and below 0 for different values of X. You can conclude that the linear model is appropriate for the Sunflowers Apparel data.

FIGURE 15.11

Plot of residuals against the square footage of a store for the Sunflowers Apparel data

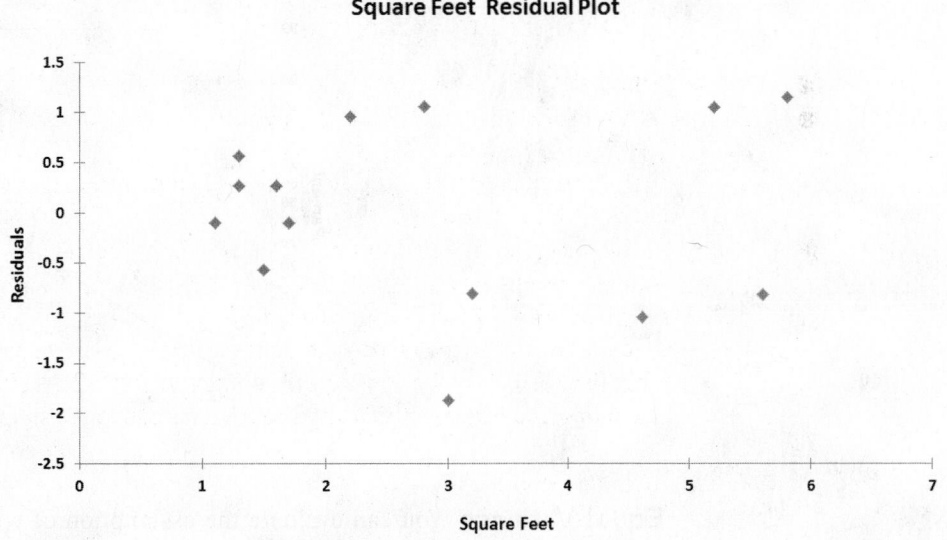

Independence You can evaluate the assumption of independence of the errors by plotting the residuals in the order or sequence in which the data were collected. If the values of Y are part of a time series (see Section 3.10), one residual may sometimes be related to the previous residual. If this relationship exists between consecutive residuals (which violates the assumption of independence), the plot of the residuals versus the time in which the data were collected will often show a cyclical pattern. Because the Sunflowers Apparel data were collected during the same time period, you do not need to evaluate the independence assumption for these data.

Normality You can evaluate the assumption of normality in the errors by organizing the residuals into a frequency distribution as shown in Table 15.3. You cannot construct a meaningful histogram because the sample size is too small. And with such a small sample size ($n = 14$), it can be difficult to evaluate the normality assumption by using a stem-and-leaf display, a boxplot, or a normal probability plot.

TABLE 15.3

Frequency Distribution of 14 Residual Values for the Sunflowers Apparel Data

Residuals	Frequency
−2.25 but less than −1.75	1
−1.75 but less than −1.25	0
−1.25 but less than −0.75	3
−0.75 but less than −0.25	1
−0.25 but less than +0.25	2
+0.25 but less than +0.75	3
+0.75 but less than +1.25	4
	14

From the normal probability plot of the residuals in Figure 15.12, the data do not appear to depart substantially from a normal distribution. The robustness of regression analysis with modest departures from normality enables you to conclude that you should not be overly concerned about departures from this normality assumption in the Sunflowers Apparel data.

FIGURE 15.12

Excel and Minitab normal probability plots of the residuals for the Sunflowers Apparel data

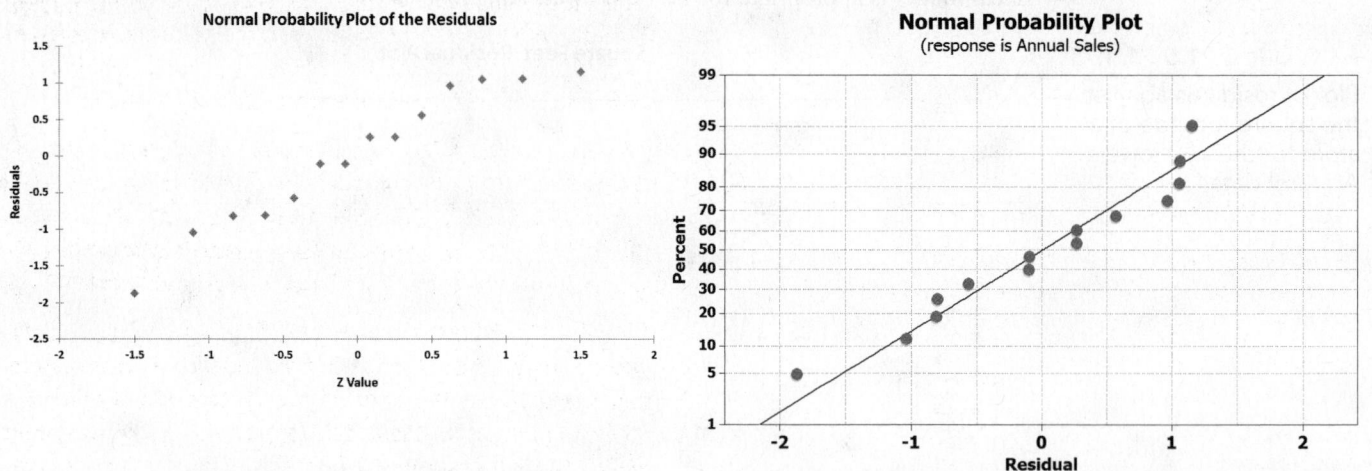

Equal Variance You can evaluate the assumption of equal variance from a plot of the residuals with X_i. For the Sunflowers Apparel data of Figure 15.11 on page 663, there do not appear to be major differences in the variability of the residuals for different X_i values. Thus, you can conclude that there is no apparent violation in the assumption of equal variance at each level of X.

To examine a case in which the equal-variance assumption is violated, observe Figure 15.13, which is a plot of the residuals with X_i for a hypothetical set of data. This plot is fan shaped because the variability of the residuals increases dramatically as X increases. Because this plot shows unequal variances of the residuals at different levels of X, the equal-variance assumption is invalid.

FIGURE 15.13
Violation of equal variance

Residuals

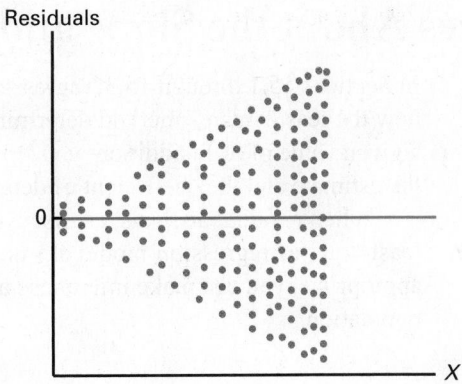

Problems for Section 15.5

LEARNING THE BASICS

15.23 The following results provide the X values, residuals, and a residual plot from a regression analysis:

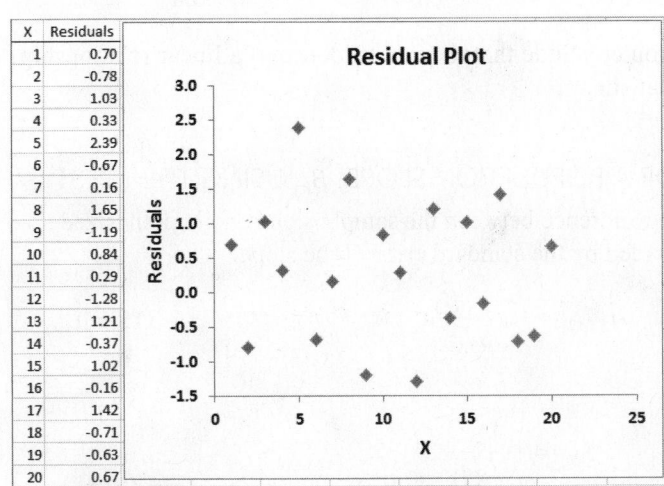

X	Residuals
1	0.70
2	-0.78
3	1.03
4	0.33
5	2.39
6	-0.67
7	0.16
8	1.65
9	-1.19
10	0.84
11	0.29
12	-1.28
13	1.21
14	-0.37
15	1.02
16	-0.16
17	1.42
18	-0.71
19	-0.63
20	0.67

Is there any evidence of a pattern in the residuals? Explain.

15.24 The following results show the X values, residuals, and a residual plot from a regression analysis:

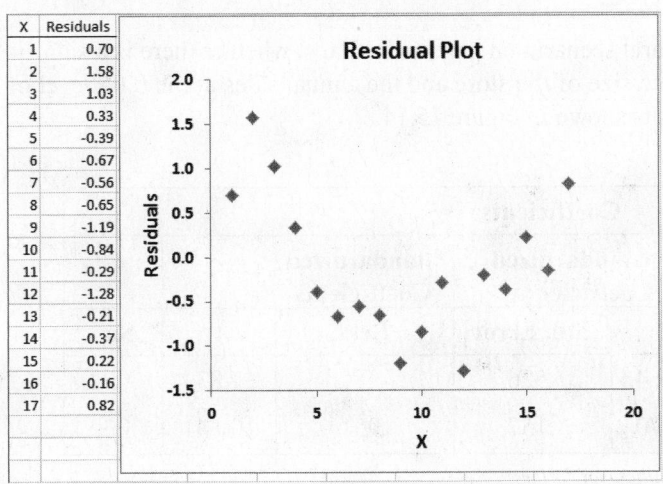

X	Residuals
1	0.70
2	1.58
3	1.03
4	0.33
5	-0.39
6	-0.67
7	-0.56
8	-0.65
9	-1.19
10	-0.84
11	-0.29
12	-1.28
13	-0.21
14	-0.37
15	0.22
16	-0.16
17	0.82

Is there any evidence of a pattern in the residuals? Explain.

APPLYING THE CONCEPTS

15.25 In Problem 15.5 on page 654, you used the summated rating to predict the cost of a restaurant meal. Perform a residual analysis for these data (stored in **Restaurants**). Evaluate whether the assumptions of regression have been seriously violated.

✓ **SELF** **15.26** In Problem 15.4 on page 654, the marketing **Test** manager used shelf space for pet food to predict weekly sales. Perform a residual analysis for these data (stored in **Petfood**). Evaluate whether the assumptions of regression have been seriously violated.

15.27 In Problem 15.7 on page 654, you used the plate gap on the bag-sealing equipment to predict the tear rating of a bag of coffee. Perform a residual analysis for these data (stored in **Starbucks**). Based on these results, evaluate whether the assumptions of regression have been seriously violated.

15.28 In Problem 15.6 on page 654, the owner of a moving company wanted to predict labor hours based on the cubic feet moved. Perform a residual analysis for these data (stored in **Moving**). Based on these results, evaluate whether the assumptions of regression have been seriously violated.

15.29 In Problem 15.9 on page 655, an agent for a real estate company wanted to predict the monthly rent for apartments, based on the size of the apartments. Perform a residual analysis for these data (stored in **Rent**). Based on these results, evaluate whether the assumptions of regression have been seriously violated.

15.30 In Problem 15.8 on page 654, you used annual revenues to predict the value of a baseball franchise. Perform a residual analysis for these data (stored in **BBRevenue2011**). Based on these results, evaluate whether the assumptions of regression have been seriously violated.

15.31 In Problem 15.10 on page 655, you used box office gross to predict DVD revenue. Perform a residual analysis for these data (stored in **Movie**). Based on these results, evaluate whether the assumptions of regression have been seriously violated.

15.6 Inferences About the Slope and Correlation Coefficient

In Sections 15.1 through 15.3, regression was used solely for descriptive purposes. You learned how the least-squares method determines the regression coefficients and how to predict Y for a given value of X. In addition, you learned how to compute and interpret the standard error of the estimate and the coefficient of determination.

When residual analysis, as discussed in Section 15.5, indicates that the assumptions of a least-squares regression model are not seriously violated and that the straight-line model is appropriate, you can make inferences about the linear relationship between the variables in the population.

t Test for the Slope

To determine the existence of a significant linear relationship between the X and Y variables, you test whether β_1 (the population slope) is equal to 0. The null and alternative hypotheses are as follows:

$$H_0: \beta_1 = 0 \ [\text{There is no linear relationship (the slope is zero).}]$$
$$H_1: \beta_1 \neq 0 \ [\text{There is a linear relationship (the slope is not zero).}]$$

If you reject the null hypothesis, you conclude that there is evidence of a linear relationship. Equation (15.15) defines the test statistic.

TESTING A HYPOTHESIS FOR A POPULATION SLOPE, β_1, USING THE t TEST

The t_{STAT} test statistic equals the difference between the sample slope and hypothesized value of the population slope divided by the standard error of the slope.

$$t_{STAT} = \frac{b_1 - \beta_1}{S_{b_1}} \tag{15.15}$$

where

$$S_{b_1} = \frac{S_{YX}}{\sqrt{SSX}}$$
$$SSX = \sum_{i=1}^{n} (X_i - \bar{X})^2$$

The t_{STAT} test statistic follows a t distribution with $n - 2$ degrees of freedom.

Return to the Sunflowers Apparel scenario on page 641. To test whether there is a significant linear relationship between the size of the store and the annual sales at the 0.05 level of significance, refer to the t test results shown in Figure 15.14.

FIGURE 15.14
SPSS t test results of the slope for the Sunflowers Apparel data

Coefficients[a]					
	Unstandardized Coefficients		**Standardized Coefficients**		
Model	**B**	**Std. Error**	**Beta**	**t**	**Sig.**
1 (Constant)	.964	.526		1.833	.092
square feet (thousands)	1.670	.157	.951	10.641	.000

a. *Dependent Variable: Annual Sales (in millions of dollars)*

From Figures 15.4 and 15.14,

$$b_1 = +1.6699 \quad n = 14 \quad S_{b_1} = 0.1569$$

and

$$t_{STAT} = \frac{b_1 - \beta_1}{S_{b_1}}$$

$$= \frac{1.6699 - 0}{0.1569} = 10.6411$$

Using the 0.05 level of significance, the critical value of t with $n - 2 = 12$ degrees of freedom is 2.1788. Because $t_{STAT} = 10.6411 > 2.1788$ or because the p-value is approximately 0, which is less than $\alpha = 0.05$, you reject H_0 (see Figure 15.15). Hence, you can conclude that there is a significant linear relationship between mean annual sales and the size of the store.

FIGURE 15.15

Testing a hypothesis about the population slope at the 0.05 level of significance, with 12 degrees of freedom

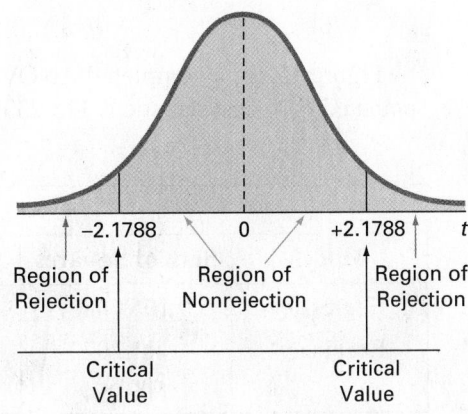

F Test for the Slope

As an alternative to the t test, in simple linear regression, you can use an F test to determine whether the slope is statistically significant. In Section 12.4, you used the F distribution to test the ratio of two variances. Equation (15.16) defines the F test for the slope as the ratio of the variance that is due to the regression (MSR) divided by the error variance ($MSE = S_{YX}^2$).

TESTING A HYPOTHESIS FOR A POPULATION SLOPE, β_1, USING THE F TEST

The F_{STAT} test statistic is equal to the regression mean square (MSR) divided by the mean square error (MSE).

$$F_{STAT} = \frac{MSR}{MSE} \qquad (15.16)$$

where

$$MSR = \frac{SSR}{1} = SSR$$

$$MSE = \frac{SSE}{n - 2}$$

The F_{STAT} test statistic follows an F distribution with 1 and $n - 2$ degrees of freedom.

Using a level of significance α, the decision rule is

$$\text{Reject } H_0 \text{ if } F_{STAT} > F_\alpha;$$

$$\text{otherwise, do not reject } H_0.$$

Table 15.4 organizes the complete set of results into an analysis of variance (ANOVA) table.

TABLE 15.4

ANOVA Table for Testing the Significance of a Regression Coefficient

Source	df	Sum of Squares	Mean Square (Variance)	F
Regression	1	SSR	$MSR = \dfrac{SSR}{1} = SSR$	$F_{STAT} = \dfrac{MSR}{MSE}$
Error	$n - 2$	SSE	$MSE = \dfrac{SSE}{n - 2}$	
Total	$n - 1$	SST		

Figure 15.16, a completed ANOVA table for the Sunflowers sales data, shows that the computed F_{STAT} test statistic is 113.2335 and the p-value is approximately 0.

FIGURE 15.16

SPSS *F*-test results for the Sunflowers Apparel data

See the "Performing Simple Linear Regression Analyses" section in Appendix 15.1 to create the worksheet that contains this.

ANOVA[b]					
Model	Sum of Squares	df	Mean Square	F	Sig.
1 Regression	105.748	1	105.748	113.234	.000[a]
Residual	11.207	12	.934		
Total	116.954	13			

a. *Predictors: (constant), square feet (thousands)*
b. *Dependent Variable: Annual Sales (in millions of dollars)*

Coefficients[a]					
	Unstandardized Coefficients		Standardized Coefficients		
Model	B	Std. Error	Beta	t	Sig.
1 (Constant)	.964	.526		1.833	.092
square feet (thousands)	1.670	.157	.951	10.641	.000

a. *Dependent Variable: Annual Sales (in millions of dollars)*

Using a level of significance of 0.05, from Table E.5, the critical value of the F distribution, with 1 and 12 degrees of freedom, is 4.75 (see Figure 15.17). Because $F_{STAT} = 113.2335 > 4.75$ or because the p-value $= 0.0000 < 0.05$, you reject H_0 and conclude that there is a significant linear relationship between the size of the store and annual sales. Because the F test in Equation (15.16) on page 667 is equivalent to the t test in Equation (15.15) on page 666, you reach the same conclusion.

FIGURE 15.17

Regions of rejection and nonrejection when testing for the significance of the slope at the 0.05 level of significance, with 1 and 12 degrees of freedom

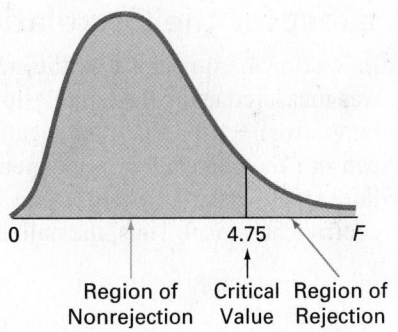

Confidence Interval Estimate for the Slope

As an alternative to testing for the existence of a linear relationship between the variables, you can construct a confidence interval estimate of β_1 using Equation (15.17).

CONFIDENCE INTERVAL ESTIMATE OF THE SLOPE, β_1

The confidence interval estimate for the population slope can be constructed by taking the sample slope, b_1, and adding and subtracting the critical t value multiplied by the standard error of the slope.

$$b_1 \pm t_{\alpha/2}S_{b_1}$$
$$b_1 - t_{\alpha/2}S_{b_1} \le \beta_1 \le b_1 + t_{\alpha/2}S_{b_1} \qquad \textbf{(15.17)}$$

where

$t_{\alpha/2}$ = critical value corresponding to an upper-tail probability of $\alpha/2$ from the t distribution with $n - 2$ degrees of freedom (i.e., a cumulative area of $1 - \alpha/2$).

From the Figure 15.14 results on page 666,

$$b_1 = 1.6699 \quad n = 14 \quad S_{b_1} = 0.1569$$

To construct a 95% confidence interval estimate, $\alpha/2 = 0.025$, and from Table E.3, $t_{\alpha/2} = 2.1788$. Thus,

$$b_1 \pm t_{\alpha/2}S_{b_1} = 1.6699 \pm (2.1788)(0.1569)$$
$$= 1.6699 \pm 0.3419$$
$$1.3280 \le \beta_1 \le 2.0118$$

Therefore, you estimate with 95% confidence that the population slope is between 1.3280 and 2.0118. Because these values are both above 0, you conclude that there is a significant linear relationship between annual sales and the size of the store. Had the interval included 0, you would have concluded that no significant relationship exists between the variables. The confidence interval indicates that for each increase of 1,000 square feet, predicted annual sales are estimated to increase by at least $1,328,000 but no more than $2,011,800.

t Test for the Correlation Coefficient

In Section 4.5 on page 174, the strength of the relationship between two numerical variables was measured using the **correlation coefficient**, r. The values of the coefficient of correlation range from -1 for a perfect negative correlation to $+1$ for a perfect positive correlation. You can use the correlation coefficient to determine whether there is a statistically significant linear relationship between X and Y. To do so, you hypothesize that the population correlation coefficient, ρ, is 0. Thus, the null and alternative hypotheses are

$$H_0: \rho = 0 \text{ (no correlation)}$$

$$H_1: \rho \neq 0 \text{ (correlation)}$$

Equation (15.18) defines the test statistic for determining the existence of a significant correlation.

TESTING FOR THE EXISTENCE OF CORRELATION

$$t_{STAT} = \frac{r - \rho}{\sqrt{\dfrac{1 - r^2}{n - 2}}} \qquad \textbf{(15.18a)}$$

where

$$r = +\sqrt{r^2} \text{ if } b_1 > 0$$

$$r = -\sqrt{r^2} \text{ if } b_1 < 0$$

The t_{STAT} test statistic follows a t distribution with $n - 2$ degrees of freedom. r is calculated as follows:

$$r = \frac{\text{cov}(X,Y)}{S_X S_Y} \qquad \textbf{(15.18b)}$$

where

$$\text{cov}(X, Y) = \frac{\displaystyle\sum_{i=1}^{n}(X_i - \overline{X})(Y_i - \overline{Y})}{n - 1}$$

$$S_X = \sqrt{\frac{\displaystyle\sum_{i=1}^{n}(X_i - \overline{X})^2}{n - 1}}$$

$$S_Y = \sqrt{\frac{\displaystyle\sum_{i=1}^{n}(Y_i - \overline{Y})^2}{n - 1}}$$

In the Sunflowers Apparel problem, $r^2 = 0.9042$ and $b_1 = +1.6699$ (see Figure 15.4 on page 647). Because $b_1 > 0$, the correlation coefficient for annual sales and store size is the positive square root of r^2, that is, $r = +\sqrt{0.9042} = +0.9509$. Using Equation (15.18a) to test the null hypothesis that there is no correlation between these two variables results in the following observed t statistic:

$$t_{STAT} = \frac{r - 0}{\sqrt{\dfrac{1 - r^2}{n - 2}}}$$

$$= \frac{0.9509 - 0}{\sqrt{\frac{1 - (0.9509)^2}{14 - 2}}} = 10.6411$$

Using the 0.05 level of significance, because $t_{STAT} = 10.6411 > 2.1788$, you reject the null hypothesis. You conclude that there is a significant association between annual sales and store size. This t_{STAT} test statistic is equivalent to the t_{STAT} test statistic found when testing whether the population slope, β_1, is equal to zero.

CASIO Calculator Instruction

Refer to Example 15.3. To test the slope and the correlation coefficient, use the Casio Calculator fx-9750GII and follow the following calculator steps:

First, enter the data in **List 1** and **List 2**.

List 1 Square Feet (X)	List 2 Annual Sales (Y)
1.7	3.7
1.6	3.9
2.8	6.7
5.6	9.5
1.3	3.4
2.2	5.6
1.3	3.7
1.1	2.7
3.2	5.5
1.5	2.9
5.2	10.7
4.6	7.6
5.8	11.8
3.0	4.1

From the **Main Menu** select

STAT F3(TEST) **F2**(t) **F3**(REG), and then set the following items:

LinearReg t Test

β & ρ	: $\neq$ (F1)
XList	: List1
YList	: List2
Freq	: 1
Save Res	: None
Execute	

Press **EXE** to obtain the result.

LinearReg tTest

$\beta \neq 0$ & $\rho \neq 0$

t	= 10.6411237
p	= 1.8227E-07
df	= 12
a	= 0.96447365
b	= 1.66986232
se	= 0.96637967
r	= 0.95088327
r^2	= 0.904179

Problems for Section 15.6

LEARNING THE BASICS

15.32 You are testing the null hypothesis that there is no linear relationship between two variables, X and Y. From your sample of $n = 10$, you determine that $r = 0.80$.
a. What is the value of the t test statistic t_{STAT}?
b. At the $\alpha = 0.05$ level of significance, what are the critical values?
c. Based on your answers to (a) and (b), what statistical decision should you make?

15.33 You are testing the null hypothesis that there is no linear relationship between two variables, X and Y. From your sample of $n = 18$, you determine that $b_1 = +4.5$ and $S_{b_1} = 1.5$.
a. What is the value of t_{STAT}?
b. At the $\alpha = 0.05$ level of significance, what are the critical values?
c. Based on your answers to (a) and (b), what statistical decision should you make?
d. Construct a 95% confidence interval estimate of the population slope, β_1.

15.34 You are testing the null hypothesis that there is no linear relationship between two variables, X and Y. From your sample of $n = 20$, you determine that $SSR = 60$ and $SSE = 40$.
a. What is the value of F_{STAT}?
b. At the $\alpha = 0.05$ level of significance, what is the critical value?
c. Based on your answers to (a) and (b), what statistical decision should you make?
d. Compute the correlation coefficient by first computing r^2 and assuming that b_1 is negative.
e. At the 0.05 level of significance, is there a significant correlation between X and Y?

APPLYING THE CONCEPTS

✓SELF Test **15.35** In Problem 15.4 on page 654, the marketing manager used shelf space for pet food to predict weekly sales. The data are stored in **Petfood**. From the results of that problem, $b_1 = 7.4$ and $S_{b_1} = 1.59$.
a. At the 0.05 level of significance, is there evidence of a linear relationship between shelf space and sales?
b. Construct a 95% confidence interval estimate of the population slope, β_1.

15.36 In Problem 15.5 on page 654, you used the summated rating of a restaurant to predict the cost of a meal. The data are stored in **Restaurants**. Using the results of that problem, $b_1 = 1.2409$ and $S_{b_1} = 0.1421$.
a. At the 0.05 level of significance, is there evidence of a linear relationship between the summated rating of a restaurant and the cost of a meal?
b. Construct a 95% confidence interval estimate of the population slope, β_1.

15.37 In Problem 15.6 on page 654, the owner of a moving company wanted to predict labor hours, based on the number of cubic feet moved. The data are stored in **Moving**. Use the results of that problem.
a. At the 0.05 level of significance, is there evidence of a linear relationship between the number of cubic feet moved and labor hours?
b. Construct a 95% confidence interval estimate of the population slope, β_1.

15.38 In Problem 15.7 on page 654, you used the plate gap in the bag-sealing equipment to predict the tear rating of a bag of coffee. The data are stored in **Starbucks**. Use the results of that problem.
a. At the 0.05 level of significance, is there evidence of a linear relationship between the plate gap of the bag-sealing machine and the tear rating of a bag of coffee?
b. Construct a 95% confidence interval estimate of the population slope, β_1.

15.39 In Problem 15.8 on page 654, you used annual revenues to predict the value of a baseball franchise. The data are stored in **BBRevenue2011**. Use the results of that problem.
a. At the 0.05 level of significance, is there evidence of a linear relationship between annual revenue and franchise value?
b. Construct a 95% confidence interval estimate of the population slope, β_1.

15.40 In Problem 15.9 on page 655, an agent for a real estate company wanted to predict the monthly rent for apartments, based on the size of the apartment. The data are stored in **Rent**. Use the results of that problem.
a. At the 0.05 level of significance, is there evidence of a linear relationship between the size of the apartment and the monthly rent?
b. Construct a 95% confidence interval estimate of the population slope, β_1.

15.41 In Problem 15.10 on page 655, you used box office gross to predict DVD revenue. The data are stored in **Movie**. Use the results of that problem.
a. At the 0.05 level of significance, is there evidence of a linear relationship between box office gross and DVD revenue?
b. Construct a 95% confidence interval estimate of the population slope, β_1.

15.42 The volatility of a stock is often measured by its beta value. You can estimate the beta value of a stock by developing a simple linear regression model, using the percentage weekly change in the stock as the dependent variable and the percentage weekly change in a market index as the independent variable. The S&P 500 Index is a common index to use. For example, if you wanted to estimate the beta value for Disney, you could use the following model, which is sometimes referred to as a *market model*:

$$(\% \text{ weekly change in Disney}) = \beta_0$$

$$+ \beta_1(\% \text{ weekly change in S \& P 500 index}) + \varepsilon$$

The least-squares regression estimate of the slope b_1 is the estimate of the beta value for Disney. A stock with a beta value of 1.0 tends to move the same as the overall market. A stock with a beta value of 1.5 tends to move 50% more than the overall market, and a stock with a beta value of 0.6 tends to move only 60% as much as the overall market. Stocks with negative beta values tend to move in the opposite direction of the overall market. The following table gives some beta values for some widely held stocks as of May 19, 2011:

a. For each of the six companies, interpret the beta value.
b. How can investors use the beta value as a guide for investing?

Company	Ticker Symbol	Beta
Procter & Gamble	PG	0.52
AT&T	T	0.59
Disney	DIS	1.19
Apple	AAPL	1.14
eBay	EBAY	1.57
Ford	F	−0.24

Source: Data extracted from **finance.yahoo.com**, May 19, 2011.

15.43 Index funds are mutual funds that try to mimic the movement of leading indexes, such as the S&P 500 or the Russell 2000. The beta values (as described in Problem 15.49) for these funds are therefore approximately 1.0, and the estimated market models for these funds are approximately

$$(\% \text{ weekly change in index fund}) =$$

$$0.0 + 1.0(\% \text{ weekly change in the index})$$

Leveraged index funds are designed to magnify the movement of major indexes. Direxion Funds is a leading provider of leveraged index and other alternative-class mutual fund products for investment advisors and sophisticated investors. Two of the company's funds are shown in the following table. (Data extracted from **www.direxionfunds.com**, May 17, 2011.)

Name	Ticker Symbol	Description
Daily Small Cap 3x Fund	TNA	300% of the Russell 2000 Index
Daily India Bull 2x Fund	INDL	200% of the Indus India Index

The estimated market models for these funds are approximately

$(\% \text{ weekly change in TNA}) = 0.0 + 3.0$
$(\% \text{ weekly change in the Russell 2000})$
$(\% \text{ weekly change in INDL}) = 0.0 + 2.0$
$(\% \text{ weekly change in the Indus India Index})$

Thus, if the Russell 2000 Index gains 10% over a period of time, the leveraged mutual fund TNA gains approximately 30%. On the downside, if the same index loses 20%, TNA loses approximately 60%.

a. The objective of the Direxion Funds Large Cap Bull 3x fund, BGU, is 300% of the performance of the Russell 1000 Index. What is its approximate market model?
b. If the Russell 1000 Index gains 10% in a year, what return do you expect BGU to have?
c. If the Russell 1000 Index loses 20% in a year, what return do you expect BGU to have?
d. What type of investors should be attracted to leveraged index funds? What type of investors should stay away from these funds?

15.44 The file Cereals contains the calories and sugar, in grams, in one serving of seven breakfast cereals:

Cereal	Calories	Sugar
Kellogg's All Bran	80	6
Kellogg's Corn Flakes	100	2
Wheaties	100	4
Nature's Path Organic Multigrain Flakes	110	4
Kellogg's Rice Krispies	130	4
Post Shredded Wheat Vanilla Almond	190	11
Kellogg's Mini Wheats	200	10

a. Compute and interpret the coefficient of correlation, r.
b. At the 0.05 level of significance, is there a significant linear relationship between calories and sugar?

15.45 Movie companies need to predict the gross receipts of an individual movie once the movie has debuted. The following results (stored in PotterMovies) are the first weekend gross, the U.S. gross, and the worldwide gross (in $millions) of the six Harry Potter movies that debuted from 2001 to 2009:

Title	First Weekend	U.S. Gross	Worldwide Gross
Sorcerer's Stone	90.295	317.558	976.458
Chamber of Secrets	88.357	261.988	878.988
Prisoner of Azkaban	93.687	249.539	795.539
Goblet of Fire	102.335	290.013	896.013
Order of the Phoenix	77.108	292.005	938.469
Half-Blood Prince	77.836	301.460	934.601

Source: Data extracted from **www.the-numbers.com/interactive/comp-Harry-Potter.php**.

a. Compute the coefficient of correlation between first weekend gross and the U.S. gross, first weekend gross and the worldwide gross, and the U.S. gross and worldwide gross.

b. At the 0.05 level of significance, is there a significant linear relationship between first weekend gross and the U.S. gross, first weekend gross and the worldwide gross, and the U.S. gross and worldwide gross?

15.46 College basketball is big business, with coaches' salaries, revenues, and expenses in millions of dollars. The file College Basketball contains the coaches' salary and revenue for college basketball at 60 of the 65 schools that played in the 2009 NCAA men's basketball tournament. (Data extracted from "Compensation for Division I Men's Basketball Coaches," *USA Today*, April 2, 2010, p. 8C; and C. Isadore, "Nothing but Net: Basketball Dollars by School," **money.cnn.com/2010/03/18/news/companies/basketball_ profits/**.)

a. Compute and interpret the coefficient of correlation, r.

b. At the 0.05 level of significance, is there a significant linear relationship between a coach's salary and revenue?

15.47 College football players trying out for the NFL are given the Wonderlic standardized intelligence test. The file Wonderlic lists the average Wonderlic scores of football players trying out for the NFL and the graduation rates for football players at the schools they attended. (Data extracted from S. Walker, "The NFL's Smartest Team," *The Wall Street Journal*, September 30, 2005, pp. W1, W10.)

a. Compute and interpret the coefficient of correlation, r.

b. At the 0.05 level of significance, is there a significant linear relationship between the average Wonderlic score of football players trying out for the NFL and the graduation rates for football players at selected schools?

c. What conclusions can you reach about the relationship between the average Wonderlic score of football players trying out for the NFL and the graduation rates for football players at selected schools?

15.7 Estimation of Mean Values and Prediction of Individual Values

In Chapter 10, you studied the concept of the confidence interval estimate of the population mean. In Example 15.2 on page 648, you used the prediction line to predict the mean value of Y for a given X. The annual sales for stores with 4,000 square feet was predicted to be 7.644 millions of dollars ($7,644,000). This estimate, however, is a *point estimate* of the population mean. This section presents methods to develop a confidence interval estimate for the mean response for a given X and for developing a prediction interval for an individual response, Y, for a given value of X.

The Confidence Interval Estimate

Equation (15.19) defines the **confidence interval estimate for the mean reponse** for a given X.

CONFIDENCE INTERVAL ESTIMATE FOR THE MEAN OF Y

$$\hat{Y}_i \pm t_{\alpha/2} S_{YX} \sqrt{h_i}$$

$$\hat{Y}_i - t_{\alpha/2} S_{YX} \sqrt{h_i} \leq \mu_{Y|X=X_i} \leq \hat{Y}_i + t_{\alpha/2} S_{YX} \sqrt{h_i} \qquad (15.19)$$

where

$$h_i = \frac{1}{n} + \frac{(X_i - \bar{X})^2}{SSX}$$

$\hat{Y}_i$ = predicted value of Y; $\hat{Y}_i = b_0 + b_1 X_i$

S_{YX} = standard error of the estimate

n = sample size

X_i = given value of X

$\mu_{Y|X=X_i}$ = mean value of Y when $X = X_i$

$$SSX = \sum_{i=1}^{n} (X_i - \bar{X})^2$$

$t_{\alpha/2}$ = critical value corresponding to an upper-tail probability of $\alpha/2$ from the t distribution with $n - 2$ degrees of freedom (i.e., a cumulative area of $1 - \alpha/2$).

The width of the confidence interval in Equation (15.19) depends on several factors. Increased variation around the prediction line, as measured by the standard error of the estimate, results in a wider interval. As you would expect, increased sample size reduces the width of the interval. In addition, the width of the interval varies at different values of X. When you predict Y for values of X close to $\overline{X}$, the interval is narrower than for predictions for X values farther away from $\overline{X}$.

In the Sunflowers Apparel example, suppose you want to construct a 95% confidence interval estimate of the mean annual sales for the entire population of stores that contain 4,000 square feet ($X = 4$). Using the simple linear regression equation,

$$\hat{Y}_i = 0.9645 + 1.6699X_i$$
$$= 0.9645 + 1.6699(4) = 7.6439 \text{ (millions of dollars)}$$

Also, given the following:

$$\overline{X} = 2.9214 \quad S_{YX} = 0.9664$$
$$SSX = \sum_{i=1}^{n}(X_i - \overline{X})^2 = 37.9236$$

From Table E.3, $t_{\alpha/2} = 2.1788$. Thus,

$$\hat{Y}_i \pm t_{\alpha/2}S_{YX}\sqrt{h_i}$$

where

$$h_i = \frac{1}{n} + \frac{(X_i - \overline{X})^2}{SSX}$$

so that

$$\hat{Y}_i \pm t_{\alpha/2}S_{YX}\sqrt{\frac{1}{n} + \frac{(X_i - \overline{X})^2}{SSX}}$$
$$= 7.6439 \pm (2.1788)(0.9664)\sqrt{\frac{1}{14} + \frac{(4 - 2.9214)^2}{37.9236}}$$
$$= 7.6439 \pm 0.6728$$

so

$$6.9711 \leq \mu_{Y/X=4} \leq 8.3167$$

Therefore, the 95% confidence interval estimate is that the mean annual sales are between $6,971,100 and $8,316,700 for the population of stores with 4,000 square feet.

The Prediction Interval

In addition to constructing a confidence interval for the mean value of Y, you can also construct a prediction interval for an individual value of Y. Although the form of this interval is similar to that of the confidence interval estimate of Equation (15.19), the prediction interval is predicting an individual value, not estimating a mean. Equation (15.20) defines the **prediction interval for an individual response, Y,** at a given value, X_i, denoted by $Y_{X=X_i}$.

PREDICTION INTERVAL FOR AN INDIVIDUAL RESPONSE, Y

$$\hat{Y}_i \pm t_{\alpha/2}S_{YX}\sqrt{1 + h_i} \qquad (15.20)$$

$$\hat{Y}_i - t_{\alpha/2}S_{YX}\sqrt{1 + h_i} \leq Y_{X=X_i} \leq \hat{Y}_i + t_{\alpha/2}S_{YX}\sqrt{1 + h_i}$$

where

$Y_{X=X_i}$ = future value of Y when $X = X_i$

$t_{\alpha/2}$ = critical value corresponding to an upper-tail probability of $\alpha/2$ from the t distribution with $n - 2$ degrees of freedom (i.e., a cumulative area of $1 - \alpha/2$)

In addition, h_i, $\hat{Y}_i$, S_{YX}, n, and X_i are defined as in Equation (15.19) on page 674.

To construct a 95% prediction interval of the annual sales for an individual store that contains 4,000 square feet ($X = 4$), you first compute $\hat{Y}_i$. Using the prediction line:

$$\hat{Y}_i = 0.9645 + 1.6699X_i$$
$$= 0.9645 + 1.6699(4)$$
$$= 7.6439 \text{ (millions of dollars)}$$

Also, given the following:

$$\overline{X} = 2.9214 \quad S_{YX} = 0.9664$$

$$SSX = \sum_{i=1}^{n}(X_i - \overline{X})^2 = 37.9236$$

From Table E.3, $t_{\alpha/2} = 2.1788$. Thus,

$$\hat{Y}_i \pm t_{\alpha/2}S_{YX}\sqrt{1 + h_i}$$

where

$$h_i = \frac{1}{n} + \frac{(X_i - \overline{X})^2}{\sum_{i=1}^{n}(X_i - \overline{X})^2}$$

so that

$$\hat{Y}_i \pm t_{\alpha/2}S_{YX}\sqrt{1 + \frac{1}{n} + \frac{(X_i - \overline{X})^2}{SSX}}$$

$$= 7.6439 \pm (2.1788)(0.9664)\sqrt{1 + \frac{1}{14} + \frac{(4 - 2.9214)^2}{37.9236}}$$

$$= 7.6439 \pm 2.2104$$

so

$$5.4335 \leq Y_{X=4} \leq 9.8543$$

Therefore, with 95% confidence, you predict that the annual sales for an individual store with 4,000 square feet is between \$5,433,500 and \$9,854,300.

Figure 15.18 presents results for the confidence interval estimate and the prediction interval for the Sunflowers Apparel data. If you compare the results of the confidence interval estimate and the prediction interval, you see that the width of the prediction interval for an individual store is much wider than the confidence interval estimate for the mean. Remember that there is much more variation in predicting an individual value than in estimating a mean value.

FIGURE 15.18

SPSS confidence interval estimate and prediction interval worksheet for the Sunflowers Apparel data

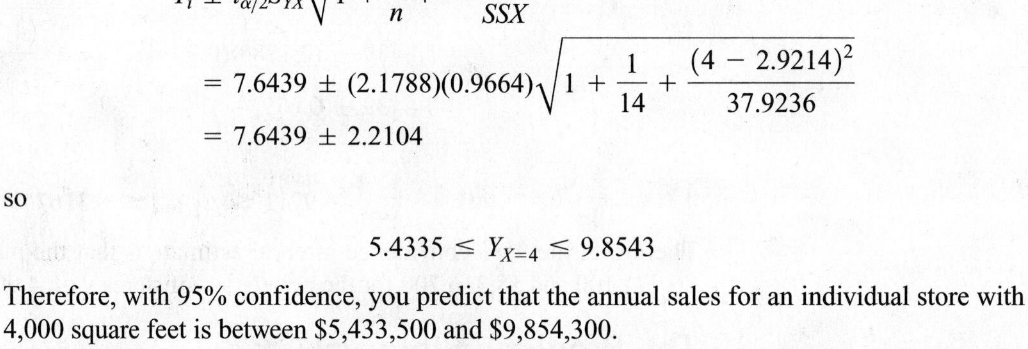

	size	sales	PRE_1	RES_1	LMCI_1	UMCI_1	LICI_1	UICI_1
1	1.7	3.7	3.80324	-0.10324	3.10247	4.50401	1.58413	6.02235
2	1.6	3.9	3.63625	0.26375	2.91459	4.35792	1.41045	5.86205
3	2.8	6.7	5.64009	1.05991	5.07582	6.20435	3.46023	7.81995
4	5.6	9.5	10.31570	-0.81570	9.24080	11.39061	7.95164	12.67977
5	1.3	3.4	3.13529	0.26471	2.34535	3.92524	0.88643	5.38416
6	2.2	5.6	4.63817	0.96183	4.02375	5.25259	2.44479	6.83155
7	1.3	3.7	3.13529	0.56471	2.34535	3.92524	0.88643	5.38416
8	1.1	2.7	2.80132	-0.10132	1.96197	3.64067	0.53463	5.06801
9	3.2	5.5	6.30803	-0.80803	5.73729	6.87877	4.12649	8.48958
10	1.5	2.9	3.46927	-0.56927	2.72572	4.21282	1.23628	5.70226
11	5.2	10.7	9.64776	1.05224	8.68671	10.60881	7.33324	11.96228
12	4.6	7.6	8.64584	-1.04584	7.84206	9.44962	6.39208	10.89960
13	5.8	11.8	10.64968	1.15032	9.51594	11.78341	8.25829	13.04106
14	3.0	4.1	5.97406	-1.87406	5.41069	6.53744	3.79443	8.15369
15								

Problems for Section 15.7

LEARNING THE BASICS

15.48 Based on a sample of $n = 20$, the least-squares method was used to develop the following prediction line: $\hat{Y}_i = 5 + 3X_i$.
In addition,

$$S_{YX} = 1.0 \quad \bar{X} = 2 \quad \sum_{i=1}^{n} (X_i - \bar{X})^2 = 20$$

a. Construct a 95% confidence interval estimate of the population mean response for $X = 2$.
b. Construct a 95% prediction interval of an individual response for $X = 2$.

15.49 Based on a sample of $n = 20$, the least-squares method was used to develop the following prediction line: $\hat{Y}_i = 5 + 3X_i$.
In addition,

$$S_{YX} = 1.0 \quad \bar{X} = 2 \quad \sum_{i=1}^{n} (X_i - \bar{X})^2 = 20$$

a. Construct a 95% confidence interval estimate of the population mean response for $X = 4$.
b. Construct a 95% prediction interval of an individual response for $X = 4$.
c. Compare the results of (a) and (b) with those of Problem 15.55 (a) and (b). Which intervals are wider? Why?

APPLYING THE CONCEPTS

15.50 In Problem 15.5 on page 654, you used the summated rating of a restaurant to predict the cost of a meal. The data are stored in Restaurants. For these data, $S_{YX} = 9.5505$ and $h_i = 0.026844$ when $X = 50$.
a. Construct a 95% confidence interval estimate of the mean cost of a meal for restaurants that have a summated rating of 50.
b. Construct a 95% prediction interval of the cost of a meal for an individual restaurant that has a summated rating of 50.
c. Explain the difference in the results in (a) and (b).

✓ SELF **15.51** In Problem 15.4 on page 654, the marketing
Test manager used shelf space for pet food to predict weekly sales. The data are stored in Petfood. For these data, $S_{YX} = 30.81$ and $h_i = 0.1373$ when $X = 8$.
a. Construct a 95% confidence interval estimate of the mean weekly sales for all stores that have 8 feet of shelf space for pet food.
b. Construct a 95% prediction interval of the weekly sales of an individual store that has 8 feet of shelf space for pet food.
c. Explain the difference in the results in (a) and (b).

15.52 In Problem 15.7 on page 654, you used the plate gap on the bag-sealing equipment to predict the tear rating of a bag of coffee. The data are stored in Starbucks.
a. Construct a 95% confidence interval estimate of the mean tear rating for all bags of coffee when the plate gap is 0.
b. Construct a 95% prediction interval of the tear rating for an individual bag of coffee when the plate gap is 0.
c. Why is the interval in (a) narrower than the interval in (b)?

15.53 In Problem 15.6 on page 654, the owner of a moving company wanted to predict labor hours based on the number of cubic feet moved. The data are stored in Moving.
a. Construct a 95% confidence interval estimate of the mean labor hours for all moves of 500 cubic feet.
b. Construct a 95% prediction interval of the labor hours of an individual move that has 500 cubic feet.
c. Why is the interval in (a) narrower than the interval in (b)?

15.54 In Problem 15.9 on page 655, an agent for a real estate company wanted to predict the monthly rent for apartments, based on the size of an apartment. The data are stored in Rent.
a. Construct a 95% confidence interval estimate of the mean monthly rental for all apartments that are 1,000 square feet in size.
b. Construct a 95% prediction interval of the monthly rental for an individual apartment that is 1,000 square feet in size.
c. Explain the difference in the results in (a) and (b).

15.55 In Problem 15.8 on page 654, you predicted the value of a baseball franchise, based on current revenue. The data are stored in BBRevenue2011.
a. Construct a 95% confidence interval estimate of the mean value of all baseball franchises that generate $150 million of annual revenue.
b. Construct a 95% prediction interval of the value of an individual baseball franchise that generates $150 million of annual revenue.
c. Explain the difference in the results in (a) and (b).

15.56 In Problem 15.10 on page 655, you used box office gross to predict DVD revenue. The data are stored in Movie. The company is about to release a movie on DVD that had a box office gross of $75 million.
a. What is the predicted DVD revenue?
b. Which interval is more useful here, the confidence interval estimate of the mean or the prediction interval for an individual response? Explain.
c. Construct and interpret the interval you selected in (b).

15.8 Pitfalls in Regression

Some of the pitfalls involved in using regression analysis are as follows:

- Lacking awareness of the assumptions of least-squares regression
- Not knowing how to evaluate the assumptions of least-squares regression
- Not knowing what the alternatives are to least-squares regression if a particular assumption is violated
- Using a regression model without knowledge of the subject matter
- Extrapolating outside the relevant range
- Concluding that a significant relationship identified in an observational study is due to a cause-and-effect relationship

The widespread availability of spreadsheet and statistical applications has made regression analysis much more feasible today than it once was. However, many users with access to such applications do not understand how to use regression analysis properly. Someone who is not familiar with either the assumptions of regression or how to evaluate the assumptions cannot be expected to know what the alternatives to least-squares regression are if a particular assumption is violated.

The data in Table 15.5 (stored in `Anscombe`) illustrate the importance of using scatter plots and residual analysis to go beyond the basic number crunching of computing the Y intercept, the slope, and r^2.

TABLE 15.5

Four Sets of Artificial Data

Data Set A		Data Set B		Data Set C		Data Set D	
X_i	Y_i	X_i	Y_i	X_i	Y_i	X_i	Y_i
10	8.04	10	9.14	10	7.46	8	6.58
14	9.96	14	8.10	14	8.84	8	5.76
5	5.68	5	4.74	5	5.73	8	7.71
8	6.95	8	8.14	8	6.77	8	8.84
9	8.81	9	8.77	9	7.11	8	8.47
12	10.84	12	9.13	12	8.15	8	7.04
4	4.26	4	3.10	4	5.39	8	5.25
7	4.82	7	7.26	7	6.42	19	12.50
11	8.33	11	9.26	11	7.81	8	5.56
13	7.58	13	8.74	13	12.74	8	7.91
6	7.24	6	6.13	6	6.08	8	6.89

Source: Data extracted from F. J. Anscombe, "Graphs in Statistical Analysis," *The American Statistician*, 27 (1973), 17–21.

Anscombe (reference 1) showed that all four data sets given in Table 15.5 have the following identical results:

$$\hat{Y}_i = 3.0 + 0.5X_i$$

$$S_{YX} = 1.237$$

$$S_{b_1} = 0.118$$

$$r^2 = 0.667$$

$$SSR = \text{Explained variation} = \sum_{i=1}^{n}(\hat{Y}_i - \bar{Y})^2 = 27.51$$

$$SSE = \text{Unexplained variation} = \sum_{i=1}^{n}(Y_i - \hat{Y}_i)^2 = 13.76$$

$$SST = \text{Total variation} = \sum_{i=1}^{n}(Y_i - \bar{Y})^2 = 41.27$$

If you stopped the analysis at this point, you would fail to observe the important differences among the four data sets.

From the scatter plots of Figure 15.19 and the residual plots of Figure 15.20, you see how different the data sets are. Each has a different relationship between X and Y. The only data set that seems to approximately follow a straight line is data set A. The residual plot for data set A does not show any obvious patterns or outlying residuals. This is certainly not true for data sets B, C, and D. The scatter plot for data set B shows that a curvilinear regression model is more appropriate. This conclusion is reinforced by the residual plot for data set B. The scatter plot and the residual plot for data set C clearly show an outlying observation. In this case, one approach used is to remove the outlier and reestimate the regression model (see reference 4). The scatter plot for data set D represents a situation in which the model is heavily dependent on the outcome of a single data point ($X_8 = 19$ and $Y_8 = 12.50$). Any regression model with this characteristic should be used with caution.

In summary, scatter plots and residual plots are of vital importance to a complete regression analysis. The information they provide is so basic to a credible analysis that you should always include these graphical methods as part of a regression analysis. Thus, a strategy you can use to help avoid the pitfalls of regression is as follows:

1. Start with a scatter plot to observe the possible relationship between X and Y.
2. Check the assumptions of regression (**l**inearity, **i**ndependence, **n**ormality, **e**qual variance) by performing a residual analysis that includes the following:
   a. Plotting the residuals versus the independent variable to determine whether the linear model is appropriate and to check for equal variance
   b. Constructing a histogram, stem-and-leaf display, boxplot, or normal probability plot of the residuals to check for normality
   c. Plotting the residuals versus time to check for independence (this step is necessary only if the data are collected over time)

FIGURE 15.19

Scatter plots for four data sets

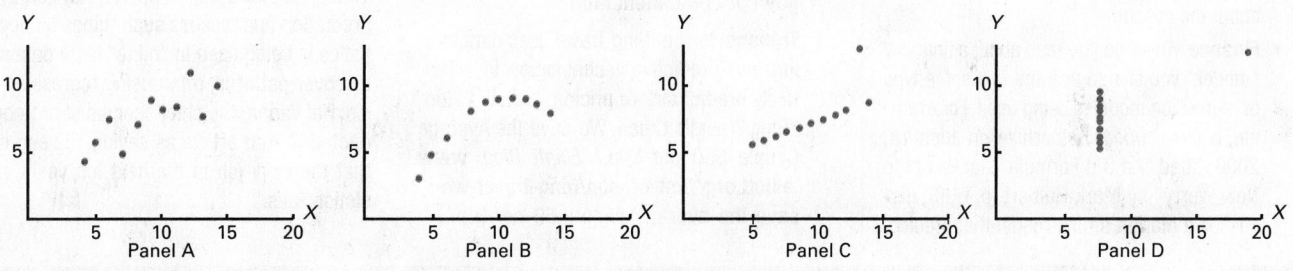

FIGURE 15.20

Residual plots for four data sets

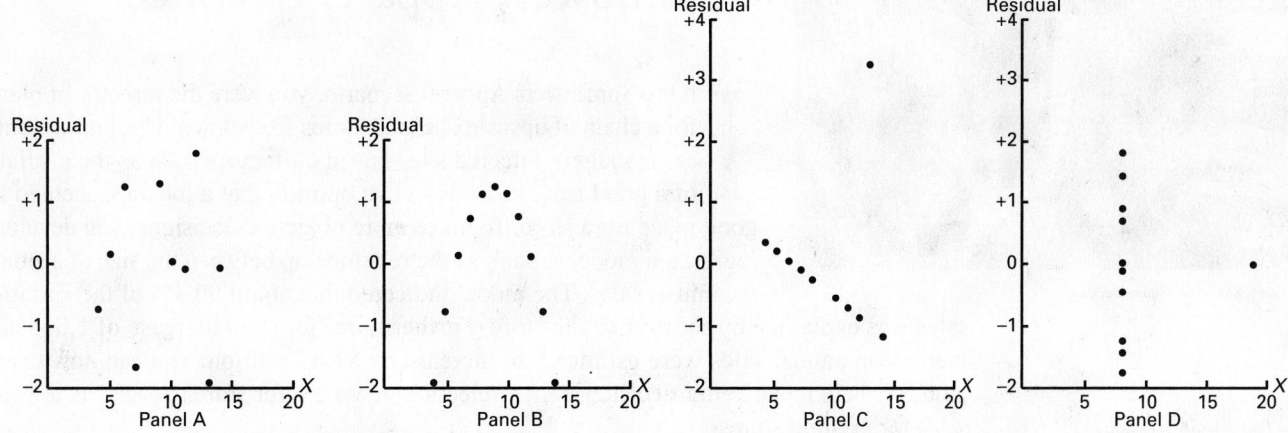

3. If there are violations of the assumptions, use alternative methods to least-squares regression or alternative least-squares models (see reference 4).

4. If there are no violations of the assumptions, carry out tests for the significance of the regression coefficients and develop confidence and prediction intervals.

5. Avoid making predictions and forecasts outside the relevant range of the independent variable.

6. Keep in mind that the relationships identified in observational studies may or may not be due to cause-and-effect relationships. Remember that, although causation implies correlation, correlation does not imply causation.

THINK ABOUT THIS   By Any Other Name

You may not have frequently heard the phrase "regression model" outside a classroom, but the basic concepts of regression can be found under a variety of names in many sectors of the economy:

- **Advertising and marketing** Managers use econometric models (in other words, regression models) to determine the effect of an advertisement on sales, based on a set of factors. In one recent example, the number of tweets that mention specific products was used to make accurate prediction of sales trends. (See H. Rui, A. Whinston, and E. Winkler, "Follow the Tweets," *The Wall Street Journal*, November 30, 2009, p. R4.) Also, managers use data mining to predict patterns of behavior of what customers will buy in the future, based on historic information about the consumer.

- **Finance** Any time you read about a financial "model," you should assume that some type of regression model is being used. For example, a *New York Times* article on June 18, 2006, titled "An Old Formula That Points to New Worry" by Mark Hulbert (p. BU8), discusses a market timing model that predicts

the returns of stocks in the next three to five years, based on the dividend yield of the stock market and the interest rate of 90-day Treasury bills.

- **Food and beverage** Enologix, a California consulting company, has developed a "formula" (a regression model) that predicts a wine's quality index, based on a set of chemical compounds found in the wine. (See D. Darlington, "The Chemistry of a 90+ Wine," *The New York Times Magazine*, August 7, 2005, pp. 36–39.)

- **Government** The Bureau of Labor Statistics uses hedonic models, a type of regression model, to adjust and manage its consumer price index ("Hedonic Quality Adjustment in the CPI," *Consumer Price Index*, **stat.bls.gov/cpi/cpihqaitem.htm**).

- **Transportation** Bing Travel uses data mining and predictive technologies to objectively predict airfare pricing. (See C. Elliott, "Bing Travel's Crean: We Save the Average Couple $50 per Trip," *Elliott Blog*, **www.elliott.org/first-person/bing-travel-we-save-the-average-couple-50-per-trip/**.)

- **Real estate** Zillow.com uses information about the features contained in a home and its location to develop estimates about the market value of the home, using a "formula" built with a proprietary model.

In a famous 2006 cover story, *BusinessWeek* predicted that statistics and probability will become core skills for businesspeople and consumers. (see S. Baker, "Why Math Will Rock Your World: More Math Geeks Are Calling the Shots in Business. Is Your Industry Next?" *BusinessWeek*, January 23, 2006, pp. 54–62.). Successful people, the article noted, would know how to use statistics, whether they are building financial models or making marketing plans. More recent articles, including S. Lohr's "For Today's Graduate, Just One Word: Statistics" (*The New York Times*, August 6, 2009, pp. A1, A3) confirm this prediction and discuss such things as how statistics is being used to "mine" large data sets to discover patterns, often using regression models. Hal Varian, the chief economist at Google, is quoted in that article as saying, "I keep saying that the sexy job in the next ten years will be statisticians."

USING STATISTICS   @Sunflowers Apparel Revisited

Dmitriy Shironosov/Shutterstock.com

In the Sunflowers Apparel scenario, you were the director of planning for a chain of upscale clothing stores for women. Until now, Sunflowers managers selected sites based on factors such as the availability of a good lease or a subjective opinion that a location seemed like a good place for a store. To make more objective decisions, you developed a regression model to analyze the relationship between the size of a store and its annual sales. The model indicated that about 90.4% of the variation in sales was explained by the size of the store. Furthermore, for each increase of 1,000 square feet, mean annual sales were estimated to increase by $1.67 million. You can now use your model to help make better decisions when selecting new sites for stores as well as to forecast sales for existing stores.

SUMMARY

As you can see from the chapter roadmap in Figure 15.21, this chapter develops the simple linear regression model and discusses the assumptions and how to evaluate them. Once you are assured that the model is appropriate, you can predict values by using the prediction line and test for the significance of the slope. In Chapter 16, regression analysis is extended to situations in which more than one independent variable is used to predict the value of a dependent variable.

FIGURE 15.21
Roadmap for simple
linear regression

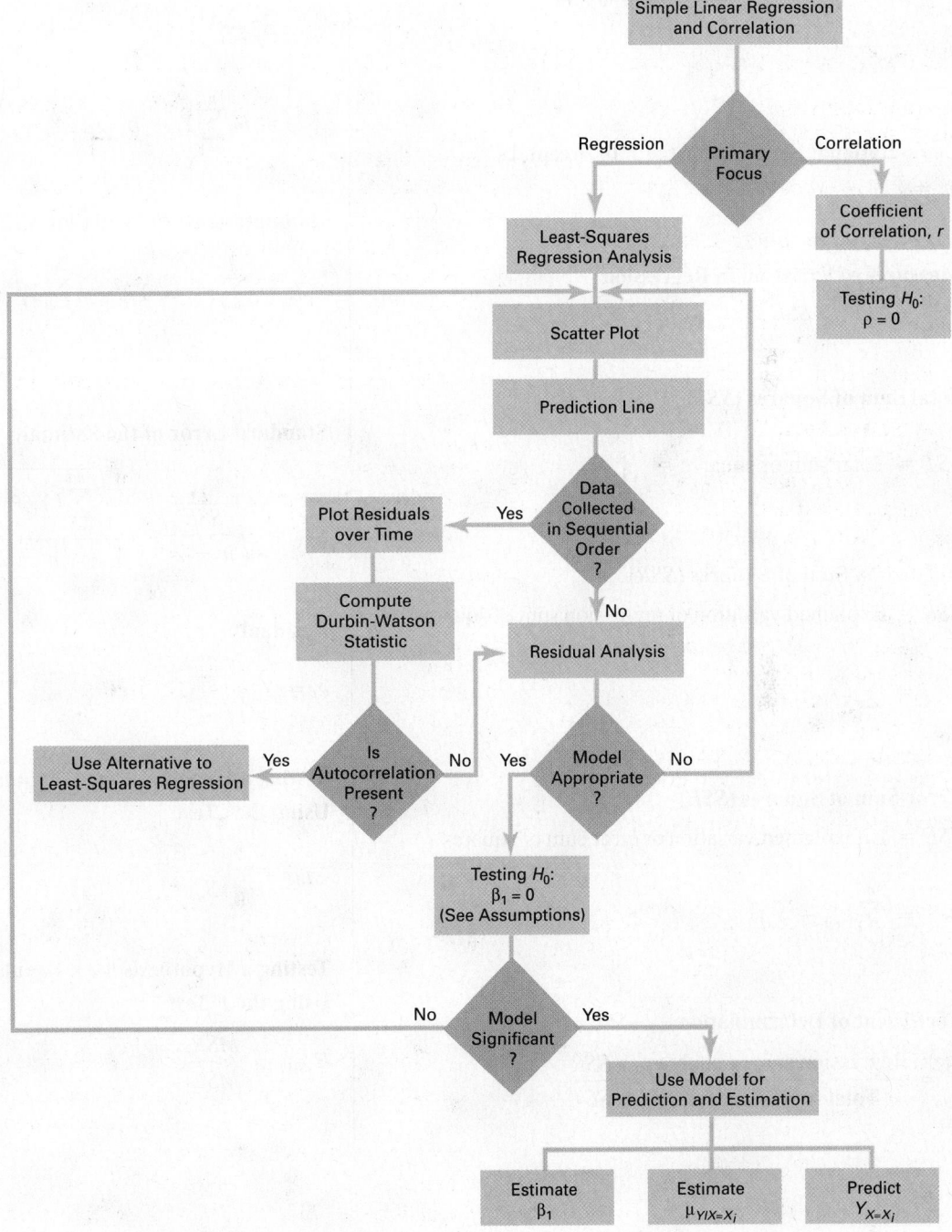

KEY EQUATIONS

Simple Linear Regression Model

$$Y_i = \beta_0 + \beta_1 X_i + \varepsilon_i$$

Simple Linear Regression Equation: The Prediction Line

$$\hat{Y}_i = b_0 + b_1 X_i$$

Computational Formula for the Slope, b_1

$$b_1 = \frac{SSXY}{SSX}$$

Computational Formula for the Y Intercept, b_0

$$b_0 = \bar{Y} - b_1 \bar{X}$$

Measures of Variation in Regression

$$SST = SSR + SSE$$

Total Sum of Squares (*SST*)

$$SST = \text{Total sum of squares} = \sum_{i=1}^{n}(Y_i - \bar{Y})^2$$

Regression Sum of Squares (*SSR*)

SSR = Explained variation or regression sum of squares

$$= \sum_{i=1}^{n}(\hat{Y}_i - \bar{Y})^2$$

Error Sum of Squares (*SSE*)

SSE = Unexplained variation or error sum of squares

$$= \sum_{i=1}^{n}(Y_i - \hat{Y}_i)^2$$

Coefficient of Determination

$$r^2 = \frac{\text{Regression sum of squares}}{\text{Total sum of squares}} = \frac{SSR}{SST}$$

Computational Formula for *SST*

$$SST = \sum_{i=1}^{n}(Y_i - \bar{Y})^2 = \sum_{i=1}^{n} Y_i^2 - \frac{\left(\sum_{i=1}^{n} Y_i\right)^2}{n}$$

Computational Formula for *SSR*

$$SSR = \sum_{i=1}^{n}(\hat{Y}_i - \bar{Y})^2$$

$$= b_0 \sum_{i=1}^{n} Y_i + b_1 \sum_{i=1}^{n} X_i Y_i - \frac{\left(\sum_{i=1}^{n} Y_i\right)^2}{n}$$

Computational Formula for *SSE*

$$SSE = \sum_{i=1}^{n}(Y_i - \hat{Y}_i)^2 = \sum_{i=1}^{n} Y_i^2 - b_0 \sum_{i=1}^{n} Y_i - b_1 \sum_{i=1}^{n} X_i Y_i$$

Standard Error of the Estimate

$$S_{YX} = \sqrt{\frac{SSE}{n-2}} = \sqrt{\frac{\sum_{i=1}^{n}(Y_i - \hat{Y}_i)^2}{n-2}}$$

Residual

$$e_i = Y_i - \hat{Y}_i$$

Testing a Hypothesis for a Population Slope, β_1, Using the *t* Test

$$t_{STAT} = \frac{b_1 - \beta_1}{S_{b_1}}$$

Testing a Hypothesis for a Population Slope, β_1, Using the *F* Test

$$F_{STAT} = \frac{MSR}{MSE}$$

Confidence Interval Estimate of the Slope, β_1

$$b_1 \pm t_{\alpha/2} S_{b_1}$$

$$b_1 - t_{\alpha/2} S_{b_1} \leq \beta_1 \leq b_1 + t_{\alpha/2} S_{b_1}$$

Testing for the Existence of Correlation

$$t_{STAT} = \frac{r - \rho}{\sqrt{\dfrac{1 - r^2}{n - 2}}}$$

$$r = \frac{cov(X,Y)}{S_X S_Y}$$

Confidence Interval Estimate for the Mean of Y

$$\hat{Y}_i \pm t_{\alpha/2} S_{YX} \sqrt{h_i}$$

$$\hat{Y}_i - t_{\alpha/2} S_{YX} \sqrt{h_i} \leq \mu_{Y|X=X_i} \leq \hat{Y}_i + t_{\alpha/2} S_{YX} \sqrt{h_i}$$

Prediction Interval for an Individual Response, Y

$$\hat{Y}_i \pm t_{\alpha/2} S_{YX} \sqrt{1 + h_i}$$

$$\hat{Y}_i - t_{\alpha/2} S_{YX} \sqrt{1 + h_i} \leq Y_{X=X_i} \leq \hat{Y}_i + t_{\alpha/2} S_{YX} \sqrt{1 + h_i}$$

KEY TERMS

CALCULATOR LESSON 18A

Lesson 18A – Simple Linear Regression

EXAMPLE 15.5   We will use the scenario "Forecasting Sales for a Clothing Store" to demonstrate how to perform simple linear regression on the calculator.

The sales for Sunflowers Apparel, a chain of apparel stores for women, have increased during the past 12 years as the chain has increased the number of its stores. Until now, Sunflowers senior managers selected sites based on subjective factors such as the availability of a good lease or the perception that a location seemed ideal for an apparel store. As the new director of planning, you need to develop a systematic approach to selecting new sites that will allow Sunflowers to make better-informed decisions for opening additional stores. This plan must be able to forecast annual sales for all potential stores under consideration. You believe that the size of the store significantly contributes to the success of a store, and you want to use this relationship in the decision-making process. You wish to predict annual sales based on the size of the store in square feet.

Table 15.6 summarizes the results of the 14 stores.

TABLE 15.6

Store	Square Feet (000)	Annual Sales (in millions of dollars)	Store	Square Feet (000)	Annual Sales (in millions of dollars)
1	1.7	3.7	8	1.1	2.7
2	1.6	3.9	9	3.2	5.5
3	2.8	6.7	10	1.5	2.9
4	5.6	9.5	11	5.2	10.7
5	1.3	3.4	12	4.6	7.6
6	2.2	5.6	13	5.8	11.8
7	1.3	3.7	14	3.0	4.1

The dependent variable, y, is the annual sales (in millions of dollars), and the independent variable, x, is the size of the store (in square feet).

1. Compute the regression coefficients – b_0 (intercept) and b_1 (slope)
To obtain the regression coefficients, use the calculator and follow these steps.

  a) From the **Main Menu** select **STAT** and press **EXE.**

  b) Enter the x values (square feet) in List 1 and the y values (annual sales) in List 2.

c) Now press **F2 (CALC)**, and then press **F6 (SET).**
The first row will be highlighted. Use the Arrow key to highlight the third row (2 Var XList : List 1).

d) Now enter the following in response to the screen prompts.

   2 Var XList   :   List 1 (F1)   *Note: You entered the x values in List 1.*

   2 Var YLIst   :   List 2 (F2)   *Note: You entered the y values in List 2.*

   2 Var Freq   :   1

e) Now press **EXIT** to return to the display of the data.

f) Now press **F3 (REG)**, and then press **F1 (X).**
The calculator will show the following results:

> **Linear Reg**
> a = 1.66986231
> b = 0.96447365
> r = 0.95088327
> r^2 = 0.904179
> y = ax + b

The values are put together to obtain the simple linear regression equation (the prediction line):

$$\hat{y} = 0.96447365 + 1.66986231x$$

The coefficient of determination, r^2, is 0.904179.

2. Hypothesis tests for the slope and correlation coefficient

At the 0.05 level of significance, is there evidence of a linear relationship between the size of the store and annual sales?

Solution:

We test for a linear relationship between the variables x and y by testing whether the population regression coefficient (slope), B, is different from zero.

$H_0: \beta_1 = 0$ (There is *not* a linear relationship.)

$H_a: \beta_1 \neq 0$ (There is a linear relationship.)

Note: Use the same data that you used for the x values (square feet) in List 1 and the y values (annual sales) in List 2.

From the **Main Menu** select

STAT   F3(TEST)   F2(t)   F3(REG), and then enter the following items.

(Note: Only use the **EXE** key after a new data entry. Otherwise, use the cursor ▼ arrow. If you accidentally hit the wrong key, use **AC/ON** or **EXIT** to go back.)

1-Sample ZInterval
$\beta \& \rho$	: $\neq$(F1)0 ▼
XList	: .List1 (F1) EXE
YList	: .List2 (F2) EXE
Freq	: 1 (F1) EXE
Execute	

Now press **EXE** or **F1**(Calc).

The calculator will show the following results:

LinearReg tTest
$\beta \neq 0 \& \rho \neq 0$
t = 10.641
p = 1.8226E-07
df = 12
a = 0.96447
b = 1.6698
y = a + bx

Use the cursor ▼ arrow to scroll down for more results.
df = 12
a = 0.96447
b = 1.6698
s = 0.96637
r = 0.95088
r^2 = 0.90417
y = a + bx

Conclusion:

p-value = 0.00000018226 < 0.05 = α, hence we reject H_0.

There is sufficient evidence to conclude that there is a linear relationship between size of the store and annual sales.

3. Compute the prediction value

What is the average annual sales if the size of the store is 1.8 (000) square feet?

Note: You have to make sure that the information in this example (in **#1**) is still recorded in the calculator and the regression calculations have been performed before you can compute the prediction value.

From the **Main Menu** select

MENU   RUN   EXE, and then enter **1.8 OPTN**.

Use the following options on the bottom of the display.

Select   **STAT (F5)** $\hat{y}$**(F2)**   **EXE**

The calculator will show the following result:

3.97022583

We interpret the value as follows:

$\hat{y} = 0.96447365 + 1.66986231\ (1.8) = 3.97022583$

We predict that the annual sales will be \$3.97022583 (in millions of dollars) if the size of the store is 1.8 (000) square feet.

4. Compute the residual

To obtain the residuals, follow the following steps.

a. From the **Main Menu** select **STAT** and press **EXE**.

b. Enter the x values (square feet) in List 1 and the y values (annual sales) in List 2.

c. While the data lists is on display, press "SHIFT" key followed by the "MENU" key.

You will see the screen displayed:

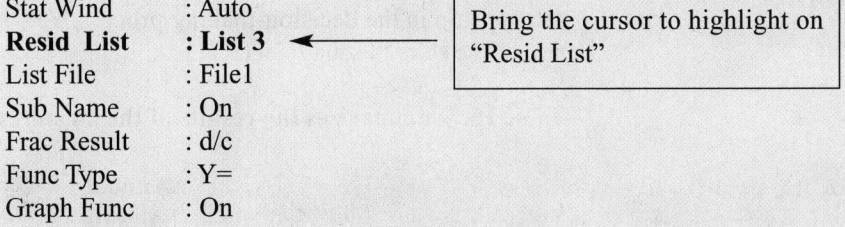

Stat Wind	: Auto
Resid List	**: List 3**
List File	: File1
Sub Name	: On
Frac Result	: d/c
Func Type	: Y=
Graph Func	: On

Bring the cursor to highlight on "Resid List"

Bring the cursor to highlight on "Resid List" and specify which list you would like to store your residual values.

After you have done with the setup, press "EXIT" key. Then run the linear regression.

CALCULATOR LESSON 18B

FX-9850GII CALCULATOR

EXAMPLE 15.6

Lesson 18B – Simple Linear Regression

We will use the scenario "Forecasting Sales for a Clothing Store" to demonstrate how to perform simple linear regression on the calculator.

The sales for Sunflowers Apparel, a chain of apparel stores for women, have increased during the past 12 years as the chain has increased the number of its stores. Until now, Sunflowers senior managers selected sites based on subjective factors such as the availability of a good lease or the perception that a location seemed ideal for an apparel store. As the new director of planning, you need to develop a systematic approach to selecting new sites that will allow Sunflowers to make better-informed decisions for opening additional stores. This plan must be able to forecast annual sales for all potential stores under consideration. You believe that the size of the store significantly contributes to the success of a store and you want to use this relationship in the decision-making process. You wish to predict annual sales based on the size of the store in square feet.

Table 15.7 summarizes the results of the 14 stores.

TABLE 15.7

Store	Square Feet (000)	Annual Sales (in millions of dollars)	Store	Square Feet (000)	Annual Sales (in millions of dollars)
1	1.7	3.7	8	1.1	2.7
2	1.6	3.9	9	3.2	5.5
3	2.8	6.7	10	1.5	2.9
4	5.6	9.5	11	5.2	10.7
5	1.3	3.4	12	4.6	7.6
6	2.2	5.6	13	5.8	11.8
7	1.3	3.7	14	3.0	4.1

The dependent variable, y, is the annual sales (in millions of dollars), and the independent variable, x, is the size of the store (in square feet).

1. Compute the regression coefficients – b_0 (intercept) and b_1 (slope)
To obtain the regression coefficients, use the calculator and follow these steps.

a) From the **Main Menu** select **STAT** and press **EXE**.

b) Enter the x values (square feet) in List 1 and the y values (annual sales) in List 2.

c) Now press **F2 (CALC)**, and then press **F6 (SET)**.
The first row will be highlighted. Use the Arrow key to highlight the third row (2 Var XList : List 1).

d) Now enter the following in response to the screen prompts.

2 Var XList	: List 1 (F1)	*Note: You entered the x values in List 1.*
2 Var YLIst	: List 2 (F2)	*Note: You entered the y values in List 2.*
2 Var Freq	: 1	

e) Now press **EXIT** to return to the display of the data.

f) Now press **F3 (REG)**, and then press **F1 (X).**

g) At this point you have two options:
    1. ax + b (corresponds to function key **F1**)
    2. a + bx (corresponds to function key **F2**)
    Select either one to change the linear regression equation.
    Suppose you select **F1 (ax + b)**.
    The calculator will show the following results:

> **Linear-Reg**
> a = 1.66986231
> b = 0.96447365
> r = 0.95088327
> r^2 = 0.904179
> y = ax + b

The values are put together to obtain the simple linear regression equation (the prediction line):

$$\hat{y} = 0.96447365 + 1.66986231x$$

The coefficient of determination, r^2, is 0.904179.

2. Hypothesis tests for the slope and correlation coefficient

At the 0.05 level of significance, is there evidence of a linear relationship between the size of the store and annual sales?

Solution:

We test for a linear relationship between the variables x and y by testing whether the population regression coefficient (slope), B, is different from zero.

$H_0: \beta_1 = 0$ (There is *not* a linear relationship.)

$H_a: \beta_1 \neq 0$ (There is a linear relationship.)

Note: Use the same data that you used for the x values (square feet) in List 1 and the y values (annual sales) in List 2.

From the **Main Menu** select

STAT F3(TEST) F2(t) F3(REG), and then enter the following items:

(Note: Only use the **EXE** key after a new data entry. Otherwise, use the cursor ▼ arrow. If you accidentally hit the wrong key, use **AC/ON** or **EXIT** to go back.)

> **1-Sample ZInterval**
> β & ρ   : ≠(F1)0   ▼
> XList   : .List1 (F1)   EXE
> YList   : .List2 (F2)   EXE
> Freq   : 1 (F1)   EXE
> Save Res   : None
> **Execute**

Now press **EXE** or **F1**(Calc).

The calculator will show the following results:

LinearReg tTest
$\beta \neq 0$ & $\rho \neq 0$
t   = 10.6411237
p   = 1.8226E-07
df = 12
a   = 0.96447365
b   = 1.66986232

Use the cursor ▼ arrow to scroll down for more results.
df = 12
a   = 0.96447365
b   = 1.66986232
se = 0.96637967
r   = 0.95088327
r^2 = 0.904179

Conclusion:

p-value = 0.00000018226 < 0.05 = α, hence we reject H_o.

There is sufficient evidence to conclude that there is a linear relationship between size of the store and annual sales.

3. Compute the prediction value

What is the average annual sales if the size of the store is 1.8 (000) square feet?

You have to make sure that the data (Table 15.1) is recorded in the calculator and the simple linear regression is performed prior to computing the prediction value.

To obtain predicted value for X=1.8, go to the main menu and select:

MENU   RUN-MAT   EXE   then enter **1.8   OPTN**   (a black key just under function key F2)

Use the following options at the bottom of the display.
Select   **STAT (F5)** $\bar{y}$**(F2)**   **EXE**

The calculator will now show the result:
3.97022583

We interpret the value as follows:

$\hat{y}$ =0.96447365 + 1.66986231 (1.8) = 3.97022583

We predict that the annual sales will be \$3.97022583 (in millions of dollars) if the size of the store is 1.8 (000) square feet.

4. Compute the residuals

You can find the residuals by following these steps.

From the **Main Menu** select

MENU   STAT   EXE   TEST(F3)   **t**(F2)   **REG**(F3)

You should see the following display on the screen:

LinearReg tTest
$\beta \& \rho$	: ≠(F1)0	▼
XList	: **List1 (F1)**	**EXE**
YList	: **List2 (F2)**	**EXE**
Freq	: **1 (F1)**	**EXE**
Save Res	: **List3**	
Execute		

Scroll to the bottom of the screen prompts until you reach **Save Res** and it is highlighted. (*Do not* press **EXE** at this point.)
Use the following options on the bottom of the display.
Select   **LIST (F2)**   and a pop-up screen will prompt you to enter List Number.

At this point enter "3" since lists 1 and 2 contain the data.

The residuals appear in List 3* as specified earlier. Press **EXIT** and you will see the residuals appear in List 3.

SPSS—Version 16—Simple Linear Regression

We will use the scenario "Forecasting Sales for a Clothing Store" to demonstrate how to perform simple linear regression using SPSS.

The dependent variable, y, is the annual sales (in millions of dollars), and the independent variable, x, is the size of the store (in square feet). You wish to predict annual sales based on the size of the store in square feet.

A random sample of 14 stores was selected with the results shown in Table 15.8.

Table 15.8 summarizes the results of the 14 stores.

TABLE 15.8

Store	Square Feet (000)	Annual Sales (in millions of dollars)	Store	Square Feet (000)	Annual Sales (in millions of dollars)
1	1.7	3.7	8	1.1	2.7
2	1.6	3.9	9	3.2	5.5
3	2.8	6.7	10	1.5	2.9
4	5.6	9.5	11	5.2	10.7
5	1.3	3.4	12	4.6	7.6
6	2.2	5.6	13	5.8	11.8
7	1.3	3.7	14	3.0	4.1

Performing a simple linear regression on SPSS—Version 16

Step 1: Open the SPSS Data Editor.

Click **Cancel** to cancel the SPSS opening window.

FIGURE 15.22

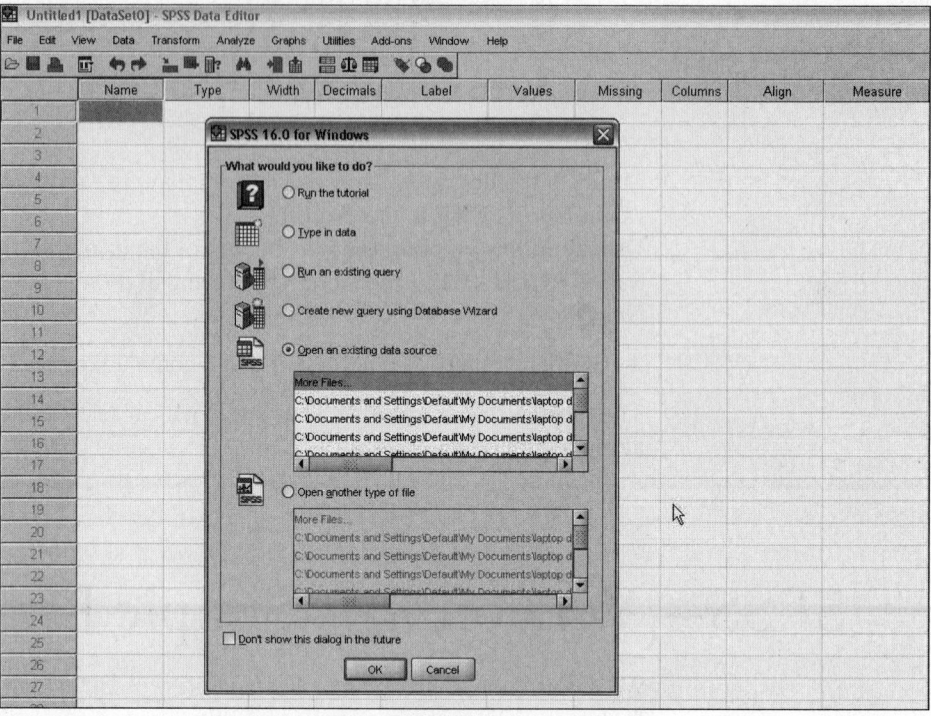

Step 2: Define the variables and give the variables a label.

Click **Variable View** (at the bottom of the window) to go to the variable view window to define the variables and fix the data at zero or one decimal places.

- Enter the variable name "size" and label it as "square feet (thousands)."

- Enter the variable name "sales" and label it as "Annual Sales (millions of dollars)."

FIGURE 15.23

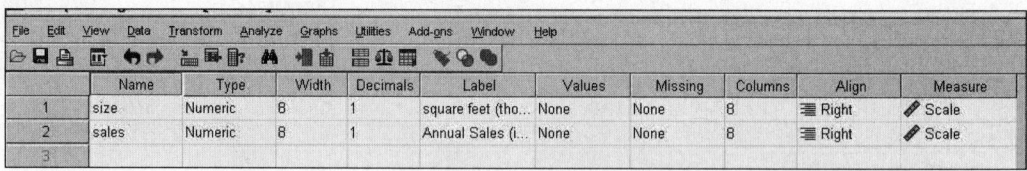

Step 3: Create a SPSS data file.

Click **Data View** to return to the data view window. Now, enter the raw data (in Table 15.8) into the appropriate columns of variables.

FIGURE 15.24

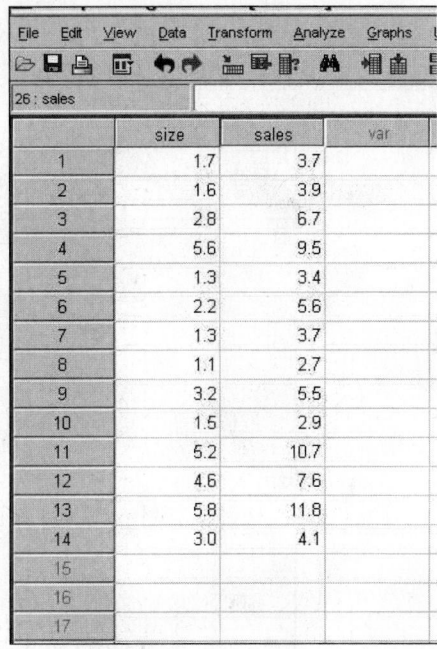

	size	sales	var
1	1.7	3.7	
2	1.6	3.9	
3	2.8	6.7	
4	5.6	9.5	
5	1.3	3.4	
6	2.2	5.6	
7	1.3	3.7	
8	1.1	2.7	
9	3.2	5.5	
10	1.5	2.9	
11	5.2	10.7	
12	4.6	7.6	
13	5.8	11.8	
14	3.0	4.1	
15			
16			
17			

After you have entered all the data, save it as "sales.sav" (or any filename).

Step 3: Perform regression analysis.

Make the following menu selections:

Analyze Regression Linear

FIGURE 15.25

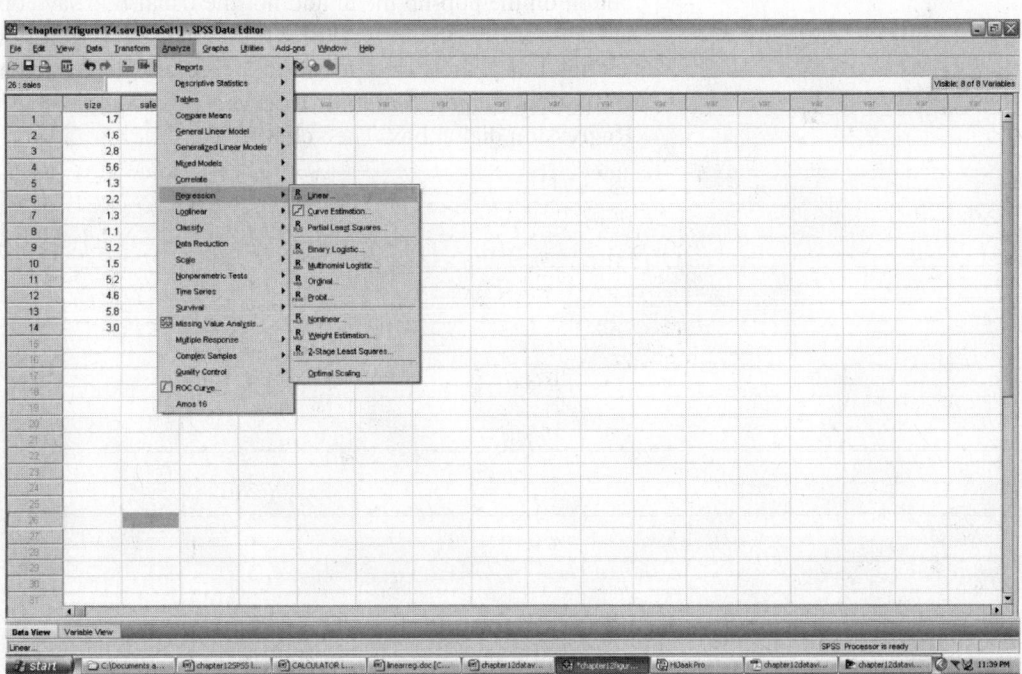

At this point, the **Linear Regression** dialog box will appear. Make these entries in the **Linear Regression** dialog box:

- Highlight the **Annual sales (or sales)** variable and click on the arrow key ( ). The variable will automatically fall into the **Dependent** box.

- Highlight the **square feet (or size)** variable and click on the arrow key ( ). The variable will fall into the **Independent(s)** box.

FIGURE 15.26

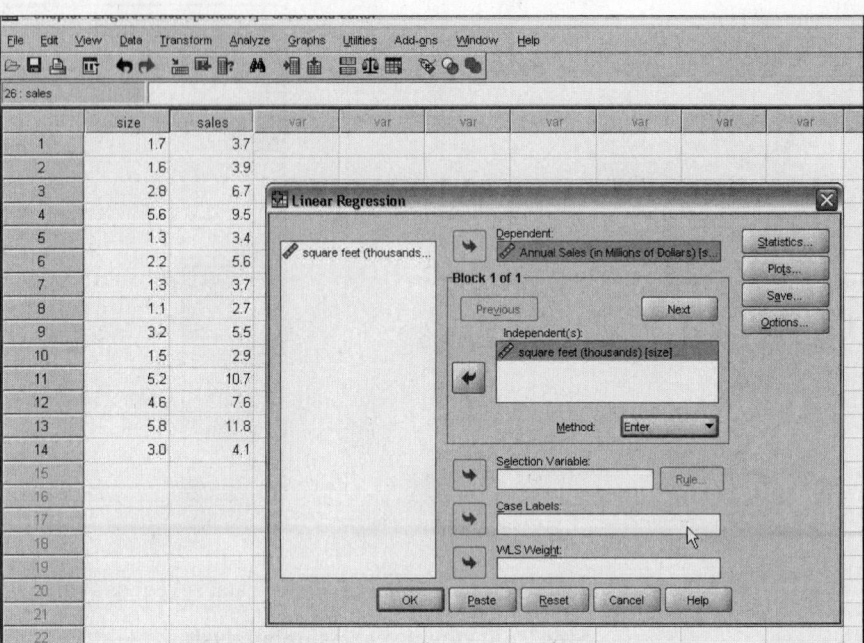

- *Obtaining Predictions and Residuals.*   Click on the save button (note that the **Save** is a button on the pop-up menu and not the usual File save option) and the **save** dialog box will pop up. In the **save** dialog box, click on **Unstandardized** in the the **Predicted Values** box. Click on **Unstandardized** in the **Residuals** box. Click on **Mean** and **Individual** in the **Prediction Intervals** box. Click on **Continue** to return to the **Linear Regression** dialog box. Then click **OK.**

FIGURE 15.27

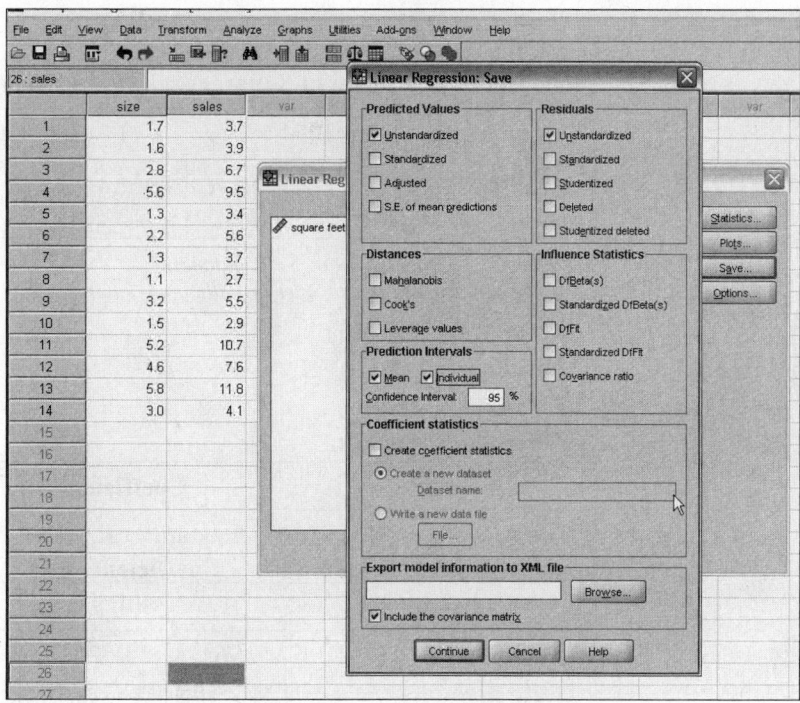

Step 3: Go to **SPSS Viewer** to obtain your SPSS results.

SPSS output:
Regression

FIGURE 15.28

Variables Entered/Removed[b]			
Model	**Variables Entered**	**Variables Removed**	**Method**
1	square feet (thousands)[a]		Enter

a. *Predictors: (constant), square feet (thousands)*
b. *Dependent Variable: Annual Sales (in millions of dollars)*

FIGURE 15.29

Model Summary				
Model	**R**	**R Square**	**Adjusted R Square**	**Std. Error of the Estimate**
1	.951[a]	.904	.896	.9664

a. *Predictors: (constant), square feet (thousands)*
b. *Dependent Variable: Annual Sales (in millions of dollars)*

FIGURE 15.30

ANOVAᵇ					
Model	Sum of Squares	df	Mean Square	F	Sig.
1 Regression	105.748	1	105.748	113.234	.000ᵃ
Residual	11.207	12	.934		
Total	116.954	13			

a. Predictors: (constant), square feet (thousands)
b. Dependent Variable: Annual Sales (in millions of dollars)

FIGURE 15.31

Coefficientsᵃ					
	Unstandardized Coefficients		Standardized Coefficients		
Model	B	Std. Error	Beta	t	Sig.
1 (Constant)	.964	.526		1.833	.092
square feet (thousands)	1.670	.157	.951	10.641	.000

a. Dependent Variable: Annual Sales (in millions of dollars)

FIGURE 15.32

Residuals Statisticsᵃ					
	Minimum	Maximum	Mean	Std. Deviation	N
Predicted Value	2.801	10.650	5.843	2.8521	14
Std. Predicted Value	−1.066	1.685	.000	1.000	14
Standard Error of Predicted Value	.259	.520	.356	.083	14
Adjusted Predicted Value	2.820	10.603	5.821	2.8263	14
Residual	−1.8741	1.1503	.0000	.9285	14
Std. Residual	−1.939	1.190	.000	.961	14
Stud. Residual	−2.013	1.413	.010	1.038	14
Deleted Residual	−2.0186	1.6200	.0215	1.0888	14
Stud. Deleted Residual	−2.368	1.481	−.009	1.104	14
Mahal. Distance	.002	2.840	.929	.886	14
Cook's Distance	.001	.407	.090	.113	14
Centred Leverage Value	.000	.218	.071	.068	14

a. Dependent Variable: Annual Sales (in millions of dollars)

Obtaining Predictions and Residuals

The confidence interval values and prediction interval values are displayed on the **SPSS Data Editor** under the variables PRE_1, RES_1, LMCI_1, UMCI_1, LICI_1, and UICI_1.

Notation:

PRE_1—Unstandardized Predicted (for Model 1)

RES_1—Unstandardized Residual (for Model 1)

LMCI_1—95% Lower Confidence Interval for y mean (for Model 1)

UMCI_1—95% Upper Confidence Interval for y mean (for Model 1)

LICI_1—95% Lower Confidence Interval for y individual (for Model 1)

UICI_1—5% Upper Confidence Interval for y individual (for Model 1)

FIGURE 15.33

File Edit View Data Transform Analyze Graphs Utilities Add-ons Window Help

31 : sales

	size	sales	PRE_1	RES_1	LMCI_1	UMCI_1	LICI_1	UICI_1
1	1.7	3.7	3.80324	-0.10324	3.10247	4.50401	1.58413	6.02235
2	1.6	3.9	3.63625	0.26375	2.91459	4.35792	1.41045	5.86205
3	2.8	6.7	5.64009	1.05991	5.07582	6.20435	3.46023	7.81995
4	5.6	9.5	10.31570	-0.81570	9.24080	11.39061	7.95164	12.67977
5	1.3	3.4	3.13529	0.26471	2.34535	3.92524	0.88643	5.38416
6	2.2	5.6	4.63817	0.96183	4.02375	5.25259	2.44479	6.83155
7	1.3	3.7	3.13529	0.56471	2.34535	3.92524	0.88643	5.38416
8	1.1	2.7	2.80132	-0.10132	1.96197	3.64067	0.53463	5.06801
9	3.2	5.5	6.30803	-0.80803	5.73729	6.87877	4.12649	8.48958
10	1.5	2.9	3.46927	-0.56927	2.72572	4.21282	1.23628	5.70226
11	5.2	10.7	9.64776	1.05224	8.68671	10.60881	7.33324	11.96228
12	4.6	7.6	8.64584	-1.04584	7.84206	9.44962	6.39208	10.89960
13	5.8	11.8	10.64968	1.15032	9.51594	11.78341	8.25829	13.04106
14	3.0	4.1	5.97406	-1.87406	5.41069	6.53744	3.79443	8.15369
15								

PROBLEMS

CHECKING YOUR UNDERSTANDING

15.57 What is the interpretation of the Y intercept and the slope in the simple linear regression equation?

15.58 What is the interpretation of the coefficient of determination?

15.59 When is the unexplained variation (i.e., error sum of squares) equal to 0?

15.60 When is the explained variation (i.e., regression sum of squares) equal to 0?

15.61 Why should you always carry out a residual analysis as part of a regression model?

15.62 What are the assumptions of regression analysis?

15.63 How do you evaluate the assumptions of regression analysis?

15.64 When and how do you use the Durbin-Watson statistic?

15.65 What is the difference between a confidence interval estimate of the mean response, $\mu_{Y|X=X_i}$, and a prediction interval of $Y_{X=X_i}$?

APPLYING THE CONCEPTS

15.66 Researchers from the Pace University Lubin School of Business conducted a study on Internet-supported courses. In one part of the study, four numerical variables were collected on 108 students in an introductory management course that met once a week for an entire semester. One variable collected was *hit consistency*. To measure hit consistency, the researchers did the following: If a student did not visit the Internet site between classes, the student was given a 0 for that time period. If a student visited the Internet site one or more times between classes, the student was given a 1 for that time period. Because there were 13 time periods, a student's score on hit consistency could range from 0 to 13.

The other three variables included the student's course average, the student's cumulative grade point average (GPA), and the total number of hits the student had on the Internet site supporting the course. The following table gives the correlation coefficient for all pairs of variables. Note that correlations marked with an * are statistically significant, using $\alpha = 0.001$:

Variable	Correlation
Course Average, Cumulative GPA	0.72*
Course Average, Total Hits	0.08
Course Average, Hit Consistency	0.37*
Cumulative GPA, Total Hits	0.12
Cumulative GPA, Hit Consistency	0.32*
Total Hits & Hit Consistency	0.64*

Source: Data extracted from D. Baugher, A. Varanelli, and E. Weisbord, "Student Hits in an Internet-Supported Course: How Can Instructors Use Them and What Do They Mean?" *Decision Sciences Journal of Innovative Education,* 1 (Fall 2003), 159–179.

a. What conclusions can you reach from this correlation analysis?

b. Are you surprised by the results, or are they consistent with your own observations and experiences?

15.67 Management of a soft-drink bottling company has the business objective of developing a method for allocating delivery costs to customers. Although one cost clearly relates to travel time within a particular route, another variable cost reflects the time required to unload the cases of soft drink at the delivery point. To begin, management decided to develop a regression model to predict delivery time based on the number of cases delivered. A sample of 20 deliveries within a territory was selected. The delivery times and the number of cases delivered were organized in the following table (and stored in Delivery):

Customer	Number of Cases	Delivery Time (Minutes)	Customer	Number of Cases	Delivery Time (Minutes)
1	52	32.1	11	161	43.0
2	64	34.8	12	184	49.4
3	73	36.2	13	202	57.2
4	85	37.8	14	218	56.8
5	95	37.8	15	243	60.6
6	103	39.7	16	254	61.2
7	116	38.5	17	267	58.2
8	121	41.9	18	275	63.1
9	143	44.2	19	287	65.6
10	157	47.1	20	298	67.3

a. Use the least-squares method to compute the regression coefficients b_0 and b_1.

b. Interpret the meaning of b_0 and b_1 in this problem.

c. Predict the delivery time for 150 cases of soft drink.

d. Should you use the model to predict the delivery time for a customer who is receiving 500 cases of soft drink? Why or why not?

e. Determine the coefficient of determination, r^2, and explain its meaning in this problem.

f. Perform a residual analysis. Is there any evidence of a pattern in the residuals? Explain.

g. At the 0.05 level of significance, is there evidence of a linear relationship between delivery time and the number of cases delivered?

h. Construct a 95% confidence interval estimate of the mean delivery time for 150 cases of soft drink and a 95% prediction interval of the delivery time for a single delivery of 150 cases of soft drink.

15.68 Measuring the height of a California redwood tree is a very difficult undertaking because these trees grow to heights of over 300 feet. People familiar with these trees understand that the height of a California redwood tree is related to other characteristics of the tree, including the diameter of the tree at the breast height of a person. The data in Redwood represent the height (in feet) and diameter (in inches) at the breast height of a person for a sample of 21 California redwood trees.

a. Assuming a linear relationship, use the least-squares method to compute the regression coefficients b_0 and b_1. State the regression equation that predicts the height of a tree based on the tree's diameter at breast height of a person.

b. Interpret the meaning of the slope in this equation.

c. Predict the height for a tree that has a breast height diameter of 25 inches.

d. Interpret the meaning of the coefficient of determination in this problem.

e. Perform a residual analysis on the results and determine the adequacy of the model.

f. Determine whether there is a significant relationship between the height of redwood trees and the breast height diameter at the 0.05 level of significance.

g. Construct a 95% confidence interval estimate of the population slope between the height of the redwood trees and breast height diameter.

15.69 You want to develop a model to predict the selling price of homes based on assessed value. A sample of 30 recently sold single-family houses in a small city is selected to study the relationship between selling price (in thousands of dollars) and assessed value (in thousands of dollars). The houses in the city were reassessed at full value one year prior to the study. The results are in House1 . (Hint: First, determine which are the independent and dependent variables.)

a. Construct a scatter plot and, assuming a linear relationship, use the least-squares method to compute the regression coefficients b_0 and b_1.

b. Interpret the meaning of the Y intercept, b_0, and the slope, b_1, in this problem.

c. Use the prediction line developed in (a) to predict the selling price for a house whose assessed value is $170,000.

d. Determine the coefficient of determination, r^2, and interpret its meaning in this problem.

e. Perform a residual analysis on your results and evaluate the regression assumptions.

f. At the 0.05 level of significance, is there evidence of a linear relationship between selling price and assessed value?

g. Construct a 95% confidence interval estimate of the population slope.

15.70 You want to develop a model to predict the assessed value of houses, based on heating area. A sample of 15 single-family houses in a city is selected. The assessed value (in thousands of dollars) and the heating area of the houses (in thousands of square feet) are recorded and stored in House2 . (Hint: First, determine which are the independent and dependent variables.)

a. Construct a scatter plot and, assuming a linear relationship, use the least-squares method to compute the regression coefficients b_0 and b_1.

b. Interpret the meaning of the Y intercept, b_0, and the slope, b_1, in this problem.

c. Use the prediction line developed in (a) to predict the assessed value for a house whose heating area is 1,750 square feet.

d. Determine the coefficient of determination, r^2, and interpret its meaning in this problem.

e. Perform a residual analysis on your results and evaluate the regression assumptions.

f. At the 0.05 level of significance, is there evidence of a linear relationship between assessed value and heating area?

15.71 The director of graduate studies at a large college of business has the objective of predicting the grade point average (GPA) of students in an MBA program. The director begins by using the Graduate Management Admission Test (GMAT) score. A sample of 20 students who have completed two years in the program is selected and stored in GPIGMAT .

a. Construct a scatter plot and, assuming a linear relationship, use the least-squares method to compute the regression coefficients b_0 and b_1.

b. Interpret the meaning of the Y intercept, b_0, and the slope, b_1, in this problem.

c. Use the prediction line developed in (a) to predict the GPA for a student with a GMAT score of 600.

d. Determine the coefficient of determination, r^2, and interpret its meaning in this problem.

e. Perform a residual analysis on your results and evaluate the regression assumptions.

f. At the 0.05 level of significance, is there evidence of a linear relationship between GMAT score and GPA?

g. Construct a 95% confidence interval estimate of the mean GPA of students with a GMAT score of 600 and a 95% prediction interval of the GPA for a particular student with a GMAT score of 600.

h. Construct a 95% confidence interval estimate of the population slope.

15.72 An accountant for a large department store has the business objective of developing a model to predict the amount of time it takes to process invoices. Data are collected from the past 32 working days, and the number of invoices processed and completion time (in hours) are stored in Invoice . (Hint: First, determine which are the independent and dependent variables.)

a. Assuming a linear relationship, use the least-squares method to compute the regression coefficients b_0 and b_1.

b. Interpret the meaning of the Y intercept, b_0, and the slope, b_1, in this problem.

c. Use the prediction line developed in (a) to predict the amount of time it would take to process 150 invoices.

d. Determine the coefficient of determination, r^2, and interpret its meaning.

e. Plot the residuals against the number of invoices processed and also against time.

f. Based on the plots in (e), does the model seem appropriate?

g. Based on the results in (e) and (f), what conclusions can you make about the validity of the prediction made in (c)?

15.73 On January 28, 1986, the space shuttle *Challenger* exploded, and seven astronauts were killed. Prior to the launch, the predicted atmospheric temperature was for freezing weather at the launch site. Engineers for Morton Thiokol (the manufacturer of the rocket motor) prepared charts to make the case that the launch should not take place due to the cold weather. These arguments were rejected, and the launch tragically took place. Upon investigation after the tragedy, experts agreed that the disaster occurred because of leaky rubber O-rings that did not seal properly due to the cold temperature. Data indicating the atmospheric temperature at the time of 23 previous launches and the O-ring damage index are stored in O-Ring .

Note: Data from flight 4 is omitted due to unknown O-ring condition.

Sources: Data extracted from *Report of the Presidential Commission on the Space Shuttle Challenger Accident,* Washington, DC, 1986, Vol. II (H1–H3); and Vol. IV (664), and *Post Challenger Evaluation of Space Shuttle Risk Assessment and Management,* Washington, DC, 1988, pp. 135–136.

a. Construct a scatter plot for the seven flights in which there was O-ring damage (O-ring damage index $\neq 0$). What conclusions, if any, can you reach about the relationship between atmospheric temperature and O-ring damage?

b. Construct a scatter plot for all 23 flights.

c. Explain any differences in the interpretation of the relationship between atmospheric temperature and O-ring damage in (a) and (b).

d. Based on the scatter plot in (b), provide reasons why a prediction should not be made for an atmospheric temperature of 31°F, the temperature on the morning of the launch of the *Challenger*.

e. Although the assumption of a linear relationship may not be valid for the set of 23 flights, fit a simple linear regression model to predict O-ring damage, based on atmospheric temperature.

f. Include the prediction line found in (e) on the scatter plot developed in (b).

g. Based on the results in (f), do you think a linear model is appropriate for these data? Explain.

h. Perform a residual analysis. What conclusions do you reach?

15.74 A baseball analyst would like to study various team statistics for the 2010 baseball season to determine which variables might be useful in predicting the number of wins achieved by teams during the season. He begins by using a team's earned run average (ERA), a measure of pitching performance, to predict the number of wins. He collects the team ERA and team wins for each of the 30 Major League Baseball teams and stores these data in BB2010 . (Hint: First, determine which are the independent and dependent variables.)

a. Assuming a linear relationship, use the least-squares method to compute the regression coefficients b_0 and b_1.

b. Interpret the meaning of the Y intercept, b_0, and the slope, b_1, in this problem.

c. Use the prediction line developed in (a) to predict the number of wins for a team with an ERA of 4.50.

d. Compute the coefficient of determination, r^2, and interpret its meaning.

e. Perform a residual analysis on your results and determine the adequacy of the fit of the model.

f. At the 0.05 level of significance, is there evidence of a linear relationship between the number of wins and the ERA?

g. Construct a 95% confidence interval estimate of the mean number of wins expected for teams with an ERA of 4.50.

h. Construct a 95% prediction interval of the number of wins for an individual team that has an ERA of 4.50.

i. Construct a 95% confidence interval estimate of the population slope.

j. The 30 teams constitute a population. In order to use statistical inference, as in (f) through (i), the data must be assumed to represent a random sample. What "population" would this sample be drawing conclusions about?

k. What other independent variables might you consider for inclusion in the model?

15.75 Can you use the annual revenues generated by National Basketball Association (NBA) franchises to predict franchise values? Figure 3.4 on page 113 shows a scatter plot of revenue with franchise value, and Figure 4.10 on page 179, shows the correlation coefficient. Now, you want to develop a simple linear regression model to predict franchise values based on revenues. (Franchise values and revenues are stored in NBAValues .)

a. Assuming a linear relationship, use the least-squares method to compute the regression coefficients b_0 and b_1.

b. Interpret the meaning of the Y intercept, b_0, and the slope, b_1, in this problem.

c. Predict the value of an NBA franchise that generates $150 million of annual revenue.

d. Compute the coefficient of determination, r^2, and interpret its meaning.

e. Perform a residual analysis on your results and evaluate the regression assumptions.

f. At the 0.05 level of significance, is there evidence of a linear relationship between the annual revenues generated and the value of an NBA franchise?

g. Construct a 95% confidence interval estimate of the mean value of all NBA franchises that generate $150 million of annual revenue.

h. Construct a 95% prediction interval of the value of an individual NBA franchise that generates $150 million of annual revenue.

i. Compare the results of (a) through (h) to those of baseball franchises in Problems 15.8, 15.20, 15.30, 15.39, and 15.55 and European soccer teams in Problem 15.76.

15.76 In Problem 15.82 you used annual revenue to develop a model to predict the franchise value of National Basketball Association (NBA) teams. Can you also use the annual revenues generated by European soccer teams to predict franchise values? (European soccer team values and revenues are stored in SoccerValues2011 .)

a. Repeat Problem 15.75 (a) through (h) for the European soccer teams.

b. Compare the results of (a) to those of baseball franchises in Problems 15.8, 15.20, 15.30, 15.39, and 15.55 and NBA franchises in Problem 15.76.

15.77 During the fall harvest season in the United States, pumpkins are sold in large quantities at farm stands. Often, instead of weighing the pumpkins prior to sale, the farm stand operator will just place the pumpkin in the appropriate circular cutout on the counter. When asked why this was done, one farmer replied, "I can tell the weight of the pumpkin from its circumference." To determine whether this was really true, the circumference and weight of each pumpkin from a sample of 23 pumpkins were determined and the results stored in Pumpkin .

a. Assuming a linear relationship, use the least-squares method to compute the regression coefficients b_0 and b_1.

b. Interpret the meaning of the slope, b_1, in this problem.

c. Predict the weight for a pumpkin that is 60 centimeters in circumference.

d. Do you think it is a good idea for the farmer to sell pumpkins by circumference instead of weight? Explain.

e. Determine the coefficient of determination, r^2, and interpret its meaning.

f. Perform a residual analysis for these data and evaluate the regression assumptions.

g. At the 0.05 level of significance, is there evidence of a linear relationship between the circumference and weight of a pumpkin?

h. Construct a 95% confidence interval estimate of the population slope, β_1.

15.78 Can demographic information be helpful in predicting sales at sporting goods stores? The file **Sporting** contains the monthly sales totals from a random sample of 38 stores in a large chain of nationwide sporting goods stores. All stores in the franchise, and thus within the sample, are approximately the same size and carry the same merchandise. The county or, in some cases, counties in which the store draws the majority of its customers is referred to here as the customer base. For each of the 38 stores, demographic information about the customer base is provided. The data are real, but the name of the franchise is not used, at the request of the company. The data set contains the following variables:

Sales—Latest one-month sales total (dollars)
Age—Median age of customer base (years)
HS—Percentage of customer base with a high school diploma
College—Percentage of customer base with a college diploma
Growth—Annual population growth rate of customer base over the past 10 years
Income—Median family income of customer base (dollars)

a. Construct a scatter plot, using sales as the dependent variable and median family income as the independent variable. Discuss the scatter plot.

b. Assuming a linear relationship, use the least-squares method to compute the regression coefficients b_0 and b_1.

c. Interpret the meaning of the Y intercept, b_0, and the slope, b_1, in this problem.

d. Compute the coefficient of determination, r^2, and interpret its meaning.

e. Perform a residual analysis on your results and determine the adequacy of the fit of the model.

f. At the 0.05 level of significance, is there evidence of a linear relationship between the independent variable and the dependent variable?

g. Construct a 95% confidence interval estimate of the population slope and interpret its meaning.

15.79 For the data of Problem 15.78, repeat (a) through (g), using Age as the independent variable.

15.80 For the data of Problem 15.78, repeat (a) through (g), using HS as the independent variable.

15.81 For the data of Problem 15.78, repeat (a) through (g), using College as the independent variable.

15.82 For the data of Problem 15.78, repeat (a) through (g), using Growth as the independent variable.

15.83 The file **CEO-Compensation** includes the total compensation (in $) of CEOs of 161 large public companies and their investment return in 2010.

Source: Data extracted from M. Krantz and B. Hansen, "CEO Pay Soars While Workers' Pay Stalls," *USA Today,* April 1, 2011, pp. 1B, 2B and **money.usatoday.com**.

a. Compute the correlation coefficient between compensation and the investment return in 2010.

b. At the 0.05 level of significance, is the correlation between compensation and the investment return in 2010 statistically significant?

c. Write a short summary of your findings in (a) and (b). Do the results surprise you?

15.84 Refer to the discussion of beta values and market models in Problem 15.42 on page 672. The S&P 500 Index tracks the overall movement of the stock market by considering the stock prices of 500 large corporations. The file **StockPrices2010** contains 2010 weekly data for the S&P 500 and three companies. The following variables are included:

WEEK—Week ending on date given
S&P—Weekly closing value for the S&P 500 Index
GE—Weekly closing stock price for General Electric
DISCA—Weekly closing stock price for Discovery Communications
GOOG—Weekly closing stock price for Google

Source: Data extracted from **finance.yahoo.com**, May 20, 2011.

a. Estimate the market model for GE. (Hint: Use the percentage change in the S&P 500 Index as the independent variable and the percentage change in GE's stock price as the dependent variable.)

b. Interpret the beta value for GE.

c. Repeat (a) and (b) for Discovery Communications.

d. Repeat (a) and (b) for Google.

e. Write a brief summary of your findings.

REPORT WRITING EXERCISE

15.85 In Problems 15.78 through 15.82, you developed regression models to predict monthly sales at a sporting goods store. Now, write a report based on the models you developed. Append to your report all appropriate charts and statistical information.

MANAGING ASHLAND MULTICOMM SERVICES

To ensure that as many trial subscriptions to the *3-For-All* service as possible are converted to regular subscriptions, the marketing department works closely with the customer support department to accomplish a smooth initial process for the trial subscription customers. To assist in this effort, the marketing department needs to accurately forecast the monthly total of new regular subscriptions.

A team consisting of managers from the marketing and customer support departments was convened to develop a better method of forecasting new subscriptions. Previously, after examining new subscription data for the prior three months, a group of three managers would develop a subjective forecast of the number of new subscriptions. Livia Salvador, who was recently hired by the company to provide expertise in quantitative forecasting methods, suggested that the department look for factors that might help in predicting new subscriptions.

Members of the team found that the forecasts in the past year had been particularly inaccurate because in some months, much more time was spent on telemarketing than in other months. Livia collected data (stored in AMS15) for the number of new subscriptions and hours spent on telemarketing for each month for the past two years.

EXERCISES

1. What criticism can you make concerning the method of forecasting that involved taking the new subscriptions data for the prior three months as the basis for future projections?

2. What factors other than number of telemarketing hours spent might be useful in predicting the number of new subscriptions? Explain.

3. **a.** Analyze the data and develop a regression model to predict the number of new subscriptions for a month, based on the number of hours spent on telemarketing for new subscriptions.

   b. If you expect to spend 1,200 hours on telemarketing per month, estimate the number of new subscriptions for the month. Indicate the assumptions on which this prediction is based. Do you think these assumptions are valid? Explain.

   c. What would be the danger of predicting the number of new subscriptions for a month in which 2,000 hours were spent on telemarketing?

DIGITAL CASE

Apply your knowledge of simple linear regression in this Digital Case, which extends the Sunflowers Apparel Using Statistics scenario from this chapter.

Leasing agents from the Triangle Mall Management Corporation have suggested that Sunflowers consider several locations in some of Triangle's newly renovated lifestyle malls that cater to shoppers with higher-than-mean disposable income. Although the locations are smaller than the typical Sunflowers location, the leasing agents argue that higher-than-mean disposable income in the surrounding community is a better predictor than store size of higher sales. The leasing agents maintain that sample data from 14 Sunflowers stores prove that this is true.

Open **Triangle_Sunflower.pdf** and review the leasing agents' proposal and supporting documents. Then answer the following questions:

1. Should mean disposable income be used to predict sales based on the sample of 14 Sunflowers stores?

2. Should the management of Sunflowers accept the claims of Triangle's leasing agents? Why or why not?

3. Is it possible that the mean disposable income of the surrounding area is not an important factor in leasing new locations? Explain.

4. Are there any other factors not mentioned by the leasing agents that might be relevant to the store leasing decision?

REFERENCES

1. Anscombe, F. J., "Graphs in Statistical Analysis," *The American Statistician*, 27 (1973), 17–21.

2. Hoaglin, D. C., and R. Welsch, "The Hat Matrix in Regression and ANOVA," *The American Statistician*, 32 (1978), 17–22.

3. Hocking, R. R., "Developments in Linear Regression Methodology: 1959–1982," *Technometrics*, 25 (1983), 219–250.

4. Kutner, M. H., C. J. Nachtsheim, J. Neter, and W. Li, *Applied Linear Statistical Models*, 5th ed. (New York: McGraw-Hill/Irwin, 2005).

5. *Microsoft Excel 2010* (Redmond, WA: Microsoft Corp., 2010).

6. *Minitab Release 16* (State College, PA: Minitab, Inc., 2010).

16 Multiple Regression

Learning Objectives

In this chapter, you learn:

- How to develop a multiple regression model
- How to interpret the regression coefficients
- How to determine which independent variables to include in the regression model
- How to determine which independent variables are most important in predicting a dependent variable
- How to use categorical independent variables in a regression model

George Bailey / Shutterstock.com

@ OmniFoods

You are the marketing manager for OmniFoods, a large food products company. The company is planning a nationwide introduction of OmniPower, a new high-energy bar. Originally marketed to runners, mountain climbers, and other athletes, high-energy bars are now popular with the general public. OmniFoods is anxious to capture a share of this thriving market.

Because the marketplace already contains several successful energy bars, you need to develop an effective marketing strategy. In particular, you need to determine the effect that price and in-store promotions will have on sales of OmniPower. Before marketing the bar nationwide, you plan to conduct a test-market study of OmniPower sales, using a sample of 34 stores in a supermarket chain. How can you extend the linear regression methods discussed in Chapter 15 to incorporate the effects of price *and* promotion into the same model? How can you use this model to improve the success of the nationwide introduction of OmniPower?

Courtesy of Sharon Rosenberg

C hapter 15 focused on simple linear regression models that use *one* numerical independent variable, X, to predict the value of a numerical dependent variable, Y. Often you can make better predictions by using *more than one* independent variable. This chapter introduces you to **multiple regression models** that use two or more independent variables to predict the value of a dependent variable.

16.1 Developing a Multiple Regression Model

The business objective facing the marketing manager at OmniFoods is to develop a model to predict monthly sales volume per store of OmniPower bars and to determine what variables influence sales. Two independent variables are considered here: the price of an OmniPower bar, as measured in cents (X_1), and the monthly budget for in-store promotional expenditures, measured in dollars (X_2). In-store promotional expenditures typically include signs and displays, in-store coupons, and free samples. The dependent variable Y is the number of OmniPower bars sold in a month. Data are collected from a sample of 34 stores in a supermarket chain selected for a test-market study of OmniPower. All the stores selected have approximately the same monthly sales volume. The data are organized and stored in OmniPower and presented in Table 16.1.

TABLE 16.1

Monthly OmniPower Sales, Price, and Promotional Expenditures

Store	Sales	Price	Promotion	Store	Sales	Price	Promotion
1	4,141	59	200	18	2,730	79	400
2	3,842	59	200	19	2,618	79	400
3	3,056	59	200	20	4,421	79	400
4	3,519	59	200	21	4,113	79	600
5	4,226	59	400	22	3,746	79	600
6	4,630	59	400	23	3,532	79	600
7	3,507	59	400	24	3,825	79	600
8	3,754	59	400	25	1,096	99	200
9	5,000	59	600	26	761	99	200
10	5,120	59	600	27	2,088	99	200
11	4,011	59	600	28	820	99	200
12	5,015	59	600	29	2,114	99	400
13	1,916	79	200	30	1,882	99	400
14	675	79	200	31	2,159	99	400
15	3,636	79	200	32	1,602	99	400
16	3,224	79	200	33	3,354	99	600
17	2,295	79	400	34	2,927	99	600

Visualizing Multiple Regression Data

With the special case of two independent variables and one dependent variable, you can visualize your data with a three-dimensional scatter plot. Figure 16.1 on page 707 presents a three-dimensional Minitab plot of the OmniPower data. This figure shows the points plotted at a height equal to their sales with drop lines down to their promotion expense and price values.

Interpreting the Regression Coefficients

When there are several independent variables, you can extend the simple linear regression model of Equation (15.1) on page 642 by assuming a linear relationship between each independent variable and the dependent variable. For example, with k independent variables, the multiple regression model is expressed in Equation (16.1).

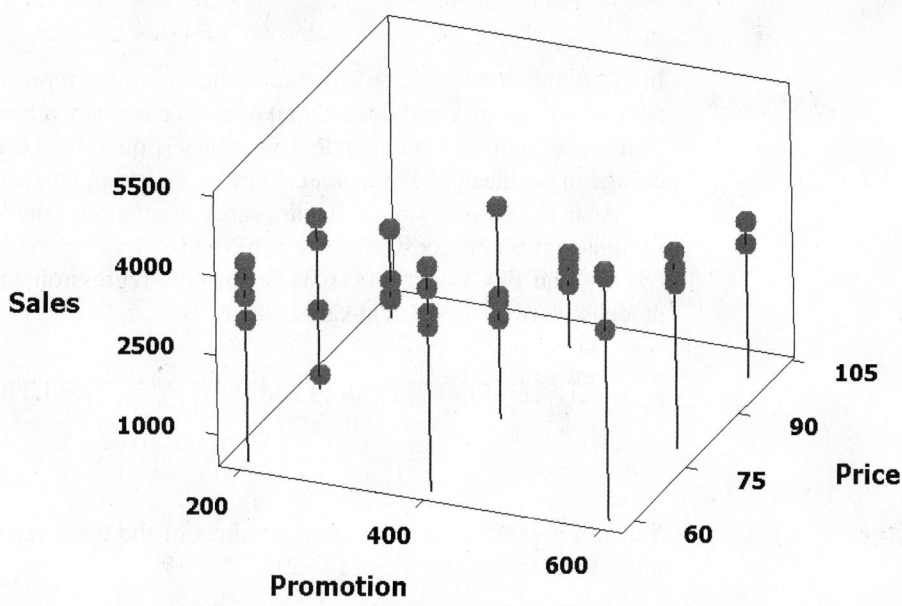

3D Scatterplot of Sales vs Price vs Promotion

MULTIPLE REGRESSION MODEL WITH k INDEPENDENT VARIABLES

$$Y_i = \beta_0 + \beta_1 X_{1i} + \beta_2 X_{2i} + \beta_3 X_{3i} + \cdots + \beta_k X_{ki} + \varepsilon_i \qquad (16.1)$$

where

$\beta_0 = Y$ intercept

$\beta_1 =$ slope of Y with variable X_1, holding variables $X_2, X_3, \ldots, X_k$ constant

$\beta_2 =$ slope of Y with variable X_2, holding variables $X_1, X_3, \ldots, X_k$ constant

$\beta_3 =$ slope of Y with variable X_3, holding variables $X_1, X_2, X_4, \ldots, X_k$ constant

.
.
.

$\beta_k =$ slope of Y with variable X_k, holding variables $X_1, X_2, X_3, \ldots, X_{k-1}$ constant

$\varepsilon_i =$ random error in Y for observation i

Equation (16.2) defines the multiple regression model with two independent variables.

MULTIPLE REGRESSION MODEL WITH TWO INDEPENDENT VARIABLES

$$Y_i = \beta_0 + \beta_1 X_{1i} + \beta_2 X_{2i} + \varepsilon_i \qquad (16.2)$$

where

$\beta_0 = Y$ intercept

$\beta_1 =$ slope of Y with variable X_1, holding variable X_2 constant

$\beta_2 =$ slope of Y with variable X_2, holding variable X_1 constant

$\varepsilon_i =$ random error in Y for observation i

Compare the multiple regression model to the simple linear regression model [Equation (15.1) on page 642]:

$$Y_i = \beta_0 + \beta_1 X_i + \varepsilon_i$$

In the simple linear regression model, the slope, β_1, represents the change in the mean of Y per unit change in X and does not take into account any other variables. In the multiple regression model with two independent variables [Equation (16.2)], the slope, β_1, represents the change in the mean of Y per unit change in X_1, taking into account the effect of X_2.

As in the case of simple linear regression, you use the least-squares method to compute sample regression coefficients (b_0, b_1, and b_2) as estimates of the population parameters (β_0, β_1, and β_2). Equation (16.3) defines the regression equation for a multiple regression model with two independent variables.

MULTIPLE REGRESSION EQUATION WITH TWO INDEPENDENT VARIABLES

$$\hat{Y}_i = b_0 + b_1 X_{1i} + b_2 X_{2i} \tag{16.3}$$

You can use SPSS to compute the values of the three regression coefficients for the OmniPower sales data (see Figure 16.2).

FIGURE 16.2

SPSS regression results worksheet for OmniPower sales data

Variables Entered/Removed[b]					Model Summary			
Model	Variables Entered	Variables Removed	Method	Model	R	R Square	Adjusted R Square	Std. Error of the Estimate
1	Promotion, Price[a]		Enter	1	.870[a]	.758	.742	638.065

a. All requested variables entered.
b. Dependent Variable: Sales

a. Predictors: (Constant), Price, Promotion

ANOVA[b]

Model		Sum of Squares	df	Mean Square	F	Sig.
1	Regression	39472730.773	2	19736365.387	48.477	.000[a]
	Residual	12620946.668	31	407127.312		
	Total	52093677.441	33			

a. Predictors: (Constant), Promotion, Price
b. Dependent Variable: Sales

Coefficients[a]

Model		Unstandardized Coefficients		Standardized Coefficients		
		B	Std. Error	Beta	t	Sig.
1	(Constant)	5837.521	628.150		9.293	.000
	Price	−53.217	6.852	−.690	−7.766	.000
	Promotion	3.613	.685	.468	5.273	.000

a. Dependent Variable: Assessed value

From Figure 16.2, the computed values of the regression coefficients are

$$b_0 = 5837.521 \quad b_1 = -53.217 \quad b_2 = 3.613$$

Therefore, the multiple regression equation is

$$\hat{Y}_i = 5{,}837.521 - 53.217X_{1i} + 3.613X_{2i}$$

where

$\hat{Y}_i$ = predicted monthly sales of OmniPower bars for store i

X_{1i} = price of OmniPower bar (in cents) for store i

X_{2i} = monthly in-store promotional expenditures (in dollars) for store i

The sample Y intercept ($b_0 = 5{,}837.5208$) estimates the number of OmniPower bars sold in a month if the price is \$0.00 and the total amount spent on promotional expenditures is also \$0.00. Because these values of price and promotion are outside the range of price and promotion used in the test-market study, and because they make no sense in the context of the problem, the value of b_0 has little or no practical interpretation.

The slope of price with OmniPower sales ($b_1 = -53.2173$) indicates that, for a given amount of monthly promotional expenditures, the predicted sales of OmniPower are estimated to decrease by 53.2173 bars per month for each 1-cent increase in the price. The slope of monthly promotional expenditures with OmniPower sales ($b_2 = 3.6131$) indicates that, for a given price, the estimated sales of OmniPower are predicted to increase by 3.6131 bars for each additional \$1 spent on promotions. These estimates allow you to better understand the likely effect that price and promotion decisions will have in the marketplace. For example, a 10-cent decrease in price is predicted to increase sales by 532.173 bars, with a fixed amount of monthly promotional expenditures. A \$100 increase in promotional expenditures is predicted to increase sales by 361.31 bars, for a given price.

Regression coefficients in multiple regression are called **net regression coefficients**; they estimate the predicted change in Y per unit change in a particular X, *holding constant the effect of the other X variables*. For example, in the study of OmniPower bar sales, for a store with a given amount of promotional expenditures, the estimated sales are predicted to decrease by 53.2173 bars per month for each 1-cent increase in the price of an OmniPower bar. Another way to interpret this "net effect" is to think of two stores with an equal amount of promotional expenditures. If the first store charges 1 cent more than the other store, the net effect of this difference is that the first store is predicted to sell 53.2173 fewer bars per month than the second store. To interpret the net effect of promotional expenditures, you can consider two stores that are charging the same price. If the first store spends \$1 more on promotional expenditures, the net effect of this difference is that the first store is predicted to sell 3.6131 more bars per month than the second store.

Predicting the Dependent Variable Y

You can use the multiple regression equation to predict values of the dependent variable. For example, what are the predicted sales for a store charging 79 cents during a month in which promotional expenditures are \$400? Using the multiple regression equation,

$$\hat{Y}_i = 5{,}837.5208 - 53.2173X_{1i} + 3.6131X_{2i}$$

with $X_{1i} = 79$ and $X_{2i} = 400$,

$$\hat{Y}_i = 5{,}837.5208 - 53.2173(79) + 3.6131(400)$$

$$= 3{,}078.57$$

Thus, you predict that stores charging 79 cents and spending \$400 in promotional expenditures will sell 3,078.57 OmniPower bars per month.

After you have developed the regression equation, done a residual analysis (see Section 16.3), and determined the significance of the overall fitted model (see Section 16.2), you can construct a confidence interval estimate of the mean value and a prediction interval for an individual value. You should rely on software to do these computations for you, given the complex nature of the computations. Figure 16.3 presents an Excel worksheet that computes a confidence interval estimate and a prediction interval for the OmniPower sales data. (The Minitab results in Figure 16.2 include these computations.)

FIGURE 16.3

SPSS confidence interval estimate and prediction interval worksheet for the OmniPower sales data

SPSS OUTPUT

The confidence interval values and prediction values are displayed on the SPSS Data Editor under the variables PRE_1, RES_1, LMCI_1, UMCI_1, LICI_1, and UICI_1.

Sales	Price	Promotion	Pre_1	RES_1	LMCI_1	UMCI_1	LICI_1	UICI_1
4141	59	200	3420.31	720.6905	2971.304	3869.315	2043.683	4796.936
3842	59	200	3420.31	421.6905	2971.304	3869.315	2043.683	4796.936
3056	59	200	3420.31	−364.31	2971.304	3869.315	2043.683	4796.936
3519	59	200	3420.31	98.69048	2971.304	3869.315	2043.683	4796.936
4226	59	400	4142.921	83.07887	3798.765	4487.078	2796.839	5489.003
4630	59	400	4142.921	487.0789	3798.765	4487.078	2796.839	5489.003
3507	59	400	4142.921	−635.921	3798.765	4487.078	2796.839	5489.003
3754	59	400	4142.921	−388.921	3798.765	4487.078	2796.839	5489.003
5000	59	600	4865.533	134.4673	4427.896	5303.17	3492.573	6238.493
5120	59	600	4865.533	254.4673	4427.896	5303.17	3492.573	6238.493
4011	59	600	4865.533	−854.533	4427.896	5303.17	3492.573	6238.493
5015	59	600	4865.533	149.4673	4427.896	5303.17	3492.573	6238.493
1916	79	200	2355.963	−439.963	2011.806	2700.119	1009.881	3702.045
675	79	200	2355.963	−1680.96	2011.806	2700.119	1009.881	3702.045
3636	79	200	2355.963	1280.037	2011.806	2700.119	1009.881	3702.045
3224	79	200	2355.963	868.0372	2011.806	2700.119	1009.881	3702.045
2295	79	400	3078.574	−783.574	2854.071	3303.077	1758.008	4399.14
2730	79	400	3078.574	−348.574	2854.071	3303.077	1758.008	4399.14
2618	79	400	3078.574	−460.574	2854.071	3303.077	1758.008	4399.14
4421	79	400	3078.574	1342.426	2854.071	3303.077	1758.008	4399.14
4113	79	600	3801.186	311.814	3428.89	4173.482	2447.636	5154.736
3746	79	600	3801.186	−55.186	3428.89	4173.482	2447.636	5154.736
3532	79	600	3801.186	−269.186	3428.89	4173.482	2447.636	5154.736
3825	79	600	3801.186	23.81399	3428.89	4173.482	2447.636	5154.736
1096	99	200	1291.616	−195.616	853.9793	1729.253	−81.3438	2664.576
761	99	200	1291.616	−530.616	853.9793	1729.253	−81.3438	2664.576
2088	99	200	1291.616	796.3839	853.9793	1729.253	−81.3438	2664.576
820	99	200	1291.616	−471.616	853.9793	1729.253	−81.3438	2664.576
2114	99	400	2014.228	99.77232	1641.932	2386.524	660.6778	3367.778
1882	99	400	2014.228	−132.228	1641.932	2386.524	660.6778	3367.778
2159	99	400	2014.228	144.7723	1641.932	2386.524	660.6778	3367.778
1602	99	400	2014.228	−412.228	1641.932	2386.524	660.6778	3367.778
3354	99	600	2736.839	617.1607	2244.978	3228.701	1345.645	4128.033
2927	99	600	2736.839	190.1607	2244.978	3228.701	1345.645	4128.033

Note: y = Monthly Sales of OmniPower bars, X1 = price of OmniPower bar (in cents), X2 = monthly in-store promotional expenditures (in dollars)
Based on Model 1
PRE – Unstandardized Predicted Value
RES – Unstandardized Residual Value
LMCI – 95% Lower Confidence Interval for y mean
UMCI – 95% Upper Confidence Interval for y mean
LICI – 95% Lower Confidence Interval for y individual
UICI – 95% Upper Confidence Interval for y individual

The 95% confidence interval estimate of the mean OmniPower sales for all stores charging 79 cents and spending $400 in promotional expenditures is 2,854.07 to 3,303.08 bars. The prediction interval for an individual store is 1,758.01 to 4,399.14 bars.

Problems for Section 16.1

LEARNING THE BASICS

16.1 For this problem, use the following multiple regression equation:

$$\hat{Y}_i = 10 + 5X_{1i} + 3X_{2i}$$

a. Interpret the meaning of the slopes.
b. Interpret the meaning of the Y intercept.

16.2 For this problem, use the following multiple regression equation:

$$\hat{Y}_i = 50 - 2X_{1i} + 7X_{2i}$$

a. Interpret the meaning of the slopes.
b. Interpret the meaning of the Y intercept.

APPLYING THE CONCEPTS

16.3 A shoe manufacturer is considering developing a new brand of running shoes. The business problem facing the marketing analyst is to determine which variables should be used to predict durability (i.e., the effect of long-term impact). Two independent variables under consideration are X_1 (FOREIMP), a measurement of the forefoot shock-absorbing capability, and X_2 (MIDSOLE), a measurement of the change in impact properties over time. The dependent variable Y is LTIMP, a measure of the shoe's durability after a repeated impact test. Data are collected from a random sample of 15 types of currently manufactured running shoes, with the following results:

Variable	Coefficients	Standard Error	t Statistic	p-Value
Intercept	−0.02686	0.06905	−0.39	0.7034
Foreimp	0.79116	0.06295	12.57	0.0000
Midsole	0.60484	0.07174	8.43	0.0000

a. State the multiple regression equation.
b. Interpret the meaning of the slopes, b_1 and b_2, in this problem.

SELF Test **16.4** A mail-order catalog business selling personal computer supplies, software, and hardware maintains a centralized warehouse. Management is currently examining the process of distribution from the warehouse. The business problem facing management relates to the factors that affect warehouse distribution costs. Cur-

rently, a small handling fee is added to each order, regardless of the amount of the order. Data collected over the past 24 months (stored in **WareCost**) indicate the warehouse distribution costs (in thousands of dollars), the sales (in thousands of dollars), and the number of orders received.

a. State the multiple regression equation.
b. Interpret the meaning of the slopes, b_1 and b_2, in this problem.
c. Explain why the regression coefficient, b_0, has no practical meaning in the context of this problem.
d. Predict the monthly warehouse distribution cost when sales are $400,000 and the number of orders is 4,500.
e. Construct a 95% confidence interval estimate for the mean monthly warehouse distribution cost when sales are $400,000 and the number of orders is 4,500.
f. Construct a 95% prediction interval for the monthly warehouse distribution cost for a particular month when sales are $400,000 and the number of orders is 4,500.
g. Explain why the interval in (e) is narrower than the interval in (f).

16.5 How does horsepower and weight affect the mileage of family sedans? Data from a sample of twenty 2011 sedans were collected and organized and stored in **Auto2011**. (Data extracted from "Top 2011 Cars," *Consumer Reports*, April 2011, pp. 28–75.) Develop a regression model to predict mileage (as measured by miles per gallon) based on the horsepower of the car's engine and the weight of the car (in pounds).

a. State the multiple regression equation.
b. Interpret the meaning of the slopes, b_1 and b_2, in this problem.
c. Explain why the regression coefficient, b_0, has no practical meaning in the context of this problem.
d. Predict the miles per gallon for cars that have 190 horsepower and weigh 3,500 pounds.
e. Construct a 95% confidence interval estimate for the mean miles per gallon for cars that have 190 horsepower and weigh 3,500 pounds.
f. Construct a 95% prediction interval for the miles per gallon for an individual car that has 190 horsepower and weighs 3,500 pounds.

16.6 The business problem facing a consumer products company is to measure the effectiveness of different types of advertising media in the promotion of its products.

Specifically, the company is interested in the effectiveness of radio advertising and newspaper advertising (including the cost of discount coupons). During a one month test period, data were collected from a sample of 22 cities with approximately equal populations. Each city is allocated a specific expenditure level for radio advertising and for newspaper advertising. The sales of the product (in thousands of dollars) and also the levels of media expenditure (in thousands of dollars) during the test month are recorded, with the following results shown below and stored in Advertise :

City	Sales ($Thousands)	Radio Adverting ($Thousands)	Newspaper Advertising ($Thousands)
1	973	0	40
2	1,119	0	40
3	875	25	25
4	625	25	25
5	910	30	30
6	971	30	30
7	931	35	35
8	1,177	35	35
9	882	40	25
10	982	40	25
11	1,628	45	45
12	1,577	45	45
13	1,044	50	0
14	914	50	0
15	1,329	55	25
16	1,330	55	25
17	1,405	60	30
18	1,436	60	30
19	1,521	65	35
20	1,741	65	35
21	1,866	70	40
22	1,717	70	40

a. State the multiple regression equation.
b. Interpret the meaning of the slopes, b_1 and b_2, in this problem.
c. Interpret the meaning of the regression coefficient, b_0.
d. Which type of advertising is more effective? Explain.

16.7 The business problem facing the director of broadcasting operations for a television station was the issue of

standby hours (i.e., hours in which unionized graphic artists at the station are paid but are not actually involved in any activity) and what factors were related to standby hours. The study included the following variables:

Standby hours (Y)—Total number of standby hours in a week
Total staff present (X_1)—Weekly total of people-days
Remote hours (X_2)—Total number of hours worked by employees at locations away from the central plant

Data were collected for 26 weeks; these data are organized and stored in Standby .
a. State the multiple regression equation.
b. Interpret the meaning of the slopes, b_1 and b_2, in this problem.
c. Explain why the regression coefficient, b_0, has no practical meaning in the context of this problem.
d. Predict the standby hours for a week in which the total staff present have 310 people-days and the remote hours are 400.
e. Construct a 95% confidence interval estimate for the mean standby hours for weeks in which the total staff present have 310 people-days and the remote hours are 400.
f. Construct a 95% prediction interval for the standby hours for a single week in which the total staff present have 310 people-days and the remote hours are 400.

16.8 Nassau County is located approximately 25 miles east of New York City. The data organized and stored in GlenCove include the appraised value, land area of the property in acres, and age, in years, for a sample of 30 single-family homes located in Glen Cove, a small city in Nassau County. Develop a multiple linear regression model to predict appraised value based on land area of the property and age, in years.
a. State the multiple regression equation.
b. Interpret the meaning of the slopes, b_1 and b_2, in this problem.
c. Explain why the regression coefficient, b_0, has no practical meaning in the context of this problem.
d. Predict the appraised value for a house that has a land area of 0.25 acres and is 45 years old.
e. Construct a 95% confidence interval estimate for the mean appraised value for houses that have a land area of 0.25 acres and are 45 years old.
f. Construct a 95% prediction interval estimate for the appraised value for an individual house that has a land area of 0.25 acres and is 45 years old.

16.2 R^2, Adjusted R^2, and the Overall F Test

This section discusses three methods you can use to evaluate the overall multiple regression model: the coefficient of multiple determination, R^2, the adjusted R^2, and the overall F test.

Coefficient of Multiple Determination

Recall from Section 15.3 that the coefficient of determination, R^2, measures the proportion of the variation in Y that is explained by the independent variable X in the simple linear regression model. In multiple regression, the **coefficient of multiple determination** represents the proportion of the variation in Y that is explained by the set of independent variables. Equation (16.4) defines the coefficient of multiple determination for a multiple regression model with two or more independent variables.

COEFFICIENT OF MULTIPLE DETERMINATION

The coefficient of multiple determination is equal to the regression sum of squares (SSR) divided by the total sum of squares (SST).

$$R^2 = \frac{\text{Regression sum of squares}}{\text{Total sum of squares}} = \frac{SSR}{SST} \qquad \textbf{(16.4)}$$

where

$\qquad SSR = $ regression sum of squares

$\qquad SST = $ total sum of squares

In the OmniPower example, from Figure 16.2 on page 708, $SSR = 39,472,730.77$ and $SST = 52,093,677.44$. Thus,

$$R^2 = \frac{SSR}{SST} = \frac{39,472,730.77}{52,093,677.44} = 0.7577$$

The coefficient of multiple determination ($R^2 = 0.7577$) indicates that 75.77% of the variation in sales is explained by the variation in the price and in the promotional expenditures. The coefficient of multiple determination also appears in the Figure 16.2 results on page 708, and is labeled R Square in the SPSS results and R-Sq in the Minitab results.

Adjusted R^2

When considering multiple regression models, some statisticians suggest that you should use the **adjusted R^2** to take into account both the number of independent variables in the model and the sample size. Reporting the adjusted R^2 is extremely important when you are comparing two or more regression models that predict the same dependent variable but have a different number of independent variables. Equation (16.5) defines the adjusted R^2.

ADJUSTED R^2

$$R^2_{adj} = 1 - \left[(1 - R^2) \frac{n-1}{n-k-1} \right] \qquad \textbf{(16.5)}$$

where k is the number of independent variables in the regression equation.

Thus, for the OmniPower data, because $R^2 = 0.7577$, $n = 34$, and $k = 2$,

$$R_{adj}^2 = 1 - \left[(1 - 0.7577)\frac{34 - 1}{34 - 2 - 1}\right]$$

$$= 1 - \left[(0.2423)\frac{33}{31}\right]$$

$$= 1 - 0.2579$$

$$= 0.7421$$

Therefore, 74.21% of the variation in sales is explained by the multiple regression model—adjusted for the number of independent variables and sample size. The adjusted R^2 also appears in the Figure 16.2 results on page 708, and is labeled Adjusted R Square in the SPSS results and R-Sq(adj) in the Minitab results.

Test for the Significance of the Overall Multiple Regression Model

You use the **overall F test** to determine whether there is a significant relationship between the dependent variable and the entire set of independent variables (the overall multiple regression model). Because there is more than one independent variable, you use the following null and alternative hypotheses:

H_0: $\beta_1 = \beta_2 = \cdots = \beta_k = 0$ (There is no linear relationship between the dependent variable and the independent variables.)

H_1: At least one $\beta_j \neq 0$, $j = 1, 2, \ldots, k$ (There is a linear relationship between the dependent variable and at least one of the independent variables.)

Equation (16.6) defines the overall F test statistic. Table 16.2 presents the ANOVA summary table.

OVERALL F TEST

The F_{STAT} test statistic is equal to the regression mean square (MSR) divided by the mean square error (MSE).

$$F_{STAT} = \frac{MSR}{MSE} \tag{16.6}$$

where

F_{STAT} = test statistic from an F distribution with k and $n - k - 1$ degrees of freedom

k = number of independent variables in the regression model

TABLE 16.2

ANOVA Summary Table for the Overall F Test

Source	Degrees of Freedom	Sum of Squares	Mean Squares (Variance)	F
Regression	k	SSR	$MSR = \dfrac{SSR}{k}$	$F_{STAT} = \dfrac{MSR}{MSE}$
Error	$n - k - 1$	SSE	$MSE = \dfrac{SSE}{n - k - 1}$	
Total	$n - 1$	SST		

FIGURE 16.4A

ANOVA Table from
the SPSS Output

ANOVA[b]					
Model	Sum of Squares	df	Mean Square	F	Sig.
1 Regression	39472730.773	2	19736365.387	48.477	.000[a]
Residual	12620946.668	31	407127.312		
Total	52093677.441	33			

a. Predictors: (Constant), Promotion, Price
b. Dependent Variable: Sales

Test statistics, F_{CALC} p-value

FIGURE 16.4

Testing for the
significance of a set of
regression coefficients at
the 0.05 level of
significance, with 2 and
31 degrees of freedom

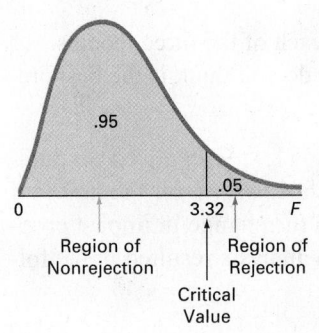

.95

.05

0   3.32 F

Region of   Region of
Nonrejection   Rejection

Critical
Value

The decision rule is

Reject H_0 at the α level of significance if $F_{STAT} > F_\alpha$;

otherwise, do not reject H_0.

Using a 0.05 level of significance, the critical value of the F distribution with 2 and 31 degrees of freedom found from Table E.5 is approximately 3.32 (see Figure 16.4). From Figure 16.4a, the F_{STAT} test statistic given in the ANOVA summary table is 48.4771. Because 48.4771 > 3.32, or because the p-value = 0.000 < 0.05, you reject H_0 and conclude that at least one of the independent variables (price and/or promotional expenditures) is related to sales.

To find the F critical value

To find the F critical value, use the Casio Calculator fx-9750GII and perform the following calculator steps.

From the **Main Menu** select

STAT F5(DIST) **F4**(F) **F3**(InvF), and then enter the following items:

Inverse F
Data   : **F2**(Var)   ▼
Area   : **0.05**   EXE
n: df   : **2**   EXE
d: df   : **31**   EXE
Save Res   : None
Execute

Now key **EXE** or **F1**(CALC).

The calculator will show the following results:

Inverse F
x-Inv = 3.30481725

The critical value is used to define the rejection and non-rejection regions as shown in the following diagram:

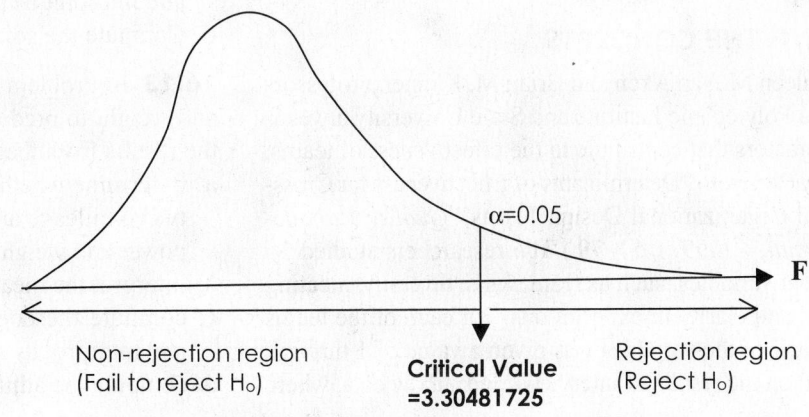

$\alpha = 0.05$

F

Non-rejection region
(Fail to reject H$_0$)

**Critical Value
=3.30481725**

Rejection region
(Reject H$_0$)

Problems for Section 16.2

LEARNING THE BASICS

16.9 The following ANOVA summary table is for a multiple regression model with two independent variables:

Source	Degrees of Freedom	Sum of Squares	Mean Squares	F
Regression	2	60		
Error	18	120		
Total	20	180		

a. Determine the regression mean square (MSR) and the mean square error (MSE).
b. Compute the overall F_{STAT} test statistic.
c. Determine whether there is a significant relationship between Y and the two independent variables at the 0.05 level of significance.
d. Compute the coefficient of multiple determination, r^2, and interpret its meaning.
e. Compute the adjusted r^2.

16.10 The following ANOVA summary table is for a multiple regression model with two independent variables:

Source	Degrees of Freedom	Sum of Squares	Mean Squares	F
Regression	2	30		
Error	10	120		
Total	12	150		

a. Determine the regression mean square (MSR) and the mean square error (MSE).
b. Compute the overall F_{STAT} test statistic.
c. Determine whether there is a significant relationship between Y and the two independent variables at the 0.05 level of significance.
d. Compute the coefficient of multiple determination, r^2, and interpret its meaning.
e. Compute the adjusted r^2.

APPLYING THE CONCEPTS

16.11 Eileen M. Van Aken and Brian M. Kleiner, professors at Virginia Polytechnic Institute and State University, investigated the factors that contribute to the effectiveness of teams. (Data extracted from "Determinants of Effectiveness for Cross-Functional Organizational Design Teams," *Quality Management Journal*, 4 (1997), 51–79.) The researchers studied 34 independent variables, such as team skills, diversity, meeting frequency, and clarity in expectations. For each of the teams studied, each of the variables was given a value of 1 through 100, based on the results of interviews and survey data, where

100 represents the highest rating. The dependent variable, team performance, was also given a value of 1 through 100, with 100 representing the highest rating. Many different regression models were explored, including the following:

Model 1

$$\text{Team performance} = \beta_0 + \beta_1(\text{Team skills}) + \varepsilon$$
$$r^2_{adj} = 0.68$$

Model 2

$$\text{Team performance} = \beta_0 + \beta_1(\text{Clarity in expectations}) + \varepsilon$$
$$r^2_{adj} = 0.78$$

Model 3

$$\text{Team performance} = \beta_0 + \beta_1(\text{Team skills})$$
$$+ \beta_2(\text{Clarity in expectations}) + \varepsilon$$
$$r^2_{adj} = 0.97$$

a. Interpret the adjusted r^2 for each of the three models.
b. Which of these three models do you think is the best predictor of team performance?

16.12 In Problem 16.3 on page 711, you predicted the durability of a brand of running shoe, based on the forefoot shock-absorbing capability and the change in impact properties over time. The regression analysis resulted in the following ANOVA summary table:

Source	Degrees of Freedom	Sum of Squares	Mean Squares	F	p-Value
Regression	2	12.61020	6.30510	97.69	0.0001
Error	12	0.77453	0.06454		
Total	14	13.38473			

a. Determine whether there is a significant relationship between durability and the two independent variables at the 0.05 level of significance.
b. Interpret the meaning of the *p*-value.
c. Compute the coefficient of multiple determination, r^2, and interpret its meaning.
d. Compute the adjusted r^2.

16.13 In Problem 16.5 on page 711, you used horsepower and weight to predict mileage (stored in Auto2011). Using the results from that problem,
a. determine whether there is a significant relationship between mileage and the two independent variables (horsepower and weight) at the 0.05 level of significance.
b. interpret the meaning of the *p*-value.
c. compute the coefficient of multiple determination, r^2, and interpret its meaning.
d. compute the adjusted r^2.

16.14 In Problem 16.4 on page 711, you used sales and number of orders to predict distribution costs at a mail-order catalog business (stored in **WareCost**). Use the results from that problem.

a. Determine whether there is a significant relationship between distribution costs and the two independent variables (sales and number of orders) at the 0.05 level of significance.

b. Interpret the meaning of the p-value.

c. Compute the coefficient of multiple determination, r^2, and interpret its meaning.

d. Compute the adjusted r^2.

16.15 In Problem 16.7 on page 712, you used the total staff present and remote hours to predict standby hours (stored in **Standby**). Use the results from that problem.

a. Determine whether there is a significant relationship between standby hours and the two independent variables (total staff present and remote hours) at the 0.05 level of significance.

b. Interpret the meaning of the p-value.

c. Compute the coefficient of multiple determination, r^2, and interpret its meaning.

d. Compute the adjusted r^2.

16.16 In Problem 16.6 on pages 711–712, you used radio advertising and newspaper advertising to predict sales (stored in **Advertise**). Use the results from that problem.

a. Determine whether there is a significant relationship between sales and the two independent variables (radio advertising and newspaper advertising) at the 0.05 level of significance.

b. Interpret the meaning of the p-value.

c. Compute the coefficient of multiple determination, r^2, and interpret its meaning.

d. Compute the adjusted r^2.

16.17 In Problem 16.8 on page 712, you used the land area of a property and the age of a house to predict appraised value (stored in **GlenCove**). Use the results from that problem.

a. Determine whether there is a significant relationship between appraised value and the two independent variables (land area of a property and age of a house) at the 0.05 level of significance.

b. Interpret the meaning of the p-value.

c. Compute the coefficient of multiple determination, r^2, and interpret its meaning.

d. Compute the adjusted r^2.

16.3 Residual Analysis for the Multiple Regression Model

In Section 15.5, you used residual analysis to evaluate the fit of the simple linear regression model. For the multiple regression model with two independent variables, you need to construct and analyze the following residual plots:

1. Residuals versus $\hat{Y}_i$

2. Residuals versus X_{1i}

3. Residuals versus X_{2i}

4. Residuals versus time

The first residual plot examines the pattern of residuals versus the predicted values of Y. If the residuals show a pattern for the predicted values of Y, there is evidence of a possible curvilinear effect in at least one independent variable, a possible violation of the assumption of equal variance (see Figure 15.13 on page 665), and/or the need to transform the Y variable.

The second and third residual plots involve the independent variables. Patterns in the plot of the residuals versus an independent variable may indicate the existence of a curvilinear effect and, therefore, the need to add a curvilinear independent variable to the multiple regression model.

The fourth plot is used to investigate patterns in the residuals in order to validate the independence assumption when the data are collected in time order. Associated with this residual plot, you can compute the Durbin-Watson statistic to determine the existence of positive autocorrelation among the residuals.

Figure 16.5 presents the residual plots for the OmniPower sales example. There is very little or no pattern in the relationship between the residuals and the predicted value of Y, the value of X_1 (price), or the value of X_2 (promotional expenditures). Thus, you can conclude that the multiple regression model is appropriate for predicting sales. There is no need to plot the residuals versus time because the data were not collected in time order.

FIGURE 16.5

Microsoft Excel residual plots for the OmniPower sales data: Panel *A*, residuals versus predicted *Y*; Panel *B*, residuals versus price; Panel *C*, residuals versus promotional expenditures

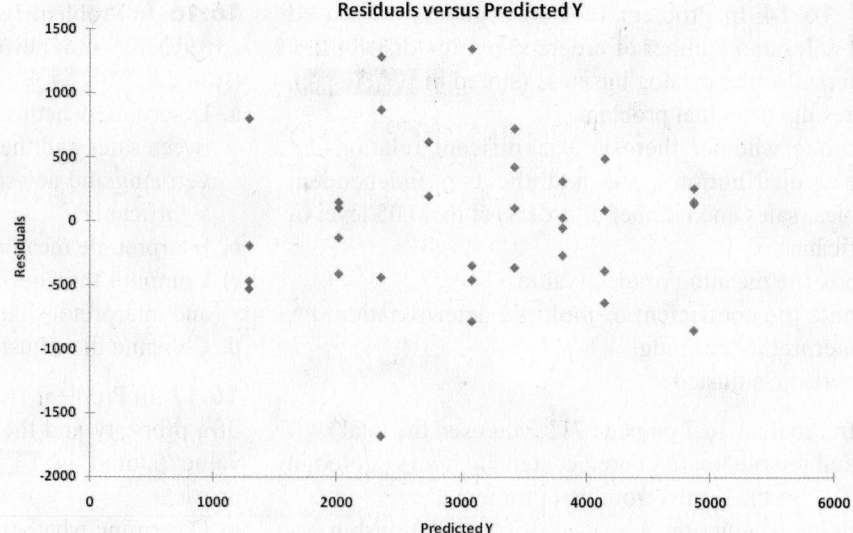

Panel A

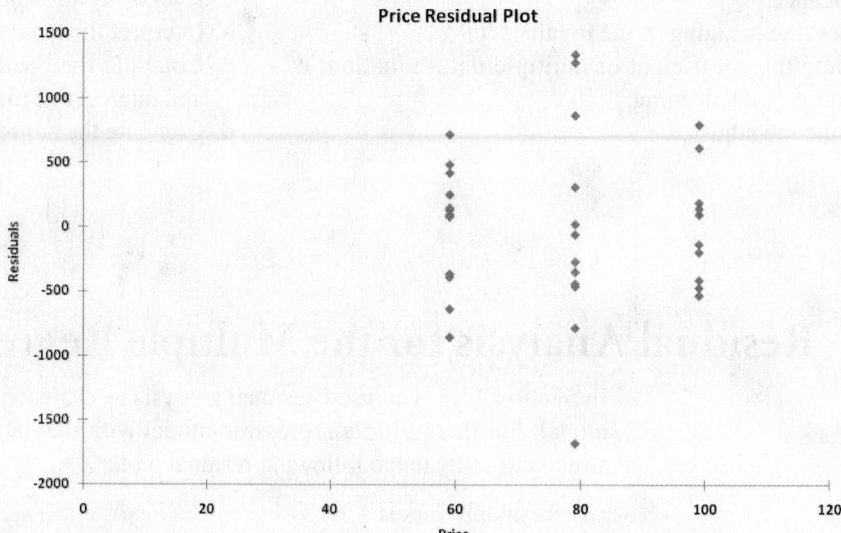

Panel B

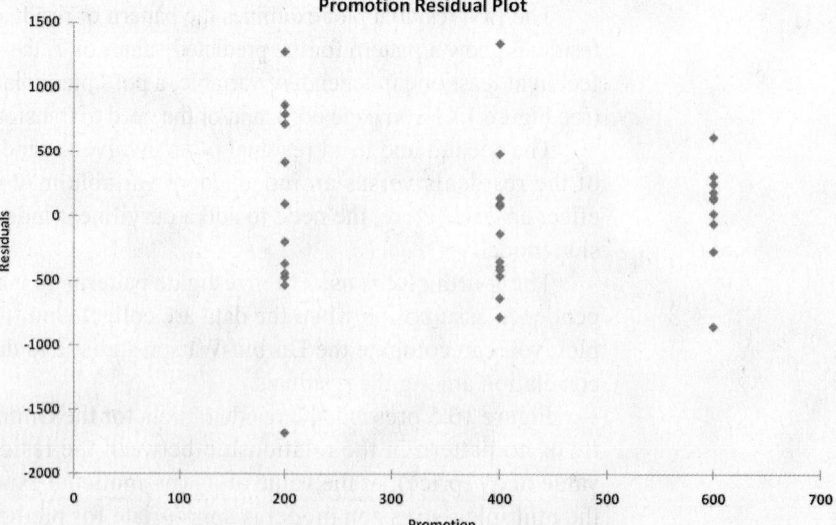

Panel C

The assumptions for simple linear regression have been discussed in Section 15.4 of Chapter 15. These assumptions are similar to that of multiple regression. The assumptions are

A. Linearity
B. Independence of errors
C. Equal variance
D. Normality of errors

The assumptions are being tested using scatterplot as a visual aid to verify if the assumptions are met. If the assumptions are violated, the multiple regression cannot be used to analyze the relationship between dependent variable and the independent variables. Next, you will learn to test the assumptions using scatterplots as illustrated in Example 16.1.

EXAMPLE 16.1

Use the Monthly OminiPower Data to Test the Assumptions for Multiple Regression

The variables used in the Monthly OmniPower data are Sales, Price and Promotional Expenditures data. The data is depicted in Table 16.1.

The dependent variable (denoted as Y) is Sales and

The independent variables (denoted as $X1$ and $X2$) are Price and Promotion respectively.

Test the Linearity Assumption

Construct the scatterplots of dependent variable against each independent variable to validate the linearity assumption. The two scatterplots are:

a. Scatterplot of Y against $X1$ as shown in Figure 16.6
b. Scatterplot of Y against $X2$ as shown in Figure 16.7

You can use SPSS to construct the scatterplots.

The linearity assumption requires you to verify if a linear relationship exists between the dependent variable and independent variable. You can visually see if the points in the scatterplot appear to fall in a straight line (i.e. no curvature). The scatterplot of sales against price shown in Figure 16.6 has a fairly straight line relationship with the responses. The scatterplot

FIGURE 16.6

A scatterplot of Y (sales) against $X1$ (sales)

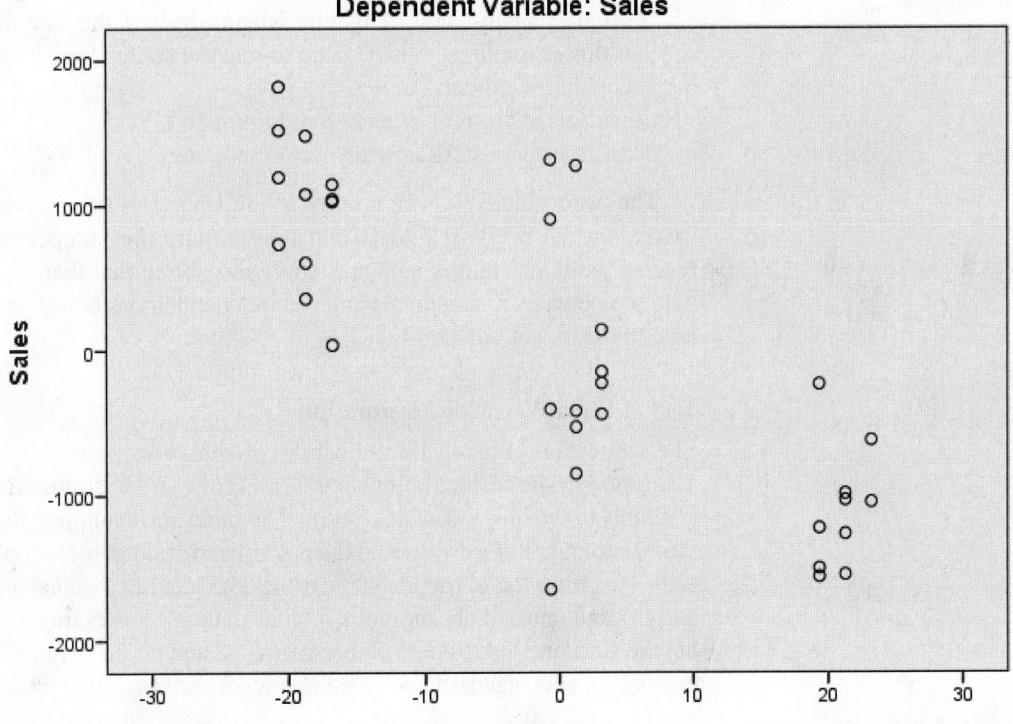

FIGURE 16.7
A scatterplot of Y (sales) against $X2$ (promotion)

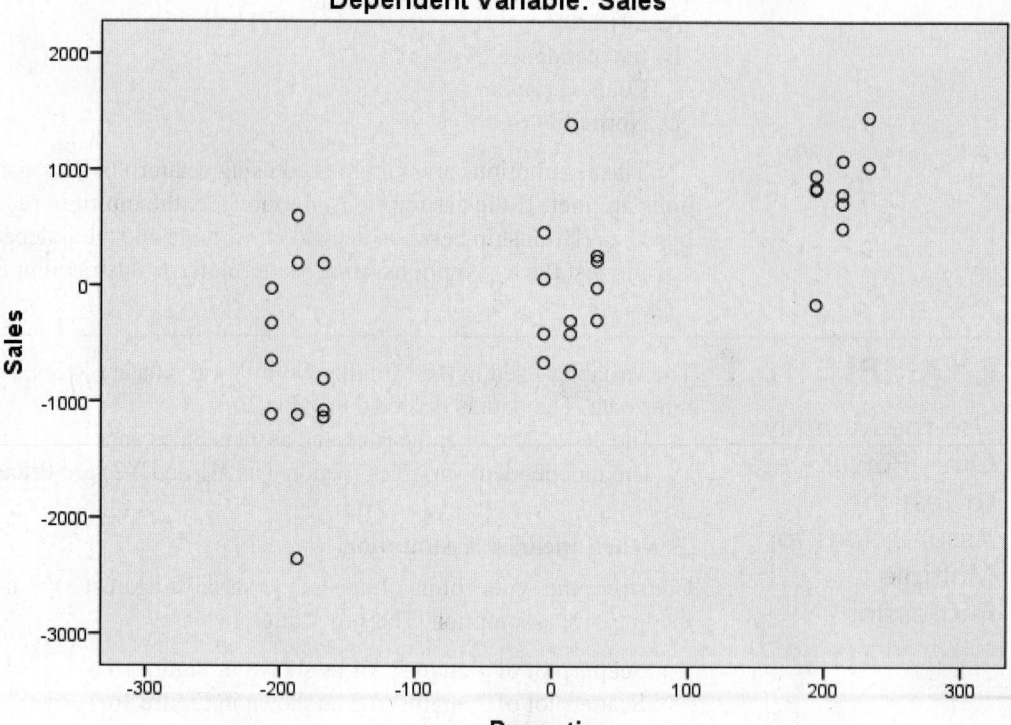

of sales and promotion shown in Figure 16.7 is also fairly linear. Studying the two scatter-plots, you can conclude that the assumption of linearity is met.

Test of Independence of Errors Assumption

As mentioned in Section 15.4, this assumption requires that the errors (ε_i) are independent of one another. To check this assumption, construct the following residual plots.

a. Residuals against time. This plot is applicable to the data that are collected in time order. For this example there is no need to plot the residuals against time since the data is not collected in time order.
b. Residuals against $X1$ as shown in Figure 16.8.
c. Residuals against $X2$ as shown in Figure 16.9.

The two residual plots containing the independent variables are used to investigate any curvature pattern in the residuals that may violate the independence assumptions. Observing residual plots in Figures 16.8 and 16.9, you notice that there is very little pattern in the relationship between the residuals and the independent variables, and therefore, the independence assumption is not violated.

Test of Equal Variance Assumption

The scatterplot of residuals against the predicted value allow you to check the equal variance assumption. The residual plot shown in Figure 16.10 is plotted with the predicted values and residuals in the unstandardized form. The other residual plot (Figure 16.11) is plotted with the standardized predicted values and standardized residuals. Both plots will give you the same results. It is common to use the standardized residual in the analysis because it is easy to identify outliers and unusual observations in your data set. For example, you can identify an outlier using the standardized residual values below –2 and above 2. In Figure 16.11, you see that there is one outlier with standardized value below –2 and two outliers with standardized value above 2.

FIGURE 16.8
A scatterplot of residual against price

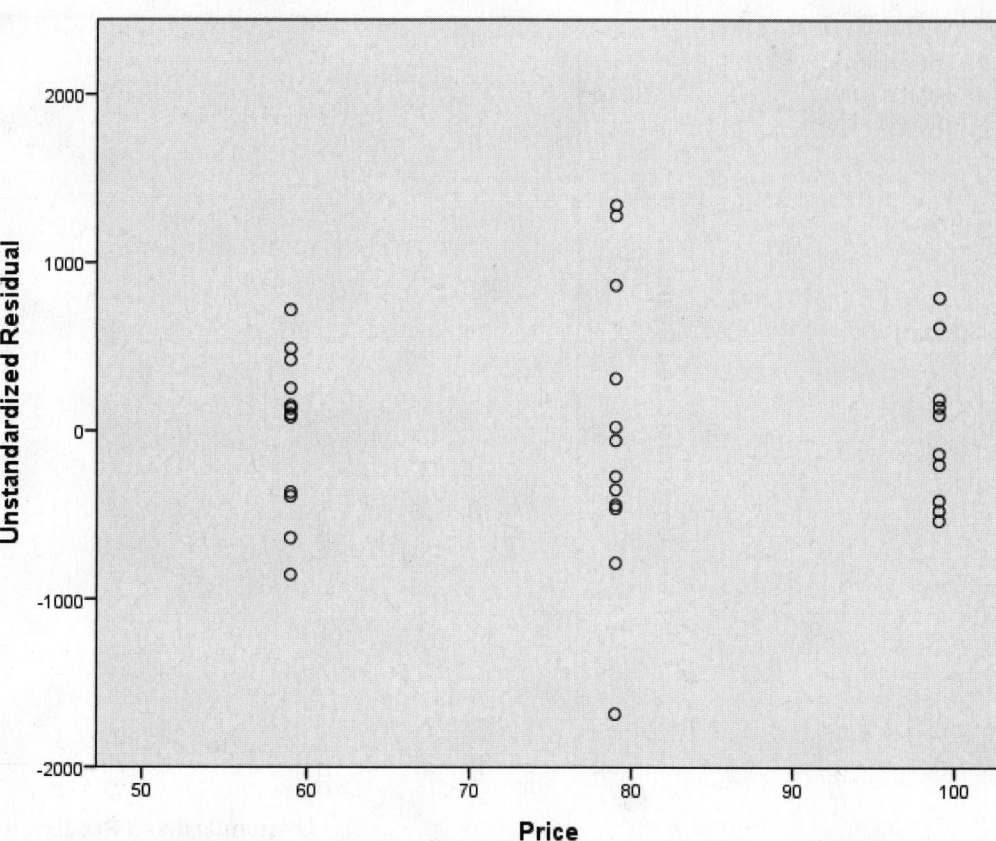

FIGURE 16.9
A scatterplot of residual against promotion

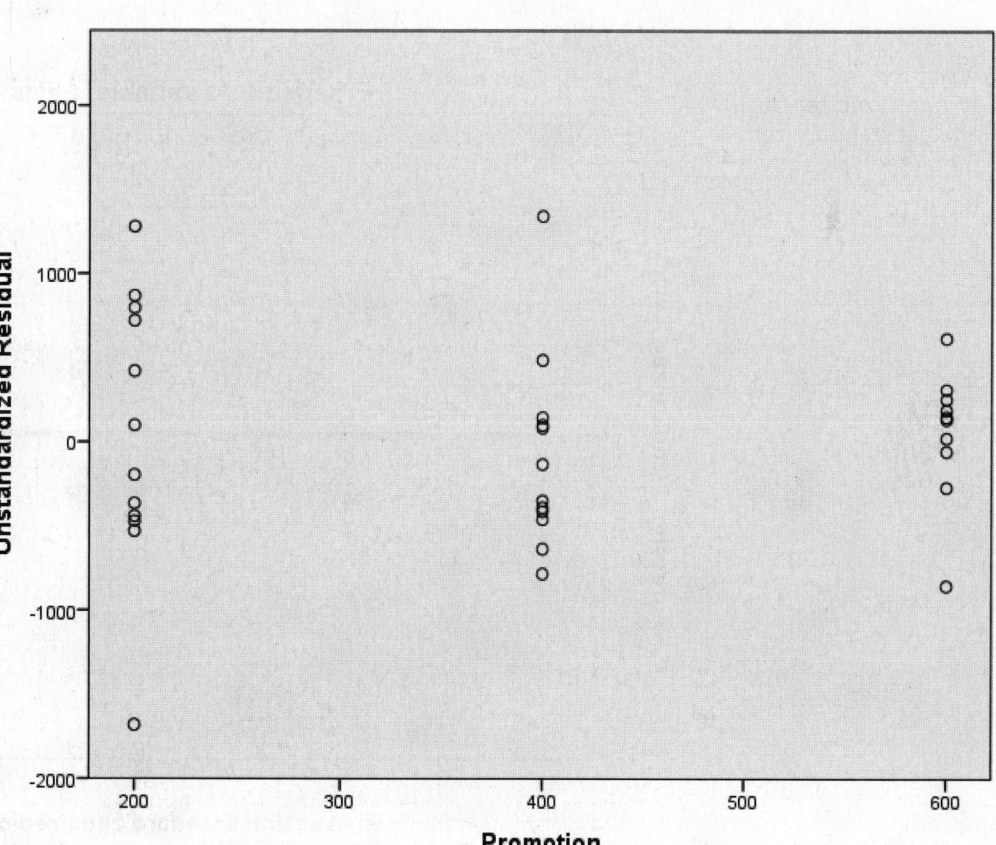

FIGURE 16.10

A scatterplot of residual against predicted value

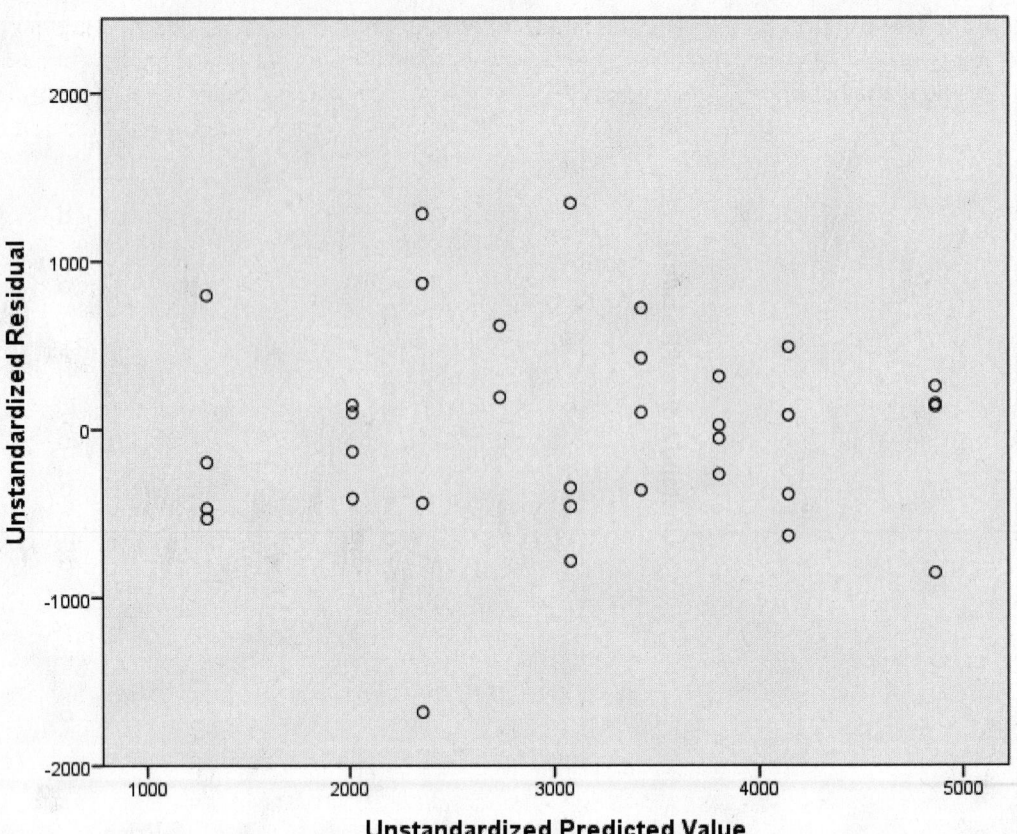

FIGURE 16.11

A scatterplot of standardized residual against standardized predicted value

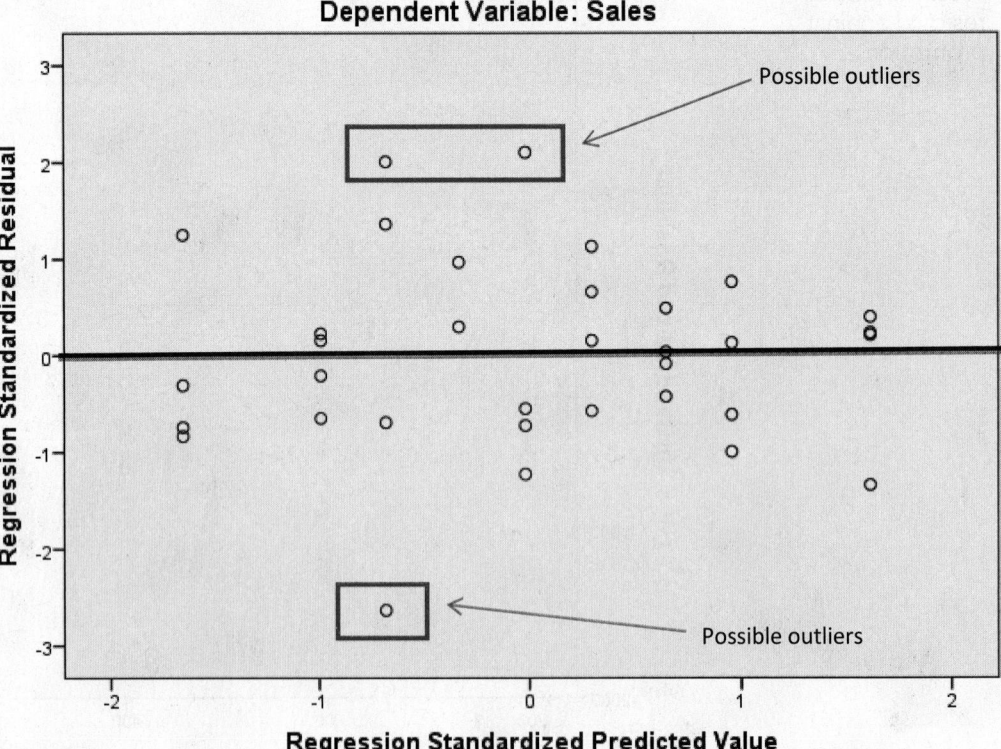

The scatterplot in Figure 16.11 should display a random pattern with points centered on the line of zero standardized residual value. The points should be evenly distributed around this line over the standardized predicted value. There is no obvious pattern in Figure 16.11 that would indicate the violation of the assumption of equal variance.

Test of Normality Assumption

To check this assumption, construct a histogram of standardized residual and a normal probability plot of standardized residual as shown in Figures 16.12 and 16.13 respectively.

The histogram of residuals in Figure 16.12 appears reasonably normal. The normal curve fitted in the histogram guide you in our examination. There is no concern that this assumption is violated.

Studying the normal probability plot (Figure 16.13), the points seemed to follow the straight line. It suggests that the normality assumption is met.

FIGURE 16.12

Histogram of standardized residuals

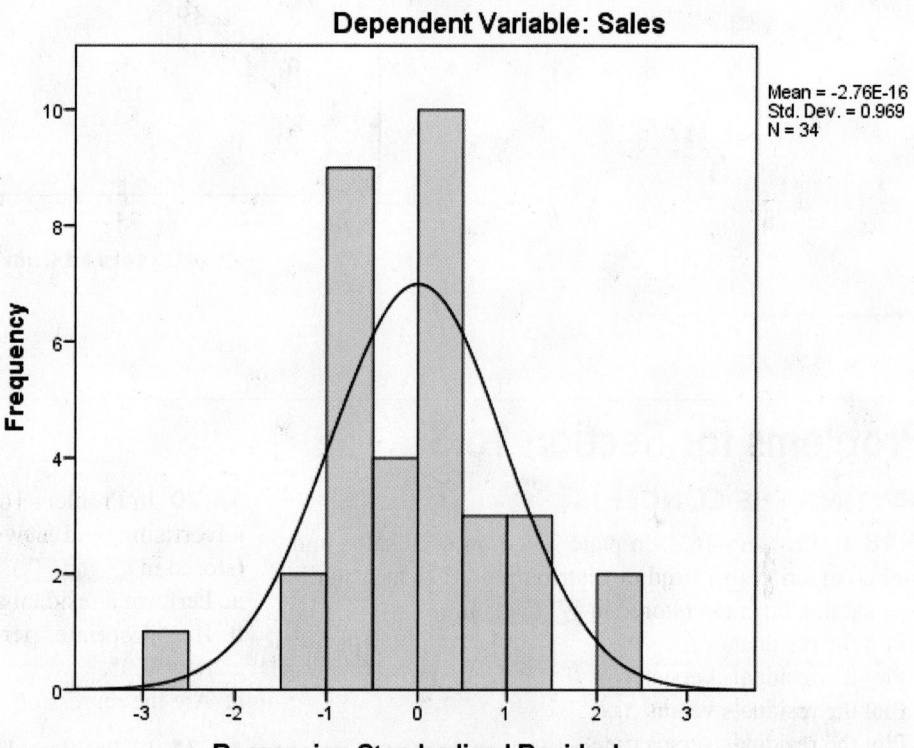

In summary, you just check the four assumptions of the regression model visually using scatterplots. You can conclude that all the four assumptions have been met and you can therefore use the regression model for inference and predictions.

FIGURE 16.13
A normal probability
plot of standardized
residuals

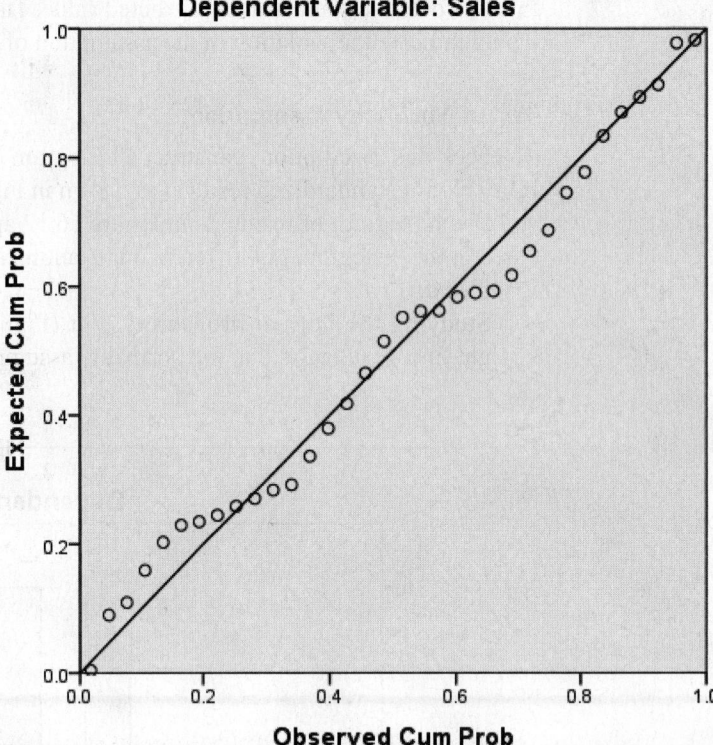

Normal P-P Plot of Regression Standardized Residual

Dependent Variable: Sales

Problems for Section 16.3

APPLYING THE CONCEPTS

16.18 In Problem 16.4 on page 711, you used sales and number of orders to predict distribution costs at a mail-order catalog business (stored in WareCost).
a. Plot the residuals versus $\hat{Y}_i$.
b. Plot the residuals versus X_{1i}.
c. Plot the residuals versus X_{2i}.
d. Plot the residuals versus time.
e. In the residual plots created in (a) through (d), is there any evidence of a violation of the regression assumptions? Explain.
f. Determine the Durbin-Watson statistic.
g. At the 0.05 level of significance, is there evidence of positive autocorrelation in the residuals?

16.19 In Problem 16.5 on page 711, you used horsepower and weight to predict mileage (stored in Auto2011).
a. Plot the residuals versus $\hat{Y}_i$
b. Plot the residuals versus X_{1i}.
c. Plot the residuals versus X_{2i}.
d. In the residual plots created in (a) through (c), is there any evidence of a violation of the regression assumptions? Explain.
e. Should you compute the Durbin-Watson statistic for these data? Explain.

16.20 In Problem 16.6 on pages 711–712, you used radio advertising and newspaper advertising to predict sales (stored in Advertise).
a. Perform a residual analysis on your results.
b. If appropriate, perform the Durbin-Watson test, using $\alpha = 0.05$.
c. Are the regression assumptions valid for these data?

16.21 In Problem 16.7 on page 712, you used the total staff present and remote hours to predict standby hours (stored in Standby).
a. Perform a residual analysis on your results.
b. If appropriate, perform the Durbin-Watson test, using $\alpha = 0.05$.
c. Are the regression assumptions valid for these data?

16.22 In Problem 16.8 on page 712, you used the land area of a property and the age of a house to predict appraised value (stored in GlenCove).
a. Perform a residual analysis on your results.
b. If appropriate, perform the Durbin-Watson test, using $\alpha = 0.05$.
c. Are the regression assumptions valid for these data?

16.4 Inferences Concerning the Population Regression Coefficients

In Section 15.7, you tested the slope in a simple linear regression model to determine the significance of the relationship between X and Y. In addition, you constructed a confidence interval estimate of the population slope. This section extends those procedures to multiple regression.

Tests of Hypothesis

In a simple linear regression model, to test a hypothesis concerning the population slope, β_1, you used Equation (15.16) on page 667:

$$t_{STAT} = \frac{b_1 - \beta_1}{S_{b_1}}$$

Equation (16.7) generalizes this equation for multiple regression.

TESTING FOR THE SLOPE IN MULTIPLE REGRESSION

$$t_{STAT} = \frac{b_j - \beta_j}{S_{b_j}} \tag{16.7}$$

where

b_j = slope of variable j with Y, holding constant the effects of all other independent variables

S_{b_j} = standard error of the regression coefficient b_j

t_{STAT} = test statistic for a t distribution with $n - k - 1$ degrees of freedom

k = number of independent variables in the regression equation

β_j = hypothesized value of the population slope for variable j, holding constant the effects of all other independent variables

---

To determine whether variable X_2 (amount of promotional expenditures) has a significant effect on sales, taking into account the price of OmniPower bars, the null and alternative hypotheses are

$$H_0: \beta_2 = 0$$
$$H_1: \beta_2 \neq 0$$

From Equation (16.7) and Figure 16.2 on page 708,

$$t_{STAT} = \frac{b_2 - \beta_2}{S_{b_2}}$$

$$= \frac{3.6131 - 0}{0.6852} = 5.2728$$

If you select a level of significance of 0.05, the critical values of t for 31 degrees of freedom from Table E.3 are -2.0395 and $+2.0395$ (see Figure 16.14).

FIGURE 16.14

Testing for significance of a regression coefficient at the 0.05 level of significance, with 31 degrees of freedom

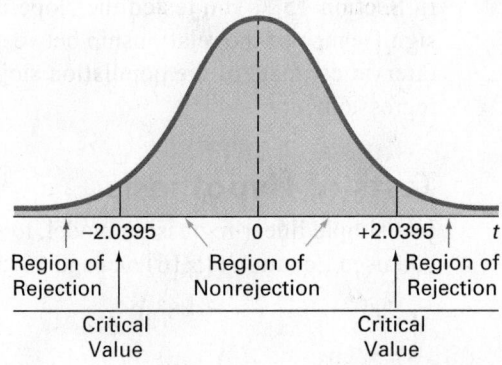

-2.0395	0	$+2.0395$ t
Region of Rejection	Region of Nonrejection	Region of Rejection
Critical Value		Critical Value

From Figure 16.4a on page 715, observe that the computed t_{STAT} test statistic is 5.2728. Because $t_{STAT} = 5.2728 > 2.0395$ or because the p-value is approximately zero, you reject H_0 and conclude that there is a significant relationship between the variable X_2 (promotional expenditures) and sales, taking into account the price, X_1. The extremely small p-value allows you to strongly reject the null hypothesis that there is no linear relationship between sales and promotional expenditures. Example 16.2 presents the test for the significance of β_1, the slope of sales with price.

FIGURE 16.14a

Coefficient table from the SPSS output

	Coefficients[a]							
	Unstandardized Coefficients		**Standardized Coefficients**				**95.0% Confidence Interval for B**	
Model	**B**	**Std. Error**	**Beta**	**t**	**Sig.**		**Lower Bound**	**Upper Bound**
1 (Constant)	5837.521	628.150		9.293	.000		4556.400	7118.642
Price	-53.217	6.852	$-.690$	-7.766	.000		-67.193	-39.242
Promotion	3.613	.685	.468	5.273	.000		2.216	5.011

a. Dependent Variable: Sales

Test statistics, t_{cal} p-value

Confidence interval estimate of slope of sales with price, β_1.

Find t critical value using calculator:

To find the t critical value, use the Casio Calculator fx-9750GII and follow the following calculator steps:

Note: Fx-9750G Plus does not have this option, therefore you have to use the Table G3 in the Appendix.

From the **Main Menu** select:

STAT   F5 (DIST)   **F2** (t)   **F3**(Invt)   then enter the following items:

Inverse Student-t
Data   : **F2**(Var)   ▼
Area   : **0.025**   **EXE**   (Note: divide α by 2 because it is a two-tailed test)
df   : **31**   **EXE**   (Note: df=n–k–1 =34–2–1=31)
Save Res : None
Execute

Now key **EXE** or **F1**(CALC)

The calculator will now show the results:

Inverse Student-t
x-Inv = 2.03951345

The critical values define the rejection and non-rejection regions.

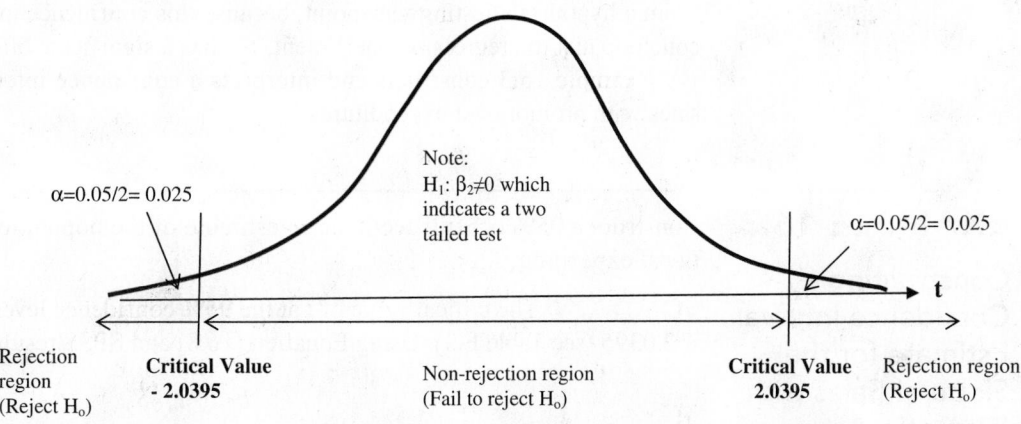

| Rejection region (Reject H_o) | Critical Value - 2.0395 | Non-rejection region (Fail to reject H_o) | Critical Value 2.0395 | Rejection region (Reject H_o) |

Note:
$H_1: \beta_2 \neq 0$ which indicates a two tailed test

$\alpha=0.05/2= 0.025$

$\alpha=0.05/2= 0.025$

EXAMPLE 16.2

Testing for the Significance of the Slope of Sales with Price

At the 0.05 level of significance, is there evidence that the slope of sales with price is different from zero?

SOLUTION From Figure 16.4a $t_{STAT} = -7.7664 < -2.0395$ (the critical value for $\alpha = 0.05$) or the p-value $= 0.0000 < 0.05$. Thus, there is a significant relationship between price, X_1, and sales, taking into account the promotional expenditures, X_2.

As shown with these two independent variables, the test of significance for a specific regression coefficient in multiple regression is a test for the significance of adding that variable into a regression model, given that the other variable is included. In other words, the t test for the regression coefficient is actually a test for the contribution of each independent variable.

Confidence Interval Estimation

Instead of testing the significance of a population slope, you may want to estimate the value of a population slope. Equation (16.8) defines the confidence interval estimate for a population slope in multiple regression.

CONFIDENCE INTERVAL ESTIMATE FOR THE SLOPE

$$b_j \pm t_{\alpha/2}S_{b_j} \tag{16.8}$$

where $t_{\alpha/2}$ is the critical value corresponding to an upper-tail probability of $\alpha/2$ from the t distribution with $n-k-1$ degrees of freedom (i.e., a cumulative area of $1 - \alpha/2$), and k is the number of independent variables.

To construct a 95% confidence interval estimate of the population slope, β_1 (the effect of price, X_1, on sales, Y, holding constant the effect of promotional expenditures, X_2), the critical value of t at the 95% confidence level with 31 degrees of freedom is 2.0395 (see Table E.3). Then, using Equation (16.8) and SPSS results in Figure 16.4a,

$$b_1 \pm t_{\alpha/2}S_{b_1}$$

$$-53.2173 \pm (2.0395)(6.8522)$$

$$-53.2173 \pm 13.9752$$

$$-67.1925 \le \beta_1 \le -39.2421$$

Taking into account the effect of promotional expenditures, the estimated effect of a 1-cent increase in price is to reduce mean sales by approximately 39.2 to 67.2 bars. You have 95% confidence that this interval correctly estimates the relationship between these variables. From a hypothesis-testing viewpoint, because this confidence interval does not include 0, you conclude that the regression coefficient, β_1, has a significant effect.

Example 16.3 constructs and interprets a confidence interval estimate for the slope of sales with promotional expenditures.

EXAMPLE 16.3

Constructing a Confidence Interval Estimate for the Slope of Sales with Promotional Expenditures

Construct a 95% confidence interval estimate of the population slope of sales with promotional expenditures.

SOLUTION The critical value of t at the 95% confidence level, with 31 degrees of freedom, is 2.0395 (see Table E.3). Using Equation (16.8) and SPSS results in Figure 16.4a,

$$b_2 \pm t_{\alpha/2}S_{b_2}$$

$$3.6131 \pm (2.0395)(0.6852)$$

$$3.6131 \pm 1.3975$$

$$2.2156 \le \beta_2 \le 5.0106$$

Thus, taking into account the effect of price, the estimated effect of each additional dollar of promotional expenditures is to increase mean sales by approximately 2.22 to 5.01 bars. You have 95% confidence that this interval correctly estimates the relationship between these variables. From a hypothesis-testing viewpoint, because this confidence interval does not include 0, you can conclude that the regression coefficient, β_2, has a significant effect.

Problems for Section 16.4

LEARNING THE BASICS

16.23 Use the following information from a multiple regression analysis:

$$n = 25 \quad b_1 = 5 \quad b_2 = 10 \quad S_{b_1} = 2 \quad S_{b_2} = 8$$

a. Which variable has the largest slope, in units of a t statistic?
b. Construct a 95% confidence interval estimate of the population slope, β_1.
c. At the 0.05 level of significance, determine whether each independent variable makes a significant contribution to the regression model. On the basis of these results, indicate the independent variables to include in this model.

16.24 Use the following information from a multiple regression analysis:

$$n = 20 \quad b_1 = 4 \quad b_2 = 3 \quad S_{b_1} = 1.2 \quad S_{b_2} = 0.8$$

a. Which variable has the largest slope, in units of a t statistic?
b. Construct a 95% confidence interval estimate of the population slope, β_1.
c. At the 0.05 level of significance, determine whether each independent variable makes a significant contribution to the regression model. On the basis of these results, indicate the independent variables to include in this model.

APPLYING THE CONCEPTS

16.25 In Problem 16.3 on page 711, you predicted the durability of a brand of running shoe, based on the forefoot shock-absorbing capability (FOREIMP) and the change in impact properties over time (MIDSOLE) for a sample of 15 pairs of shoes. Use the following results:

Variable	Coefficient	Standard Error	t Statistic	p-value
Intercept	−0.02686	0.06905	−0.39	0.7034
Foreimp	0.79116	0.06295	12.57	0.0000
Midsole	0.60484	0.07174	8.43	0.0000

a. Construct a 95% confidence interval estimate of the population slope between durability and forefoot shock-absorbing capability.
b. At the 0.05 level of significance, determine whether each independent variable makes a significant contribution to the regression model. On the basis of these results, indicate the independent variables to include in this model.

✓SELF Test **16.26** In Problem 16.4 on page 711, you used sales and number of orders to predict distribution costs at a mail-order catalog business (stored in **WareCost**). Use the results from that problem.
a. Construct a 95% confidence interval estimate of the population slope between distribution cost and sales.
b. At the 0.05 level of significance, determine whether each independent variable makes a significant contribution to the regression model. On the basis of these results, indicate the independent variables to include in this model.

16.27 In Problem 16.5 on page 711, you used horsepower and weight to predict mileage (stored in **Auto2011**). Use the results from that problem.

a. Construct a 95% confidence interval estimate of the population slope between mileage and horsepower.
b. At the 0.05 level of significance, determine whether each independent variable makes a significant contribution to the regression model. On the basis of these results, indicate the independent variables to include in this model.

16.28 In Problem 16.6 on pages 711–712, you used radio advertising and newspaper advertising to predict sales (stored in **Advertise**). Use the results from that problem.
a. Construct a 95% confidence interval estimate of the population slope between sales and radio advertising.
b. At the 0.05 level of significance, determine whether each independent variable makes a significant contribution to the regression model. On the basis of these results, indicate the independent variables to include in this model.

16.29 In Problem 16.7 on page 712, you used the total number of staff present and remote hours to predict standby hours (stored in **Standby**). Use the results from that problem.
a. Construct a 95% confidence interval estimate of the population slope between standby hours and total number of staff present.
b. At the 0.05 level of significance, determine whether each independent variable makes a significant contribution to the regression model. On the basis of these results, indicate the independent variables to include in this model.

16.30 In Problem 16.8 on page 712, you used land area of a property and age of a house to predict appraised value (stored in **GlenCove**). Use the results from that problem.
a. Construct a 95% confidence interval estimate of the population slope between appraised value and land area of a property.
b. At the 0.05 level of significance, determine whether each independent variable makes a significant contribution to the regression model. On the basis of these results, indicate the independent variables to include in this model.

16.5 Using Dummy Variables and Interaction Terms in Regression Models

The multiple regression models discussed in Sections 16.1 through 16.4 assumed that each independent variable is a numerical variable. For example, in Section 16.1, you used price and promotional expenditures, two numerical independent variables, to predict the monthly sales of OmniPower energy bars. However, for some models, you might want to include the effect of a categorical independent variable. For example, to predict the monthly sales of the OmniPower bars, you might want to include the categorical variable shelf location (not end-aisle or end-aisle) in the model.

Dummy Variables

To include a categorical independent variable in a regression model, you use a **dummy variable**. A dummy variable recodes the categories of a categorical variable using the numeric values 0 and 1. Where appropriate, the value of 0 is assigned to the absence of a characteristic and the value 1 is assigned to the presence of the characteristic. If a given categorical independent variable has only two categories, such as shelf location in the previous example, then you can define one dummy variable, X_d, to represent the two categories as

$$X_d = 0 \text{ if the observation is in category 1 (not end-aisle in the example)}$$

$$X_d = 1 \text{ if the observation is in category 2 (end-aisle in the example)}$$

To illustrate using dummy variables in regression, consider a business problem that involves developing a model for predicting the assessed value of houses ($000), based on the size of the house (in thousands of square feet) and whether the house has a fireplace. To include the categorical variable for the presence of a fireplace, the dummy variable X_2 is defined as

$$X_2 = 0 \text{ if the house does not have a fireplace}$$

$$X_2 = 1 \text{ if the house has a fireplace}$$

Data collected from a sample of 15 houses are organized and stored in House3 . Table 16.3 presents the data. In the last column of Table 16.3, you can see how the categorical values are converted to numerical values.

TABLE 16.3

Predicting Assessed Value, Based on Size of House and Presence of a Fireplace

Assessed Value	Size	Fireplace	Fireplace Coded
234.4	2.00	Yes	1
227.4	1.71	No	0
225.7	1.45	No	0
235.9	1.76	Yes	1
229.1	1.93	No	0
220.4	1.20	Yes	1
225.8	1.55	Yes	1
235.9	1.93	Yes	1
228.5	1.59	Yes	1
229.2	1.50	Yes	1
236.7	1.90	Yes	1
229.3	1.39	Yes	1
224.5	1.54	No	0
233.8	1.89	Yes	1
226.8	1.59	No	0

Assuming that the slope of assessed value with the size of the house is the same for houses that have and do not have a fireplace, the multiple regression model is

$$Y_i = \beta_0 + \beta_1 X_{1i} + \beta_2 X_{2i} + \varepsilon_i$$

where

Y_i = assessed value, in thousands of dollars, for house i

β_0 = Y intercept

X_{1i} = size of the house, in thousands of square feet, for house i

β_1 = slope of assessed value with size of the house, holding constant the presence or absence of a fireplace

X_{2i} = dummy variable representing the absence or presence of a fireplace for house i

β_2 = net effect of the presence of a fireplace on assessed value, holding constant the size of the house

ε_i = random error in Y for house i

Figure 16.16 illustrates the SPSS results for this model.

FIGURE 16.15

SPSS regression results worksheet for the regression model that includes size of the house and presence of fireplace

Model Summary[b]

Variables Entered/Removed[b]

Model	Variables Entered	Variables Removed	Method
1	Square feet (thousands)[a]		Enter
1	size, fireplace[a]		Enter

a. *All requested variables entered.*
b. *Dependent Variable: Assessed value*

Model Summary

Model	R	R Square	Adjusted R Square	Std. Error of the Estimate
1	.901[a]	.811	.780	2.2626

a. *Predictors: (Constant), size, fireplace*

ANOVA[b]

Model		Sum of Squares	df	Mean Square	F	Sig.
1	Regression	263.704	2	131.852	25.756	.000[a]
	Residual	61.432	12	5.119		
	Total	325.136	14			

a. *Predictors: (Constant), size, fireplace*
b. *Dependent Variable: Assessed value*

Coefficients[a]

Model		Unstandardized Coefficients B	Std. Error	Standardized Coefficients Beta	t	Sig.
1	(Constant)	200.090	4.352		45.980	.000
	fireplace	3.853	1.241	.390	3.104	.009
	size	16.186	2.574	.790	6.287	.000

From Figure 16.15, the regression equation is

$$\hat{Y}_i = 200.0905 + 16.1858X_{1i} + 3.8530X_{2i}$$

For houses without a fireplace, you substitute $X_2 = 0$ into the regression equation:

$$\hat{Y}_i = 200.0905 + 16.1858X_{1i} + 3.8530X_{2i}$$

$$= 200.0905 + 16.1858X_{1i} + 3.8530(0)$$

$$= 200.0905 + 16.1858X_{1i}$$

For houses with a fireplace, you substitute $X_2 = 1$ into the regression equation:

$$\hat{Y}_i = 200.0905 + 16.1858X_{1i} + 3.8530X_{2i}$$
$$= 200.0905 + 16.1858X_{1i} + 3.8530(1)$$
$$= 203.9435 + 16.1858X_{1i}$$

In this model, the regression coefficients are interpreted as follows:

1. Holding constant whether a house has a fireplace, for each increase of 1.0 thousand square feet in the size of the house, the mean assessed value is estimated to increase by 16.186 thousand dollars (i.e., $16,186.00).
2. Holding constant the size of the house, the presence of a fireplace is estimated to increase the mean assessed value of the house by 3.853 thousand dollars (i.e., $3,853).

In Figure 16.15, the t_{CALC} test statistic for the slope of the size of the house with assessed value is 6.287, and the p-value is approximately 0.000; the t_{CALC} test statistic for presence of a fireplace is 3.104, and the p-value is 0.009. Thus, each of the two variables makes a significant contribution to the model at a level of significance of 0.01. In addition, the coefficient of multiple determination indicates that 81.11% of the variation in assessed value is explained by variation in the size of the house and whether the house has a fireplace.

Interactions

In all the regression models discussed so far, the effect an independent variable has on the dependent variable has been assumed to be independent of the other independent variables in the model. An **interaction** occurs if the effect of an independent variable on the dependent variable changes according to the *value* of a second independent variable. For example, it is possible that advertising might have a large effect on the sales of a product when the price of a product is low. However, if the price of the product is too high, increases in advertising will not dramatically change sales. In this case, price and advertising are said to interact. In other words, you cannot make general statements about the effect of advertising on sales. The effect that advertising has on sales is *dependent* on the price. You use an **interaction term** (sometimes referred to as a **cross-product term**) to model an interaction effect in a regression model.

To illustrate the concept of interaction and use of an interaction term, return to the example concerning the assessed values of homes. In the regression model, you assumed that the effect the size of the house has on the assessed value is independent of whether the house has a fireplace. In other words, you assumed that the slope of assessed value with size is the same for houses with fireplaces as it is for houses without fireplaces. If these two slopes are different, then an interaction exists between the size of the house and the presence of a fireplace.

To evaluate the possibility of an interaction, you first define an interaction term that equals the product of the independent variable X_1 (size of house) and the dummy variable X_2 (fireplace). You then test whether this interaction variable makes a significant contribution to the regression model. If the interaction is significant, you cannot use the original model for prediction. For the data of Table 16.3, let

$$X_3 = X_1 \times X_2$$

Figure 16.16 illustrates SPSS results for this regression model, which includes the size of the house, X_1; the presence of a fireplace, X_2; and the interaction of X_1 and X_2 (which is defined as X_3).

To test for the existence of an interaction, you use the null hypothesis

$$H_0: \beta_3 = 0$$

versus the alternative hypothesis

$$H_1: \beta_3 \neq 0.$$

In Figure 16.16, the t_{CALC} test statistic for the interaction of size and fireplace is 1.483. Because $t_{CALC} = 1.483 < 2.201$ or the p-value $= 0.1661 > 0.05$, you do not reject the null hypothesis. Therefore, the interaction does not make a significant contribution to the model, given that size and presence of a fireplace are already included. You can conclude that the slope of assessed value with size is the same for houses with fireplaces and without fireplaces.

FIGURE 16.16

SPSS regression results worksheet for a regression model that includes size, presence of fireplace, and interaction of size and fireplace

Variables Entered/Removed[b]

Model	Variables Entered	Variables Removed	Method
1	Interaction, size, fireplace[a]		Enter

a. All requested variables entered.
b. Dependent Variable: Assessed value

Model Summary

Model	R	R Square	Adjusted R Square	Std. Error of the Estimate
1	.918[a]	.843	.800	2.1573

a. Predictors: (Constant), interaction, size, fireplace

ANOVA[b]

Model		Sum of Squares	df	Mean Square	F	Sig.
1	Regression	273.944	3	91.315	19.621	.000[a]
	Residual	51.192	11	4.654		
	Total	325.136	14			

a. Predictors: (Constant), interaction, size, fireplace
b. Dependent Variable: Assessed value

Coefficients[a]

Model		Unstandardized Coefficients B	Std. Error	Standardized Coefficients Beta	t	Sig.
1	(Constant)	212.952	9.612		22.154	.000
	fireplace	−11.840	10.646	−1.199	−1.112	.290
	size	8.362	5.817	.408	1.438	.178
	interaction	9.518	6.416	1.664	1.483	.166

a. Dependent Variable: Assessed value

Multiple Regression Practice Questions

USING QUESTION 16.1

The data in the file (Redwood) include height, diameter at breast height of a person, and bark thickness for a sample of 21 California redwood trees. The data are shown in the table below.

Height	Diameter at Breast Height	Bark Thickness
122	20	1.1
193.5	36	2.8
166.5	18	2
82	10	1.2
133.5	21	2
156	29	1.4
172.5	51	1.8
81	11	1.1
148	26	2.5
113	12	1.5
84	13	1.4
164	40	2.3
203.3	52	2
174	30	2.5
159	22	3
205	42	2.6
223.5	45	4.3
195	54	4
232.5	39	2.2
190.5	36	3.5
100	8	1.4

The SPSS outputs are shown below:

Descriptive Statistics

	Mean	Std. Deviation	N
Height	157.083	46.3199	21
Diameter at breast height	29.29	14.792	21
Bark thickness	2.219	.9163	21

Model Summary[c]

Model	R	R Square	Adjusted R Square	Std. Error of the Estimate
1	.854[a]	.729	.715	24.7486
2	.886[b]	.786	.762	22.5982

a. Predictors: (Constant), Diameter at breast height
b. Predictors: (Constant), Diameter at breast height, Bark thickness
c. Dependent Variable: Height

ANOVA[a]

Model		Sum of Squares	df	Mean Square	F	Sig.
1	Regression	31273.267	1	31273.267	51.059	.000[b]
	Residual	11637.400	19	612.495		
	Total	42910.667	20			
2	Regression	33718.478	2	16859.239	33.013	.000[c]
	Residual	9192.189	18	510.677		
	Total	42910.667	20			

a. Dependent Variable: Height
b. Predictors: (Constant), Diameter at breast height
c. Predictors: (Constant), Diameter at breast height, Bark thickness

Coefficients[a]

Model		Unstandardized Coefficients B	Unstandardized Coefficients Std. Error	Standardized Coefficients Beta	t	Sig.	95.0% Confidence Interval for B Lower Bound	95.0% Confidence Interval for B Upper Bound
1	(Constant)	78.796	12.215		6.451	.000	53.230	104.362
	Diameter at breast height	2.673	.374	.854	7.146	.000	1.890	3.456
2	(Constant)	62.141	13.503		4.602	.000	33.772	90.510
	Diameter at breast height	2.057	.443	.657	4.645	.000	1.126	2.987
	Bark thickness	15.642	7.148	.309	2.188	.042	.624	30.660

a. Dependent Variable: Height

CHARTS

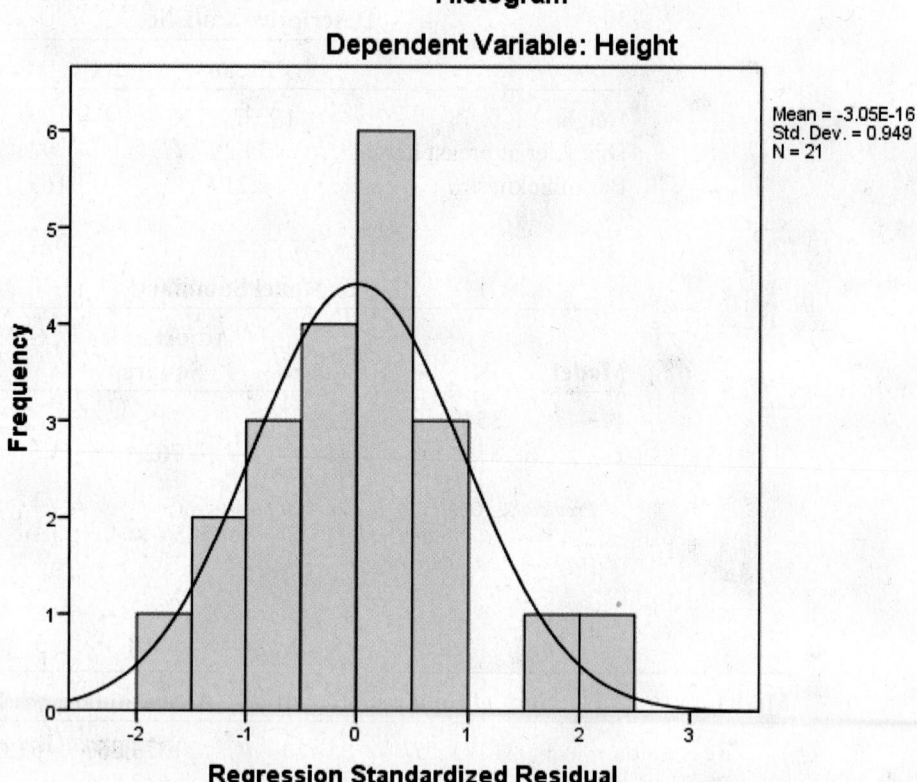

Histogram

Dependent Variable: Height

Mean = -3.05E-16
Std. Dev. = 0.949
N = 21

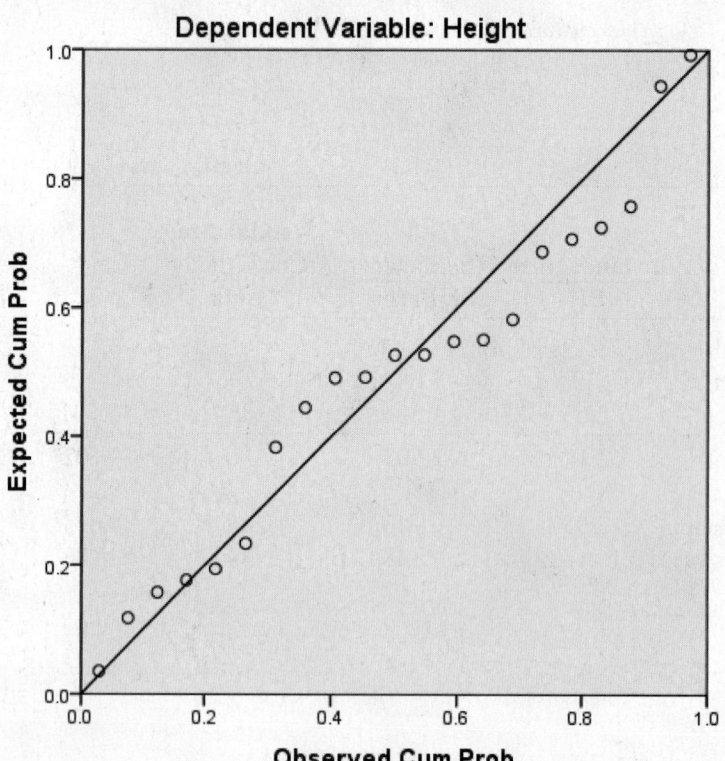

Normal P-P Plot of Regression Standardized Residual

Dependent Variable: Height

Scatterplot
Dependent Variable: Height

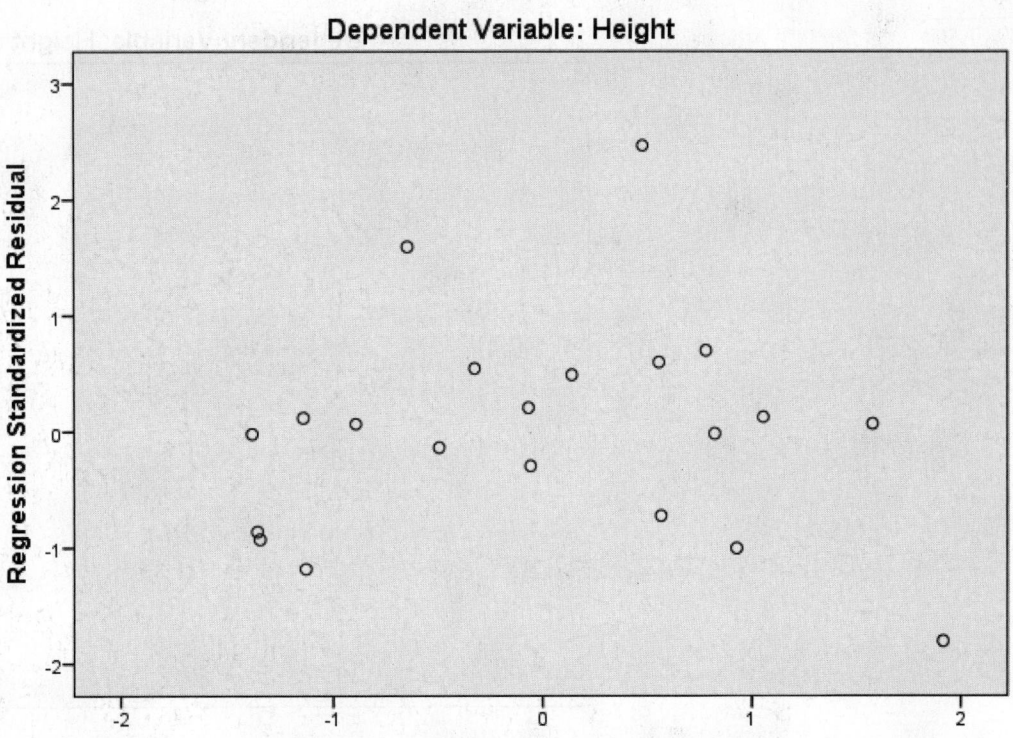

Partial Regression Plot
Dependent Variable: Height

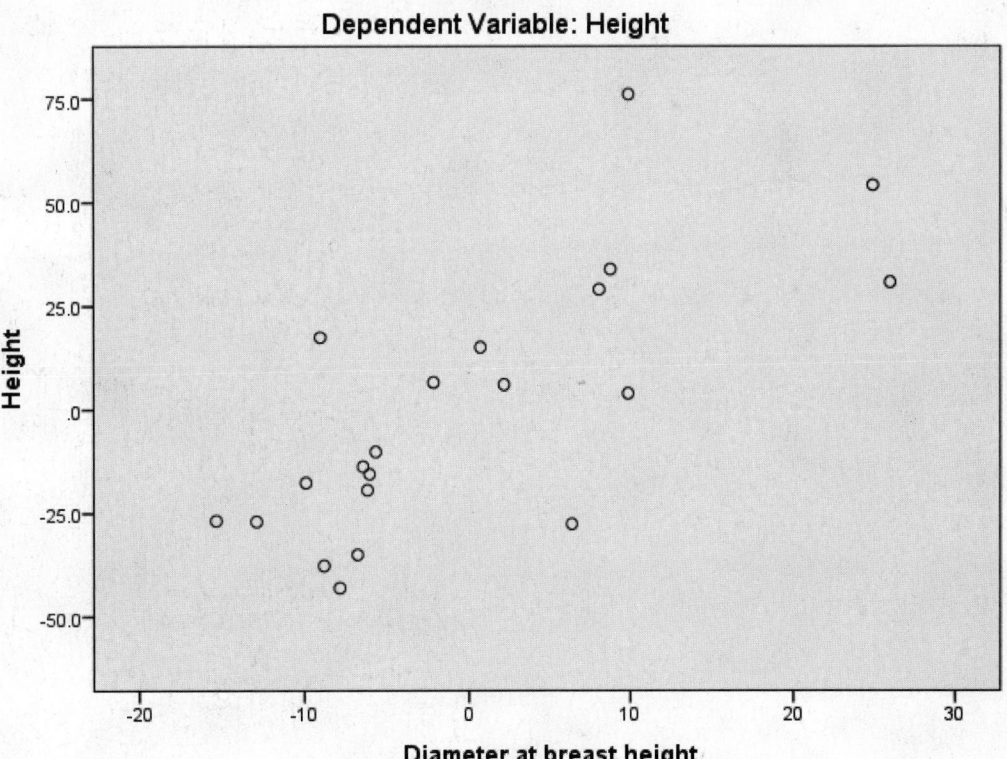

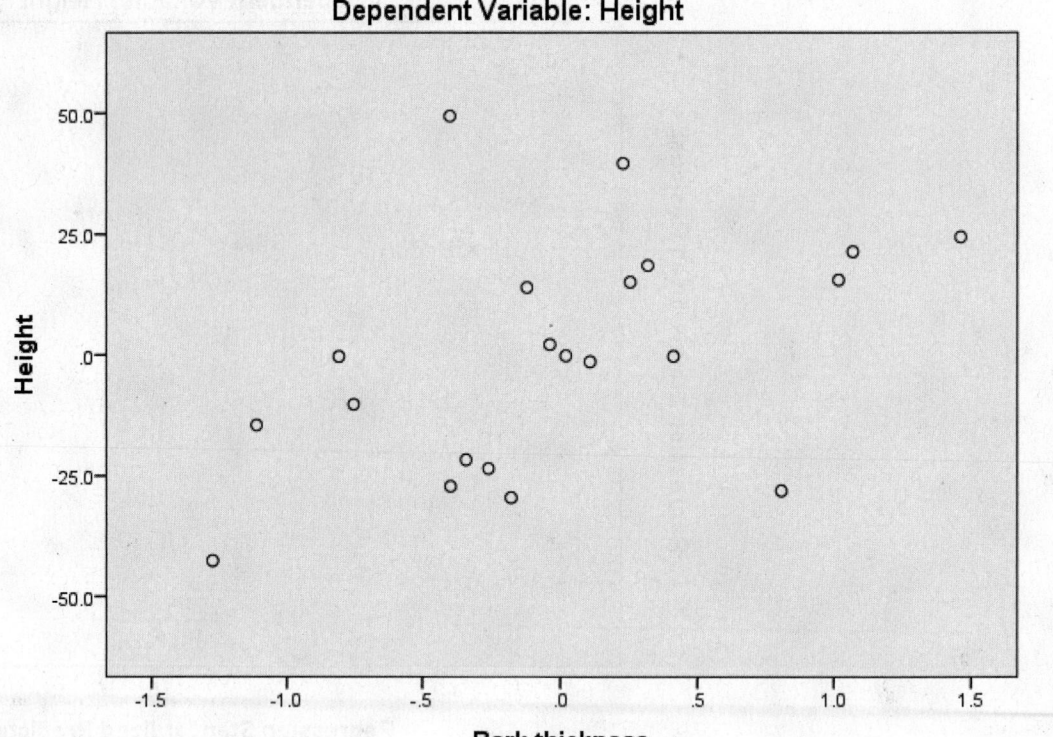

PRE_2	RES_2	LMCI_2	UMCI_2	LICI_2	UICI_2	Height	Diameter at Breast Height	Bark Thickness
120.4814	1.51864	103.7586	137.2042	70.14533	170.8174	122	20	1.1
179.9798	13.52017	167.6055	192.3541	130.9167	229.0429	193.5	36	2.8
130.4456	36.05444	116.8649	144.0262	81.0644	179.8267	166.5	18	2
101.4784	−19.4784	83.75755	119.1993	50.80206	152.1548	82	10	1.2
136.6157	−3.1157	124.5615	148.6699	87.63235	185.5991	133.5	21	2
143.6843	12.31568	127.7298	159.6389	93.59827	193.7704	156	29	1.4
195.1887	−22.6887	168.4161	221.9614	140.6833	249.6941	172.5	51	1.8
101.971	−20.971	84.21302	119.7289	51.28162	152.6603	81	11	1.1
154.7202	−6.72016	142.4363	167.0041	105.6798	203.7605	148	26	2.5
110.2844	2.71562	94.11167	126.4571	60.12842	160.4404	113	12	1.5
110.7769	−26.7769	94.93321	126.6206	60.72607	160.8278	84	13	1.4
180.3858	−16.3858	166.5026	194.2689	130.9206	229.851	164	40	2.3
200.3738	2.87621	174.8175	225.9301	146.4555	254.2921	203.3	52	2
162.947	11.05298	151.9011	173.993	114.202	211.692	174	30	2.5
154.3142	4.68579	134.5156	174.1129	102.8744	205.754	159	22	3
189.1918	15.80825	175.2686	203.1149	139.7153	238.6682	205	42	2.6
221.953	1.54705	195.1885	248.7174	167.4516	276.4543	223.5	45	4.3
235.7708	−40.7708	211.9219	259.6197	182.6405	288.9012	195	54	4
176.7649	55.73511	162.8949	190.6349	127.3034	226.2264	232.5	39	2.2
190.9291	−0.42909	171.863	209.9952	139.7668	242.0914	190.5	36	3.5
100.4934	−0.49335	82.03281	118.9539	49.55362	151.4331	100	8	1.4

Based on Model 2

PRE—Unstandardized Predicted

RES—Unstandardized Residual

LMCI—95% Lower Confidence Interval for y mean

UMCI—95% Upper Confidence Interval for y mean

LICI—95% Lower Confidence Interval for y individual

UICI—95% Upper Confidence Interval for y individual

Note: Independent variable, Y: height of a tree
 Dependent variable, X1: diameter at breast height
 Dependent variable, X2: thickness of the bark

Use the SPSS outputs to answer the following questions:

1. Are the regression assumptions valid for these data? Justify your answers with the appropriate charts.

2. State the multiple regression equation that predicts the height of a tree based on the tree's diameter at breast height and the thickness of the bark.

3. Interpret the meaning of the coefficients in this equation (corresponds to model 2 in the SPSS output).

4. At the 0.05 level of significance, is the linear model 2 useful for predicting the height of a tree?

5. Predict the height for a tree that has a breast height diameter of 25 inches and a bark thickness of 2 inches.

6. For model 2, what is the forecast error (or residual) of the height for a tree that has a breast height diameter of 25 inches and a bark thickness of 2 inches?

7. At the 0.05 level of significance, determine whether each independent variable makes a significant contribution to the regression model 2. Indicate the most appropriate regression model for this set of data.

8. Based on model 2, construct a 95% confidence interval estimate of the population slope for diameter at breast height and thickness of the bark.

9. Based on model 2, construct a 95% confidence interval estimate of the mean height for trees that have a breast-height diameter of 25 inches and a bark thickness of 2 inches.

10. Based on model 2, construct a 95% confidence interval estimate of the height for an individual tree that has a breast-height diameter of 25 inches and a bark thickness of 2 inches.

11. What is the coefficient of multiple determination for model 2? And interpret its meaning.

12. Of the two models given in the SPSS output, which model appears to be the more efficient? Why?

13. State the multiple regression equation for model 1.

14. At the 0.05 level of significance, is the linear model 1 useful for predicting the height of a tree?

USING QUESTION 16.2

Nassau County is located approximately 25 miles east of New York City. Data in the file (Glen Cove) include the appraised value, land area of the property in acres, house size (square feet), age, rooms, baths and garage for a sample of 30 single-family homes located in Glen Cove, a small city in Nassau County. The data are shown in the table below.

Address	Appraised Value	Land (acres)	House Size (square feet)	Age	Rooms	Baths	Garage
9 Sycamore Road	466.0	0.2297	2448	46	7	3.5	2
21 Jefferson St.	364.0	0.2192	1942	51	7	2.5	1
38 Hitching Post Lane	429.0	0.1630	2073	29	5	3	2
4 Poppy Lane	548.4	0.4608	2707	18	8	2.5	1
5 Daniel Drive	405.9	0.2549	2042	46	7	1.5	1
15 Francis Terrace	374.1	0.2290	2089	88	7	2	0
23 Guilfoy Street	315.0	0.1808	1433	48	7	2	0
17 Carlyle Drive	749.7	0.5015	2991	7	9	2.5	1
8 Craft Avenue	217.7	0.2229	1008	52	5	1	0
22 Beechwood Ct.	635.7	0.1300	3202	15	8	2.5	2
14 Fox Street	350.7	0.1763	2230	54	8	2	0
7 Raynham Road	455.0	0.4200	1848	48	7	2	1
2 Jerome Drive	356.2	0.2520	2100	46	6	2	0
7 Valentine Street	271.7	0.1148	1846	12	5	3	1
38 Jefferson Street	304.3	0.1693	1331	64	5	1	1
15 Inwood Road	288.4	0.1714	1344	52	8	1	0
29 Meadowfield Lane	396.7	0.3849	1822	44	6	2	1
13 Westland Drive	613.5	0.6545	2479	46	6	2.5	2
79 Valentine Street	314.1	0.1722	1605	52	6	3	0
13 Fairmont Place	363.5	0.1435	2080	78	11	2	0
1 Prestwick Terrace	364.3	0.2755	2410	71	6	1	1
11 Clement Street	305.1	0.1148	1753	97	8	2	0
7 Woodland Road	441.7	0.3636	1884	45	7	2	2
36 Elm Avenue	353.1	0.1474	2050	41	10	2	2
17 Duke Place	463.3	0.2281	2978	40	6	2.5	2
12 Prospect Avenue	320.0	0.4626	2132	82	7	1	0
1 Buckeye Road	332.8	0.1889	1551	54	6	2	0
30 Ann Street	276.6	0.1228	1129	44	5	1	0
26 Broadfield Place	397.0	0.1492	1674	34	7	2	1
16 Jackson Street	221.9	0.0852	1184	94	5	1	0

The SPSS outputs are shown below:

Descriptive Statistics

	Mean	Std. Deviation	N
Appraised Value	389.849	120.3881	30
Land (acres)	.246293	.1372620	30
House Size (square feet)	1978.83	550.875	30
Age	49.93	22.490	30
Rooms	6.83	1.487	30
Baths	2.000	.6948	30
Garage	.80	.805	30

Model Summary[e]

Model	R	R Square	Adjusted R Square	Std. Error of the Estimate
1	.828[a]	.686	.675	68.6650
2	.879[b]	.773	.756	59.4552
3	.911[c]	.830	.810	52.4795
4	.920[d]	.847	.807	52.8354

a. Predictors: (Constant), House Size (square feet)
b. Predictors: (Constant), House Size (square feet), Land (acres)
c. Predictors: (Constant), House Size (square feet), Land (acres), Age
d. Predictors: (Constant), Garage, Rooms, Land (acres), Baths, Age, House Size (square feet)
e. Dependent Variable: Appraised Value

ANOVA[a]

Model		Sum of Squares	df	Mean Square	F	Sig.
1	Regression	288288.833	1	288288.833	61.144	.000[b]
	Residual	132016.709	28	4714.882		
	Total	420305.542	29			
2	Regression	324862.616	2	162431.308	45.950	.000[c]
	Residual	95442.927	27	3534.923		
	Total	420305.542	29			
3	Regression	348699.010	3	116233.003	42.204	.000[d]
	Residual	71606.532	26	2754.097		
	Total	420305.542	29			
4	Regression	356099.115	6	59349.853	21.260	.000[e]
	Residual	64206.427	23	2791.584		
	Total	420305.542	29			

a. Dependent Variable: Appraised Value
b. Predictors: (Constant), House Size (square feet)
c. Predictors: (Constant), House Size (square feet), Land (acres)
d. Predictors: (Constant), House Size (square feet), Land (acres), Age
e. Predictors: (Constant), Garage, Rooms, Land (acres), Baths, Age, House Size (square feet)

Coefficients[a]

Model		Unstandardized Coefficients B	Std. Error	Standardized Coefficients Beta	t	Sig.
1	(Constant)	31.694	47.488		.667	.510
	House Size (square feet)	.181	.023	.828	7.819	.000
2	(Constant)	20.209	41.273		.490	.628
	House Size (square feet)	.151	.022	.693	6.862	.000
	Land (acres)	284.755	88.527	.325	3.217	.003
3	(Constant)	136.794	53.830		2.541	.017
	House Size (square feet)	.129	.021	.589	6.157	.000
	Land (acres)	276.088	78.196	.315	3.531	.002
	Age	−1.399	.476	−.261	−2.942	.007
4	(Constant)	83.064	68.789		1.208	.240
	Land (acres)	292.184	80.883	.333	3.612	.001
	House Size (square feet)	.101	.028	.460	3.597	.002
	Age	−1.253	.551	−.234	−2.273	.033
	Rooms	10.690	7.542	.132	1.417	.170
	Baths	6.279	18.476	.036	.340	.737
	Garage	15.971	16.754	.107	.953	.350

a. Dependent Variable: Appraised Value

CHARTS

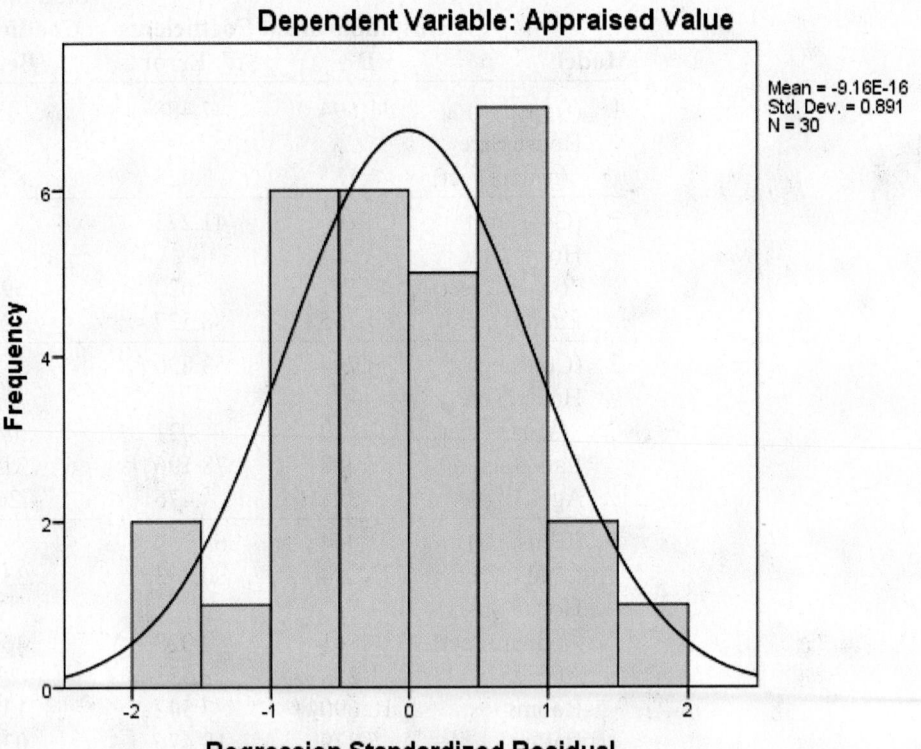

Histogram

Dependent Variable: Appraised Value

Mean = -9.16E-16
Std. Dev. = 0.891
N = 30

Regression Standardized Residual

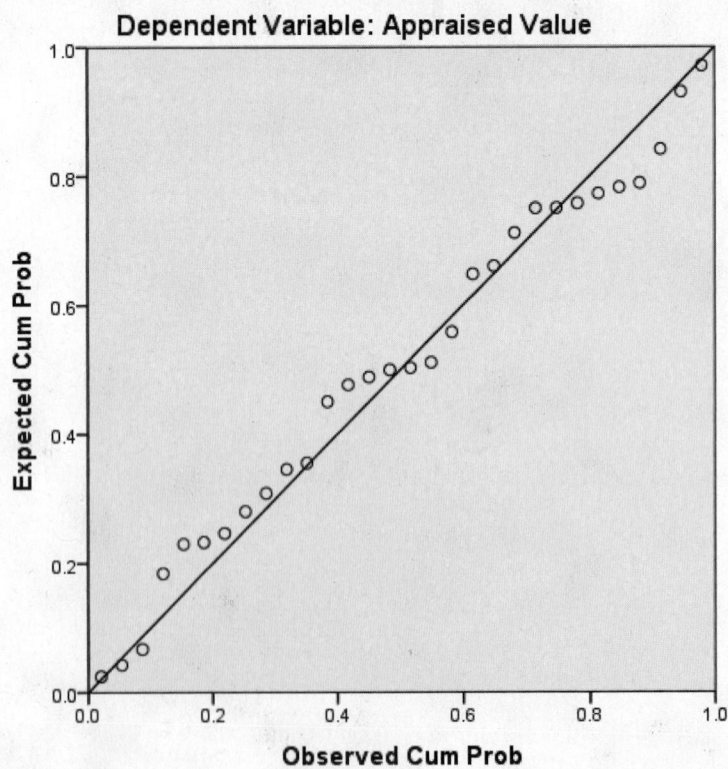

Normal P-P Plot of Regression Standardized Residual

Dependent Variable: Appraised Value

Observed Cum Prob

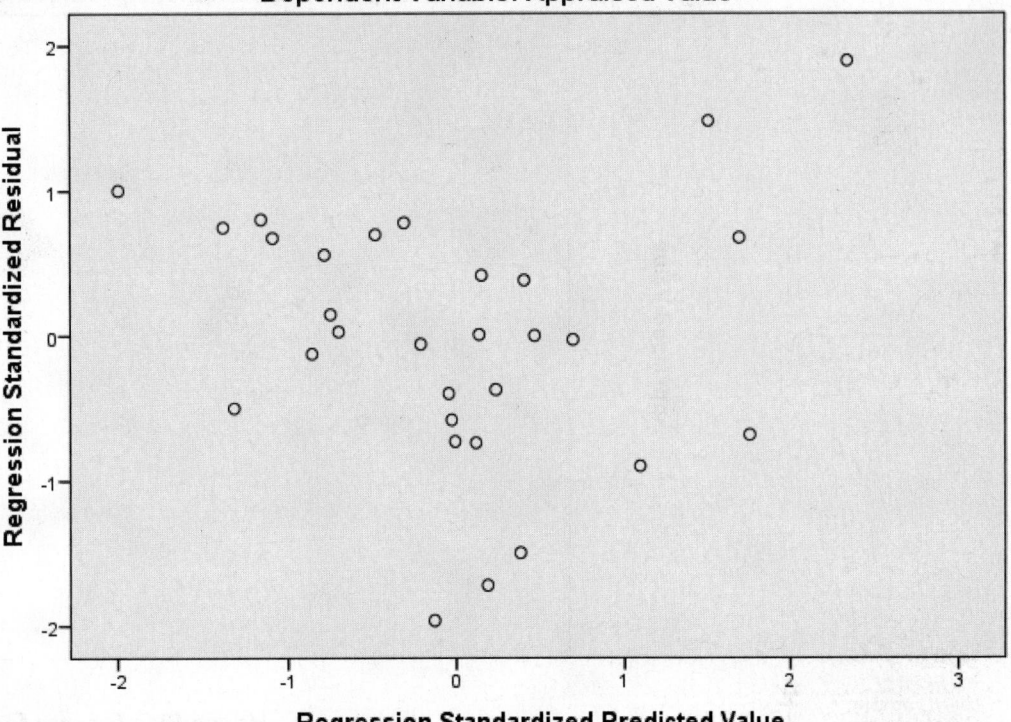

Scatterplot

Dependent Variable: Appraised Value

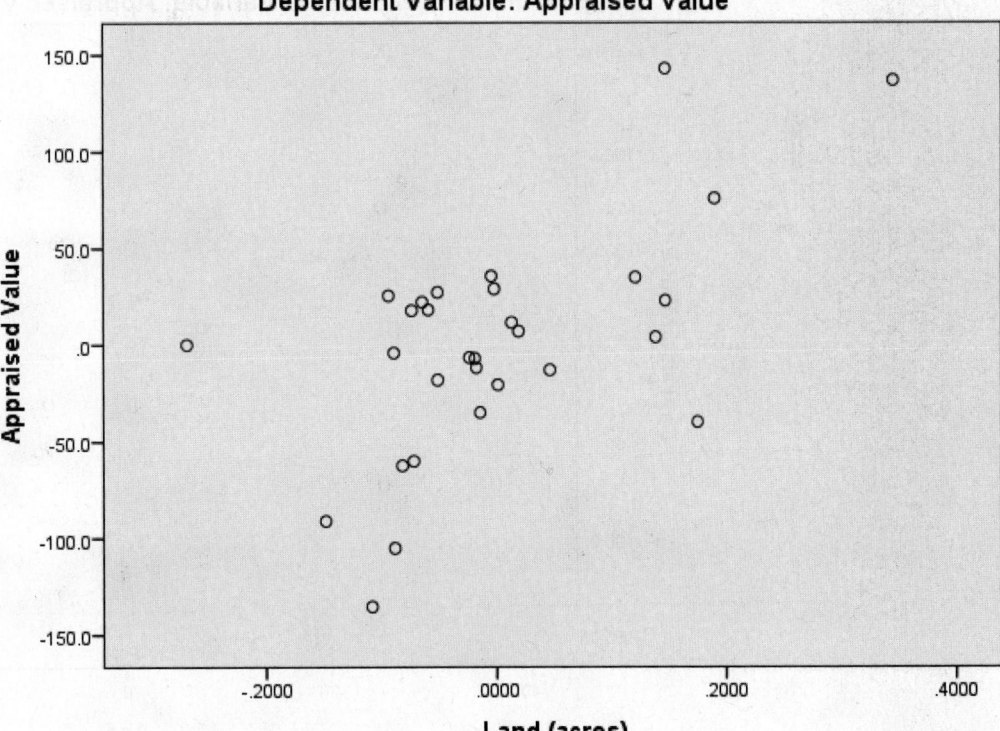

Partial Regression Plot

Dependent Variable: Appraised Value

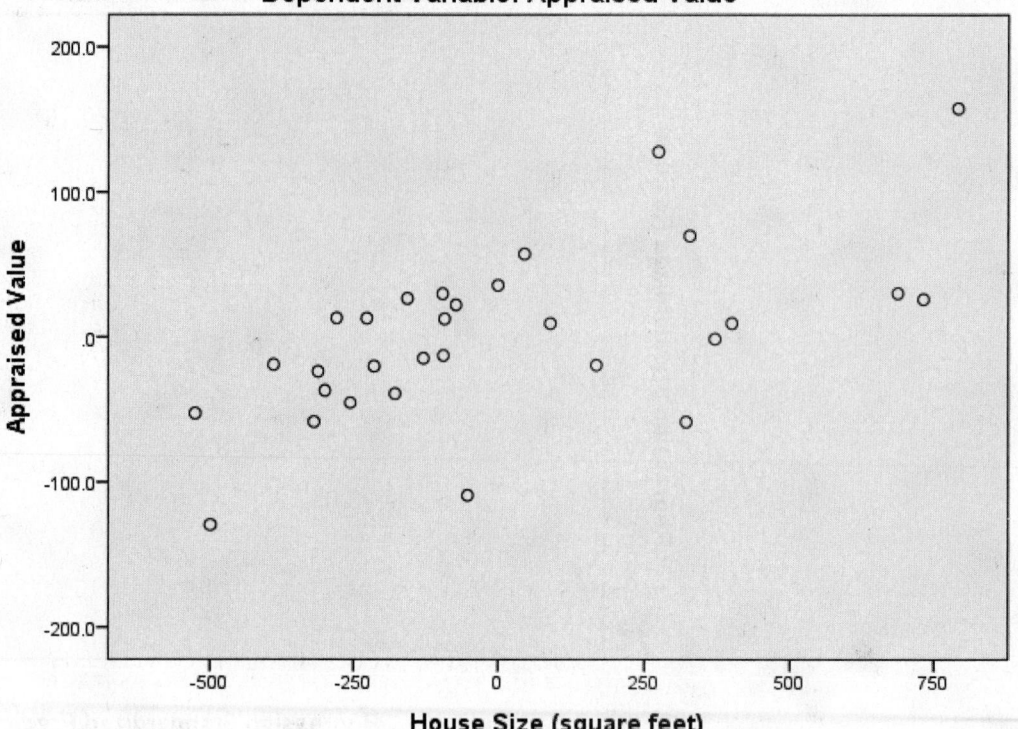

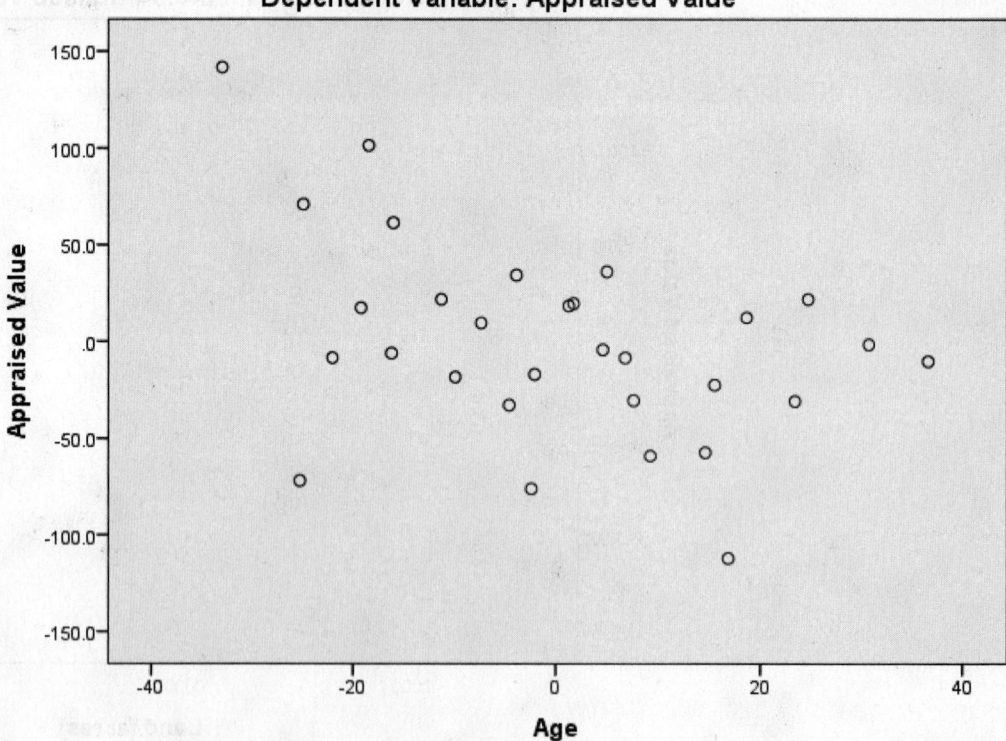

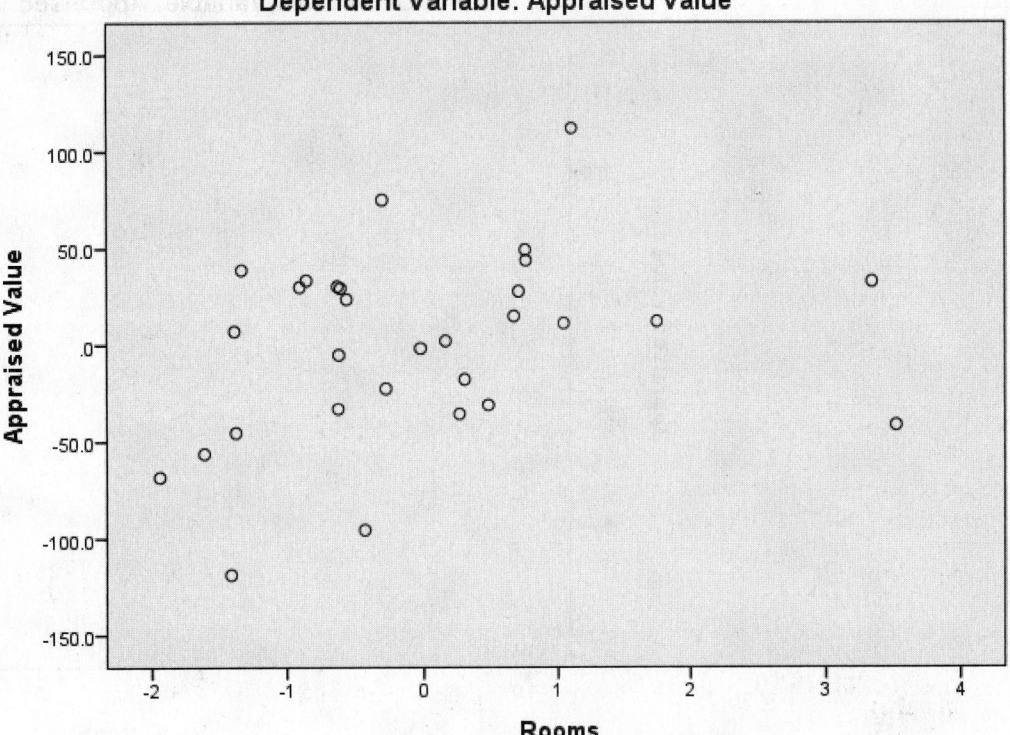

Partial Regression Plot

Dependent Variable: Appraised Value

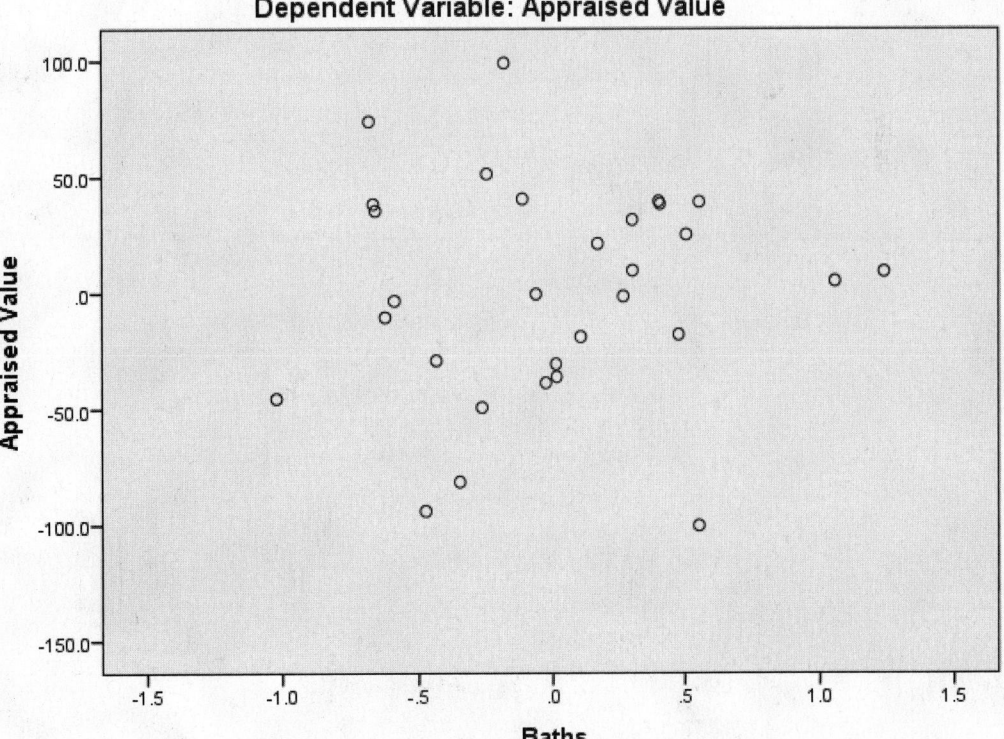

Partial Regression Plot

Dependent Variable: Appraised Value

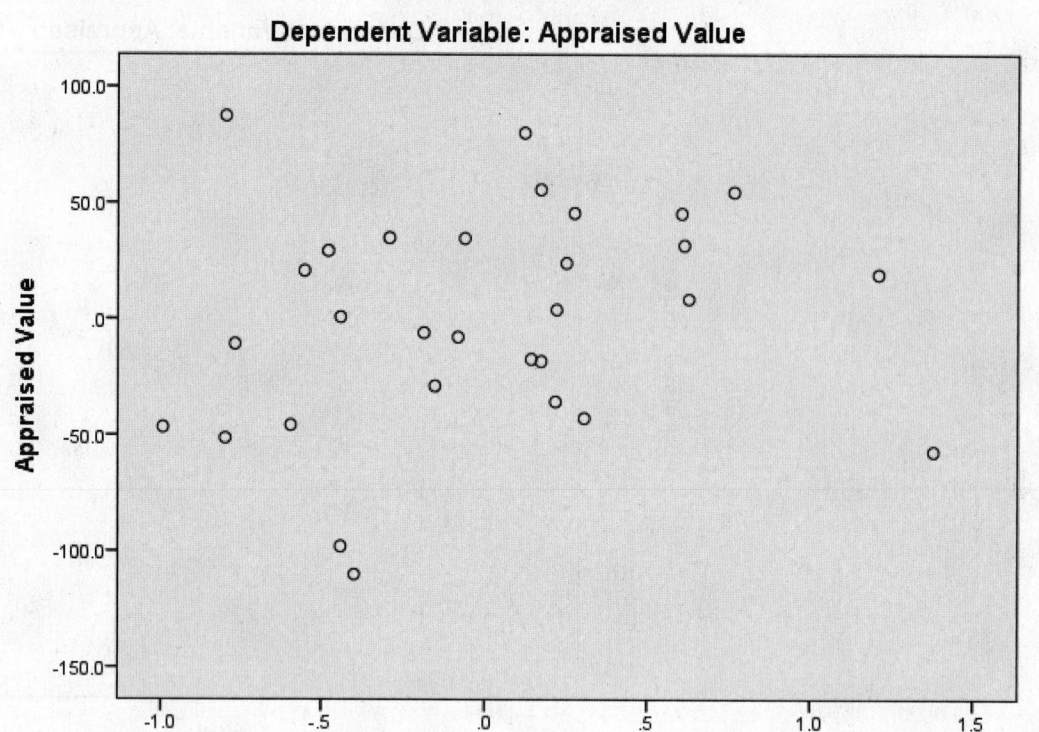

Partial Regression Plot

Dependent Variable: Appraised Value

Pre_4	Res_4	LMCI_4	UMCI_4	LICI_4	UICI_4	Appraised Value	Land (acres)	House Size (square feet)	Age	Rooms	Baths	Garage
467.49	−1.49	410.01	524.96	344.00	590.98	466.00	0.23	2448.00	46.00	7.00	3.50	2.00
385.01	−21.01	356.16	413.85	271.97	498.05	364.00	0.22	1942.00	51.00	7.00	2.50	1.00
407.07	21.93	354.41	459.73	285.75	528.39	429.00	0.16	2073.00	29.00	5.00	3.00	2.00
584.60	−36.20	534.05	635.14	464.18	705.02	548.40	0.46	2707.00	18.00	8.00	2.50	1.00
405.48	0.42	374.89	436.08	291.98	518.98	405.90	0.25	2042.00	46.00	7.00	1.50	1.00
337.17	36.93	287.37	386.96	217.06	457.27	374.10	0.23	2089.00	88.00	7.00	2.00	0.00
307.24	7.76	269.48	345.00	191.60	422.88	315.00	0.18	1433.00	48.00	7.00	2.00	0.00
649.53	100.21	582.66	716.41	521.40	777.67	749.70	0.50	2991.00	7.00	9.00	2.50	1.00
244.12	−26.42	194.90	293.35	124.25	363.99	217.70	0.22	1008.00	52.00	5.00	1.00	0.0
557.46	78.24	487.18	627.75	427.52	687.41	635.70	0.13	3202.00	15.00	8.00	2.50	2.00
389.26	−38.56	348.14	430.38	272.48	506.04	350.70	0.18	2230.00	54.00	8.00	2.00	0.00
434.84	20.16	395.13	474.56	318.55	551.13	455.00	0.42	1848.00	48.00	7.00	2.00	1.00
386.95	−30.75	344.02	429.87	269.52	504.37	356.20	0.25	2100.00	46.00	6.00	2.00	0.00
375.49	-103.79	317.05	433.93	251.55	499.43	271.70	0.11	1846.00	12.00	5.00	3.00	1.00
261.88	42.42	212.13	311.63	141.79	381.97	304.30	0.17	1331.00	64.00	5.00	1.00	1.00
294.94	−6.54	244.90	344.98	174.73	415.15	288.40	0.17	1344.00	52.00	8.00	1.00	0.00
416.30	−19.60	381.61	450.98	301.63	530.97	396.70	0.38	1822.00	44.00	6.00	2.00	1.00
577.76	35.74	505.91	649.60	446.96	708.55	613.50	0.65	2479.00	46.00	6.00	2.50	2.00
312.60	1.50	255.01	370.20	189.06	436.15	314.10	0.17	1605.00	52.00	6.00	3.00	0.00
366.57	−3.07	298.37	434.77	237.74	495.40	363.50	0.14	2080.00	78.00	11.00	2.00	0.00
403.35	−39.05	343.37	463.33	278.68	528.03	364.30	0.28	2410.00	71.00	6.00	1.00	1.00
269.41	35.69	213.38	325.45	146.59	392.24	305.10	0.11	1753.00	97.00	8.00	2.00	0.00
441.72	−0.02	389.80	493.63	320.72	562.72	441.70	0.36	1884.00	45.00	7.00	2.00	2.00
432.33	−79.23	359.85	504.80	301.18	563.47	353.10	0.15	2050.00	41.00	10.00	2.00	2.00
510.88	−47.58	452.22	569.54	386.83	634.92	463.30	0.23	2978.00	40.00	6.00	2.50	2.00
410.99	−90.99	352.48	469.49	287.01	534.96	320.00	0.46	2132.00	82.00	7.00	1.00	0.00
303.27	29.57	269.65	336.88	188.91	417.62	332.80	0.19	1551.00	54.00	6.00	2.00	0.00
237.07	39.53	184.51	289.64	115.79	358.36	276.60	0.12	1129.00	44.00	5.00	1.00	0.00
355.77	41.23	319.85	391.69	240.72	470.82	397.00	0.15	1674.00	34.00	7.00	2.00	1.00
168.94	52.96	114.99	222.89	47.06	290.83	221.90	0.09	1184.00	94.00	5.00	1.00	0.00

Based on Model 4
PRE—Unstandardized Predicted
RES—Unstandardized Residual
LMCI—95% Lower Confidence Interval for y mean
UMCI—95% Upper Confidence Interval for y mean
LICI—95% Lower Confidence Interval for y individual
UICI—95% Upper Confidence Interval for y individual

Note: Independent variable: the appraised value
Dependent variables: land area of the property in acres, house size (square feet), age, rooms, baths and garage

Use the SPSS outputs to answer the following questions:

1. Are the regression assumptions valid for these data? Justify your answers with the appropriate charts.

2. State the multiple regression equation for model 1.

3. State the multiple regression equation for model 2.

4. State the multiple regression equation for model 3.

5. State the multiple regression equation for model 4.

6. Of the four models given in the SPSS outputs, which model appears to be the most efficient? Why?

7. At the 0.05 level of significance, is the linear model 1 useful for predicting the appraised value of a single-family home?

8. At the 0.05 level of significance, is the linear model 2 useful for predicting the appraised value of a single-family home?

9. At the 0.05 level of significance, is the linear model 3 useful for predicting the appraised value of a single-family home?

10. At the 0.05 level of significance, is the linear model 4 useful for predicting the appraised value of a single-family home?

11. Use model 4 to predict the appraised value of a single-family home that has a land area of 0.2297 acres, house size of 2448 square feet, age of 46 years, 7 rooms, 3.5 baths and 2 garages.

12. For model 4, what is the forecast error (or residual) of appraised value of a single-family home that has a land area of 0.2297 acres, house size of 2448 square feet, age of 46 years, 7 rooms, 3.5 baths and 2 garages?

13. At the 0.05 level of significance, determine whether each independent variable makes a significant contribution to the regression model 4. Indicate the most appropriate regression model for this set of data.

14. Based on model 4, construct a 95% confidence interval estimate of the mean appraised value of a single-family home that has a land area of 0.2297 acres, house size of 2448 square feet, age of 46 years, 7 rooms, 3.5 baths and 2 garages.

15. Based on model 4, construct a 95% confidence interval estimate of the appraised value of a single-family home that has a land area of 0.2297 acres, house size of 2448 square feet, age of 46 years, 7 rooms, 3.5 baths and 2 garages.

16. What is the coefficient of multiple determination for model 4? And interpret its meaning.

USING QUESTION 16.3

Many factors determine the attendance at Major League Baseball games. These factors can include when the game is played, the weather, the opponent, and whether the team is having a good season. In an effort to increase ticket sales, ball clubs run promotions such as free concerts after the game or giveaways of team hats or bobbleheads of star players (T.C. Boyd and T.C. Krehbiel, "An Analysis of the Effects of Specific Promotion Types on Attendance at Major League Baseball Games," *American Journal of Business,* 2006, 21, pp. 21–32).

The data file (**Phillies**) include the following variables for a recent season:

Attendance—Paid attendance for each Philadelphia Phillies home game

Temp—High temperature for the day

Win—Team's winning percentage at the time of the game

OpWin—opponent team's winning percentage at the time of the game

Weekend—Dummy variable, 1 if game played on Friday, Saturday, or Sunday; 0 otherwise

Promotion—Dummy variable, 1 if a promotion was held; 0 if no promotion was held

A regression analysis using attendance as the dependent variable and the other five variables as independent variables was performed and the SPSS results were provided.

The data are shown in the table below.

Attendance	Temp	Win	OpWin	Weekend	Promotion
18,591	48	531	469	1	1
18,073	49	531	469	1	1
14,502	67	500	500	0	0
13,020	75	429	571	0	0
14,542	66	500	500	0	0
14,111	65	556	444	0	0
13,366	57	500	556	1	0
15,606	73	455	600	1	0
19,195	78	417	636	1	1
12,138	57	368	474	0	0
12,250	61	400	450	0	0
12,249	62	381	476	0	0
15,257	65	325	434	1	0
16,205	66	345	414	1	0
32,411	71	367	400	1	1
12,321	82	387	467	0	0
13,216	77	406	452	0	0
12,476	89	424	438	0	0
20,504	77	441	647	1	0
32,634	89	457	629	1	1
21,114	79	444	639	1	1
21,090	60	409	545	0	0
22,640	67	422	533	0	0
26,405	74	435	522	0	0
15,455	91	404	491	1	0
16,601	89	396	500	1	0
19,223	85	407	491	1	1
14,942	78	418	491	0	0
13,039	91	411	500	0	0
16,888	63	444	469	1	0
20,634	70	438	477	1	0

(continued)

Attendance	Temp	Win	OpWin	Weekend	Promotion
41,079	81	446	470	1	1
17,424	81	439	493	0	0
21,905	82	433	500	0	1
22,132	85	441	493	0	1
17,039	84	435	556	1	0
18,759	86	441	548	1	0
38,158	88	437	554	1	1
18,422	90	456	500	0	0
20,826	95	463	494	0	0
50,396	97	457	500	0	1
12,303	99	463	518	1	0
44,143	88	458	524	1	1
15,228	86	452	529	1	0
17,393	86	453	529	1	1
23,541	93	467	429	0	0
27,672	92	473	424	0	1
20,422	69	470	629	1	0
23,570	73	468	635	1	0
25,012	83	458	643	1	0
27,330	94	471	552	0	0
22,595	95	467	557	0	0
20,380	94	472	551	0	0
17,076	86	477	556	1	0
23,506	82	481	551	1	0
28,186	84	477	555	1	1
20,259	86	473	558	0	0
14,046	99	470	359	0	0
14,509	99	475	356	0	0
14,289	93	479	353	0	0
31,117	93	483	559	1	0
20,242	95	488	555	1	1
58,493	96	484	558	1	1
16,126	86	496	500	0	0
13,821	74	500	496	0	0
14,268	67	496	500	0	0
18,335	80	504	464	1	0
21,747	85	500	468	1	1
24,047	86	496	471	1	1
13,514	93	493	475	0	0
14,345	91	490	486	0	1
14,345	91	487	489	0	1
12,247	82	483	487	0	0
13,167	77	486	490	0	0
13,718	84	486	438	1	0
16,621	85	486	442	1	0
23,054	81	490	439	1	1
15,807	80	500	630	0	0
14,516	77	503	626	0	0

The SPSS outputs are shown below:

Model Summary[b]

Model	R	R Square	Adjusted R Square	Std. Error of the Estimate
1	.345[a]	.119	.084	8296.787

a. Predictors: (Constant), OpWin, Temp, Win
b. Dependent Variable: Attendance

ANOVA[a]

Model		Sum of Squares	df	Mean Square	F	Sig.
1	Regression	699691116.010	3	233230372.003	3.388	.022[b]
	Residual	5162750420.369	75	68836672.272		
	Total	5862441536.380	78			

a. Dependent Variable: Attendance
b. Predictors: (Constant), OpWin, Temp, Win

Coefficients[a]

Model		Unstandardized Coefficients B	Unstandardized Coefficients Std. Error	Standardized Coefficients Beta	t	Sig.	95.0% Confidence Interval for B Lower Bound	95.0% Confidence Interval for B Upper Bound
1	(Constant)	−8820.597	13031.698		−.677	.501	−3478.071	17139.877
	Temp	203.665	79.116	.281	2.574	.012	46.058	361.272
	Win	−3.001	22.404	−.015	−.134	.894	−47.632	41.630
	OpWin	27.249	14.089	.211	1.934	.057	−.817	55.316

a. Dependent Variable: Attendance

CHARTS

Histogram

Dependent Variable: Attendance

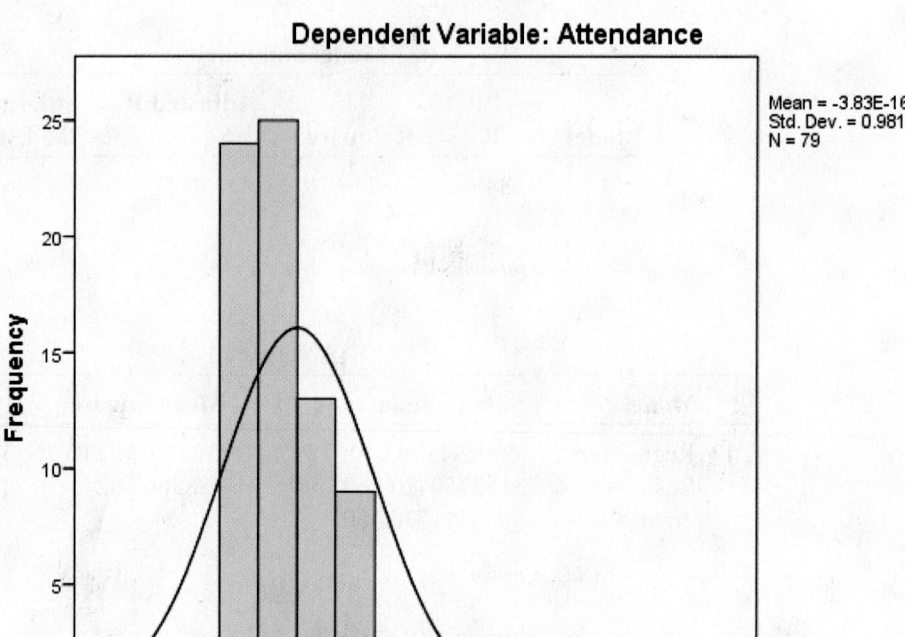

Mean = -3.83E-16
Std. Dev. = 0.981
N = 79

Normal P-P Plot of Regression Standardized Residual

Dependent Variable: Attendance

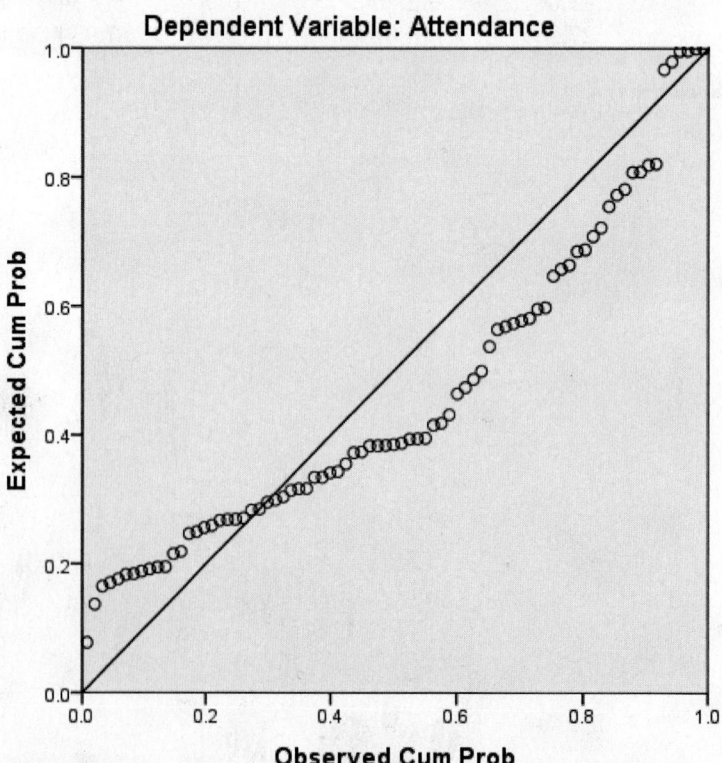

Scatterplot

Dependent Variable: Attendance

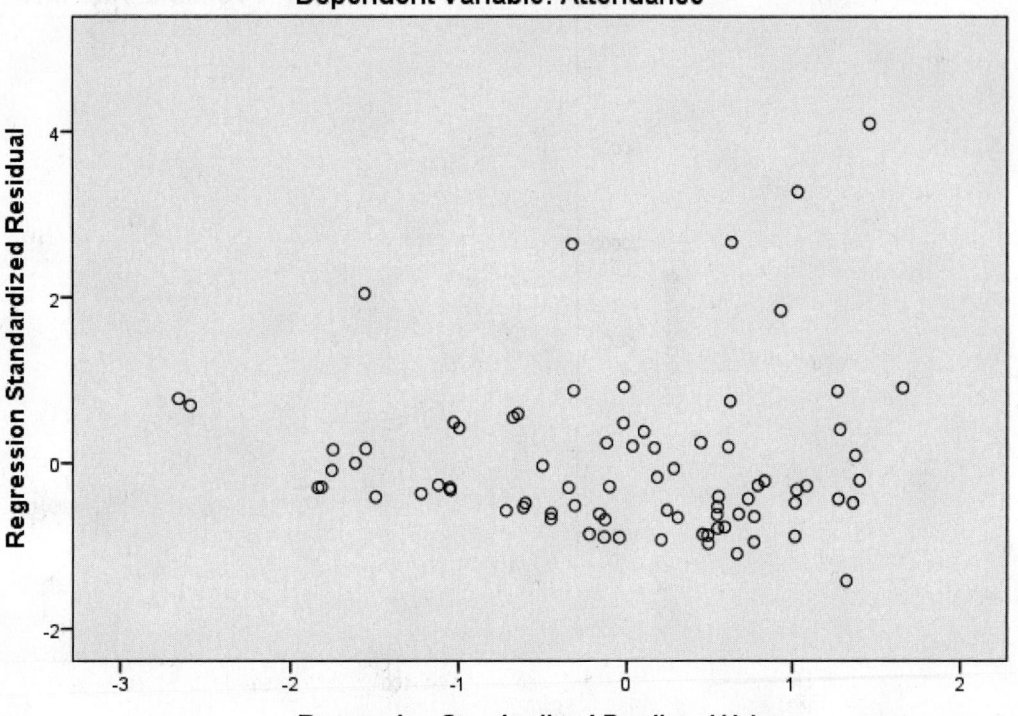

Partial Regression Plot

Dependent Variable: Attendance

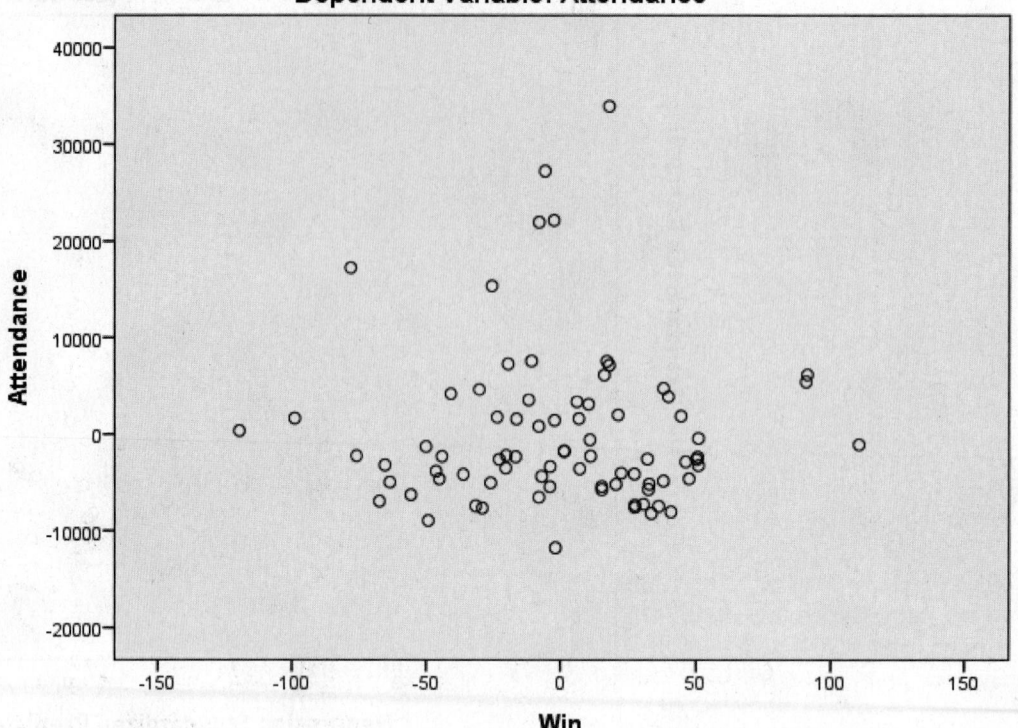

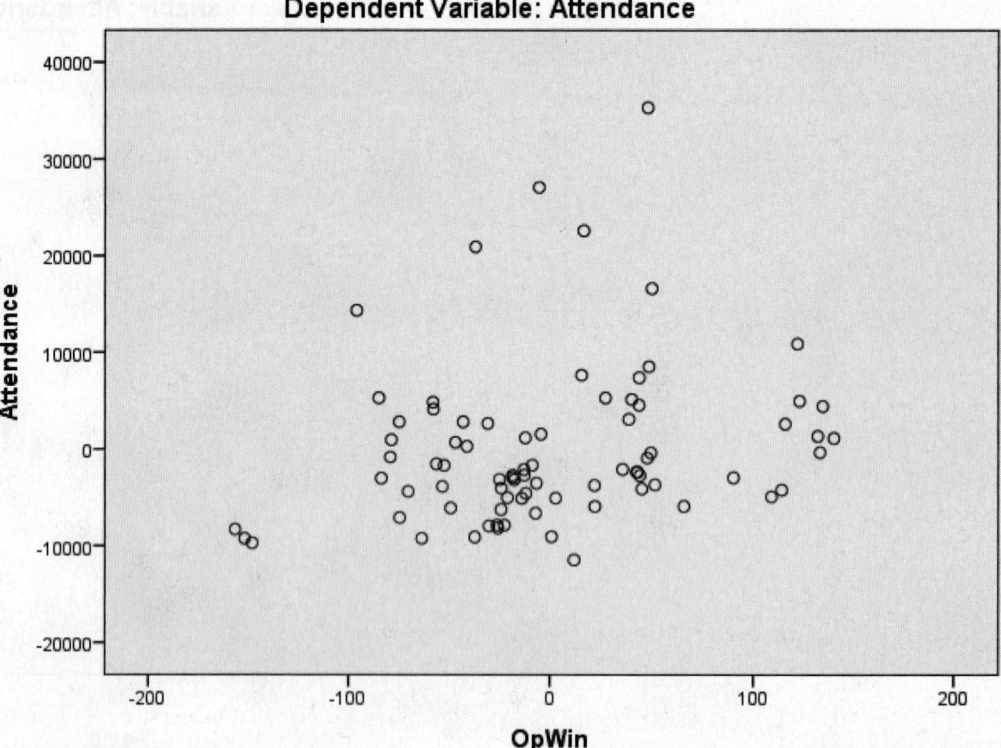

Attendance	Temp	Win	OpWin	Weekend	Promotion	PRE_1	RES_1	LMCI_1	UMCI_1	LICI_1	UICI_1
18591	48	531	469	1	1	12141.66	6449.337	5237.852	19045.47	−5770.31	30053.64
18073	49	531	469	1	1	12345.33	5727.672	5568.641	19122.01	−5518.04	30208.69
14502	67	500	500	0	0	16949.07	−2447.07	13327.16	20570.97	28.82554	33869.31
13020	75	429	571	0	0	20726.17	−7706.17	17745.44	23706.91	3931.498	37520.85
14542	66	500	500	0	0	16745.4	−2203.4	13017.09	20473.72	−197.936	33688.74
14111	65	556	444	0	0	14847.71	−736.706	8743.11	20952.3	−2771.67	32467.08
13366	57	500	556	1	0	16438.38	−3072.38	11553.84	21322.92	−796.327	33673.09
15606	73	455	600	1	0	21031.05	−5425.05	17667.04	24395.06	4164.128	37897.96
19195	78	417	636	1	1	23144.39	−3949.39	18614.91	27673.88	6006.931	40281.85
12138	57	368	474	0	0	14600.09	−2462.09	9144.693	20055.48	−2805.02	32005.19
12250	61	400	450	0	0	14664.72	−2414.72	10224.55	19104.9	−2449.35	31778.8
12249	62	381	476	0	0	15633.89	−3384.89	11006.03	20261.76	−1529.83	32797.62
15257	65	325	434	1	0	15268.48	−11.4811	8739.099	21797.86	−2502.54	33039.5
16205	66	345	414	1	0	14867.14	1337.864	8910.457	20823.81	−2701.54	32435.81
32411	71	367	400	1	1	15437.94	16973.06	10210.35	20665.54	−1897.11	32773
12321	82	387	467	0	0	19443.94	−7122.94	15723.66	23164.23	2502.372	36385.52
13216	77	406	452	0	0	17959.86	−4743.86	14738.23	21181.48	1120.759	34798.95
12476	89	424	438	0	0	19968.33	−7492.33	16670.78	23265.87	3114.539	36822.11
20504	77	441	647	1	0	23168.44	−2664.44	18734.67	27602.21	6056.03	40280.86
32634	89	457	629	1	1	25073.92	7560.084	20963.96	29183.88	8042.53	42105.3
21114	79	444	639	1	1	23348.77	−2234.77	19159.38	27538.17	6298.044	40399.5
21090	60	409	545	0	0	17022.74	4067.262	12765.25	21280.23	−44.8505	34090.33
22640	67	422	533	0	0	18082.39	4557.614	14883.07	21281.7	1247.542	34917.23
26405	74	435	522	0	0	19169.28	7235.717	16841.41	21497.16	2478.108	35860.46
15455	91	404	491	1	0	21879.9	−6424.9	18353.4	25406.39	4979.821	38779.97
16601	89	396	500	1	0	21741.82	−5140.82	18109.59	25374.05	4819.366	38664.27
19223	85	407	491	1	1	20648.9	−1425.9	17626.83	23670.98	3846.84	37450.96
14942	78	418	491	0	0	19190.23	−4248.23	16645.95	21734.51	2467.503	35912.96
13039	91	411	500	0	0	22104.13	−9065.13	18798.07	25410.2	5248.675	38959.59
16888	63	444	469	1	0	15457.74	1430.26	11925.51	18989.97	−1443.53	32359.01
20634	70	438	477	1	0	17119.4	3514.602	14405.3	19833.49	369.9905	33868.81
41079	81	446	470	1	1	19144.96	21934.04	16967.28	21322.64	2474.067	35815.85
17424	81	439	493	0	0	19792.7	−2368.7	17746.17	21839.24	3138.435	36446.97
21905	82	433	500	0	1	20205.12	1699.88	18050.63	22359.61	3537.242	36873
22132	85	441	493	0	1	20601.36	1530.64	18453.97	22748.75	3934.399	37268.32
17039	84	435	556	1	0	22132.41	−5093.41	19516.44	24748.38	5398.625	38866.2
18759	86	441	548	1	0	22303.74	−3544.74	19810.49	24796.99	5588.698	39018.78
38158	88	437	554	1	1	22886.57	15271.43	20105.81	25667.33	6126.232	39646.91
18422	90	456	500	0	0	21765.41	−3343.41	19388.12	24142.7	5067.275	38463.55
20826	95	463	494	0	0	22599.24	−1773.24	19666.58	25531.89	5813.027	39385.44
50396	97	457	500	0	1	23188.07	27207.93	20014.89	26361.24	6358.173	40017.96
12303	99	463	518	1	0	24067.88	−11764.9	20635.8	27499.96	7187.255	40948.51
44143	88	458	524	1	1	22006.07	22136.93	19772.33	24239.8	5327.76	38684.37
15228	86	452	529	1	0	21752.99	−6524.99	19602.64	23903.34	5085.647	38420.33
17393	86	453	529	1	1	21749.99	−4356.99	19606.55	23893.43	5083.535	38416.44
23541	93	467	429	0	0	20408.69	3132.309	16927.06	23890.33	3517.921	37299.46
27672	92	473	424	0	1	20050.77	7621.228	16506.84	23594.7	3147.051	36954.49
20422	69	470	629	1	0	20961.6	−539.599	16710.43	25212.77	3895.588	38027.61

(continued)

Attendance	Temp	Win	OpWin	Weekend	Promotion	PRE_1	RES_1	LMCI_1	UMCI_1	LICI_1	UICI_1
23570	73	468	635	1	0	21945.76	1624.242	17789.67	26101.84	4903.183	38988.33
25012	83	458	643	1	0	24230.42	781.5843	20002.43	28458.4	7170.163	41290.67
27330	94	471	552	0	0	23952.02	3377.976	20876.04	27028.01	7140.183	40763.87
22595	95	467	557	0	0	24303.94	−1708.94	21071.59	27536.29	7462.789	41145.09
20380	94	472	551	0	0	23921.77	−3541.77	20852.53	26991.02	7111.163	40732.38
17076	86	477	556	1	0	22413.69	−5337.69	19878.9	24948.49	5692.404	39134.98
23506	82	481	551	1	0	21450.78	2055.218	19036.72	23864.84	4747.368	38154.2
28186	84	477	555	1	1	21979.11	6206.886	19536.17	24422.06	5271.501	38686.73
20259	86	473	558	0	0	22480.2	−2221.2	19958.22	25002.18	5760.845	39199.55
14046	99	470	359	0	0	19714.22	−5668.22	14327.28	25101.16	2330.453	37097.99
14509	99	475	356	0	0	19617.47	−5108.47	14132.39	25102.54	2203.039	37031.9
14289	93	479	353	0	0	18301.73	−4012.73	13093.07	23510.38	972.3726	35631.08
31117	93	483	559	1	0	23903.09	7213.909	20751.17	27055.01	7077.19	40728.99
20242	95	488	555	1	1	24186.42	−3944.42	20824.84	27548	7319.984	41052.85
58493	96	484	558	1	1	24483.84	34009.16	21034.75	27932.92	7599.745	41367.93
16126	86	496	500	0	0	20830.71	−4704.71	18173.49	23487.92	4090.422	37570.99
13821	74	500	496	0	0	18265.72	−4444.72	15240.25	21291.2	1463.051	35068.4
14268	67	496	500	0	0	16961.07	−2693.07	13446.56	20475.58	63.49248	33858.65
18335	80	504	464	1	0	18603.73	−268.73	15415.88	21791.58	1771.062	35436.4
21747	85	500	468	1	1	19743.06	2003.942	16728.85	22757.26	2942.41	36543.71
24047	86	496	471	1	1	20040.48	4006.525	17149.34	22931.61	3261.471	36819.48
13514	93	493	475	0	0	21584.13	−8070.13	18390.41	24777.86	4750.35	38417.91
14345	91	490	486	0	1	21485.55	−7140.55	18607.34	24363.75	4708.767	38262.33
14345	91	487	489	0	1	21576.3	−7231.3	18779.47	24373.13	4813.287	38339.31
12247	82	483	487	0	0	19700.82	−7453.82	17385.88	22015.76	3011.444	36390.2
13167	77	486	490	0	0	18755.24	−5588.24	16272.1	21238.38	2041.702	35468.78
13718	84	486	438	1	0	18763.93	−5045.93	15650.42	21877.44	1945.179	35582.68
16621	85	486	442	1	0	19076.59	−2455.59	16018.14	22135.04	2267.948	35885.23
23054	81	490	439	1	1	18168.18	4885.823	14990.63	21345.73	1337.456	34998.9
15807	80	500	630	0	0	23139.13	−7332.13	18948.46	27329.8	6088.088	40190.17
14516	77	503	626	0	0	22410.13	−7894.13	18195.43	26624.84	5353.168	39467.1

Based on Model 1

PRE—Unstandardized Predicted

RES—Unstandardized Residual

LMCI—95% Lower Confidence Interval for y mean

UMCI—95% Upper Confidence Interval for y mean

LICI—95% Lower Confidence Interval for y individual

UICI—95% Upper Confidence Interval for y individual

Note: Independent variable: Attendance
Dependent variables: Temp, Win, OpWin, Weekend, and Promotion

Use the SPSS results to answer the following questions:

1. Are the regression assumptions valid for these data? Justify your answers with the appropriate charts.

2. Interpret the regression coefficients in (1).

3. State the multiple regression equation.

4. Predict the attendance for a Philadelphia Phillies home game that is held when the high temperature of the day is 48 (Temp=48), the team's winning percentage at the time of the game is 531 (Win=531), the opponent team's winning percentage at the time of the game is 469 (OpWin=469) and the game is played on Friday, Saturday or Sunday (Weekend=1), and promotion is being held (Promotion=1).

5. What is the forecast error (or residual) of attendance for a Philadelphia Phillies home game that is held when the high temperature of the day is 48 (Temp=48), the team's winning percentage at the time of the game is 531 (Win=531), the opponent team's winning percentage at the time of the game is 469 (OpWin=469) and the game is played on Friday, Saturday or Sunday (Weekend=1), and promotion is being held (Promotion=1)?

6. At the 0.05 level of significance, is the linear regression model useful for predicting the attendance for a Philadelphia Phillies home game?

7. At the 0.05 level of significance, determine which independent variables significantly influenced attendance?

8. What is the coefficient of multiple determination? And interpret its meaning.

9. Construct a 95% confidence interval estimate of the population slope between attendance and temperature of the day (Temp).

10. Construct a 95% confidence interval estimate of the population slope between attendance and the team's winning percentage at the time of the game (Win).

11. Construct a 95% confidence interval estimate of the population slope between attendance and the opponent team's winning percentage at the time of the game (OpWin).

12. Construct a 95% confidence interval estimate of the mean attendance for a Philadelphia Phillies home game that is held when the high temperature of the day is 48 (Temp=48), the team's winning percentage at the time of the game is 531 (Win=531), the opponent team's winning percentage at the time of the game is 469 (OpWin=469) and the game is played on Friday, Saturday or Sunday (Weekend=1), and promotion is being held (Promotion=1).

13. Based on model 4, construct a 95% confidence interval estimate of the Philadelphia Phillies home game that is held when the high temperature of the day is 48 (Temp=48), the team's winning percentage at the time of the game is 531 (Win=531), the opponent team's winning percentage at the time of the game is 469 (OpWin=469) and the game is played on Friday, Saturday or Sunday (Weekend=1), and promotion is being held (Promotion=1).

Problems for Section 16.5

LEARNING THE BASICS

16.31 Suppose X_1 is a numerical variable and X_2 is a dummy variable and the regression equation for a sample of $n = 20$ is

$$\hat{Y}_i = 6 + 4X_{1i} + 2X_{2i}$$

a. Interpret the regression coefficient associated with variable X_1.
b. Interpret the regression coefficient associated with variable X_2.

16.32 Suppose that in Problem 16.31, the t_{test} test statistic for testing the contribution of X_2 is 3.27. At the 0.05 level of significance, is there evidence that variable X_2 makes a significant contribution to the model?

APPLYING THE CONCEPTS

16.33 The chair of the accounting department plans to develop a regression model to predict the grade point average in accounting for those students who are graduating and have completed the accounting major, based on the student's SAT score and whether the student received a grade of B or higher in the introductory statistics course ($0 = $ no and $1 = $ yes).
a. Explain the steps involved in developing a regression model for these data. Be sure to indicate the particular models you need to evaluate and compare.
b. Suppose the regression coefficient for the variable whether the student received a grade of B or higher in the introductory statistics course is $+0.30$. How do you interpret this result?

16.34 A real estate association in a suburban community would like to study the relationship between the size of a single-family house (as measured by the number of rooms) and the selling price of the house (in thousands of dollars). Two different neighborhoods are included in the study, one on the east side of the community ($=0$) and the other on the west side ($=1$). A random sample of 20 houses was selected, with the results stored in **Neighbor**. For (a) through (j), do not include an interaction term.
a. State the multiple regression equation that predicts the selling price, based on the number of rooms and the neighborhood.
b. Interpret the regression coefficients in (a).
c. Predict the selling price for a house with nine rooms that is located in an east-side neighborhood. Construct a 95% confidence interval estimate and a 95% prediction interval.
d. Perform a residual analysis on the results and determine whether the regression assumptions are valid.
e. Is there a significant relationship between selling price and the two independent variables (rooms and neighborhood) at the 0.05 level of significance?

f. At the 0.05 level of significance, determine whether each independent variable makes a contribution to the regression model. Indicate the most appropriate regression model for this set of data.
g. Construct and interpret a 95% confidence interval estimate of the population slope of the relationship between selling price and number of rooms.
h. Construct and interpret a 95% confidence interval estimate of the population slope of the relationship between selling price and neighborhood.
i. Compute and interpret the adjusted r^2.
j. What assumption do you need to make about the slope of selling price with number of rooms?
k. Add an interaction term to the model and, at the 0.05 level of significance, determine whether it makes a significant contribution to the model.
l. On the basis of the results of (f) and (k), which model is most appropriate? Explain.

16.35 The marketing manager of a large supermarket chain faced the business problem of determining the effect on the sales of pet food of shelf space and whether the product was placed at the front ($=1$) or back ($=0$) of the aisle. Data are collected from a random sample of 12 equal-sized stores. The results are shown in the following table (and organized and stored in **Petfood**):

Store	Shelf Space (Feet)	Location	Weekly Sales ($)
1	5	Back	160
2	5	Front	220
3	5	Back	140
4	10	Back	190
5	10	Back	240
6	10	Front	260
7	15	Back	230
8	15	Back	270
9	15	Front	280
10	20	Back	260
11	20	Back	290
12	20	Front	310

For (a) through (l), do not include an interaction term.
a. State the multiple regression equation that predicts weekly sales based on shelf space and location.
b. Interpret the regression coefficients in (a).
c. Predict the weekly sales of pet food for a store with 8 feet of shelf space situated at the back of the aisle. Construct a 95% confidence interval estimate and a 95% prediction interval.
d. Perform a residual analysis on the results and determine whether the regression assumptions are valid.

e. Is there a significant relationship between sales and the two independent variables (shelf space and aisle position) at the 0.05 level of significance?

f. At the 0.05 level of significance, determine whether each independent variable makes a contribution to the regression model. Indicate the most appropriate regression model for this set of data.

g. Construct and interpret 95% confidence interval estimates of the population slope of the relationship between sales and shelf space and between sales and aisle location.

h. Compare the slope in (b) with the slope for the simple linear regression model of Problem 15.4 on page 654. Explain the difference in the results.

i. Compute and interpret the meaning of the coefficient of multiple determination, r^2.

j. Compute and interpret the adjusted r^2.

k. Compare r^2 with the r^2 value computed in Problem 15.16 (a) on page 661.

l. What assumption about the slope of shelf space with sales do you need to make in this problem?

m. Add an interaction term to the model and, at the 0.05 level of significance, determine whether it makes a significant contribution to the model.

n. On the basis of the results of (f) and (m), which model is most appropriate? Explain.

16.36 In mining engineering, holes are often drilled through rock, using drill bits. As a drill hole gets deeper, additional rods are added to the drill bit to enable additional drilling to take place. It is expected that drilling time increases with depth. This increased drilling time could be caused by several factors, including the mass of the drill rods that are strung together. The business problem relates to whether drilling is faster using dry drilling holes or wet drilling holes. Using dry drilling holes involves forcing compressed air down the drill rods to flush the cuttings and drive the hammer. Using wet drilling holes involves forcing water rather than air down the hole. Data have been collected from a sample of 50 drill holes that contains measurements of the time to drill each additional 5 feet (in minutes), the depth (in feet), and whether the hole was a dry drilling hole or a wet drilling hole. The data are organized and stored in **Drill**. Develop a model to predict additional drilling time, based on depth and type of drilling hole (dry or wet). For (a) through (j) do not include an interaction term.

Source: Data extracted from R. Penner and D. G. Watts, "Mining Information," *The American Statistician*, 45, 1991, pp. 4–9.

a. State the multiple regression equation.

b. Interpret the regression coefficients in (a).

c. Predict the additional drilling time for a dry drilling hole at a depth of 100 feet. Construct a 95% confidence interval estimate and a 95% prediction interval.

d. Perform a residual analysis on the results and determine whether the regression assumptions are valid.

e. Is there a significant relationship between additional drilling time and the two independent variables (depth

and type of drilling hole) at the 0.05 level of significance?

f. At the 0.05 level of significance, determine whether each independent variable makes a contribution to the regression model. Indicate the most appropriate regression model for this set of data.

g. Construct a 95% confidence interval estimate of the population slope for the relationship between additional drilling time and depth.

h. Construct a 95% confidence interval estimate of the population slope for the relationship between additional drilling time and the type of hole drilled.

i. Compute and interpret the adjusted r^2.

j. What assumption do you need to make about the slope of additional drilling time with depth?

k. Add an interaction term to the model and, at the 0.05 level of significance, determine whether it makes a significant contribution to the model.

l. On the basis of the results of (f) and (k), which model is most appropriate? Explain.

16.37 The owner of a moving company typically has his most experienced manager predict the total number of labor hours that will be required to complete an upcoming move. This approach has proved useful in the past, but the owner has the business objective of developing a more accurate method of predicting labor hours. In a preliminary effort to provide a more accurate method, the owner has decided to use the number of cubic feet moved and whether there is an elevator in the apartment building as the independent variables and has collected data for 36 moves in which the origin and destination were within the borough of Manhattan in New York City and the travel time was an insignificant portion of the hours worked. The data are organized and stored in **Moving**. For (a) through (j), do not include an interaction term.

a. State the multiple regression equation for predicting labor hours, using the number of cubic feet moved and whether there is an elevator.

b. Interpret the regression coefficients in (a).

c. Predict the labor hours for moving 500 cubic feet in an apartment building that has an elevator and construct a 95% confidence interval estimate and a 95% prediction interval.

d. Perform a residual analysis on the results and determine whether the regression assumptions are valid.

e. Is there a significant relationship between labor hours and the two independent variables (cubic feet moved and whether there is an elevator in the apartment building) at the 0.05 level of significance?

f. At the 0.05 level of significance, determine whether each independent variable makes a contribution to the regression model. Indicate the most appropriate regression model for this set of data.

g. Construct a 95% confidence interval estimate of the population slope for the relationship between labor hours and cubic feet moved.

h. Construct a 95% confidence interval estimate for the relationship between labor hours and the presence of an elevator.

i. Compute and interpret the adjusted r^2.

j. What assumption do you need to make about the slope of labor hours with cubic feet moved?

k. Add an interaction term to the model and, at the 0.05 level of significance, determine whether it makes a significant contribution to the model.

l. On the basis of the results of (f) and (k), which model is most appropriate? Explain.

SELF **16.38** In Problem 16.4 on page 711, you used sales **Test** and orders to predict distribution cost (stored in **WareCost**). Develop a regression model to predict distribution cost that includes sales, orders, and the interaction of sales and orders.

a. At the 0.05 level of significance, is there evidence that the interaction term makes a significant contribution to the model?

b. Which regression model is more appropriate, the one used in (a) or the one used in Problem 16.4? Explain.

16.39 Zagat's publishes restaurant ratings for various locations in the United States. The file **Restaurants** contains the Zagat rating for food, décor, service, and cost per person for a sample of 50 restaurants located in a city and 50 restaurants located in a suburb. Develop a regression model to predict the cost per person, based on a variable that represents the sum of the ratings for food, décor, and service and a dummy variable concerning location (city vs. suburban). For (a) through (l), do not include an interaction term.

Sources: Extracted from *Zagat Survey 2010, New York City Restaurants*; and *Zagat Survey 2009–2010, Long Island Restaurants*.

a. State the multiple regression equation.

b. Interpret the regression coefficients in (a).

c. Predict the cost for a restaurant with a summated rating of 60 that is located in a city and construct a 95% confidence interval estimate and a 95% prediction interval.

d. Perform a residual analysis on the results and determine whether the regression assumptions are satisfied.

e. Is there a significant relationship between price and the two independent variables (summated rating and location) at the 0.05 level of significance?

f. At the 0.05 level of significance, determine whether each independent variable makes a contribution to the regression model. Indicate the most appropriate regression model for this set of data.

g. Construct a 95% confidence interval estimate of the population slope for the relationship between cost and summated rating.

h. Compare the slope in (b) with the slope for the simple linear regression model of Problem 15.5 on page 654. Explain the difference in the results.

i. Compute and interpret the meaning of the coefficient of multiple determination.

j. Compute and interpret the adjusted r^2.

k. Compare r^2 with the r^2 value computed in Problem 15.17 (b) on page 661.

l. What assumption about the slope of cost with summated rating do you need to make in this problem?

m. Add an interaction term to the model and, at the 0.05 level of significance, determine whether it makes a significant contribution to the model.

n. On the basis of the results of (f) and (m), which model is most appropriate? Explain.

16.40 In Problem 16.6 on pages 711–712, you used radio advertising and newspaper advertising to predict sales (stored in **Advertise**). Develop a regression model to predict sales that includes radio advertising, newspaper advertising, and the interaction of radio advertising and newspaper advertising.

a. At the 0.05 level of significance, is there evidence that the interaction term makes a significant contribution to the model?

b. Which regression model is more appropriate, the one used in this problem or the one used in Problem 16.6? Explain.

16.41 In Problem 16.5 on page 711, horsepower and weight were used to predict miles per gallon (stored in **Auto2011**). Develop a regression model that includes horsepower, weight, and the interaction of horsepower and weight to predict miles per gallon.

a. At the 0.05 level of significance, is there evidence that the interaction term makes a significant contribution to the model?

b. Which regression model is more appropriate, the one used in this problem or the one used in Problem 16.5? Explain.

16.42 In Problem 16.7 on page 712, you used total staff present and remote hours to predict standby hours (stored in **Standby**). Develop a regression model to predict standby hours that includes total staff present, remote hours, and the interaction of total staff present and remote hours.

a. At the 0.05 level of significance, is there evidence that the interaction term makes a significant contribution to the model?

b. Which regression model is more appropriate, the one used in this problem or the one used in Problem 16.7? Explain.

George Bailey / Shutterstock.com

USING STATISTICS @ OmniFoods Revisited

In the Using Statistics scenario, you were the marketing manager for OmniFoods, a large food products company planning a nationwide introduction of a new high-energy bar, OmniPower. You needed to determine the effect that price and in-store promotions would have on sales of OmniPower in order to develop an effective marketing strategy. A sample of 34 stores in a supermarket chain was selected for a test-market study. The stores charged between 59 and 99 cents per bar and were given an in-store promotion budget between $200 and $600.

At the end of the one-month test-market study, you performed a multiple regression analysis on the data. Two independent variables were considered: the price of an OmniPower bar and the monthly budget for in-store promotional expenditures. The dependent variable was the number of OmniPower bars sold in a month. The coefficient of determination indicated that 75.8% of the variation in sales was explained by knowing the price charged and the amount spent on in-store promotions. The model indicated that the predicted sales of OmniPower are estimated to decrease by 532 bars per month for each 10-cent increase in the price, and the predicted sales are estimated to increase by 361 bars for each additional $100 spent on promotions.

After studying the relative effects of price and promotion, OmniFoods needs to set price and promotion standards for a nationwide introduction (obviously, lower prices and higher promotion budgets lead to more sales, but they do so at a lower profit margin). You determined that if stores spend $400 a month for in-store promotions and charge 79 cents, the 95% confidence interval estimate of the mean monthly sales is 2,854 to 3,303 bars. OmniFoods can multiply the lower and upper bounds of this confidence interval by the number of stores included in the nationwide introduction to estimate total monthly sales. For example, if 1,000 stores are in the nationwide introduction, then total monthly sales should be between 2.854 million and 3.308 million bars.

SUMMARY

In this chapter, you learned how multiple regression models allow you to use two or more independent variables to predict the value of a dependent variable. You also learned how to include categorical independent variables and interaction terms in regression models. Figure 16.17 presents a roadmap of the chapter.

FIGURE 16.17
Roadmap for multiple
regression

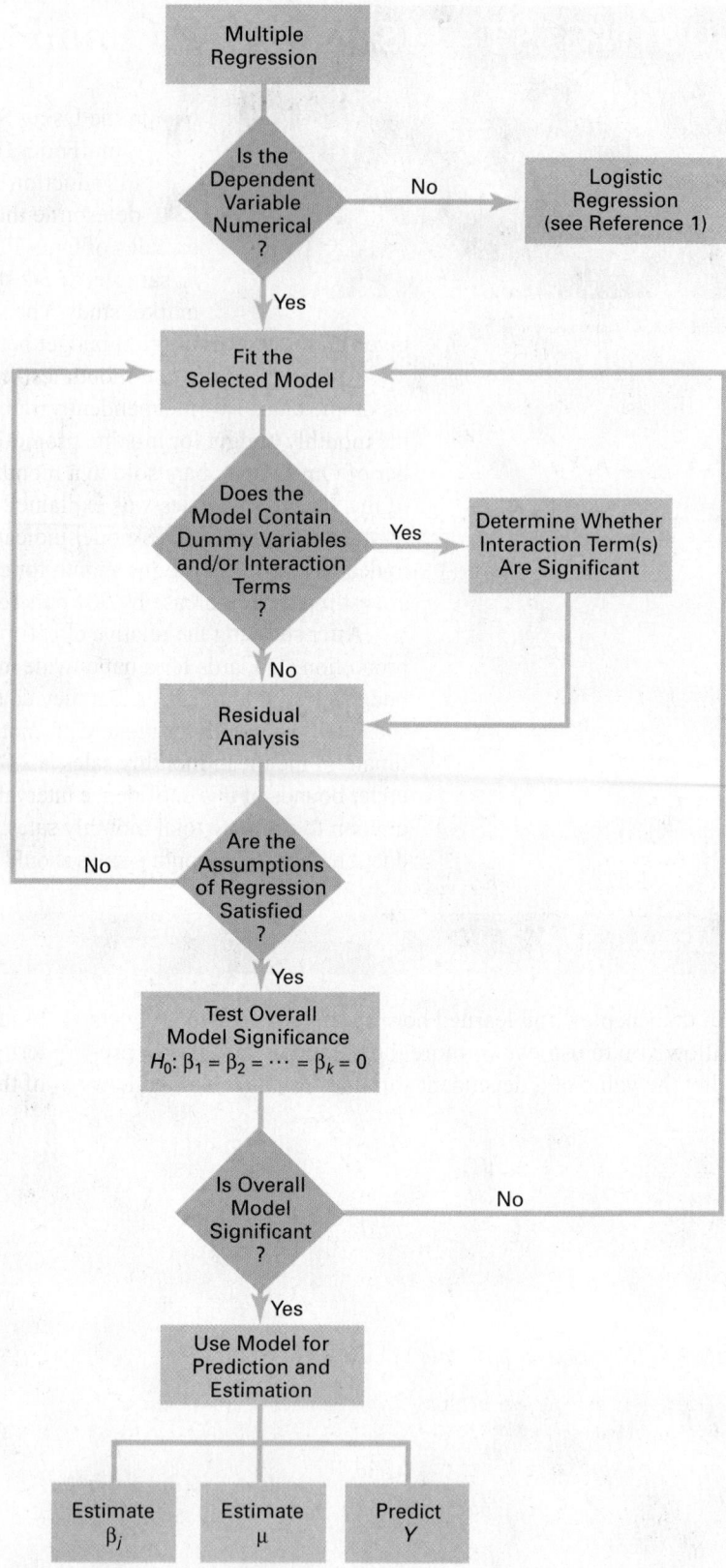

KEY EQUATIONS

Multiple Regression Model with k Independent Variables

$$Y_i = \beta_0 + \beta_1 X_{1i} + \beta_2 X_{2i} + \beta_3 X_{3i} + \cdots + \beta_k X_{ki} + \varepsilon_i$$

Multiple Regression Model with Two Independent Variables

$$Y_i = \beta_0 + \beta_1 X_{1i} + \beta_2 X_{2i} + \varepsilon_i$$

Multiple Regression Equation with Two Independent Variables

$$\hat{Y}_i = b_0 + b_1 X_{1i} + b_2 X_{2i}$$

Coefficient of Multiple Determination

$$r^2 = \frac{\text{Regression sum of squares}}{\text{Total sum of squares}} = \frac{SSR}{SST}$$

Adjusted r^2

$$r^2_{\text{adj}} = 1 - \left[(1 - r^2) \frac{n-1}{n-k-1} \right]$$

Overall F Test

$$F_{STAT} = \frac{MSR}{MSE}$$

Testing for the Slope in Multiple Regression

$$t_{STAT} = \frac{b_j - \beta_j}{S_{b_j}}$$

Confidence Interval Estimate for the Slope

$$b_j \pm t_{\alpha/2} S_{b_j}$$

KEY TERMS

adjusted R^2 713
coefficient of multiple
    determination   713
cross-product term   732

dummy variable   729
interaction   732
interaction term   732
multiple regression model   706

net regression
    coefficient   709
overall F test   714

PROBLEMS

CHECKING YOUR UNDERSTANDING

16.43 What is the difference between r^2 and adjusted r^2?

16.44 How does the interpretation of the regression coefficients differ in multiple regression and simple linear regression?

16.45 Why and how do you use dummy variables?

16.46 How can you evaluate whether the slope of the dependent variable with an independent variable is the same for each level of the dummy variable?

16.47 Under what circumstances do you include an interaction term in a regression model?

16.48 When a dummy variable is included in a regression model that has one numerical independent variable, what assumption do you need to make concerning the slope between the dependent variable, Y, and the numerical independent variable, X?

APPLYING THE CONCEPTS

16.49 Increasing customer satisfaction typically results in increased purchase behavior. For many products, there is more than one measure of customer satisfaction. In many of these instances, purchase behavior can increase dramatically with an increase in any one of the customer satisfaction measures, not necessarily all of them at the same time. Gunst and Barry ("One Way to Moderate Ceiling Effects," *Quality Progress*, October 2003, pp. 83–85) consider a product with two satisfaction measures, X_1 and X_2, that range from the lowest level of satisfaction, 1, to the highest level of satisfaction, 7. The dependent variable, Y, is a measure of purchase behavior, with the highest value generating the most sales. The following regression equation is presented:

$$\hat{Y}_i = -3.888 + 1.449 X_{1i} + 1.462 X_{2i} - 0.190 X_{1i} X_{2i}$$

Suppose that X_1 is the perceived quality of the product and X_2 is the perceived value of the product. (Note: If the customer thinks the product is overpriced, he or she perceives it to be of low value and vice versa.)

a. What is the predicted purchase behavior when $X_1 = 2$ and $X_2 = 2$?
b. What is the predicted purchase behavior when $X_1 = 2$ and $X_2 = 7$?
c. What is the predicted purchase behavior when $X_1 = 7$ and $X_2 = 2$?
d. What is the predicted purchase behavior when $X_1 = 7$ and $X_2 = 7$?
e. What is the regression equation when $X_2 = 2$? What is the slope for X_1 now?
f. What is the regression equation when $X_2 = 7$? What is the slope for X_1 now?
g. What is the regression equation when $X_1 = 2$? What is the slope for X_2 now?
h. What is the regression equation when $X_1 = 7$? What is the slope for X_2 now?
i. Discuss the implications of (a) through (h) within the context of increasing sales for this product with two customer satisfaction measures.

16.50 The owner of a moving company typically has his most experienced manager predict the total number of labor hours that will be required to complete an upcoming move. This approach has proved useful in the past, but the owner has the business objective of developing a more accurate method of predicting labor hours. In a preliminary effort to provide a more accurate method, the owner has decided to use the number of cubic feet moved and the number of pieces of large furniture as the independent variables and has collected data for 36 moves in which the origin and destination were within the borough of Manhattan in New York City and the travel time was an insignificant portion of the hours worked. The data are organized and stored in **Moving**.

a. State the multiple regression equation.
b. Interpret the meaning of the slopes in this equation.
c. Predict the labor hours for moving 500 cubic feet with two large pieces of furniture.
d. Perform a residual analysis on your results and determine whether the regression assumptions are valid.
e. Determine whether there is a significant relationship between labor hours and the two independent variables (the number of cubic feet moved and the number of pieces of large furniture) at the 0.05 level of significance.
f. Determine the p-value in (e) and interpret its meaning.
g. Interpret the meaning of the coefficient of multiple determination in this problem.
h. Determine the adjusted r^2.
i. At the 0.05 level of significance, determine whether each independent variable makes a significant contribution to

the regression model. Indicate the most appropriate regression model for this set of data.
j. Determine the p-values in (i) and interpret their meaning.
k. Construct a 95% confidence interval estimate of the population slope between labor hours and the number of cubic feet moved. How does the interpretation of the slope here differ from that in Problem 15.37 on page 672?

16.51 Professional basketball has truly become a sport that generates interest among fans around the world. More and more players come from outside the United States to play in the National Basketball Association (NBA). You want to develop a regression model to predict the number of wins achieved by each NBA team, based on field goal (shots made) percentage for the team and for the opponent. The data are stored in **NBA2011**.

a. State the multiple regression equation.
b. Interpret the meaning of the slopes in this equation.
c. Predict the number of wins for a team that has a field goal percentage of 45% and an opponent field goal percentage of 44%.
d. Perform a residual analysis on your results and determine whether the regression assumptions are valid.
e. Is there a significant relationship between number of wins and the two independent variables (field goal percentage for the team and for the opponent) at the 0.05 level of significance?
f. Determine the p-value in (e) and interpret its meaning.
g. Interpret the meaning of the coefficient of multiple determination in this problem.
h. Determine the adjusted r^2.
i. At the 0.05 level of significance, determine whether each independent variable makes a significant contribution to the regression model. Indicate the most appropriate regression model for this set of data.
j. Determine the p-values in (i) and interpret their meaning.

16.52 A sample of 30 recently sold single-family houses in a small city is selected. Develop a model to predict the selling price (in thousands of dollars), using the assessed value (in thousands of dollars) as well as time (in months since reassessment). The houses in the city had been reassessed at full value one year prior to the study. The results are stored in **House1**.

a. State the multiple regression equation.
b. Interpret the meaning of the slopes in this equation.
c. Predict the selling price for a house that has an assessed value of $170,000 and was sold 12 months after reassessment.
d. Perform a residual analysis on your results and determine whether the regression assumptions are valid.
e. Determine whether there is a significant relationship between selling price and the two independent variables (assessed value and time period) at the 0.05 level of significance.

f. Determine the *p*-value in (e) and interpret its meaning.

g. Interpret the meaning of the coefficient of multiple determination in this problem.

h. Determine the adjusted r^2.

i. At the 0.05 level of significance, determine whether each independent variable makes a significant contribution to the regression model. Indicate the most appropriate regression model for this set of data.

j. Determine the *p*-values in (i) and interpret their meaning.

k. Construct a 95% confidence interval estimate of the population slope between selling price and assessed value. How does the interpretation of the slope here differ from that in Problem 15.69 on page 698?

16.53 Measuring the height of a California redwood tree is very difficult because these trees grow to heights over 300 feet. People familiar with these trees understand that the height of a California redwood tree is related to other characteristics of the tree, including the diameter of the tree at the breast height of a person (in inches) and the thickness of the bark of the tree (in inches). The file `Redwood` contains the height, diameter at breast height of a person, and bark thickness for a sample of 21 California redwood trees.

a. State the multiple regression equation that predicts the height of a tree, based on the tree's diameter at breast height and the thickness of the bark.

b. Interpret the meaning of the slopes in this equation.

c. Predict the height for a tree that has a breast height diameter of 25 inches and a bark thickness of 2 inches.

d. Interpret the meaning of the coefficient of multiple determination in this problem.

e. Perform a residual analysis on the results and determine whether the regression assumptions are valid.

f. Determine whether there is a significant relationship between the height of redwood trees and the two independent variables (breast-height diameter and bark thickness) at the 0.05 level of significance.

g. Construct a 95% confidence interval estimate of the population slope between the height of redwood trees and breast-height diameter and between the height of redwood trees and the bark thickness.

h. At the 0.05 level of significance, determine whether each independent variable makes a significant contribution to the regression model. Indicate the independent variables to include in this model.

i. Construct a 95% confidence interval estimate of the mean height for trees that have a breast-height diameter of 25 inches and a bark thickness of 2 inches, along with a prediction interval for an individual tree.

16.54 Develop a model to predict the assessed value (in thousands of dollars), using the size of the houses (in thousands of square feet) and the age of the houses (in years) from the following table (stored in `House2`):

House	Assessed Value ($Thousands)	Size of House (Thousands of Square Feet)	Age (Years)
1	184.4	2.00	3.42
2	177.4	1.71	11.50
3	175.7	1.45	8.33
4	185.9	1.76	0.00
5	179.1	1.93	7.42
6	170.4	1.20	32.00
7	175.8	1.55	16.00
8	185.9	1.93	2.00
9	178.5	1.59	1.75
10	179.2	1.50	2.75
11	186.7	1.90	0.00
12	179.3	1.39	0.00
13	174.5	1.54	12.58
14	183.8	1.89	2.75
15	176.8	1.59	7.17

a. State the multiple regression equation.

b. Interpret the meaning of the slopes in this equation.

c. Predict the assessed value for a house that has a size of 1,750 square feet and is 10 years old.

d. Perform a residual analysis on the results and determine whether the regression assumptions are valid.

e. Determine whether there is a significant relationship between assessed value and the two independent variables (size and age) at the 0.05 level of significance.

f. Determine the *p*-value in (e) and interpret its meaning.

g. Interpret the meaning of the coefficient of multiple determination in this problem.

h. Determine the adjusted r^2.

i. At the 0.05 level of significance, determine whether each independent variable makes a significant contribution to the regression model. Indicate the most appropriate regression model for this set of data.

j. Determine the *p*-values in (i) and interpret their meaning.

k. Construct a 95% confidence interval estimate of the population slope between assessed value and size. How does the interpretation of the slope here differ from that of Problem 15.70 on page 699?

l. The real estate assessor's office has been publicly quoted as saying that the age of a house has no bearing on its assessed value. Based on your answers to (a) through (k), do you agree with this statement? Explain.

16.55 A baseball analyst, wants to determine which variables are important in predicting a team's wins in a given season. He has collected data related to wins, earned run average (ERA), and runs scored for the 2010 season (stored in `BB2010`). Develop a model to predict the number of wins based on ERA and runs scored.

a. State the multiple regression equation.

b. Interpret the meaning of the slopes in this equation.

c. Predict the number of wins for a team that has an ERA of 4.50 and has scored 750 runs.

d. Perform a residual analysis on the results and determine whether the regression assumptions are valid.

e. Is there a significant relationship between number of wins and the two independent variables (ERA and runs scored) at the 0.05 level of significance?

f. Determine the p-value in (e) and interpret its meaning.

g. Interpret the meaning of the coefficient of multiple determination in this problem.

h. Determine the adjusted r^2.

i. At the 0.05 level of significance, determine whether each independent variable makes a significant contribution to the regression model. Indicate the most appropriate regression model for this set of data.

j. Determine the p-values in (i) and interpret their meaning.

k. Construct a 95% confidence interval estimate of the population slope between wins and ERA.

l. Which is more important in predicting wins—pitching, as measured by ERA, or offense, as measured by runs scored? Explain.

16.56 Referring to Problem 16.55, suppose that in addition to using ERA to predict the number of wins, Crazy Dave wants to include the league (0 = American, 1 = National) as an independent variable. Develop a model to predict wins based on ERA and league. For (a) through (j), do not include an interaction term.

a. State the multiple regression equation.

b. Interpret the slopes in (a).

c. Predict the number of wins for a team with an ERA of 4.50 in the American League. Construct a 95% confidence interval estimate for all teams and a 95% prediction interval for an individual team.

d. Perform a residual analysis on the results and determine whether the regression assumptions are valid.

e. Is there a significant relationship between wins and the two independent variables (ERA and league) at the 0.05 level of significance?

f. At the 0.05 level of significance, determine whether each independent variable makes a contribution to the regression model. Indicate the most appropriate regression model for this set of data.

g. Construct a 95% confidence interval estimate of the population slope for the relationship between wins and ERA.

h. Construct a 95% confidence interval estimate of the population slope for the relationship between wins and league.

i. Compute and interpret the adjusted r^2.

j. What assumption do you have to make about the slope of wins with ERA?

k. Add an interaction term to the model and, at the 0.05 level of significance, determine whether it makes a significant contribution to the model.

l. On the basis of the results of (f) and (k), which model is most appropriate? Explain.

16.57 You are a real estate broker who wants to compare property values in Glen Cove and Roslyn (which are located approximately 8 miles apart). In order to do so, you will analyze the data in GCRoslyn , a file that includes samples of houses from Glen Cove and Roslyn. Making sure to include the dummy variable for location (Glen Cove or Roslyn), develop a regression model to predict appraised value, based on the land area of a property, the age of a house, and location. Be sure to determine whether any interaction terms need to be included in the model.

16.58 A recent article discussed a metal deposition process in which a piece of metal is placed in an acid bath and an alloy is layered on top of it. The business objective of engineers working on the process was to reduce variation in the thickness of the alloy layer. To begin, the temperature and the pressure in the tank holding the acid bath are to be studied as independent variables. Data are collected from 50 samples. The results are organized and stored in Thickness . (Data extracted from J. Conklin, "It's a Marathon, Not a Sprint," *Quality Progress*, June 2009, pp. 46–49.)

Develop a multiple regression model that uses temperature and the pressure in the tank holding the acid bath to predict the thickness of the alloy layer. Be sure to perform a thorough residual analysis. The article suggests that there is a significant interaction between the pressure and the temperature in the tank. Do you agree?

16.59 Starbucks Coffee Co. uses a data-based approach to improving the quality and customer satisfaction of its products. When survey data indicated that Starbucks needed to improve its package sealing process, an experiment was conducted (data extracted from L. Johnson and S. Burrows, "For Starbucks, It's In the Bag," *Quality Progress*, March 2011, pp. 17–23) to determine the factors in the bag-sealing equipment that might be affecting the ease of opening the bag without tearing the inner liner of the bag. Among the factors that could affect the rating of the ability of the bag to resist tears were the viscosity, pressure, and plate gap on the bag-sealing equipment. Data was collected on 19 bags in which the plate gap was varied. The results are stored in the file Starbucks . Develop a multiple regression model that uses the viscosity, pressure, and plate gap on the bag-sealing equipment to predict the tear rating of the bag. Be sure to perform a thorough residual analysis. Do you think that you need to use all three independent variables in the model? Explain.

MANAGING ASHLAND MULTICOMM SERVICES

In its continuing study of the *3-For-All* subscription solicitation process, a marketing department team wants to test the effects of two types of structured sales presentations (personal formal and personal informal) and the number of hours spent on telemarketing on the number of new subscriptions. The staff has recorded these data in the file **AMS13** for the past 24 weeks.

Analyze these data and develop a multiple regression model to predict the number of new subscriptions for a week, based on the number of hours spent on telemarketing and the sales presentation type. Write a report, giving detailed findings concerning the regression model used.

DIGITAL CASE

Apply your knowledge of multiple regression models in this Digital Case, which extends the OmniFoods Using Statistics scenario from this chapter.

To ensure a successful test marketing of its OmniPower energy bars, the OmniFoods marketing department has contracted with In-Store Placements Group (ISPG), a merchandising consultancy. ISPG will work with the grocery store chain that is conducting the test-market study. Using the same 34-store sample used in the test-market study, ISPG claims that the choice of shelf location and the presence of in-store OmniPower coupon dispensers both increase sales of the energy bars.

Open **Omni_ISPGMemo.pdf** to review the ISPG claims and supporting data. Then answer the following questions:

1. Are the supporting data consistent with ISPG's claims? Perform an appropriate statistical analysis to confirm (or discredit) the stated relationship between sales and the two independent variables of product shelf location and the presence of in-store OmniPower coupon dispensers.

2. If you were advising OmniFoods, would you recommend using a specific shelf location and in-store coupon dispensers to sell OmniPower bars?

3. What additional data would you advise collecting in order to determine the effectiveness of the sales promotion techniques used by ISPG?

REFERENCES

1. Hosmer, D. W., and S. Lemeshow, *Applied Logistic Regression*, 2nd ed. (New York: Wiley, 2001).
2. Kutner, M., C. Nachtsheim, J. Neter, and W. Li, *Applied Linear Statistical Models*, 5th ed. (New York: McGraw-Hill/Irwin, 2005).
3. *Microsoft Excel 2010* (Redmond, WA: Microsoft Corp., 2010).
4. *Minitab Release 16* (State College, PA: Minitab, Inc., 2010).

SPSS—Version 16—Multiple Regression

Suppose the professor wanted to develop a model to predict the students' marks at the end of the QMS 202 course as measured in percentage based on how frequently they missed class, number of problems solved, total hours spent studying, and how frequently they sought help from the teaching assistant.

The dependent variable, Y, is the final QMS 202 marks (in percentage). Three independent variables are the following:

- Number of lectures missed during the semester (X_1)
- Total number of problems solved (X_2)
- Total hours spent per week studying for QMS 202 (X_3)
- Total number of times the student sought the teaching assistant's help (X_4)

A random sample of 35 students who enrolled in the QMS 202 course was selected with the results shown in Table 16.4.

TABLE 16.4

Data for Multiple Regression Model to Predict QMS202 Marks

Student	y = QMS 202 Marks	X1 = Number of lectures missed during the semester	X2 = Total number of problems solved	X3 = Total hours spent studying for QMS 202	X4 = Total number of times the student sought the teaching assistant's help
1	90	0	100	24.2	11
2	60	5	20	5.3	2
3	45	9	5	1.2	0
4	85	1	50	11.5	5
5	72	3	45	8.6	6
6	96	1	110	22.3	12
7	50	6	10	3.5	4
8	65	3	34	7.8	5
9	87	2	78	10.4	11
10	88	1	77	11.6	10
11	78	2	50	9.2	8
12	73	3	49	10.3	10
13	59	5	22	6.4	4
14	49	7	6	2.6	0
15	94	0	110	25.4	12
16	55	4	21	4.5	5
17	52	5	20	5.8	3
18	63	3	40	8.9	4

19	51	6	20	4.0	3
20	93	1	107	19.1	12
21	50	7	15	3.3	5
22	65	4	30	6.4	4
23	87	1	80	11.6	12
24	88	0	87	12.2	11
25	78	1	55	10.1	9
26	73	4	51	14.2	11
27	56	6	30	5.5	3
28	44	9	3	1.6	0
29	95	0	115	23.8	12
30	56	7	27	3.9	4
31	52	6	24	3.4	5
32	63	5	46	5.5	2
33	56	8	23	3.7	1
34	98	0	150	23.8	12
35	71	1	48	3.9	6

Performing a multiple regression on SPSS—Version 16

Step 1: Open the SPSS Data Editor.

Click **cancel** to cancel the SPSS opening window.

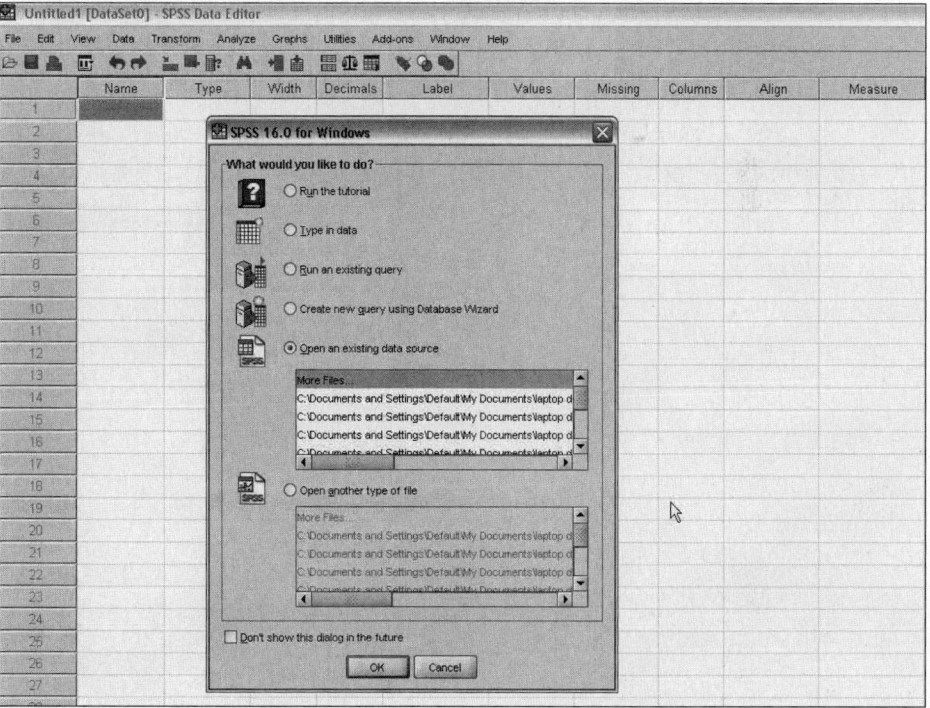

Step 2: Define the variables and give the variables a label.

Click **Variable View** (at the bottom of the window) to go to the variable view window to define the variables and fix the data at zero or one decimal places.

- Give variable name—"student" to trace the respondent's responses if there is a data entry error.

- Give variable name—"y" and label it as "QMS 202 Marks."

- Give variable name—"x1" and label it as "Number of lectures missed during the semester."

- Give variable name—"x2" and label it as "Total number of problems solved."

- Give variable name—"x3" and label it as "Total hours spent studying for QMS 202."

- Give variable name—"x4" and label it as "Total number of times the student seeks the teaching assistant's help."

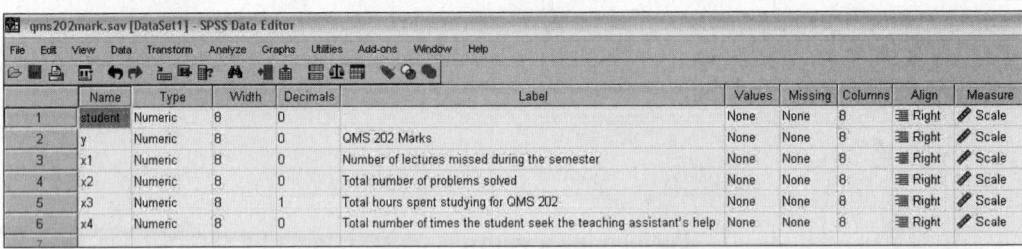

	Name	Type	Width	Decimals	Label	Values	Missing	Columns	Align	Measure
1	student	Numeric	8	0		None	None	8	Right	Scale
2	y	Numeric	8	0	QMS 202 Marks	None	None	8	Right	Scale
3	x1	Numeric	8	0	Number of lectures missed during the semester	None	None	8	Right	Scale
4	x2	Numeric	8	0	Total number of problems solved	None	None	8	Right	Scale
5	x3	Numeric	8	1	Total hours spent studying for QMS 202	None	None	8	Right	Scale
6	x4	Numeric	8	0	Total number of times the student seek the teaching assistant's help	None	None	8	Right	Scale
7										

Step 3: Create an SPSS data file.

Click **Data View** to return to the data view window. Now, enter the raw data (in Table 16.4) into the appropriate columns of variables.

	student	y	x1	x2	x3	x4
1	1	90	0	100	24.2	11
2	2	60	5	20	5.3	2
3	3	45	9	5	1.2	0
4	4	85	1	50	11.5	5
5	5	72	3	45	8.6	6
6	6	96	1	110	22.3	12
7	7	50	6	10	3.5	4
8	8	65	3	34	7.8	5
9	9	87	2	78	10.4	11
10	10	88	1	77	11.6	10
11	11	78	2	50	9.2	8
12	12	73	3	49	10.3	10
13	13	59	5	22	6.4	4
14	14	49	7	6	2.6	0
15	15	94	0	110	25.4	12
16	16	55	4	21	4.5	5
17	17	52	5	20	5.8	3
18	18	63	3	40	8.9	4
19	19	51	6	20	4.0	3
20	20	93	1	107	19.1	12
21	21	50	7	15	3.3	5
22	22	65	4	30	6.4	4
23	23	87	1	80	11.6	12
24	24	88	0	87	12.2	11
25	25	78	1	55	10.1	9
26	26	73	4	51	14.2	11
27	27	56	6	30	5.5	3
28	28	44	9	3	1.6	0
29	29	95	0	115	23.8	12
30	30	56	7	27	3.9	4
31	31	52	6	24	3.4	5

After you have entered all the data, save the file as "qms202mark.sav" (or any filename).

Step 4: Perform regression analysis.

Make the following menu selections:

Analyze → Regression → Linear

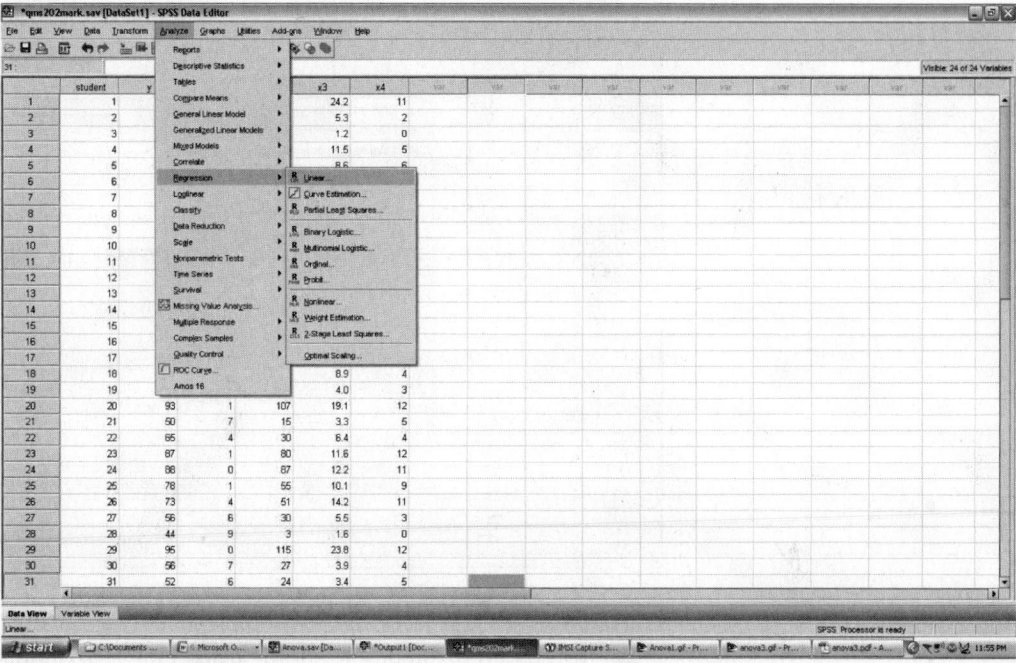

At this point, the **Linear Regression** dialog box will appear. Make these entries in the **Linear Regression** dialog box:

- Highlight the **QMS 202 Marks** variable and click the arrow key. The variable will automatically fall into the **Dependent** box (→).

- Highlight each x_1, x_2, x_3, and x_4 variable and click the arrow key. The variable will fall into the **Independent(s)** box (→).

- Click the **Enter** button next to the **Method.** Select **stepwise** as the method to develop several multiple regression models.

Note: The **Stepwise** method uses a step-by-step algorithm that starts building a regression model with one independent variable. At each step the algorithm checks to see if any of the variables (already included in the model) can be removed and adds a variable (not yet included in the model) by examining the fit of the model. The algorithm stops when there are no more significant independent variables to be considered.

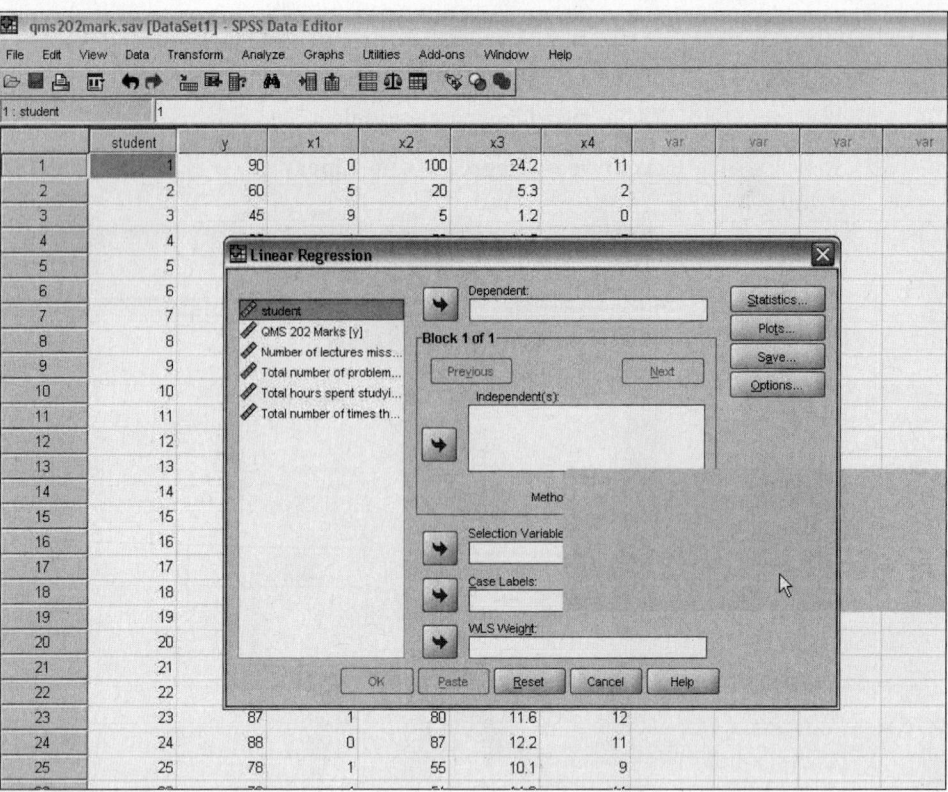

- *Obtaining Predictions and Residuals*   Click the save button (note that **Save** is a button on the pop-up menu and is not the usual File save option) and the **save** dialog box will pop up. In the **save** dialog box, click on **Unstandardized** in the the **Predicted Values** box. Click on **Unstandardized** in the **Residuals** box. Click on **Mean** and **Individual** in the **Prediction Intervals** box. Click on **Continue** to return to the **Linear Regression** dialog box. Then click **OK.**

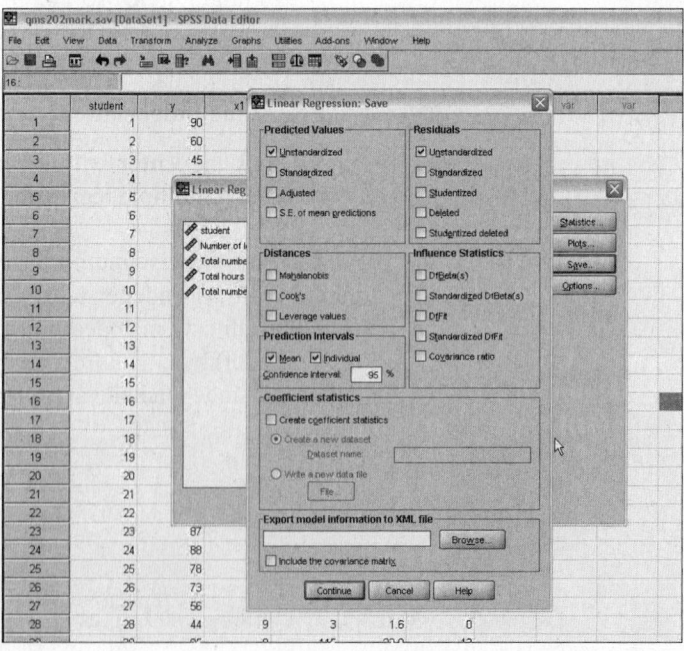

Step 5: Go to SPSS Viewer to obtain your SPSS results.

SPSS output:
Regression

							Model Summary[c]
Model	R	R Square	Adjusted R Square	Std. Error of the Estimate
1	.948[a]	.898	.895	5.541
2	.975[b]	.952	.949	3.874

a. *Predictors: (Constant), Total number of problems solved*
b. *Predictors: (Constant), Total number of problems solved, Number of lectures missed during the semester*
c. *Dependent Variable: QMS 202 Marks*

ANOVA[c]

Model		Sum of Squares	df	Mean Square	F	Sig.
1	Regression	8906.850	1	8906.850	290.062	.000[a]
	Residual	1013.322	33	30.707		
	Total	9920.171	34			
2	Regression	9439.916	2	4719.958	314.497	.000[b]
	Residual	480.255	32	15.008		
	Total	9920.171	34			

a. *Predictors: (Constant), Total number of problems solved*
b. *Predictors: (Constant), Total number of problems solved, Number of lectures missed during the semester*
c. *Dependent Variable: QMS 202 Marks*

Coefficients[a]

Model		Unstandardized Coefficients B	Std. Error	Standardized Coefficients Beta	t	Sig.
1	(Constant)	47.864	1.584		30.208	.000
	Total number of problems solved	.433	.025	.948	17.031	.000
2	(Constant)	66.176	3.266		20.261	.000
	Total number of problems solved	.262	.034	.574	7.781	.000
	Number of lectures missed during the semester	−2.703	.454	−.440	−5.960	.000

a. *Dependent Variable: QMS 202 Marks*

Obtaining Predictions and Residuals

The confidence interval values and prediction interval values are displayed on the **SPSS Data Editor** under the variables PRE_1, RES_1, LMCI_1, UMCI_1, LICI_1 and UICI_1.

Notation:

PRE_1—Unstandardized Predicted (for Model 1)

RES_1—Unstandardized Residual (for Model 1)

LMCI_1—95% Lower Confidence Interval for y mean (for Model 1)

UMCI_1—95% Upper Confidence Interval for y mean (for Model 1)

LICI_1—95% Lower Confidence Interval for y individual (for Model 1)

UICI_1—5% Upper Confidence Interval for y individual (for Model 1)

	student	y	x1	x2	x3	x4	PRE_1	RES_1	LMCI_1	UMCI_1	LICI_1	UICI_1
1	1	90	0	100	24.2	11	92.42439	-2.42439	90.14242	94.70635	84.20995	100.63882
2	2	60	5	20	5.3	2	57.90953	2.09047	56.12041	59.69865	49.81814	66.00091
3	3	45	9	5	1.2	0	43.15942	1.84058	40.00047	46.31836	34.65951	51.65933
4	4	85	1	50	11.5	5	76.59692	8.40308	73.83760	79.35623	68.23729	84.95654
5	5	72	3	45	8.6	6	69.87807	2.12193	68.27996	71.47619	61.82677	77.92938
6	6	96	1	110	22.3	12	92.34603	3.65397	89.57978	95.11228	83.98411	100.70795
7	7	50	6	10	3.5	4	52.58147	-2.58147	50.60136	54.56157	44.44572	60.71721
8	8	65	3	34	7.8	5	66.99074	-1.99074	64.89777	69.08370	58.82679	75.15468
9	9	87	2	78	10.4	11	81.24329	5.75671	79.56637	82.92022	73.17598	89.31061
10	10	88	1	77	11.6	10	83.68402	4.31598	81.83363	85.53440	75.57887	91.78917
11	11	78	2	50	9.2	8	73.89371	4.10629	71.89270	75.89472	65.75285	82.03457
12	12	73	3	49	10.3	10	70.92801	2.07199	69.45388	72.40215	62.90040	78.95663
13	13	59	5	22	6.4	4	58.43450	0.56550	56.71665	60.15234	50.35857	66.51042
14	14	49	7	6	2.6	0	48.82832	0.17168	46.66977	50.98687	40.64731	57.00933
15	15	94	0	110	25.4	12	95.04924	-1.04924	92.50056	97.59792	86.75675	103.34172
16	16	55	4	21	4.5	5	60.87522	-5.87522	58.70999	63.04045	52.69245	69.05799
17	17	52	5	20	5.8	3	57.90953	-5.90953	56.12041	59.69865	49.81814	66.00091
18	18	63	3	40	8.9	4	68.56565	-5.56565	66.76493	70.36636	60.47169	76.65960
19	19	51	6	20	4.0	3	55.20632	-4.20632	53.42214	56.99050	47.11603	63.29661
20	20	93	1	107	19.1	12	91.55857	1.44143	88.94270	94.17445	83.24519	99.87196
21	21	50	7	15	3.3	5	51.19068	-1.19068	49.04963	53.33174	43.01428	59.36709
22	22	65	4	30	6.4	4	63.23759	1.76241	61.51281	64.96237	55.16019	71.31499
23	23	87	1	80	11.6	12	84.47147	2.52853	82.63208	86.31086	76.36882	92.57412
24	24	88	0	87	12.2	11	89.01208	-1.01208	86.78851	91.23565	80.81367	97.21048
25	25	78	1	55	10.1	9	77.90934	0.09066	75.39568	80.42301	69.62755	86.19113
26	26	73	4	51	14.2	11	68.74978	4.25022	67.35271	70.14685	60.73595	76.76360
27	27	56	6	30	5.5	3	57.83117	-1.83117	55.98994	59.67241	49.72810	65.93424
28	28	44	9	3	1.6	0	42.63445	1.36555	39.52208	45.74682	34.15173	51.11716
29	29	95	0	115	23.8	12	96.36166	-1.36166	93.62413	99.09920	88.00920	104.71413
30	30	56	7	27	3.9	4	54.34051	1.65949	51.95856	56.72246	46.09774	62.58328
31	31	52	6	24	3.4	5	56.25626	-4.25626	54.48067	58.03185	48.16786	64.34466

CHAPTER 16 EXCEL GUIDE

EG16.1 Developing a Multiple Regression Model

Interpreting the Regression Coefficients

PHStat2 Use **Multiple Regression** to perform a multiple regression analysis. For example, to perform the Figure 16.2 analysis of the OmniPower sales data on page 708, open to the **DATA worksheet** of the **OmniPower workbook**. Select **PHStat → Regression → Multiple Regression**, and in the procedure's dialog box (shown below):

1. Enter **A1:A35** as the **Y Variable Cell Range**.
2. Enter **B1:C35** as the **X Variables Cell Range**.
3. Check **First cells in both ranges contain label**.
4. Enter **95** as the **Confidence level for regression coefficients**.
5. Check **Regression Statistics Table** and **ANOVA and Coefficients Table**.
6. Enter a **Title** and click **OK**.

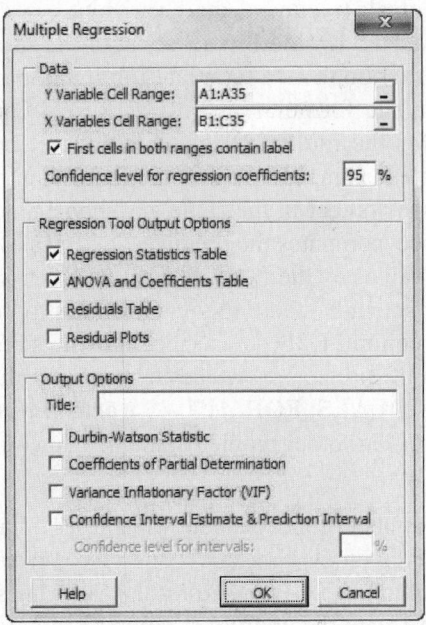

The procedure creates a worksheet that contains a copy of your data in addition to the regression results worksheet shown in Figure 16.2. For more information about these worksheets, read the following *In-Depth Excel* section.

In-Depth Excel Use the **COMPUTE worksheet** of the **Multiple Regression workbook**, partially shown in

Figure 16.2 on page 708, as a template for performing multiple regression. Columns A through I of this worksheet duplicate the visual design of the Analysis ToolPak regression worksheet. The worksheet uses the regression data in the **MRData worksheet** to perform the regression analysis for the OmniPower sales data.

Figure 16.2 does not show the columns K through N Calculations area. This area contains a **LINEST(*cell range of Y variable, cell range of X variable,* True, True)** array formula in the cell range L2:N6 and calculations for the *t* test of the slope (see Section 15.6 on page 666). The array formula computes the b_2, b_1, and b_0 coefficients in cells L2, M2, and N2; the b_2, b_1, and b_0 standard error in cells L3, M3, and N3; r^2 and the standard error of the estimate in cells L4 and M4; the *F* test statistic and error *df* in cells L5 and M5; and *SSR* and *SSE* in cells L6 and M6. (The rest of the cell range, N4, N5, and N6, displays the **#N/A** message. This is not an error.)

Open to the **COMPUTE_FORMULAS worksheet** to examine all the formulas in the worksheet.

To perform multiple regression analyses for other data, paste the regression data into the MRData worksheet. Paste the values for the *Y* variable into column A. Paste the values for the *X* variables into consecutive columns, starting with column B. Then, open to the COMPUTE worksheet and enter the confidence level in cell L8. Select the area to hold the array formula. The current array formula is in 5-row-by-3-column range of cells that starts with cell L2. If you have more than two independent variables, extend this range, adding a column for each independent variable in excess of two. For example, for three independent variables, select the 5-row-by-4-column range that starts with cell L2. Adjust the array formula, and then, while holding down the **Control** and **Shift** keys (or the **Apple** key on a Mac), press the **Enter** key.

Analysis ToolPak Use **Regression** to perform a multiple regression analysis. For example, to perform the Figure 16.2 analysis of the OmniPower sales data on page 708, open to the **DATA worksheet** of the **OmniPower workbook** and:

1. Select **Data → Data Analysis**.
2. In the Data Analysis dialog box, select **Regression** from the **Analysis Tools** list and then click **OK**.

In the Regression dialog box (shown on page 778):

3. Enter **A1:A35** as the **Input Y Range** and enter **B1:C35** as the **Input X Range**.
4. Check **Labels** and check **Confidence Level** and enter **95** in its box.

5. Click **New Worksheet Ply**.
6. Click **OK**.

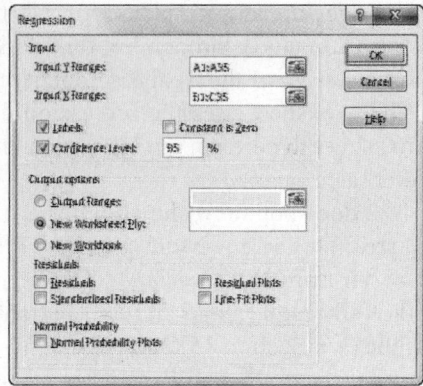

Predicting the Dependent Variable Y

PHStat2 Use the "Interpreting the Regression Coefficients" *PHStat2* instructions but replace step 6 with the following steps 6 through 8:

6. Check **Confidence Interval Estimate & Prediction Interval** and enter **95** as the percentage for **Confidence level for intervals**.
7. Enter a **Title** and click **OK**.
8. In the new worksheet, enter **79** in cell **B6** and enter **400** in cell **B7**.

These steps create a new worksheet that is discussed in the following *In-Depth Excel* instructions.

In-Depth Excel Use the **CIEandPI** worksheet of the **Multiple Regression workbook**, shown in Figure 16.3 on page 710, as a template for computing confidence interval estimates and prediction intervals for a multiple regression model with two independent variables. The worksheet contains the data and formulas for the OmniPower sales example shown in Figure 16.3. The worksheet uses several array formulas to use functions that perform matrix operations to compute the matrix product X'X (in cell range B9:D11), the inverse of the X'X matrix (in cell range B13:D15), the product of X'G multiplied by the inverse of X'X (in cell range B17:D17), and the predicted Y (in cell B21). (Open to the **CIEandPI_FORMULAS worksheet** to examine all formulas.)

Modifying this worksheet for other models with more than two independent variables requires knowledge that is beyond the scope of this book. For other models with two independent variables, paste the data for those variables into columns B and C of the **MRArray worksheet** and adjust the number of entries in column A (all of which are **1**). Then open to the COMPUTE worksheet and edit the array formula in cell range B9:D11 and edit the labels in cells A6 and A7.

EG16.2 R^2, Adjusted R^2, and the Overall F Test

The coefficient of multiple determination, R^2, the adjusted R^2, and the overall F test are all computed as part of creating the multiple regression results worksheet using the Section EG16.1 instructions. If you use either the *PHStat2* or *In-Depth Excel* instructions, formulas are used to compute these results in the **COMPUTE worksheet**. Formulas in cells B5, B7, B13, C12, C13, D12, and E12 copy values computed by an array formula in cell range L2:N6 and in cell F12, the expression **FDIST(F test statistic, 1, error degrees of freedom)** computes the p-value for the overall F test.

EG16.3 Residual Analysis for the Multiple Regression Model

PHStat2 Use the Section EG16.1 "Interpreting the Regression Coefficients" *PHStat2* instructions. Modify step 5 by checking **Residuals Table** and **Residual Plots** in addition to checking **Regression Statistics Table** and **ANOVA and Coefficients Table**.

In-Depth Excel Create a worksheet that calculates residuals and then create a scatter plot of the original X variable and the residuals (plotted as the Y variable).

Use the **RESIDUALS worksheet** of the **Multiple Regression workbook** as a template for creating a residuals worksheet. The formulas in this worksheet compute the residuals for the multiple regression model for the OmniPower sales example by using the regression data in the **MRData worksheet** in the same workbook. In column D, the worksheet computes the predicted Y values by multiplying the X_1 values by the b_1 coefficient and the X_2 values by the b_2 coefficient and adding these products to the b_0 coefficient. In column F, the worksheet computes residuals by subtracting the predicted Y values from the Y values. (Open to the **RESIDUALS_FORMULAS worksheet** to examine all formulas.) For other problems, modify this worksheet as follows:

1. If the number of independent variables is greater than 2, select column D, right-click, and click **Insert** from the shortcut menu. Repeat this step as many times as necessary to create the additional columns to hold all the X variables.
2. Paste the data for the X variables into columns, starting with column B.
3. Paste Y values in column E (or in the second-to-last column if there are more than two X variables).
4. For sample sizes smaller than 34, delete the extra rows. For sample sizes greater than 34, copy the predicted Y and residuals formulas down through the row containing the last pair of X and Y values. Also, add the new observation numbers in column A.

To create residual plots, use copy-and-paste special values (see Appendix Section F.6) to paste data values on a new worksheet in the proper order before applying the Section EG2.6 scatter plot instructions.

Analysis ToolPak Use the Section EG16.1 *Analysis Tool-Pak* instructions. Modify step 5 by checking **Residuals** and **Residual Plots** before clicking **New Worksheet Ply** and then **OK**. (Note that the **Residuals Plots** option creates residual plots only for each independent variable.)

EG16.4 Inferences Concerning the Population Regression Coefficients

The regression results worksheets created by using the EG16.1 instructions include the information needed to make the inferences discussed in Section 16.4.

EG16.5 Using Dummy Variables and Interaction Terms in Regression Models

Dummy Variables

Use **Find and Replace** to create a dummy variable from a two-level categorical variable. Before using **Find and Replace**, copy and paste the categorical values to another column in order to preserve the original values.

For example, to create a dummy variable named FireplaceCoded from the two-level categorical variable Fire-place as shown in Table 16.3 on page 730, open to the **DATA worksheet** of the **House3 workbook** and:

1. Copy and paste the **Fireplace** values in column **C** to column D (the first empty column).
2. Select column **D**.
3. Press **Ctrl+H** (the keyboard shortcut for **Find and Replace**).

In the Find and Replace dialog box:

4. Enter **Yes** in the **Find what** box and enter **1** in the **Replace with** box.
5. Click **Replace All**. If a message box to confirm the replacement appears, click **OK** to continue.
6. Enter **No** in the **Find what** box and enter **0** in the **Replace with** box.
7. Click **Replace All**. If a message box to confirm the replacement appears, click **OK** to continue.
8. Click **Close**.

Interactions

To create an interaction term, add a column of formulas that multiply one independent variable by another. For example, if the first independent variable appeared in column B and the second independent variable appeared in column C, enter the formula = **B2** * **C2** in the row 2 cell of an empty new column and then copy the formula down through all rows of data to create the interaction.

Appendices

A.1 Rules for Arithmetic Operations

RULE	EXAMPLE
1. $a + b = c$ and $b + a = c$	$2 + 1 = 3$ and $1 + 2 = 3$
2. $a + (b + c) = (a + b) + c$	$5 + (7 + 4) = (5 + 7) + 4 = 16$
3. $a - b = c$ but $b - a \neq c$	$9 - 7 = 2$ but $7 - 9 \neq 2$
4. $(a)(b) = (b)(a)$	$(7)(6) = (6)(7) = 42$
5. $(a)(b + c) = ab + ac$	$(2)(3 + 5) = (2)(3) + (2)(5) = 16$
6. $a \div b \neq b \div a$	$12 \div 3 \neq 3 \div 12$
7. $\dfrac{a + b}{c} = \dfrac{a}{c} + \dfrac{b}{c}$	$\dfrac{7 + 3}{2} = \dfrac{7}{2} + \dfrac{3}{2} = 5$
8. $\dfrac{a}{b + c} \neq \dfrac{a}{b} + \dfrac{a}{c}$	$\dfrac{3}{4 + 5} \neq \dfrac{3}{4} + \dfrac{3}{5}$
9. $\dfrac{1}{a} + \dfrac{1}{b} = \dfrac{b + a}{ab}$	$\dfrac{1}{3} + \dfrac{1}{5} = \dfrac{5 + 3}{(3)(5)} = \dfrac{8}{15}$
10. $\left(\dfrac{a}{b}\right)\left(\dfrac{c}{d}\right) = \left(\dfrac{ac}{bd}\right)$	$\left(\dfrac{2}{3}\right)\left(\dfrac{6}{7}\right) = \left(\dfrac{(2)(6)}{(3)(7)}\right) = \dfrac{12}{21}$
11. $\dfrac{a}{b} \div \dfrac{c}{d} = \dfrac{ad}{bc}$	$\dfrac{5}{8} \div \dfrac{3}{7} = \left(\dfrac{(5)(7)}{(8)(3)}\right) = \dfrac{35}{24}$

A.2 Rules for Algebra: Exponents and Square Roots

RULE	EXAMPLE
1. $(X^a)(X^b) = X^{a+b}$	$(4^2)(4^3) = 4^5$
2. $(X^a)^b = X^{ab}$	$(2^2)^3 = 2^6$
3. $(X^a/X^b) = X^{a-b}$	$\dfrac{3^5}{3^3} = 3^2$
4. $\dfrac{X^a}{X^a} = X^0 = 1$	$\dfrac{3^4}{3^4} = 3^0 = 1$
5. $\sqrt{XY} = \sqrt{X}\sqrt{Y}$	$\sqrt{(25)(4)} = \sqrt{25}\sqrt{4} = 10$
6. $\sqrt{\dfrac{X}{Y}} = \dfrac{\sqrt{X}}{\sqrt{Y}}$	$\sqrt{\dfrac{16}{100}} = \dfrac{\sqrt{16}}{\sqrt{100}} = 0.40$

A.3 Rules for Logarithms

Base 10

Log is the symbol used for base-10 logarithms:

RULE	EXAMPLE
1. $\log(10^a) = a$	$\log(100) = \log(10^2) = 2$
2. If $\log(a) = b$, then $a = 10^b$	If $\log(a) = 2$, then $a = 10^2 = 100$
3. $\log(ab) = \log(a) + \log(b)$	$\log(100) = \log[(10)(10)] = \log(10) + \log(10)$
	$= 1 + 1 = 2$
4. $\log(a^b) = (b)\log(a)$	$\log(1{,}000) = \log(10^3) = (3)\log(10) = (3)(1) = 3$
5. $\log(a/b) = \log(a) - \log(b)$	$\log(100) = \log(1{,}000/10) = \log(1{,}000) - \log(10)$
	$= 3 - 1 = 2$

EXAMPLE

Take the base-10 logarithm of each side of the following equation:

$$Y = \beta_0 \beta_1^X \varepsilon$$

SOLUTION: Apply rules 3 and 4:

$$\log(Y) = \log(\beta_0 \beta_1^X \varepsilon)$$
$$= \log(\beta_0) + \log(\beta_1^X) + \log(\varepsilon)$$
$$= \log(\beta_0) + X\log(\beta_1) + \log(\varepsilon)$$

Base e

ln is the symbol used for base e logarithms, commonly referred to as natural logarithms. e is Euler's number, and $e \cong 2.718282$:

RULE	EXAMPLE
1. $\ln(e^a) = a$	$\ln(7.389056) = \ln(e^2) = 2$
2. If $\ln(a) = b$, then $a = e^b$	If $\ln(a) = 2$, then $a = e^2 = 7.389056$
3. $\ln(ab) = \ln(a) + \ln(b)$	$\ln(100) = \ln[(10)(10)]$
	$= \ln(10) + \ln(10) = 2.302585 + 2.302585 = 4.605170$
4. $\ln(a^b) = (b)\ln(a)$	$\ln(1{,}000) = \ln(10^3) = 3\ln(10) = 3(2.302585) = 6.907755$
5. $\ln(a/b) = \ln(a) - \ln(b)$	$\ln(100) = \ln(1{,}000/10) = \ln(1{,}000) - \ln(10)$
	$= 6.907755 - 2.302585 = 4.605170$

EXAMPLE

Take the base e logarithm of each side of the following equation:

$$Y = \beta_0 \beta_1^X \varepsilon$$

SOLUTION: Apply rules 3 and 4:

$$\ln(Y) = \ln(\beta_0 \beta_1^X \varepsilon)$$
$$= \ln(\beta_0) + \ln(\beta_1^X) + \ln(\varepsilon)$$
$$= \ln(\beta_0) + X\ln(\beta_1) + \ln(\varepsilon)$$

A.4 Summation Notation

The symbol Σ, the Greek capital letter sigma, represents "taking the sum of." Consider a set of n values for variable X. The expression $\sum_{i=1}^{n} X_i$ means to take the sum of the n values for variable X. Thus:

$$\sum_{i=1}^{n} X_i = X_1 + X_2 + X_3 + \cdots + X_n$$

The following problem illustrates the use of the symbol Σ. Consider five values of a variable X: $X_1 = 2, X_2 = 0, X_3 = -1, X_4 = 5$, and $X_5 = 7$. Thus:

$$\sum_{i=1}^{5} X_i = X_1 + X_2 + X_3 + X_4 + X_5 = 2 + 0 + (-1) + 5 + 7 = 13$$

In statistics, the squared values of a variable are often summed. Thus:

$$\sum_{i=1}^{n} X_i^2 = X_1^2 + X_2^2 + X_3^2 + \cdots + X_n^2$$

and, in the example above:

$$\sum_{i=1}^{5} X_i^2 = X_1^2 + X_2^2 + X_3^2 + X_4^2 + X_5^2$$

$$= 2^2 + 0^2 + (-1)^2 + 5^2 + 7^2$$

$$= 4 + 0 + 1 + 25 + 49$$

$$= 79$$

$\sum_{i=1}^{n} X_i^2$, the summation of the squares, is *not* the same as $\left(\sum_{i=1}^{n} X_i \right)^2$, the square of the sum:

$$\sum_{i=1}^{n} X_i^2 \neq \left(\sum_{i=1}^{n} X_i \right)^2$$

In the example given above, the summation of squares is equal to 79. This is not equal to the square of the sum, which is $13^2 = 169$.

Another frequently used operation involves the summation of the product. Consider two variables, X and Y, each having n values. Then:

$$\sum_{i=1}^{n} X_i Y_i = X_1 Y_1 + X_2 Y_2 + X_3 Y_3 + \cdots + X_n Y_n$$

Continuing with the previous example, suppose there is a second variable, Y, whose five values are $Y_1 = 1, Y_2 = 3, Y_3 = -2, Y_4 = 4$, and $Y_5 = 3$. Then,

$$\sum_{i=1}^{n} X_i Y_i = X_1 Y_1 + X_2 Y_2 + X_3 Y_3 + X_4 Y_4 + X_5 Y_5$$

$$= (2)(1) + (0)(3) + (-1)(-2) + (5)(4) + (7)(3)$$

$$= 2 + 0 + 2 + 20 + 21$$

$$= 45$$

In computing $\sum\limits_{i=1}^{n} X_i Y_i$, you need to realize that the first value of X is multiplied by the first value of Y, the second value of X is multiplied by the second value of Y, and so on. These products are then summed in order to compute the desired result. However, the summation of products is *not* equal to the product of the individual sums:

$$\sum_{i=1}^{n} X_i Y_i \neq \left(\sum_{i=1}^{n} X_i \right) \left(\sum_{i=1}^{n} Y_i \right)$$

In this example,

$$\sum_{i=1}^{5} X_i = 13$$

and

$$\sum_{i=1}^{5} Y_i = 1 + 3 + (-2) + 4 + 3 = 9$$

so that

$$\left(\sum_{i=1}^{5} X_i \right) \left(\sum_{i=1}^{5} Y_i \right) = (13)(9) = 117$$

However,

$$\sum_{i=1}^{5} X_i Y_i = 45$$

The following table summarizes these results:

VALUE	X_i	Y_i	$X_i Y_i$
1	2	1	2
2	0	3	0
3	−1	−2	2
4	5	4	20
5	7	3	21
	$\sum\limits_{i=1}^{5} X_i = 13$	$\sum\limits_{i=1}^{5} Y_i = 9$	$\sum\limits_{i=1}^{5} X_i Y_i = 45$

Rule 1 The summation of the values of two variables is equal to the sum of the values of each summed variable:

$$\sum_{i=1}^{n} (X_i + Y_i) = \sum_{i=1}^{n} X_i + \sum_{i=1}^{n} Y_i$$

Thus,

$$\sum_{i=1}^{5} (X_i + Y_i) = (2 + 1) + (0 + 3) + (-1 + (-2)) + (5 + 4) + (7 + 3)$$

$$= 3 + 3 + (-3) + 9 + 10$$

$$= 22$$

$$\sum_{i=1}^{5} X_i + \sum_{i=1}^{5} Y_i = 13 + 9 = 22$$

Rule 2   The summation of a difference between the values of two variables is equal to the difference between the summed values of the variables:

$$\sum_{i=1}^{n}(X_i - Y_i) = \sum_{i=1}^{n}X_i - \sum_{i=1}^{n}Y_i$$

Thus,

$$\sum_{i=1}^{5}(X_i - Y_i) = (2 - 1) + (0 - 3) + (-1 - (-2)) + (5 - 4) + (7 - 3)$$

$$= 1 + (-3) + 1 + 1 + 4$$

$$= 4$$

$$\sum_{i=1}^{5}X_i - \sum_{i=1}^{5}Y_i = 13 - 9 = 4$$

Rule 3   The sum of a constant times a variable is equal to that constant times the sum of the values of the variable:

$$\sum_{i=1}^{n}cX_i = c\sum_{i=1}^{n}X_i$$

where c is a constant. Thus, if $c = 2$,

$$\sum_{i=1}^{5}cX_i = \sum_{i=1}^{5}2X_i = (2)(2) + (2)(0) + (2)(-1) + (2)(5) + (2)(7)$$

$$= 4 + 0 + (-2) + 10 + 14$$

$$= 26$$

$$c\sum_{i=1}^{5}X_i = 2\sum_{i=1}^{5}X_i = (2)(13) = 26$$

Rule 4   A constant summed n times will be equal to n times the value of the constant.

$$\sum_{i=1}^{n}c = nc$$

where c is a constant. Thus, if the constant $c = 2$ is summed 5 times,

$$\sum_{i=1}^{5}c = 2 + 2 + 2 + 2 + 2 = 10$$

$$nc = (5)(2) = 10$$

EXAMPLE

Suppose there are six values for the variables X and Y, such that $X_1 = 2, X_2 = 1, X_3 = 5, X_4 = -3, X_5 = 1, X_6 = -2$ and $Y_1 = 4, Y_2 = 0, Y_3 = -1, Y_4 = 2, Y_5 = 7$, and $Y_6 = -3$. Compute each of the following:

(a) $\sum_{i=1}^{6}X_i$

(b) $\sum_{i=1}^{6}Y_i$

(c) $\sum_{i=1}^{6}X_i^2$

(d) $\sum_{i=1}^{6}Y_i^2$

(e) $\sum_{i=1}^{6}X_iY_i$

(f) $\sum_{i=1}^{6}(X_i + Y_i)$

(g) $\displaystyle\sum_{i=1}^{6}(X_i - Y_i)$ (i) $\displaystyle\sum_{i=1}^{6}(cX_i)$, where $c = -1$

(h) $\displaystyle\sum_{i=1}^{6}(X_i - 3Y_i + 2X_i^2)$ (j) $\displaystyle\sum_{i=1}^{6}(X_i - 3Y_i + c)$, where $c = +3$

Answers
(a) 4   (b) 9   (c) 44   (d) 79   (e) 10   (f) 13   (g) −5   (h) 65   (i) −4   (j) −5

References

1. Bashaw, W. L., *Mathematics for Statistics* (New York: Wiley, 1969).
2. Lanzer, P., *Basic Math: Fractions, Decimals, Percents* (Hicksville, NY: Video Aided Instruction, 2006).
3. Levine, D. and A. Brandwein, *The MBA Primer: Business Statistics*, 3rd ed. (Cincinnati, OH: Cengage Publishing, 2011).
4. Levine, D., *Statistics* (Hicksville, NY: Video Aided Instruction, 2006).
5. Shane, H., *Algebra 1* (Hicksville, NY: Video Aided Instruction, 2006).

A.5 Statistical Symbols

+	add	×	multiply
−	subtract	÷	divide
=	equal to	≠	not equal to
≅	approximately equal to	<	less than
>	greater than	≤	less than or equal to
≥	greater than or equal to		

A.6 Greek Alphabet

GREEK LETTER		LETTER NAME	ENGLISH EQUIVALENT	GREEK LETTER		LETTER NAME	ENGLISH EQUIVALENT
A	α	Alpha	a	N	ν	Nu	n
B	β	Beta	b	Ξ	ξ	Xi	x
Γ	γ	Gamma	g	O	o	Omicron	ŏ
Δ	δ	Delta	d	Π	π	Pi	p
E	ε	Epsilon	ĕ	P	ρ	Rho	r
Z	ζ	Zeta	z	Σ	σ	Sigma	s
H	η	Eta	ē	T	τ	Tau	t
Θ	θ	Theta	th	Y	υ	Upsilon	u
I	ι	Iota	i	Φ	ϕ	Phi	ph
K	κ	Kappa	k	X	χ	Chi	ch
Λ	λ	Lambda	l	Ψ	ψ	Psi	ps
M	μ	Mu	m	Ω	ω	Omega	ō

B.1 Objects in a Window

When you open Excel or Minitab, you see a window that contains the objects listed in Table B.1 and shown in Figure B.1 on page 789. To effectively use Excel or Minitab, you must be familiar with these objects and their names.

TABLE B.1

Common Window
Elements

Number	Element	Function
❶	Title bar	Displays the name of the program and contains the Minimize, Resize, and Close buttons for the program window. You drag and drop the title bar to reposition a program window onscreen.
❷	Minimize, Resize, and Close buttons	Changes the display of the program window. **Minimize** hides the window without closing the program, **Resize** permits you to change the size of the window, and **Close** removes the window from the screen and closes the program. A second set of these buttons that appear below the first set perform the three actions for the currently active workbook.
❸	Menu Bar and Toolbars	The menu bar is a horizontal list of words, where each word represents either a command operation or leads to another list of choices. Toolbars are sets of graphical icons that represent commands. The toolbar icons serve as shortcuts to menu bar choices. (Minitab and Excel 2003)
❹	Ribbon	A selectable area that combines the functions of a menu bar and toolbars. In the Ribbon, commands are arranged in a series of **tabs,** and the tabs are further divided into **groups.** Some groups contain **launcher buttons** that display additional choices presented in a dialog box or as a **gallery,** a set of pictorial choices. (Excel 2007 and Excel 2010)
❺	Workbook area	Displays the currently open worksheets. In Excel, this area usually displays the currently active worksheet in the workbook and shows the other worksheets as **sheet tabs** near the bottom of the workbook area.
❻	Scroll bar	Allows you to move through a worksheet vertically or horizontally to reveal rows and columns that cannot otherwise be seen.

FIGURE B.1

Minitab, Excel 2010, and
Excel 2007 windows (with
number labels keyed to
Table B.1)

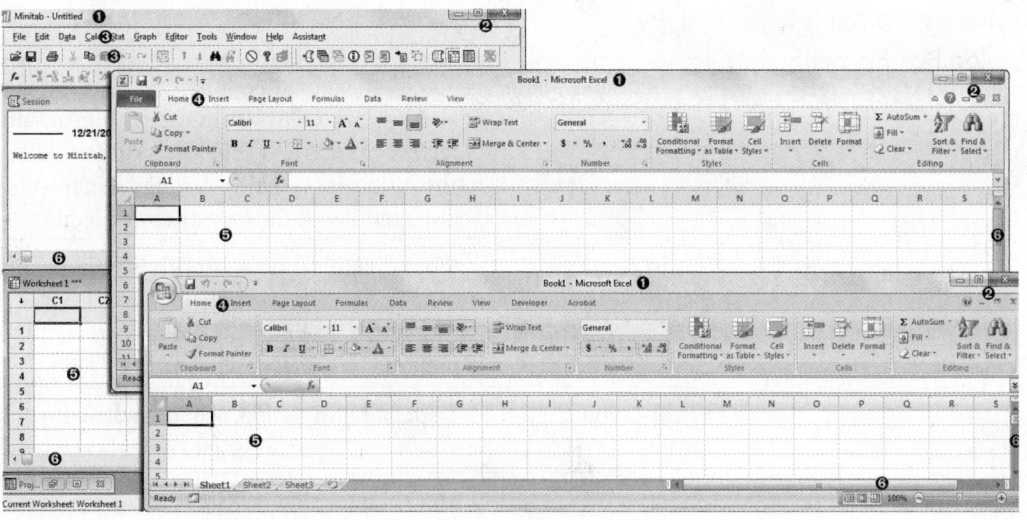

B.2 Basic Mouse Operations

To interact with the objects in a window, you frequently use a mouse (or some other pointing device). Mouse operations can be divided into four types and assume a mouse with two buttons, one designated as the primary button (typically the left button) and the other button designated as the secondary button (typically the right button).

Click, **select**, **check**, and **clear** are operations in which you move the mouse pointer over an object and press the primary button. **Click** is used when pressing the primary button completes an action, as in "click (the) **OK** (button)." **Select** is used when pressing the primary button to choose or highlight one choice from a list of choices. **Check** is used when pressing the primary button places a checkmark in the dialog box's check box. (**Clear** reverses this action, removing the checkmark.)

Double-click is an operation in which two clicks are made in rapid succession. Most double-click operations enable an object for following use, such as double-clicking a chart in order to make changes to the chart. **Right-click** is an operation in which you move the mouse pointer over an object and press the *secondary* button. In the Excel Guide instructions, you will often right-click an object in order to display a pop-up **shortcut menu** of context-sensitive command operations.

Drag is an operation in which you hold down the primary button over an object and then move the mouse. (The drag operation ends when you release the mouse button.) Dragging is done to select multiple objects, such as selecting all the cells in a cell range, as well as to physically move an object to another part of the screen. The related **drag-and-drop** operation permits you to move one object over another to trigger an action. You drag the first object across the screen, and when the first object is over the second object, you release the primary mouse button. (In most cases, releasing the primary button causes the first object to reappear in its original position onscreen.)

Without a working knowledge of these mousing operations, you will find it difficult to understand and follow the instructions presented in the end-of-chapter Excel and Minitab Guides.

B.3 Dialog Box Interactions

When you interact with either Excel or Minitab, you will see **dialog boxes**, pop-up windows that contain messages or ask you to make entries or selections. Table B.2 identifies and defines the common objects found in dialog boxes which are shown in Figure B.2 on page 790.

TABLE B.2
Dialog Box Elements

Element	Function
Command button	A clickable area that tells a program to take some action. For example, a dialog box **OK button** causes a program to take an action using the current entries and selections of the dialog box. A dialog box **Cancel button** closes a dialog box and cancels the pending operation associated with the entries and selections in the dialog box.
List box	A box that displays a list of clickable choices. If a list exceeds the dimensions of a list box, list boxes display **scroll buttons** or **sliders** (not shown in Figure B.2) that can be clicked to reveal choices not currently displayed.
Drop-down list	A special button that, when clicked, displays a list of choices from which you typically select one choice.
Edit box	An area into which entries can be typed. Some edit boxes also contain drop-down lists or **spinner buttons** that can be used to make entries. A cell range edit box typically contains a clickable button that allows you to drag the mouse over a cell range as an alternative to typing the cell range.
Set of option buttons	A set of buttons that represent a set of mutually exclusive choices. Clicking one option button clears all the other option buttons in the set.
Check box	A clickable area that represents an optional action. A check box displays either a checkmark or nothing, depending on whether the optional action has been selected. Unlike with option buttons, clicking a check box does not affect the status of other check boxes, and more than one check box can be checked at a time. Clicking a check box that already contains a checkmark *clears* the check box. (To distinguish between the two states, instructions in this book use the verbs *check* and *clear*.)

FIGURE B.2

Excel 2010 Open (partially obscured) and Minitab Print dialog boxes

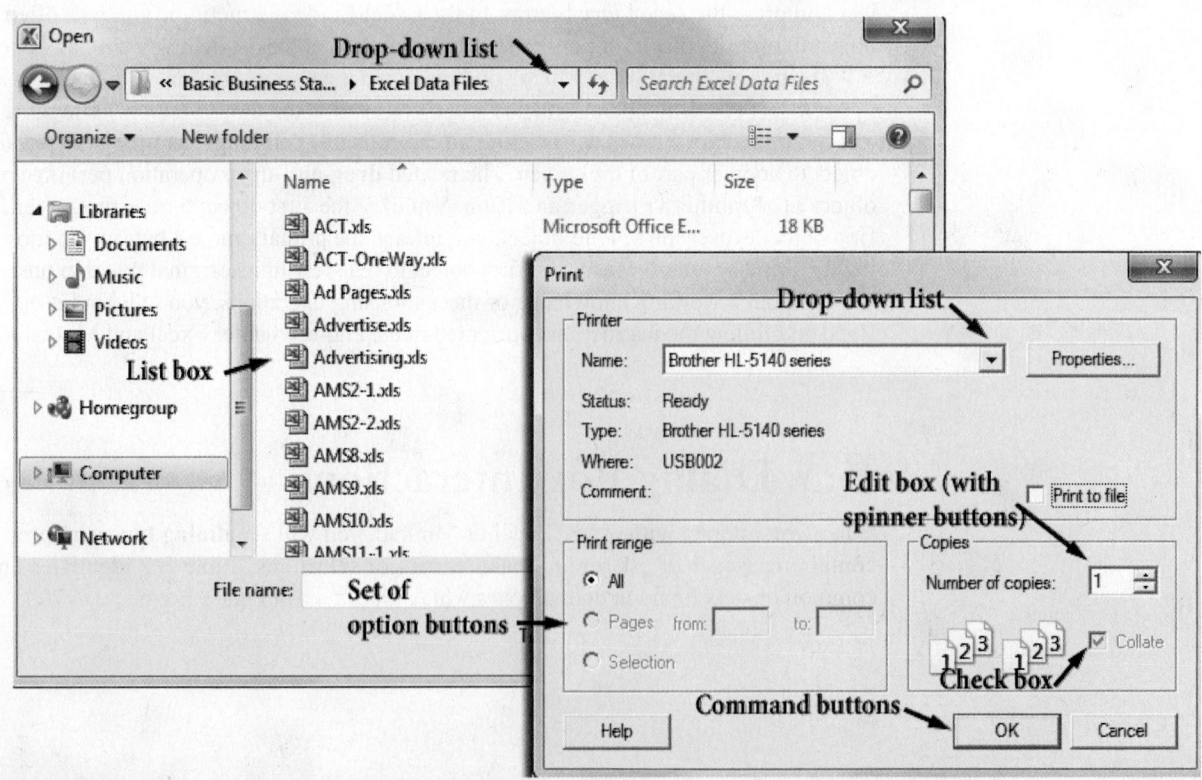

B.4 Unique Features

Excel 2007 This version of Excel uniquely features the **Office Button**, the circular logo in the upper left of the window that displays a menu of basic computing commands when clicked (see Figure B.1). The Office Button functions much like the File menu in Excel 2003 and Minitab and the File tab in Excel 2010.

Minitab All versions of Minitab use a session manager, a window in which results are added as a continuous log. (All Minitab results, other than charts, shown in this book have been copied from a session manager log.)

Minitab 16 Minitab 16 includes an Assistant feature that helps guide you through the choice of the statistical method to use. The Assistant appears as an additional choice on the Minitab menu bar and also provides direct clickable shortcuts to menu choices that might otherwise require several different mouse clicks to select. The Assistant is not explicitly used in this book due to its uniqueness to Minitab 16.

Software Configuration Details

D.1 Checking for and Applying Updates

Excel

To check for and apply Excel updates, your system must be connected to the Internet. You can check and apply updates using one of two methods. If Internet Explorer is the default web browser on your system, use the Excel "check for updates" feature. In Excel 2010, select **File → Help → Check for Updates** and follow the instructions that appear on the web page that is displayed. In Excel 2007, click the **Office Button** and then **Excel Options** (at the bottom of the Office Button menu window). In the Excel options dialog box, click **Resources** in the left pane and then in the right pane click **Check for Updates** and follow the instructions that appear on the web page that is displayed.

If the first method fails for any reason, you can manually download Excel and Microsoft Office updates by opening a web browser and going to **office.microsoft.com/officeupdate**. On the web page that is displayed, you can find download links arranged by popularity as well as by product version. If you use this second method, you need to know the exact version and status of your copy of Excel. In Excel 2010, select **File → Help** and note the information under the heading "About Microsoft Excel." In Excel 2007, click the **Office Button** and then **Excel Options**. In the Excel options dialog box, click **Resources** in the left pane and then in the right pane note the detail line under the heading "about Microsoft Office Excel 2007." The numbers and codes that follow the words "Microsoft Office Excel" indicate the version number and updates already applied.

If you use Mac Excel, select **Help → Check for Updates** to begin Microsoft AutoUpdate for Mac, similar to Microsoft Update, described above, for checking and applying updates.

Special Notes About the Windows Update Service   If you use a Microsoft Windows–based system and have previously turned on the Windows Update service, your system has not necessarily downloaded and applied all Excel updates. If you use Windows Update, you can upgrade for free to the Microsoft Update service that searches for and downloads updates for all Microsoft products, including Excel and Office. (You can learn more about the Microsoft Update service by visiting **www.microsoft.com/security/updates/mu.aspx**.)

Minitab

To check for and apply Minitab updates, your system must be connected to the Internet. Select **Help → Check for Updates**. Follow directions, if any, that appear in the Minitab Software Update Manager dialog box. If there are no new updates, you will see a dialog box that states "There are no updates available." Click **OK** in that dialog box and then click **Cancel** in the Update Manager dialog box to continue with your Minitab session.

D.2 Concise Instructions for Installing PHStat2

If your system can run the Microsoft Windows–based Excel 2003, Excel 2007, or Excel 2010, you can download, install, and use PHStat2. Before using PHStat2:

- Check for and apply all Excel updates by using the instructions in Section D.1.
- Download and read the PHStat2 readme file for the latest information about PHStat2.
- Download the PHStat2 setup program.

- Run the PHStat2 setup program to install PHStat2 on your system, taking note of the technical requirements listed in the PHStat2 readme file.
- Configure Excel to use PHStat2 (see Appendix Section D.3).

The PHStat2 setup program copies the PHStat2 files to your system and adds entries in the Windows registry file on your system. Run the setup program only after first logging on to Windows using a user account that has administrator privileges. (Running the setup program with a Windows user account that does not include these privileges will prevent the setup program from properly installing PHStat2.)

If your system runs Windows Vista, Windows 7, or certain third-party security programs, you may see messages asking you to "permit" or "allow" specific system operations as the setup program executes. If you do not give the setup program the necessary permissions, PHStat2 will *not* be properly installed on your computer.

After the setup completes, check the installation by opening PHStat2. If the installation ran properly, Excel will display a PHStat menu in the Add-Ins tab of the Office Ribbon (Excel 2007 or Excel 2010) or the Excel menu bar (Excel 2003). If you have skipped checking for and applying necessary Excel updates, or if some of the updates were unable to be applied, when you first attempt to use PHStat2, you may see a "Compile Error" message that talks about a "hidden module." If this occurs, repeat the process of checking for and applying updates to Excel. (If the bandwidth of the Internet connection is limited, you may need to use another connection.)

As you use PHStat2, check the download page or the MyStatLab course for this book to see if any free updates are available. Additional information about updates may also be available at the Pearson Education PHStat2 website, **www.pearsonhighered.com/phstat**. For more information about PHStat2 without going online, read Appendix Section G.1 on page 817.

D.3 Configuring Excel for PHStat2 Usage

To configure Excel security settings for PHStat2 usage:

1. In Excel 2010, select **File → Options**. In Excel 2007, click the Office Button and then click **Excel Options** (at the bottom of the Office Button menu window).

In the Excel Options dialog box:

2. Click **Trust Center** in the left pane and then click **Trust Center Settings** in the right pane (see the top of Figure D.1 on page 794).

In the Trust Center dialog box:

3. Click **Add-ins** in the next left pane, and in the Add-ins right pane clear all of the checkboxes (see the bottom left of Figure D.1).
4. Click **Macro Settings** in the left pane, and in the Macro Settings right pane click **Disable all macros with notification** and check **Trust access to the VBA object model** (see the bottom right of Figure D.1).
5. Click **OK** to close the Trust Center dialog box.

Back in the Excel Options dialog box:

6. Click **OK** to finish.

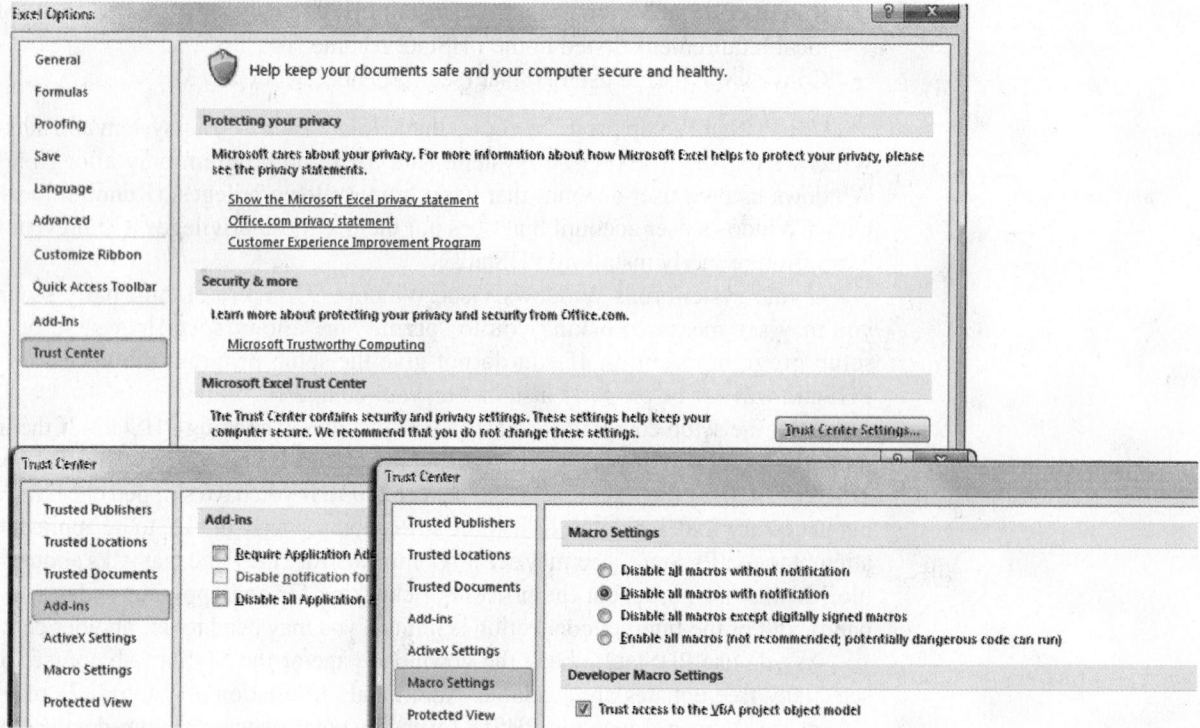

FIGURE D.1

Configuring Excel security settings

On some systems that have stringent security settings, you might need to modify step 5. For such systems, in step 5, click **Trusted Locations** in the left pane and then, in the Trusted Locations right pane, click **Add new location** to add the folder path to the PHStat2 add-in (typically C:\Program Files\PHStat2) and then click **OK**.

When you open PHStat2, Excel will display a Microsoft Excel Security Notice dialog box (shown below). Click **Enable Macros** to enable PHStat2 to open and function.

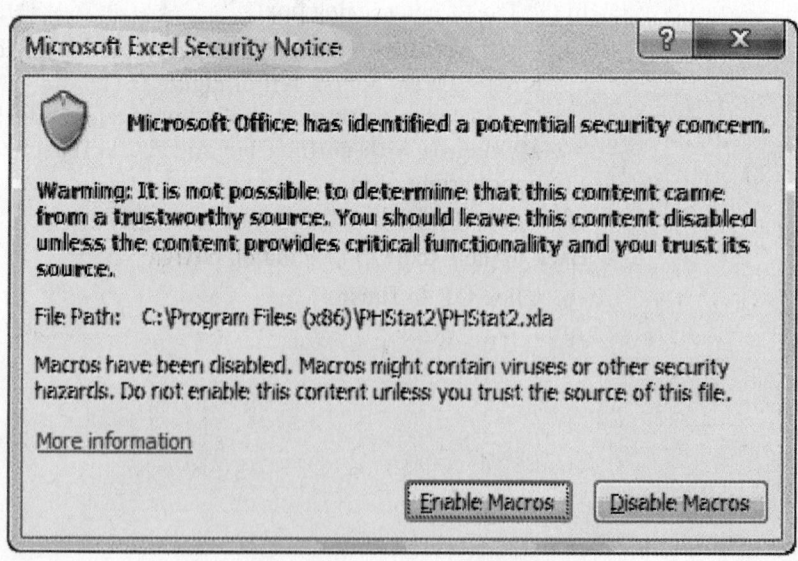

D.4 Using the Visual Explorations Add-in Workbook

To use the Visual Explorations add-in workbook, first download the set of three files that comprise Visual Explorations from this book's companion website. Place the three files together in a folder of your choosing. Next, use the Section D.3 instructions for configuring Excel for PHStat2 usage. Then open the **Visual Explorations.xla** file in Excel and use the VisualExplorations menu in the **Add-Ins** tab to select individual procedures.

D.5 Checking for the Presence of the Analysis ToolPak

To check for the presence of the Analysis ToolPak add-in (needed only if you will be using the *Analysis ToolPak* Excel Guide instructions):

1. In Excel 2010, select **File → Options**. In Excel 2007, click the **Office Button** and then click **Excel Options** (at the bottom of the Office Button menu window).

In the Excel Options dialog box:

2. Click **Add-Ins** in the left pane and look for the entry **Analysis ToolPak** in the right pane, under **Active Application Add-ins**.
3. If the entry appears, click **OK**.

If the entry does not appear in the **Active Application Add-ins** list, click **Go**. In the Add-Ins dialog box, check **Analysis ToolPak** in the **Add-Ins available** list and click **OK**. If Analysis ToolPak does not appear in the list, rerun the Microsoft Office setup program to install this component.

The Analysis ToolPak add-in is not included and is not available for Mac Excel 2008 but is included in other versions of Mac Excel.

TABLE E.1
Table of Random Numbers

	Column							
Row	**00000** **12345**	**00001** **67890**	**11111** **12345**	**11112** **67890**	**22222** **12345**	**22223** **67890**	**33333** **12345**	**33334** **67890**
01	49280	88924	35779	00283	81163	07275	89863	02348
02	61870	41657	07468	08612	98083	97349	20775	45091
03	43898	65923	25078	86129	78496	97653	91550	08078
04	62993	93912	30454	84598	56095	20664	12872	64647
05	33850	58555	51438	85507	71865	79488	76783	31708
06	97340	03364	88472	04334	63919	36394	11095	92470
07	70543	29776	10087	10072	55980	64688	68239	20461
08	89382	93809	00796	95945	34101	81277	66090	88872
09	37818	72142	67140	50785	22380	16703	53362	44940
10	60430	22834	14130	96593	23298	56203	92671	15925
11	82975	66158	84731	19436	55790	69229	28661	13675
12	30987	71938	40355	54324	08401	26299	49420	59208
13	55700	24586	93247	32596	11865	63397	44251	43189
14	14756	23997	78643	75912	83832	32768	18928	57070
15	32166	53251	70654	92827	63491	04233	33825	69662
16	23236	73751	31888	81718	06546	83246	47651	04877
17	45794	26926	15130	82455	78305	55058	52551	47182
18	09893	20505	14225	68514	47427	56788	96297	78822
19	54382	74598	91499	14523	68479	27686	46162	83554
20	94750	89923	37089	20048	80336	94598	26940	36858
21	70297	34135	53140	33340	42050	82341	44104	82949
22	85157	47954	32979	26575	57600	40881	12250	73742
23	11100	02340	12860	74697	96644	89439	28707	25815
24	36871	50775	30592	57143	17381	68856	25853	35041
25	23913	48357	63308	16090	51690	54607	72407	55538
26	79348	36085	27973	65157	07456	22255	25626	57054
27	92074	54641	53673	54421	18130	60103	69593	49464
28	06873	21440	75593	41373	49502	17972	82578	16364
29	12478	37622	99659	31065	83613	69889	58869	29571
30	57175	55564	65411	42547	70457	03426	72937	83792
31	91616	11075	80103	07831	59309	13276	26710	73000
32	78025	73539	14621	39044	47450	03197	12787	47709
33	27587	67228	80145	10175	12822	86687	65530	49325
34	16690	20427	04251	64477	73709	73945	92396	68263
35	70183	58065	65489	31833	82093	16747	10386	59293
36	90730	35385	15679	99742	50866	78028	75573	67257
37	10934	93242	13431	24590	02770	48582	00906	58595
38	82462	30166	79613	47416	13389	80268	05085	96666
39	27463	10433	07606	16285	93699	60912	94532	95632
40	02979	52997	09079	92709	90110	47506	53693	49892
41	46888	69929	75233	52507	32097	37594	10067	67327
42	53638	83161	08289	12639	08141	12640	28437	09268
43	82433	61427	17239	89160	19666	08814	37841	12847
44	35766	31672	50082	22795	66948	65581	84393	15890
45	10853	42581	08792	13257	61973	24450	52351	16602
46	20341	27398	72906	63955	17276	10646	74692	48438
47	54458	90542	77563	51839	52901	53355	83281	19177
48	26337	66530	16687	35179	46560	00123	44546	79896
49	34314	23729	85264	05575	96855	23820	11091	79821
50	28603	10708	68933	34189	92166	15181	66628	58599
51	66194	28926	99547	16625	45515	67953	12108	57846
52	78240	43195	24837	32511	70880	22070	52622	61881
53	00833	88000	67299	68215	11274	55624	32991	17436
54	12111	86683	61270	58036	64192	90611	15145	01748
55	47189	99951	05755	03834	43782	90599	40282	51417
56	76396	72486	62423	27618	84184	78922	73561	52818
57	46409	17469	32483	09083	76175	19985	26309	91536

TABLE E.1

Table of Random Numbers (*continued*)

Row	00000 12345	00001 67890	11111 12345	11112 67890	22222 12345	22223 67890	33333 12345	33334 67890
58	74626	22111	87286	46772	42243	68046	44250	42439
59	34450	81974	93723	49023	58432	67083	36876	93391
60	36327	72135	33005	28701	34710	49359	50693	89311
61	74185	77536	84825	09934	99103	09325	67389	45869
62	12296	41623	62873	37943	25584	09609	63360	47270
63	90822	60280	88925	99610	42772	60561	76873	04117
64	72121	79152	96591	90305	10189	79778	68016	13747
65	95268	41377	25684	08151	61816	58555	54305	86189
66	92603	09091	75884	93424	72586	88903	30061	14457
67	18813	90291	05275	01223	79607	95426	34900	09778
68	38840	26903	28624	67157	51986	42865	14508	49315
69	05959	33836	53758	16562	41081	38012	41230	20528
70	85141	21155	99212	32685	51403	31926	69813	58781
71	75047	59643	31074	38172	03718	32119	69506	67143
72	30752	95260	68032	62871	58781	34143	68790	69766
73	22986	82575	42187	62295	84295	30634	66562	31442
74	99439	86692	90348	66036	48399	73451	26698	39437
75	20389	93029	11881	71685	65452	89047	63669	02656
76	39249	05173	68256	36359	20250	68686	05947	09335
77	96777	33605	29481	20063	09398	01843	35139	61344
78	04860	32918	10798	50492	52655	33359	94713	28393
79	41613	42375	00403	03656	77580	87772	86877	57085
80	17930	00794	53836	53692	67135	98102	61912	11246
81	24649	31845	25736	75231	83808	98917	93829	99430
82	79899	34061	54308	59358	56462	58166	97302	86828
83	76801	49594	81002	30397	52728	15101	72070	33706
84	36239	63636	38140	65731	39788	06872	38971	53363
85	07392	64449	17886	63632	53995	17574	22247	62607
86	67133	04181	33874	98835	67453	59734	76381	63455
87	77759	31504	32832	70861	15152	29733	75371	39174
88	85992	72268	42920	20810	29361	51423	90306	73574
89	79553	75952	54116	65553	47139	60579	09165	85490
90	41101	17336	48951	53674	17880	45260	08575	49321
91	36191	17095	32123	91576	84221	78902	82010	30847
92	62329	63898	23268	74283	26091	68409	69704	82267
93	14751	13151	93115	01437	56945	89661	67680	79790
94	48462	59278	44185	29616	76537	19589	83139	28454
95	29435	88105	59651	44391	74588	55114	80834	85686
96	28340	29285	12965	14821	80425	16602	44653	70467
97	02167	58940	27149	80242	10587	79786	34959	75339
98	17864	00991	39557	54981	23588	81914	37609	13128
99	79675	80605	60059	35862	00254	36546	21545	78179
100	72335	82037	92003	34100	29879	46613	89720	13274

Source: Partially extracted from the Rand Corporation, *A Million Random Digits with 100,000 Normal Deviates* (Glencoe, IL, The Free Press, 1955).

TABLE E.2

The Cumulative Standardized Normal Distribution

Entry represents area under the cumulative standardized
normal distribution from $-\infty$ to Z

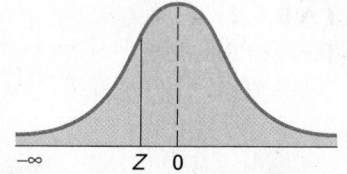

	Cumulative Probabilities									
Z	0.00	0.01	0.02	0.03	0.04	0.05	0.06	0.07	0.08	0.09
−6.0	0.000000001									
−5.5	0.000000019									
−5.0	0.000000287									
−4.5	0.000003398									
−4.0	0.000031671									
−3.9	0.00005	0.00005	0.00004	0.00004	0.00004	0.00004	0.00004	0.00004	0.00003	0.00003
−3.8	0.00007	0.00007	0.00007	0.00006	0.00006	0.00006	0.00006	0.00005	0.00005	0.00005
−3.7	0.00011	0.00010	0.00010	0.00010	0.00009	0.00009	0.00008	0.00008	0.00008	0.00008
−3.6	0.00016	0.00015	0.00015	0.00014	0.00014	0.00013	0.00013	0.00012	0.00012	0.00011
−3.5	0.00023	0.00022	0.00022	0.00021	0.00020	0.00019	0.00019	0.00018	0.00017	0.00017
−3.4	0.00034	0.00032	0.00031	0.00030	0.00029	0.00028	0.00027	0.00026	0.00025	0.00024
−3.3	0.00048	0.00047	0.00045	0.00043	0.00042	0.00040	0.00039	0.00038	0.00036	0.00035
−3.2	0.00069	0.00066	0.00064	0.00062	0.00060	0.00058	0.00056	0.00054	0.00052	0.00050
−3.1	0.00097	0.00094	0.00090	0.00087	0.00084	0.00082	0.00079	0.00076	0.00074	0.00071
−3.0	0.00135	0.00131	0.00126	0.00122	0.00118	0.00114	0.00111	0.00107	0.00103	0.00100
−2.9	0.0019	0.0018	0.0018	0.0017	0.0016	0.0016	0.0015	0.0015	0.0014	0.0014
−2.8	0.0026	0.0025	0.0024	0.0023	0.0023	0.0022	0.0021	0.0021	0.0020	0.0019
−2.7	0.0035	0.0034	0.0033	0.0032	0.0031	0.0030	0.0029	0.0028	0.0027	0.0026
−2.6	0.0047	0.0045	0.0044	0.0043	0.0041	0.0040	0.0039	0.0038	0.0037	0.0036
−2.5	0.0062	0.0060	0.0059	0.0057	0.0055	0.0054	0.0052	0.0051	0.0049	0.0048
−2.4	0.0082	0.0080	0.0078	0.0075	0.0073	0.0071	0.0069	0.0068	0.0066	0.0064
−2.3	0.0107	0.0104	0.0102	0.0099	0.0096	0.0094	0.0091	0.0089	0.0087	0.0084
−2.2	0.0139	0.0136	0.0132	0.0129	0.0125	0.0122	0.0119	0.0116	0.0113	0.0110
−2.1	0.0179	0.0174	0.0170	0.0166	0.0162	0.0158	0.0154	0.0150	0.0146	0.0143
−2.0	0.0228	0.0222	0.0217	0.0212	0.0207	0.0202	0.0197	0.0192	0.0188	0.0183
−1.9	0.0287	0.0281	0.0274	0.0268	0.0262	0.0256	0.0250	0.0244	0.0239	0.0233
−1.8	0.0359	0.0351	0.0344	0.0336	0.0329	0.0322	0.0314	0.0307	0.0301	0.0294
−1.7	0.0446	0.0436	0.0427	0.0418	0.0409	0.0401	0.0392	0.0384	0.0375	0.0367
−1.6	0.0548	0.0537	0.0526	0.0516	0.0505	0.0495	0.0485	0.0475	0.0465	0.0455
−1.5	0.0668	0.0655	0.0643	0.0630	0.0618	0.0606	0.0594	0.0582	0.0571	0.0559
−1.4	0.0808	0.0793	0.0778	0.0764	0.0749	0.0735	0.0721	0.0708	0.0694	0.0681
−1.3	0.0968	0.0951	0.0934	0.0918	0.0901	0.0885	0.0869	0.0853	0.0838	0.0823
−1.2	0.1151	0.1131	0.1112	0.1093	0.1075	0.1056	0.1038	0.1020	0.1003	0.0985
−1.1	0.1357	0.1335	0.1314	0.1292	0.1271	0.1251	0.1230	0.1210	0.1190	0.1170
−1.0	0.1587	0.1562	0.1539	0.1515	0.1492	0.1469	0.1446	0.1423	0.1401	0.1379
−0.9	0.1841	0.1814	0.1788	0.1762	0.1736	0.1711	0.1685	0.1660	0.1635	0.1611
−0.8	0.2119	0.2090	0.2061	0.2033	0.2005	0.1977	0.1949	0.1922	0.1894	0.1867
−0.7	0.2420	0.2388	0.2358	0.2327	0.2296	0.2266	0.2236	0.2206	0.2177	0.2148
−0.6	0.2743	0.2709	0.2676	0.2643	0.2611	0.2578	0.2546	0.2514	0.2482	0.2451
−0.5	0.3085	0.3050	0.3015	0.2981	0.2946	0.2912	0.2877	0.2843	0.2810	0.2776
−0.4	0.3446	0.3409	0.3372	0.3336	0.3300	0.3264	0.3228	0.3192	0.3156	0.3121
−0.3	0.3821	0.3783	0.3745	0.3707	0.3669	0.3632	0.3594	0.3557	0.3520	0.3483
−0.2	0.4207	0.4168	0.4129	0.4090	0.4052	0.4013	0.3974	0.3936	0.3897	0.3859
−0.1	0.4602	0.4562	0.4522	0.4483	0.4443	0.4404	0.4364	0.4325	0.4286	0.4247
−0.0	0.5000	0.4960	0.4920	0.4880	0.4840	0.4801	0.4761	0.4721	0.4681	0.4641

TABLE E.2

The Cumulative Standardized Normal Distribution (*continued*)

Entry represents area under the cumulative standardized
normal distribution from $-\infty$ to Z

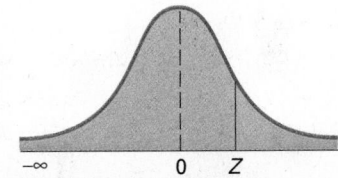

	Cumulative Probabilities									
Z	0.00	0.01	0.02	0.03	0.04	0.05	0.06	0.07	0.08	0.09
0.0	0.5000	0.5040	0.5080	0.5120	0.5160	0.5199	0.5239	0.5279	0.5319	0.5359
0.1	0.5398	0.5438	0.5478	0.5517	0.5557	0.5596	0.5636	0.5675	0.5714	0.5753
0.2	0.5793	0.5832	0.5871	0.5910	0.5948	0.5987	0.6026	0.6064	0.6103	0.6141
0.3	0.6179	0.6217	0.6255	0.6293	0.6331	0.6368	0.6406	0.6443	0.6480	0.6517
0.4	0.6554	0.6591	0.6628	0.6664	0.6700	0.6736	0.6772	0.6808	0.6844	0.6879
0.5	0.6915	0.6950	0.6985	0.7019	0.7054	0.7088	0.7123	0.7157	0.7190	0.7224
0.6	0.7257	0.7291	0.7324	0.7357	0.7389	0.7422	0.7454	0.7486	0.7518	0.7549
0.7	0.7580	0.7612	0.7642	0.7673	0.7704	0.7734	0.7764	0.7794	0.7823	0.7852
0.8	0.7881	0.7910	0.7939	0.7967	0.7995	0.8023	0.8051	0.8078	0.8106	0.8133
0.9	0.8159	0.8186	0.8212	0.8238	0.8264	0.8289	0.8315	0.8340	0.8365	0.8389
1.0	0.8413	0.8438	0.8461	0.8485	0.8508	0.8531	0.8554	0.8577	0.8599	0.8621
1.1	0.8643	0.8665	0.8686	0.8708	0.8729	0.8749	0.8770	0.8790	0.8810	0.8830
1.2	0.8849	0.8869	0.8888	0.8907	0.8925	0.8944	0.8962	0.8980	0.8997	0.9015
1.3	0.9032	0.9049	0.9066	0.9082	0.9099	0.9115	0.9131	0.9147	0.9162	0.9177
1.4	0.9192	0.9207	0.9222	0.9236	0.9251	0.9265	0.9279	0.9292	0.9306	0.9319
1.5	0.9332	0.9345	0.9357	0.9370	0.9382	0.9394	0.9406	0.9418	0.9429	0.9441
1.6	0.9452	0.9463	0.9474	0.9484	0.9495	0.9505	0.9515	0.9525	0.9535	0.9545
1.7	0.9554	0.9564	0.9573	0.9582	0.9591	0.9599	0.9608	0.9616	0.9625	0.9633
1.8	0.9641	0.9649	0.9656	0.9664	0.9671	0.9678	0.9686	0.9693	0.9699	0.9706
1.9	0.9713	0.9719	0.9726	0.9732	0.9738	0.9744	0.9750	0.9756	0.9761	0.9767
2.0	0.9772	0.9778	0.9783	0.9788	0.9793	0.9798	0.9803	0.9808	0.9812	0.9817
2.1	0.9821	0.9826	0.9830	0.9834	0.9838	0.9842	0.9846	0.9850	0.9854	0.9857
2.2	0.9861	0.9864	0.9868	0.9871	0.9875	0.9878	0.9881	0.9884	0.9887	0.9890
2.3	0.9893	0.9896	0.9898	0.9901	0.9904	0.9906	0.9909	0.9911	0.9913	0.9916
2.4	0.9918	0.9920	0.9922	0.9925	0.9927	0.9929	0.9931	0.9932	0.9934	0.9936
2.5	0.9938	0.9940	0.9941	0.9943	0.9945	0.9946	0.9948	0.9949	0.9951	0.9952
2.6	0.9953	0.9955	0.9956	0.9957	0.9959	0.9960	0.9961	0.9962	0.9963	0.9964
2.7	0.9965	0.9966	0.9967	0.9968	0.9969	0.9970	0.9971	0.9972	0.9973	0.9974
2.8	0.9974	0.9975	0.9976	0.9977	0.9977	0.9978	0.9979	0.9979	0.9980	0.9981
2.9	0.9981	0.9982	0.9982	0.9983	0.9984	0.9984	0.9985	0.9985	0.9986	0.9986
3.0	0.99865	0.99869	0.99874	0.99878	0.99882	0.99886	0.99889	0.99893	0.99897	0.99900
3.1	0.99903	0.99906	0.99910	0.99913	0.99916	0.99918	0.99921	0.99924	0.99926	0.99929
3.2	0.99931	0.99934	0.99936	0.99938	0.99940	0.99942	0.99944	0.99946	0.99948	0.99950
3.3	0.99952	0.99953	0.99955	0.99957	0.99958	0.99960	0.99961	0.99962	0.99964	0.99965
3.4	0.99966	0.99968	0.99969	0.99970	0.99971	0.99972	0.99973	0.99974	0.99975	0.99976
3.5	0.99977	0.99978	0.99978	0.99979	0.99980	0.99981	0.99981	0.99982	0.99983	0.99983
3.6	0.99984	0.99985	0.99985	0.99986	0.99986	0.99987	0.99987	0.99988	0.99988	0.99989
3.7	0.99989	0.99990	0.99990	0.99990	0.99991	0.99991	0.99992	0.99992	0.99992	0.99992
3.8	0.99993	0.99993	0.99993	0.99994	0.99994	0.99994	0.99994	0.99995	0.99995	0.99995
3.9	0.99995	0.99995	0.99996	0.99996	0.99996	0.99996	0.99996	0.99996	0.99997	0.99997
4.0	0.999968329									
4.5	0.999996602									
5.0	0.999999713									
5.5	0.999999981									
6.0	0.999999999									

TABLE E.3
Critical Values of t

For a particular number of degrees of freedom, entry represents the critical value of t corresponding to the cumulative probability $(1 - \alpha)$ *and a specified upper-tail area* (α).

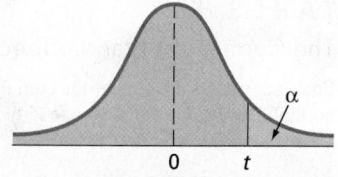

	Cumulative Probabilities					
	0.75	0.90	0.95	0.975	0.99	0.995
	Upper-Tail Areas					
Degrees of Freedom	0.25	0.10	0.05	0.025	0.01	0.005
1	1.0000	3.0777	6.3138	12.7062	31.8207	63.6574
2	0.8165	1.8856	2.9200	4.3027	6.9646	9.9248
3	0.7649	1.6377	2.3534	3.1824	4.5407	5.8409
4	0.7407	1.5332	2.1318	2.7764	3.7469	4.6041
5	0.7267	1.4759	2.0150	2.5706	3.3649	4.0322
6	0.7176	1.4398	1.9432	2.4469	3.1427	3.7074
7	0.7111	1.4149	1.8946	2.3646	2.9980	3.4995
8	0.7064	1.3968	1.8595	2.3060	2.8965	3.3554
9	0.7027	1.3830	1.8331	2.2622	2.8214	3.2498
10	0.6998	1.3722	1.8125	2.2281	2.7638	3.1693
11	0.6974	1.3634	1.7959	2.2010	2.7181	3.1058
12	0.6955	1.3562	1.7823	2.1788	2.6810	3.0545
13	0.6938	1.3502	1.7709	2.1604	2.6503	3.0123
14	0.6924	1.3450	1.7613	2.1448	2.6245	2.9768
15	0.6912	1.3406	1.7531	2.1315	2.6025	2.9467
16	0.6901	1.3368	1.7459	2.1199	2.5835	2.9208
17	0.6892	1.3334	1.7396	2.1098	2.5669	2.8982
18	0.6884	1.3304	1.7341	2.1009	2.5524	2.8784
19	0.6876	1.3277	1.7291	2.0930	2.5395	2.8609
20	0.6870	1.3253	1.7247	2.0860	2.5280	2.8453
21	0.6864	1.3232	1.7207	2.0796	2.5177	2.8314
22	0.6858	1.3212	1.7171	2.0739	2.5083	2.8188
23	0.6853	1.3195	1.7139	2.0687	2.4999	2.8073
24	0.6848	1.3178	1.7109	2.0639	2.4922	2.7969
25	0.6844	1.3163	1.7081	2.0595	2.4851	2.7874
26	0.6840	1.3150	1.7056	2.0555	2.4786	2.7787
27	0.6837	1.3137	1.7033	2.0518	2.4727	2.7707
28	0.6834	1.3125	1.7011	2.0484	2.4671	2.7633
29	0.6830	1.3114	1.6991	2.0452	2.4620	2.7564
30	0.6828	1.3104	1.6973	2.0423	2.4573	2.7500
31	0.6825	1.3095	1.6955	2.0395	2.4528	2.7440
32	0.6822	1.3086	1.6939	2.0369	2.4487	2.7385
33	0.6820	1.3077	1.6924	2.0345	2.4448	2.7333
34	0.6818	1.3070	1.6909	2.0322	2.4411	2.7284
35	0.6816	1.3062	1.6896	2.0301	2.4377	2.7238
36	0.6814	1.3055	1.6883	2.0281	2.4345	2.7195
37	0.6812	1.3049	1.6871	2.0262	2.4314	2.7154
38	0.6810	1.3042	1.6860	2.0244	2.4286	2.7116
39	0.6808	1.3036	1.6849	2.0227	2.4258	2.7079
40	0.6807	1.3031	1.6839	2.0211	2.4233	2.7045
41	0.6805	1.3025	1.6829	2.0195	2.4208	2.7012
42	0.6804	1.3020	1.6820	2.0181	2.4185	2.6981
43	0.6802	1.3016	1.6811	2.0167	2.4163	2.6951
44	0.6801	1.3011	1.6802	2.0154	2.4141	2.6923
45	0.6800	1.3006	1.6794	2.0141	2.4121	2.6896
46	0.6799	1.3002	1.6787	2.0129	2.4102	2.6870
47	0.6797	1.2998	1.6779	2.0117	2.4083	2.6846
48	0.6796	1.2994	1.6772	2.0106	2.4066	2.6822

Degrees of Freedom	Cumulative Probabilities					
	0.75	0.90	0.95	0.975	0.99	0.995
	Upper-Tail Areas					
	0.25	0.10	0.05	0.025	0.01	0.005
49	0.6795	1.2991	1.6766	2.0096	2.4049	2.6800
50	0.6794	1.2987	1.6759	2.0086	2.4033	2.6778
51	0.6793	1.2984	1.6753	2.0076	2.4017	2.6757
52	0.6792	1.2980	1.6747	2.0066	2.4002	2.6737
53	0.6791	1.2977	1.6741	2.0057	2.3988	2.6718
54	0.6791	1.2974	1.6736	2.0049	2.3974	2.6700
55	0.6790	1.2971	1.6730	2.0040	2.3961	2.6682
56	0.6789	1.2969	1.6725	2.0032	2.3948	2.6665
57	0.6788	1.2966	1.6720	2.0025	2.3936	2.6649
58	0.6787	1.2963	1.6716	2.0017	2.3924	2.6633
59	0.6787	1.2961	1.6711	2.0010	2.3912	2.6618
60	0.6786	1.2958	1.6706	2.0003	2.3901	2.6603
61	0.6785	1.2956	1.6702	1.9996	2.3890	2.6589
62	0.6785	1.2954	1.6698	1.9990	2.3880	2.6575
63	0.6784	1.2951	1.6694	1.9983	2.3870	2.6561
64	0.6783	1.2949	1.6690	1.9977	2.3860	2.6549
65	0.6783	1.2947	1.6686	1.9971	2.3851	2.6536
66	0.6782	1.2945	1.6683	1.9966	2.3842	2.6524
67	0.6782	1.2943	1.6679	1.9960	2.3833	2.6512
68	0.6781	1.2941	1.6676	1.9955	2.3824	2.6501
69	0.6781	1.2939	1.6672	1.9949	2.3816	2.6490
70	0.6780	1.2938	1.6669	1.9944	2.3808	2.6479
71	0.6780	1.2936	1.6666	1.9939	2.3800	2.6469
72	0.6779	1.2934	1.6663	1.9935	2.3793	2.6459
73	0.6779	1.2933	1.6660	1.9930	2.3785	2.6449
74	0.6778	1.2931	1.6657	1.9925	2.3778	2.6439
75	0.6778	1.2929	1.6654	1.9921	2.3771	2.6430
76	0.6777	1.2928	1.6652	1.9917	2.3764	2.6421
77	0.6777	1.2926	1.6649	1.9913	2.3758	2.6412
78	0.6776	1.2925	1.6646	1.9908	2.3751	2.6403
79	0.6776	1.2924	1.6644	1.9905	2.3745	2.6395
80	0.6776	1.2922	1.6641	1.9901	2.3739	2.6387
81	0.6775	1.2921	1.6639	1.9897	2.3733	2.6379
82	0.6775	1.2920	1.6636	1.9893	2.3727	2.6371
83	0.6775	1.2918	1.6634	1.9890	2.3721	2.6364
84	0.6774	1.2917	1.6632	1.9886	2.3716	2.6356
85	0.6774	1.2916	1.6630	1.9883	2.3710	2.6349
86	0.6774	1.2915	1.6628	1.9879	2.3705	2.6342
87	0.6773	1.2914	1.6626	1.9876	2.3700	2.6335
88	0.6773	1.2912	1.6624	1.9873	2.3695	2.6329
89	0.6773	1.2911	1.6622	1.9870	2.3690	2.6322
90	0.6772	1.2910	1.6620	1.9867	2.3685	2.6316
91	0.6772	1.2909	1.6618	1.9864	2.3680	2.6309
92	0.6772	1.2908	1.6616	1.9861	2.3676	2.6303
93	0.6771	1.2907	1.6614	1.9858	2.3671	2.6297
94	0.6771	1.2906	1.6612	1.9855	2.3667	2.6291
95	0.6771	1.2905	1.6611	1.9853	2.3662	2.6286
96	0.6771	1.2904	1.6609	1.9850	2.3658	2.6280
97	0.6770	1.2903	1.6607	1.9847	2.3654	2.6275
98	0.6770	1.2902	1.6606	1.9845	2.3650	2.6269
99	0.6770	1.2902	1.6604	1.9842	2.3646	2.6264
100	0.6770	1.2901	1.6602	1.9840	2.3642	2.6259
110	0.6767	1.2893	1.6588	1.9818	2.3607	2.6213
120	0.6765	1.2886	1.6577	1.9799	2.3578	2.6174
∞	0.6745	1.2816	1.6449	1.9600	2.3263	2.5758

TABLE E.4

Critical Values of χ^2

For a particular number of degrees of freedom, entry represents the critical value of χ^2 corresponding to the cumulative probability $(1 - \alpha)$ and a specified upper-tail area (α).

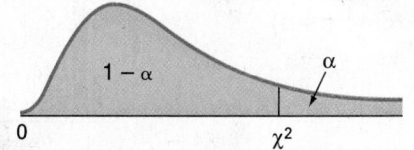

Degrees of Freedom	Cumulative Probabilities											
	0.005	0.01	0.025	0.05	0.10	0.25	0.75	0.90	0.95	0.975	0.99	0.995
	Upper-Tail Areas (α)											
	0.995	0.99	0.975	0.95	0.90	0.75	0.25	0.10	0.05	0.025	0.01	0.005
1			0.001	0.004	0.016	0.102	1.323	2.706	3.841	5.024	6.635	7.879
2	0.010	0.020	0.051	0.103	0.211	0.575	2.773	4.605	5.991	7.378	9.210	10.597
3	0.072	0.115	0.216	0.352	0.584	1.213	4.108	6.251	7.815	9.348	11.345	12.838
4	0.207	0.297	0.484	0.711	1.064	1.923	5.385	7.779	9.488	11.143	13.277	14.860
5	0.412	0.554	0.831	1.145	1.610	2.675	6.626	9.236	11.071	12.833	15.086	16.750
6	0.676	0.872	1.237	1.635	2.204	3.455	7.841	10.645	12.592	14.449	16.812	18.548
7	0.989	1.239	1.690	2.167	2.833	4.255	9.037	12.017	14.067	16.013	18.475	20.278
8	1.344	1.646	2.180	2.733	3.490	5.071	10.219	13.362	15.507	17.535	20.090	21.955
9	1.735	2.088	2.700	3.325	4.168	5.899	11.389	14.684	16.919	19.023	21.666	23.589
10	2.156	2.558	3.247	3.940	4.865	6.737	12.549	15.987	18.307	20.483	23.209	25.188
11	2.603	3.053	3.816	4.575	5.578	7.584	13.701	17.275	19.675	21.920	24.725	26.757
12	3.074	3.571	4.404	5.226	6.304	8.438	14.845	18.549	21.026	23.337	26.217	28.299
13	3.565	4.107	5.009	5.892	7.042	9.299	15.984	19.812	22.362	24.736	27.688	29.819
14	4.075	4.660	5.629	6.571	7.790	10.165	17.117	21.064	23.685	26.119	29.141	31.319
15	4.601	5.229	6.262	7.261	8.547	11.037	18.245	22.307	24.996	27.488	30.578	32.801
16	5.142	5.812	6.908	7.962	9.312	11.912	19.369	23.542	26.296	28.845	32.000	34.267
17	5.697	6.408	7.564	8.672	10.085	12.792	20.489	24.769	27.587	30.191	33.409	35.718
18	6.265	7.015	8.231	9.390	10.865	13.675	21.605	25.989	28.869	31.526	34.805	37.156
19	6.844	7.633	8.907	10.117	11.651	14.562	22.718	27.204	30.144	32.852	36.191	38.582
20	7.434	8.260	9.591	10.851	12.443	15.452	23.828	28.412	31.410	34.170	37.566	39.997
21	8.034	8.897	10.283	11.591	13.240	16.344	24.935	29.615	32.671	35.479	38.932	41.401
22	8.643	9.542	10.982	12.338	14.042	17.240	26.039	30.813	33.924	36.781	40.289	42.796
23	9.260	10.196	11.689	13.091	14.848	18.137	27.141	32.007	35.172	38.076	41.638	44.181
24	9.886	10.856	12.401	13.848	15.659	19.037	28.241	33.196	36.415	39.364	42.980	45.559
25	10.520	11.524	13.120	14.611	16.473	19.939	29.339	34.382	37.652	40.646	44.314	46.928
26	11.160	12.198	13.844	15.379	17.292	20.843	30.435	35.563	38.885	41.923	45.642	48.290
27	11.808	12.879	14.573	16.151	18.114	21.749	31.528	36.741	40.113	43.194	46.963	49.645
28	12.461	13.565	15.308	16.928	18.939	22.657	32.620	37.916	41.337	44.461	48.278	50.993
29	13.121	14.257	16.047	17.708	19.768	23.567	33.711	39.087	42.557	45.722	49.588	52.336
30	13.787	14.954	16.791	18.493	20.599	24.478	34.800	40.256	43.773	46.979	50.892	53.672

For larger values of degrees of freedom (df) the expression $Z = \sqrt{2\chi^2} - \sqrt{2(df) - 1}$ may be used and the resulting upper-tail area can be found from the cumulative standardized normal distribution (Table E.2).

TABLE E.5

Critical Values of F

For a particular combination of numerator and denominator degrees of freedom, entry represents the critical values of F corresponding to the cumulative probability $(1 - \alpha)$ and a specified upper-tail area (α).

$\alpha = 0.05$

Cumulative Probabilities = 0.95

Upper-Tail Areas = 0.05

Numerator, df_1

Denominator, df_2	1	2	3	4	5	6	7	8	9	10	12	15	20	24	30	40	60	120	∞
1	161.40	199.50	215.70	224.60	230.20	234.00	236.80	238.90	240.50	241.90	243.90	245.90	248.00	249.10	250.10	251.10	252.20	253.30	254.30
2	18.51	19.00	19.16	19.25	19.30	19.33	19.35	19.37	19.38	19.40	19.41	19.43	19.45	19.45	19.46	19.47	19.48	19.49	19.50
3	10.13	9.55	9.28	9.12	9.01	8.94	8.89	8.85	8.81	8.79	8.74	8.70	8.66	8.64	8.62	8.59	8.57	8.55	8.53
4	7.71	6.94	6.59	6.39	6.26	6.16	6.09	6.04	6.00	5.96	5.91	5.86	5.80	5.77	5.75	5.72	5.69	5.66	5.63
5	6.61	5.79	5.41	5.19	5.05	4.95	4.88	4.82	4.77	4.74	4.68	4.62	4.56	4.53	4.50	4.46	4.43	4.40	4.36
6	5.99	5.14	4.76	4.53	4.39	4.28	4.21	4.15	4.10	4.06	4.00	3.94	3.87	3.84	3.81	3.77	3.74	3.70	3.67
7	5.59	4.74	4.35	4.12	3.97	3.87	3.79	3.73	3.68	3.64	3.57	3.51	3.44	3.41	3.38	3.34	3.30	3.27	3.23
8	5.32	4.46	4.07	3.84	3.69	3.58	3.50	3.44	3.39	3.35	3.28	3.22	3.15	3.12	3.08	3.04	3.01	2.97	2.93
9	5.12	4.26	3.86	3.63	3.48	3.37	3.29	3.23	3.18	3.14	3.07	3.01	2.94	2.90	2.86	2.83	2.79	2.75	2.71
10	4.96	4.10	3.71	3.48	3.33	3.22	3.14	3.07	3.02	2.98	2.91	2.85	2.77	2.74	2.70	2.66	2.62	2.58	2.54
11	4.84	3.98	3.59	3.36	3.20	3.09	3.01	2.95	2.90	2.85	2.79	2.72	2.65	2.61	2.57	2.53	2.49	2.45	2.40
12	4.75	3.89	3.49	3.26	3.11	3.00	2.91	2.85	2.80	2.75	2.69	2.62	2.54	2.51	2.47	2.43	2.38	2.34	2.30
13	4.67	3.81	3.41	3.18	3.03	2.92	2.83	2.77	2.71	2.67	2.60	2.53	2.46	2.42	2.38	2.34	2.30	2.25	2.21
14	4.60	3.74	3.34	3.11	2.96	2.85	2.76	2.70	2.65	2.60	2.53	2.46	2.39	2.35	2.31	2.27	2.22	2.18	2.13
15	4.54	3.68	3.29	3.06	2.90	2.79	2.71	2.64	2.59	2.54	2.48	2.40	2.33	2.29	2.25	2.20	2.16	2.11	2.07
16	4.49	3.63	3.24	3.01	2.85	2.74	2.66	2.59	2.54	2.49	2.42	2.35	2.28	2.24	2.19	2.15	2.11	2.06	2.01
17	4.45	3.59	3.20	2.96	2.81	2.70	2.61	2.55	2.49	2.45	2.38	2.31	2.23	2.19	2.15	2.10	2.06	2.01	1.96
18	4.41	3.55	3.16	2.93	2.77	2.66	2.58	2.51	2.46	2.41	2.34	2.27	2.19	2.15	2.11	2.06	2.02	1.97	1.92
19	4.38	3.52	3.13	2.90	2.74	2.63	2.54	2.48	2.42	2.38	2.31	2.23	2.16	2.11	2.07	2.03	1.98	1.93	1.88
20	4.35	3.49	3.10	2.87	2.71	2.60	2.51	2.45	2.39	2.35	2.28	2.20	2.12	2.08	2.04	1.99	1.95	1.90	1.84
21	4.32	3.47	3.07	2.84	2.68	2.57	2.49	2.42	2.37	2.32	2.25	2.18	2.10	2.05	2.01	1.96	1.92	1.87	1.81
22	4.30	3.44	3.05	2.82	2.66	2.55	2.46	2.40	2.34	2.30	2.23	2.15	2.07	2.03	1.98	1.91	1.89	1.84	1.78
23	4.28	3.42	3.03	2.80	2.64	2.53	2.44	2.37	2.32	2.27	2.20	2.13	2.05	2.01	1.96	1.91	1.86	1.81	1.76
24	4.26	3.40	3.01	2.78	2.62	2.51	2.42	2.36	2.30	2.25	2.18	2.11	2.03	1.98	1.94	1.89	1.84	1.79	1.73
25	4.24	3.39	2.99	2.76	2.60	2.49	2.40	2.34	2.28	2.24	2.16	2.09	2.01	1.96	1.92	1.87	1.82	1.77	1.71
26	4.23	3.37	2.98	2.74	2.59	2.47	2.39	2.32	2.27	2.22	2.15	2.07	1.99	1.95	1.90	1.85	1.80	1.75	1.69
27	4.21	3.35	2.96	2.73	2.57	2.46	2.37	2.31	2.25	2.20	2.13	2.06	1.97	1.93	1.88	1.84	1.79	1.73	1.67
28	4.20	3.34	2.95	2.71	2.56	2.45	2.36	2.29	2.24	2.19	2.12	2.04	1.96	1.91	1.87	1.82	1.77	1.71	1.65
29	4.18	3.33	2.93	2.70	2.55	2.43	2.35	2.28	2.22	2.18	2.10	2.03	1.94	1.90	1.85	1.81	1.75	1.70	1.64
30	4.17	3.32	2.92	2.69	2.53	2.42	2.33	2.27	2.21	2.16	2.09	2.01	1.93	1.89	1.84	1.79	1.74	1.68	1.62
40	4.08	3.23	2.84	2.61	2.45	2.34	2.25	2.18	2.12	2.08	2.00	1.92	1.84	1.79	1.74	1.69	1.64	1.58	1.51
60	4.00	3.15	2.76	2.53	2.37	2.25	2.17	2.10	2.04	1.99	1.92	1.84	1.75	1.70	1.65	1.59	1.53	1.47	1.39
120	3.92	3.07	2.68	2.45	2.29	2.17	2.09	2.02	1.96	1.91	1.83	1.75	1.66	1.61	1.55	1.50	1.43	1.35	1.25
∞	3.84	3.00	2.60	2.37	2.21	2.10	2.01	1.94	1.88	1.83	1.75	1.67	1.57	1.52	1.46	1.39	1.32	1.22	1.00

$\alpha = 0.025$

Cumulative Probabilities = 0.975

Upper-Tail Areas = 0.025

Numerator, df_1

Denominator, df_2	1	2	3	4	5	6	7	8	9	10	12	15	20	24	30	40	60	120	∞
1	647.80	799.50	864.20	899.60	921.80	937.10	948.20	956.70	963.30	968.60	976.70	984.90	993.10	997.20	1,001.00	1,006.00	1,010.00	1,014.00	1,018.00
2	38.51	39.00	39.17	39.25	39.30	39.33	39.36	39.39	39.39	39.40	39.41	39.43	39.45	39.46	39.46	39.47	39.48	39.49	39.50
3	17.44	16.04	15.44	15.10	14.88	14.73	14.62	14.54	14.47	14.42	14.34	14.25	14.17	14.12	14.08	14.04	13.99	13.95	13.90
4	12.22	10.65	9.98	9.60	9.36	9.20	9.07	8.98	8.90	8.84	8.75	8.66	8.56	8.51	8.46	8.41	8.36	8.31	8.26
5	10.01	8.43	7.76	7.39	7.15	6.98	6.85	6.76	6.68	6.62	6.52	6.43	6.33	6.28	6.23	6.18	6.12	6.07	6.02
6	8.81	7.26	6.60	6.23	5.99	5.82	5.70	5.60	5.52	5.46	5.37	5.27	5.17	5.12	5.07	5.01	4.96	4.90	4.85
7	8.07	6.54	5.89	5.52	5.29	5.12	4.99	4.90	4.82	4.76	4.67	4.57	4.47	4.42	4.36	4.31	4.25	4.20	4.14
8	7.57	6.06	5.42	5.05	4.82	4.65	4.53	4.43	4.36	4.30	4.20	4.10	4.00	3.95	3.89	3.84	3.78	3.73	3.67
9	7.21	5.71	5.08	4.72	4.48	4.32	4.20	4.10	4.03	3.96	3.87	3.77	3.67	3.61	3.56	3.51	3.45	3.39	3.33
10	6.94	5.46	4.83	4.47	4.24	4.07	3.95	3.85	3.78	3.72	3.62	3.52	3.42	3.37	3.31	3.26	3.20	3.14	3.08
11	6.72	5.26	4.63	4.28	4.04	3.88	3.76	3.66	3.59	3.53	3.43	3.33	3.23	3.17	3.12	3.06	3.00	2.94	2.88
12	6.55	5.10	4.47	4.12	3.89	3.73	3.61	3.51	3.44	3.37	3.28	3.18	3.07	3.02	2.96	2.91	2.85	2.79	2.72
13	6.41	4.97	4.35	4.00	3.77	3.60	3.48	3.39	3.31	3.25	3.15	3.05	2.95	2.89	2.84	2.78	2.72	2.66	2.60
14	6.30	4.86	4.24	3.89	3.66	3.50	3.38	3.29	3.21	3.15	3.05	2.95	2.84	2.79	2.73	2.67	2.61	2.55	2.49
15	6.20	4.77	4.15	3.80	3.58	3.41	3.29	3.20	3.12	3.06	2.96	2.86	2.76	2.70	2.64	2.59	2.52	2.46	2.40
16	6.12	4.69	4.08	3.73	3.50	3.34	3.22	3.12	3.05	2.99	2.89	2.79	2.68	2.63	2.57	2.51	2.45	2.38	2.32
17	6.04	4.62	4.01	3.66	3.44	3.28	3.16	3.06	2.98	2.92	2.82	2.72	2.62	2.56	2.50	2.44	2.38	2.32	2.25
18	5.98	4.56	3.95	3.61	3.38	3.22	3.10	3.01	2.93	2.87	2.77	2.67	2.56	2.50	2.44	2.38	2.32	2.26	2.19
19	5.92	4.51	3.90	3.56	3.33	3.17	3.05	2.96	2.88	2.82	2.72	2.62	2.51	2.45	2.39	2.33	2.27	2.20	2.13
20	5.87	4.46	3.86	3.51	3.29	3.13	3.01	2.91	2.84	2.77	2.68	2.57	2.46	2.41	2.35	2.29	2.22	2.16	2.09
21	5.83	4.42	3.82	3.48	3.25	3.09	2.97	2.87	2.80	2.73	2.64	2.53	2.42	2.37	2.31	2.25	2.18	2.11	2.04
22	5.79	4.38	3.78	3.44	3.22	3.05	2.93	2.84	2.76	2.70	2.60	2.50	2.39	2.33	2.27	2.21	2.14	2.08	2.00
23	5.75	4.35	3.75	3.41	3.18	3.02	2.90	2.81	2.73	2.67	2.57	2.47	2.36	2.30	2.24	2.18	2.11	2.04	1.97
24	5.72	4.32	3.72	3.38	3.15	2.99	2.87	2.78	2.70	2.64	2.54	2.44	2.33	2.27	2.21	2.15	2.08	2.01	1.94
25	5.69	4.29	3.69	3.35	3.13	2.97	2.85	2.75	2.68	2.61	2.51	2.41	2.30	2.24	2.18	2.12	2.05	1.98	1.91
26	5.66	4.27	3.67	3.33	3.10	2.94	2.82	2.73	2.65	2.59	2.49	2.39	2.28	2.22	2.16	2.09	2.03	1.95	1.88
27	5.63	4.24	3.65	3.31	3.08	2.92	2.80	2.71	2.63	2.57	2.47	2.36	2.25	2.19	2.13	2.07	2.00	1.93	1.85
28	5.61	4.22	3.63	3.29	3.06	2.90	2.78	2.69	2.61	2.55	2.45	2.34	2.23	2.17	2.11	2.05	1.98	1.91	1.83
29	5.59	4.20	3.61	3.27	3.04	2.88	2.76	2.67	2.59	2.53	2.43	2.32	2.21	2.15	2.09	2.03	1.96	1.89	1.81
30	5.57	4.18	3.59	3.25	3.03	2.87	2.75	2.65	2.57	2.51	2.41	2.31	2.20	2.14	2.07	2.01	1.94	1.87	1.79
40	5.42	4.05	3.46	3.13	2.90	2.74	2.62	2.53	2.45	2.39	2.29	2.18	2.07	2.01	1.94	1.88	1.80	1.72	1.64
60	5.29	3.93	3.34	3.01	2.79	2.63	2.51	2.41	2.33	2.27	2.17	2.06	1.94	1.88	1.82	1.74	1.67	1.58	1.48
120	5.15	3.80	3.23	2.89	2.67	2.52	2.39	2.30	2.22	2.16	2.05	1.94	1.82	1.76	1.69	1.61	1.53	1.43	1.31
∞	5.02	3.69	3.12	2.79	2.57	2.41	2.29	2.19	2.11	2.05	1.94	1.83	1.71	1.64	1.57	1.48	1.39	1.27	1.00

continued

TABLE E.5
Critical Values of F (continued)

Cumulative Probabilities = 0.99

Upper-Tail Areas = 0.01

Numerator, df_1

Denominator, df_2	1	2	3	4	5	6	7	8	9	10	12	15	20	24	30	40	60	120	∞
1	4,052.00	4,999.50	5,403.00	5,625.00	5,764.00	5,859.00	5,928.00	5,982.00	6,022.00	6,056.00	6,106.00	6,157.00	6,209.00	6,235.00	6,261.00	6,287.00	6,313.00	6,339.00	6,366.00
2	98.50	99.00	99.17	99.25	99.30	99.33	99.36	99.37	99.39	99.40	99.42	99.43	44.45	99.46	99.47	99.47	99.48	99.49	99.50
3	34.12	30.82	29.46	28.71	28.24	27.91	27.67	27.49	27.35	27.23	27.05	26.87	26.69	26.60	26.50	26.41	26.32	26.22	26.13
4	21.20	18.00	16.69	15.98	15.52	15.21	14.98	14.80	14.66	14.55	14.37	14.20	14.02	13.93	13.84	13.75	13.65	13.56	13.46
5	16.26	13.27	12.06	11.39	10.97	10.67	10.46	10.29	10.16	10.05	9.89	9.72	9.55	9.47	9.38	9.29	9.20	9.11	9.02
6	13.75	10.92	9.78	9.15	8.75	8.47	8.26	8.10	7.98	7.87	7.72	7.56	7.40	7.31	7.23	7.14	7.06	6.97	6.88
7	12.25	9.55	8.45	7.85	7.46	7.19	6.99	6.84	6.72	6.62	6.47	6.31	6.16	6.07	5.99	5.91	5.82	5.74	5.65
8	11.26	8.65	7.59	7.01	6.63	6.37	6.18	6.03	5.91	5.81	5.67	5.52	5.36	5.28	5.20	5.12	5.03	4.95	4.86
9	10.56	8.02	6.99	6.42	6.06	5.80	5.61	5.47	5.35	5.26	5.11	4.96	4.81	4.73	4.65	4.57	4.48	4.40	4.31
10	10.04	7.56	6.55	5.99	5.64	5.39	5.20	5.06	4.94	4.85	4.71	4.56	4.41	4.33	4.25	4.17	4.08	4.00	3.91
11	9.65	7.21	6.22	5.67	5.32	5.07	4.89	4.74	4.63	4.54	4.40	4.25	4.10	4.02	3.94	3.86	3.78	3.69	3.60
12	9.33	6.93	5.95	5.41	5.06	4.82	4.64	4.50	4.39	4.30	4.16	4.01	3.86	3.78	3.70	3.62	3.54	3.45	3.36
13	9.07	6.70	5.74	5.21	4.86	4.62	4.44	4.30	4.19	4.10	3.96	3.82	3.66	3.59	3.51	3.43	3.34	3.25	3.17
14	8.86	6.51	5.56	5.04	4.69	4.46	4.28	4.14	4.03	3.94	3.80	3.66	3.51	3.43	3.35	3.27	3.18	3.09	3.00
15	8.68	6.36	5.42	4.89	4.56	4.32	4.14	4.00	3.89	3.80	3.67	3.52	3.37	3.29	3.21	3.13	3.05	2.96	2.87
16	8.53	6.23	5.29	4.77	4.44	4.20	4.03	3.89	3.78	3.69	3.55	3.41	3.26	3.18	3.10	3.02	2.93	2.81	2.75
17	8.40	6.11	5.18	4.67	4.34	4.10	3.93	3.79	3.68	3.59	3.46	3.31	3.16	3.08	3.00	2.92	2.83	2.75	2.65
18	8.29	6.01	5.09	4.58	4.25	4.01	3.84	3.71	3.60	3.51	3.37	3.23	3.08	3.00	2.92	2.84	2.75	2.66	2.57
19	8.18	5.93	5.01	4.50	4.17	3.94	3.77	3.63	3.52	3.43	3.30	3.15	3.00	2.92	2.84	2.76	2.67	2.58	2.49
20	8.10	5.85	4.94	4.43	4.10	3.87	3.70	3.56	3.46	3.37	3.23	3.09	2.94	2.86	2.78	2.69	2.61	2.52	2.42
21	8.02	5.78	4.87	4.37	4.04	3.81	3.64	3.51	3.40	3.31	3.17	3.03	2.88	2.80	2.72	2.64	2.55	2.46	2.36
22	7.95	5.72	4.82	4.31	3.99	3.76	3.59	3.45	3.35	3.26	3.12	2.98	2.83	2.75	2.67	2.58	2.50	2.40	2.31
23	7.88	5.66	4.76	4.26	3.94	3.71	3.54	3.41	3.30	3.21	3.07	2.93	2.78	2.70	2.62	2.54	2.45	2.35	2.26
24	7.82	5.61	4.72	4.22	3.90	3.67	3.50	3.36	3.26	3.17	3.03	2.89	2.74	2.66	2.58	2.49	2.40	2.31	2.21
25	7.77	5.57	4.68	4.18	3.85	3.63	3.46	3.32	3.22	3.13	2.99	2.85	2.70	2.62	2.54	2.45	2.36	2.27	2.17
26	7.72	5.53	4.64	4.14	3.82	3.59	3.42	3.29	3.18	3.09	2.96	2.81	2.66	2.58	2.50	2.42	2.33	2.23	2.13
27	7.68	5.49	4.60	4.11	3.78	3.56	3.39	3.26	3.15	3.06	2.93	2.78	2.63	2.55	2.47	2.38	2.29	2.20	2.10
28	7.64	5.45	4.57	4.07	3.75	3.53	3.36	3.23	3.12	3.03	2.90	2.75	2.60	2.52	2.44	2.35	2.26	2.17	2.06
29	7.60	5.42	4.54	4.04	3.73	3.50	3.33	3.20	3.09	3.00	2.87	2.73	2.57	2.49	2.41	2.33	2.23	2.14	2.03
30	7.56	5.39	4.51	4.02	3.70	3.47	3.30	3.17	3.07	2.98	2.84	2.70	2.55	2.47	2.39	2.30	2.21	2.11	2.01
40	7.31	5.18	4.31	3.83	3.51	3.29	3.12	2.99	2.89	2.80	2.66	2.52	2.37	2.29	2.20	2.11	2.02	1.92	1.80
60	7.08	4.98	4.13	3.65	3.34	3.12	2.95	2.82	2.72	2.63	2.50	2.35	2.20	2.12	2.03	1.94	1.84	1.73	1.60
120	6.85	4.79	3.95	3.48	3.17	2.96	2.79	2.66	2.56	2.47	2.34	2.19	2.03	1.95	1.86	1.76	1.66	1.53	1.38
∞	6.63	4.61	3.78	3.32	3.02	2.80	2.64	2.51	2.41	2.32	2.18	2.04	1.88	1.79	1.70	1.59	1.47	1.32	1.00

Cumulative Probabilities = 0.995

Upper-Tail Areas = 0.005

$\alpha = 0.005$

Denominator, df_2	Numerator, df_1																		
	1	2	3	4	5	6	7	8	9	10	12	15	20	24	30	40	60	120	∞
1	16,211.00	20,000.00	21,615.00	22,500.00	23,056.00	23,437.00	23,715.00	23,925.00	24,091.00	24,224.00	24,426.00	24,630.00	24,836.00	24,910.00	25,044.00	25,148.00	25,253.00	25,359.00	25,465.00
2	198.50	199.00	199.20	199.20	199.30	199.30	199.40	199.40	199.40	199.40	199.40	199.40	199.40	199.50	199.50	199.50	199.50	199.50	199.50
3	55.55	49.80	47.47	46.19	45.39	44.84	44.43	44.13	43.88	43.69	43.39	43.08	42.78	42.62	42.47	42.31	42.15	41.99	41.83
4	31.33	26.28	24.26	23.15	22.46	21.97	21.62	21.35	21.14	20.97	20.70	20.44	20.17	20.03	19.89	19.75	19.61	19.47	19.32
5	22.78	18.31	16.53	15.56	14.94	14.51	14.20	13.96	13.77	13.62	13.38	13.15	12.90	12.78	12.66	12.53	12.40	12.27	12.11
6	18.63	14.54	12.92	12.03	11.46	11.07	10.79	10.57	10.39	10.25	10.03	9.81	9.59	9.47	9.36	9.24	9.12	9.00	8.88
7	16.24	12.40	10.88	10.05	9.52	9.16	8.89	8.68	8.51	8.38	8.18	7.97	7.75	7.65	7.53	7.42	7.31	7.19	7.08
8	14.69	11.04	9.60	8.81	8.30	7.95	7.69	7.50	7.34	7.21	7.01	6.81	6.61	6.50	6.40	6.29	6.18	6.06	5.95
9	13.61	10.11	8.72	7.96	7.47	7.13	6.88	6.69	6.54	6.42	6.23	6.03	5.83	5.73	5.62	5.52	5.41	5.30	5.19
10	12.83	9.43	8.08	7.34	6.87	6.54	6.30	6.12	5.97	5.85	5.66	5.47	5.27	5.17	5.07	4.97	4.86	4.75	4.61
11	12.23	8.91	7.60	6.88	6.42	6.10	5.86	5.68	5.54	5.42	5.24	5.05	4.86	4.75	4.65	4.55	4.44	4.34	4.23
12	11.75	8.51	7.23	6.52	6.07	5.76	5.52	5.35	5.20	5.09	4.91	4.72	4.53	4.43	4.33	4.23	4.12	4.01	3.90
13	11.37	8.19	6.93	6.23	5.79	5.48	5.25	5.08	4.94	4.82	4.64	4.46	4.27	4.17	4.07	3.97	3.87	3.76	3.65
14	11.06	7.92	6.68	6.00	5.56	5.26	5.03	4.86	4.72	4.60	4.43	4.25	4.06	3.96	3.86	3.76	3.66	3.55	3.41
15	10.80	7.70	6.48	5.80	5.37	5.07	4.85	4.67	4.54	4.42	4.25	4.07	3.88	3.79	3.69	3.58	3.48	3.37	3.26
16	10.58	7.51	6.30	5.64	5.21	4.91	4.69	4.52	4.38	4.27	4.10	3.92	3.73	3.64	3.54	3.44	3.33	3.22	3.11
17	10.38	7.35	6.16	5.50	5.07	4.78	4.56	4.39	4.25	4.14	3.97	3.79	3.61	3.51	3.41	3.31	3.21	3.10	2.98
18	10.22	7.21	6.03	5.37	4.96	4.66	4.44	4.28	4.14	4.03	3.86	3.68	3.50	3.40	3.30	3.20	3.10	2.99	2.87
19	10.07	7.09	5.92	5.27	4.85	4.56	4.34	4.18	4.04	3.93	3.76	3.59	3.40	3.31	3.21	3.11	3.00	2.89	2.78
20	9.94	6.99	5.82	5.17	4.76	4.47	4.26	4.09	3.96	3.85	3.68	3.50	3.32	3.22	3.12	3.02	2.92	2.81	2.69
21	9.83	6.89	5.73	5.09	4.68	4.39	4.18	4.02	3.88	3.77	3.60	3.43	3.24	3.15	3.05	2.95	2.84	2.73	2.61
22	9.73	6.81	5.65	5.02	4.61	4.32	4.11	3.94	3.81	3.70	3.54	3.36	3.18	3.08	2.98	2.88	2.77	2.66	2.55
23	9.63	6.73	5.58	4.95	4.54	4.26	4.05	3.88	3.75	3.64	3.47	3.30	3.12	3.02	2.92	2.82	2.71	2.60	2.48
24	9.55	6.66	5.52	4.89	4.49	4.20	3.99	3.83	3.69	3.59	3.42	3.25	3.06	2.97	2.87	2.77	2.66	2.55	2.43
25	9.48	6.60	5.46	4.84	4.43	4.15	3.94	3.78	3.64	3.54	3.37	3.20	3.01	2.92	2.82	2.72	2.61	2.50	2.38
26	9.41	6.54	5.41	4.79	4.38	4.10	3.89	3.73	3.60	3.49	3.33	3.15	2.97	2.87	2.77	2.67	2.56	2.45	2.33
27	9.34	6.49	5.36	4.74	4.34	4.06	3.85	3.69	3.56	3.45	3.28	3.11	2.93	2.83	2.73	2.63	2.52	2.41	2.29
28	9.28	6.44	5.32	4.70	4.30	4.02	3.81	3.65	3.52	3.41	3.25	3.07	2.89	2.79	2.69	2.59	2.48	2.37	2.25
29	9.23	6.40	5.28	4.66	4.26	3.98	3.77	3.61	3.48	3.38	3.21	3.04	2.86	2.76	2.66	2.56	2.45	2.33	2.21
30	9.18	6.35	5.24	4.62	4.23	3.95	3.74	3.58	3.45	3.34	3.18	3.01	2.82	2.73	2.63	2.52	2.42	2.30	2.18
40	8.83	6.07	4.98	4.37	3.99	3.71	3.51	3.35	3.22	3.12	2.95	2.78	2.60	2.50	2.40	2.30	2.18	2.06	1.93
60	8.49	5.79	4.73	4.14	3.76	3.49	3.29	3.13	3.01	2.90	2.74	2.57	2.39	2.29	2.19	2.08	1.96	1.83	1.69
120	8.18	5.54	4.50	3.92	3.55	3.28	3.09	2.93	2.81	2.71	2.54	2.37	2.19	2.09	1.98	1.87	1.75	1.61	1.43
∞	7.88	5.30	4.28	3.72	3.35	3.09	2.90	2.74	2.62	2.52	2.36	2.19	2.00	1.90	1.79	1.67	1.53	1.36	1.00

TABLE E.6

Critical Values of the Studentized Range, Q

Upper 5% Points ($\alpha = 0.05$)

Denominator, df	Numerator, df																		
	2	3	4	5	6	7	8	9	10	11	12	13	14	15	16	17	18	19	20
1	17.97	26.98	32.82	37.08	40.41	43.12	45.40	47.36	49.07	50.59	51.96	53.20	54.33	55.36	56.32	57.22	58.04	58.83	59.56
2	6.09	8.33	9.80	10.88	11.74	12.44	13.03	13.54	13.99	14.39	14.75	15.08	15.38	15.65	15.91	16.14	16.37	16.57	16.77
3	4.50	5.91	6.83	7.50	8.04	8.48	8.85	9.18	9.46	9.72	9.95	10.15	10.35	10.53	10.61	10.84	10.98	11.11	11.24
4	3.93	5.04	5.76	6.29	6.71	7.05	7.35	7.60	7.83	8.03	8.21	8.37	8.53	8.66	8.79	8.91	9.03	9.13	9.23
5	3.64	4.60	5.22	5.67	6.03	6.33	6.58	6.80	7.00	7.17	7.32	7.47	7.60	7.72	7.83	7.93	8.03	8.12	8.21
6	3.46	4.34	4.90	5.31	5.63	5.90	6.12	6.32	6.49	6.65	6.79	6.92	7.03	7.14	7.24	7.34	7.43	7.51	7.59
7	3.34	4.17	4.68	5.06	5.36	5.61	5.82	6.00	6.16	6.30	6.43	6.55	6.66	6.76	6.85	6.94	7.02	7.10	7.17
8	3.26	4.04	4.53	4.89	5.17	5.40	5.60	5.77	5.92	6.05	6.18	6.29	6.39	6.48	6.57	6.65	6.73	6.80	6.87
9	3.20	3.95	4.42	4.76	5.02	5.24	5.43	5.60	5.74	5.87	5.98	6.09	6.19	6.28	6.36	6.44	6.51	6.58	6.64
10	3.15	3.88	4.33	4.65	4.91	5.12	5.31	5.46	5.60	5.72	5.83	5.93	6.03	6.11	6.20	6.27	6.34	6.41	6.47
11	3.11	3.82	4.26	4.57	4.82	5.03	5.20	5.35	5.49	5.61	5.71	5.81	5.90	5.98	6.06	6.13	6.20	6.27	6.33
12	3.08	3.77	4.20	4.51	4.75	4.95	5.12	5.27	5.40	5.51	5.62	5.71	5.80	5.88	5.95	6.02	6.09	6.15	6.21
13	3.06	3.74	4.15	4.45	4.69	4.89	5.05	5.19	5.32	5.43	5.53	5.63	5.71	5.79	5.86	5.93	6.00	6.06	6.11
14	3.03	3.70	4.11	4.41	4.64	4.83	4.99	5.13	5.25	5.36	5.46	5.55	5.64	5.71	5.79	5.85	5.92	5.97	6.03
15	3.01	3.67	4.08	4.37	4.60	4.78	4.94	5.08	5.20	5.31	5.40	5.49	5.57	5.65	5.72	5.79	5.85	5.90	5.96
16	3.00	3.65	4.05	4.33	4.56	4.74	4.90	5.03	5.15	5.26	5.35	5.44	5.52	5.59	5.66	5.73	5.79	5.84	5.90
17	2.98	3.63	4.02	4.30	4.52	4.71	4.86	4.99	5.11	5.21	5.31	5.39	5.47	5.54	5.61	5.68	5.73	5.79	5.84
18	2.97	3.61	4.00	4.28	4.50	4.67	4.82	4.96	5.07	5.17	5.27	5.35	5.43	5.50	5.57	5.63	5.69	5.74	5.79
19	2.96	3.59	3.98	4.25	4.47	4.65	4.79	4.92	5.04	5.14	5.23	5.32	5.39	5.46	5.53	5.59	5.65	5.70	5.75
20	2.95	3.58	3.96	4.23	4.45	4.62	4.77	4.90	5.01	5.11	5.20	5.28	5.36	5.43	5.49	5.55	5.61	5.66	5.71
24	2.92	3.53	3.90	4.17	4.37	4.54	4.68	4.81	4.92	5.01	5.10	5.18	5.25	5.32	5.38	5.44	5.49	5.55	5.59
30	2.89	3.49	3.85	4.10	4.30	4.46	4.60	4.72	4.82	4.92	5.00	5.08	5.15	5.21	5.27	5.33	5.38	5.43	5.48
40	2.86	3.44	3.79	4.04	4.23	4.39	4.52	4.64	4.74	4.82	4.90	4.98	5.04	5.11	5.16	5.22	5.27	5.31	5.36
60	2.83	3.40	3.74	3.98	4.16	4.31	4.44	4.55	4.65	4.73	4.81	4.88	4.94	5.00	5.06	5.11	5.15	5.20	5.24
120	2.80	3.36	3.69	3.92	4.10	4.24	4.36	4.47	4.56	4.64	4.71	4.78	4.84	4.90	4.95	5.00	5.04	5.09	5.13
∞	2.77	3.31	3.63	3.86	4.03	4.17	4.29	4.39	4.47	4.55	4.62	4.68	4.74	4.80	4.85	4.89	4.93	4.97	5.01

continued

TABLE E.6

Critical Values of the Studentized Range, Q

Upper 1% Points ($\alpha = 0.01$)

Denominator, df	Numerator, df																		
	2	3	4	5	6	7	8	9	10	11	12	13	14	15	16	17	18	19	20
1	90.03	135.00	164.30	185.60	202.20	215.80	227.20	237.00	245.60	253.20	260.00	266.20	271.80	277.00	281.80	286.30	290.40	294.30	298.00
2	14.04	19.02	22.29	24.72	26.63	28.20	29.53	30.68	31.69	32.59	33.40	34.13	34.81	35.43	36.00	36.53	37.03	37.50	37.95
3	8.26	10.62	12.17	13.33	14.24	15.00	15.64	16.20	16.69	17.13	17.53	17.89	18.22	18.52	18.81	19.07	19.32	19.55	19.77
4	6.51	8.12	9.17	9.96	10.58	11.10	11.55	11.93	12.27	12.57	12.84	13.09	13.32	13.53	13.73	13.91	14.08	14.24	14.40
5	5.70	6.98	7.80	8.42	8.91	9.32	9.67	9.97	10.24	10.48	10.70	10.89	11.08	11.24	11.40	11.55	11.68	11.81	11.93
6	5.24	6.33	7.03	7.56	7.97	8.32	8.61	8.87	9.10	9.30	9.49	9.65	9.81	9.95	10.08	10.21	10.32	10.43	10.54
7	4.95	5.92	6.54	7.01	7.37	7.68	7.94	8.17	8.37	8.55	8.71	8.86	9.00	9.12	9.24	9.35	9.46	9.55	9.65
8	4.75	5.64	6.20	6.63	6.96	7.24	7.47	7.68	7.86	8.03	8.18	8.31	8.44	8.55	8.66	8.76	8.85	8.94	9.03
9	4.60	5.43	5.96	6.35	6.66	6.92	7.13	7.32	7.50	7.65	7.78	7.91	8.03	8.13	8.23	8.33	8.41	8.50	8.57
10	4.48	5.27	5.77	6.14	6.43	6.67	6.87	7.06	7.21	7.36	7.49	7.60	7.71	7.81	7.91	7.99	8.08	8.15	8.23
11	4.39	5.15	5.62	5.97	6.25	6.48	6.67	6.84	6.99	7.13	7.25	7.36	7.47	7.56	7.65	7.73	7.81	7.88	7.95
12	4.32	5.04	5.50	5.84	6.10	6.32	6.51	6.67	6.81	6.94	7.06	7.17	7.26	7.36	7.44	7.52	7.59	7.66	7.73
13	4.26	4.96	5.40	5.73	5.98	6.19	6.37	6.53	6.67	6.79	6.90	7.01	7.10	7.19	7.27	7.35	7.42	7.49	7.55
14	4.21	4.90	5.32	5.63	5.88	6.09	6.26	6.41	6.54	6.66	6.77	6.87	6.96	7.05	7.13	7.20	7.27	7.33	7.40
15	4.17	4.84	5.25	5.56	5.80	5.99	6.16	6.31	6.44	6.56	6.66	6.76	6.85	6.93	7.00	7.07	7.14	7.20	7.26
16	4.13	4.79	5.19	5.49	5.72	5.92	6.08	6.22	6.35	6.46	6.56	6.66	6.74	6.82	6.90	6.97	7.03	7.09	7.15
17	4.10	4.74	5.14	5.43	5.66	5.85	6.01	6.15	6.27	6.38	6.48	6.57	6.66	6.73	6.81	6.87	6.94	7.00	7.05
18	4.07	4.70	5.09	5.38	5.60	5.79	5.94	6.08	6.20	6.31	6.41	6.50	6.58	6.66	6.73	6.79	6.85	6.91	6.97
19	4.05	4.67	5.05	5.33	5.55	5.74	5.89	6.02	6.14	6.25	6.34	6.43	6.51	6.59	6.65	6.72	6.78	6.84	6.89
20	4.02	4.64	5.02	5.29	5.51	5.69	5.84	5.97	6.09	6.19	6.29	6.37	6.45	6.52	6.59	6.65	6.71	6.77	6.82
24	3.96	4.55	4.91	5.17	5.37	5.54	5.69	5.81	5.92	6.02	6.11	6.19	6.26	6.33	6.39	6.45	6.51	6.56	6.61
30	3.89	4.46	4.80	5.05	5.24	5.40	5.54	5.65	5.76	5.85	5.93	6.01	6.08	6.14	6.20	6.26	6.31	6.36	6.41
40	3.83	4.37	4.70	4.93	5.11	5.27	5.39	5.50	5.60	5.69	5.76	5.84	5.90	5.96	6.02	6.07	6.12	6.17	6.21
60	3.76	4.28	4.60	4.82	4.99	5.13	5.25	5.36	5.45	5.53	5.60	5.67	5.73	5.79	5.84	5.89	5.93	5.97	6.02
120	3.70	4.20	4.50	4.71	4.87	5.01	5.12	5.21	5.30	5.38	5.44	5.51	5.56	5.61	5.66	5.71	5.75	5.79	5.83
∞	3.64	4.12	4.40	4.60	4.76	4.88	4.99	5.08	5.16	5.23	5.29	5.35	5.40	5.45	5.49	5.54	5.57	5.61	5.65

Source: Extracted from H. L. Harter and D. S. Clemm, "The Probability Integrals of the Range and of the Studentized Range—Probability Integral, Percentage Points, and Moments of the Range," *Wright Air Development Technical Report 58–484*, Vol. 1, 1959.

TABLE E.7

Critical Values, d_L and d_U, of the Durbin-Watson Statistic, D (Critical Values Are One-Sided)[a]

	α = 0.05										α = 0.01									
	k = 1		k = 2		k = 3		k = 4		k = 5		k = 1		k = 2		k = 3		k = 4		k = 5	
n	d_L	d_U	d_L	d_U	d_L	d_U	d_L	d_U	d_L	d_U	d_L	d_U	d_L	d_U	d_L	d_U	d_L	d_U	d_L	d_U
15	1.08	1.36	.95	1.54	.82	1.75	.69	1.97	.56	2.21	.81	1.07	.70	1.25	.59	1.46	.49	1.70	.39	1.96
16	1.10	1.37	.98	1.54	.86	1.73	.74	1.93	.62	2.15	.84	1.09	.74	1.25	.63	1.44	.53	1.66	.44	1.90
17	1.13	1.38	1.02	1.54	.90	1.71	.78	1.90	.67	2.10	.87	1.10	.77	1.25	.67	1.43	.57	1.63	.48	1.85
18	1.16	1.39	1.05	1.53	.93	1.69	.82	1.87	.71	2.06	.90	1.12	.80	1.26	.71	1.42	.61	1.60	.52	1.80
19	1.18	1.40	1.08	1.53	.97	1.68	.86	1.85	.75	2.02	.93	1.13	.83	1.26	.74	1.41	.65	1.58	.56	1.77
20	1.20	1.41	1.10	1.54	1.00	1.68	.90	1.83	.79	1.99	.95	1.15	.86	1.27	.77	1.41	.68	1.57	.60	1.74
21	1.22	1.42	1.13	1.54	1.03	1.67	.93	1.81	.83	1.96	.97	1.16	.89	1.27	.80	1.41	.72	1.55	.63	1.71
22	1.24	1.43	1.15	1.54	1.05	1.66	.96	1.80	.86	1.94	1.00	1.17	.91	1.28	.83	1.40	.75	1.54	.66	1.69
23	1.26	1.44	1.17	1.54	1.08	1.66	.99	1.79	.90	1.92	1.02	1.19	.94	1.29	.86	1.40	.77	1.53	.70	1.67
24	1.27	1.45	1.19	1.55	1.10	1.66	1.01	1.78	.93	1.90	1.04	1.20	.96	1.30	.88	1.41	.80	1.53	.72	1.66
25	1.29	1.45	1.21	1.55	1.12	1.66	1.04	1.77	.95	1.89	1.05	1.21	.98	1.30	.90	1.41	.83	1.52	.75	1.65
26	1.30	1.46	1.22	1.55	1.14	1.65	1.06	1.76	.98	1.88	1.07	1.22	1.00	1.31	.93	1.41	.85	1.52	.78	1.64
27	1.32	1.47	1.24	1.56	1.16	1.65	1.08	1.76	1.01	1.86	1.09	1.23	1.02	1.32	.95	1.41	.88	1.51	.81	1.63
28	1.33	1.48	1.26	1.56	1.18	1.65	1.10	1.75	1.03	1.85	1.10	1.24	1.04	1.32	.97	1.41	.90	1.51	.83	1.62
29	1.34	1.48	1.27	1.56	1.20	1.65	1.12	1.74	1.05	1.84	1.12	1.25	1.05	1.33	.99	1.42	.92	1.51	.85	1.61
30	1.35	1.49	1.28	1.57	1.21	1.65	1.14	1.74	1.07	1.83	1.13	1.26	1.07	1.34	1.01	1.42	.94	1.51	.88	1.61
31	1.36	1.50	1.30	1.57	1.23	1.65	1.16	1.74	1.09	1.83	1.15	1.27	1.08	1.34	1.02	1.42	.96	1.51	.90	1.60
32	1.37	1.50	1.31	1.57	1.24	1.65	1.18	1.73	1.11	1.82	1.16	1.28	1.10	1.35	1.04	1.43	.98	1.51	.92	1.60
33	1.38	1.51	1.32	1.58	1.26	1.65	1.19	1.73	1.13	1.81	1.17	1.29	1.11	1.36	1.05	1.43	1.00	1.51	.94	1.59
34	1.39	1.51	1.33	1.58	1.27	1.65	1.21	1.73	1.15	1.81	1.18	1.30	1.13	1.36	1.07	1.43	1.01	1.51	.95	1.59
35	1.40	1.52	1.34	1.58	1.28	1.65	1.22	1.73	1.16	1.80	1.19	1.31	1.14	1.37	1.08	1.44	1.03	1.51	.97	1.59
36	1.41	1.52	1.35	1.59	1.29	1.66	1.24	1.73	1.18	1.80	1.21	1.32	1.15	1.38	1.10	1.44	1.04	1.51	.99	1.59
37	1.42	1.53	1.36	1.59	1.31	1.66	1.25	1.72	1.19	1.80	1.22	1.32	1.16	1.38	1.11	1.45	1.06	1.51	1.00	1.59
38	1.43	1.54	1.37	1.59	1.32	1.66	1.26	1.72	1.21	1.79	1.23	1.33	1.18	1.39	1.12	1.45	1.07	1.52	1.02	1.58
39	1.43	1.54	1.38	1.60	1.33	1.66	1.27	1.72	1.22	1.79	1.24	1.34	1.19	1.39	1.14	1.45	1.09	1.52	1.03	1.58
40	1.44	1.54	1.39	1.60	1.34	1.66	1.29	1.72	1.23	1.79	1.25	1.34	1.20	1.40	1.15	1.46	1.10	1.52	1.05	1.58
45	1.48	1.57	1.43	1.62	1.38	1.67	1.34	1.72	1.29	1.78	1.29	1.38	1.24	1.42	1.20	1.48	1.16	1.53	1.11	1.58
50	1.50	1.59	1.46	1.63	1.42	1.67	1.38	1.72	1.34	1.77	1.32	1.40	1.28	1.45	1.24	1.49	1.20	1.54	1.16	1.59
55	1.53	1.60	1.49	1.64	1.45	1.68	1.41	1.72	1.38	1.77	1.36	1.43	1.32	1.47	1.28	1.51	1.25	1.55	1.21	1.59
60	1.55	1.62	1.51	1.65	1.48	1.69	1.44	1.73	1.41	1.77	1.38	1.45	1.35	1.48	1.32	1.52	1.28	1.56	1.25	1.60
65	1.57	1.63	1.54	1.66	1.50	1.70	1.47	1.73	1.44	1.77	1.41	1.47	1.38	1.50	1.35	1.53	1.31	1.57	1.28	1.61
70	1.58	1.64	1.55	1.67	1.52	1.70	1.49	1.74	1.46	1.77	1.43	1.49	1.40	1.52	1.37	1.55	1.34	1.58	1.31	1.61
75	1.60	1.65	1.57	1.68	1.54	1.71	1.51	1.74	1.49	1.77	1.45	1.50	1.42	1.53	1.39	1.56	1.37	1.59	1.34	1.62
80	1.61	1.66	1.59	1.69	1.56	1.72	1.53	1.74	1.51	1.77	1.47	1.52	1.44	1.54	1.42	1.57	1.39	1.60	1.36	1.62
85	1.62	1.67	1.60	1.70	1.57	1.72	1.55	1.75	1.52	1.77	1.48	1.53	1.46	1.55	1.43	1.58	1.41	1.60	1.39	1.63
90	1.63	1.68	1.61	1.70	1.59	1.73	1.57	1.75	1.54	1.78	1.50	1.54	1.47	1.56	1.45	1.59	1.43	1.61	1.41	1.64
95	1.64	1.69	1.62	1.71	1.60	1.73	1.58	1.75	1.56	1.78	1.51	1.55	1.49	1.57	1.47	1.60	1.45	1.62	1.42	1.64
100	1.65	1.69	1.63	1.72	1.61	1.74	1.59	1.76	1.57	1.78	1.52	1.56	1.50	1.58	1.48	1.60	1.46	1.63	1.44	1.65

[a] n = number of observations; k = number of independent variables.

Source: Computed from TSP 4.5 based on R. W. Farebrother, "A Remark on Algorithms AS106, AS153, and AS155: The Distribution of a Linear Combination of Chi-Square Random Variables," *Journal of the Royal Statistical Society*, Series C (Applied Statistics), 1984, 29, p. 323–333.

TABLE E.8
Control Chart Factors

Number of Observations in Sample/Subgroup (n)	d_2	d_3	D_3	D_4	A_2
2	1.128	0.853	0	3.267	1.880
3	1.693	0.888	0	2.575	1.023
4	2.059	0.880	0	2.282	0.729
5	2.326	0.864	0	2.114	0.577
6	2.534	0.848	0	2.004	0.483
7	2.704	0.833	0.076	1.924	0.419
8	2.847	0.820	0.136	1.864	0.373
9	2.970	0.808	0.184	1.816	0.337
10	3.078	0.797	0.223	1.777	0.308
11	3.173	0.787	0.256	1.744	0.285
12	3.258	0.778	0.283	1.717	0.266
13	3.336	0.770	0.307	1.693	0.249
14	3.407	0.763	0.328	1.672	0.235
15	3.472	0.756	0.347	1.653	0.223
16	3.532	0.750	0.363	1.637	0.212
17	3.588	0.744	0.378	1.622	0.203
18	3.640	0.739	0.391	1.609	0.194
19	3.689	0.733	0.404	1.596	0.187
20	3.735	0.729	0.415	1.585	0.180
21	3.778	0.724	0.425	1.575	0.173
22	3.819	0.720	0.435	1.565	0.167
23	3.858	0.716	0.443	1.557	0.162
24	3.895	0.712	0.452	1.548	0.157
25	3.931	0.708	0.459	1.541	0.153

Source: Reprinted from *ASTM-STP 15D* by kind permission of the American Society for Testing and Materials.

TABLE E.9

The Standardized Normal Distribution

Entry represents area under the standardized normal
distribution from the mean to Z

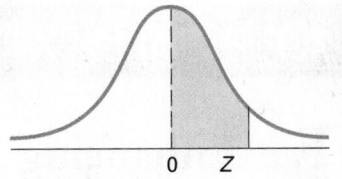

Z	.00	.01	.02	.03	.04	.05	.06	.07	.08	.09
0.0	.0000	.0040	.0080	.0120	.0160	.0199	.0239	.0279	.0319	.0359
0.1	.0398	.0438	.0478	.0517	.0557	.0596	.0636	.0675	.0714	.0753
0.2	.0793	.0832	.0871	.0910	.0948	.0987	.1026	.1064	.1103	.1141
0.3	.1179	.1217	.1255	.1293	.1331	.1368	.1406	.1443	.1480	.1517
0.4	.1554	.1591	.1628	.1664	.1700	.1736	.1772	.1808	.1844	.1879
0.5	.1915	.1950	.1985	.2019	.2054	.2088	.2123	.2157	.2190	.2224
0.6	.2257	.2291	.2324	.2357	.2389	.2422	.2454	.2486	.2518	.2549
0.7	.2580	.2612	.2642	.2673	.2704	.2734	.2764	.2794	.2823	.2852
0.8	.2881	.2910	.2939	.2967	.2995	.3023	.3051	.3078	.3106	.3133
0.9	.3159	.3186	.3212	.3238	.3264	.3289	.3315	.3340	.3365	.3389
1.0	.3413	.3438	.3461	.3485	.3508	.3531	.3554	.3577	.3599	.3621
1.1	.3643	.3665	.3686	.3708	.3729	.3749	.3770	.3790	.3810	.3830
1.2	.3849	.3869	.3888	.3907	.3925	.3944	.3962	.3980	.3997	.4015
1.3	.4032	.4049	.4066	.4082	.4099	.4115	.4131	.4147	.4162	.4177
1.4	.4192	.4207	.4222	.4236	.4251	.4265	.4279	.4292	.4306	.4319
1.5	.4332	.4345	.4357	.4370	.4382	.4394	.4406	.4418	.4429	.4441
1.6	.4452	.4463	.4474	.4484	.4495	.4505	.4515	.4525	.4535	.4545
1.7	.4554	.4564	.4573	.4582	.4591	.4599	.4608	.4616	.4625	.4633
1.8	.4641	.4649	.4656	.4664	.4671	.4678	.4686	.4693	.4699	.4706
1.9	.4713	.4719	.4726	.4732	.4738	.4744	.4750	.4756	.4761	.4767
2.0	.4772	.4778	.4783	.4788	.4793	.4798	.4803	.4808	.4812	.4817
2.1	.4821	.4826	.4830	.4834	.4838	.4842	.4846	.4850	.4854	.4857
2.2	.4861	.4864	.4868	.4871	.4875	.4878	.4881	.4884	.4887	.4890
2.3	.4893	.4896	.4898	.4901	.4904	.4906	.4909	.4911	.4913	.4916
2.4	.4918	.4920	.4922	.4925	.4927	.4929	.4931	.4932	.4934	.4936
2.5	.4938	.4940	.4941	.4943	.4945	.4946	.4948	.4949	.4951	.4952
2.6	.4953	.4955	.4956	.4957	.4959	.4960	.4961	.4962	.4963	.4964
2.7	.4965	.4966	.4967	.4968	.4969	.4970	.4971	.4972	.4973	.4974
2.8	.4974	.4975	.4976	.4977	.4977	.4978	.4979	.4979	.4980	.4981
2.9	.4981	.4982	.4982	.4983	.4984	.4984	.4985	.4985	.4986	.4986
3.0	.49865	.49869	.49874	.49878	.49882	.49886	.49889	.49893	.49897	.49900
3.1	.49903	.49906	.49910	.49913	.49916	.49918	.49921	.49924	.49926	.49929
3.2	.49931	.49934	.49936	.49938	.49940	.49942	.49944	.49946	.49948	.49950
3.3	.49952	.49953	.49955	.49957	.49958	.49960	.49961	.49962	.49964	.49965
3.4	.49966	.49968	.49969	.49970	.49971	.49972	.49973	.49974	.49975	.49976
3.5	.49977	.49978	.49978	.49979	.49980	.49981	.49981	.49982	.49983	.49983
3.6	.49984	.49985	.49985	.49986	.49986	.49987	.49987	.49988	.49988	.49989
3.7	.49989	.49990	.49990	.49990	.49991	.49991	.49992	.49992	.49992	.49992
3.8	.49993	.49993	.49993	.49994	.49994	.49994	.49994	.49995	.49995	.49995
3.9	.49995	.49995	.49996	.49996	.49996	.49996	.49996	.49996	.49997	.49997

F.1 Enhancing Workbook Presentation

You can enhance workbook presentation by using common formatting commands and rearranging the order of the worksheets and chart sheets in a workbook.

Table F.1 presents the shortcuts for worksheet formatting operations used to create the Excel Guide workbooks and the results shown throughout this book. These shortcuts can be found in the Home tab of the Excel Office Ribbon (see Figure F.1 on page 813).

TABLE F.1

Shortcuts to Common Formatting Operations

Number	Operation Name	Use
❶	Font Face and Font Size	Changes the text font face and size for cell entries and chart labels. Worksheets shown in this book have been formatted as **Calibri 11**. Many DATA worksheets have been formatted as **Arial 10**.
❷	Boldface	Toggles on (or off) boldface text style for the currently selected object.
❸	Italic	Toggles on (or off) italic text style for the currently selected object.
❹	Borders	Displays a gallery of choices that permit drawing lines (borders) around a cell or cell range.
❺	Fill Color	Displays a gallery of choices for the background color of a cell. Immediately to the right of **Fill Color** is the related **Font Color** (not used in any example in this book).
❻	Align Text	Aligns the display of the contents of a worksheet cell. Three buttons are available: **Align Text Left**, **Center**, and **Align Text Right**.
❼	Merge & Center	Merges (combines) adjacent cells into one cell and centers the display of the contents of that cell. In Excel 2007, this button is also a drop-down list that offers additional **Merge** and **Unmerge** choices.
❽	Percent	Formats the display of a number value in a cell as a percentage. The value 1 displays as 100%, the value 0.01 displays as 1%. To the immediate left of **Percent** is **Currency**, which formats values as dollars and cents. Do not confuse **Currency** formatting with the symbol used to identify absolute cell references.
❾	Increase Decimal and Decrease Decimal	Adjusts the number of decimal places to display a number value in a cell.
❿	Format	Displays a gallery of choices that affect the row height and column width of a cell. The most common usage is to select a column and then select **Format → AutoFit Column Width**.

FIGURE F.1

Home tab of the Excel Office Ribbon (with number labels keyed to Table F.1)

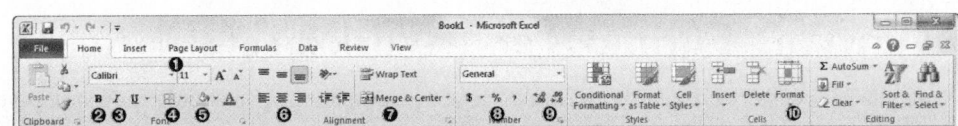

Use the **Move or Copy** command to rearrange the order of the worksheets and chart sheets in a workbook. To move or copy a worksheet, right-click the worksheet sheet tab and click **Move or Copy** in the shortcut menu that appears. In the Move or Copy dialog box, select the destination workbook from the **To book** drop-down list—select **(new book)** to place the worksheet in a new workbook—and select a position for the worksheet in the **Before sheet** list. If making a copy, also check **Create a copy**. Click **OK** to complete the move or copy operation.

Worksheet cell formatting can also be done through the **Format Cells** command. When editing a worksheet, right-click a cell and then click **Format Cells** from the shortcut menu. In the Format Cells dialog box that appears, you can perform all the formatting operations discussed in Table F.1 and more.

F.2 Useful Keyboard Shortcuts

In Excel, certain keys or keystroke combinations (one or more keys held down as you press another key) are keyboard shortcuts that act as alternate means of executing common operations. Table F.2 presents some common shortcuts that represent some of the common Excel operations described in this book. (Keystroke combinations are shown using a plus sign, as in **Ctrl+C**, which means "while holding down the **Ctrl** key, press the **C** key.")

TABLE F.2

Useful Keyboard Shortcuts

Key	Operation
Backspace	Erases typed characters to the left of the current position, one character at a time.
Delete	Erases characters to the right of the cursor, one character at a time.
Enter or Tab	Finalizes an entry typed into a worksheet cell. Implied by the use of the verb *enter* in the Excel Guides.
Esc	Cancels an action or a dialog box. Equivalent to the dialog box **Cancel** button.
F1	Displays the Excel help system.
Ctrl+C	Copies the currently selected worksheet entry or chart label.
Ctrl+V	Pastes the currently copied object into the currently selected worksheet cell or chart label.
Ctrl+X	Cuts the currently selected worksheet entry or chart label. You cut, and not delete, something in order to paste it somewhere else.
Ctrl+B	Toggles on (or off) boldface text style for the currently selected object.
Ctrl+I	Toggles on (or off) italic text style for the currently selected object.
Ctrl+F	Finds a **Find what** value.
Ctrl+H	Replaces a **Find what** value with the **Replace with** value.
Ctrl+Z	Undoes the last operation.
Ctrl+Y	Redoes the last operation.
Ctrl+`	Toggles on (or off) formulas view of worksheet.
Ctrl+Shift+Enter	Enters an array formula.

Note: Using the copy-and-paste keyboard shortcut, Ctrl+C and Ctrl+V, to copy formulas from one worksheet cell to another is subject to the same type of adjustment.

F.3 Verifying Formulas and Worksheets

If you use formulas in your worksheets, you should review and verify formulas before you use their results. To view the formulas in a worksheet, press Ctrl+` (grave accent key). To restore the original view, the results of the formulas, press Ctrl+` a second time.

As you create and use more complicated worksheets, you might want to visually examine the relationships among a formula and the cells it uses (called the *precedents*) and the cells that use the results of the formula (the *dependents*). Select **Formulas → Trace Precedents** (or **Trace Dependents**). When you are finished, clear all trace arrows by selecting **Formulas → Remove Arrows**.

F.4 Chart Formatting

Excel incorrectly formats the charts created by the *In-Depth Excel* instructions. Use the formatting adjustments in Table F.3 to properly format charts you create. Before applying these adjustments, relocate a chart to its own chart sheet. To do so, right-click the chart background and click **Move Chart** from the shortcut menu. In the Move Chart dialog box, click **New Sheet**, enter a name for the new chart sheet, and click **OK**.

TABLE F.3
Excel Chart Formatting
Adjustments

Layout Tab Selection	Notes
Chart Title → Above Chart	In the box that is added to the chart, double-click **Chart Title** and enter an appropriate title.
Axes Titles → Primary Horizontal Axis Title → Title Below Axis	In the box that is added to the chart, double-click **Axis Title** and enter an appropriate title.
Axes Titles → Primary Vertical Axis Title → Rotated Title	In the box that is added to the chart, double-click **Axis Title** and enter an appropriate title.
Axes Titles → Secondary Horizontal → Axis Title → None and **Axes Titles → Secondary Vertical Axis Title → Rotated Title**	Only for charts that contain secondary axes.
Legend → None	Turns off the chart legend.
Data Labels → None	Turns off the display of values at plotted points or bars in the charts.
Data Table → None	Turns off the display of a summary table on the chart sheet.
Axes → Primary Horizontal Axis → Show Left to Right Axis (or **Show Default Axis**, if listed)	Turns on the display of the X axis.
Axes → Primary Vertical Axis → Show Default Axis	Turns on the display of the Y axis.
Gridlines → Primary Horizontal Gridlines → None	Turns off the improper horizontal gridlines.
Gridlines → Primary Vertical Gridlines → None	Turns off the improper vertical gridlines.

Use all of the adjustments in Table F.3, unless a particular set of charting instructions tells you otherwise. To apply the adjustments, you must be open to the chart sheet that contains the chart to be adjusted. All adjustments are made by first selecting the **Layout** tab (under the Chart Tools heading). If a Layout tab selection cannot be made, the adjustment does not apply to the type of chart being adjusted. (Excel hides or disables chart formatting choices that do not apply to a particular chart type.)

Occasionally, when you open to a chart sheet, the chart is either too large to be fully seen or too small, surrounded by a chart frame mat that is too large. Click the **Zoom Out** or **Zoom In** buttons, located in the lower-right portion of the Excel window frame, to adjust the display.

F.5   Creating Histograms for Discrete Probability Distributions

You can create a histogram for a discrete probability distribution based on a discrete probabilities table. For example, to create a histogram based on the Figure 6.2 binomial probabilities worksheet on page 256, open to the **COMPUTE worksheet** of the **Binomial workbook**. Select the cell range **B14:B18**, the probabilities in the Binomial Probabilities Table, and:

1. Select **Insert → Column** and select the first **2-D Column** gallery choice (**Clustered Column**).
2. Right-click the chart background and click **Select Data**.

In the Select Data Source dialog box:

3. Click **Edit** under the **Horizontal (Categories) Axis Labels** heading.
4. In the Axis Labels dialog box, enter **=COMPUTE!A14:A18** the cell range of the X axis values. (This cell range must be entered as a formula in the form =*SheetName!CellRange*.) Then, click **OK** to return to the Select Data Source dialog box.
5. Click **OK**.

In the chart:

6. Right-click inside a bar and click **Format Data Series** in the shortcut menu.

In the Format Data Series dialog box:

7. Click **Series Options** in the left pane. In the Series Options right pane, change the **Gap Width** slider to **Large Gap**. Click **Close**.

Relocate the chart to a chart sheet and adjust the chart formatting by using the instructions in Section F.4.

F.6   Pasting with Paste Special

Pasting data from one worksheet to another can sometimes cause unexpected side effects. When the two worksheets are in different workbooks, a simple paste creates an external link to the original workbook. This can lead to errors later if the first workbook is unavailable when the second one is being used. Even pasting between worksheets in the same workbook can lead to problems if what is being pasted is a cell range of formulas.

To avoid such side effects, use **Paste Special** in these special situations. To use this operation, copy the original cell range as you would do normally and select the cell or cell range to be the target of the paste. Right-click the target and click **Paste Special** from the shortcut menu. In the Paste Special dialog box (shown on page 816), click **Values** and then click **OK**. For the first case, Paste Special Values pastes the current values of the cells in the first workbook and not formulas that use cell references to the first workbook. For the second case, Paste Special Values pastes the current evaluation of the formulas copied and not the formulas themselves.

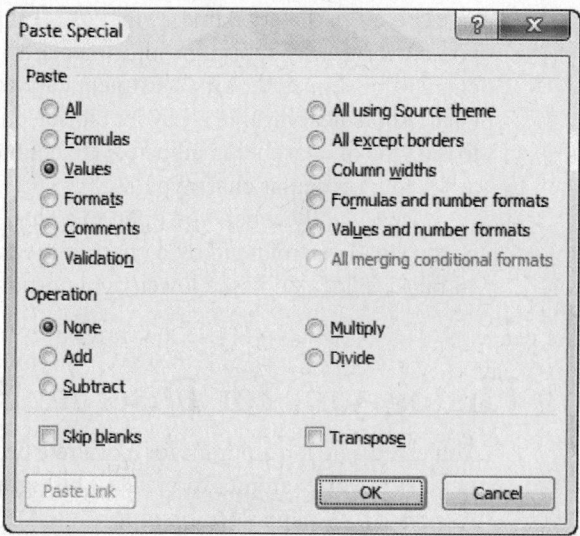

If you use PHStat2 and have data for a procedure in the form of formulas, use Paste Special Values to create columns of equivalent values before using the procedure. (PHStat2 will not work properly if data for a procedure are in the form of formulas.) Paste Special can paste other types of information, including cell formatting information. For a full discussion of Paste Special, see the Excel help system.

G.1 PHStat2 FAQs

What is PHStat2?
PHStat2 is software that makes operating Windows-based Microsoft Excel as distraction free as possible. As a student studying statistics, you can focus mainly on learning statistics and not worry about having to fully master Excel first. PHStat2 contains just about all the statistical methods taught in an introductory statistics course that can be illustrated using Excel.

Which versions of Excel are compatible with PHStat2?
PHStat2 works with Excel 2003 and 32-bit versions of Excel 2007 and Excel 2010. PHStat2 does not work with any Excel version for the Mac. (Mac users can use virtualizing software to run Microsoft Windows and Excel 2003, 2007, or 2010 on their systems in order to use PHStat2.)

How do I get started using PHStat2?
Read the instructions in Section D.2 on page 792 and complete the checklist. As that section states, be sure to completely review the PHStat2 readme file before attempting to add PHStat2 to your system.

Where can I find help if I have problems setting up PHStat2?
If you need help when you set up PHStat2, first review the "Troubleshooting PHStat2" section of the downloadable PHStat2 readme file. If you require additional assistance, visit the PHStat2 website (**www.pearsonhighered.com/phstat**) and go to the web page for your version (see next question) to see if there is any additional information to help you. If necessary, click the **Contact Pearson Technical Support** to contact Pearson Education Customer Technical Support. (Technical Support staff cannot answer questions about the statistical applications of PHStat2 or questions about specific PHStat2 procedures.)

How can I identify which PHStat2 version I have?
Open Microsoft Excel with PHStat2 and select **PHStat → Help for PHStat**. In the dialog box that appears, note the XLA and DLL version numbers. If you downloaded and installed the PHStat2 version designed for this book, both of these numbers will not be lower than 3.3.

How can I be sure that my version of PHStat2 is up-to-date?
The PHStat2 setup program that you can download as part of the online resources for this book will always be the most up-to-date version for use with this book. Slight revisions of PHStat2 may occur during the lifetime of this edition. Those revisions will be noted on the PHStat2 website

(**www.pearsonhighered.com/phstat**) and reflected in the copy of the PHStat2 setup program you can download.

Where can I find tips for using PHStat2?
While your classmates and instructor can be the best sources of tips, you can check for any tips that may be posted on the new third-party PHStat2 community website **phstatcommunity.org** that, at the time of publication of this book, was scheduled to be activated by Fall 2011.

G.2 Excel FAQs

What does "Compatibility Mode" in the title bar mean?
Excel displays "Compatibility Mode" when the workbook you are currently using has been previously stored using the **.xls** file format that is compatible with all Excel versions. Compatibility Mode does not affect Excel functionality but will cause Excel to review your workbook for exclusive-to-Excel-2007-or-2010 formatting properties and objects the next time you save the workbook. (To preserve exclusive features in Excel 2010, select **File → Save As** and select **Excel Workbook (*.xlsx)** from the **Save as type** drop-down list. To preserve exclusive features in Excel 2007, click the **Office Button**, move the mouse pointer over **Save As**, and in the Save As gallery, click **Excel Workbook** to save the workbook in the **.xlsx** file format.)

If you open any of the Excel data or Excel Guide workbooks for this book, you will see "Compatibility Mode," as all workbooks for this book have been stored using the **.xls** format. Generally, it makes little difference whether you use compatibility mode or not. The one exception is when working with PivotTables.

In Excel 2010, how can I specify the custom settings that you recommend?
Select **File → Options**. In the Excel Options dialog box, click **Formulas** in the left pane, and in the **Formulas** right pane, click **Automatic** under Workbook Calculation and verify that all check boxes are checked except **Enable iterative calculation**, **R1C1 reference style**, and **Formulas referring to empty cells**.

In Excel 2007, how can I specify the custom settings that you recommend?
Click the **Office Button** and then click **Excel Options**. In the Excel Options dialog box, click **Formulas** in the left pane, and in the **Formulas** right pane, click **Automatic** under Workbook Calculation and verify that all check boxes

are checked except **Enable iterative calculation**, **R1C1 reference style**, and **Formulas referring to empty cells**.

What Excel security settings will allow the PHStat2 or Visual Explorations add-in to function properly?

Use the instructions in Appendix Section D.3 on page 793 for configuring Excel for PHStat2 for both add-ins.

I do not see the menu for the Visual Explorations (or PHStat2) add-in that I opened. Where is it?

Unlike earlier versions of Excel that allowed add-ins to add menus to the menu bar, Excel 2007 and 2010 places all add-in menus under the Add-ins tab. In order to see the menu, click **Add-ins** and then click the name of the add-in menu.

How can I install the Analysis ToolPak?

Close Excel and rerun the Microsoft Office or Microsoft Excel setup program. When the setup program runs, choose the option that allows you to add components which will be labeled either as **Change** or **Add or Remove Features**. (If you use Windows 7, open the **Programs and Features** Control Panel applet, select the entry for your version or Office or Excel, and then click **Change** at the top of the list of programs.)

In the Installation Options screen, double-click **Microsoft Office Excel** and then double-click **Add-ins.** Click the **Analysis ToolPak** drop-down list button and select **Run from My Computer**. (You may need access to the original Microsoft Office setup program to complete this task.) Upon successful installation, you will see **Data Analysis** as a choice in the **Analysis** group of the **Data** tab when you next open Excel.

Answers to Selected Problems

CHAPTER 1

1.1 (a) ordinal **(b)** ordinal **(c)** nominal **(d)** ordinal **(e)** nominal **(f)** nominal **(g)** ordinal **(h)** nominal **(i)** ordinal **(j)** nominal

1.2

Question	Measurement Scale	Discrete/ Continuous
What is your age?	Ratio	Discrete
Do you have a driver's license?	Nominal	Discrete
What is your gender?	Nominal	Discrete
Do you have any medical conditions?	Nominal	Discrete

1.3 (I) Question 1: Which year did the registered nurse employed in Nursing?

Question 2: How old are you?

(II) Year = Interval.

(III) Age = Ratio discrete.

1.4

QUESTION	Measurement Scale
1. What is your household income?	Ratio-discrete
2. What is your gender (sex)?	Nominal
3. Where is your place of birth?	Nominal
4. What is your religious observation?	Ordinal
5. Did you volunteer in the past?	Nominal
6. What is your sense of belonging to community?	Ordinal
7. Which region did you come from?	Nominal
8. What is your educational level?	Ordinal

1.5 Ratio-discrete.

CHAPTER 2

2.1 (b) The Pareto chart is best for portraying these data because it not only sorts the frequencies in descending order but also provides the cumulative line on the same chart. **(c)** You can conclude that friends/family account for the largest percentage, 45%. When other, news media, and online user reviews are added to friends/family, this accounts for 83%.

2.3 (b) 88%. **(d)** The Pareto chart allows you to see which sources account for most of the electricity.

2.5 (b) Since electricity consumption is spread over many types of appliances, a bar chart may be best in showing which types of appliances used the most electricity. **(c)** Air conditioning, lighting, and clothes washers/other accounted for 58% of the residential electricity use in the United States.

2.7 (b) A higher percentage of females enjoy shopping for clothing.

2.9 The percentage of online retailers who require three or more clicks to be removed from an e-mail list has increased drastically from 2008 to 2009.

CHAPTER 3

3.1 (a) $L = 3$ and $H = 574$; Stem: 0, 1, 2, 3, 4, 5; Stem Unit: 100

(b) $L = 1$ and $H = 48$; Stem: 0, 0, 1, 1, 2, 2, 3, 3, 4, 4; Stem Unit: 10

(c) $L = 13,002,000$ and $H = 37,000,000$; Stem: 1, 1, 2, 2, 3, 3; Stem Unit: 10,000,000

(d) $L = 11,398,000$ and $H = 376,956,000$; Stem: 0, 0, 1, 1, 2, 2, 3, 3; Stem Unit: 100,000,000

(e) $L = 6,460$ and $H = 139,000$; Stem: 0, 0, 0, 0, 0, 1, 1; Stem Unit: 100,000

(f) $L = -81.1$ and $H = 9.2$; Stem: −8, −7, −6, −5, −4, −3, −2, −1, −0, 0; Stem Unit: 10

(g) $L = -19.9$ and $H = 10.7$; Stem: −1, −1, −0, −0, 0, 0, 1; Stem Unit: 10

(h) $L = -106.6$ and $H = 25.1$; Stem: −1, −0, −0, −0, −0, −0, 0, 0; Stem Unit: 100

3.2 (a)

Stem (10)	Leaf
0	6 6 7
0	9
1	0 0 0 0 0 0 1
1	2
1	5
1	6
1	8
2	0
2	3
2	
2	
2	9

(b) $L = -0.04$ and $H = 0.09$; Stem: −0.0, −0.0, −0.0, 0.0, 0.0, 0.0, 0.0, 0.0; Stem Unit: face value

(c) $L = -0.24$ and $H = 0.84$; Stem: −0.2, −0.1, −0.0, 0.0, 0.1, 0.2, 0.3, 0.4, 0.5, 0.6, 0.7, 0.8; Stem Unit: face value

(d) $L = -0.06$ and $H = 0$; Stem: −0.06, −0.05, −0.04, −0.03, −0.02, −0.01, −0.00; Stem Unit: face value

3.4 (a) $L = 5,613$ and $H = 93,221$; Stem: 0, 1, 2, 3, 4, 5, 6, 7, 8, 9; Stem Unit: 10,000

(b) $L = -1,670$ and $H = 2,356$; Stem: −1, −1, −0, −0, 0, 0, 1, 1, 2; Stem Unit: 1,000

(c) $L = -234$ and $H = 323$; Stem: −2, −1, −1, −0, −0, 0, 0, 1, 1, 2, 2, 3; Stem Unit: 100

(d) $L = 0$ and $H = 83$; Stem: 0, 1, 2, 3, 4, 5, 6, 7, 8; Stem Unit: 10

(e) $L = 13$ and $H = 409$; Stem: 0, 0, 1, 1, 2, 2, 3, 3, 4; Stem Unit: 100

3.6 (a)

Revenue Rank	Number of Companies
0 and under 20	14
20 and under 40	8
40 and under 60	7
60 and under 80	2
80 and under 100	0
100 and under 120	1
Total	32

cw = 25 is feasible
First class = 0 and under 25
Last class = 100 and under 125

(b)

Market Capitalization	Number of Companies
0 and under 5,000	2
5,000 and under 10,000	8
10,000 and under 15,000	11
15,000 and under 20,000	4
20,000 and under 25,000	2
25,000 and under 30,000	2
30,000 and under 35,000	0
35,000 and under 40,000	1
Total	30

(c)

P/E Ratio	Number of Companies
7.5 and under 10.0	3
10.0 and under 12.5	5
12.5 and under 15.0	12
15.0 and under 17.5	3
17.5 and under 20.0	1
20.0 and under 22.5	1
22.5 and under 25.0	2
25.0 and under 27.5	1
27.5 and under 30.0	2
Total	30

cw = 5 is feasible
First class = 5.00 and under 10.00
Last class = 25.00 and under 30.00

(d)

Per Share Data–Price/Sales	Number of Companies
0.00 and under 0.50	2
0.50 and under 1.00	8
1.00 and under 1.50	11
1.50 and under 2.00	4
2.00 and under 2.50	4
2.50 and under 3.00	0
3.00 and under 3.50	0
3.50 and under 4.00	1
Total	30

(e)

Debt/Equity Ratio	Number of Companies
0.0 and under 0.2	2
0.2 and under 0.4	9
0.4 and under 0.6	8
0.6 and under 0.8	2
0.8 and under 1.0	4
1.0 and under 1.2	2
1.2 and under 1.4	1
1.4 and under 1.6	1
1.6 and under 1.8	2
1.8 and under 2.0	1
Total	32

(f)

Revenue % Change	Number of Companies
-25 and under 0	10
0 and under 25	20
25 and under 50	1
50 and under 75	0
75 and under 100	0
100 and under 125	1
Total	32

(g)

Earnings per Share–Latest Year	Number of Companies
1.00 and under 1.50	1
1.50 and under 2.00	5
2.00 and under 2.50	1
2.50 and under 3.00	9
3.00 and under 3.50	5
3.50 and under 4.00	5
4.00 and under 4.50	1
4.50 and under 5.00	0
5.00 and under 5.50	1
Total	28

cw = 1 is feasible
First class = 1.00 and under 2.00
Last class = 5.00 and under 6.00

(h)

Number of Employees	Number of Companies
0 and under 25,000	22
25,000 and under 50,000	5
50,000 and under 75,000	3
75,000 and under 100,000	0
100,000 and under 125,000	1
125,000 and under 150,000	1
Total	32

3.7 (a)

Revenue Amount 2007($)	Number of Companies
15,000,000 and under 20,000,000	4
20,000,000 and under 22,000,000	7
25,000,000 and under 30,000,000	6
30,000,000 and under 35,000,000	3
35,000,000 and under 40,000,000	0
40,000,000 and under 45,000,000	1
Total	21

(b)

Profit Amount 2007($)	Number of Companies
0 and under 1,000,000	4
1,000,000 and under 2,000,000	1
2,000,000 and under 3,000,000	5
3,000,000 and under 4,000,000	4
4,000,000 and under 5,000,000	4
5,000,000 and under 6,000,000	1
Total	19

(c)

Revenue Change (%)	Number of Companies
-15.0 and under -10.0	1
-10.0 and under -5.0	0
-5.0 and under 0.0	3
0.0 and under 5.0	5
5.0 and under 10.0	1
10.0 and under 15.0	5
15.0 and under 20.0	2
20.0 and under 25.0	3
25.0 and under 30.0	1
Total	21

CW = 10 is feasible
First class = -20.0 and under -10.0
Last class = 20.0 and under 30.0

(d)

Profit Change (%)	Number of Companies
-250 and under 0	5
0 and under 250	12
250 and under 500	1
500 and under 750	0
750 and under 1,000	0
1,000 and under 1,250	1
Total	19

3.8 (a)

Volume	Number of Companies
0 and under 200,000	16
200,000 and under 400,000	3
400,000 and under 600,000	0
600,000 and under 800,000	0
800,000 and under 1,000,000	1
Total	20

(b)

High/Ask Price	Number of Companies
0.00 and under 10.00	11
10.00 and under 20.00	3
20.00 and under 30.00	4
30.00 and under 40.00	1
40.00 and under 50.00	0
50.00 and under 60.00	1
Total	20

(c)

Low/Bid Price	Number of Companies
0.00 and under 10.00	11
10.00 and under 20.00	4
20.00 and under 30.00	3
30.00 and under 40.00	1
40.00 and under 50.00	0
50.00 and under 60.00	1
Total	20

(d)

Close/Previous Price	Number of Companies
0.00 and under 10.00	11
10.00 and under 20.00	4
20.00 and under 30.00	3
30.00 and under 40.00	1
40.00 and under 50.00	0
50.00 and under 60.00	1
Total	20

(e)

Net Change	Number of Companies
-0.50 and under 0.00	4
0.00 and under 0.50	10
0.50 and under 1.00	2
1.00 and under 1.50	2
1.50 and under 2.00	2
Total	20

(f)

52 Week High Price	Number of Companies
0.00 and under 10.00	5
10.00 and under 20.00	5
20.00 and under 30.00	6
30.00 and under 40.00	1
40.00 and under 50.00	1
50.00 and under 60.00	2
Total	20

(g)

52 Week Low Price	Number of Companies
0.00 and under 5.00	12
5.00 and under 10.00	1
10.00 and under 15.00	4
15.00 and under 20.00	2
20.00 and under 25.00	1
Total	20

3.9 (a) Manulife Mix Funds   L = 10.21   H = 14.38

Valuation ($)	# of Funds
10.00 and under 11.00	6
11.00 and under 12.00	9
12.00 and under 13.00	12
13.00 and under 14.00	2
14.00 and under 15.00	1
Total	30

(b) Manulife Mix Funds   L = −0.12   H = 0.04

Change ($)	# of Funds
−0.12 and under −0.10	1
−0.10 and under −0.08	0
−0.08 and under −0.06	2
−0.06 and under −0.04	4
−0.04 and under −0.02	9
−0.02 and under 0.00	10
0.00 and under 0.02	2
0.02 and under 0.04	1
0.04 and under 0.06	1
Total	30

(c) Manulife Mix Funds   L = −0.94   H = 0.35

Percent Change	# of Funds
−1.00 and under −0.75	1
−0.75 and under −0.50	3
−0.50 and under −0.25	11
−0.25 and under 0.00	11
0.00 and under 0.25	3
0.25 and under 0.50	1
Total	30

(d) CI-Clarica Mutual Funds   L = 8.44   H = 21.02

Valuation ($)	# of Funds
7.50 and under 10.00	5
10.00 and under 12.50	12
12.50 and under 15.00	12
15.00 and under 17.50	5
17.50 and under 20.00	1
20.00 and under 22.50	1
Total	36

(e) Transamerica Growsafe 75/100   L = 2.86   H = 6.12

Valuation ($)	# of Funds
2.00 and under 3.00	1
3.00 and under 4.00	5
4.00 and under 5.00	15
5.00 and under 6.00	13
6.00 and under 7.00	1
Total	35

(f) Transamerica Growsafe 75/100   L = −1.19   H = 0.75

Valuation ($)	# of Funds
−1.50 and under −1.00	1
−1.00 and under −0.50	1
−0.50 and under 0.00	16
0.00 and under 0.50	16
0.50 and under 1.00	1
Total	35

3.10 (a) 32% **(b)** $22,000) **(c)** $29,000

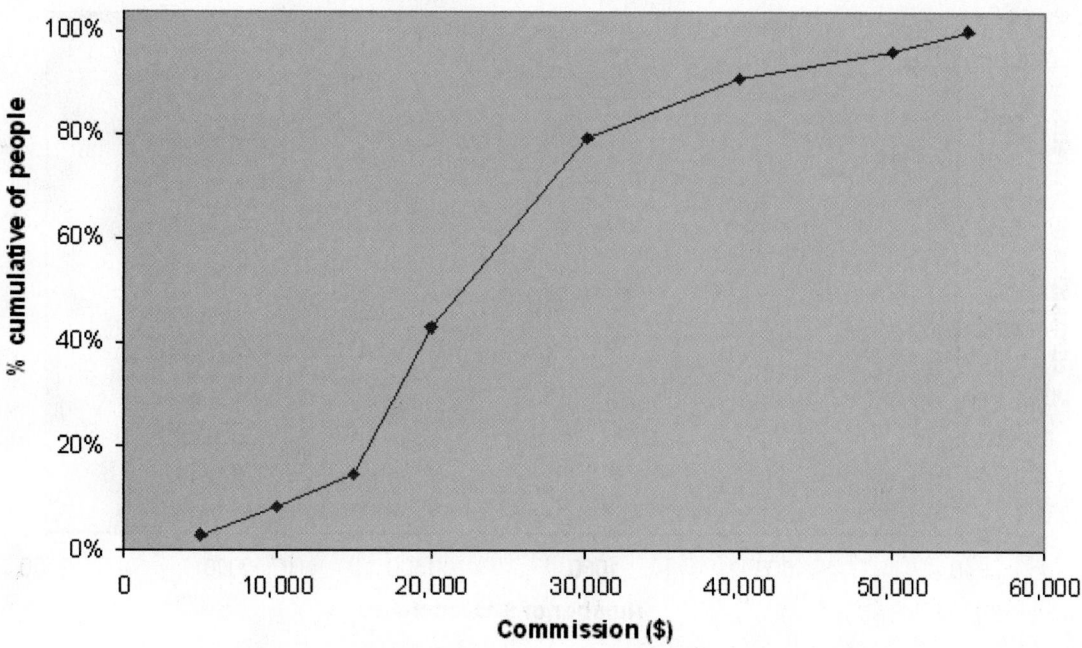

3.11 (a) 51 **(b)** 16%

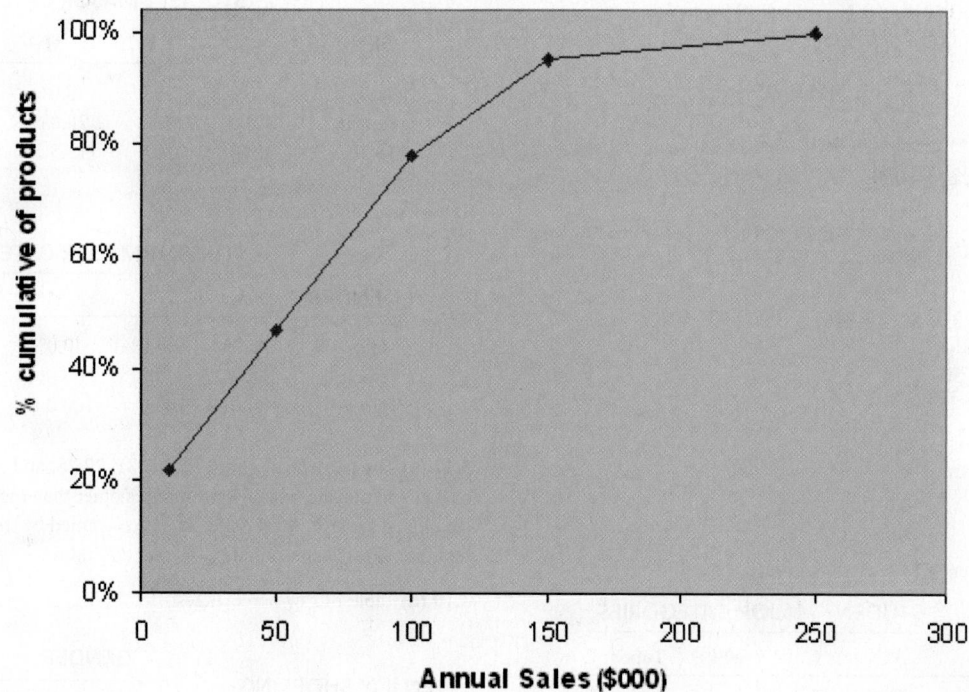

3.12 (a) 46% **(b)** 450 sharesz

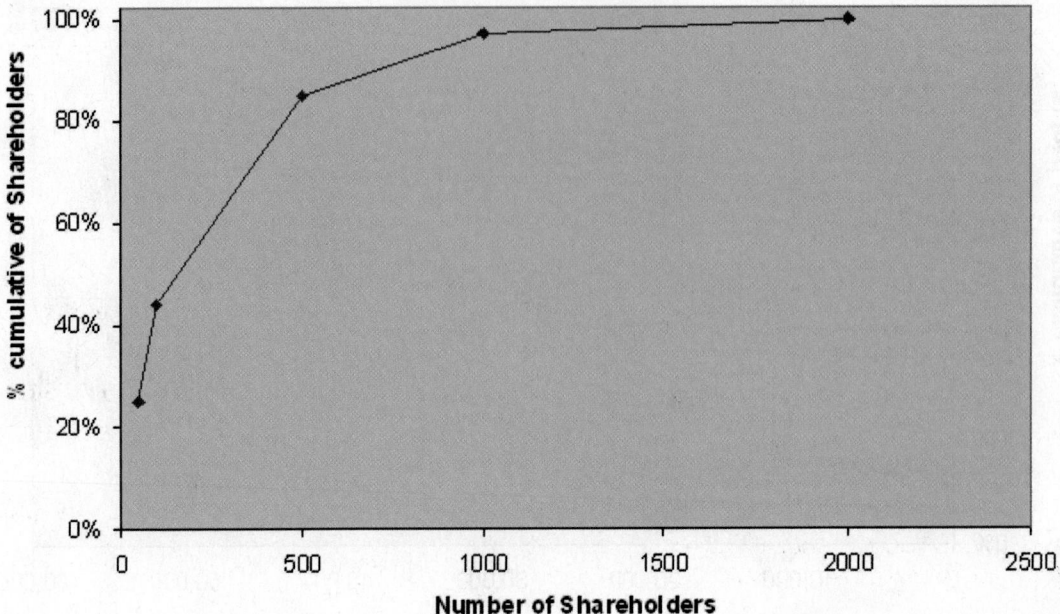

3.13 (a)

(a) $\left[10\left(\dfrac{25}{100}\right)+\dfrac{1}{2}\right]=3; x_3=2990$

(b) $\left[10\left(\dfrac{50}{100}\right)+\dfrac{1}{2}\right]=5.5; \dfrac{x_5+x_6}{2}=\dfrac{3461+3959}{2}=3710$

(c) $\left[10\left(\dfrac{75}{100}\right)+\dfrac{1}{2}\right]=8; x_8=6499$

(d) $\left[10\left(\dfrac{80}{100}\right)+\dfrac{1}{2}\right]=8.5; \dfrac{x_8+x_9}{2}=\dfrac{6499+9291}{2}=7895$

(e) $\left[10\left(\dfrac{43}{100}\right)+\dfrac{1}{2}\right]=4.8\Rightarrow 5; x_5=3461$

(f) $\left[10\left(\dfrac{67}{100}\right)+\dfrac{1}{2}\right]=7.2\Rightarrow 7; x_7=6170$

3.15 (a) Table of frequencies for all student responses:

GENDER	STUDENT MAJOR CATEGORIES			
	A	C	M	Totals
Male	14	9	2	25
Female	6	6	3	15
Totals	20	15	5	40

(b) Table based on total percentages:

GENDER	STUDENT MAJOR CATEGORIES			
	A	C	M	Totals
Male	35.0%	22.5%	5.0%	62.5%
Female	15.0	15.0	7.5	37.5
Totals	50.0	37.5	12.5	100.0

Table based on row percentages:

GENDER	STUDENT MAJOR CATEGORIES			
	A	C	M	Totals
Male	56.0%	36.0%	8.0%	100.0%
Female	40.0	40.0	20.0	100.0
Totals	50.0	37.5	12.5	100.0

Table based on column percentages;

GENDER	STUDENT MAJOR CATEGORIES			
	A	C	M	Totals
Male	70.0%	60.0%	40.0%	62.5%
Female	30.0	40.0	60.0	37.5
Totals	100.0	100.0	100.0	100.0

3.17 (a) The percentages are 17.18, 5.21, 22.28, and 55.33. **(b)** More than half the oil consumed is from countries other than the U.S., Japan, and developed Europe. More than 20% is consumed by the U.S. and slightly less than 20% is consumed by developed Europe.

3.19 (a) Table of row percentages:

ENJOY SHOPPING FOR CLOTHING	GENDER		
	Male	Female	Total
Yes	46%	54%	100%
No	53	47	100
Total	50	50	100

Table of column percentages:

ENJOY SHOPPING FOR CLOTHING	GENDER		
	Male	Female	Total
Yes	44%	51%	47%
No	56	49	53
Total	100	100	100

Table of total percentages:

ENJOY SHOPPING FOR CLOTHING	GENDER		
	Male	Female	Total
Yes	22%	25%	47%
No	28	25	53
Total	50	50	100

(b) A higher percentage of females enjoy shopping for clothing.

3.21 The percentage of online retailers who require three or more clicks to be removed from an e-mail list has increased drastically from 2008 to 2009.

3.22 (b) Yes, there is a strong positive relationship between X and Y. As X increases, so does Y.

3.24 (c) There appears to be very little relationship between the first weekend gross and either the U.S. gross or the worldwide gross of Harry Potter movies.

3.26 (a) and (c) There appears to be a positive relationship between the coaches' salary and revenue. Yes, this is borne out by the data.

3.28 (b) There is a great deal of variation in the returns from decade to decade. Most of the returns are between 5% and 15%. The 1950s, 1980s, and 1990s had exceptionally high returns, and only the 1930s and 2000s had negative returns.

3.30 (b) There has been a slight decline in movie attendance between 2001 and 2010. During that time, movie attendance increased from 2002 to 2004 but then decreased to a level below that in 2001.

3.48 (c) The publisher gets the largest portion (64.8%) of the revenue. About half (32.3%) of the revenue received by the publisher covers manufacturing costs. The publisher's marketing and promotion account for the next largest share of the revenue, at 15.4%. Author, bookstore employee salaries and benefits, and publisher administrative costs and taxes each account for around 10% of the revenue, whereas the publisher after-tax profit, bookstore operations, bookstore pretax profit, and freight constitute the "trivial few" allocations of the revenue. Yes, the bookstore gets twice the revenue of the authors.

3.50 (b) The pie chart may be best since with only three categories, it enables you to see the portion of the whole in each category. **(d)** The pie chart may be best since, with only four categories it enables you to see the portion of the whole in each category. **(e)** The online content is not copy-edited or fact-checked as carefully as print content. Only 41% of the online content is copy-edited as carefully as print content and only 57% of the online content is fact-checked as carefully as the print content.

3.52 (a)

DESSERT ORDERED	GENDER		
	Male	Female	Total
Yes	71%	29%	100%
No	48	52	100
Total	53	47	100

DESSERT ORDERED	GENDER		
	Male	Female	Total
Yes	30%	14%	23%
No	70	86	77
Total	100	100	100

DESSERT ORDERED	GENDER		
	Male	Female	Total
Yes	16%	7%	23%
No	37	40	77
Total	53	47	100

DESSERT ORDERED	BEEF ENTRÉE		
	Yes	No	Total
Yes	52%	48%	100%
No	25	75	100
Total	31	69	100

DESSERT ORDERED	BEEF ENTRÉE		
	Yes	No	Total
Yes	38%	16%	23%
No	62	84	77
Total	100	100	100

DESSERT ORDERED	BEEF ENTRÉE		
	Yes	No	Total
Yes	12%	11%	23%
No	19	58	77
Total	31	69	100

(b) If the owner is interested in finding out the percentage of males and females who order dessert or the percentage of those who order a beef entrée and a dessert among all patrons, the table of total percentages is most informative. If the owner is interested in the effect of gender on ordering of dessert or the effect of ordering a beef entrée on the ordering of dessert, the table of column percentages will be most informative. Because dessert is usually ordered after the main entrée, and the owner has no direct control over the gender of patrons, the table of row percentages is not very useful here. **(c)** 30% of the men ordered desserts, compared to 14% of the women; men are more than twice as likely to order dessert as women. Almost 38% of the patrons ordering a beef entrée ordered dessert, compared to 16% of patrons ordering all other entrées. Patrons ordering beef are more than 2.3 times as likely to order dessert as patrons ordering any other entrée.

3.54 (a) 23575R15 accounts for over 80% of the warranty claims. **(b)** 91.82% of the warranty claims are from the ATX model. **(c)** Tread separation accounts for 73.23% of the warranty claims among the ATX model. **(d)** The number of claims is evenly distributed among the three incidents; other/unknown incidents account for almost 40% of the claims, tread separation accounts for about 35% of the claims, and blowout accounts for about 25% of the claims.

3.56 (c) The alcohol percentage is concentrated between 4% and 6%, with the largest concentration between 4% and 5%. The calories are concentrated between 140 and 160. The carbohydrates are concentrated between 12 and 15. There are outliers in the percentage of alcohol in both tails. The outlier in the lower tail is due to the non-alcoholic beer O'Doul's with only a 0.4% alcohol content. There are a few beers with alcohol content as high as around 11.5%. There are a few beers with calorie content as high as 330 and carbohydrates as high as 32.1. There is a strong positive relationship between percentage alcohol and calories, and calories and carbohydrates and a moderately positive relationship between percentage alcohol and carbohydrates.

3.58 (c) The one-year CD rate is concentrated above 1.20. The five-year CD rate is concentrated between 2.2 and 2.5. In general, the five-year CD has the higher yield. There does not appear to be any relationship between the one-year CD rate and the five-year CD rate at the various banks.

3.60 (a)

Frequency (Boston)

Weight (Boston)	Frequency	Percentage
3,015 but less than 3,050	2	0.54%
3,050 but less than 3,085	44	11.96
3,085 but less than 3,120	122	33.15
3,120 but less than 3,155	131	35.60
3,155 but less than 3,190	58	15.76
3,190 but less than 3,225	7	1.90
3,225 but less than 3,260	3	0.82
3,260 but less than 3,295	1	0.27

(b)

Frequency (Vermont)

Weight (Vermont)	Frequency	Percentage
3,550 but less than 3,600	4	1.21%
3,600 but less than 3,650	31	9.39
3,650 but less than 3,700	115	34.85
3,700 but less than 3,750	131	39.70
3,750 but less than 3,800	36	10.91
3,800 but less than 3,850	12	3.64
3,850 but less than 3,900	1	0.30

(d) 0.54% of the Boston shingles pallets are underweight, and 0.27% are overweight. 1.21% of the Vermont shingles pallets are underweight, and 3.94% are overweight.

3.62 (c)

Calories	Frequency	Percentage	Limit	Percentage Less Than
50 but less than 100	3	12%	100	12%
100 but less than 150	3	12	150	24
150 but less than 200	9	36	200	60
200 but less than 250	6	24	250	84
250 but less than 300	3	12	300	96
300 but less than 350	0	0	350	96
350 but less than 400	1	4	400	100

Cholesterol	Frequency	Percentage	Limit	Percentage Less Than
0 but less than 50	2	8%	50	8%
50 but less than 100	17	68	100	76
100 but less than 150	4	16	150	92
150 but less than 200	1	4	200	96
200 but less than 250	0	0	250	96
250 but less than 300	0	0	300	96
300 but less than 350	0	0	350	96
350 but less than 400	0	0	400	96
400 but less than 450	0	0	450	96
450 but less than 500	1	4	500	100

The sampled fresh red meats, poultry, and fish vary from 98 to 397 calories per serving, with the highest concentration between 150 to 200 calories. One protein source, spareribs, with 397 calories, is more than 100 calories above the next-highest-caloric food. The protein content of the sampled foods varies from 16 to 33 grams, with 68% of the values falling between 24 and 32 grams. Spareribs and fried liver are both very different from other foods sampled—the former on calories and the latter on cholesterol content.

3.64 (b) There is a downward trend in the amount filled. **(c)** The amount filled in the next bottle will most likely be below 1.894 liter. **(d)** The scatter plot of the amount of soft drink filled against time reveals the trend of the data, whereas a histogram only provides information on the distribution of the data.

CHAPTER 4

4.1 (a) $1295 per office **(b)** $410 per person

4.2 (a) 21.78 **(b)** $76.17 **(c)** $21.56 **(d)** 89.4

4.3 40.2%

4.4 $1.50

4.5 $0.94

4.6 $16.67

4.7 (a) 10.5 hours **(b)** $29.0 **(c)** 28.90

4.8 (a) $2,639.03 **(b)** 422,245.25 **(c)** 22.25%

4.9 (a) $24,752.21 **(b)** 7,989.35

4.10 (a) mean = 375, median = 350, Mean is a better measure. **(b)** $450

4.11 (a) $398 **(b)** $5.88 million **(c)** Median **(d)** $5.2 million. Illinois and Pennsylvania

4.12 33 days

4.13 (a) 2 star: mean = $23,200 per room, 3-star:mean = $53,500 per room **(b)** Median = 201 rooms **(c)** $8.5 million

4.14 (a) $29,353.441 **(b)** 3.02%

4.15 (a) $1509.14 **(b)** 126 people

4.16 12,202 students

4.17 17.49 hours

4.18 $210,303.41

4.19 (a) Mean = $4.14 billion US **(b)** $64,150 US **(c)** 61,497.33

(b) If quality is measured by central tendency, Grade X tires provide slightly better quality because X's mean and median are both equal to the expected value, 575 mm. If, however, quality is measured by consistency, Grade Y provides better quality because, even though Y's mean is only slightly larger than the mean for Grade X, Y's standard deviation is much smaller. The range in values for Grade Y is 5 mm compared to the range in values for Grade X, which is 16 mm.

(c)

	Grade X	Grade Y, Altered
Mean	575	577.4
Median	575	575
Standard deviation	6.40	6.11

When the fifth Y tire measures 588 mm rather than 578 mm, Y's mean inner diameter becomes 577.4 mm, which is larger than X's mean inner diameter, and Y's standard deviation increases from 2.07 mm to 6.11 mm. In this case, X's tires are providing better quality in terms of the mean inner diameter, with only slightly more variation among the tires than Y's.

4.41 (a) ,Mean $= \dfrac{63.26}{9} = 7.0289$

Median $= 5th$ ranked value $= 7.38$

(b) Variance $= (4.20 - 7.0289)^2 + (5.03 - 7.0289)^2 + (5.86 - 7.0289)^2$
$$+ (6.45 - 7.0289)^2 + (7.38 - 7.0289)^2$$
$$+ (7.54 - 7.0289)^2 + (8.46 - 7.0289)^2$$
$$+ (8.47 - 7.0289)^2 + (9.87 - 7.0289)^2$$
$$= \dfrac{26.2809}{9 - 1} = 3.2851,$$

Standard deviation $= \sqrt{3.2851} = 1.8125$,range $= 9.87 - 4.20 = 5.67$,

Coefficient of variation $= \dfrac{1.8125}{7.0289} \times 100\% = 25.79\%$

(c) The mean is only slightly smaller than the median, so the data are only slightly left-skewed. **(d)** The mean cost is \$7.03, and the median cost is \$7.38. The average scatter of cost around the mean is \$1.81. The difference between the highest cost and the lowest cost is \$5.67.

4.43 (a) Mean $= 21.12$, median $= 22$, mode $= 22$ **(b)** $S^2 = 5.2767$,

$S = 2.2971$, range $= 10$, coefficient of variation $= 10.88\%$, and Z scores are $-0.49, 1.25, 0.38, 0.82, -0.49, 0.38, -0.05, 0.38, 0.38, -0.92, 0.38, 0.38, 2.12, -0.93, -0.93, 0.82, 1.25, -0.05, -0.05, -0.93, -0.05, 0.38, 0.38, -2.23, -2.23.$ **(c)** Because the mean is slightly less than the median, the data are slightly left-skewed. **(d)** The distributions of MPG of the sedans is right-skewed, while the MPG of the SUVs is slightly right-skewed. The mean MPG of sedans is 4.66 higher than that of SUVs. The average scatter and the range of the MPG of sedans is much higher than that for SUVs.

4.45 (a) Mean $= 0.9257$, median $= 0.88$ **(b)** Variance $= 0.1071$, standard deviation $= 0.3273$, range $= 0.96$, $CV = 35.36\%$. There is no outlier because none of the Z scores has an absolute value that is greater than 3.0. **(c)** The data appear to be right-skewed because the mean is greater than the median.

4.47 (a) Mean $= 82.3333$, median $= 77.0$. **(b)** Range $= 48$, variance $= 327.0667$, standard deviation $= 18.085$ **(c)** The price paid by U.S. travelers is right-skewed because the mean is greater than the median. **(d) (a)** Mean $= 90.6667$, median $= 77$. **(b)** Range $= 98$,

variance $= 1,297.0667$, standard deviation $= 36.0148$. **(c)** The price is now more skewed because the mean is much greater than the median due to the higher price in the first city (160).

4.49 (a) Mean $= 7.11$, median $= 6.68$. **(b)** Variance $= 4.336$, standard deviation $= 2.082$, range $= 6.67$, $CV = 29.27\%$.

(c) Because the mean is greater than the median, the distribution is right-skewed. **(d)** The mean and median are both greater than 5 minutes. The distribution is right-skewed, meaning that there are some unusually high values. Further, 13 of the 15 bank customers sampled (or 86.7%) had waiting times greater than 5 minutes. So the customer is likely to experience a waiting time in excess of 5 minutes. The manager overstated the bank's service record in responding that the customer would "almost certainly" not wait longer than 5 minutes for service.

4.55 (a) 4, 9, 5. **(b)** 3, 4, 7, 9, 12. **(c)** The distances between the median and the extremes are close, 4 and 5, but the differences in the tails are different (1 on the left and 3 on the right), so this distribution is slightly right-skewed. **(d)** In Problem 3.2 (d), because mean $=$ median, the distribution is symmetric. The box part of the graph is symmetric, but the tails show right-skewness.

4.57 (a) $-6.5, 8, 14.5$. **(b)** $-8, -6.5, 7, 8, 9$. **(c)** The shape is left-skewed. **(d)** This is consistent with the answer in Problem 3.4 (d).

4.59 (a) $Q_1 = \dfrac{14 + 1}{4} = 3.75$ ranked value $=$ 4th ranked value $=$ \$0.68,

$Q_3 = \dfrac{3(14 + 1)}{4} = \dfrac{45}{4} = 11.25$ ranked value $=$ 11th ranked value $=$ \$1.14,

Interquartile range $= 1.14 - 0.68 = \$0.46$. **(b)** Five-number summary: 0.55 0.68 0.88 1.14 1.51. **(c)** The distribution is right-skewed.

4.61 (a) $Q_1 = 19.5$, $Q_3 = 22$, interquartile range $= 2.5$. **(b)** Five-number summary: 16 19.5 22 22 26. **(c)** The MPG of SUVs is left skewed since the distance from the smallest value to the median is greater than the distance from the median to the largest value, the distance from the smallest value to the first quartile is greater than the distance from the third quartile to the largest value, and the distance from the first quartile to the median is greater than the distance from the median to the third quartile.

4.63 (a) Commercial district five-number summary: 0.38 3.2 4.5 5.55 6.46. Residential area five-number summary: 3.82 5.64 6.68 8.73 10.49. **(b)** Commercial district: The distribution is left-skewed. Residential area: The distribution is slightly right-skewed. **(c)** The central tendency of the waiting times for the bank branch located in the commercial district of a city is lower than that of the branch located in the residential area. There are a few long waiting times for the branch located in the residential area, whereas there are a few exceptionally short waiting times for the branch located in the commercial area.

4.65 (a)

Average of 3-Year Return	Risk			
Type	Above Average	Average	Below Average	Grand Total
Intermediate government	5.6515	5.7862	4.8214	5.4367
Short-term corporate	-0.0440	2.6355	3.2294	2.1156
Grand total	3.1966	4.1583	3.9484	3.7761

(b)

StdDev of 3-Year Return	Risk			
Type	Above Average	Average	Below Average	Grand Total
Intermediate government	2.4617	1.1457	1.2784	1.8066
Short-term corporate	3.6058	1.7034	1.4886	2.6803
Grand total	4.1197	2.1493	1.6001	2.8227

(c) Across the three different risk levels, intermediate government funds have the highest average three-year returns but the lowest standard deviation. **(d)** Similarly to the 2006–2008 three-year returns, intermediate government funds have the highest average three-year returns but the lowest standard deviation across the three different risk levels.

4.67 (a)

Average of Return 2008		Risk			
Type	Fees	Above Average	Average	Below Average	Grand Total
Intermediate government	No	9.0294	6.9053	4.0368	6.5709
	Yes	3.8863	7.1700	4.5444	4.9937
Intermediate government total		6.5358	6.99656	4.200	5.9576
Short-term corporate	No	10.7315	−1.6174	0.4600	−3.2607
	Yes	−10.2000	−1.6250	0.7250	−3.5941
Short-term corporate total		−10.6252	−1.6140	0.492	−3.3237
Grand total		−0.8612	2.5450	2.1661	1.316

(b)

StdDev of Return 2008		Risk			
Type	Fees	Above Average	Average	Below Average	Grand Total
Intermediate government	No	5.6635	3.6998	3.5178	4.7322
	Yes	6.5778	2.8744	3.2055	5.0712
Intermediate government total		6.5675	3.3870	3.3694	4.8999
Short-term corporate	No	8.6070	4.0613	3.3503	7.1587
	Yes	7.2928	5.4013	3.5790	6.9786
Short-term corporate total		8.2199	4.3480	3.3220	7.0874
Grand total		11.2319	5.8231	3.8020	7.6530

(c) The intermediate government funds have the highest average 2008 returns but the lowest standard deviation among all different combinations of risk level and whether there is a fee charged with the exception that they have the highest average 2008 returns and the highest standard deviation among the below average risk funds that do not charge a fee. **(d)** In contrast to the 2008 returns, the intermediate government funds have the lowest average 2009 returns for all combinations of risk level and whether the funds charged a fee with the except of the below average risk funds that do not charge a fee where the intermediate government funds have the highest average 2008 returns. Unlike the 2008 returns, the intermediate government funds have the lowest standard deviations only among the above average risk funds that do not charge a fee, the average risk funds that either charge a fee or do not charge a fee, and the below average risk funds that charge a fee.

4.74 41.6 years

4.75 $1370

4.76 (a) 28.4 **(b)** 27.5 **(c)** 8.84

4.77 (a) 6.67 **(b)** Mean = $124 and s = $21.43 **(c)** Mean = 3.1 and s = 1.4

4.78 (a) Mean = 79.4% and s = 5.79% **(b)** Mean = 88.9% and s = 5.37%, The average grades of Queen's are higher

4.79

Statistics	Mayor's Salary	Councillor's Salary
Mean	60022.77	24251.82
Median	54758	22640
s	15251.82	13122.07
Min	45000	10664
Q1	50684.5	13750
Q3	65906	28764
Max	101084	63915
CV	25%	54%

4.80

Statistics	Cable Revenue	Advertising Revenue
Mean	0.339	0.175
Median	0.3	0.145
s	0.313	0.177
Min	0.05	0.02
Q1	0.165	0.06
Q3	0.365	0.21
Max	1.25	0.66
CV	92%	101%

c)

Statistics	2000	1989
Mean	$16.96 million	$17.54 million

4.81

	1995	1996
CV	71%	80%

4.82 Mean = 5.7172
S = 4.249

4.83

	Revenue	Net Income
CV	56%	60%

4.84

	March	April
CV	102%	73%

4.85 $28.32 million

4.86 (a) Mean = 6.15 and s = 1.68 **(b)** Men: Mean = 267.14 Women: Mean = 280 **(c)** 48.07

4.87 (a) Mean = 15.37 **(b)** 120.51

4.88 (a)

	1993	1994
Median	504.5	754

b)

	1994	1995
CV	47%	40%

CHAPTER 5

5.2 (a) Simple events include selecting a red ball. **(b)** Selecting a white ball. **(c)** The sample space consists of the 12 red balls and the 8 white balls.

5.4 (a) 60/100 = 3/5 = 0.6. **(b)** 10/100 = 1/10 = 0.1. **(c)** 35/100 = 7/20 = 0.35. **(d)** 9/10 = 0.9.

5.6 (a) Mutually exclusive, not collectively exhaustive. **(b)** Not mutually exclusive, not collectively exhaustive. **(c)** Mutually exclusive, not collectively exhaustive. **(d)** Mutually exclusive, collectively exhaustive.

5.8 (a) Needs three or more clicks to be removed from an email list. **(b)** Needs three or more clicks to be removed from an email list in 2009. **(c)** Does not need three or more clicks to be removed from an email list. **(d)** "Needs three or more clicks to be removed from an email list in 2009" is a joint event because it consists of two characteristics.

5.10 (a) A respondent who answers quickly. **(b)** A respondent who answers quickly who is over 70 years old. **(c)** A respondent who does not answer quickly. **(d)** A respondent who answers quickly and is over 70 years old is a joint event because it consists of two characteristics, answering quickly and being over 70 years old.

5.12 (a) $796/3,790 = 0.21$. **(b)** $1,895/3,790 = 0.50$. **(c)** $796/3,790 + 1,895/3,790 - 550/3,790 = 2,141/3790 = 0.5649$. **(d)** The probability of "is engaged with their workplace *or* is a U.S. worker" includes the probability of "is engaged with their workplace" plus the probability of "is a U.S. worker" minus the joint probability of "is engaged with their workplace *and* is a U.S. worker."

5.14 (a) $514/1,085$. **(b)** $76/1,085$. **(c)** $781/1,085$ **(d)** $1,085/1,085 = 1.00$.

5.16 (a) $10/30 = 1/3 = 0.33$. **(b)** $20/60 = 1/3 = 0.33$. **(c)** $40/60 = 2/3 = 0.67$. **(d)** Because $P(A/B) = P(A) = 1/3$, events A and B are independent.

5.18 $\frac{1}{2} = 0.5$.

5.20 Because $P(A \text{ and } B) = 0.20$ and $P(A)P(B) = 0.12$, events A and B are not independent.

5.22 (a) $536/1,000 = 0.536$. **(b)** $707/1,000 = 0.707$. **(c)** $P(\text{Answers quickly}) = 1,243/2,000 = 0.6215$ which is not equal to $P(\text{Answers quickly} \mid \text{between 12 and 50}) = 0.536$. Therefore, answers quickly and age are not independent.

5.24 (a) $550/1,895 = 0.2902$. **(b)** $1,345/1,895 = 0.7098$. **(c)** $246/1,895 = 0.1298$. **(d)** $1,649/1,895 = 0.8702$.

5.26 (a) $0.025/0.6 = 0.0417$. **(b)** $0.015/0.4 = 0.0375$. **(c)** Because $P(\text{Needs warranty repair} \mid \text{Manufacturer based in U.S.}) = 0.0417$ and $P(\text{Needs warranty repair}) = 0.04$, the two events are not independent.

5.28 (a) 0.0045. **(b)** 0.012. **(c)** 0.0059. **(d)** 0.0483.

5.30 0.095.

5.32 (a) 0.736. **(b)** 0.997.

5.34 (a) $P(B' \mid O) = \dfrac{(0.5)(0.3)}{(0.5)(0.3) + (0.25)(0.7)} = 0.4615$.

(b) $P(O) = 0.175 + 0.15 = 0.325$.

5.36 (a) $P(\text{Huge success} \mid \text{Favorable review}) = 0.099/0.459 = 0.2157$; $P(\text{Moderate success} \mid \text{Favorable review}) = 0.14/0.459 = 0.3050$; $P(\text{Break even} \mid \text{Favorable review}) = 0.16/0.459 = 0.3486$; $P(\text{Loser} \mid \text{Favorable review}) = 0.06/0.459 = 0.1307$. **(b)** $P(\text{Favorable review}) = 0.459$.

5.38 $3^{10} = 59,049$.

5.40 (a) $2^7 = 128$. **(b)** $6^7 = 279,936$. **(c)** There are two mutually exclusive and collectively exhaustive outcomes in (a) and six in (b).

5.42 $(8)(4)(3)(3) = 288$.

5.44 $5! = (5)(4)(3)(2)(1) = 120$. Not all the orders are equally likely because the teams have a different probability of finishing first through fifth.

5.46 $n! = 6! = 720$.

5.48 $\dfrac{10!}{4!6!} = 210$.

5.50 $4,950$.

5.60 (a)

	Age		
Goals	**18–25**	**26–40**	**Total**
Getting Rich	405	310	715
Other	95	190	285
Total	500	500	1,000

(b) Simple event: "Has a goal of getting rich." Joint event: "Has a goal of getting rich and is between 18–25 years old." **(c)** $P(\text{Has a goal of getting rich}) = 715/1,000 = 0.715$. **(d)** $P(\text{Has a goal of getting rich and is in the 26–40-year-old group}) = 310/1000 = 0.31$. **(e)** Not independent.

5.62 (a) $99/200$. **(b)** $127/200$. **(c)** $129/200$. **(d)** $29/200$. **(f)** $10/100$.

5.64 (a) 0.4712. **(b)** Because the probability that a fatality involved a rollover, given that the fatality involved an SUV, a van, or a pickup is 0.4712, which is almost twice the probability that a fatality involved a rollover with any vehicle type, at 0.24, SUVs, vans, and pickups are generally more prone to rollover accidents.

CHAPTER 6

6.2 (a) $\mu = 0(0.10) + 1(0.20) + 2(0.45) + 3(0.15) + 4(0.05) + 5(0.05) = 2.0$.

(b) $\sigma = \sqrt{\begin{array}{l}(0-2)^2(0.10) + (1-2)^2(0.20) + (2-2)^2(0.45) + \\ (3-2)^2(0.15) + (4-2)^2(0.05) + (5-2)^2(0.05)\end{array}}$ $= 1.183$.

6.4 (a)

X	$P(X)$
$\$-1$	$21/36$
$\$+1$	$15/36$

(b)

X	$P(X)$
$\$-1$	$21/36$
$\$+1$	$15/36$

(c)

X	$P(X)$
$\$-1$	$30/36$
$\$+4$	$6/36$

(d) $-\$0.167$ for each method of play.

6.6 (a) 2.1058. **(b)** 1.4671.

6.8 (a) $E(X) = \$66.20$; $E(Y) = \$63.01$. **(b)** $\sigma_X = \$57.22$; $\sigma_Y = \$195.22$. **(c)** Based on the expected value criteria, you would choose the common stock fund. However, the common stock fund also has a standard deviation more than three times higher than that for the corporate bond fund. An investor should carefully weigh the increased risk. **(d)** If you chose the common stock fund, you would need to assess your reaction to the small possibility that you could lose virtually all of your entire investment.

6.9 Probability distribution

P	X
0.02	50,000
0.12	35,000
0.5	20,000
0.25	10,000
0.08	0
0.03	−10,000

$E(X) = 50,000(0.02) + 35,000(0.12) + 20,000(0.5) + 10,000(0.25) + 0(0.8) − 10,000(0.03) = 17,400$

6.10 $80,000

6.11 (a)

# years	X	P(X)
1	$2.00	0.5
2	3.50	0.2
3	4.50	0.2
5	6.50	0.1

(b) $406.25 for 125 subscribers

6.12 (a) Project 3 **(b)** Project 3 has the lowest relative variability

6.13 Country C: $E(X) = \$2,000$

6.14 Tire C: $E(X) = \$282,000$

6.15 QMS should order 11 units: $E(X) = 67$

6.16 (a) 0.2770. **(b)** 0.0936. **(c)** 1.75 children.

6.17 (a) 0.0601. **(b)** 0.9 def. chips. **(c)** 0.1920.

6.18 (a) 0.9981. **(b)** 0.0135.

6.19 0.1495.

6.20 (a) 0.9254. **(b)** 0.5489.

6.22 (a) 0.2128. **(b)** 0.3153. **(c)** 0.9294. **(d)** $\mu = 4.95$ $\sigma = 0.9307$. **(e)** that a flight is on time or not on time and each flight is independent of all other flights.

6.24 (a) 0.0834. **(b)** 0.2351. **(c)** 0.6169. **(d)** 0.3831.

6.26 Given $\pi = 0.848$ and $n = 3$,

(a) $P(X = 3) = \dfrac{n!}{x!(n-x)!}\pi^x(1-\pi)^{n-x} = \dfrac{3!}{3!0!}(0.848)^3(0.152)^0 = 0.6098.$

(b) $P(X = 0) = \dfrac{n!}{x!(n-x)!}\pi^x(1-\pi)^{n-x} = \dfrac{3!}{0!3!}(0.848)^0(0.152)^3 = 0.0035.$

(c) $P(X \geq 2) = P(X = 2) + P(X = 3)$
$= \dfrac{3!}{2!1!}(0.848)^2(0.152)^1 + \dfrac{3!}{3!0!}(0.848)^3(0.152)^0 = 0.9377.$

(d) $E(X) = n\pi = 3(0.848) = 2.544$ $\sigma_X = \sqrt{n\pi(1-\pi)}$
$= \sqrt{3(0.848)(0.152)} = 0.6218$

6.28 0.0527.

6.29 (a) 0.1353. **(b)** 0.3712.

6.30 (a) 0.2231. **(b)** 0.3423.

6.31 (a) 0.0174. **(b)** 0.9975.

6.32 (a) 0.2707. **(b)** 0.2149.

6.33 (a) 0.6310. **(b)** 0.8488.

6.35 (a) $P(X < 5) = P(X = 0) + P(X = 1) + P(x = 2) + P(X = 3) + P(X = 4)$
$= \dfrac{e^{-6}(6)^0}{0!} + \dfrac{e^{-6}(6)^1}{1!} + \dfrac{e^{-6}(6)^2}{2!} + \dfrac{e^{-6}(6)^3}{3!} + \dfrac{e^{-6}(6)^4}{4!}$

$= 0.002479 + 0.014873 + 0.044618 + 0.089235 + 0.133853$
$= 0.2851.$

(b) $P(X = 5) = \dfrac{e^{-6}(6)^5}{5!} = 0.1606.$

(c) $P(X \geq 5) = 1 - P(X < 5) = 1 - 0.2851 = 0.7149.$

(d) $P(X = 4 \text{ or } X = 5) = P(X = 4) + P(X = 5) = \dfrac{e^{-6}(6)^4}{4!} + \dfrac{e^{-6}(6)^5}{5!}$
$= 0.2945.$

6.37 (a) $P(X = 0) = 0.0296.$ **(b)** $P(X \geq 1) = 0.9704.$
(c) $P(X \geq 2) = 0.8662.$

6.39 (a) 0.0176. **(b)** 0.9093. **(c)** 0.9220.

6.41 (a) 0.2618. **(b)** 0.8478. **(c)** Because Ford had a lower mean rate of problems per car in 2009 compared to Dodge, the probability of a randomly selected Ford having zero problems and the probability of no more than two problems are both higher than Dodge.

6.43 (a) 0.2441. **(b)** 0.8311. **(c)** Because Dodge had a lower mean rate of problems per car in 2009 compared to 2008, the probability of a randomly selected Dodge having zero problems and the probability of no more than two problems are both lower in 2009 than in 2008.

6.49 (a) 0.64. **(b)** 0.64. **(c)** 0.3020. **(d)** 0.0060. **(e)** The assumption of independence may not be true.

6.51 (a) If $\pi = 0.50$ and $n = 12$, $P(X \geq 9) = 0.0730.$
(b) If $\pi = 0.75$ and $n = 12$, $P(X \geq 9) = 0.6488.$

6.53 (a) 0.1074. **(b)** 0.2684. **(c)** 0.6242. **(d)** Mean = 2.0, standard deviation = 1.2649. **(e)** Since the percentage of bills containing an error is lower in this problem, the probability is higher in (a) and (b) of this problem and lower in (c).

6.55 (a) $\mu = n\pi = 13.6$ **(b)** $\sigma = \sqrt{n\pi(1-\rho)} = 2.0861.$
(c) $P(X = 15) = 0.1599.$ **(d)** $P(X \leq 10) = 0.0719.$
(e) $P(X \geq 10) = 0.9721.$

6.57 (a) If $\pi = 0.50$ and $n = 39$, $P(X \geq 34) = 0.00000121.$
(b) If $\pi = 0.70$ and $n = 39$, $P(X \geq 34) = 0.0109.$ **(c)** If $\pi = 0.90$ and $n = 39$, $P(X \geq 34) = 0.8097.$ **(d)** Based on the results in (a)–(c), the probability that the Standard & Poor's 500 Index will increase if there is an early gain in the first five trading days of the year is very likely to be close to 0.90 because that yields a probability of 80.97% that at least 34 of the 39 years the Standard & Poor's 500 Index will increase the entire year.

6.59 (a) The assumptions needed are (i) the probability that a golfer loses a golf ball in a given interval is constant, (ii) the probability that a golfer loses more than one golf ball approaches 0 as the interval gets smaller, and (iii) the probability that a golfer loses a golf ball is independent from interval to interval. **(b)** 0.0067. **(c)** 0.6160. **(d)** 0.3840.

CHAPTER 7

7.1 (a) 0.1056 **(b)** 10.56% **(c)** 75,995 km

7.2 (a) 0.9522 **(b)** 0.9902 **(c)** 0.3829 **(d)** $2.9 million

7.3 (a) 0.7340 **(b)** 92 papers

7.4 (a) 0.8944 **(b)** IQ = 74

7.5 (a) Stocks: P(lose) = 0.2736   Bonds: P(lose) = 0.2727
(b) Stocks: 0.4498   Bonds: 0.1272 **(c)** 29.7%

7.6 (a) 0.7430 **(b)** 2.42% **(c)** GPA = 3.59

7.8 (a) $P(34 < X < 50) = P(-1.33 < Z < 0) = 0.4082.$
(b) $P(X < 30) + P(X > 60) = P(Z < -1.67) + P(Z > 0.83) = 0.0475 + (1.0 - 0.7967) = 0.2508.$ **(c)** $P(Z < -0.84) \cong 0.20$,

$Z = -0.84 = \dfrac{X - 50}{12}$, $X = 50 - 0.84(12) = 39.92$ thousand miles, or

39,920 miles. **(d)** The smaller standard deviation makes the absolute Z values larger. **(a)** $P(34 < X < 50) = P(-1.60 < Z < 0) = 0.4452.$
(b) $P(X < 30) + P(X > 60) = P(Z < -2.00) + P(Z > 1.00) = 0.0228 + (1.0 - 0.8413) = 0.1815.$ **(c)** $X = 50 - 0.84(10) = 41.6$ thousand miles, or 41,600 miles.

7.10 (a) 0.9878. **(b)** 0.8185. **(c)** 86.16%. **(d)** Option 1: Because your score of 81% on this exam represents a Z score of 1.00, which is below the minimum Z score of 1.28, you will not earn an A grade on the exam under this grading option. Option 2: Because your score of 68% on this exam represents a Z score of 2.00, which is well above the minimum Z score of 1.28, you will earn an A grade on the exam under this grading option. You should prefer Option 2.

7.12 (a) 0.9461. **(b)** 0.0032. **(c)** 0.0045. **(d)** 29.6714.

7.27 With 39 values, the smallest of the standard normal quantile values covers an area under the normal curve of 0.025. The corresponding Z value is -1.96. The middle (20th) value has a cumulative area of 0.50 and a corresponding Z value of 0.0. The largest of the standard normal quantile values covers an area under the normal curve of 0.975, and its corresponding Z value is $+1.96$.

7.29 (a) Mean $= 21.12$, median $= 22$, $S = 2.2971$, range $= 10$, $6S = 6(2.2971) = 13.7826$, interquartile range $= 2.5$, $1.33(2.2971) = 3.0551$. The mean is slightly less than the median. The range is much less than $6S$, and the interquartile range is less than $1.33S$. **(b)** The normal probability plot does not appear to be highly skewed. The data may be symmetrical but not normally distributed.

7.31 (a) Mean $= 1{,}040.863$, median $= 981$, range $= 1{,}732$, $6(S) = 2{,}571.2310$, interquartile range $= 593$, $1.33(S) = 569.9562$. There are 62.75%, 78.43%, and 94.12% of the observations that fall within 1, 1.28, and 2 standard deviations of the mean, respectively, as compared to the approximate theoretical 66.67%, 80%, and 95%. Because the mean is slightly larger than the median, the interquartile range is slightly larger than 1.33 times the standard deviation, and the range is much smaller than 6 times the standard deviation, the data appear to deviate slightly from the normal distribution. **(b)** The normal probability plot suggests that the data appear to be slightly right-skewed.

7.33 (a) Interquartile range $= 0.0025$, $S = 0.0017$, range $= 0.008$, $1.33(S) = 0.0023$, $6(S) = 0.0102$. Because the interquartile range is close to $1.33S$ and the range is also close to $6S$, the data appear to be approximately normally distributed. **(b)** The normal probability plot suggests that the data appear to be approximately normally distributed.

7.35 (a) Five-number summary: 82 127 148.5 168 213; mean $= 147.06$, mode $= 130$, range $= 131$, interquartile range $= 41$, standard deviation $= 31.69$. The mean is very close to the median. The five-number summary suggests that the distribution is approximately symmetric around the median. The interquartile range is very close to $1.33S$. The range is about $50 below $6S$. In general, the distribution of the data appears to closely resemble a normal distribution. **(b)** The normal probability plot confirms that the data appear to be approximately normally distributed.

7.43 (a) 0.4772. **(b)** 0.9544. **(c)** 0.0456. **(d)** 1.8835. **(e)** 1.8710 and 2.1290.

7.45 (a) 0.2734. **(b)** 0.2038. **(c)** 4.404 ounces. **(d)** 4.188 ounces and 5.212 ounces.

7.47 (a) Waiting time will more closely resemble an exponential distribution. **(b)** Seating time will more closely resemble a normal distribution. **(c)** Both the histogram and normal probability plot suggest that waiting time more closely resembles an exponential distribution. **(d)** Both the histogram and normal probability plot suggest that seating time more closely resembles a normal distribution.

7.49 (a) 0.999968 **(b)** 0.0668 **(c)** 0.0013 **(d)** 1.6653 **(e)** 0.8080 to 1.592 .

CHAPTER 8

8.2 Sample without replacement: Read from left to right in three-digit sequences and continue unfinished sequences from the end of the row to the beginning of the next row:
Row 05: 338 505 855 551 438 855 077 186 579 488 767 833 170
Rows 05–06: 897
Row 06: 340 033 648 847 204 334 639 193 639 411 095 924
Rows 06–07: 707
Row 07: 054 329 776 100 871 007 255 980 646 886 823 920 461
Row 08: 893 829 380 900 796 959 453 410 181 277 660 908 887
Rows 08–09: 237
Row 09: 818 721 426 714 050 785 223 801 670 353 362 449
Rows 09–10: 406
Note: All sequences above 902 and duplicates are discarded.

8.4 A simple random sample would be less practical for personal interviews because of travel costs (unless interviewees are paid to go to a central interviewing location).

8.6 Here all members of the population are equally likely to be selected, and the sample selection mechanism is based on chance. But selection of two elements is not independent; for example, if A is in the sample, we know that B is also and that C and D are not.

8.8 (a)
Row 16: 2323 6737 5131 8888 1718 0654 6832 4647 6510 4877
Row 17: 4579 4269 2615 1308 2455 7830 5550 5852 5514 7182
Row 18: 0989 3205 0514 2256 8514 4642 7567 8896 2977 8822
Row 19: 5438 2745 9891 4991 4523 6847 9276 8646 1628 3554
Row 20: 9475 0899 2337 0892 0048 8033 6945 9826 9403 6858
Row 21: 7029 7341 3553 1403 3340 4205 0823 4144 1048 2949
Row 22: 8515 7479 5432 9792 6575 5760 0408 8112 2507 3742
Row 23: 1110 0023 4012 8607 4697 9664 4894 3928 7072 5815
Row 24: 3687 1507 7530 5925 7143 1738 1688 5625 8533 5041
Row 25: 2391 3483 5763 3081 6090 5169 0546
Note: All sequences above 5,000 are discarded. There were no repeating sequences.

(b) 089 189 289 389 489 589 689 789 889 989
1089 1189 1289 1389 1489 1589 1689 1789 1889 1989
2089 2189 2289 2389 2489 2589 2689 2789 2889 2989
3089 3189 3289 3389 3489 3589 3689 3789 3889 3989
4089 4189 4289 4389 4489 4589 4689 4789 4889 4989

(c) With the single exception of invoice 0989, the invoices selected in the simple random sample are not the same as those selected in the systematic sample. It would be highly unlikely that a simple random sample would select the same units as a systematic sample.

8.10 Before accepting the results of a survey of college students, you might want to know, for example: Who funded the survey? Why was it conducted? What was the population from which the sample was selected? What sampling design was used? What mode of response was used: a personal interview, a telephone interview, or a mail survey? Were interviewers trained? Were survey questions field-tested? What questions were asked? Were the questions clear, accurate, unbiased, and valid? What operational definition of "vast majority" was used? What was the response rate? What was the sample size?

8.12 (a) The four types of survey errors are coverage error, nonresponse error, sampling error, and measurement error. **(b)** When people who answer the survey tell you what they think you want to hear, rather than what they really believe, this is the halo effect, which is a source of measurement error. Also, every survey will have sampling error that reflects the chance differences from sample to sample, based on the probability of particular individuals being selected in the particular sample.

8.14 Before accepting the results of the survey, you might want to know, for example: Who funded the study? Why was it conducted? What was the population from which the sample was selected? What sampling design was used? What mode of response was used: a personal interview, a telephone interview, or a mail survey? Were interviewers trained? Were survey questions field-tested? What other questions were asked? Were the questions clear, accurate, unbiased, and valid? What was the response rate? What was the margin of error? What was the sample size? What frame was used?

8.16 (a) Virtually 0. **(b)** 0.1587. **(c)** 0.0139. **(d)** 50.195.

8.18 (a) Both means are equal to 6. This property is called unbiasedness. **(c)** The distribution for $n = 3$ has less variability. The larger sample size has resulted in sample means being closer to μ.

8.20 (a) When $n = 2$, because the mean is larger than the median, the distribution of the sales price of new houses is skewed to the right, and so is the sampling distribution of $\overline{X}$ although it will be less skewed than the population. **(b)** If you select samples of $n = 100$, the shape of the sampling distribution of the sample mean will be very close to a normal distribution, with a mean of \$272,400 and a standard deviation of \$9,000. **(c)** 0.9989. **(d)** 0.3611

8.22 (a) $P(\overline{X} > 3) = P(Z > -1.00) = 1.0 - 0.1587 = 0.8413$. **(b)** $P(Z < 1.04) = 0.85; \overline{X} = 3.10 + 1.04(0.1) = 3.204$. **(c)** To be able to use the standardized normal distribution as an approximation for the area under the curve, you must assume that the population is approximately symmetrical. **(d)** $P(Z < 1.04) = 0.85; \overline{X} = 3.10 + 1.04(0.05) = 3.152$.

8.23 (a) 0.8351 **(b)** 108.4 kw

8.24 0.2424

8.25 4 years

8.26 (a) 0.2195 **(b)** 0.0933 **(c)** 4.2 proposals

8.27 (a) 0.0008 **(b)** 0.1030

8.28 74.6%

8.29 (a) 451 hours **(b)** 0.3085

8.30 (a) 0.9608 **(b)** 0.9802

8.31 (a) 50 managers **(b)** \$252,802

8.32 (a) 0.8571 **(b)** 0.2084

8.33A 2.28%

8.33B (a) 0.8781 **(b)** 0.8943

8.34 (a) 0.2375 **(b)** 0.0766 **(c)** 0.000003 **(d)** 0.0032

8.35 399 bags

8.36 1072 days

8.37 (a) 0.0938 **(b)** 1692 drills

8.38 9.52%

8.39 0.0002

8.40 (a) 0.0004 **(b)** 40.8 minutes

8.41 (a) 0.2051 **(b)** \$60,702

8.42 (a) 0.3366 **(b)** 21%

8.51 (a) 0.40. **(b)** 0.0704.

8.53 (a) $\pi = 0.501, \sigma_p = \sqrt{\dfrac{\pi(1 - \pi)}{n}} = \sqrt{\dfrac{0.501(1 - 0.501)}{100}} = 0.05$

$P(p > 0.55) = P(Z > 0.98) = 1.0 - 0.8365 = 0.1635$.

(b) $\pi = 0.60, \sigma_p = \sqrt{\dfrac{\pi(1 - \pi)}{n}} = \sqrt{\dfrac{0.6(1 - 0.6)}{100}} = 0.04899$.

$P(p > 0.55) = P(Z > -1.021) = 1.0 - 0.1539 = 0.8461$.

(c) $\pi = 0.49, \sigma_p = \sqrt{\dfrac{\pi(1 - \pi)}{n}} = \sqrt{\dfrac{0.49(1 - 0.49)}{100}} = 0.05$

$P(p > 0.55) = P(Z > 1.20) = 1.0 - 0.8849 = 0.1151$.

(d) Increasing the sample size by a factor of 4 decreases the standard error by a factor of 2.

(a) $P(p > 0.55) = P(Z > 1.96) = 1.0 - 0.9750 = 0.0250$.
(b) $P(p > 0.55) = P(Z > -2.04) = 1.0 - 0.0207 = 0.9793$.
(c) $P(p > 0.55) = P(Z > 2.40) = 1.0 - 0.9918 = 0.0082$.

8.55 (a) 0.7889. **(b)** 0.6746. **(c)** 0.8857. **(d) (a)** 0.9458. **(b)** 0.9377. **(c)** 0.9920.

8.57 (a) 0.8422 **(b)** The probability is 90% that the sample percentage will be contained within 5.58% (0.3042 to 0.4158) symmetrically around the population percentage. **(c)** The probability is 95% that the sample percentage will be contained within 6.65% (0.2935 to 0.4265) symmetrically around the population percentage.

8.59 (a) 0.0336. **(b)** 0.0000. **(c)** Increasing the sample size by a factor of 5 decreases the standard error by a factor of $\sqrt{5}$. The sampling distribution of the proportion becomes more concentrated around the true proportion of 0.59 and, hence, the probability in (b) becomes smaller than that in (a).

8.71 (a) 0.4999. **(b)** 0.00009. **(c)** 0. **(d)** 0. **(e)** 0.7518.

8.73 (a) 0.8944. **(b)** 4.617; 4.783. **(c)** 4.641.

8.75 (a) 0.5319. **(b)** 0.9538. **(c)** 0.9726.

CHAPTER 9

9.1 $\overline{R} = 0.67$
$UCL_R = D_4\overline{R} = 2.282(0.67) = 1.53$
$LCL_R = D_3\overline{R} = 0(0.67) = 0$

$\overline{\overline{X}} = 75.448$

$UCL_X = \overline{\overline{X}} + A_2\overline{R} = 75.448 + (0.729)(0.67) = 75.936$

$LCL_X = \overline{\overline{X}} - A_2\overline{R} = 75.448 - (0.729)(0.67) = 74.960$

9.2 $\overline{R} = 0.338$

$UCL_R = D_4\overline{R} = 2.004(0.338) = 0.677$

$LCL_R = D_3\overline{R} = 0(0.338) = 0$

$\overline{\overline{X}} = 35.399$

$UCL_X = \overline{\overline{X}} + A_2\overline{R} = 35.399 + (0.483)(0.338) = 35.562$

$LCL_X = \overline{\overline{X}} - A_2\overline{R} = 35.399 - (0.483)(0.338) = 35.236$

9.3 $\overline{R} = 23.7$

$UCL_R = D_4\overline{R} = 2.114(23.7) = 50.1$

$LCL_R = D_3\overline{R} = 0(23.7) = 0$

$\overline{\overline{X}} = 104$

$UCL_X = \overline{\overline{X}} + A_2\overline{R} = 104 + (0.577)(23.7) = 117.7$

$LCL_X = \overline{\overline{X}} - A_2\overline{R} = 104 - (0.577)(23.7) = 90.3$

9.4 $\overline{R} = 25.3$

$UCL_R = D_4\overline{R} = 2.282(25.3) = 57.7$

$LCL_R = D_3\overline{R} = 0(25.0) = 0$

$\overline{\overline{X}} = 382.33$

$UCL_X = \overline{\overline{X}} + A_2\overline{R} = 382.33 + (0.729)(25.3) = 400.77$

$LCL_X = \overline{\overline{X}} - A_2\overline{R} = 382.33 - (0.729)(25.3) = 363.89$

9.5 $\overline{R} = 2.71$

$UCL_R = D_4\overline{R} = 2.114(2.71) = 5.73$

$LCL_R = D_3\overline{R} = 0(2.71) = 0$

$\overline{\overline{X}} = 15.53$

$UCL_X = \overline{\overline{X}} + A_2\overline{R} = 15.53 + (0.577)(2.71) = 17.09$

$LCL_X = \overline{\overline{X}} - A_2\overline{R} = 15.53 - (0.577)(2.71) = 13.97$

9.6 $\overline{R} = 1.36$

$UCL_R = D_4\overline{R} = 2.004(1.36) = 2.73$

$LCL_R = D_3\overline{R} = 0(1.36) = 0$

$\overline{\overline{X}} = 200.47$

$UCL_X = \overline{\overline{X}} + A_2\overline{R} = 200.47 + (0.483)(1.36) = 201.13$

$LCL_X = \overline{\overline{X}} - A_2\overline{R} = 200.47 - (0.483)(1.36) = 199.81$

9.8 (a) Day 4, Day 3. **(b)** LCL = 0.0397, UCL = 0.2460. **(c)** No, proportions are within control limits.

9.10 (a) $n = 500, \overline{p} = 761/16{,}000 = 0.0476$.

$$UCL = \overline{p} + 3\sqrt{\frac{\overline{p}(1 - \overline{p})}{n}}$$

$$= 0.0476 + 3\sqrt{\frac{0.0476(1 - 0.0476)}{500}} = 0.0761$$

$$LCL = \overline{p} - 3\sqrt{\frac{\overline{p}(1 - \overline{p})}{n}}$$

$$= 0.0476 - 3\sqrt{\frac{0.0476(1 - 0.0476)}{500}} = 0.0190$$

(b) Because the individual points are distributed around $\overline{p}$ without any pattern and all the points are within the control limits, the process is in a state of statistical control.

9.12 (a) UCL = 0.0176, LCL = 0.0082. The proportion of unacceptable cans is below the LCL on Day 4. There is evidence of a pattern over time because the last eight points are all above the mean, and most of the earlier points are below the mean. Therefore, this process is out of control.

9.14 (a) UCL = 0.1431, LCL = 0.0752. Days 9, 26, and 30 are above the UCL. Therefore, this process is out of control.

9.21 (a) The main reason that service quality is lower than product quality is because the former involves human interaction, which is prone to variation. Also, the most critical aspects of a service are often timeliness and professionalism, and customers can always perceive that the service could be done more quickly and with greater professionalism. For products, customers often cannot perceive a better or more ideal product than the one they are getting. For example, a new laptop is better and contains more interesting features than any laptop the owner has ever imagined. **(b)** Both services and products are the results of processes. However, measuring services is often harder because of the dynamic variation due to the human interaction between the service provider and the customer. Product quality is often a straightforward measurement of a static physical characteristic such as the amount of sugar in a can of soda. Categorical data are also more common in service quality. **(c)** Yes. **(d)** Yes.

9.23 (a) $\overline{p} = 0.2702$, LCL = 0.1700, UCL = 0.3703. **(b)** Yes, RudyBird's market share is in control before the in-store promotion. **(c)** All seven days of the in-store promotion are above the UCL. The promotion increased market share.

9.25 (a) $\overline{p} = 0.75175$, LCL = 0.62215, UCL = 0.88135. Although none of the points are outside the control limits, there is a clear pattern over time, with the last 13 points above the center line. Therefore, this process is not in control. **(b)** Because the increasing trend begins around Day 20, this change in method would be the assignable cause. **(c)** The control chart would have been developed using the first 20 days, and then a different control chart would be used for the final 20 points because they represent a different process.

9.27 (a) $\overline{p} = 0.1198$, LCL = 0.0205, UCL = 0.2191. **(b)** Day 24 is below the LCL; therefore, the process is out of control. **(c)** Special causes of variation should be investigated to improve the process. Next, the process should be improved to decrease the proportion of undesirable trades.

9.29 Separate p charts should be developed for each food for each shift:

Kidney—Shift 1: $\overline{p} = 0.01395$, UCL = 0.02678, LCL = 0.00112. Although there are no points outside the control limits, there is a strong increasing trend in nonconformances over time.

Kidney—Shift 2: $\overline{p} = 0.01829$, UCL = 0.03329, LCL = 0.00329. Although there are no points outside the control limits, there is a strong increasing trend in nonconformances over time.

Shrimp—Shift 1: $\overline{p} = 0.006995$, UCL = 0.01569, LCL = 0. There are no points outside the control limits, and there is no pattern over time.

Shrimp—Shift 2: $\overline{p} = 0.01023$, UCL = 0.021, LCL = 0. There are no points outside the control limits, and there is no pattern over time.

The team needs to determine the reasons for the increase in nonconformances for the kidney product. The production volume for kidney is clearly decreasing for both shifts. This can be observed from a plot of the production volume over time. The team needs to investigate the reasons for this.

CHAPTER 10

10.2 $114.68 \le \mu \le 135.32$.

10.4 Yes, it is true because 5% of intervals will not include the population mean.

10.6 (a) You would compute the mean first because you need the mean to compute the standard deviation. If you had a sample, you would compute the sample mean. If you had the population mean, you would compute the population standard deviation. **(b)** If you have a sample, you are computing the sample standard deviation, not the population standard deviation needed in Equation (8.1). If you have a population and have computed the population mean and population standard deviation, you don't need a confidence interval estimate of the population mean because you already know the mean.

10.8 Equation (10.1) assumes that you know the population standard deviation. Because you are selecting a sample of 100 from the population, you are computing a sample standard deviation, not the population standard deviation.

10.10 (a) $\bar{X} \pm Z \cdot \dfrac{\sigma}{\sqrt{n}} = 350 \pm 1.96 \cdot \dfrac{100}{\sqrt{64}}$; $325.50 \le \mu \le 374.50$.
(b) No, the manufacturer cannot support a claim that the bulbs have a mean of 400 hours. Based on the data from the sample, a mean of 400 hours would represent a distance of 4 standard deviations above the sample mean of 350 hours. **(c)** No. Because σ is known and $n = 64$, from the Central Limit Theorem, you know that the sampling distribution of $\bar{X}$ is approximately normal. **(d)** The confidence interval is narrower, based on a population standard deviation of 80 hours rather than the original standard deviation of 100 hours. $\bar{X} \pm Z \cdot \dfrac{\sigma}{\sqrt{n}} = 350 \pm 1.96 \cdot \dfrac{80}{\sqrt{64}}$, $330.4 \le$ $\mu \le 369.6$. Based on the smaller standard deviation, a mean of 400 hours would represent a distance of 5 standard deviations above the sample mean of 350 hours. No, the manufacturer cannot support a claim that the bulbs have a mean life of 400 hours.

10.12 (a) 2.2622. **(b)** 3.2498. **(c)** 2.0395. **(d)** 1.9977. **(e)** 1.7531.

10.14 $-0.12 \le \mu \le 11.84$, $2.00 \le \mu \le 6.00$. The presence of the outlier increases the sample mean and greatly inflates the sample standard deviation.

10.16 (a) $32 \pm (2.0096)(9)/\sqrt{50}$; $29.44 \le \mu \le 34.56$ **(b)** The quality improvement team can be 95% confident that the population mean turnaround time is between 29.44 hours and 34.56 hours. **(c)** The project was a success because the initial turnaround time of 68 hours does not fall within the interval.

10.18 (a) $5.64 \le \mu \le 8.42$. **(b)** You can be 95% confident that the population mean amount spent for lunch at a fast-food restaurant is between $5.64 and $8.42.

10.20 (a) $20.17 \le \mu \le 22.07$. **(b)** You can be 95% confident that the population mean miles per gallon of 2011 small SUVs is between 20.17 and 22.07. **(c)** Because the 95% confidence interval for population mean miles per gallon of 2011 small SUVs overlaps with that for the population mean miles per gallon of 2011 family sedans, you are unable to conclude that the population mean miles per gallon of 2011 small SUVs is lower than that of 2011 family sedans.

10.22 (a) $31.12 \le \mu \le 54.96$. **(b)** The number of days is approximately normally distributed. **(c)** No, the outliers skew the data. **(d)** Because the sample size is fairly large, at $n = 50$, the use of the t distribution is appropriate.

10.24 (a) $\$0.7367 \le \$1.1147$. **(b)** That the population distribution is normally distributed. **(c)** Both the normal probability plot and the boxplot show that the distribution of the cost of dark chocolate bars is right-skewed.

10.26 $0.19 \le \pi \le 0.31$.

10.28 (a) $p = \dfrac{X}{n} = \dfrac{135}{500} = 0.27$, $p \pm Z\sqrt{\dfrac{p(1-p)}{n}} = 0.27 \pm$

$2.58\sqrt{\dfrac{0.27(0.73)}{500}}$; $0.2189 \le \pi \le 0.3211$. **(b)** The manager in charge of

promotional programs concerning residential customers can infer that the proportion of households that would purchase an additional telephone line if it were made available at a substantially reduced installation cost is somewhere between 0.22 and 0.32, with 99% confidence.

10.30 (a) $0.4762 \le \pi \le 0.5638$. **(b)** No, you cannot, because the interval estimate includes 0.50 (50%). **(c)** $0.5062 \le \pi \le 0.5338$. Yes, you can, because the interval is above 0.50 (50%). **(d)** The larger the sample size, the narrower the confidence interval, holding everything else constant.

10.32 (a) $0.784 \le \pi \le 0.816$. **(b)** $0.5099 \le \pi \le 0.5498$. **(c)** Many more people think that e-mail messages are easier to misinterpret.

10.34 $n = 35$.

10.36 $n = 1{,}041$.

10.38 (a) $n = \dfrac{Z^2\sigma^2}{e^2} = \dfrac{(1.96)^2(400)^2}{50^2} = 245.86$. Use $n = 246$.

(b) $n = \dfrac{Z^2\sigma^2}{e^2} = \dfrac{(1.96)^2(400)^2}{25^2} = 983.41$. Use $n = 984$.

10.40 $n = 97$.

10.42 (a) $n = 167$. **(b)** $n = 97$.

10.44 (a) $n = 246$. **(b)** $n = 385$. **(c)** $n = 554$. **(d)** When there is more variability in the population, a larger sample is needed to accurately estimate the mean.

10.46 (a) $p = 0.28$; $0.2522 \le \pi \le 0.3078$. **(b)** $p = 0.19$; $0.1657 \le$ $\pi \le 0.2143$. **(c)** $p = 0.07$; $0.0542 \le \pi \le 0.0858$. **(d) (a)** $n = 1{,}937$. **(b)** $n = 1{,}479$. **(c)** $n = 626$.

10.48 (a) If you conducted a follow-up study to estimate the population proportion of individuals who view oil companies favorably, you would use $\pi = 0.84$ in the sample size formula because it is based on past information on the proportion. **(b)** $n = 574$.

10.54 $940.50 \le \mu \le 1007.50$. Based on the evidence gathered from the sample of 34 stores, the 95% confidence interval for the mean per-store count in all of the franchise's stores is from 940.50 to 1,007.50. With a 95% level of confidence, the franchise can conclude that the mean per-store count in all its stores is somewhere between 940.50 and 1,007.50, which is larger than the original 900 mean per-store count before the price reduction. Hence, reducing coffee prices is a good strategy to increase the mean customer count.

10.56 (a) $14.085 \le \mu \le 16.515$. **(b)** $0.530 \le \pi \le 0.820$. **(c)** $n = 25$. **(d)** $n = 784$. **(e)** If a single sample were to be selected for both purposes, the larger of the two sample sizes ($n = 784$) should be used.

10.58 (a) $8.049 \le \mu \le 11.351$. **(b)** $0.284 \le \pi \le 0.676$. **(c)** $n = 35$. **(d)** $n = 121$. **(e)** If a single sample were to be selected for both purposes, the larger of the two sample sizes ($n = 121$) should be used.

10.60 (a) $\$25.80 \le \mu \le \$31.24$. **(b)** $0.3037 \le \pi \le 0.4963$. **(c)** $n = 97$. **(d)** $n = 423$. **(e)** If a single sample were to be selected for both purposes, the larger of the two sample sizes ($n = 423$) should be used.

10.62 (a) $\$36.66 \le \mu \le \$40.42$. **(b)** $0.2027 \le \pi \le 0.3973$. **(c)** $n = 110$. **(d)** $n = 423$. **(e)** If a single sample were to be selected for both purposes, the larger of the two sample sizes ($n = 423$) should be used.

10.64 (a) $n = 27$. **(b)** $\$1{,}581.24 \le \mu \le 1{,}727.30$.

10.66 (a) $8.41 \le \mu \le 8.43$. **(b)** With 95% confidence, the population mean width of troughs is somewhere between 8.41 and 8.43 inches.

(c) The assumption is valid as the width of the troughs is approximately normally distributed.

10.68 (a) $0.2425 \leq \mu \leq 0.2856$. **(b)** $0.1975 \leq \mu \leq 0.2385$. **(c)** The amounts of granule loss for both brands are skewed to the right, but the sample sizes are large enough. **(d)** Because the two confidence intervals do not overlap, you can conclude that the mean granule loss of Boston shingles is higher than that of Vermont shingles.

CHAPTER 11

11.2 Because $Z_{STAT} = +2.21 > 1.96$, reject H_0.

11.4 Reject H_0 if $Z_{STAT} < -2.58$ or if $Z_{STAT} > 2.58$.

11.6 p-value $= 0.0456$.

11.8 p-value $= 0.1676$.

11.10 H_0: Defendant is guilty; H_1: Defendant is innocent. A Type I error would be not convicting a guilty person. A Type II error would be convicting an innocent person.

11.12 H_0: $\mu = 20$ minutes. 20 minutes is adequate travel time between classes. H_1: $\mu \neq 20$ minutes. 20 minutes is not adequate travel time between classes.

11.14 (a) $Z_{STAT} = \dfrac{350 - 375}{\frac{100}{\sqrt{64}}} = -2.0$. Because $Z_{STAT} = -2.00 < -1.96$, reject H_0. **(b)** p-value $= 0.0456$. **(c)** $325.5 \leq \mu \leq 374.5$. **(d)** The conclusions are the same.

11.16 (a) Because $-2.58 < Z_{STAT} = -1.7678 < 2.58$, do not reject H_0. **(b)** p-value $= 0.0771$. **(c)** $0.9877 \leq \mu \leq 1.0023$. **(d)** The conclusions are the same.

11.18 $t_{STAT} = 2.00$.

11.20 ± 2.1315.

11.22 No, you should not use a t test because the original population is left-skewed, and the sample size is not large enough for the t test to be valid.

11.24 (a) $t_{STAT} = (3.57 - 3.70)/0.8/\sqrt{64} = -1.30$. Because $-1.9983 < t_{STAT} = -1.30 < 1.9983$ and p-value $= 0.1984 > 0.05$, there is no evidence that the population mean waiting time is different from 3.7 minutes. **(b)** Because $n = 64$, the central limit theorem should ensure that the sampling distribution of the mean is approximately normal. In general, the t test is appropriate for this sample size except for the case where the population is extremely skewed or bimodal.

11.26 (a) $-1.9842 < t_{STAT} = 1.1364 < 1.9842$. There is no evidence that the population mean retail value of the greeting cards is different from \$2.50. **(b)** p-value $= 0.2585 > 0.05$. The probability of getting a t_{STAT} statistic greater than $+1.1364$ or less than -1.1364, given that the null hypothesis is true, is 0.2585.

11.28 (a) Because $-2.306 < t_{STAT} = 0.8754 < 2.306$, do not reject H_0. There is not enough evidence to conclude that the mean amount spent for lunch at a fast food restaurant, is different from \$6.50. **(b)** The p-value is 0.4069. If the population mean is \$6.50, the probability of observing a sample of nine customers that will result in a sample mean farther away from the hypothesized value than this sample is 0.4069. **(c)** The distribution of the amount spent is normally distributed. **(d)** With a small sample size, it is difficult to evaluate the assumption of normality. However, the distribution may be symmetric because the mean and the median are close in value.

11.30 (a) Because $-2.0096 < t_{STAT} = 0.114 < 2.0096$, do not reject H_0. There is no evidence that the mean amount is different from 2 liters. **(b)** p-value $= 0.9095$. **(d)** Yes, the data appear to have met the normality assumption. **(e)** The amount of fill is decreasing over time so the values are not independent. Therefore, the t test is invalid.

11.32 (a) Because $t_{STAT} = -5.9355 < -2.0106$, reject H_0. There is enough evidence to conclude that mean widths of the troughs is different from 8.46 inches. **(b)** The population distribution is normal. **(c)** Although the distribution of the widths is left-skewed, the large sample size means that the validity of the t test is not seriously affected although the data is left skewed, the large sample size allows you to use the t distribution.

11.34 (a) Because $-2.68 < t_{STAT} = 0.094 < 2.68$, do not reject H_0. There is no evidence that the mean amount is different from 5.5 grams. **(b)** $5.462 \leq \mu \leq 5.542$. **(c)** The conclusions are the same.

11.36 p-value $= 0.0228$.

11.38 p-value $= 0.0838$.

11.40 p-value $= 0.9162$.

11.42 $t_{STAT} = 2.7638$.

11.44 $t_{STAT} = -2.5280$.

11.46 (a) $t_{STAT} = -1.7094 < -1.6604$. There is evidence that the population mean waiting time is less than 36.5 hours. **(b)** p-value $= 0.0453 < 0.05$. The probability of getting a t_{STAT} statistic less than -1.7094, given that the null hypothesis is true, is 0.0453.

11.48 (a) $t_{STAT} = (32 - 68)/9/\sqrt{50} = -28.2843$. Because $t_{STAT} = -28.2843 < -2.4049$, reject H_0. p-value $= 0.0000 < 0.01$, reject H_0. **(b)** The probability of getting a sample mean of 32 minutes or less if the population mean is 68 minutes is 0.0000.

11.50 (a) H_0: $\mu \leq 900$; H_1: $\mu > 900$. **(b)** A Type I error occurs when you conclude that the mean number of customers increased above 900 when in fact the mean number of customers is not greater than 900. A Type II error occurs when you conclude that the mean number of customers is not greater than 900 when in fact the mean number of customers has increased above 900. **(c)** Because $t_{STAT} = 4.4947 > 2.4448$ or p-value $= 0.0000 < 0.01$, reject H_0. There is enough evidence to conclude the population mean number of customers is greater than 900. **(d)** The probability that the sample mean is 900 customers or more when the null hypothesis is true is 0.0000.

11.52 $p = 0.22$.

11.54 Do not reject H_0.

11.56 (a) $Z_{STAT} = 1.4726$, p-value $= 0.0704$. Because $Z_{STAT} = 1.47 < 1.645$ or $0.0704 > 0.05$, do not reject H_0. There is no evidence to show that more than 19.2% of students at your university use the Mozilla Foundation web browser. **(b)** $Z_{STAT} = 2.9451$, p-value $= 0016$. Because $Z_{STAT} = 2.9451 > 1.645$, reject H_0. There is evidence to show that more than 19.2% of students at your university use the Mozilla Foundation web browser. **(c)** The sample size had a major effect on being able to reject the null hypothesis. **(d)** You would be very unlikely to reject the null hypothesis with a sample of 20.

11.58 H_0: $\pi = 0.6$; H_1: $\pi \neq 0.6$. Decision rule: If $Z_{STAT} > 1.96$ or $Z_{STAT} < -1.96$, reject H_0.

$$p = \frac{650}{1,000} = 0.65$$

Test statistic:

$$Z_{STAT} = \frac{p - \pi}{\sqrt{\dfrac{\pi(1 - \pi)}{n}}} = \frac{0.65 - 0.60}{\sqrt{\dfrac{0.6(1 - 0.6)}{1,000}}} = 3.2275$$

Because $Z_{STAT} = 3.2275 > 1.96$ or p-value $= 0.0012 < 0.05$, reject H_0 and conclude that there is evidence that the percentage of young job seekers who prefer to look for a job in a place they want to reside is different from 60%.

11.60 (a) H_0: $\pi \le 0.08$. No more than 8% of students at your school are omnivores. H_1: $\pi > 0.08$. More than 8% of students at your school are omnivores. **(b)** $Z_{STAT} = 3.6490 > 1.645$; p-value $= 0.0001316$. Because $Z_{STAT} = 3.6490 > 1.645$ or p-value $= 0.0001316 < 0.05$, reject H_0. There is enough evidence to show that the percentage of omnivores at your school is greater than 8%.

11.70 (a) Buying a site that is not profitable. **(b)** Not buying a profitable site. **(c)** Type I. **(d)** If the executives adopt a less stringent rejection criterion by buying sites for which the computer model predicts moderate or large profit, the probability of committing a Type I error will increase. Many more of the sites the computer model predicts that will generate moderate profit may end up not being profitable at all. On the other hand, the less stringent rejection criterion will lower the probability of committing a Type II error because more potentially profitable sites will be purchased.

11.72 (a) Because $t_{STAT} = 3.248 > 2.0010$, reject H_0. **(b)** p-value $= 0.0019$. **(c)** Because $Z_{STAT} = -0.32 > -1.645$, do not reject H_0. **(d)** Because $-2.0010 < t_{STAT} = 0.75 < 2.0010$, do not reject H_0. **(e)** Because $Z_{STAT} = -1.61 > -1.645$, do not reject H_0.

11.74 (a) Because $t_{STAT} = -1.69 > -1.7613$, do not reject H_0. **(b)** The data are from a population that is normally distributed. **(d)** With the exception of one extreme value, the data are approximately normally distributed. **(e)** There is insufficient evidence to state that the waiting time is less than five minutes.

11.76 (a) Because $t_{STAT} = -1.47 > -1.6896$, do not reject H_0. **(b)** p-value $= 0.0748$. If the null hypothesis is true, the probability of obtaining a t_{STAT} of -1.47 or more extreme is 0.0748. **(c)** Because $t_{STAT} = -3.10 < -1.6973$, reject H_0. **(d)** p-value $= 0.0021$. If the null hypothesis is true, the probability of obtaining a t_{STAT} of -3.10 or more extreme is 0.0021. **(e)** The data in the population are assumed to be normally distributed. **(g)** Both boxplots suggest that the data are skewed slightly to the right, more so for the Boston shingles. However, the very large sample sizes mean that the results of the t test are relatively insensitive to the departure from normality.

11.78 (a) $t_{STAT} = -21.61$, reject H_0. **(b)** p-value $= 0.0000$. **(c)** $t_{STAT} = -27.19$, reject H_0. **(d)** p-value $= 0.0000$. **(e)** Because of the large sample sizes, you do not need to be concerned with the normality assumption.

CHAPTER 12

12.2 (a) $t = 3.8959$. **(b)** $df = 21$. **(c)** 2.5177. **(d)** Because $t_{STAT} = 3.8959 > 2.5177$, reject H_0.

12.4 $3.73 \le \mu_1 - \mu_2 \le 12.27$.

12.6 Because $t_{STAT} = 2.6762 < 2.9979$ or p-value $= 0.0158 > 0.01$, do not reject H_0. There is no evidence of a difference in the means of the two populations.

12.8 (a) Because $t_{STAT} = 5.7883 > 1.6581$ or p-value $= 0.0000 < 0.05$, reject H_0. There is evidence that the mean amount of Goldfish crackers eaten by children is higher for those who watched food ads than for those who did not watch food ads. **(b)** $5.79 \le \mu_1 - \mu_2 \le 11.81$. **(c)** The results cannot be compared because (a) is a one-tail test and (b) is a confidence interval that is comparable only to the results of a two-tail test.

12.10 (a) H_0: $\mu_1 = \mu_2$, where Populations: $1 = $ Males, $2 = $ Females. H_1: $\mu_1 \ne \mu_2$. Decision rule: $df = 170$. If $t_{STAT} < -1.974$ or $t_{STAT} > 1.974$, reject H_0.

Test statistic:

$$S_p^2 = \frac{(n_1 - 1)(S_1^2) + (n_2 - 1)(S_2^2)}{(n_1 - 1) + (n_2 - 1)}$$

$$= \frac{(99)(13.35^2) + (71)(9.42^2)}{99 + 71} = 140.8489$$

$$t_{STAT} = \frac{(\bar{X}_1 - \bar{X}_2) - (\mu_1 - \mu_2)}{\sqrt{S_p^2 \left(\dfrac{1}{n_1} + \dfrac{1}{n_2}\right)}}$$

$$= \frac{(40.26 - 36.85) - 0}{\sqrt{140.8489 \left(\dfrac{1}{100} + \dfrac{1}{72}\right)}} = 1.859.$$

Decision: Because $-1.974 < t_{STAT} = 1.859 < 1.974$, do not reject H_0. There is not enough evidence to conclude that the mean computer anxiety experienced by males and females is different. **(b)** p-value $= 0.0648$. **(c)** In order to use the pooled-variance t test, you need to assume that the populations are normally distributed with equal variances.

12.12 (a) Because $t_{STAT} = -4.1343 < -2.0484$, reject H_0. **(b)** p-value $= 0.0003$. **(c)** The populations of waiting times are approximately normally distributed. **(d)** $-4.2292 \le \mu_1 - \mu_2 \le -1.4268$.

12.14 (a) Because $t_{STAT} = 4.10 > 2.024$, reject H_0. There is evidence of a difference in the mean surface hardness between untreated and treated steel plates. **(b)** p-value $= 0.0002$. The probability that two samples have a mean difference of 9.3634 or more is 0.0002 if there is no difference in the mean surface hardness between untreated and treated steel plates. **(c)** You need to assume that the population distribution of hardness of both untreated and treated steel plates is normally distributed. **(d)** $4.7447 \le \mu_1 - \mu_2 \le 13.9821$.

12.16 (a) Because $t_{STAT} = -7.8124 < -1.9845$ or p-value $= 0.0000 < 0.05$, reject H_0. There is evidence of a difference in the mean number of calls for cell phone users under age 12 and cell phone users who are between 13 and 17 years of age. **(b)** You must assume that each of the two independent populations is normally distributed.

12.18 (a) 2.20. **(b)** 2.57. **(c)** 3.50.

12.20 (a) Population B: $S^2 = 25$. **(b)** 1.5625.

12.22 $df_{numerator} = 24$, $df_{denominator} = 24$.

12.24 Because $F_{STAT} = 1.2109 < 2.27$, do not reject H_0.

12.26 (a) Because $F_{STAT} = 1.2995 < 3.18$, do not reject H_0. **(b)** Because $F_{STAT} = 1.2995 < 2.62$, do not reject H_0.

12.28 (a) H_0: $\sigma_1^2 = \sigma_2^2$. H_1: $\sigma_1^2 \neq \sigma_2^2$.

Decision rule: If $F_{STAT} > 1.556$, reject H_0.

Test statistic: $F_{STAT} = \dfrac{S_1^2}{S_2^2} = \dfrac{(13.35)^2}{(9.42)^2} = 2.008$.

Decision: Because $F_{STAT} = 2.008 > 1.556$, reject H_0. There is evidence to conclude that the two population variances are different. **(b)** p-value $= 0.0022$. **(c)** The test assumes that each of the two populations is normally distributed. **(d)** Based on (a) and (b), a separate-variance t test should be used.

12.30 (a) Because $F_{STAT} = 5.1802 > 2.34$ or p-value $= 0.0002 < 0.05$, reject H_0. There is evidence of a difference in the variability of the battery life between the two types of digital cameras. **(b)** p-value $= 0.0002$. The probability of obtaining a sample that yields a test statistic more extreme than 5.1802 is 0.0002 if there is no difference in the two population variances. **(c)** The test assumes that each of the two populations are normally distributed. **(d)** Based on (a) and (b), a separate-variance t test should be used.

12.32 Because $F_{STAT} = 2.7684 > 2.2693$, or p-value $= 0.0156 < 0.05$, reject H_0. There is evidence of a difference in the variance of the yield at the two time periods.

12.33 $df = 19$.

12.35 (a) $t_{STAT} = (-1.5566)/(1.424)/\sqrt{9} = -3.2772$. Because $t_{STAT} = -3.2772 < -2.306$ or p-value $= 0.0112 < 0.05$, reject H_0. There is enough evidence of a difference in the mean summated ratings between the two brands. **(b)** You must assume that the distribution of the differences between the two ratings is approximately normal. **(c)** p-value $= 0.0112$. The probability of obtaining a mean difference in ratings that results in a test statistic that deviates from 0 by 3.2772 or more in either direction is 0.0112 if there is no difference in the mean summated ratings between the two brands. **(d)** $-2.6501 \leq \mu_D \leq -0.4610$. You are 95% confident that the mean difference in summated ratings between brand A and brand B is somewhere between -2.6501 and -0.4610.

12.37 (a) Because $-2.2622 < t_{STAT} = 0.0332 < 2.2622$ or p-value $= 0.9743 > 0.05$, do not reject H_0. There is not enough evidence to conclude that there is a difference between the mean prices between Costco and store brands. **(b)** You must assume that the distribution of the differences between the prices is approximately normal. **(c)** $-\$1.612 \leq \mu_D \leq \$1.66$. You are 95% confident that the mean difference between the prices is between $-\$1.612$ and $\$1.66$. **(d)** The results in (a) and (c) are the same. The hypothesized value of 0 for the difference in the price of shopping items between Costco and store brands is within the 95% confidence interval.

12.39 (a) Because $t_{STAT} = 1.8425 < 1.943$, do not reject H_0. There is not enough evidence to conclude that the mean bone marrow microvessel density is higher before the stem cell transplant than after the stem cell transplant. **(b)** p-value $= 0.0575$. The probability that the t statistic for the mean difference in microvessel density is 1.8425 or more is 5.75% if the mean density is not higher before the stem cell transplant than after the stem cell transplant. **(c)** $-28.26 \leq \mu_D \leq 200.55$. You are 95% confident that the mean difference in bone marrow microvessel density before and after the stem cell transplant is somewhere between -28.26 and 200.55. **(d)** that the distribution of the difference before and after the stem cell transplant is normally distributed.

12.41 (a) Because $t_{STAT} = -9.3721 < -2.4258$, reject H_0. There is evidence that the mean strength is lower at two days than at seven days. **(b)** The population of differences in strength is approximately normally distributed. **(c)** $p = 0.000$.

12.43 (a) Because $-2.58 \leq Z_{STAT} = -0.58 \leq 2.58$, do not reject H_0. **(b)** $-0.273 \leq \pi_1 - \pi_2 \leq 0.173$.

12.45 (a) H_0: $\pi_1 \leq \pi_2$. H_1: $\pi_1 > \pi_2$. Populations: $1 = 2009, 2 = 2008$. **(b)** Because $Z_{STAT} = 5.3768 > 1.6449$ or p-value $= 0.0000 < 0.05$, reject H_0. There is sufficient evidence to conclude that the population proportion of large online retailers who require three or more clicks to be removed from an e-mail list is greater in 2009 than in 2008. **(c)** Yes, the result in (b) makes it appropriate to claim that the population proportion of large online retailers who require three or more clicks to be removed from an e-mail list is greater in 2009 than in 2008.

12.47 (a) H_0: $\pi_1 = \pi_2$. H_1: $\pi_1 \neq \pi_2$. Decision rule: If $|Z_{STAT}| > 2.58$, reject H_0.

Test statistic: $\bar{p} = \dfrac{X_1 + X_2}{n_1 + n_2} = \dfrac{707 + 536}{1,000 + 1,000} = 0.6215$

$Z_{STAT} = \dfrac{(p_1 - p_2) - (\pi_2 - \pi_2)}{\sqrt{\bar{p}(1 - \bar{p})\left(\dfrac{1}{n_1} + \dfrac{1}{n_2}\right)}} = \dfrac{(0.707 - 0.536) - 0}{\sqrt{0.6215(1 - 0.6215)\left(\dfrac{1}{1,000} + \dfrac{1}{1,000}\right)}}$.

$Z_{STAT} = 7.8837 > 2.58$, reject H_0. There is evidence of a difference in the proportion who believe that e-mail messages should be answered quickly between the two age groups. **(b)** p-value $= 0.0000$. The probability of obtaining a difference in proportions that gives rise to a test statistic below -7.8837 or above $+7.8837$ is 0.0000 if there is no difference in the proportion of people in the two age groups who believe that e-mail messages should be answered quickly.

12.49 (a) Because $Z_{STAT} = 7.2742 > 1.96$, reject H_0. There is evidence of a difference in the proportion of adults and users ages 12–17 who oppose ads. **(b)** p-value $= 0.0000$. The probability of obtaining a difference in proportions that is 0.16 or more in either direction is 0.0000 if there is no difference between the proportion of adults and users ages 12–17 who oppose ads.

12.62 (a) \$0.59 coffee: $t_{STAT} = 2.8167 > 1.7613$ (or p-value $= 0.0069 < 0.05$, so reject H_0. There is evidence that reducing the price to \$0.59 has increased mean daily customer count. \$0.79 coffee: $t_{STAT} = 2.0894 > 1.7613$ (or p-value $= 0.0277 < 0.05$), so reject H_0. There is evidence that reducing the price to \$0.79 has increased mean daily customer count. **(b)** Because $F_{STAT} = 1.3407 < 2.9786$, or p-value $= 0.5906 > 0.05$, do not reject H_0. There is not enough evidence of a difference in the variance of the daily customer count for \$0.59 and \$0.79 coffee. Because $-2.0484 < t_{STAT} = 0.7661 < 2.0484$ or p-value $= 0.4500 > 0.05$, do not reject H_0. There is insufficient evidence of a difference in the mean daily customer count for \$0.59 and \$0.79 coffee. **(c)** Since both \$0.59 and \$0.79 coffee increased daily customer count, you should recommend that the price of coffee should be reduced. However, since there is no significant difference in the mean daily customer count between the two prices, you should price the coffee at \$0.79 per 12-ounce cup.

12.64 (a) Because $F_{STAT} = 1.2007 < 2.0244$, or p-value $= 0.5804 > 0.05$, do not reject H_0. There is not enough evidence of a difference in the variance of the salary of Master Black Belts and Green Belts. **(b)** The pooled-variance t test. **(c)** Because $t_{STAT} = 4.9747 > 1.6604$ or p-value $= 0.0000 < 0.05$, reject H_0. There is evidence that the mean salary of Master Black Belts is higher than the mean salary of Green Belts.

12.66 (a) Because $F_{STAT} = 22.7067 > F_\alpha = 1.6275$, reject H_0. There is enough evidence to conclude that there is a difference between the variances in age of students at the Western school and at the Eastern school. **(b)** Because there is a difference between the variances in the age of students at the Western school and at the Eastern school, schools should take that into account when designing their curriculum to accommodate the larger variance in age of students in the state university in the Western United States. **(c)** It is more appropriate to use a separate-variance t test. **(d)** Because $F_{STAT} = 1.3061 < 1.6275$, do not reject H_0. There is not enough evidence to conclude that there is a difference between the variances in years of spreadsheet usage of students at the Western school and at the Eastern school. **(e)** Using the pooled-variance t test, because $t_{STAT} = -4.6650 < -2.5978$, reject H_0. There is enough evidence of a difference in the mean years of spreadsheet usage of students at the Western school and at the Eastern school.

12.68 (a) Because $t_{STAT} = 3.3282 > 1.8595$, reject H_0. There is enough evidence to conclude that the introductory computer students required more than a mean of 10 minutes to write and run a program in Visual Basic. **(b)** Because $t_{STAT} = 1.3636 < 1.8595$, do not reject H_0. There is not enough evidence to conclude that the introductory computer students required more than a mean of 10 minutes to write and run a program in Visual Basic. **(c)** Although the mean time necessary to complete the assignment increased from 12 to 16 minutes as a result of the increase in one data value, the standard deviation went from 1.8 to 13.2, which reduced the value of t statistic. **(d)** Because $F_{STAT} = 1.2308 < 3.8549$, do not reject H_0. There is not enough evidence to conclude that the population variances are different for the Introduction to Computers students and computer majors. Hence, the pooled-variance t test is a valid test to determine whether computer majors can write a Visual Basic program in less time than introductory students, assuming that the distributions of the time needed to write a Visual Basic program for both the Introduction to Computers students and the computer majors are approximately normally distributed. Because $t_{STAT} = 4.0666 > 1.7341$, reject H_0. There is enough evidence that the mean time is higher for Introduction to Computers students than for computer majors. **(e)** p-value $= 0.000362$. If the true population mean amount of time needed for Introduction to Computer students to write a Visual Basic program is no more than 10 minutes, the probability of observing a sample mean greater than the 12 minutes in the current sample is 0.0362%. Hence, at a 5% level of significance, you can conclude that the population mean amount of time needed for Introduction to Computer students to write a Visual Basic program is more than 10 minutes. As illustrated in part **(d)**, in which there is not enough evidence to conclude that the population variances are different for the Introduction to Computers students and computer majors, the pooled-variance t test performed is a valid test to determine whether computer majors can write a Visual Basic program in less time than introductory students, assuming that the distribution of the time needed to write a Visual Basic program for both the Introduction to Computers students and the computer majors are approximately normally distributed.

12.70 From the boxplot and the summary statistics, both distributions are approximately normally distributed. $F_{STAT} = 1.056 < 1.89$. There is insufficient evidence to conclude that the two population variances are significantly different at the 5% level of significance. $t_{STAT} = -5.084 < -1.99$. At the 5% level of significance, there is sufficient evidence to reject the null hypothesis of no difference in the mean life of the bulbs between the two manufacturers. You can conclude that there is a significant difference in the mean life of the bulbs between the two manufacturers.

12.72 Playing a game on a video game system: Because $Z_{STAT} = 15.74 > 1.96$ and p-value $= 0.0000 < 0.05$, reject H_0. There is evidence that there is a difference between boys and girls in the proportion who played a game on a video game system. Reading a book for fun: Because $Z_{STAT} = -2.1005 < -1.96$ and p-value $= 0.0357 < 0.05$, reject H_0.

There is evidence that there is a difference between boys and girls in the proportion who have read a book for fun. Gave product advice to parents: Because $-1.96 < Z_{STAT} = 0.7427 < 1.96$ and p-value $= 0.4576 > 0.05$, do not reject H_0. There is insufficient evidence that there is a difference between boys and girls in the proportion who gave product advice to parents. Shopped at a mall: Because $Z_{STAT} = -6.7026 < -1.96$ and p-value $= 0.0000 < 0.05$, reject H_0. There is evidence that there is a difference between boys and girls in the proportion who shopped at a mall.

12.74 The normal probability plots suggest that the two populations are not normally distributed. An F test is inappropriate for testing the difference in two variances. The sample variances for Boston and Vermont shingles are 0.0203 and 0.015, respectively. Because $t_{STAT} = 3.015 > 1.967$ or p-value $= 0.0028 < \alpha = 0.05$, reject H_0. There is sufficient evidence to conclude that there is a difference in the mean granule loss of Boston and Vermont shingles.

12.76 Population 1 = foreign large-cap blend, 2 = small-cap blend, 3 = mid-cap blend, 4 = Large-cap blend, 5 = diversified emerging markets; Three-year return: Levene test: $F_{STAT} = 0.4148$. Since the p-value $= 0.7971 > 0.05$, do not reject H_0. There is insufficient evidence to show a difference in the variance of the three-year return among the 5 different types of mutual funds at a 5% level of significance. $F_{STAT} = 14.3127$. Since the p-value is virtually zero, reject H_0. There is sufficient evidence to show a difference in the mean three-year returns among the five different types of mutual funds at a 5% level of significance. Critical range = 2.83. Groups 3 and 4. (Mid-cap blend and large-cap blend) have lower three-year returns than diversified emerging markets. All other comparisons are not significant. Five-year return: Levene test: $F_{STAT} = 0.9671$. Since the p-value $= 0.4349 > 0.05$, do not reject H_0. There is insufficient evidence to show a difference in the variance of the five-year return among the 5 different types of mutual funds at a 5% level of significance. $F_{STAT} = 62.4531$ Since the p-value is virtually zero, reject H_0. There is sufficient evidence to show a difference in the mean five-year returns among the five different types of mutual funds at a 5% level of significance. Critical range = 2.3171. At the 5% level of significance, there is sufficient evidence that the mean five-year returns of the diversified emerging market funds is significantly higher than the others. Also, the mean five-year returns of the large-cap blend funds are significantly lower than that of the foreign large-cap funds. Ten-year return: Levene test: $F_{STAT} = 0.7854$. Since the p-value $= 0.5407 > 0.05$, do not reject H_0. There is insufficient evidence to show a difference in the variance of return among the five different types of mutual funds at a 5% level of significance. $F_{STAT} = 11.9951$. Since the p-value is virtually zero, reject H_0. There is sufficient evidence to show a difference in the mean 10-year returns among the five different types of mutual funds at a 5% level of significance. Critical range = 3.3372. At the 5% level of significance, there is sufficient evidence that the mean 10-year returns of the diversified emerging market funds is significantly higher than the others. Expense ratio: Levene test: $F_{STAT} = 0.59$. Since the p-value $= 0.6716 > 0.05$, do not reject H_0. There is insufficient evidence to show a difference in the variance in expense ratios among the 5 different types of mutual funds at a 5% level of significance. $F_{STAT} = 4.1069$. Since the p-value $= 0.0064 < 0.05$, reject H_0. There is sufficient evidence to show a difference in the mean expense ratio among the five different types of mutual funds at a 5% level of significance. Critical range = 0.479. At the 5% level of significance, there is sufficient evidence that the mean expense ratio of the diversified emerging market funds is significantly higher than the foreign large-cap funds.

CHAPTER 13

13.2 (a) $SSW = 150.$ **(b)** $MSA = 15.$ **(c)** $MSW = 5.$ **(d)** $F_{STAT} = 3.$

13.4 (a) 2. **(b)** 18. **(c)** 20.

13.6 (a) Reject H_0 if $F_{STAT} > 2.95$; otherwise, do not reject H_0. **(b)** Because $F_{STAT} = 4 > 2.95$, reject H_0. **(c)** The table does not have 28 degrees of freedom in the denominator, so use the next larger critical value, $Q_\alpha = 3.90.$ **(d)** Critical range $= 6.166.$

13.8 (a) $H_0: \mu_A = \mu_B = \mu_C = \mu_D$ and H_1: At least one mean is different.

$$MSA = \frac{SSA}{c-1} = \frac{1,986.475}{3} = 662.1583.$$

$$MSW = \frac{SSW}{n-c} = \frac{495.5}{36} = 13.76389.$$

$$F_{STAT} = \frac{MSA}{MSW} = \frac{662.1583}{13.76389} = 48.1084.$$

$$F_{0.05,3,36} = 2.8663.$$

Because the p-value is approximately 0 and $F_{STAT} = 48.1084 > 2.8663$, reject H_0. There is sufficient evidence of a difference in the mean strength of the four brands of trash bags.
(b) Critical range $= Q_\alpha \sqrt{\dfrac{MSW}{2}\left(\dfrac{1}{n_j} + \dfrac{1}{n_{j'}}\right)} = 3.79 \sqrt{\dfrac{13.7639}{2}\left(\dfrac{1}{10} + \dfrac{1}{10}\right)}$

$= 4.446.$

From the Tukey-Kramer procedure, there is a difference in mean strength between Kroger and Tuffstuff, Glad and Tuffstuff, and Hefty and Tuffstuff. **(c)** ANOVA output for Levene's test for homogeneity of variance:

$$MSA = \frac{SSA}{c-1} = \frac{24.075}{3} = 8.025.$$

$$MSW = \frac{SSW}{n-c} = \frac{198.2}{36} = 5.5056.$$

$$F_{STAT} = \frac{MSA}{MSW} = \frac{8.025}{5.5056} = 1.4576.$$

$$F_{0.05,3,36} = 2.8663.$$

Because p-value $= 0.2423 > 0.05$ and $F_{STAT} = 1.4576 < 2.8663$, do not reject H_0. There is insufficient evidence to conclude that the variances in strength among the four brands of trash bags are different. **(d)** From the results in (a) and (b), Tuffstuff has the lowest mean strength and should be avoided.

13.10 (a) Because $F_{STAT} = 12.56 > 2.76$, reject H_0. **(b)** Critical range $= 4.67$. Advertisements A and B are different from Advertisements C and D. Advertisement E is only different from Advertisement D. **(c)** Because $F_{STAT} = 1.927 < 2.76$, do not reject H_0. There is no evidence of a significant difference in the variation in the ratings among the five advertisements. **(d)** The advertisements underselling the pen's characteristics had the highest mean ratings, and the advertisements overselling the pen's characteristics had the lowest mean ratings. Therefore, use an advertisement that undersells the pen's characteristics and avoid advertisements that oversell the pen's characteristics.

13.12 (a) Because the p-value for this test, 0.922, is greater than the level of significance, $\alpha = 0.05$ (or the computed F test statistic, 0.0817, is less than the critical value $F = 3.6823$), you cannot reject the null hypothesis. You conclude that there is insufficient evidence of a difference in the mean yield between the three methods used in the cleansing step. **(b)** Because there is no evidence of a difference between the methods, you should not develop any multiple comparisons. **(c)** Because the p-value

for this test, 0.8429, is greater than the level of significance, $\alpha = 0.05$ (or the computed F test statistic, 0.1728, is less than the critical value, $F = 3.6823$), you cannot reject the null hypothesis. You conclude that there is insufficient evidence of a difference in the variation in the yield between the three methods used in the cleansing step. **(d)** Because there is no evidence of a difference in the variation between the methods, the validity of the conclusion reached in (a) is not affected.

13.14 (a) Because $F_{STAT} = 53.03 > 2.92$, reject H_0.
(b) Critical range $= 5.27$ (using 30 degrees of freedom). Designs 3 and 4 are different from Designs 1 and 2. Designs 1 and 2 are different from each other. **(c)** The assumptions are that the samples are randomly and independently selected (or randomly assigned), the original populations of distances are approximately normally distributed, and the variances are equal. **(d)** Because $F_{STAT} = 2.093 < 2.92$, do not reject H_0. There is no evidence of a significant difference in the variation in the distance among the four designs. **(e)** The manager should choose Design 3 or 4.

13.28 (a) Because $F_{STAT} = 22.7067 > F_\alpha = 1.6275$, reject H_0. There is enough evidence to conclude that there is a difference between the variances in age of students at the Western school and at the Eastern school. **(b)** Because there is a difference between the variances in the age of students at the Western school and at the Eastern school, schools should take that into account when designing their curriculum to accommodate the larger variance in age of students in the state university in the Western United States. **(c)** It is more appropriate to use a separate-variance t test. **(d)** Because $F_{STAT} = 1.3061 < 1.6275$, do not reject H_0. There is not enough evidence to conclude that there is a difference between the variances in years of spreadsheet usage of students at the Western school and at the Eastern school. **(e)** Using the pooled-variance t test, because $t_{STAT} = -4.6650 < -2.5978$, reject H_0. There is enough evidence of a difference in the mean years of spreadsheet usage of students at the Western school and at the Eastern school.

13.30 (a) Because $t_{STAT} = 3.3282 > 1.8595$, reject H_0. There is enough evidence to conclude that the introductory computer students required more than a mean of 10 minutes to write and run a program in Visual Basic. **(b)** Because $t_{STAT} = 1.3636 < 1.8595$, do not reject H_0. There is not enough evidence to conclude that the introductory computer students required more than a mean of 10 minutes to write and run a program in Visual Basic. **(c)** Although the mean time necessary to complete the assignment increased from 12 to 16 minutes as a result of the increase in one data value, the standard deviation went from 1.8 to 13.2, which reduced the value of t statistic. **(d)** Because $F_{STAT} = 1.2308 < 3.8549$, do not reject H_0. There is not enough evidence to conclude that the population variances are different for the Introduction to Computers students and computer majors. Hence, the pooled-variance t test is a valid test to determine whether computer majors can write a Visual Basic program in less time than introductory students, assuming that the distributions of the time needed to write a Visual Basic program for both the Introduction to Computers students and the computer majors are approximately normally distributed. Because $t_{STAT} = 4.0666 > 1.7341$, reject H_0. There is enough evidence that the mean time is higher for Introduction to Computers students than for computer majors. **(e)** p-value $= 0.000362$. If the true population mean amount of time needed for Introduction to Computer students to write a Visual Basic program is no more than 10 minutes, the probability of observing a sample mean greater than the 12 minutes in the current sample is 0.0362%. Hence, at a 5% level of significance, you can conclude that the population mean amount of time needed for Introduction to Computer students to write a Visual Basic program is more than 10 minutes. As illustrated in part **(d)**, in which there is not enough evidence to conclude that the population variances are different for the Introduction to Computers students and computer majors, the pooled-variance t test performed is a valid test to determine whether computer majors can write a Visual Basic program in less time than introductory students, assuming that the distribution of the time needed to write a Visual Basic program for both the Introduction to Computers students and the computer majors are approximately normally distributed.

13.32 From the boxplot and the summary statistics, both distributions are approximately normally distributed. $F_{STAT} = 1.056 < 1.89$. There is insufficient evidence to conclude that the two population variances are significantly different at the 5% level of significance. $t_{STAT} = -5.084 < -1.99$. At the 5% level of significance, there is sufficient evidence to reject the null hypothesis of no difference in the mean life of the bulbs between the two manufacturers. You can conclude that there is a significant difference in the mean life of the bulbs between the two manufacturers.

13.36 The normal probability plots suggest that the two populations are not normally distributed. An F test is inappropriate for testing the difference in two variances. The sample variances for Boston and Vermont shingles are 0.0203 and 0.015, respectively. Because $t_{STAT} = 3.015 > 1.967$ or p-value $= 0.0028 < \alpha = 0.05$, reject H_0. There is sufficient evidence to conclude that there is a difference in the mean granule loss of Boston and Vermont shingles.

CHAPTER 14

14.2 (a) For $df = 1$ and $\alpha = 0.05$, $\chi_\alpha^2 = 3.841$. **(b)** For $df = 1$ and $\alpha = 0.025$, $\chi^2 = 5.024$. **(c)** For $df = 1$ and $\alpha = 0.01$, $\chi_\alpha^2 = 6.635$.

14.4 (a) All $f_e = 25$. **(b)** Because $\chi_{STAT}^2 = 4.00 > 3.841$, reject H_0.

14.6 (b) Because $\chi_{STAT}^2 = 28.9102 > 3.841$, reject H_0. There is enough evidence to conclude that there is a significant difference between the proportion of retail websites that require three or more clicks to be removed from an email list in 2009 as compared to 2008. p-value $= 0.0000$. The probability of obtaining a test statistic of 28.9102 or larger when the null hypothesis is true is 0.0000. **(c)** You should not compare the results in (a) to those of Problem 10.30 (b) because that was a one-tail test.

14.8 (a) H_0: $\pi_1 = \pi_2$. H_1: $\pi_1 \neq \pi_2$. Because $\chi_{STAT}^2 = (536 - 621.5)^2/621.5 + (464 - 378.5)^2/378.5 + (707 - 621.5)^2/621.5 + (293 - 378.5)^2/378.5 = 62.152 > 6.635$, reject H_0. There is evidence of a difference in the proportion who believe that e-mail messages should be answered quickly between the two age groups. **(b)** p-value $= 0.0000$. The probability of obtaining a difference in proportions that gives rise to a test statistic greater than 62.152 is 0.0000 if there is no difference in the proportion of people in the two age groups who believe that e-mail messages should be answered quickly. **(c)** The results of (a) and (b) are exactly the same as those of Problem 10.32. The χ^2 in (a) and the Z in Problem 10.32 (a) satisfy the relationship that $\chi^2 = 62.152 = Z^2 = (7.8837)^2$, and the p-value in (b) is exactly the same as the p-value computed in Problem 10.32 (b).

14.10 (a) Since $\chi_{STAT}^2 = 52.9144 > 3.841$, reject H_0. There is evidence that there is a significant difference between the proportion of adults and users ages 12–17 who oppose ads on websites. **(b)** p-value 0.0000. The probability of obtaining a test statistic of 52.9144 or larger when the null hypothesis is true is 0.0000.

14.12 (a) The expected frequencies for the first row are 20, 30, and 40. The expected frequencies for the second row are 30, 45, and 60. **(b)** Because $\chi_{STAT}^2 = 12.5 > 5.991$, reject H_0.

14.14 (a) Because the calculated test statistic $\chi_{STAT}^2 = 48.6268 > 9.4877$, reject H_0 and conclude that there is a difference in the proportion who oppose ads on websites between the age groups. **(b)** The p-value is virtually 0. The probability of a test statistic greater than 48.6268 or more is approximately 0 if there is no difference between the age groups in the proportion who oppose ads on websites.

14.16 (a) H_0: $\pi_1 = \pi_2 = \pi_3$. H_1: At least one proportion differs.

f_0	f_e	$(f_0 - f_e)$	$(f_0 - f_e)^2/f_e$
48	42.667	5.333	0.667
152	157.333	−5.333	0.181
56	42.667	13.333	4.166
144	157.333	−13.333	1.130
24	42.667	−18.667	8.167
176	157.333	18.667	2.215
			16.526

Decision rule: $df = (c - 1) = (3 - 1) = 2$. If $\chi_{STAT}^2 > 5.9915$, reject H_0.

Test statistic: $\chi_{STAT}^2 = \sum_{all\ cells} \dfrac{(f_0 - f_e)}{f_e} = 16.526$.

Decision: Because $\chi_{STAT}^2 = 16.526 > 5.9915$, reject H_0. There is a significant difference in the age groups with respect to major grocery shopping day. **(b)** p-value $= 0.0003$. The probability that the test statistic is greater than or equal to 16.526 is 0.0003, if the null hypothesis is true.

14.18 (a) Because $\chi_{STAT}^2 = 6.50 > 5.9915$, reject H_0. There is evidence of a difference in the percentage who often listen to rock music among the age groups. **(b)** p-value $= 0.0388$.

14.20 $df = (r - 1)(c - 1) = (3 - 1)(4 - 1) = 6$.

14.22 $\chi_{STAT}^2 = 92.1028 > 16.919$, reject H_0 and conclude that there is evidence of a relationship between the type of dessert ordered and the type of entrée ordered.

14.24 (a) H_0: There is no relationship between the commuting time of company employees and the level of stress-related problems observed on the job. H_1: There is a relationship between the commuting time of company employees and the level of stress-related problems observed on the job.

f_0	f_e	$(f_0 - f_e)$	$(f_0 - f_e)^2/f_e$
9	12.1379	−3.1379	0.8112
17	20.1034	−3.1034	0.4791
18	11.7586	6.2414	3.3129
5	5.2414	−0.2414	0.0111
8	8.6810	−0.6810	0.0534
6	5.0776	0.9224	0.1676
18	14.6207	3.3793	0.7811
28	24.2155	3.7845	0.5915
7	14.1638	−7.1638	3.6233
			9.8311

Decision rule: If $\chi_{STAT}^2 > 13.277$, reject H_0.

Test statistic: $\chi_{STAT}^2 = \sum_{all\ cells} \dfrac{(f_0 - f_e)^2}{f_e} = 9.8311$.

Decision: Because $\chi^2_{STAT} = 9.8311 < 13.277$, do not reject H_0. There is insufficient evidence to conclude that there is a relationship between the commuting time of company employees and the level of stress-related problems observed on the job. **(b)** Because $\chi^2_{STAT} = 9.831 > 9.488$, reject H_0. There is enough evidence at the 0.05 level to conclude that there is a relationship.

14.26 Because $\chi^2_{STAT} = 129.520 > 21.026$, reject H_0. There is a relationship between when the decision is made of what to have for dinner and the type of household.

14.30 (a) Because $\chi^2_{STAT} = 0.412 < 3.841$, do not reject H_0. There is insufficient evidence to conclude that there is a relationship between a student's gender and pizzeria selection. **(b)** Because $\chi^2_{STAT} = 2.624 < 3.841$, do not reject H_0. There is insufficient evidence to conclude that there is a relationship between a student's gender and pizzeria selection. **(c)** Because $\chi^2_{STAT} = 4.956 < 5.991$, do not reject H_0. There is insufficient evidence to conclude that there is a relationship between price and pizzeria selection. **(d)** p-value $= 0.0839$. The probability of a sample that gives a test statistic equal to or greater than 4.956 is 8.39% if the null hypothesis of no relationship between price and pizzeria selection is true.

14.32 (a) Because $\chi^2_{STAT} = 11.895 < 12.592$, do not reject H_0. There is not enough evidence to conclude that there is a relationship between the attitudes of employees toward the use of self-managed work teams and employee job classification. **(b)** Because $\chi^2_{STAT} = 3.294 < 12.592$, do not reject H_0. There is insufficient evidence to conclude that there is a relationship between the attitudes of employees toward vacation time without pay and employee job classification.

CHAPTER 15

15.2 (a) Yes. **(b)** No. **(c)** No. **(d)** Yes.

15.4 (a) The scatter plot shows a positive linear relationship. **(b)** For each increase in shelf space of an additional foot, predicted weekly sales are estimated to increase by $7.40. **(c)** $\hat{Y} = 145 + 7.4X = 145 + 7.4(8) = 204.2$, or $204.20.

15.6 (b) $b_0 = -2.37, b_1 = 0.0501$ **(c)** For every cubic foot increase in the amount moved, predicted labor hours are estimated to increase by 0.0501. **(d)** 22.67 labor hours.

15.8 (b) $b_0 = -501.7008, b_1 = 5.0077$. **(c)** For each additional million-dollar increase in revenue, the value is predicted to increase by an estimated $5.0077 million. Literal interpretation of b_0 is not meaningful because an operating franchise cannot have zero revenue. **(d)** 249.4485 million.

15.10 (b) $b_0 = 10.473, b_1 = 0.3839$. **(c)** For each increase of one million dollars of box office gross, the predicted DVD revenue is estimated to increase by $0.3839 million. **(d)** $\hat{Y} = b_0 + b_1 X$. $\hat{Y} = 10.473 + 0.3839(75) = \$39.2658$ million.

15.12 $r^2 = 0.90$. 90% of the variation in the dependent variable can be explained by the variation in the independent variable.

15.14 $r^2 = 0.75$. 75% of the variation in the dependent variable can be explained by the variation in the independent variable.

15.16 (a) $r^2 = \dfrac{SSR}{SST} = \dfrac{20,535}{30,025} = 0.684$. 68.4% of the variation in sales can be explained by the variation in shelf space.

(b) $S_{YX} = \sqrt{\dfrac{SSE}{n-2}} = \sqrt{\dfrac{\sum_{i=1}^{n}(Y_i - \hat{Y}_i)^2}{n-2}} = \sqrt{\dfrac{9,490}{10}} = 30.8058.$

(c) Based on (a) and (b), the model should be useful for predicting sales.

15.18 (a) $r^2 = 0.8892$. 88.92% of the variation in labor hours can be explained by the variation in cubic feet moved. **(b)** $S_{YX} = 5.0314$ **(c)** Based on (a) and (b), the model should be very useful for predicting the labor hours.

15.20 (a) $r^2 = 0.9542$. 95.42% of the variation in the value of a baseball franchise can be explained by the variation in its annual revenue. **(b)** $S_{YX} = 58.9821$. **(c)** Based on (a) and (b), the model should be very useful for predicting the value of a baseball franchise.

15.22 (a) $r^2 = 0.5452$. 54.52% of the variation in DVD revenue can be explained by the variation in box office gross. **(b)** $S_{YX} = 15.3782$. The variation of DVD revenue around the prediction line is $15.3782 million. The typical difference between actual DVD revenue and the predicted DVD revenue using the regression equation is approximately $15.3782 million. **(c)** Based on (a) and (b), the model is useful for predicting DVD revenue. **(d)** Other variables that might explain the variation in DVD revenue could be the amount spent on advertising, the timing of the release of the DVDs, and the type of movie.

15.24 A residual analysis of the data indicates a pattern, with sizable clusters of consecutive residuals that are either all positive or all negative. This pattern indicates a violation of the assumption of linearity. A curvilinear model should be investigated.

15.26 There does not appear to be a pattern in the residual plot. The assumptions of regression do not appear to be seriously violated.

15.28 Based on the residual plot, there does not appear to be a curvilinear pattern in the residuals. The assumptions of normality and equal variance do not appear to be seriously violated.

15.30 Based on the residual plot, there appears to be a nonlinear pattern in the residuals. A curvilinear model should be investigated. There is some right-skewness in the residuals, and there is some violation of the equal-variance assumption.

15.33 (a) 3.00. **(b)** ± 2.1199. **(c)** Reject H_0. There is evidence that the fitted linear regression model is useful. **(d)** $1.32 \le \beta_1 \le 7.68$.

15.35 (a) $t_{STAT} = \dfrac{b_1 - \beta_1}{S_{b_1}} = \dfrac{7.4}{1.59} = 4.65 > 2.2281$. Reject H_0. There is evidence of a linear relationship between shelf space and sales. **(b)** $b_1 \pm t_{\alpha/2}S_{b_1} = 7.4 \pm 2.2281(1.59)$ $3.86 \le \beta_1 \le 10.94$.

15.37 (a) $t_{STAT} = 16.52 > 2.0322$; reject H_0. There is evidence of a linear relationship between the number of cubic feet moved and labor hours. **(b)** $0.0439 \le \beta_1 \le 0.0562$.

15.39 (a) $t_{STAT} = 24.1555 > 2.0484$ or because the p-value is approximately 0, reject H_0 at the 5% level of significance. There is evidence of a linear relationship between annual revenue and franchise value. **(b)** $4.5830 \le \beta_1 \le 5.4323$.

15.41 (a) $t_{STAT} = 4.8964 > 2.086$ or because the p-value is virtually $0 < 0.05$; reject H_0. There is evidence of a linear relationship between box office gross and sales of DVDs. **(b)** $3.3072 \le \beta_1 \le 5.3590$.

15.43 (a) (% daily change in BGU) $= b_0 + 3.0$ (% daily change in Russell 1000 index). **(b)** If the Russell 1000 gains 10% in a year, BGU is expected to gain an estimated 30%. **(c)** If the Russell 1000 loses 20% in a year, BGU is expected to lose an estimated 60%. **(d)** Risk takers will be attracted to leveraged funds, and risk-averse investors will stay away.

15.45 (a), (b) First weekend and U.S. gross: $r = 0.2526, t_{STAT} = -0.5221 < 2.7764, p$-value $= 0.6292 > 0.05$. Do not reject H_0. At the 0.05 level of significance, there is a insufficient evidence of a linear relationship between

First weekend sales and U.S. gross. First weekend and worldwide gross: $r = 0.4149$, $t_{STAT} = -0.912 < 2.7764$, p-value $= 0.4134 > 0.05$. Do not reject H_0. At the 0.05 level of significance, there is a insufficient evidence of a linear relationship between first weekend sales and worldwide gross. U.S. gross and worldwide gross: $r = 0.9414$, $t_{STAT} = 5.5807 > 2.7764$, p-value $= 0.0051 < 0.05$. Reject H_0. At the 0.05 level of significance, there is evidence of a linear relationship between U.S. gross and worldwide gross.

15.47 (a) $r = 0.5497$. There appears to be a moderate positive linear relationship between the average Wonderlic score of football players trying out for the NFL and the graduation rate for football players at selected schools. **(b)** $t_{STAT} = 3.9485$, p-value $= 0.0004 < 0.05$. Reject H_0. At the 0.05 level of significance, there is a significant linear relationship between the average Wonderlic score of football players trying out for the NFL and the graduation rate for football players at selected schools. **(c)** There is a significant linear relationship between the average Wonderlic score of football players trying out for the NFL and the graduation rate for football players at selected schools, but the positive linear relationship is only moderate.

15.49 (a) $15.95 \le \mu_{Y|X=4} \le 18.05$. **(b)** $14.651 \le Y_{X=4} \le 19.349$.

15.51 (a) $\hat{Y} = 145 + 7.4(8) = 204.2$ $\hat{Y} \pm t_{\alpha/2}S_{YX}\sqrt{h_i}$

$$= 204.2 \pm 2.2281(30.81)\sqrt{0.1373}$$

$$178.76 \le \mu_{Y|X=8} \le 229.64.$$

(b) $\hat{Y} \pm t_{\alpha/2}S_{YX}\sqrt{1 + h_i}$

$$= 204.2 \pm 2.2281(30.81)\sqrt{1 + 0.1373}$$

$$131.00 \le Y_{X=8} \le 277.40.$$

(c) Part (b) provides a prediction interval for the individual response given a specific value of the independent variable, and part (a) provides an interval estimate for the mean value, given a specific value of the independent variable. Because there is much more variation in predicting an individual value than in estimating a mean value, a prediction interval is wider than a confidence interval estimate.

15.53 (a) $20.799 \le \mu_{Y|X=500} \le 24.542$. **(b)** $12.276 \le Y_{X=500} \le 33.065$. **(c)** You can estimate a mean more precisely than you can predict a single observation.

15.55 (a) $217.4561 \le \mu_{Y|X=150} \le 281.441$. **(b)** $124.4653 \le Y_{X=150} \le 374.4318$. **(c)** Part (b) provides a prediction interval for an individual response given a specific value of X, and part (a) provides a confidence interval estimate for the mean value, given a specific value of X. Because there is much more variation in predicting an individual value than in estimating a mean, the prediction interval is wider than the confidence interval.

15.67 (a) $b_0 = 24.84$, $b_1 = 0.14$. **(b)** For each additional case, the predicted delivery time is estimated to increase by 0.14 minutes. **(c)** 45.84. **(d)** No, 500 is outside the relevant range of the data used to fit the regression equation. **(e)** $r^2 = 0.972$. **(f)** There is no obvious pattern in the residuals, so the assumptions of regression are met. The model appears to be adequate. **(g)** $t_{STAT} = 24.88 > 2.1009$; reject H_0. **(h)** $44.88 \le \mu_{Y|X=150} \le 46.80$. $41.56 \le Y_{X=150} \le 50.12$.

15.69 (a) $b_0 = -122.3439$, $b_1 = 1.7817$. **(b)** For each additional thousand dollars in assessed value, the estimated selling price of a house increases by $1.7817 thousand. The estimated selling price of a house with a 0 assessed value is -122.3439 thousand. However, this interpretation is not meaningful because the assessed value cannot be below 0. **(c)** $\hat{Y} = -122.3439 + 1.78171X = -122.3439 +$

$1.78171(170) = 180.5475$ thousand dollars. **(d)** $r^2 = 0.9256$. So 92.56% of the variation in selling price can be explained by the variation in assessed value. **(e)** Neither the residual plot nor the normal probability plot reveals any potential violation of the linearity, equal variance, and normality assumptions. **(f)** $t_{STAT} = 18.6648 > 2.0484$, p-value is virtually 0. Because p-value < 0.05, reject H_0. There is evidence of a linear relationship between selling price and assessed value. **(g)** $1.5862 \le \beta_1 \le 1.9773$.

15.71 (a) $b_0 = 0.30$, $b_1 = 0.00487$. **(b)** For each additional point on the GMAT score, the predicted GPA is estimated to increase by 0.00487. Because a GMAT score of 0 is not possible, the Y intercept does not have a practical interpretation. **(c)** 3.222. **(d)** $r^2 = 0.798$. **(e)** There is no obvious pattern in the residuals, so the assumptions of regression are met. The model appears to be adequate. **(f)** $t_{STAT} = 8.43 > 2.1009$; reject H_0. **(g)** $3.144 \le \mu_{Y|X=600} \le 3.301$, $2.866 \le Y_{X=600} \le 3.559$. **(h)** $.00366 \le \beta_1 \le .00608$.

15.73 (a) There is no clear relationship shown on the scatter plot. **(c)** Looking at all 23 flights, when the temperature is lower, there is likely to be some O-ring damage, particularly if the temperature is below 60 degrees. **(d)** 31 degrees is outside the relevant range, so a prediction should not be made. **(e)** Predicted $Y = 18.036 - 0.240X$, where $X =$ temperature and $Y =$ O-ring damage **(g)** A nonlinear model would be more appropriate. **(h)** The appearance on the residual plot of a nonlinear pattern indicates that a nonlinear model would be better. It also appears that the normality assumption is invalid.

15.75 (a) $b_0 = -6.2448$, $b_1 = 2.9576$. **(b)** For each additional million-dollar increase in revenue, the franchise value will increase by an estimated $2.9576 million. Literal interpretation of b_0 is not meaningful because an operating franchise cannot have zero revenue. **(c)** $437.3901 million. **(d)** $r^2 = 0.981$. 98.1% of the variation in the value of an NBA franchise can be explained by the variation in its annual revenue. **(e)** There does not appear to be a pattern in the residual plot. The assumptions of regression do not appear to be seriously violated. **(f)** $t_{STAT} = 38.0207 > 2.0484$ or because the p-value is approximately 0, reject H_0 at the 5% level of significance. There is evidence of a linear relationship between annual revenue and franchise value. **(g)** $431.0467 \le \mu_{Y|X=150} \le 443.7334$. **(h)** $408.8257 \le Y_{X=150} \le 465.9544$. **(i)** The strength of the relationship between revenue and value is stronger for baseball and NBA franchises than for European soccer teams.

15.77 (a) $b_0 = -2,629.222$, $b_1 = 82.472$. **(b)** For each additional centimeter in circumference, the weight is estimated to increase by 82.472 grams. **(c)** 2,319.08 grams. **(d)** Yes, since circumference is a very strong predictor of weight. **(e)** $r^2 = 0.937$. **(f)** There appears to be a nonlinear relationship between circumference and weight. **(g)** p-value is virtually $0 < 0.05$; reject H_0. **(h)** $72.7875 \le \beta_1 \le 92.156$.

15.79 (b) $\hat{Y} = 931,626.16 + 21,782.76X$. **(c)** $b_1 = 21,782.76$ For each increase of the median age of the customer base by one year, the latest one-month sales total is estimated to increase by $21,782.76. $b_0 = 931,626.16$ Since age cannot be 0, there is no direct interpretation for b_0. **(d)** $r^2 = 0.0017$. Only 0.17% of the total variation in the franchise's latest one-month sales total can be explained by using the median age of the customer base. **(e)** The residuals are very evenly spread out across different ranges of median age. **(f)** Because $-2.0281 < t_{STAT} = 0.2482 < 2.0281$, do not reject H_0. There is insufficient evidence to conclude that there is a linear relationship between the one-month sales total and the median age of the customer base. **(g)** $-156,181.50 \le \beta_1 \le 199,747.02$.

15.81 (a) There is a positive linear relationship between total sales and the percentage of the customer base with a college diploma. **(b)** $\hat{Y} = 789,847.38 + 35,854.15X$. **(c)** $b_1 = 35,854.15$ For each increase of 1% of the customer base having received a college diploma, the latest one-month mean sales total is estimated to increase by \$35,854.15. $b_0 = 789,847.38$ Although this is outside the range of the data, it would mean that the estimated sales when the percentage of the customer base with a college diploma was 0 would be \$789,847.38 **(d)** $r^2 = 0.1036$. 10.36% of the total variation in the franchise's latest one-month sales total can be explained by the percentage of the customer base with a college diploma. **(e)** The residuals are evenly spread out around zero. **(f)** Because $t_{STAT} = 2.0392 > 2.0281$, reject H_0. There is enough evidence to conclude that there is a linear relationship between one-month sales total and percentage of customer base with a college diploma. **(g)** $b_1 \pm t_{\alpha/2} S_{b_1} = 35,854.15 \pm 2.0281(17,582.269)$, $195.75 \le \beta_1 \le 71,512.60$.

15.83 (a) The correlation between compensation and stock performance is -0.0389. **(b)** $t_{STAT} = -0.4912 > -1.96$; p-value $= 0.6239 > 0.05$. The correlation between compensation and stock performance is not significant. **(c)** The lack of correlation between compensation and stock performance was surprising (or maybe it shouldn't have been!).

CHAPTER 16

16.2 (a) For each one-unit increase in X_1, you estimate that Y will decrease 2 units, holding X_2 constant. For each one-unit increase in X_2, you estimate that Y will increase 7 units, holding X_1 constant. **(b)** The Y intercept, equal to 50, estimates the value of Y when both X_1 and X_2 are 0.

16.4 (a) $\hat{Y} = -2.72825 + 0.047114X_1 + 0.011947X_2$. **(b)** For a given number of orders, for each increase of \$1,000 in sales, the distribution cost is estimated to increase by \$47.114. For a given amount of sales, for each increase of one order, the distribution cost is estimated to increase by \$11.95. **(c)** The interpretation of b_0 has no practical meaning here because it would represent the estimated distribution cost when there were no sales and no orders. **(d)** $\hat{Y} = -2.72825 + 0.047114(400) + 0.011947(4500) = 69.878$, or \$69,878. **(e)** $\$66,419.93 \le \mu_{Y|X} \le \$73,337.01$. **(f)** $\$59,380.61 \le Y_X \le \$80,376.33$. **(g)** The interval in (e) is narrower because it is estimating the mean value, not an individual value.

16.6 (a) $\hat{Y} = 156.4 + 13.081X_1 + 16.795X_2$. **(b)** For a given amount of newspaper advertising, each increase by \$1,000 in radio advertising is estimated to result in an increase in sales of \$13,081. For a given amount of radio advertising, each increase by \$1,000 in newspaper advertising is estimated to result in an increase in sales of \$16,795. **(c)** When there is no money spent on radio advertising and newspaper advertising, the estimated mean sales is \$156,430.44. **(d)** Holding the other independent variable constant, newspaper advertising seems to be more effective because its slope is greater.

16.8 (a) $\hat{Y} = 400.8057 + 456.4485X_1 - 2.4708X_2$ where $X_1 =$ land area, $X_2 =$ age. **(b)** For a given age, each increase by one acre in land area is estimated to result in an increase in appraised value by \$456.45 thousands. For a given land area, each increase of one year in age is estimated to result in a decrease in appraised value by \$2.47 thousands. **(c)** The interpretation of b_0 has no practical meaning here because it would represent the estimated appraised value of a new house that has no land area. **(d)** $\hat{Y} = 400.8057 + 456.4485(0.25) - 2.4708(45) = \$403.73$ thousands. **(e)** $372.7370 \le \mu_{Y|X} \le 434.7243$. **(f)** $235.1964 \le Y_X \le 572.2649$.

16.10 (a) $MSR = 15, MSE = 12$. **(b)** 1.25. **(c)** $F_{STAT} = 1.25 < 4.10$; do not reject H_0. **(d)** 0.20. **(e)** 0.04.

16.12 (a) $F_{STAT} = 97.69 > 3.89$. Reject H_0. There is evidence of a significant linear relationship with at least one of the independent variables. **(b)** p-value $= 0.0001$. **(c)** $r^2 = 0.9421$. 94.21% of the variation in the long-

term ability to absorb shock can be explained by variation in forefoot absorbing capability and variation in midsole impact. **(d)** $r^2_{adj} = 0.935$.

16.14 (a) $F_{STAT} = 74.13 > 3.467$; reject H_0. **(b)** p-value $= 0$. **(c)** $r^2 = 0.8759$. 87.59% of the variation in distribution cost can be explained by variation in sales and variation in number of orders. **(d)** $r^2_{adj} = 0.8641$.

16.16 (a) $F_{STAT} = 40.16 > 3.522$. Reject H_0. There is evidence of a significant linear relationship. **(b)** p-value < 0.001. **(c)** $r^2 = 0.8087$. 80.87% of the variation in sales can be explained by variation in radio advertising and variation in newspaper advertising. **(d)** $r^2_{adj} = 0.7886$.

16.18 (a)–(e) Based on a residual analysis, there is no evidence of a violation of the assumptions of regression. **(f)** $D = 2.26$ **(g)** $D = 2.26 > 1.55$. There is no evidence of positive autocorrelation in the residuals.

16.20 (a) There appears to be a quadratic relationship in the plot of the residuals against both radio and newspaper advertising. **(b)** Since the data are not collected over time, the Durbin-Watson test is not appropriate. **(c)** Curvilinear terms for both of these explanatory variables should be considered for inclusion in the model.

16.22 (a) The residual analysis reveals no patterns. **(b)** Since the data are not collected over time, the Durbin-Watson test is not appropriate. **(c)** There are no apparent violations in the assumptions.

16.24 (a) Variable X_2 has a larger slope in terms of the t statistic of 3.75 than variable X_1, which has a smaller slope in terms of the t statistic of 3.33. **(b)** $1.46824 \le \beta_1 \le 6.53176$. **(c)** For X_1: $t_{STAT} = 4/1.2 = 3.33 > 2.1098$, with 17 degrees of freedom for $\alpha = 0.05$. Reject H_0. There is evidence that X_1 contributes to a model already containing X_2. For X_2: $t_{STAT} = 3/0.8 = 3.75 > 2.1098$, with 17 degrees of freedom for $\alpha = 0.05$. Reject H_0. There is evidence that X_2 contributes to a model already containing X_1. Both X_1 and X_2 should be included in the model.

16.26 (a) 95% confidence interval on β_1: $b_1 \pm tS_{b_1}, 0.0471 \pm 2.0796$ (0.0203), $0.0049 \le \beta_1 \le 0.0893$. **(b)** For X_1: $t_{STAT} = b_1/S_{b_1} = 0.0471/0.0203 = 2.32 > 2.0796$. Reject H_0. There is evidence that X_1 contributes to a model already containing X_2. For X_2: $t_{STAT} = b_1/S_{b_1} = 0.0112/0.0023 = 5.31 > 2.0796$. Reject H_0. There is evidence that X_2 contributes to a model already containing X_1. Both X_1 (sales) and X_2 (orders) should be included in the model.

16.28 (a) $9.398 \le \beta_1 \le 16.763$. **(b)** For X_1: $t_{STAT} = 7.43 > 2.093$. Reject H_0. There is evidence that X_1 contributes to a model already containing X_2. For X_2: $t_{STAT} = 5.67 > 2.093$. Reject H_0. There is evidence that X_2 contributes to a model already containing X_1. Both X_1 (radio advertising) and X_2 (newspaper advertising) should be included in the model.

16.30 (a) $227.5865 \le \beta_1 \le 685.3104$. **(b)** For X_1: $t_{STAT} = 4.0922$ and p-value $= 0.0003$. Because p-value < 0.05, reject H_0. There is evidence that X_1 contributes to a model already containing X_2. For X_2: $t_{STAT} = -3.6295$ and p-value $= 0.0012$. Because p-value < 0.05 reject H_0. There is evidence that X_2 contributes to a model already containing X_1. Both X_1 (land area) and X_2 (age) should be included in the model.

16.32 Because $t_{STAT} = 3.27 > 2.1098$, reject H_0. Variable X_2 makes a significant contribution to the model.

16.34 (a) $\hat{Y} = 243.7371 + 9.2189X_1 + 12.6967X_2$, where $X_1 =$ number of rooms and $X_2 =$ neighborhood (east $= 0$) **(b)** Holding constant the effect of neighborhood, for each additional room, the selling price is estimated to increase by 9.2189 thousands of dollars, or $9,218.9. For a given number of rooms, a west neighborhood is estimated to increase the selling price over an east neighborhood by 12.6967 thousands of dollars, or $12,696.7. **(c)** $\hat{Y} = 243.7371 + 9.2189(9) + 12.6967(0) = 326.7076$, or $326,707.6$. $\$309,560.04 \leq Y_X \leq \$343,855.1$. $\$321,471.44 \leq \mu_{Y|X} \leq \$331,943.71$. **(d)** Based on a residual analysis, the model appears to be adequate. **(e)** $F_{STAT} = 55.39$, the p-value is virtually 0. Because p-value < 0.05, reject H_0. There is evidence of a significant relationship between selling price and the two independent variables (rooms and neighborhood). **(f)** For X_1:$t_{STAT} = 8.9537$, the p-value is virtually 0. Reject H_0. Number of rooms makes a significant contribution and should be included in the model. For X_2:$t_{STAT} = 3.5913$, p-value $= 0.0023 < 0.05$, Reject H_0. Neighborhood makes a significant contribution and should be included in the model. Based on these results, the regression model with the two independent variables should be used. **(g)** $7.0466 \leq \beta_1 \leq 11.3913$. **(h)** $5.2378 \leq \beta_2 \leq 20.1557$. **(i)** $r^2_{adj} = 0.851$. **(j)** The slope of selling price with number of rooms is the same, regardless of whether the house is located in an east or west neighborhood. **(k)** $\hat{Y} = 253.95 + 8.032X_1 - 5.90X_2 + 2.089X_1X_2$. For $X_1 X_2$, p-value $= 0.330$. Do not reject H_0. There is no evidence that the interaction term makes a contribution to the model. **(l)** The model in (b) should be used.

16.36 (a) Predicted time $= 8.01 + 0.00523$ Depth $- 2.105$ Dry. **(b)** Holding constant the effect of type of drilling, for each foot increase in depth of the hole, the drilling time is estimated to increase by 0.00523 minutes. For a given depth, a dry drilling hole is estimated to reduce the drilling time over wet drilling by 2.1052 minutes. **(c)** 6.428 minutes, $6.210 \leq \mu_{Y|X} \leq 6.646$, $4.923 \leq Y_X \leq 7.932$. **(d)** The model appears to be adequate. **(e)** $F_{STAT} = 111.11 > 3.09$; reject H_0. **(f)** $t_{STAT} = 5.03 > 1.9847$; reject H_0. $t_{STAT} = -14.03 < -1.9847$; reject H_0. Include both variables. **(g)** $0.0032 \leq \beta_1 \leq 0.0073$. **(h)** $-2.403 \leq \beta_2 \leq -1.808$. **(i)** 69.0%. **(j)** The slope of the additional drilling time with the depth of the hole is the same, regardless of the type of drilling method used. **(k)** The p-value of the interaction term $= 0.462 > 0.05$, so the term is not significant and should not be included in the model. **(l)** The model in part (b) should be used.

16.38 (a) $\hat{Y} = 31.5594 + 0.0296X_1 + 0.0041X_2 + 0.000017159X_1X_2$, where $X_1 =$ sales, $X_2 =$ orders, p-value $= 0.3249 > 0.05$. Do not reject H_0. There is not enough evidence that the interaction term makes a contribution to the model. **(b)** Because there is insufficient evidence of any interaction effect between sales and orders, the model in Problem 13.4 should be used.

16.40 (a) The p-value of the interaction term $= 0.002 < 0.05$, so the term is significant and should be included in the model. **(b)** Use the model developed in this problem.

16.42 (a) For $X_1 X_2$, p-value $= 0.2353 > 0.05$. Do not reject H_0. There is insufficient evidence that the interaction term makes a contribution to the model. **(b)** Because there is not enough evidence of an interaction effect between total staff present and remote hours, the model in Problem 13.7 should be used.

16.50 (a) $\hat{Y} = -3.9152 + 0.0319X_1 + 4.2228X_2$, where $X_1 =$ number cubic feet moved and $X_2 =$ number of pieces of large furniture. **(b)** Holding constant the number of pieces of large furniture, for each additional cubic foot moved, the labor hours are estimated to increase by 0.0319. Holding constant the amount of cubic feet moved, for each additional piece of large furniture, the labor hours are estimated to increase by 4.2228. **(c)** $\hat{Y} = -3.9152 + 0.0319(500) + 4.2228 (2) = 20.4926$. **(d)** Based on a residual analysis, the errors appear to be normally distributed. The equal-variance assumption might be violated because the variances appear to be larger around the center region of both independent variables. There might also be violation of the linearity

assumption. A model with quadratic terms for both independent variables might be fitted. **(e)** $F_{STAT} = 228.80$, p-value is virtually 0. Because p-value < 0.05, reject H_0. There is evidence of a significant relationship between labor hours and the two independent variables (the amount of cubic feet moved and the number of pieces of large furniture). **(f)** The p-value is virtually 0. The probability of obtaining a test statistic of 228.80 or greater is virtually 0 if there is no significant relationship between labor hours and the two independent variables (the amount of cubic feet moved and the number of pieces of large furniture). **(g)** $r^2 = 0.9327$. 93.27% of the variation in labor hours can be explained by variation in the number of cubic feet moved and the number of pieces of large furniture. **(h)** $r^2_{adj} = 0.9287$. **(i)** For X_1: $t_{STAT} = 6.9339$, the p-value is virtually 0. Reject H_0. The number of cubic feet moved makes a significant contribution and should be included in the model. For X_2: $t_{STAT} = 4.6192$, the p-value is virtually 0. Reject H_0. The number of pieces of large furniture makes a significant contribution and should be included in the model. Based on these results, the regression model with the two independent variables should be used. **(j)** For X_1: $t_{STAT} = 6.9339$, the p-value is virtually 0. The probability of obtaining a sample that will yield a test statistic farther away than 6.9339 is virtually 0 if the number of cubic feet moved does not make a significant contribution, holding the effect of the number of pieces of large furniture constant. For X_2: $t_{STAT} = 4.6192$, the p-value is virtually 0. The probability of obtaining a sample that will yield a test statistic farther away than 4.6192 is virtually 0 if the number of pieces of large furniture does not make a significant contribution, holding the effect of the amount of cubic feet moved constant. **(k)** $0.0226 \leq \beta_1 \leq 0.0413$. You are 95% confident that the mean labor hours will increase by between 0.0226 and 0.0413 for each additional cubic foot moved, holding constant the number of pieces of large furniture. In Problem 12.44, you are 95% confident that the labor hours will increase by between 0.0439 and 0.0562 for each additional cubic foot moved, regardless of the number of pieces of large furniture.

16.52 (a) $\hat{Y} = -120.0483 + 1.7506X_1 + 0.3680X_2$, where $X_1 =$ assessed value and $X_2 =$ time since assessment. **(b)** Holding constant the time period, for each additional thousand dollars of assessed value, the selling price is estimated to increase by 1.7506 thousand dollars. Holding constant the assessed value, for each additional month since assessment, the selling price is estimated to increase by 0.3680 thousand dollars. **(c)** $\hat{Y} = -120.0483 + 1.7506(170) + 0.3680(12) = 181.9692$ thousand dollars. **(d)** Based on a residual analysis, the model appears to be adequate. **(e)** $F_{STAT} = 223.46$, the p-value is virtually 0. Because p-value < 0.05, reject H_0. There is evidence of a significant relationship between selling price and the two independent variables (assessed value and time since assessment). **(f)** The p-value is virtually 0. The probability of obtaining a test statistic of 223.46 or greater is virtually 0 if there is no significant relationship between selling price and the two independent variables (assessed value and time since assessment). **(g)** $r^2 = 0.9430$. 94.30% of the variation in selling price can be explained by variation in assessed value and time since assessment. **(h)** $r^2_{adj} = 0.9388$. **(i)** For X_1: $t_{STAT} = 20.4137$, the p-value is virtually 0. Reject H_0. The assessed value makes a significant contribution and should be included in the model. For X_2: $t_{STAT} = 2.8734$, p-value $= 0.0078 < 0.05$. Reject H_0. The time since assessment makes a significant contribution and should be included in the model. Based on these results, the regression model with the two independent variables should be used. **(j)** For X_1: $t_{STAT} = 20.4137$, the p-value is virtually 0. The probability of obtaining a sample that will yield a test statistic farther away than 20.4137 is virtually 0 if the assessed value does not make a significant contribution, holding time since assessment constant. For X_2: $t_{STAT} = 2.8734$, the p-value is virtually 0. The probability of obtaining a sample that will yield a test statistic farther away than 2.8734 is virtually 0 if the time since assessment does not make a significant contribution holding the effect of the assessed value constant. **(k)** $1.5746 \leq \beta_1 \leq 1.9266$. You are 95% confident that the selling price will increase by an amount somewhere between $1.5746 thousand and $1.9266 thousand for each additional thousand-dollar increase in assessed value, holding constant the time since assessment. In Problem 12.76, you are 95% confident that the selling price will increase by an amount somewhere between $1.5862 thousand and $1.9773 thousand for each additional thousand-dollar increase in assessed value, regardless of the time since assessment.

16.54 (a) $\hat{Y} = 163.7751 + 10.7252X_1 - 0.2843X_2$, where X_1 = size and X_2 = age. **(b)** Holding age constant, for each additional thousand square feet, the assessed value is estimated to increase by $10.7252 thousand. Holding size constant, for each additional year, the assessed value is estimated to decrease by $0.2843 thousand. **(c)** $\hat{Y} = 163.7751 + 10.7252(1.75) - 0.2843(10) = 179.7017$ thousand dollars. **(d)** Based on a residual analysis, the errors appear to be normally distributed. The equal-variance assumption appears to be valid. There might be a violation of the linearity assumption for age. You might want to include a quadratic term in the model for age. **(e)** $F_{STAT} = 28.58, p\text{-value} = 0.0000272776$. Because $p\text{-value} = 0.0000 < 0.05$, reject H_0. There is evidence of a significant relationship between assessed value and the two independent variables (size and age). **(f)** $p\text{-value} = 0.0000272776$. The probability of obtaining an F_{STAT} test statistic of 28.58 or greater is virtually 0 if there is no significant relationship between assessed value and the two independent variables (size and age). **(g)** $r^2 = 0.8265$. 82.65% of the variation in assessed value can be explained by variation in size and age. **(h)** $r^2_{adj} = 0.7976$. **(i)** For X_1: $t_{STAT} = 3.5581, p\text{-value} = 0.0039 < 0.05$. Reject H_0. The size of a house makes a significant contribution and should be included in the model. For X_2: $t_{STAT} = -3.4002$, $p\text{-value} = 0.0053 < 0.05$. Reject H_0. The age of a house makes a significant contribution and should be included in the model. Based on these results, the regression model with the two independent variables should be used. **(j)** For X_1: $p\text{-value} = 0.0039$. The probability of obtaining a sample that will yield a test statistic farther away than 3.5581 is 0.0039 if the size of a house does not make a significant contribution, holding age constant. For X_2: $p\text{-value} = 0.0053$. The probability of obtaining a sample that will yield a test statistic farther away than -3.4002 is 0.0053 if the age of a house does not make a significant contribution, holding the effect of the size constant. **(k)** $4.1572 \le \beta_1 \le 17.2928$. You are 95% confident that the mean assessed value will increase by an amount somewhere between $4.1575 thousand and $17.2928 thousand for each additional thousand-square-foot increase in the size of a house, holding constant the age. In Problem 12.77, you are 95% confident that the mean assessed value will increase by an amount somewhere between $9.4695 thousand and $23.7972 thousand for each additional thousand-square-foot increase in heating area, regardless of the age. **(l)** Based on your answers to (b) through (k), the age of a house does have an effect on its assessed value.

16.56 (a) $\hat{Y} = 157.8976 - 18.4490X_1 - 3.2787X_2$, where X_1 = ERA and X_2 = league (American = 0, National = 1) **(b)** Holding constant the effect of the league, for each additional ERA, the number of wins is estimated to decrease by 18.4490. For a given ERA, a team in the National League is estimated to have 3.2787 fewer wins than a team in the American League. **(c)** 74.8771 wins Confidence interval: 69.6315 to 80.1227 Prediction interval: 57.3027 to 92.4515. **(d)** There is no apparent violation of the assumptions.

(e) $F_{STAT} = 12.7768 > 3.35, p\text{-value} = 0.0001$. Because $p\text{-value} < 0.05$, reject H_0. There is evidence of a significant relationship between wins and the two independent variables (ERA and league). **(f)** For X_1: $t_{STAT} = -5.0424 < -2.0518$, the $p\text{-value}$ is virtually 0. Reject H_0. ERA makes a significant contribution and should be included in the model. For X_2: $t_{STAT} = -1.0844 > -2.0518$, $p\text{-value} = 0.0502 > 0.05$. Do not reject H_0. The league does not make a significant contribution and should not be included in the model. Based on these results, the regression model with only the ERA as the independent variable should be used. **(g)** $-25.9562 \le \beta_1 \le -10.9418$. **(h)** $-9.4825 \le \beta_2 \le 2.9250$. **(i)** $r^2 = 0.4862$. 48.62% of the variation in wins can be explained by the variation in ERA and league. **(j)** The slope of the number of wins with ERA is the same, regardless of whether the team belongs to the American League or the National League. **(k)** For X_1X_2: $t_{STAT} = -0.2802 > -2.0555$ the $p\text{-value}$ is 0.7815 > 0.05. Do not reject H_0. There is no evidence that the interaction term makes a contribution to the model. **(m)** The model with one independent variable (ERA) should be used.

16.58 The r^2 of the multiple regression is very low, at 0.0645. Only 6.45% of the variation in thickness can be explained by the variation of pressure and temperature. The F test statistic for the combined significant of pressure and temperature is 1.621, with $p\text{-value} = 0.2085$. Hence, at a 5% level of significance, there is not enough evidence to conclude that both pressure and temperature affect thickness. The $p\text{-value}$ of the t test for the significance of pressure is 0.8307 > 0.05. Hence, there is insufficient evidence to conclude that pressure affects thickness, holding constant the effect of temperature. The $p\text{-value}$ of the t test for the significance of temperature is 0.0820, which is also > 0.05. There is insufficient evidence to conclude that temperature affects thickness at the 5% level of significance, holding constant the effect of pressure. Hence, neither pressure nor temperature affects thickness individually.

The normal probability plot does not suggest any potential violation of the normality assumption. The residual plots do not indicate potential violation of the equal variance assumption. The temperature residual plot, however, suggests that there might be a nonlinear relationship between temperature and thickness.

The r^2 of the multiple regression model is very low, at 0.0734. Only 7.34% of the variation in thickness can be explained by the variation of pressure, temperature, and the interaction of the two. The F test statistic for the model that includes pressure and temperature is 1.214, with a $p\text{-value}$ of 0.3153. Hence, at a 5% level of significance, there is insufficient evidence to conclude that pressure, temperature, and the interaction of the two affect thickness. The $p\text{-value}$ of the t test for the significance of pressure, temperature, and the interaction term are 0.5074, 0.4053, and 0.5111, respectively, which are all greater than 5%. Hence, there is insufficient evidence to conclude that pressure, temperature, or the interaction individually affects thickness, holding constant the effect of the other variables.

The pattern in the normal probability plot and residual plots is similar to that in the regression without the interaction term. Hence the article's suggestion that there is a significant interaction between the pressure and the temperature in the tank cannot be validated.